W9-CAY-821

PEARSON   ALWAYS LEARNING

Marvin L. Bittinger • David J. Ellenbogen • Barbara L. Johnson

Elementary & Intermediate Algebra
Concepts & Applications, Volume 1

Second Custom Edition for Math 151, 151A and 151B

Taken from:
Elementary & Intermediate Algebra: Concepts & Applications, Sixth Edition
by Marvin L. Bittinger, David J. Ellenbogen, and Barbara L. Johnson

Taken from:

Elementary & Intermediate Algebra: Concepts & Applications, Sixth Edition
by Marvin L. Bittinger, David J. Ellenbogen, and Barbara L. Johnson
Copyright © 2014, 2010, 2006 by Pearson Education, Inc.
Upper Saddle River, New Jersey 07458

All rights reserved. No part of this book may be reproduced, in any form or by any means, without permission in writing from the publisher.

This special edition published in cooperation with Pearson Learning Solutions.

All trademarks, service marks, registered trademarks, and registered service marks are the property of their respective owners and are used herein for identification purposes only.

Pearson Learning Solutions, 501 Boylston Street, Suite 900, Boston, MA 02116
A Pearson Education Company
www.pearsoned.com

Printed in the United States of America

4 5 6 7 8 9 10 V092 18 17 16 15 14

000200010271767684

JL

ISBN 10: 1-269-31109-3
ISBN 13: 978-1-269-31109-0

Contents

CHAPTER 4

Polynomials   229

CHAPTER 5

Polynomials and Factoring   303

CHAPTER 6

Rational Expressions and Equations   373

A KEY TO THE ICONS IN THE EXERCISE SETS

 Concept reinforcement exercises, indicated by blue exercise numbers, provide basic practice with the new concepts and vocabulary.

Aha!   Exercises labeled *Aha!* indicate the first time that a new insight can greatly simplify a problem and help students be alert to using that insight on following exercises. They are not more difficult.

▦   Calculator exercises are designed to be worked using either a scientific calculator or a graphing calculator.

⊟   Graphing calculator exercises are designed to be worked using a graphing calculator and often provide practice for concepts discussed in the Technology Connections.

▱   Writing exercises are designed to be answered using one or more complete sentences.

✓   A check mark in the annotated instructor's edition indicates Synthesis exercises that the authors consider particularly beneficial for students.

Preface

Welcome to the sixth edition of *Elementary and Intermediate Algebra: Concepts and Applications!* As always, our goal is to present content that is easy to understand yet of enough depth to allow success in future courses. You will recognize many proven features, applications, and explanations; you will also find new material developed as a result of our experience in the classroom as well as from insights from faculty and students throughout North America.

This text is intended for students with a firm background in *arithmetic*. It is one of three texts in an algebra series that also includes *Elementary Algebra: Concepts and Applications*, Ninth Edition, and *Intermediate Algebra: Concepts and Applications*, Ninth Edition.

Approach

Our goal is to help today's students learn and retain mathematical concepts. To achieve this, we feel that we must prepare developmental-mathematics students for the transition from "skills-oriented" elementary algebra courses to more "concept-oriented" college-level mathematics courses. This requires the development of critical thinking skills: to reason mathematically, to communicate mathematically, and to identify and solve mathematical problems. Following are aspects of our approach that we use to help meet the challenges we all face when teaching developmental mathematics.

Problem Solving

We use problem solving and applications to motivate the students wherever possible, and we include real-life applications and problem-solving techniques throughout the text. Problem solving encourages students to think about how mathematics can be used, and it helps to prepare them for more advanced material in future courses.

In Chapter 2, we introduce our five-step process for solving problems: (1) Familiarize, (2) Translate, (3) Carry out, (4) Check, and (5) State the answer. Repeated use of this problem-solving strategy throughout the text provides students with a starting point for any type of problem they encounter, and frees them to focus on the unique aspects of the particular problem. We often use estimation and carefully checked guesses to help with the *Familiarize* and *Check* steps (see pp. 113 and 422).

What's New in the Ninth Edition?

In addition to the following new features and other changes in this edition, including a new design, we have rewritten many key topics in response to user and reviewer feedback and have made significant improvements in design, art, pedagogy, and an expanded supplements package. Detailed information about the content changes outlined on p. ix is available in the form of a conversion guide. Please ask your Pearson representative for more information.

Applications

Interesting applications of mathematics help motivate students and instructors. In the new edition, we have updated real-world data problems and examples to include subjects such as renewable energy (p. 109), graduate-school acceptance (pp. 140 and 611), and zipline rides (p. 676). For a complete list of applications and the page numbers on which they can be found, please refer to the Index of Applications at the back of the book.

Pedagogy

New! **Your Turn Exercises.** After every example, students are directed to work a similar exercise. This provides immediate reinforcement of concepts and skills. Answers to these exercises appear at the end of each exercise set. (See pp. 89 and 343.)

New! **Exploring the Concept.** Appearing once in almost every chapter, this feature encourages students to think about or visualize a concept. These activities lead into Interactive Figures available in MyMathLab. Students can manipulate iFigs to further explore and solidify their understanding of the concepts. (See pp. 194, 349, and 674.)

Revised! **Connecting the Concepts.** Appearing at least once in every chapter, this feature summarizes concepts from several sections or chapters and illustrates connections between them. It includes a set of mixed exercises to help students make these connections. (See pp. 217, 350, and 658.)

Algebraic–Graphical Connections.   Appearing occasionally throughout the text, this feature draws attention to visualizations of algebraic concepts. (See pp. 506 and 698.)

Technology Connections.   These optional features in each chapter help students use a graphing calculator or a graphing calculator app to visualize concepts. Exercises are included with many of these features, and additional exercises in many exercise sets are marked with a graphing calculator icon to indicate more practice with this optional use of technology. (See pp. 176, 180, and 666.)

Student Notes.   Comments in the margin are addressed directly to students in a conversational tone. Ranging from suggestions for avoiding common mistakes to how to best read new notation, they give students extra explanation of the mathematics appearing on that page. (See pp. 106, 204, and 322.)

Study Skills.   We offer one study tip in every section. Ranging from time management to test preparation, these suggestions for successful study habits apply to any college course and any level of student. (See pp. 154, 287, and 312.)

New!   **Mid-Chapter Review.**   In the middle of every chapter, we offer a brief summary of the concepts covered in the first part of the chapter, two guided solutions to help students work step-by-step through solutions, and a set of mixed review exercises. (See pp. 103, 202, and 335.)

Exercise Sets

New!   **Vocabulary and Reading Check.**   These exercises begin every exercise set and are designed to encourage the student to read the section. Students who can complete these exercises should be prepared to work the remaining exercises in the exercise set. (See pp. 108, 259, and 351.)

Concept Reinforcement Exercises.   These true/false, matching, and fill-in-the-blank exercises appearing near the beginning of many exercise sets build students' confidence and comprehension. Answers to all concept reinforcement exercises appear in the answer section at the back of the book. (See pp. 139, 159, and 208.)

Aha! Exercises.   These exercises are not more difficult than their neighboring exercises; in fact, they can be solved more quickly, without lengthy computation, if the student has the proper insight. Designed to reward students who "look before they leap," the icon indicates the first time a new insight applies, and then it is up to the student to determine when to use that insight on subsequent exercises. (See pp. 236, 401, and 647.)

Revised!   **Skill Review Exercises.**   These exercises appear in every section beginning with Section 1.2. Taken together, each chapter's Skill Review exercises review all the major concepts covered in previous chapters in the text. Often these exercises focus on a single topic, such as solving equations, from multiple perspectives. (See pp. 386, 451, and 509.)

Synthesis Exercises.   Synthesis exercises appear in each exercise set following the Skill Review exercises. Students will need to use skills and concepts from earlier sections to solve these problems, and this will help them develop deeper insights into the current topic. The synthesis exercises are a real strength of the text, and in the annotated instructor's edition, the authors have placed a ✓ next to selected synthesis exercises that they suggest instructors "check out" and consider assigning. These exercises are not more difficult than the others, but they do use previously learned concepts and skills in ways that may be especially beneficial to students as they prepare for future topics. (See pp. 162, 201, and 394.)

Writing Exercises.   Two basic writing exercises appear just before the Skill Review exercises, and at least two more challenging exercises appear in the Synthesis exercises. Writing exercises aid student comprehension by requiring students to use critical thinking to explain concepts in one or more complete sentences. Because correct answers may vary, the only writing exercises for which answers appear at the back of the text are those in the chapter Review Exercises. (See pp. 189, 245, and 756.)

New!   **Quick Quiz.**   Beginning with the second section in each chapter, a five-question Quick Quiz appears near the end of each exercise set. Containing questions from sections already covered in the chapter, these quizzes provide a short but consistent review of the material in the chapter and help students prepare for a chapter test. (See pp. 363 and 531.)

New!   **Prepare to Move On.**   Beginning with Chapter 2, this short set of exercises appears at the end of every exercise set, and reviews concepts and skills previously covered in the text that will be used in the next section of the text. (See pp. 112 and 318.)

End of Chapter

Chapter Resources.   These learning resources appear at the end of each chapter, making them easy to integrate into lessons at the most appropriate time. The mathematics necessary to use the resource has been presented by the end of the section indicated with each resource.

- **Translating for Success** and **Visualizing for Success.** These matching exercises help students learn to translate word problems to mathematical language and to graph equations and inequalities. (See pp. 221 and 364.)
- **Collaborative Activity.** Students who work in groups generally outperform those who do not, so these optional activities direct them to explore mathematics together. Additional collaborative activities and suggestions for directing collaborative learning appear in the *Instructor's Resources Manual with Tests and Mini Lectures.* (See pp. 222, 365, and 566.)

New!
- **Decision Making: Connection.** Although many applications throughout the text involve decision-making situations, this feature specifically applies the math of each chapter to a context in which students may be involved in decision making. (See pp. 294, 433, and 492.)

Revised!
Study Summary.   At the end of each chapter, this synopsis gives students a fast and effective review of key chapter terms and concepts. Concepts are paired with worked-out examples and practice exercises. (See pp. 146 and 567.)

Chapter Review and Test.   A thorough chapter review and a practice test help prepare students for a test covering the concepts presented in each chapter. (See pp. 369 and 693.)

New!
Quick Response (QR) Codes.   These have been added to each chapter test, allowing students to link directly to chapter test prep videos with step-by-step solutions to all chapter test exercises. This effective tool allows students to receive help studying exactly when they need it at point of use.

Cumulative Review.   This review appears after every chapter beginning with Chapter 2 to help students retain and apply their knowledge from previous chapters. (See pp. 228 and 440.)

New Design

While incorporating a new layout, a fresh palette of colors, and new features, we retain an open look and a typeface that is easy to read. In addition, we continue to pay close attention to the pedagogical use of color to ensure that it is used to present concepts in the clearest possible manner.

Content Changes

The exposition, examples, and exercises have been carefully reviewed and, as appropriate, revised or replaced.

An increased focus on connections and concepts is made in Exploring the Concept, Connecting the Concepts, and Decision Making: Connection features. This focus is invaluable for student comprehension. In addition, concept and skill review has been expanded in Quick Quiz, Mid-Chapter Review, Study Summary, Skill Review, and Prepare to Move On features, which are described in more detail in the preceding Pedagogy section.

Other content changes include the following.

- Examples and exercises that use real data are updated or replaced with current applications.
- Chapter 1 now discusses the use of prime factorizations to find the LCM of two numbers. Learning this method will prepare students to find the LCM of two polynomials.
- Chapter 2 includes an introduction to motion problems as well as an explanation of percent increase and percent decrease.
- Section 3.7 now provides a comprehensive discussion of finding equations of lines.
- The explanation of simplifying powers of i in Section 10.8 is rewritten to provide students with a better understanding of the concept.
- Composition of functions in Section 12.1 is explained in greater detail to help students move from a concrete example to function notation.
- The optional connection to technology has been revised to include new calculator operating systems and graphing calculator applications for mobile devices.

ANCILLARIES

The following ancillaries are available to help both instructors and students use this text more effectively.

Supplements

NEW! Integrated Bittinger Video Program and MyMathGuide

Bittinger Video Program, available in MyMathLab and on DVD, includes closed captioning and the following video types:

NEW! To-the-Point Objective Videos
- Concise, interactive, and objective based.
- View a whole section, choose an objective, or go straight to an example.
- Interactive Your Turn Video Check pauses for students to work problems and check answers.
- Seamlessly integrated with *MyMathGuide: Notes, Practice, and Video Path*.

Chapter Test Prep Videos
- Step-by-step solution for every problem in the Chapter Tests.
- Also available on YouTube, and by scanning the QR code on the Chapter Test pages in the text.

ISBNs: 0-321-84882-9/978-0-321-84882-6

NEW! MyMathGuide: Notes, Practice, and Video Path
- Guided, hands-on learning for traditional, lab-based, hybrid, and online courses.
- Designed to correlate with *To-the-Point Objective Videos*.
- Highlights key concepts, skills, and definitions for each learning objective.
- Quick Review of key vocabulary terms and vocabulary practice problems.
- Examples with guided solutions and similar Your Turn exercises for practice.
- Space to write questions and notes and to show work.
- Additional Practice Exercises with Readiness Checks.
- Available in MyMathLab and printed.

ISBNs: 0-321-84876-4/978-0-321-84876-5

Student's Solutions Manual
by Christine Verity
- Contains completely worked-out solutions with step-by-step annotations for all the odd-numbered exercises in the text, with the exception of the writing exercises. Also contains all solutions to Chapter Review, Chapter Test, and Connecting the Concepts exercises.
- Available in MyMathLab and printed.

ISBNs: 0-321-84877-2/978-0-321-84877-2

Annotated Instructor's Edition
- Provides answers to all text exercises in color next to the corresponding problems.
- Includes Teaching Tips.
- Icons identify writing and graphing calculator exercises.

ISBNs: 0-321-84881-0/978-0-321-84881-9

Instructor's Solutions Manual (download only)
by Christine Verity
- Contains fully worked-out solutions to the odd-numbered exercises and brief solutions to the even-numbered exercises in the exercise sets.
- Available for download at www.pearsonhighered.com or in MyMathLab.

Instructor's Resource Manual (download only) with Tests and Mini Lectures
by Laurie Hurley
- Includes resources designed to help both new and adjunct faculty with course preparation and classroom management.
- Offers helpful teaching tips correlated to the sections of the text.
- Contains two multiple-choice tests per chapter, six free-response tests per chapter, and eight final exams.
- Available for download at www.pearsonhighered.com or in MyMathLab.

PowerPoint® Lecture Slides (download only)
- Present key concepts and definitions from the text.
- Available for download at www.pearsonhighered.com or in MyMathLab.

TestGen®

TestGen® (www.pearsoned.com/testgen) enables instructors to build, edit, print, and administer tests using a computerized bank of questions developed to cover all the objectives of the text. TestGen is algorithmically based, allowing instructors to create multiple equivalent versions of the same question or test with the click of a button. Instructors can also modify test bank questions or add new questions. The software and testbank are available for download from Pearson Education's online catalog.

AVAILABLE FOR STUDENTS AND INSTRUCTORS

MyMathLab® Online Course (access code required)

The Bittinger courses include all of MyMathLab's robust features, plus these additional highlights:

New!   Two MyMathLab course options are now available:

- **Standard MyMathLab courses** allow instructors to build their course their way, offering maximum flexibility and control over all aspects of assignment creation.

New!

- **Ready-to-Go courses** provide students with all the same great MyMathLab features, but make it easier for instructors to get started.

Both Bittinger course options include one pre-made pre-test and post-test for every chapter, section-lecture homework, and a chapter review quiz linked to personalized homework.

New!   **Increased coverage** of skill-building, conceptual, and applications exercises, **plus new problem types,** provide even more flexibility when creating homework.

New!   **Interactive Figures**, available for key concepts, foster conceptual understanding for visual and tactile learners. Exploring the Concept in the text leads into iFigs available in MML. Students manipulate iFigs to explore concepts and solidify their understanding.

New!   **Bittinger Video Program** includes all new To-the-Point Objective Videos and Chapter Test Prep Videos.

New!   *MyMathGuide: Notes, Practice, and Video Path* can be viewed and printed.

MathXL® Online Course (access code required)

MathXL® is the homework and assessment engine that runs MyMathLab. (MyMathLab is MathXL plus a learning management system.)

With MathXL, instructors can

- Create, edit, and assign online homework and tests using algorithmically generated exercises correlated at the objective level to the textbook.
- Create and assign their own online exercises and import TestGen tests for added flexibility.
- Maintain records of all student work tracked in MathXL's online gradebook.

With MathXL, students can

- Take chapter tests in MathXL and receive personalized study plans and/or personalized homework assignments based on their test results.
- Use the study plan and/or the homework to link directly to tutorial exercises for the objectives they need to study.
- Access supplemental animations and video clips directly from selected exercises.

MathXL is available to qualified adopters. For more information, visit our website at www.mathxl.com, or contact your Pearson representative.

Acknowledgments

An outstanding team of professionals was involved in the production of this text. Judy Henn, Laurie Hurley, Helen Medley, Joanne Koratich, Monroe Street, and Holly Martinez carefully checked the book for accuracy and offered thoughtful suggestions. Michelle Lanosga and Daniel Johnson provided exceptional research support, and Christine Verity, Laurie Hurley, and Lisa Collette did remarkable work in preparing supplements. Special thanks are due Nelson Carter and Katherine Carter for their outstanding work on videos.

Martha Morong, of Quadrata, Inc., provided editorial and production services of the highest quality, and Geri Davis, of the Davis Group, Inc., performed superb work as designer, art editor, and photo researcher. Bill Melvin and Network Graphics provided the accurate and creative illustrations and graphs.

The team at Pearson deserves special thanks. Executive Editor Cathy Cantin, Executive Content Editor Kari Heen, Senior Production Supervisor Ron Hampton, Content Editor Katherine Minton, and Editorial Assistant Kerianne Okie provided many fine suggestions, coordinated tasks and schedules, and remained involved and accessible throughout the project. Marketing Manager Rachel Ross skillfully kept in touch with the needs of faculty. Editor in Chief Maureen O'Connor and Editorial Director Chris Hoag deserve credit for assembling this fine team.

We also thank the students at Indiana University Purdue University Indianapolis and the Community College of Vermont and the following professors for their thoughtful reviews and insightful comments.

Darla Aguilar, *Pima Community College–Desert Vista Campus*; Michael Anzzolin, *Waubonsee Community College*; Jan Archibald, *Ventura College*; Ruben Arenas, *East Los Angeles College*; Don Brown, *Macon State College*; Manuel Caramés, *Miami-Dade College–North Campus*; Gary Carpenter, *Pima Community College, Northwest Campus*; Tim Chappell, *Penn Valley Community College*; Phong Chau, *Glendale Community College*; Krista Cohlmia, *Odessa College*; Ola Disu, *Tarrant County College*; Theresa Evans, *Odessa College*; Anissa Florence, *University of Louisville*; Sandy Gordon, *Central Carolina Technical College*; Sharon Hamsa, *Longview Community College*; Doug Harley, *Del Mar College*; Cynthia Harris, *Triton College*; Geoffrey Hirsch, *Ohlone College*; Pat Horacek, *Pensacola Junior College*; Glenn Jablonski, *Triton College*; Joseph Kazimir, *East Los Angeles College*; Sally Keely, *Clark College*; Jennifer Kumi Burkett, *Triton College*; Ana Leon, *Louisville Community College*; Linda Lohman, *Jefferson Community and Technical College*; Bob Martin, *Tarrant County College*; Caroline Martinson, *Jefferson Community and Technical College*; Eric Moller, *Del Mar College*; Agashi Nwogbaga, *Wesley College*; Miriam Pack, *Glendale Community College*; Michelle Parsons, *San Diego Mesa College*; Amy Petty, *South Suburban College*; Anthony Precella, *Del Mar College*; Timothy Precella, *Del Mar College*; Thomas Pulver, *Waubonsee Community College*; Angela Redmon, *Wenatchee Valley College*; Richard Rupp, *Del Mar College*; Mehdi Sadatmousavi, *Pima Community College*; Ahmad Shafiee, *Del Mar College*; Jane Thompson, *Waubonsee Community College*; Ann Thrower, *Kilgore College*

Finally, a special thank-you to all those who so generously agreed to discuss their professional use of mathematics in our chapter openers. These dedicated people all share a desire to make math more meaningful to students. We cannot imagine a finer set of role models.

M.L.B.
D.J.E.
B.L.J.

Introduction to Algebraic Expressions

NUMBER OF SONGS PURCHASED	AMOUNT PAID
2	$1.98
3	2.97
5	4.95
10	9.90

The Media May Change, But the Music Remains.

Thomas Edison's phonograph, patented in 1877, was the first successful method of recording music. At first, music was recorded on cylinders. During the next century, the media evolved to records, then to tapes, and then to CDs. Today, most of the 100,000 albums released each year are available electronically, and online music sales are soaring, due in part to the ability to purchase single tracks. Can you use the data in the table shown to write an equation that *models* the cost of single-track downloads? (*See Example 7 in Section 1.1.*)

It's true—even as a musician, I am not exempt from using math, because music is math.

Myra Flynn, a singer/songwriter from Randolph, Vermont, uses math in harmonies, time signatures, tuning systems, and all music theory. Putting an album out requires the use of even more math: calculating the number of hours worked in the studio, payments for producers and musicians, hard-copy and digital distribution regionally, and ticket and concert sales.

P roblem solving is the focus of this text. In Chapter 1, we lay the foundation for the problem-solving approach that is developed in Chapter 2 and used in all chapters that follow. This foundation includes a review of arithmetic, a discussion of real numbers and their properties, and an examination of how real numbers are added, subtracted, multiplied, divided, and raised to powers.

1.1   Introduction to Algebra

Evaluating Algebraic Expressions   ▪   Translating to Algebraic Expressions   ▪   Translating to Equations

This section introduces some basic concepts and expressions used in algebra. Our focus is on the wordings and expressions that often arise in real-world problems.

Evaluating Algebraic Expressions

Probably the greatest difference between arithmetic and algebra is the use of *variables*. Suppose that n represents the number of tickets sold in one day for a U2 concert and that each ticket costs $60. Then a total of 60 times n, or $60 \cdot n$, dollars will be collected for tickets.

The letter n is a **variable** because it can represent any one of a set of numbers.

The number 60 is a **constant** because it does not change.

The multiplication sign $\cdot$ is an **operation sign** because it indicates the **operation** of multiplication.

The expression $60 \cdot n$ is a **variable expression** because it contains a variable.

An **algebraic expression** consists of variables and/or numerals, often with operation signs and grouping symbols. Other examples of algebraic expressions are:

$t - 37$;   This contains the variable t, the constant 37, and the operation of subtraction.

$(s + t) \div 2$.   This contains the variables s and t, the constant 2, grouping symbols, and the operations of addition and division.

Multiplication can be written in several ways. For example, "60 times n" can be written as $60 \cdot n$, $60 \times n$, $60(n)$, $60 * n$, or simply (and usually) $60n$. Division can also be represented by a fraction bar: $\frac{9}{7}$, or $9/7$, means $9 \div 7$.

To **evaluate** an algebraic expression, we **substitute** a number for each variable in the expression and calculate the result. This result is called the **value** of the expression. The table below lists several values of the expression $60 \cdot n$.

Student Notes

Notation like "$60 \times n$" is not often used in algebra because the "$\times$" symbol can be misread as a variable.

Cost per Ticket (in dollars), 60	Number of Tickets Sold, n	Total Collected (in dollars), $60n$
60	150	9,000
60	200	12,000
60	250	15,000

Student Notes

At the end of each example in this text, you will see YOUR TURN. This directs you to try an exercise similar to the example. The answers to these exercises appear at the end of each exercise set.

EXAMPLE 1 Evaluate each expression for the given values.

a) $x + y$ for $x = 37$ and $y = 28$

b) $5ab$ for $a = 2$ and $b = 3$

SOLUTION

a) We substitute 37 for x and 28 for y and carry out the addition:

$$x + y = (37) + (28) = 65. \quad \text{Using parentheses when substituting is not always necessary but is never incorrect.}$$

The value of the expression is 65.

b) We substitute 2 for a and 3 for b and multiply:

$$5ab = 5 \cdot 2 \cdot 3 = 10 \cdot 3 = 30. \quad 5ab \text{ means 5 times } a \text{ times } b.$$

1. Evaluate $m - n$ for $m = 100$ and $n = 64$.

YOUR TURN

EXAMPLE 2 The area of a triangle with a base of length b and a height of length h is given by the formula $A = \frac{1}{2}bh$. Find the area when b is 8 m (meters) and h is 6.4 m.

SOLUTION We substitute 8 m for b and 6.4 m for h and then multiply:

$$A = \frac{1}{2}bh$$
$$= \frac{1}{2}(8\,\text{m})(6.4\,\text{m})$$
$$= \frac{1}{2}(8)(6.4)(\text{m})(\text{m})$$
$$= 4(6.4)\,\text{m}^2$$
$$= 25.6\,\text{m}^2, \text{ or } 25.6 \text{ square meters.}$$

2. Using the formula given in Example 2, find the area of a triangle when b is 30 in. (inches) and h is 10 in.

Note that we use square units for area and $(\text{m})(\text{m}) = \text{m}^2$.

YOUR TURN

Translating to Algebraic Expressions

Before attempting to translate problems to equations, we need to be able to translate certain phrases to algebraic expressions. Any variable can be used to represent an unknown quantity; however, it is helpful to choose a descriptive letter. For example, w suggests weight and p suggests population or price. It is important to write down what each variable represents, as well as the unit in which it is measured.

Important Words	Sample Phrase or Sentence	Variable Definition	Translation
Addition (+)			
added to	700 lb was added to the car's weight.	Let w represent the car's weight, in pounds.	$w + 700$
sum of	The sum of a number and 12	Let n represent the number.	$n + 12$
plus	53 plus some number	Let x represent "some number."	$53 + x$
more than	8000 more than Detroit's population	Let p represent Detroit's population.	$p + 8000$
increased by	Alex's original guess, increased by 4	Let n represent Alex's original guess.	$n + 4$
Subtraction (−)			
subtracted from	2 g was subtracted from the weight.	Let w represent the weight, in grams.	$w - 2$
difference of	The difference of two scores	Let m represent the larger score and n represent the smaller score.	$m - n$
minus	A team of size s, minus 2 players	Let s represent the number of players.	$s - 2$
less than	50 lb less than the weight of the lumber	Let w represent the weight of the lumber, in pounds.	$w - 50$
decreased by	The car's speed, decreased by 8 mph	Let s represent the car's speed, in miles per hour.	$s - 8$
Multiplication (·)			
multiplied by	The number of guests, multiplied by 3	Let g represent the number of guests.	$g \cdot 3$
product of	The product of two numbers	Let m and n represent the numbers.	$m \cdot n$
times	5 times the dog's weight	Let w represent the dog's weight, in pounds.	$5w$
twice	Twice the wholesale cost	Let c represent the wholesale cost.	$2c$
of	$\frac{1}{2}$ of Rita's salary	Let s represent Rita's salary.	$\frac{1}{2}s$
Division (÷)			
divided by	A 2-lb coffee cake, divided by 3	*No variables are required for translation.*	$2 \div 3$
quotient of	The quotient of 14 and 7	*No variables are required for translation.*	$14 \div 7$
divided into	4 divided into the delivery fee	Let f represent the delivery fee.	$f \div 4$
ratio of	The ratio of $500 to the price of a new car	Let p represent the price of a new car, in dollars.	$500/p$
per	There were 18 students per teacher.	*No variables are required for translation.*	$18/1$

EXAMPLE 3 Translate each phrase to an algebraic expression.

a) Four less than Ava's height, in inches

b) Eighteen more than a number

c) A day's pay, in dollars, divided by eight

SOLUTION To help think through a translation, we sometimes begin with a specific number in place of a variable.

a) If the height were 60, then 4 less than 60 would mean $60 - 4$. If we use h to represent "Ava's height, in inches," the translation of "Four less than Ava's height, in inches" is $h - 4$.

b) If we knew the number to be 10, the translation would be $10 + 18$, or $18 + 10$. If we use t to represent "a number," the translation of "Eighteen more than a number" is $t + 18$, or $18 + t$.

3. Translate to an algebraic expression: Twenty less than the number of students registered for the course.

c) We let d represent "a day's pay, in dollars." If the pay were $78, the translation would be $78 \div 8$, or $\frac{78}{8}$. Thus our translation of "A day's pay, in dollars, divided by eight" is $d \div 8$, or $d/8$.

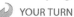 YOUR TURN

> *CAUTION!* The order in which we subtract and divide affects the answer! Answering $4 - h$ or $8 \div d$ in Examples 3(a) and 3(c) is incorrect.

EXAMPLE 4 Translate each phrase to an algebraic expression.

a) Half of some number

b) Seven pounds more than twice Owen's weight

c) Six less than the product of two numbers

d) Nine times the difference of a number and 10

e) Eighty-two percent of last year's enrollment

SOLUTION

Phrase	Variable(s)	Algebraic Expression
a) Half of some number	Let n represent the number.	$\frac{1}{2}n$, or $\frac{n}{2}$, or $n \div 2$
b) Seven pounds more than twice Owen's weight	Let w represent Owen's weight, in pounds.	$2w + 7$, or $7 + 2w$
c) Six less than the product of two numbers	Let m and n represent the numbers.	$mn - 6$
d) Nine times the difference of a number and 10	Let a represent the number.	$9(a - 10)$
e) Eighty-two percent of last year's enrollment	Let r represent last year's enrollment.	82% of r, or $0.82r$

YOUR TURN

Translating to Equations

The **equal** symbol, $=$, indicates that the expressions on either side of the equal sign represent the same number. An **equation** is a number sentence with the verb $=$.

It is important to be able to distinguish between expressions and equations. Compare the descriptions in the table below.

Expression	Equation
No $=$ sign appears.	An $=$ sign appears.
Compare to an English *phrase*, like "The interesting book."	Compare to an English *sentence*, like "The book was interesting."
May be of any length: x $3(x - 5) + 4y - 17(3 - y).$	May be of any length: $x = 7$ $3(x - 5) + 4y = 17(3 - y).$

Although we do not study equations until Chapter 2, we can translate certain problem situations to equations now. The words "is the same as," "equal," "is," "are," "was," and "were" often translate to "$=$."

> **Words indicating equality ($=$):** "is the same as," "equal," "is," "are," "was," "were," "represents"

Student Notes

Try looking for "than" or "from" in a phrase and writing what follows it first. Then add or subtract the necessary quantity. (See Examples 4b and 4c.)

4. Translate to an algebraic expression: Half of the sum of two numbers.

When translating a problem to an equation, we first translate phrases to algebraic expressions, and then the entire statement to an equation containing those expressions.

EXAMPLE 5 Translate the following problem to an equation.

What number plus 478 is 1019?

SOLUTION We let y represent the unknown number. The translation then comes almost directly from the English sentence.

Note that "what number plus 478" translates to "$y + 478$" and "is" translates to "$=$."

5. Translate to an equation: What number times 12 is 672?

YOUR TURN

Sometimes it helps to reword a problem before translating.

EXAMPLE 6 Translate the following problem to an equation.

The Siduhe River Bridge in China is the world's highest bridge. At 1550 ft, it is 270 ft higher than the Baluarte Bridge in Mexico. How high is the Baluarte Bridge?

Source: www.highestbridges.com

Baluarte Bridge, Mexico

SOLUTION We let h represent the height, in feet, of the Baluarte Bridge. A rewording and a translation are as follows:

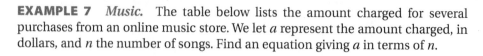

YOUR TURN

6. Translate to an equation: Valley College has 13 science instructors. There are 5 more science instructors than math instructors. How many math instructors are there?

When we translate a problem into mathematical language, we say that we **model** the problem. A **mathematical model** is a mathematical representation of a real-world situation. Note that the word *model* can be used as either a verb or a noun.

Information about a problem is often given as a set of numbers, called **data.** Sometimes data follow a pattern that can be modeled using an equation.

EXAMPLE 7 *Music.* The table below lists the amount charged for several purchases from an online music store. We let a represent the amount charged, in dollars, and n the number of songs. Find an equation giving a in terms of n.

Number of Songs Purchased, n	Amount Charged, a
2	$1.98
3	2.97
5	4.95
10	9.90

SOLUTION To write an equation for a **in terms of** n means that a will be on one side of the equal sign and an expression involving n will be on the other side.

We look for a pattern in the data. Since the amount charged increases as the number of songs increases, we can try dividing the amount by the number of songs:

$$1.98/2 = 0.99; \qquad 4.95/5 = 0.99;$$
$$2.97/3 = 0.99; \qquad 9.90/10 = 0.99.$$

7. Suppose that an online music store charges \$2.58 for 2 songs, \$3.87 for 3 songs, and \$12.90 for 10 songs. Using the same variables as in Example 7, find an equation giving a in terms of n.

The quotient is the same, 0.99, for each pair of numbers. Thus each song costs \$0.99. We reword and translate as follows:

Rewording: The amount charged is 0.99 times the number of songs.

Translating: a = 0.99 $\cdot$ n

 YOUR TURN

Technology Connection

Technology Connections are activities that make use of features that are common to most graphing calculators. In some cases, students may find the user's manual for their particular calculator helpful for exact keystrokes.

Although all graphing calculators are not the same, most share the following characteristics.

Screen. The large screen can show graphs and tables as well as the expressions entered. The screen has a different layout for different functions. Computations are performed in the **home screen**. On many calculators, the home screen is accessed by pressing `2ND` `QUIT`. The **cursor** shows location on the screen, and the **contrast** (set by `2ND` ⌃ or `2ND` ⌄) determines how dark the characters appear.

Keypad. There are options written above the keys as well as on them. To access those above the keys, we press

`2ND` or `ALPHA` and then the key. Expressions are usually entered as they would appear in print. For example, to evaluate $3xy + x$ for $x = 65$ and $y = 92$, we press 3 `×` 65 `×` 92 `+` 65 and then `ENTER`. The value of the expression, 18005, will appear at the right of the screen.

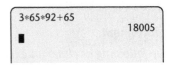

```
3*65*92+65
                        18005
■
```

Evaluate each of the following.

1. $27a - 18b$, for $a = 136$ and $b = 13$
2. $19xy - 9x + 13y$, for $x = 87$ and $y = 29$

Study Skills

Get the Facts

Throughout this textbook, you will find a feature called Study Skills. These tips are intended to help improve your math study skills. On the first day of class, we recommend that you complete this chart.

 Chapter Resources:
Translating for Success, p. 69;
Collaborative Activity
(Teamwork), p. 70

1.1   EXERCISE SET

FOR EXTRA HELP

MyMathLab® *Math XL*

PRACTICE   WATCH   READ   REVIEW

⟶ Vocabulary and Reading Check

Choose from the following list of words to complete each statement. Not every word will be used.

constant   model
equation   operation
evaluate   variable
expression

1. In the expression $4 + x$, the number 4 is a(n) _____.

2. To _____ an algebraic expression, we substitute a number for each variable and carry out the operations.

3. When we translate a problem into mathematical language, we say that we _____ the problem.

4. A(n) _____ contains an equal sign.

⟶ Concept Reinforcement

Classify each of the following as either an expression or an equation.

5. $10n - 1$

6. $3x = 21$

7. $2x - 5 = 9$

8. $5(x + 2)$

9. $45 = a - 1$

10. $4a - 5b$

11. $2x - 3y = 8$

12. $r(t + 7) + 5$

Evaluating Algebraic Expressions

Evaluate.

13. $5a$, for $a = 9$

14. $11y$, for $y = 7$

15. $12 - r$, for $r = 4$

16. $t + 8$, for $t = 2$

17. $\dfrac{a}{b}$, for $a = 45$ and $b = 9$

18. $\dfrac{c + d}{3}$, for $c = 14$ and $d = 13$

19. $\dfrac{x + y}{4}$, for $x = 2$ and $y = 14$

20. $\dfrac{m}{n}$, for $m = 54$ and $n = 9$

21. $\dfrac{p - q}{7}$, for $p = 55$ and $q = 20$

22. $\dfrac{9m}{q}$, for $m = 6$ and $q = 18$

23. $\dfrac{5z}{y}$, for $z = 9$ and $y = 15$

24. $\dfrac{m - n}{2}$, for $m = 20$ and $n = 8$

Substitute to find the value of each expression.

25. *Hockey.* The area of a rectangle with base b and height h is bh. A regulation hockey goal is 6 ft wide and 4 ft high. Find the area of the opening.

6 ft

4 ft

26. *Orbit Time.* A communications satellite orbiting 300 mi above the earth travels about 27,000 mi in one orbit. The time, in hours, for an orbit is

$$\dfrac{27{,}000}{v},$$

where v is the velocity, in miles per hour. How long will an orbit take at a velocity of 1125 mph?

27. *Zoology.* A great white shark has triangular teeth. Each tooth measures about 5 cm across the base and has a height of 6 cm. Find the surface area of the front side of one such tooth. (See Example 2.)

6 cm

5 cm

28. *Work Time.* Justin takes three times as long to do a job as Carl does. Suppose t represents the time it takes Carl to do the job. Then $3t$ represents the time it takes Justin. How long does it take Justin if Carl takes **(a)** 30 sec? **(b)** 90 sec? **(c)** 2 min?

29. *Area of a Parallelogram.* The area of a parallelogram with base b and height h is bh. Edward Tufte's

sculpture *Spring Arcs* is in the shape of a parallelogram with base 67 ft and height 12 ft. What is the area of the parallelogram?

Source: edwardtufte.com

Spring Arcs *(2004), Edward Tufte. Solid stainless steel,* 12' × 67'.

30. *Women's Softball.* A softball player's batting average is h/a, where h is the number of hits and a is the number of "at bats." In the 2011 Women's College World Series, Michelle Moultrie of the Florida Gators had 13 hits in 24 at bats. What was her batting average? Round to the nearest thousandth.

Translating to Algebraic Expressions

Translate to an algebraic expression.

31. 5 more than Ron's age

32. The product of 4 and a

33. 6 times b

34. 7 more than Patti's weight

35. 9 less than c

36. 4 less than d

37. 6 increased by q

38. 11 increased by z

39. The difference of p and t

40. m subtracted from n

41. x less than y

42. 2 less than Kurt's age

43. x divided by w

44. The quotient of two numbers

45. The sum of the box's length and height

46. The sum of d and f

47. The product of 9 and twice m

48. Abby's speed minus twice the wind speed

49. Thirteen less than one quarter of some number

50. Four less than ten times a number

51. Five times the difference of two numbers

52. One third of the sum of two numbers

53. 64% of the women attending

54. 38% of a number

Translating to Equations

Translate each problem to an equation. Do not solve.

55. What number added to 73 is 201?

56. Seven times what number is 1596?

57. When 42 is multiplied by a number, the result is 2352. Find the number.

58. When 345 is added to a number, the result is 987. Find the number.

59. *Chess.* A chess board has 64 squares. If pieces occupy 19 squares, how many squares are unoccupied?

60. *Hours Worked.* A carpenter charges $35 per hour. How many hours did she work if she billed a total of $3640?

61. *Recycling.* Currently, Americans recycle 34% of all municipal solid waste. This is the same as recycling 82 million tons per year. What is the total amount of waste generated per year?

Source: U.S. EPA, Municipal Solid Waste Department

62. *Travel to Work.* In 2009, the average commuting time to work in New York was 31.4 min. The average commuting time in North Dakota was 15.4 min shorter. How long was the average commute in North Dakota?

Source: American Community Survey

63. *Nutrition.* The number of grams f of dietary fiber recommended daily for children depends on the age a of the child, as shown in the table below. Find an equation for f in terms of a.

Age of Child, a (in years)	Grams of Dietary Fiber Recommended Daily, f
3	8
4	9
5	10
6	11
7	12
8	13

Source: The American Health Foundation

64. *Tuition.* The table below lists the tuition costs for students taking various numbers of hours of classes. Find an equation for the cost c of tuition for a student taking h hours of classes.

Number of Class Hours, h	Tuition, c
12	$1200
15	1500
18	1800
21	2100

65. *Postage Rates.* The U.S. Postal Service charges extra for packages that must be processed by hand. The table below lists machinable and nonmachinable costs for certain packages. Find an equation for the nonmachinable cost n in terms of the machinable cost m.

Weight (in pounds)	Machinable Cost, m	Nonmachinable Cost, n
1	$2.74	$4.95
2	3.08	5.29
3	3.42	5.63

Source: pe.usps.gov

66. *Foreign Currency.* On Emily's trip to Italy, she used her debit card to withdraw money. The table below lists the amounts r that she received and the amounts s that were subtracted from her account. Find an equation for r in terms of s.

Amount Received, r (in U.S. dollars)	Amount Subtracted, s (in U.S. dollars)
$150	$153
75	78
120	123

67. *Number of Drivers.* The table below lists the number of vehicle miles v traveled annually per household by the number of drivers d in the household. Find an equation for v in terms of d.

Number of Drivers, d	Number of Vehicle Miles Traveled, v
1	10,000
2	20,000
3	30,000
4	40,000

Source: Energy Information Administration

68. *Meteorology.* The table below lists the number of centimeters of water w to which various amounts of snow s will melt under certain conditions. Find an equation for w in terms of s.

Depth of Snow, s (in centimeters)	Depth of Water, w (in centimeters)
120	12
135	13.5
160	16
90	9

Translating to Algebraic Expressions and Equations

In each of Exercises 69–76, match the phrase or sentence with the appropriate expression or equation from the column on the right.

69. ____ Twice the sum of two numbers

70. ____ Five less than a number is twelve.

71. ____ Twelve more than a number is five.

72. ____ Half of the product of two numbers

73. ____ Three times the sum of a number and five

74. ____ Twice the sum of two numbers is 48.

75. ____ One less than the product of two numbers is 48.

76. ____ Six more than the quotient of two numbers

a) $\dfrac{x}{y} + 6$

b) $2(x + y) = 48$

c) $\dfrac{1}{2} \cdot a \cdot b$

d) $t + 12 = 5$

e) $ab - 1 = 48$

f) $2(m + n)$

g) $3(t + 5)$

h) $x - 5 = 12$

To the student and the instructor: Writing exercises, denoted by 📋, should be answered using one or more English sentences. Because answers to many writing exercises will vary, solutions are not listed in the answers at the back of the book.

77. What is the difference between a variable, a variable expression, and an equation?

78. What does it mean to evaluate an algebraic expression?

Synthesis

To the student and the instructor: Synthesis exercises *are designed to challenge students to extend the concepts or skills studied in each section. Many synthesis exercises will require the assimilation of skills and concepts from several sections.*

79. If the lengths of the sides of a square are doubled, is the area doubled? Why or why not?

80. Write a problem that translates to
$$2006 + t = 2014.$$

81. Signs of Distinction charges $120 per square foot for handpainted signs. The town of Belmar commissioned a triangular sign with a base of 3 ft and a height of 2.5 ft. How much will the sign cost?

82. Find the area that is shaded.

83. Evaluate $\dfrac{x - y}{3}$ when x is twice y and $x = 12$.

84. Evaluate $\dfrac{x + y}{2}$ when y is twice x and $x = 6$.

85. Evaluate $\dfrac{a + b}{4}$ when a is twice b and $a = 16$.

86. Evaluate $\dfrac{a - b}{3}$ when a is three times b and $a = 18$.

Answer each question with an algebraic expression.

87. If $w + 3$ is a whole number, what is the next whole number after it?

88. If $d + 2$ is an odd number, what is the preceding odd number?

Translate to an algebraic expression.

89. The perimeter of a rectangle with length l and width w (perimeter means distance around)

90. The perimeter of a square with side s (perimeter means distance around)

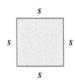

91. Ellie's race time, assuming she took 5 sec longer than Dion and Dion took 3 sec longer than Molly. Assume that Molly's time was t seconds.

92. Kade's age 7 years from now if he is 2 years older than Monique and Monique is a years old

93. If the height of a triangle is doubled, is its area also doubled? Why or why not?

YOUR TURN ANSWERS: SECTION 1.1

1. 36   **2.** 150 in^2 **3.** Let n represent the number of students registered for the course; $n - 20$ **4.** Let x and y represent the numbers; $\frac{1}{2}(x + y)$ **5.** Let x represent the number; $x \cdot 12 = 672$.   **6.** Let m represent the number of math instructors; $13 = m + 5$ **7.** $a = 1.29n$

1.2 The Commutative, Associative, and Distributive Laws

The Commutative Laws ▪ The Associative Laws ▪ The Distributive Law ▪ The Distributive Law and Factoring

Study Skills

Learn by Example

The examples in each section are designed to prepare you for success with the exercise set. Study the step-by-step solutions of the examples, noting that color is used to indicate substitutions and to call attention to the new steps in multistep examples. The time you spend studying the examples will save you valuable time when you do your assignment.

The commutative, associative, and distributive laws discussed in this section enable us to write *equivalent expressions* that will simplify our work.

The expressions $4 + 4 + 4$, $3 \cdot 4$, and $4 \cdot 3$ all represent the same number, 12. Expressions that represent the same number are said to be **equivalent**. The equivalent expressions $t + 18$ and $18 + t$ are both translations of "eighteen more than a number." These expressions are equivalent because they represent the same number for any value of t. We can illustrate this by making some choices for t.

When $t = 3$, $t + 18 = 3 + 18 = 21$
and $18 + t = 18 + 3 = 21$.

When $t = 40$, $t + 18 = 40 + 18 = 58$
and $18 + t = 18 + 40 = 58$.

The Commutative Laws

Recall that changing the order in addition or multiplication does not change the result. Equations like $3 + 78 = 78 + 3$ and $5 \cdot 14 = 14 \cdot 5$ illustrate this idea and show that addition and multiplication are **commutative**.

THE COMMUTATIVE LAWS

> ***For Addition.***   For any numbers a and b,
>
> $$a + b = b + a.$$
>
> (Changing the order of addition does not affect the answer.)
>
> ***For Multiplication.***   For any numbers a and b,
>
> $$ab = ba.$$
>
> (Changing the order of multiplication does not affect the answer.)

EXAMPLE 1   Use the commutative laws to write an expression equivalent to each of the following: **(a)** $y + 5$; **(b)** $9x$; **(c)** $7 + ab$.

SOLUTION

a) $y + 5$ is equivalent to $5 + y$ by the commutative law of addition.

b) $9x$ is equivalent to $x \cdot 9$ by the commutative law of multiplication.

c) $7 + ab$ is equivalent to $ab + 7$ by the commutative law of *addition*.

$7 + ab$ is also equivalent to $7 + ba$ by the commutative law of *multiplication*.

$7 + ab$ is also equivalent to $ba + 7$ by the two commutative laws, used together.

1. Use the commutative law of addition to write an expression equivalent to $7a + 3$.

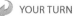 YOUR TURN

The Associative Laws

Parentheses can be used to indicate groupings. We generally simplify within the parentheses first. For example,

$$3 + (8 + 4) = 3 + 12 = 15$$

and

$$(3 + 8) + 4 = 11 + 4 = 15.$$

Similarly,

$$4 \cdot (2 \cdot 3) = 4 \cdot 6 = 24$$

and

$$(4 \cdot 2) \cdot 3 = 8 \cdot 3 = 24.$$

Note that, so long as only addition or only multiplication appears in an expression, changing the grouping does not change the result. Equations such as $3 + (7 + 5) = (3 + 7) + 5$ and $4(5 \cdot 3) = (4 \cdot 5)3$ illustrate that addition and multiplication are **associative**.

THE ASSOCIATIVE LAWS

For Addition. For any numbers a, b, and c,

$$a + (b + c) = (a + b) + c.$$

(Numbers can be grouped in any manner for addition.)

For Multiplication. For any numbers a, b, and c,

$$a \cdot (b \cdot c) = (a \cdot b) \cdot c.$$

(Numbers can be grouped in any manner for multiplication.)

EXAMPLE 2 Use an associative law to write an expression equivalent to each of the following: **(a)** $y + (z + 3)$; **(b)** $(8x)y$.

SOLUTION

a) $y + (z + 3)$ is equivalent to $(y + z) + 3$ by the associative law of addition.

b) $(8x)y$ is equivalent to $8(xy)$ by the associative law of multiplication.

YOUR TURN

2. Use the associative law of multiplication to write an expression equivalent to $37(mp)$.

When only addition or only multiplication is involved, parentheses do not change the result. For that reason, we sometimes omit them altogether. Thus,

$$x + (y + 7) = x + y + 7 \quad \text{and} \quad l(wh) = lwh.$$

A sum such as $(5 + 1) + (3 + 5) + 9$ can be simplified by pairing numbers that add to 10. The associative and commutative laws allow us to do this:

$$(5 + 1) + (3 + 5) + 9 = 5 + 5 + 9 + 1 + 3$$
$$= 10 + 10 + 3 = 23.$$

EXAMPLE 3 Use the commutative and/or associative laws of addition to write two expressions equivalent to $(7 + x) + 3$. Then simplify.

SOLUTION

$$(7 + x) + 3 = (x + 7) + 3 \qquad \text{Using the commutative law; } (x + 7) + 3 \text{ is one equivalent expression.}$$

$$= x + (7 + 3) \qquad \text{Using the associative law; } x + (7 + 3) \text{ is another equivalent expression.}$$

$$= x + 10 \qquad \text{Simplifying}$$

3. Use the commutative and/or associative laws of multiplication to write two expressions equivalent to $2(x \cdot 3)$. Then simplify.

YOUR TURN

Student Notes

To remember the names *commutative*, *associative*, and *distributive*, first understand the concept. Next, use everyday life to link each word to the concept. For example, think of *commuting* to and from college as changing the order of appearance.

The Distributive Law

The *distributive law* is probably the single most important law for manipulating algebraic expressions. Unlike the commutative and associative laws, the distributive law uses multiplication together with addition.

The distributive law relates expressions like $5(x + 2)$ and $5x + 10$, which involve both multiplication and addition. When two numbers are multiplied, the result is a **product**. The parts of the product are called **factors**. When two numbers are added, the result is a **sum**. The parts of the sum are called **terms**.

$5(x + 2)$ is a product. The factors are 5 and $(x + 2)$.

This factor is a sum. Its terms are x and 2.

$5x + 10$ is a sum. The terms are $5x$ and 10.

This term is a product. Its factors are 5 and x.

In general, a term is a number, a variable, or a product or a quotient of numbers and/or variables. Terms are separated by plus signs.

EXAMPLE 4 List the terms in the expression $3s + st + \dfrac{2s}{t}$.

SOLUTION Terms are separated by plus signs, so the terms in $3s + st + \dfrac{2s}{t}$ are $3s$, st, and $\dfrac{2s}{t}$.

4. List the terms in the expression $5x + 3y$.

YOUR TURN

EXAMPLE 5 List the factors in the expression $x(3 + y)$.

SOLUTION Factors are parts of products, so the factors in $x(3 + y)$ are x and $(3 + y)$.

5. List the factors in the expression $4 \cdot x \cdot y$.

YOUR TURN

You have already used the distributive law although you may not have realized it at the time. To illustrate, try to multiply $3 \cdot 21$ mentally. Many people find the product, 63, by thinking of 21 as $20 + 1$ and then multiplying 20 by 3 and 1 by 3. The sum of the two products, $60 + 3$, is 63. Note that if the 3 does not multiply *both* 20 and 1, the result will not be correct.

We can compute $4(7 + 2)$ in two ways. As in the discussion of $3(20 + 1)$ above, to compute $4(7 + 2)$, we can multiply both 7 and 2 by 4 and add the results:

$$4(7 + 2) = 4 \cdot 7 + 4 \cdot 2 = 28 + 8 = 36.$$

By first adding inside the parentheses, we get the same result in a different way:

$$4(7 + 2) = 4(9) = 36.$$

Student Notes

The distributive law involves both addition *and* multiplication. Do not try to "distribute" when only multiplication is involved. For example, $5(3 \cdot x) = (5 \cdot 3) \cdot x = 15x$ (by the associative law of multiplication). *It is incorrect to write* $5(3 \cdot x) = (5 \cdot 3)(5 \cdot x).$

THE DISTRIBUTIVE LAW

For any numbers a, b, and c,

$$a(b + c) = ab + ac.$$

(The product of a number and a sum can be written as the sum of two products.)

EXAMPLE 6   Multiply: $3(x + 2)$.

SOLUTION   Since $x + 2$ cannot be simplified unless a value for x is given, we use the distributive law:

$$3(x + 2) = 3 \cdot x + 3 \cdot 2 \qquad \text{Using the distributive law}$$
$$= 3x + 6. \qquad \text{Note that } 3 \cdot x \text{ is the same as } 3x.$$

6. Multiply: $5(3 + y)$.

YOUR TURN

The distributive law can also be used when more than two terms are inside the parentheses.

EXAMPLE 7   Multiply: $6(s + 2 + 5w)$.

SOLUTION

$$6(s + 2 + 5w) = 6 \cdot s + 6 \cdot 2 + 6 \cdot 5w \qquad \text{Using the distributive law}$$
$$= 6s + 12 + (6 \cdot 5)w \qquad \text{Using the associative law for multiplication}$$
$$= 6s + 12 + 30w$$

7. Multiply: $4(5a + 6m + 1)$.

YOUR TURN

Because of the commutative law of multiplication, the distributive law can be used on the "right": $(b + c)a = ba + ca$.

EXAMPLE 8   Multiply: $(c + 4)5$.

SOLUTION

$$(c + 4)5 = c \cdot 5 + 4 \cdot 5 \qquad \text{Using the distributive law on the right}$$
$$= 5c + 20 \qquad \text{Using the commutative law; } c \cdot 5 = 5c$$

8. Multiply: $(11 + y)2$.

YOUR TURN

CAUTION!   To use the distributive law for removing parentheses, be sure to multiply *each* term inside the parentheses by the multiplier outside. Thus,

$$a(b + c) \neq ab + c \quad \text{but} \quad a(b + c) = ab + ac.$$

The Distributive Law and Factoring

If we use the distributive law in reverse, we have the basis of a process called **factoring**: $ab + ac = a(b + c)$. To **factor** an expression means to write an equivalent expression that is a product. Recall that the parts of the product are called **factors**. Note that "factor" can be used as either a verb or a noun. A **common factor** is a factor that appears in every term in an expression.

EXAMPLE 9   Use the distributive law to factor each of the following.

a) $3x + 3y$ **b)** $7x + 21y + 7$

SOLUTION

a) By the distributive law,

$$3x + 3y = 3(x + y).\qquad \text{The common factor for } 3x \text{ and } 3y \text{ is } 3.$$

b) $7x + 21y + 7 = 7 \cdot x + 7 \cdot 3y + 7 \cdot 1$ The common factor is 7.

$$= 7(x + 3y + 1)$$ Using the distributive law.

 Be sure to include both the 1 and the common factor, 7.

9. Use the distributive law to factor $15x + 5$.
_____

 YOUR TURN

To check our factoring, we multiply to see if the original expression is obtained. For example, to check the **factorization** in Example 9(b), note that

$$7(x + 3y + 1) = 7 \cdot x + 7 \cdot 3y + 7 \cdot 1$$
$$= 7x + 21y + 7.$$

Since $7x + 21y + 7$ is what we started with in Example 9(b), we have a check.

1.2   EXERCISE SET

FOR EXTRA HELP   MyMathLab® Math XL

PRACTICE   WATCH   READ   REVIEW

Vocabulary and Reading Check

Choose from the following list of words to complete each statement. Not every word will be used.

associative   factors
commutative   product
distributive   sum
equivalent   terms

1. _____ expressions represent the same number.

2. Changing the order of multiplication does not affect the answer. This is an example of a(n) _____ law.

3. The result of addition is called a(n) _____ .

4. The numbers in a product are called _____ .

Concept Reinforcement

Determine whether each statement illustrates a commutative law, an associative law, or a distributive law.

5. $8 + x = x + 8$ **6.** $5b(c) = 5(bc)$

7. $x(y + z) = xy + xz$ **8.** $3(t + 4) = 3(4 + t)$

9. $5(x + 2) = (x + 2)5$ **10.** $2a + 2b = 2(a + b)$

The Commutative Laws

Use the commutative law of addition to write an equivalent expression.

11. $11 + t$ **12.** $a + 2$

13. $4 + 8x$ **14.** $ab + c$

15. $9x + 3y$ **16.** $3a + 7b$

17. $5(a + 1)$ **18.** $9(x + 5)$

Use the commutative law of multiplication to write an equivalent expression.

19. $7x$

20. xy

21. st

22. $13m$

23. $5 + ab$

24. $x + 3y$

25. $5(a + 1)$

26. $9(x + 5)$

The Associative Laws

Use the associative law of addition to write an equivalent expression.

27. $(x + 8) + y$

28. $(5 + m) + r$

29. $u + (v + 7)$

30. $x + (2 + y)$

31. $(ab + c) + d$

32. $(m + np) + r$

Use the associative law of multiplication to write an equivalent expression.

33. $(10x)y$

34. $(4u)v$

35. $2(ab)$

36. $9(7r)$

37. $3[2(a + b)]$

38. $5[x(2 + y)]$

The Commutative and Associative Laws

Use the commutative and/or associative laws to write two equivalent expressions. Answers may vary.

39. $s + (t + 6)$

40. $7 + (v + w)$

41. $(17a)b$

42. $x(3y)$

Use the commutative and/or associative laws to show why the expression on the left is equivalent to the expression on the right. Write a series of steps with labels, as in Example 3.

43. $(1 + x) + 2$ is equivalent to $x + 3$

44. $(2a)4$ is equivalent to $8a$

45. $(m \cdot 3)7$ is equivalent to $21m$

46. $4 + (9 + x)$ is equivalent to $x + 13$

The Distributive Law

List the terms in each expression.

47. $x + xyz + 1$

48. $9 + 17a + abc$

49. $2a + \dfrac{a}{3b} + 5b$

50. $3xy + 20 + \dfrac{4a}{b}$

51. $4x + 4y$

52. $14 + 2y$

List the factors in each expression.

53. $5n$

54. uv

55. $3(x + y)$

56. $(a + b)12$

57. $7 \cdot a \cdot b$

58. $m \cdot n \cdot 2$

59. $(a - b)(x - y)$

60. $(3 - a)(b + c)$

Multiply.

61. $2(x + 15)$

62. $3(x + 5)$

63. $4(1 + a)$

64. $7(1 + y)$

65. $10(9x + 6)$

66. $9(6m + 7)$

67. $5(r + 2 + 3t)$

68. $4(5x + 8 + 3p)$

69. $(a + b)2$

70. $(x + 2)7$

71. $(x + y + 2)5$

72. $(2 + a + b)6$

The Distributive Law and Factoring

Use the distributive law to factor each of the following. Check by multiplying.

73. $2a + 2b$

74. $5y + 5z$

75. $7 + 7y$

76. $13 + 13x$

77. $32x + 2$

78. $20a + 5$

79. $5x + 10 + 15y$

80. $3 + 27b + 6c$

81. $7a + 35b$

82. $3x + 24y$

83. $44x + 11y + 22z$

84. $14a + 56b + 7$

The Commutative, Associative, and Distributive Laws

Fill in each blank with the law that justifies that step.

85. $3(2 + x)$
$= 3(x + 2)$ _____
$= 3 \cdot x + 3 \cdot 2$ _____
$= 3x + 6$ Multiplying

86. $(y + 4)5$
$= 5(y + 4)$ _____
$= 5 \cdot y + 5 \cdot 4$ _____
$= 5y + 20$ Multiplying

87. $7(2x + 3y)$
$= 7(2x) + 7(3y)$ _____
$= (7 \cdot 2)x + (7 \cdot 3)y$ _____
$= 14x + 21y$ Multiplying

88. $(4a + 2)8$
$= 8(4a + 2)$ _____
$= 8(4a) + 8(2)$ _____
$= (8 \cdot 4)a + 8(2)$ _____
$= 32a + 16$ Multiplying

 89. Is subtraction commutative? Why or why not?

 90. Is division associative? Why or why not?

Synthesis

 91. Give an example illustrating the distributive law, and identify the terms and the factors in your example. Explain how you can identify terms and factors in an expression.

92. Explain how the distributive, commutative, and associative laws can be used to show that $2(3x + 4y)$ is equivalent to $6x + 8y$.

Fill in each blank with the law that justifies that step.

93. $[2(x + 1)] + 3x$
$= [2 \cdot x + 2 \cdot 1] + 3x$ _____
$= [2x + 2] + 3x$ Multiplying
$= 2x + [2 + 3x]$ _____
$= 2x + [3x + 2]$ _____
$= [2x + 3x] + 2$ _____
$= [(2 + 3)x] + 2$ _____
$= [5x] + 2$ Adding
$= 5x + 2$

94. $12a + 4(b + 5)$
$= (4 \cdot 3)a + 4(b + 5)$ Writing 12 as a product
$= 4(3a) + 4(b + 5)$ _____
$= 4(3a) + 4(b) + 4(5)$ _____
$= 4(3a + b + 5)$ _____

Tell whether the expressions in each pairing are equivalent. Then explain why or why not.

95. $8 + 4(a + b)$ and $4(2 + a + b)$

96. $5(a \cdot b)$ and $5 \cdot a \cdot 5 \cdot b$

97. $7 \div 3m$ and $m \cdot 3 \div 7$

98. $(rt + st)5$ and $5t(r + s)$

99. $30y + x \cdot 15$ and $5[2(x + 3y)]$

100. $[c(2 + 3b)]5$ and $10c + 15bc$

101. Evaluate the expressions $3(2 + x)$ and $6 + x$ for $x = 0$. Do your results indicate that $3(2 + x)$ and $6 + x$ are equivalent? Why or why not?

102. Factor $15x + 40$. Then evaluate both $15x + 40$ and the factorization for $x = 4$. Do your results *guarantee* that the factorization is correct? Why or why not? (*Hint:* See Exercise 101.)

103. Aidan, Beth, and Cody consistently work more than 40 hours every week. The first 40 hours are paid at a regular pay rate of $10 per hour. The number of hours over 40 are paid at an overtime pay rate that is one and one-half times the regular pay rate. Each of the employees calculates the week's wages using a different formula.

- Aidan multiplies his overtime hours by 1.5, adds this to his regular hours, and then multiplies the sum by 10.
- Beth multiplies her regular hours by 10, then multiplies her overtime hours by 10 and then by 1.5. Finally, she adds the two amounts together.
- Cody multiplies his overtime hours by 15 and adds this to 400.

Let x represent the number of overtime hours worked in one week.

a) Write an algebraic expression for each method of calculating wages.

b) Use the commutative, associative, and distributive laws to show that all three methods of calculating wages yield the same total.

YOUR TURN ANSWERS: SECTION 1.2

1. $3 + 7a$ **2.** $(37m)p$ **3.** $2(3x); (2 \cdot 3)x; 6x;$ answers may vary   **4.** $5x, 3y$ **5.** $4, x, y$ **6.** $15 + 5y$
7. $20a + 24m + 4$ **8.** $22 + 2y$ **9.** $5(3x + 1)$

QUICK QUIZ: SECTIONS 1.1 AND 1.2

To the student and the instructor: Beginning in the second section of each chapter, every exercise set contains a short quiz reviewing content already taught in the chapter. The numbers in brackets immediately following the directions or exercise indicate the section in which the skill was introduced. The answers to all quiz exercises appear at the back of the book. Continuous review of chapter content is excellent preparation for a chapter test.

1. Evaluate $x - y$ for $x = 17$ and $y = 8$.   [1.1]

2. Translate to an algebraic expression: Twice the sum of m and 3.   [1.1]

3. Translate to an equation. Do not solve. One-third of what number is 18?   [1.1]

4. Multiply: $3(x + 5y + 7)$.   [1.2]

5. Factor: $14a + 7t + 7$.   [1.2]

1.3 Fraction Notation

Factors and Prime Factorizations ● Multiplication, Division, and Simplification of Fractions ● Addition and Subtraction of Fractions

This section covers multiplication, addition, subtraction, and division with fractions, including fraction expressions that contain variables.

An example of **fraction notation** for a number is

$$\frac{2}{3}. \quad \begin{array}{l} \leftarrow \text{Numerator} \\ \leftarrow \text{Denominator} \end{array}$$

The top number is called the **numerator,** and the bottom number is called the **denominator**.

Factors and Prime Factorizations

We first review how *natural numbers* are factored. **Natural numbers** can be thought of as the counting numbers:

$$1, 2, 3, 4, 5, \dots.$$

(The dots indicate that the established pattern continues without ending.)

Since factors are parts of products, to factor a number, we express it as a product of two or more numbers.

Several factorizations of 12 are

$$1 \cdot 12, \quad 2 \cdot 6, \quad 3 \cdot 4, \quad 2 \cdot 2 \cdot 3.$$

It is easy to overlook a factor of a number if the factorizations are not written methodically.

EXAMPLE 1 List all factors of 18.

SOLUTION Beginning at 1, we check all natural numbers to see if they are factors of 18. If they are, we write the factorization. We stop when we have already included the next natural number in a factorization.

1 is a factor of every number.	$1 \cdot 18$
2 is a factor of 18.	$2 \cdot 9$
3 is a factor of 18.	$3 \cdot 6$
4 is *not* a factor of 18.	
5 is *not* a factor of 18.	

6 is the next natural number, but we have already listed 6 as a factor in the product $3 \cdot 6$.

We stop at 6 because any natural number greater than 6 would be paired with a factor less than 6. (Remember that multiplication is commutative.)

We now write the factors of 18, going down the above list of factorizations writing the first factors and then up the list writing the second factors:

$$1, \quad 2, \quad 3, \quad 6, \quad 9, \quad 18.$$

 YOUR TURN

Student Notes

If you are asked to "find the factors" of a number, your answer will be a list of numbers. If you are asked to "find a factorization" of a number, your answer will be a product. For example:

The factors of 12 are 1, 2, 3, 4, 6, 12.

A factorization of 12 is $2 \cdot 2 \cdot 3$.

1. List all factors of 54.

Some numbers have only two different factors, the number itself and 1. Such numbers are called **prime**.

PRIME NUMBER

A *prime number* is a natural number that has exactly two different factors: the number itself and 1. The first several primes are 2, 3, 5, 7, 11, 13, 17, 19, and 23.

If a natural number other than 1 is not prime, we call it **composite**.

EXAMPLE 2   Label each number as prime, composite, or neither: 29, 4, 1.

SOLUTION

29 is prime. It has exactly two different factors, 29 and 1.

4 is not prime. It has three different factors, 1, 2, and 4. It is composite.

1 is not prime. It does not have two *different* factors. The number 1 is not considered composite. It is neither prime nor composite.

2. Label 21 as prime, composite, or neither.

YOUR TURN

Every composite number can be factored into a product of prime numbers. Such a factorization is called the **prime factorization** of that composite number.

EXAMPLE 3   Find the prime factorization of 36.

SOLUTION   We first factor 36 in any way that we can, such as

$$36 = 4 \cdot 9.$$

Since 4 and 9 are not prime, we factor them:

$$36 = 4 \cdot 9$$
$$= 2 \cdot 2 \cdot 3 \cdot 3. \qquad \text{2 and 3 are both prime.}$$

3. Find the prime factorization of 100.

The prime factorization of 36 is $2 \cdot 2 \cdot 3 \cdot 3$.

YOUR TURN

Student Notes

When writing a factorization, you are writing an equivalent expression for the original number. Some students do this with a tree diagram:

$$36 = 4 \quad \cdot \quad 9$$
$$36 = 2 \cdot 2 \cdot 3 \cdot 3$$

All prime

Multiplication, Division, and Simplification of Fractions

Recall from arithmetic that fractions are multiplied as follows.

MULTIPLICATION OF FRACTIONS

For any two fractions a/b and c/d,

$$\frac{a}{b} \cdot \frac{c}{d} = \frac{ac}{bd}.$$

(The numerator of the product is the product of the two numerators. The denominator of the product is the product of the two denominators.)

EXAMPLE 4 Multiply: **(a)** $\dfrac{2}{3} \cdot \dfrac{5}{7}$; **(b)** $\dfrac{4}{x} \cdot \dfrac{8}{y}$; **(c)** $9 \cdot \dfrac{7}{n}$.

SOLUTION We multiply numerators as well as denominators.

a) $\dfrac{2}{3} \cdot \dfrac{5}{7} = \dfrac{2 \cdot 5}{3 \cdot 7} = \dfrac{10}{21}$
   b) $\dfrac{4}{x} \cdot \dfrac{8}{y} = \dfrac{4 \cdot 8}{x \cdot y} = \dfrac{32}{xy}$

4. Multiply: $\dfrac{2}{x} \cdot \dfrac{3}{7}$.

c) $9 \cdot \dfrac{7}{n} = \dfrac{9}{1} \cdot \dfrac{7}{n} = \dfrac{9 \cdot 7}{1 \cdot n} = \dfrac{63}{n}$ 9 can be written $\dfrac{9}{1}$

 YOUR TURN

Any nonzero number divided by itself is 1.

FRACTION NOTATION FOR 1

For any number a, except 0,

$$\dfrac{a}{a} = 1.$$

Two numbers whose product is 1 are **reciprocals**, or **multiplicative inverses**, of each other. All numbers, except zero, have reciprocals. For example,

the reciprocal of $\dfrac{2}{3}$ is $\dfrac{3}{2}$ because $\dfrac{2}{3} \cdot \dfrac{3}{2} = \dfrac{6}{6} = 1$;

the reciprocal of 9 is $\dfrac{1}{9}$ because $9 \cdot \dfrac{1}{9} = \dfrac{9}{1} \cdot \dfrac{1}{9} = \dfrac{9}{9} = 1$;

the reciprocal of $\dfrac{1}{4}$ is 4 because $\dfrac{1}{4} \cdot 4 = \dfrac{1}{4} \cdot \dfrac{4}{1} = \dfrac{4}{4} = 1$.

Reciprocals are used to rewrite division in an equivalent form that uses multiplication.

DIVISION OF FRACTIONS

To divide two fractions, multiply by the reciprocal of the divisor:

$$\dfrac{a}{b} \div \dfrac{c}{d} = \dfrac{a}{b} \cdot \dfrac{d}{c}.$$

EXAMPLE 5 Divide: $\dfrac{1}{2} \div \dfrac{3}{5}$.

SOLUTION

$$\dfrac{1}{2} \div \dfrac{3}{5} = \dfrac{1}{2} \cdot \dfrac{5}{3}$$ $\dfrac{5}{3}$ is the reciprocal of $\dfrac{3}{5}$.

5. Divide: $\dfrac{3}{4} \div \dfrac{5}{7}$.

$$= \dfrac{5}{6}$$

 YOUR TURN

Multiplying a number by 1 gives that same number because of the *identity property of* 1. A similar property can be stated for division.

Study Skills

Do the Exercises

- When you complete an odd-numbered exercise, you can check your answers at the back of the book. If you miss any, closely examine your work, and if necessary, consult your instructor for guidance.

- Do some even-numbered exercises, even if none are assigned. Because there are no answers given for them, you will gain practice doing exercises in a context similar to taking a quiz or a test. Check your answers later with a friend or your instructor.

THE IDENTITY PROPERTY OF 1

For any number a,

$$a \cdot 1 = 1 \cdot a = a.$$

(Multiplying a number by 1 gives that same number.) The number 1 is called the *multiplicative identity*.

For example, we can multiply $\frac{4}{5} \cdot \frac{6}{6}$ to find an expression equivalent to $\frac{4}{5}$. Since $\frac{6}{6} = 1$, the expression $\frac{4}{5} \cdot \frac{6}{6}$ is equivalent to $\frac{4}{5} \cdot 1$, or simply $\frac{4}{5}$. We have

$$\frac{4}{5} \cdot \frac{6}{6} = \frac{4 \cdot 6}{5 \cdot 6} = \frac{24}{30}.$$

Thus, $\frac{24}{30}$ is equivalent to $\frac{4}{5}$.

We reverse these steps by "removing a factor equal to 1"—in this case, $\frac{6}{6}$. By removing a factor that equals 1, we can *simplify* an expression like $\frac{24}{30}$ to an equivalent expression like $\frac{4}{5}$.

To simplify, we factor the numerator and the denominator, looking for the largest factor common to both. This is sometimes made easier by writing prime factorizations. After identifying common factors, we can express the fraction as a product of two fractions, one of which is in the form a/a.

EXAMPLE 6   Simplify: **(a)** $\dfrac{15}{40}$; **(b)** $\dfrac{36}{24}$.

SOLUTION

a) Note that 5 is a factor of both 15 and 40:

$$\frac{15}{40} = \frac{3 \cdot 5}{8 \cdot 5} \qquad \text{Factoring the numerator and the denominator, using the common factor, 5}$$

$$= \frac{3}{8} \cdot \frac{5}{5} \qquad \text{Rewriting as a product of two fractions; } \frac{5}{5} = 1$$

$$= \frac{3}{8} \cdot 1 = \frac{3}{8}. \qquad \text{Using the identity property of 1 (removing a factor equal to 1)}$$

b) $\dfrac{36}{24} = \dfrac{2 \cdot 2 \cdot 3 \cdot 3}{2 \cdot 2 \cdot 2 \cdot 3}$ Writing the prime factorizations and identifying common factors; 12/12 could also be used.

$$= \frac{3}{2} \cdot \frac{2 \cdot 2 \cdot 3}{2 \cdot 2 \cdot 3} \qquad \text{Rewriting as a product of two fractions; } \frac{2 \cdot 2 \cdot 3}{2 \cdot 2 \cdot 3} = 1$$

$$= \frac{3}{2} \cdot 1 = \frac{3}{2} \qquad \text{Using the identity property of 1}$$

6. Simplify: $\dfrac{35}{30}$.

YOUR TURN

It is always wise to check your result to see if any common factors of the numerator and the denominator remain. (This will not occur if prime factorizations are used correctly.) If common factors remain, repeat the process by removing another factor equal to 1 to simplify your result.

"Canceling" is a shortcut that you may have used for removing a factor equal to 1 when working with fraction notation. With *great* concern, we mention it as a possible way to speed up your work. Canceling can be used only when removing common factors in numerators and denominators. Canceling *cannot* be used in sums or differences. Our concern is that "canceling" be used with understanding. Example 6(b) might have been done faster as follows:

$$\frac{36}{24} = \frac{2 \cdot 2 \cdot 3 \cdot 3}{2 \cdot 2 \cdot 2 \cdot 3} = \frac{3}{2}, \quad \text{or} \quad \frac{36}{24} = \frac{3 \cdot \cancel{12}}{2 \cdot \cancel{12}} = \frac{3}{2}, \quad \text{or} \quad \frac{\overset{3}{\overset{18}{\cancel{36}}}}{\underset{12}{\underset{2}{\cancel{24}}}} = \frac{3}{2}.$$

> **CAUTION!**   Unfortunately, canceling is often performed incorrectly:
>
> $$\frac{\cancel{2} + 3}{\cancel{2}} \neq 3, \qquad \frac{\cancel{4} - 1}{\cancel{4} - 2} \neq \frac{1}{2}, \qquad \frac{1\cancel{5}}{\cancel{5}4} \neq \frac{1}{4}.$$
>
> The above cancellations are incorrect because the expressions canceled are *not* factors. For example, in $2 + 3$, the 2 and the 3 are not factors. Correct simplifications are as follows:
>
> $$\frac{2 + 3}{2} = \frac{5}{2}, \qquad \frac{4 - 1}{4 - 2} = \frac{3}{2}, \qquad \frac{15}{54} = \frac{5 \cdot \cancel{3}}{18 \cdot \cancel{3}} = \frac{5}{18}.$$
>
> *Remember*: **If you can't factor, you can't cancel! If in doubt, don't cancel!**

Sometimes it is helpful to use 1 as a factor in the numerator or the denominator when simplifying.

EXAMPLE 7   Simplify: $\dfrac{9}{72}$.

SOLUTION

$$\frac{9}{72} = \frac{1 \cdot 9}{8 \cdot 9} \qquad \text{Factoring and using the identity property of 1 to write 9 as } 1 \cdot 9$$

$$= \frac{1 \cdot \cancel{9}}{8 \cdot \cancel{9}} = \frac{1}{8} \qquad \text{Simplifying by removing a factor equal to 1: } \frac{9}{9} = 1$$

YOUR TURN

Addition and Subtraction of Fractions

When denominators are the same, fractions are added or subtracted by adding or subtracting numerators and keeping the same denominator.

> **ADDITION AND SUBTRACTION OF FRACTIONS**
>
> For any two fractions a/d and b/d,
>
> $$\frac{a}{d} + \frac{b}{d} = \frac{a + b}{d} \quad \text{and} \quad \frac{a}{d} - \frac{b}{d} = \frac{a - b}{d}. \qquad \text{Note that the denominators are the same.}$$

Student Notes

The following rules can help you quickly determine whether 2, 3, or 5 is a factor of a number.

2 is a factor of a number if the number is even (the ones digit is 0, 2, 4, 6, or 8).

3 is a factor of a number if the sum of its digits is divisible by 3.

5 is a factor of a number if its ones digit is 0 or 5.

7. Simplify: $\dfrac{6}{18}$.

> **CAUTION!**   When adding or subtracting fractions with the same denominator, add or subtract only the numerators. The denominator does not change.

EXAMPLE 8 Add and simplify: $\dfrac{4}{8} + \dfrac{5}{8}$.

SOLUTION The common denominator is 8. We add the numerators and keep the common denominator:

$$\frac{4}{8} + \frac{5}{8} = \frac{4+5}{8} = \frac{9}{8}. \qquad \text{You can think of this as } 4 \cdot \tfrac{1}{8} + 5 \cdot \tfrac{1}{8} = 9 \cdot \tfrac{1}{8}, \text{ or } \tfrac{9}{8}.$$

8. Add and simplify: $\dfrac{2}{5} + \dfrac{4}{5}$.

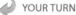 YOUR TURN

In arithmetic, we often write $1\tfrac{1}{8}$ rather than the "improper" fraction $\tfrac{9}{8}$. In algebra, $\tfrac{9}{8}$ is generally more useful and is quite "proper" for our purposes.

When denominators are different, we use the identity property of 1 and multiply to find a common denominator. Then we add, as in Example 8.

A common denominator is a number that is divisible by each fraction's denominator. One method of finding a common denominator uses prime factorizations.

FINDING A COMMON DENOMINATOR USING PRIME FACTORIZATIONS

1. Find the prime factorization of each denominator.
2. Choose one factorization.
3. Multiply that factorization by any factors of the other denominator that it lacks.

EXAMPLE 9 Add: $\dfrac{7}{8} + \dfrac{5}{12}$.

SOLUTION We follow the steps listed above to find a common denominator.

1. $8 = 2 \cdot 2 \cdot 2$ Find the prime factorization of each denominator.
    $12 = 2 \cdot 2 \cdot 3$

2. $2 \cdot 2 \cdot 2$ Choose one factorization.

3. $2 \cdot 2 \cdot 2 \cdot 3$ The factorization of 8 is "missing" the factor 3 from the factorization of 12.

The common denominator is thus $2 \cdot 2 \cdot 2 \cdot 3$, or 24. It is divisible by both 8 and 12. We multiply both $\tfrac{7}{8}$ and $\tfrac{5}{12}$ by suitable forms of 1 to obtain two fractions with denominators of 24:

$$\frac{7}{8} + \frac{5}{12} = \frac{7}{8} \cdot \frac{3}{3} + \frac{5}{12} \cdot \frac{2}{2} \qquad \text{Multiplying by 1. Since } 8 \cdot 3 = 24, \text{ we multiply } \tfrac{7}{8} \text{ by } \tfrac{3}{3}. \text{ Since } 12 \cdot 2 = 24, \text{ we multiply } \tfrac{5}{12} \text{ by } \tfrac{2}{2}.$$

$$= \frac{21}{24} + \frac{10}{24} \qquad \text{Performing the multiplication}$$

$$= \frac{31}{24}. \qquad \text{Adding fractions}$$

9. Add: $\dfrac{9}{8} + \dfrac{4}{5}$.

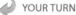 YOUR TURN

After adding, subtracting, multiplying, or dividing, we may still need to simplify the answer.

EXAMPLE 10   Perform the indicated operation and, if possible, simplify.

a) $\dfrac{7}{10} - \dfrac{1}{5}$

b) $8 \cdot \dfrac{5}{12}$

c) $\dfrac{\frac{5}{6}}{\frac{25}{9}}$

SOLUTION

a) $\dfrac{7}{10} - \dfrac{1}{5} = \dfrac{7}{10} - \dfrac{1}{5} \cdot \dfrac{2}{2}$ Using 10 as the common denominator

$= \dfrac{7}{10} - \dfrac{2}{10}$

$= \dfrac{5}{10} = \dfrac{1 \cdot \cancel{5}}{2 \cdot \cancel{5}} = \dfrac{1}{2}$ Removing a factor equal to 1: $\dfrac{5}{5} = 1$

b) $8 \cdot \dfrac{5}{12} = \dfrac{8 \cdot 5}{12}$ Multiplying numerators and denominators. Think of 8 as $\frac{8}{1}$.

$= \dfrac{2 \cdot 2 \cdot 2 \cdot 5}{2 \cdot 2 \cdot 3}$ Factoring; $\dfrac{4 \cdot 2 \cdot 5}{4 \cdot 3}$ can also be used.

$= \dfrac{\cancel{2} \cdot \cancel{2} \cdot 2 \cdot 5}{\cancel{2} \cdot \cancel{2} \cdot 3}$ Removing a factor equal to 1: $\dfrac{2 \cdot 2}{2 \cdot 2} = 1$

$= \dfrac{10}{3}$ Simplifying

c) $\dfrac{\frac{5}{6}}{\frac{25}{9}} = \dfrac{5}{6} \div \dfrac{25}{9}$ Rewriting horizontally. Remember that a fraction bar indicates division.

$= \dfrac{5}{6} \cdot \dfrac{9}{25}$ Multiplying by the reciprocal of $\frac{25}{9}$

$= \dfrac{5 \cdot 3 \cdot 3}{2 \cdot 3 \cdot 5 \cdot 5}$ Writing as one fraction and factoring

$= \dfrac{\cancel{5} \cdot \cancel{3} \cdot 3}{2 \cdot \cancel{3} \cdot \cancel{5} \cdot 5}$ Removing a factor equal to 1: $\dfrac{5 \cdot 3}{3 \cdot 5} = 1$

$= \dfrac{3}{10}$ Simplifying

10. Subtract and, if possible, simplify:

$\dfrac{9}{20} - \dfrac{1}{4}.$

 YOUR TURN

Technology Connection

Many calculators can perform operations using fraction notation. You may find an option n/d on a key or in a **menu** of options that appears when a key is pressed. To select an item from a menu, we highlight its number and press **ENTER** or simply press the number of the item.

For example, to add $\frac{2}{15} + \frac{7}{12}$, we first press **MATH** ▷ ⌃ **ENTER** to choose the n/d option in the MATH NUM submenu. An empty fraction template will appear on the screen. We then press ② ⌄ ① ⑤ to enter the numerator and the denominator of the first fraction. Next, we press ▷ to move outside of the fraction and then press ⊕. To enter the second fraction, we press **MATH** ▷ ⌃ **ENTER** again and then enter the numerator and the denominator of the second fraction. We press **ENTER** to calculate the result.

$$\frac{2}{15} + \frac{7}{12}$$

$$\frac{43}{60}$$

Since a fraction bar indicates division, we can enter $\frac{2}{15} + \frac{7}{12}$ as $2/15 + 7/12$. The answer is typically given in decimal notation. To convert this to fraction notation, we press **MATH** and select the FRAC option. The notation ANS ▶ FRAC shows that the calculator will convert .7166666667 to fraction notation.

```
2/15+7/12
                    .7166666667
Ans▶Frac
                           43/60
```

We see that $\frac{2}{15} + \frac{7}{12} = \frac{43}{60}$.

1.3   EXERCISE SET

FOR EXTRA HELP

MyMathLab® Math XL   PRACTICE   WATCH READ   REVIEW

🢂 Vocabulary and Reading Check

Choose from the following list of words to complete each statement. Not every word will be used.

add	numerator
composite	opposite
denominator	prime
multiply	reciprocal

1. The top number in a fraction is called the _____.

2. A(n) _____ number has exactly two different factors.

3. To divide two fractions, multiply by the _____ of the divisor.

4. We need a common denominator in order to _____ fractions.

🢂 Concept Reinforcement

In each of Exercises 5–8, match the description with a number from the list on the right.

5. ____ A factor of 35   a) 2

6. ____ A number that has 3 as a factor   b) 7

7. ____ An odd composite number   c) 60

8. ____ The only even prime number   d) 65

To the student and the instructor: *Beginning in this section, selected exercises are marked with the symbol* Aha! *. Students who pause to inspect an Aha! exercise should find the answer more readily than those who proceed mechanically. This is done to discourage rote memorization. Some later "Aha!" exercises in this exercise set are unmarked, to encourage students to always pause before working a problem.*

Factors and Prime Factorizations

Label each of the following numbers as prime, composite, or neither.

9. 9	**10.** 15	**11.** 41	**12.** 49
13. 77	**14.** 37	**15.** 2	**16.** 1
17. 0	**18.** 16		

List all the factors of each number.

19. 50	**20.** 70	**21.** 42	**22.** 60

Find the prime factorization of each number. If the number is prime, state this.

23. 39	**24.** 34	**25.** 30
26. 98	**27.** 27	**28.** 54
29. 150	**30.** 56	**31.** 31
32. 180	**33.** 210	**34.** 79
35. 115	**36.** 143	

Simplification of Fractions

Simplify.

37. $\dfrac{21}{35}$ **38.** $\dfrac{20}{26}$ **39.** $\dfrac{16}{56}$

40. $\dfrac{72}{27}$ **41.** $\dfrac{12}{48}$ **42.** $\dfrac{18}{84}$

43. $\dfrac{52}{13}$ **44.** $\dfrac{132}{11}$ **45.** $\dfrac{19}{76}$

46. $\dfrac{17}{51}$ **47.** $\dfrac{150}{25}$ **48.** $\dfrac{180}{36}$

49. $\dfrac{42}{50}$ **50.** $\dfrac{75}{80}$ **51.** $\dfrac{120}{82}$

52. $\dfrac{75}{45}$ **53.** $\dfrac{210}{98}$ **54.** $\dfrac{140}{350}$

Multiplication, Division, Addition, and Subtraction of Fractions

Perform the indicated operation and, if possible, simplify.

55. $\dfrac{1}{2} \cdot \dfrac{3}{5}$ **56.** $\dfrac{11}{10} \cdot \dfrac{8}{5}$ **57.** $\dfrac{9}{2} \cdot \dfrac{4}{3}$

Aha! **58.** $\dfrac{11}{12} \cdot \dfrac{12}{11}$ **59.** $\dfrac{1}{8} + \dfrac{3}{8}$ **60.** $\dfrac{1}{2} + \dfrac{1}{8}$

61. $\dfrac{4}{9} + \dfrac{13}{18}$ **62.** $\dfrac{4}{5} + \dfrac{8}{15}$ **63.** $\dfrac{3}{a} \cdot \dfrac{b}{7}$

64. $\dfrac{x}{5} \cdot \dfrac{y}{z}$ **65.** $\dfrac{4}{n} + \dfrac{6}{n}$ **66.** $\dfrac{9}{x} - \dfrac{5}{x}$

67. $\dfrac{3}{10} + \dfrac{8}{15}$ **68.** $\dfrac{7}{8} + \dfrac{5}{12}$ **69.** $\dfrac{11}{7} - \dfrac{4}{7}$

70. $\dfrac{12}{5} - \dfrac{2}{5}$ **71.** $\dfrac{13}{18} - \dfrac{4}{9}$ **72.** $\dfrac{13}{15} - \dfrac{11}{45}$

Aha! **73.** $\dfrac{20}{30} - \dfrac{2}{3}$ **74.** $\dfrac{5}{7} - \dfrac{5}{21}$ **75.** $\dfrac{7}{6} \div \dfrac{3}{5}$

76. $\dfrac{7}{5} \div \dfrac{10}{3}$ **77.** $12 \div \dfrac{4}{9}$ **78.** $\dfrac{9}{4} \div 9$

Aha! **79.** $\dfrac{7}{13} \div \dfrac{7}{13}$ **80.** $\dfrac{1}{10} \div \dfrac{1}{5}$ **81.** $\dfrac{\frac{2}{7}}{\frac{5}{3}}$

82. $\dfrac{\frac{3}{8}}{\frac{1}{5}}$ **83.** $\dfrac{9}{\frac{1}{2}}$ **84.** $\dfrac{\frac{3}{7}}{6}$

85. Under what circumstances would the sum of two fractions be easier to compute than the product of the same two fractions?

86. Under what circumstances would the product of two fractions be easier to compute than the sum of the same two fractions?

Synthesis

87. Bryce insists that $(2 + x)/8$ is equivalent to $(1 + x)/4$. What mistake do you think is being made and how could you demonstrate to Bryce that the two expressions are not equivalent?

88. *Research.* Mathematicians use computers to determine whether very large numbers are prime. Find the largest prime number currently known, and describe how it was found.

89. In the following table, the top number can be factored in such a way that the sum of the factors is the bottom number. For example, in the first column, 56 is factored as $7 \cdot 8$, since $7 + 8 = 15$, the bottom number. Find the missing numbers in each column.

Product	56	63	36	72	140	96	168
Factor	7						
Factor	8						
Sum	15	16	20	38	24	20	29

90. *Packaging.* Tritan Candies uses two sizes of boxes, 6 in. long and 8 in. long. These are packed end to end in larger cartons to be shipped. What is the shortest-length carton that will accommodate boxes of either size without any room left over? (Each carton must contain boxes of only one size; no mixing is allowed.)

Simplify.

91. $\dfrac{16 \cdot 9 \cdot 4}{15 \cdot 8 \cdot 12}$ **92.** $\dfrac{9 \cdot 8xy}{2xy \cdot 36}$

93. $\dfrac{45pqrs}{9prst}$ **94.** $\dfrac{247}{323}$

95. $\dfrac{15 \cdot 4xy \cdot 9}{6 \cdot 25x \cdot 15y}$

96. $\dfrac{10x \cdot 12 \cdot 25y}{2z \cdot 30x \cdot 20y}$

97. $\dfrac{\frac{27ab}{15mn}}{\frac{18bc}{25np}}$

98. $\dfrac{\frac{45xyz}{24ab}}{\frac{30xz}{32ac}}$

99. $\dfrac{5\frac{3}{4}rs}{4\frac{1}{2}st}$

100. $\dfrac{3\frac{5}{7}mn}{2\frac{4}{5}np}$

Find the area of each figure.

101.

102.

103. Find the perimeter of a square with sides of length $3\frac{5}{9}$ m.

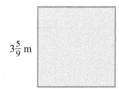

104. Find the perimeter of the rectangle in Exercise 101.

105. Find the total length of the edges of a cube with sides of length $2\frac{3}{10}$ cm.

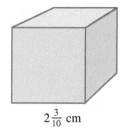

$2\frac{3}{10}$ cm

⮕ **YOUR TURN ANSWERS: SECTION 1.3**

1. 1, 2, 3, 6, 9, 18, 27, 54   **2.** Composite   **3.** $2 \cdot 2 \cdot 5 \cdot 5$
4. $\dfrac{6}{7x}$ **5.** $\dfrac{21}{20}$ **6.** $\dfrac{7}{6}$ **7.** $\dfrac{1}{3}$ **8.** $\dfrac{6}{5}$ **9.** $\dfrac{77}{40}$ **10.** $\dfrac{1}{5}$

QUICK QUIZ: SECTIONS 1.1–1.3

1. Translate to an algebraic expression: 4 less than the width of a box.   [1.1]

2. Use a commutative law to write an expression equivalent to $5(x + 3)$. There is more than one correct answer.   [1.2]

3. Find the prime factorization of 40.   [1.3]

4. Simplify: $\dfrac{54}{66}$.   [1.3]

5. Add and, if possible, simplify: $\dfrac{4}{x} + \dfrac{7}{x}$.   [1.3]

1.4   Positive and Negative Real Numbers

Whole Numbers and Integers   ▪   The Rational Numbers   ▪   Real Numbers and Order   ▪   Absolute Value

A **set** is a collection of objects. The set containing 1, 3, and 7 is usually written $\{1, 3, 7\}$. In this section, we examine some important sets of numbers.

Whole Numbers and Integers

Whole numbers = {0, 1, 2, 3, ...}

The set of **whole numbers** can be written as $\{0, 1, 2, 3, \dots\}$. We represent this set using dots on the number line, as shown at left.

To create the set of integers, we include all whole numbers, along with their *opposites*. To find the opposite of a number, we locate the number that is the same distance from 0 but on the other side of 0 on the number line. For example,

the opposite of 1 is negative 1, written -1;

and

the opposite of 3 is negative 3, written -3.

Student Notes

It is not uncommon in mathematics for a symbol to have more than one meaning in different contexts. The symbol "−" in 5 − 3 indicates subtraction. The same symbol in −10 indicates the opposite of 10, or negative 10.

The **integers** consist of all whole numbers and their opposites. Note that, except for 0, opposites occur in pairs. Thus, 5 is the opposite of −5, just as −5 is the opposite of 5. The number 0 acts as its own opposite.

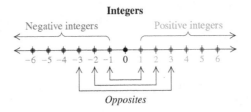

Integers

SET OF INTEGERS

The set of integers $= \{\ldots, -4, -3, -2, -1, 0, 1, 2, 3, 4, \ldots\}.$

Integers are associated with many real-world problems and situations.

EXAMPLE 1   State which integer(s) corresponds to each situation.

a) In 2011, there was $13.7 trillion in outstanding mortgage debt in the United States.

> **Source**: Board of Governors of the Federal Reserve System

b) Badwater Basin in Death Valley, California, is 282 ft below sea level.

SOLUTION

a) The integer −13,700,000,000,000 corresponds to a debt of $13.7 trillion.

b) The integer −282 corresponds to 282 ft below sea level. The elevation is −282 ft.

1. State what integers correspond to this situation: The highest temperature ever recorded in a desert was 136 degrees Fahrenheit (°F) at Al-Aziziyah in the Sahara, Libya. The coldest temperature ever recorded in a desert was 4°F below zero in the McMurdo Dry Valleys, Antarctica.

> **Source**: Guinness World Records

 YOUR TURN

The Rational Numbers

A number like $\frac{5}{9}$, although built out of integers, is not itself an integer. Another set of numbers, the **rational numbers**, contains integers, fractions, and decimals. Some examples of rational numbers are

$$\frac{5}{9}, \quad -\frac{4}{7}, \quad 95, \quad -16, \quad 0, \quad \frac{-35}{8}, \quad 2.4, \quad -0.31.$$

The number $-\frac{4}{7}$ can be written as $\frac{-4}{7}$ or $\frac{4}{-7}$. Indeed, every number listed above can be written as an integer over an integer. For example, 95 can be written as $\frac{95}{1}$ and 2.4 can be written as $\frac{24}{10}$. In this manner, any *ratio*nal number can be expressed as the *ratio* of two integers. Rather than attempt to list all rational numbers, we use this idea of ratio to describe the set as follows.

Try to Get Ahead

Try to keep one section ahead of your instructor. If you study ahead of your lectures, you can concentrate on what is being explained in class, rather than trying to write everything down. You can then write notes on only special points or questions related to what is happening in class.

> **SET OF RATIONAL NUMBERS**
>
> The set of rational numbers $= \left\{ \dfrac{a}{b} \,\middle|\, a \text{ and } b \text{ are integers and } b \neq 0 \right\}$.
>
> This is read "the set of all numbers a over b, such that a and b are integers and b does not equal zero."

To *graph* a number is to mark its location on the number line.

EXAMPLE 2   Graph each of the following rational numbers: **(a)** $\frac{5}{2}$; **(b)** -3.2; **(c)** $\frac{11}{8}$.

SOLUTION

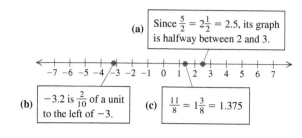

(a) Since $\frac{5}{2} = 2\frac{1}{2} = 2.5$, its graph is halfway between 2 and 3.

(b) -3.2 is $\frac{2}{10}$ of a unit to the left of -3.

(c) $\frac{11}{8} = 1\frac{3}{8} = 1.375$

2. Graph -1.1 on the number line.

YOUR TURN

Every rational number can be written using fraction notation or decimal notation.

EXAMPLE 3   Convert to decimal notation: $-\frac{5}{8}$.

SOLUTION   We first find decimal notation for $\frac{5}{8}$. Since $\frac{5}{8}$ means $5 \div 8$, we divide.

$$
\begin{array}{r}
0.6\,2\,5 \\
8\overline{)5.0\,0\,0} \\
\underline{4\,8} \\
2\,0 \\
\underline{1\,6} \\
4\,0 \\
\underline{4\,0} \\
0
\end{array}
$$

$\longleftarrow$ The remainder is 0.

3. Convert $-\dfrac{7}{4}$ to decimal notation.

Thus, $\frac{5}{8} = 0.625$, so $-\frac{5}{8} = -0.625$.

YOUR TURN

Because the division in Example 3 ends with the remainder 0, we consider -0.625 a **terminating decimal**. If we are "bringing down" zeros and a remainder reappears, we have a **repeating decimal**, as shown in the next example.

EXAMPLE 4   Convert to decimal notation: $\frac{7}{11}$.

SOLUTION   We divide:

$$
\begin{array}{r}
0.6\,3\,6\,3\ldots \\
11\overline{)7.0\,0\,0\,0} \\
\underline{6\,6} \\
4\,0 \\
\underline{3\,3} \\
7\,0 \\
\underline{6\,6} \\
4\,0
\end{array}
$$

4 reappears as a remainder, so the pattern of 6's and 3's in the quotient will repeat.

4. Convert $-\frac{1}{6}$ to decimal notation.

We abbreviate repeating decimals by writing a bar over the repeating part—in this case, $0.\overline{63}$. Thus, $\frac{7}{11} = 0.\overline{63}$.

YOUR TURN

Although we do not prove it here, every rational number can be expressed as either a terminating decimal or a repeating decimal, and every terminating decimal or repeating decimal is a rational number.

Real Numbers and Order

Some numbers, when written in decimal form, neither terminate nor repeat. Such numbers are called **irrational numbers**. These numbers cannot be expressed as a ratio of two integers.

What sort of numbers are irrational? One example is π (the Greek letter *pi*, read "pie"), which is used to find the area and the circumference of a circle: $A = \pi r^2$ and $C = 2\pi r$.

Another irrational number, $\sqrt{2}$ (read "the square root of 2"), is the length of the diagonal of a square with sides of length 1. It is also the number that, when multiplied by itself, gives 2. No rational number can be multiplied by itself to get 2, although some approximations come close:

1.4 is an *approximation* of $\sqrt{2}$ because $(1.4)(1.4) = 1.96$;

1.41 is a better approximation because $(1.41)(1.41) = 1.9881$;

1.4142 is an even better approximation because $(1.4142)(1.4142) = 1.99996164$.

To approximate $\sqrt{2}$ on some calculators, we simply press ② and then ⎷ . With other calculators, we press ⎷ ② **ENTER**. If needed, consult your manual.

EXAMPLE 5   Graph the real number $\sqrt{3}$ on the number line.

SOLUTION   We use a calculator and approximate: $\sqrt{3} \approx 1.732$ ("$\approx$" means "approximately equals"). Then we locate this number on the number line.

5. Graph $\sqrt{5}$ on the number line.

YOUR TURN

Not every square root is irrational. For example, $\sqrt{9} = 3$, so $\sqrt{9}$ is a rational number.

The rational numbers and the irrational numbers together correspond to all the points on the number line and make up what is called the **real-number system**.

Technology Connection

To approximate $\sqrt{3}$ on some graphing calculators, we press $\boxed{\sqrt{}}$ and then enter 3. Some calculators require the use of parentheses around the 3.

Approximate each of the following to nine decimal places.

1. $\sqrt{5}$
2. $\sqrt{7}$
3. $\sqrt{13}$
4. $\sqrt{27}$

> **SET OF REAL NUMBERS**
>
> The set of real numbers = The set of all numbers corresponding to points on the number line.

The following figure shows the relationships among various kinds of numbers.

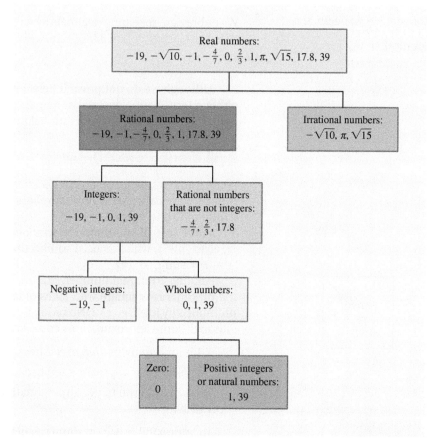

EXAMPLE 6 Which numbers in the following group are **(a)** whole numbers? **(b)** integers? **(c)** rational numbers? **(d)** irrational numbers? **(e)** real numbers?

$$-38, \quad -\frac{8}{5}, \quad 0, \quad 0.\overline{3}, \quad 4.5, \quad \sqrt{30}, \quad 52$$

SOLUTION

a) 0 and 52 are whole numbers.

b) -38, 0, and 52 are integers.

c) -38, $-\frac{8}{5}$, 0, $0.\overline{3}$, 4.5, and 52 are rational numbers.

d) $\sqrt{30}$ is an irrational number.

e) -38, $-\frac{8}{5}$, 0, $0.\overline{3}$, 4.5, $\sqrt{30}$, and 52 are real numbers.

6. Which numbers in the following group are integers?

$$5, \quad -15, \quad 0, \quad -3.6, \quad \frac{2}{3}$$

YOUR TURN

EXPLORING 🔍 THE CONCEPT

Use the number line shown at right to answer the following questions.

1. Graph the numbers 2 and 5.
   a) Which number is farther to the right on the number line?
   b) Which number is greater?
2. Graph the numbers 2 and −5.
   a) Which number is farther to the right on the number line?
   b) Which number is greater?
3. Graph the numbers −2 and −5.
   a) Which number is farther to the right on the number line?
   b) Which number is greater?
4. Why is 4 > 1, but −4 < −1?

ANSWERS

1. (a) 5; (b) 5   2. (a) 2; (b) 2   3. (a) −2; (b) −2
4. 4 is to the right of 1 on the number line, and −1 is to the right of −4 on the number line.

Real numbers are named in order on the number line, with larger numbers farther to the right. For any two numbers, the one to the left is less than the one to the right. We use the symbol **<** to mean "**is less than**." The sentence −8 < 6 means "−8 is less than 6." The symbol **>** means "**is greater than**." The sentence −3 > −7 means "−3 is greater than −7."

EXAMPLE 7 Use either < or > for ▓ to write a true sentence.

a) 2 ▓ 9
b) −3.45 ▓ 1.32
c) 6 ▓ −12
d) −18 ▓ −5
e) $\frac{7}{11}$ ▓ $\frac{5}{8}$

SOLUTION

a) Since 2 is to the left of 9 on the number line, we know that 2 is less than 9, so 2 < 9.

b) Since −3.45 is to the left of 1.32, we have −3.45 < 1.32.

c) Since 6 is to the right of −12, we have 6 > −12.

d) Since −18 is to the left of −5, we have −18 < −5.

e) We convert to decimal notation: $\frac{7}{11} = 0.\overline{63}$ and $\frac{5}{8} = 0.625$. Thus, $\frac{7}{11} > \frac{5}{8}$.

We also could have used a common denominator: $\frac{7}{11} = \frac{56}{88} > \frac{55}{88} = \frac{5}{8}$.

7. Use either < or > for ▓ to write a true sentence: −8 ▓ −9.

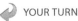 YOUR TURN

Student Notes

It is important to remember that just because an equation or inequality is written or printed, it is not necessarily *true*. For instance, 6 = 7 is an equation and 2 > 5 is an inequality. Of course, both statements are *false*.

Sentences like "$a < −5$" and "$−3 > −8$" are **inequalities**. It may be helpful to think of an inequality sign as "opening" toward the larger number, or as being widest next to the larger number.

Note that $a > 0$ means that a represents a positive real number and $a < 0$ means that a represents a negative real number.

Statements like $a \leq b$ and $b \geq a$ are also inequalities. We read $a \leq b$ as "a **is less than or equal to** b" and $a \geq b$ as "a **is greater than or equal to** b."

EXAMPLE 8 Write a second inequality with the same meaning as $−11 \leq −3$.

SOLUTION Every inequality can be written in two ways:

$−11 \leq −3$ has the same meaning as $−3 \geq −11$.

If we read both inequalities, we say that

$−11$ is less than or equal to $−3$,   and

$−3$ is greater than or equal to $−11$.

These statements have the same meaning.

8. Write a second inequality with the same meaning as $5 > y$.

YOUR TURN

Technology Connection

Graphing calculators use the notation $|2|$ or abs (2) to indicate the absolute value of 2. This is often accessed using the NUM option of the MATH key. When entering negative numbers, be sure to use the ⊝ key and *not* the ⊖ key.

Absolute Value

The distance that a number is from 0 on the number line is called the **absolute value** of the number.

Distance is never negative, so numbers that are opposites have the same absolute value. If a number is nonnegative, its absolute value is the number itself. If a number is negative, its absolute value is its opposite.

> ### ABSOLUTE VALUE
> We write $|a|$, read "the absolute value of a," to represent the number of units that a is from zero.

EXAMPLE 9 Find each absolute value: **(a)** $|-3|$; **(b)** $|7.2|$; **(c)** $|0|$.

SOLUTION

a) $|-3| = 3$ since -3 is 3 units from 0.

b) $|7.2| = 7.2$ since 7.2 is 7.2 units from 0.

c) $|0| = 0$ since 0 is 0 units from itself.

9. Find the absolute value: $|-18|$.

YOUR TURN

1.4 EXERCISE SET

FOR EXTRA HELP

 MyMathLab® MathXL
PRACTICE   WATCH   READ   REVIEW

Vocabulary and Reading Check

Choose from the following list of words to complete each statement. Not every word will be used.

absolute value   rational number
integer   repeating
irrational number   terminating
opposite   whole number

1. Since $\frac{3}{20} = 0.15$, we can write $\frac{3}{20}$ as a(n) _____ decimal.

2. If a number is a(n) _____, it is either a whole number or the opposite of a whole number.

3. 0 is the only _____ that is not a natural number.

4. A number like $\sqrt{5}$, which cannot be written precisely in fraction notation or decimal notation, is an example of a(n) _____.

5. The _____ of 1 is -1.

6. When two numbers are opposites, they have the same _____.

Concept Reinforcement

Translate each phrase to an algebraic expression.

7. The opposite of n

8. The absolute value of x

9. -10 is less than x

10. 6 is greater than or equal to y

Whole Numbers and Integers

State which real numbers correspond to each situation.

11. *Student Loans and Grants.* The maximum amount that an independent undergraduate first-year student can borrow with a Direct Stafford Loan is $9500. The maximum annual award for the Landscape Architecture Foundation Scholarship is $5000.

Sources: www.studentaid.ed.gov and www.collegescholarships.org

12. Using a NordicTrack exercise machine, Kylie burned 150 calories. She then drank an isotonic drink containing 65 calories.

13. *Record Temperature.* The highest temperature recorded in Alaska is 100 degrees Fahrenheit (°F) at Fort Yukon. The lowest temperature recorded in Alaska is 80°F below zero at Prospect Creek Camp.

Source: www.netstate.com

14. The Dead Sea is 1349 ft below sea level, whereas Mt. Everest is 29,035 ft above sea level.

Source: National Geographic

15. *Stock Market.* The Dow Jones Industrial Average is an indicator of the stock market. On September 29, 2008, the Dow Jones fell a record 777.68 points. On October 13, 2008, the Dow Jones gained a record 936.42 points.

Sources: CME Group Index Services, LLC; Dow Jones Indexes

16. Ignition occurs 10 sec before liftoff. A spent fuel tank is detached 235 sec after liftoff.

17. Kittling County Volunteers received a technology grant of $10,000 and spent $4500 to update its website.

18. Mina deposited $650 in a savings account. Two weeks later, she withdrew $180.

19. The New York Giants gained 8 yd on the first play. They lost 5 yd on the next play.

20. In the 2011 British Open Championship, golfer Rory McIlroy finished 7 over par. In the U.S. Open Championship, he finished 16 under par.

Source: PGA Tour Inc.

The Rational Numbers

Graph each rational number on the number line.

21. -2 **22.** 5

23. -4.3 **24.** 3.87

25. $\frac{10}{3}$ **26.** $-\frac{17}{5}$

Write decimal notation for each number.

27. $\frac{7}{8}$ **28.** $-\frac{1}{8}$ **29.** $-\frac{3}{4}$

30. $\frac{11}{6}$ **31.** $-\frac{7}{6}$ **32.** $-\frac{5}{12}$

33. $\frac{2}{3}$ **34.** $\frac{1}{4}$ **35.** $-\frac{1}{2}$

36. $-\frac{1}{9}$ Aha! **37.** $\frac{13}{100}$ **38.** $-\frac{9}{20}$

Real Numbers and Order

Graph each irrational number on the number line.

39. $\sqrt{5}$ **40.** $\sqrt{92}$

41. $-\sqrt{22}$ **42.** $-\sqrt{54}$

Write a true sentence using either $<$ or $>$.

43. $5 \quad 0$ **44.** $8 \quad -8$

45. $-9 \quad 9$ **46.** $0 \quad -7$

47. $-8 \quad -5$ **48.** $-4 \quad -3$

49. $-5 \quad -11$ **50.** $-3 \quad -4$

51. $-12.5 \quad -10.2$ **52.** $-10.3 \quad -14.5$

53. $\frac{5}{12} \quad \frac{11}{25}$ **54.** $-\frac{14}{17} \quad -\frac{27}{35}$

For each of the following, write a second inequality with the same meaning.

55. $-2 > x$ **56.** $a > 9$

57. $10 \leq y$ **58.** $-12 \geq t$

For Exercises 59–64, consider the following list:

$$-83, \quad -4.7, \quad 0, \quad \tfrac{5}{9}, \quad 2.\overline{16}, \quad \pi, \quad \sqrt{17}, \quad 62.$$

59. List all rational numbers.

60. List all natural numbers.

61. List all integers.

62. List all irrational numbers.

63. List all real numbers.

64. List all nonnegative integers.

Absolute Value

Find each absolute value.

65. $|-58|$

66. $|-47|$

67. $|-12.2|$

68. $|4.3|$

69. $|\sqrt{2}|$

70. $|-456|$

71. $\left|-\frac{9}{7}\right|$

72. $|-\sqrt{3}|$

73. $|0|$

74. $\left|-\frac{3}{4}\right|$

75. $|x|$, for $x = -8$

76. $|a|$, for $a = -5$

 77. Is every integer a rational number? Why or why not?

78. Is every integer a natural number? Why or why not?

Synthesis

 79. Is the absolute value of a number always positive? Why or why not?

80. How many rational numbers are there between 0 and 1? Justify your answer.

81. Does "nonnegative" mean the same thing as "positive"? Why or why not?

List in order from least to greatest.

82. $13, -12, 5, -17$

83. $-23, 4, 0, -17$

84. $-\frac{2}{3}, \frac{1}{2}, -\frac{3}{4}, -\frac{5}{6}, \frac{3}{8}, \frac{1}{6}$

85. $\frac{4}{5}, \frac{4}{3}, \frac{4}{8}, \frac{4}{6}, \frac{4}{9}, \frac{4}{2}, -\frac{4}{3}$

Write a true sentence using either $<$, $>$, or $=$.

86. $|-5|$ $|-2|$

87. $|4|$ ▢ $|-7|$

88. $|-8|$ ▢ $|8|$

89. $|23|$ ▢ $|-23|$

Solve. Consider only integer replacements.

Aha! **90.** $|x| = 19$

91. $|x| < 3$

92. $2 < |x| < 5$

Given that $0.3\overline{3} = \frac{1}{3}$ and $0.6\overline{6} = \frac{2}{3}$, express each of the following as a ratio of two integers.

93. $0.1\overline{1}$

94. $0.9\overline{9}$

95. $5.5\overline{5}$

96. $7.7\overline{7}$

Translate to an inequality.

97. A number a is negative.

98. A number x is nonpositive.

99. The distance from x to 0 is no more than 10.

100. The distance from t to 0 is at least 20.

To the student and the instructor: *The calculator icon, 🖩, indicates those exercises designed to be solved with a calculator.*

101. When Helga's calculator gives a decimal value for $\sqrt{2}$ and that value is promptly squared, the result is 2. Yet when that same decimal approximation is entered by hand and then squared, the result is not exactly 2. Why do you suppose this is?

102. Is the following statement true? Why or why not?
$$\sqrt{a^2} = |a| \quad \text{for any real number } a.$$

↘ YOUR TURN ANSWERS: SECTION 1.4

1. $136; -4$ **2.**

```
      -1.1
 +--+--●--+--+--+--+--+
-4  -2  0     2     4
```

3. -1.75

4. $-0.1\overline{6}$ **5.**

```
                  √5
 +--+--+--+--+--+--●--+
-4  -2  0     2     4
```

6. $5, -15, 0$

7. $>$ **8.** $y < 5$ **9.** 18

QUICK QUIZ: SECTIONS 1.1–1.4

1. Evaluate $12 - c$ for $c = 11$. [1.1]

2. Factor: $5x + 5y + 15$. [1.2]

3. Subtract and, if possible, simplify: $\frac{1}{2} - \frac{1}{3}$. [1.3]

4. Divide and, if possible, simplify: $\frac{4}{5} \div \frac{2}{5}$. [1.3]

5. Write a true sentence using either $<$ or $>$: $0 \,\square\, -0.5$. [1.4]

Mid-Chapter Review

An introduction to algebra involves learning some basic laws and terms.

Commutative Laws: $a + b = b + a$; $ab = ba$
Associative Laws: $a + (b + c) = (a + b) + c$; $a(bc) = (ab)c$
Distributive Law: $a(b + c) = ab + ac$

GUIDED SOLUTIONS

1. Evaluate $\dfrac{x - y}{3}$ for $x = 22$ and $y = 10$.   [1.1]*

Solution

$$\frac{x - y}{3} = \frac{\boxed{} - \boxed{}}{3} \quad \text{Substituting}$$

$$= \frac{\boxed{}}{3} \quad \text{Subtracting}$$

$$= \boxed{} \quad \text{Dividing}$$

2. Factor: $14x + 7$.   [1.2]

Solution

$$14x + 7 = \boxed{} \cdot 2x + \boxed{} \cdot 1$$

Factoring each term using a common factor

$$= \boxed{} (2x + 1) \quad \text{Factoring out the common factor}$$

MIXED REVIEW

Evaluate.   [1.1]

3. $x + y$, for $x = 3$ and $y = 12$

4. $\dfrac{2a}{5}$, for $a = 10$

Translate to an algebraic expression.   [1.1]

5. 10 less than d

6. The product of 8 and the number of hours worked

7. Translate to an equation. Do not solve.   [1.1]
Janine's class has 27 students. This is 5 fewer than the number originally enrolled. How many students originally enrolled in the class?

8. Determine whether 8 is a solution of $13t = 94$. [1.1]

9. Use the commutative law of addition to write an expression equivalent to $7 + 10x$.   [1.2]

10. Use the associative law of multiplication to write an expression equivalent to $3(ab)$.   [1.2]

Multiply.   [1.2]

11. $4(2x + 8)$

12. $3(2m + 5n + 10)$

Factor.   [1.2]

13. $18x + 15$

14. $9c + 12d + 3$

15. Find the prime factorization of 84.   [1.3]

16. Simplify: $\frac{135}{315}$.

Perform the indicated operation and, if possible, simplify.   [1.3]

17. $\dfrac{11}{12} - \dfrac{3}{8}$

18. $\dfrac{8}{15} \div \dfrac{6}{11}$

19. Graph -2.5 on the number line.   [1.4]

20. Write decimal notation for $-\frac{3}{20}$.   [1.4]

Write a true sentence using either < or >.   [1.4]

21. $-16 \ \square \ -24$

22. $-\frac{3}{22} \ \square \ -\frac{2}{15}$

23. Write a second inequality with the same meaning as $x \geq 9$.   [1.4]

Find the absolute value.   [1.4]

24. $|-5.6|$

25. $|0|$

---

*The *section reference* [1.1] refers to Chapter 1, Section 1. The concept reviewed in Guided Solution 1 was developed in this section.

1.5 Addition of Real Numbers

Adding with the Number Line ▪ Adding Without the Number Line ▪ Problem Solving ▪ Combining Like Terms

We now consider addition of real numbers. To gain understanding, we will use the number line first and then develop rules that allow us to add without the number line.

Adding with the Number Line

To add $a + b$ on the number line, we start at a and move according to b.

a) If b is positive, we move to the right (the positive direction).

b) If b is negative, we move to the left (the negative direction).

c) If b is 0, we stay at a.

EXAMPLE 1 Add: $-4 + 9$.

SOLUTION To add on the number line, we locate the first number, -4, and then move 9 units to the right. Note that it requires 4 units to reach 0. The difference between 9 and 4 is where we finish.

$$-4 + 9 = 5$$

1. Use the number line to add $-3 + 5$.

YOUR TURN

EXAMPLE 2 Add: $3 + (-5)$.

SOLUTION We locate the first number, 3, and then move 5 units to the left. Note that it requires 3 units to reach 0. The difference between 5 and 3 is 2, so we finish 2 units to the left of 0, at -2.

$$3 + (-5) = -2$$

2. Use the number line to add $1 + (-4)$.

YOUR TURN

EXAMPLE 3 Add: $-4 + (-3)$.

SOLUTION After locating -4, we move 3 units to the left. We finish a total of 7 units to the left of 0, at -7.

$$-4 + (-3) = -7$$

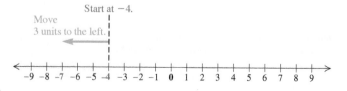

3. Use the number line to add $-2 + (-1)$.

YOUR TURN

EXAMPLE 4 Add: −5.2 + 0.

SOLUTION We locate −5.2 and move 0 units. Thus we finish where we started, at −5.2.

$$-5.2 + 0 = -5.2$$

4. Use the number line to add −4 + 0.

YOUR TURN

From Examples 1–4, we can develop the following rules.

RULES FOR ADDITION OF REAL NUMBERS

1. *Positive numbers*: Add as usual. The answer is positive.
2. *Negative numbers*: Add absolute values and make the answer negative (see Example 3).
3. *A positive number and a negative number*: Subtract the smaller absolute value from the greater absolute value. Then:

    a) If the positive number has the greater absolute value, the answer is positive (see Example 1).
    b) If the negative number has the greater absolute value, the answer is negative (see Example 2).
    c) If the numbers have the same absolute value, the answer is 0.

4. *One number is zero*: The sum is the other number (see Example 4).

Rule 4 is known as the **identity property of 0**.

IDENTITY PROPERTY OF 0

For any real number *a*,

$$a + 0 = 0 + a = a.$$

(Adding 0 to a number gives that same number.) The number 0 is called the *additive identity*.

Adding Without the Number Line

Student Notes

Parentheses are essential when a negative sign follows an operation. Just as we would never write 8 ÷ ×2, it is improper to write −12 + −7.

The rules listed above can be used without drawing the number line.

EXAMPLE 5 Add without using the number line.

a) −12 + (−7)   b) −1.4 + 8.5
c) −36 + 21   d) 1.5 + (−1.5)
e) $-\frac{7}{8} + 0$ f) $\frac{2}{3} + \left(-\frac{5}{8}\right)$

Study Skills

Two (or a Few More) Heads Are Better Than One

Consider forming a study group with some of your classmates. Exchange telephone numbers, schedules, and any e-mail addresses so that you can coordinate study time for homework and tests.

5. Add without using the number line:

$2.3 + (-9.1)$.

SOLUTION

a) $-12 + (-7) = -19$

Two negatives. *Think:* Add the absolute values, 12 and 7, to get 19. Make the answer *negative*, -19.

b) $-1.4 + 8.5 = 7.1$

A negative and a positive. *Think:* The difference of absolute values is $8.5 - 1.4$, or 7.1. The positive number has the greater absolute value, so the answer is *positive*, 7.1.

c) $-36 + 21 = -15$

A negative and a positive. *Think:* The difference of absolute values is $36 - 21$, or 15. The negative number has the greater absolute value, so the answer is *negative*, -15.

d) $1.5 + (-1.5) = 0$

A negative and a positive. *Think:* Since the numbers are opposites, they have the same absolute value and the answer is 0.

e) $-\dfrac{7}{8} + 0 = -\dfrac{7}{8}$

One number is zero. The sum is the other number, $-\frac{7}{8}$.

f) $\dfrac{2}{3} + \left(-\dfrac{5}{8}\right) = \dfrac{16}{24} + \left(-\dfrac{15}{24}\right)$

$= \dfrac{1}{24}$

This is similar to part (b) above. We find a common denominator and then add.

YOUR TURN

If we are adding several numbers, some positive and some negative, the commutative and associative laws allow us to add all the positives, then add all the negatives, and then add the results. Of course, we can also add from left to right, if we prefer.

EXAMPLE 6   Add: $15 + (-2) + 7 + 14 + (-5) + (-12)$.

SOLUTION

$15 + (-2) + 7 + 14 + (-5) + (-12)$

$= 15 + 7 + 14 + (-2) + (-5) + (-12)$ Using the commutative law of addition

$= (15 + 7 + 14) + [(-2) + (-5) + (-12)]$ Using the associative law of addition

$= 36 + (-19)$ Adding the positives; adding the negatives

$= 17$ Adding a positive and a negative

6. Add:

$-3 + 10 + (-11) + (-1) + 4$.

YOUR TURN

Problem Solving

EXAMPLE 7   *Credit-Card Interest Rates.*   During one four-week period in 2011, the national average credit-card interest rate dropped 0.09%, then rose 0.16%, stayed the same, and then dropped 0.02%. By how much did the national average credit-card interest rate change?

Source: CreditCards.com Weekly Credit Card Rate Report

SOLUTION   The problem translates to a sum:

Rewording: The 1st   the 2nd   the 3rd   the 4th   the total
change plus change plus change plus change is   change.

Translating: -0.09 $+$ 0.16 $+$ 0 $+$ (-0.02) $=$ Total change

Adding from left to right, we have

$$-0.09 + 0.16 + 0 + (-0.02) = 0.07 + 0 + (-0.02) = 0.07 + (-0.02) = 0.05.$$

The national average credit-card interest rate rose 0.05% over the four-week period.

YOUR TURN

7. Refer to Example 7. In a different four-week period, the interest rate rose 0.01%, dropped 0.08%, dropped 0.01%, and then did not change. By how much did the interest rate change?

Combining Like Terms

When two terms have variable factors that are exactly the same, like $5a$ and $-7a$, the terms are called **like**, or **similar, terms**. Constants like 6 and 2 are also considered to be like terms. The distributive law enables us to **combine**, or **collect, like terms** in order to form equivalent expressions.

EXAMPLE 8   Combine like terms to form equivalent expressions.

a) $-7x + 9x$

b) $2a + (-3b) + (-5a) + 9b$

c) $6 + y + (-3.5y) + 2$

SOLUTION

a) $-7x + 9x = (-7 + 9)x$ Using the distributive law

$\qquad\qquad = 2x$ Adding -7 and 9

b) $2a + (-3b) + (-5a) + 9b$

$\qquad = 2a + (-5a) + (-3b) + 9b$ Using the commutative law of addition

$\qquad = (2 + (-5))a + (-3 + 9)b$ Using the distributive law

$\qquad = -3a + 6b$ Adding

c) $6 + y + (-3.5y) + 2 = y + (-3.5y) + 6 + 2$ Using the commutative law of addition

$\qquad\qquad = (1 + (-3.5))y + 6 + 2$ Using the distributive law

$\qquad\qquad = -2.5y + 8$ Adding

8. Combine like terms to form an equivalent expression:

$$-9x + 5 + 13x + (-11).$$

YOUR TURN

1.5   EXERCISE SET   FOR EXTRA HELP   MyMathLab® Math XL
PRACTICE   WATCH   READ   REVIEW

Vocabulary and Reading Check

Choose from the following list of words to complete each statement. Words may be used more than once or not at all.

add   identity   like   negative
positive   subtract   zero

1. To add $-3 + (-6)$, _____ 3 and 6 and make the answer _____.

2. To add $-1 + 8$, _____ 1 from 8 and make the answer _____.

3. To add $-11 + 5$, _____ 5 from 11 and make the answer _____.

4. The number 0 is called the additive _____.

5. The addition $-7 + 0 = -7$ illustrates the _____ property of 0.

6. The expressions $5x$ and $-9x$ are examples of _____ terms.

Concept Reinforcement

In each of Exercises 7–12, match the term with a like term from the column on the right.

7. ___ $8n$ a) $-3z$

8. ___ $7m$ b) $5x$

9. ___ 43 c) $2t$

10. ___ $28z$ d) $-4m$

11. ___ $-2x$ e) 9

12. ___ $-9t$ f) $-3n$

Adding with the Number Line

Add using the number line.

13. $5 + (-8)$ 14. $2 + (-5)$

15. $-6 + 10$ 16. $-3 + 8$

17. $-7 + 0$ 18. $-6 + 0$

19. $-3 + (-5)$ 20. $-4 + (-6)$

Adding Without the Number Line

Add. Do not use the number line except as a check.

21. $-6 + (-5)$ 22. $-8 + (-12)$

23. $10 + (-15)$ 24. $12 + (-22)$

25. $12 + (-12)$ 26. $17 + (-17)$

27. $-24 + (-17)$ 28. $-17 + (-25)$

29. $-13 + 13$ 30. $-31 + 31$

31. $20 + (-11)$ 32. $8 + (-5)$

33. $-36 + 0$ 34. $0 + (-74)$

35. $-3 + 14$ 36. $25 + (-6)$

37. $-24 + (-19)$ 38. $11 + (-9)$

39. $19 + (-19)$ 40. $-20 + (-6)$

41. $23 + (-5)$ 42. $-15 + (-7)$

43. $69 + (-85)$ 44. $-63 + 13$

45. $-3.6 + 2.8$ 46. $-6.5 + 4.7$

47. $-5.4 + (-3.7)$ 48. $-3.8 + (-9.4)$

49. $\frac{4}{5} + \left(\frac{-1}{5}\right)$ 50. $\frac{-2}{7} + \frac{3}{7}$

51. $\frac{-4}{7} + \frac{-2}{7}$ 52. $\frac{-5}{9} + \frac{-2}{9}$

53. $-\frac{2}{5} + \frac{1}{3}$ 54. $-\frac{4}{13} + \frac{1}{2}$

55. $\frac{-4}{9} + \frac{2}{3}$ 56. $\frac{1}{9} + \left(\frac{-1}{3}\right)$

57. $35 + (-14) + (-19) + (-5)$

58. $-28 + (-44) + 17 + 31 + (-94)$

Ahа! 59. $-4.9 + 8.5 + 4.9 + (-8.5)$

60. $24 + 3.1 + (-44) + (-8.2) + 63$

Problem Solving

Solve. Write your answer as a complete sentence.

61. *Gasoline Prices.* During one month, the price of a gallon of 87-octane gasoline dropped 15¢, then dropped 3¢, and then rose 17¢. By how much did the price change during that period?

62. *Natural Gas Prices.* During one winter, the price of a gallon of natural gas dropped 2¢, then rose 25¢, and then dropped 43¢. By how much did the price change during that period?

63. *Telephone Bills.* Chloe's cell-phone bill for July was $82. She sent a check for $50 and then ran up $63 in charges for August. What was her new balance?

64. *Profits and Losses.* The following table lists the profits and losses of Premium Sales over a 3-year period. Find the profit or loss after this period of time.

Year	Profit or loss
2010	$-\$26{,}500$
2011	$-\$10{,}200$
2012	$+\$32{,}400$

65. *Yardage Gained.* In an intramural football game, the quarterback attempted passes with the following results.

First try	13-yd loss
Second try	12-yd gain
Third try	21-yd gain

Find the total gain (or loss).

66. *Account Balance.* Omari has $450 in a checking account. He writes a check for $530, makes a deposit of $75, and then writes a check for $90. What is the balance in the account?

67. *Lake Level.* Between September 2009 and September 2010, the elevation of the Great Salt Lake dropped $\frac{2}{5}$ ft, rose $\frac{9}{10}$ ft, and dropped $\frac{6}{5}$ ft. By how much did the level change?

Source: U.S. Geological Survey

68. *Credit-Card Bills.* Logan's credit-card bill indicates that he owes $470. He sends a check to the credit-card company for $45, charges another $160 in merchandise, and then pays off another $500 of his bill. What is Logan's new balance?

69. *Peak Elevation.* The tallest mountain in the world, as measured from base to peak, is Mauna Kea in Hawaii. From a base 19,684 ft below sea

level, it rises 33,480 ft. What is the elevation of its peak?

Source: Guinness World Records 2007

70. *Class Size.* During the first two weeks of the semester, 5 students withdrew from Hailey's algebra class, 8 students were added to the class, and 4 students were dropped as "no-shows." By how many students did the original class size change?

Combining Like Terms

Combine like terms to form an equivalent expression.

71. $7a + 10a$

72. $3x + 8x$

73. $-3x + 12x$

74. $-2m + (-7m)$

75. $7m + (-9m)$

76. $-4x + 4x$

77. $-8y + (-2y)$

78. $10n + (-17n)$

79. $-3 + 8x + 4 + (-10x)$

80. $8a + 5 + (-a) + (-3)$

81. $6m + 9n + (-9n) + (-10m)$

82. $-11s + (-8t) + (-3s) + 8t$

83. $-4x + 6.3 + (-x) + (-10.2)$

84. $-7 + 10.5y + 13 + (-11.5y)$

Find the perimeter of each figure.

85.

86.

87.

88.

89.

90.

91. Explain in your own words why the sum of two negative numbers is negative.

92. Without performing the actual addition, explain why the sum of all integers from -10 to 10 is 0.

Synthesis

93. Under what circumstances will the sum of one positive number and several negative numbers be positive?

94. Is it possible to add real numbers without knowing how to calculate $a - b$ with a and b both nonnegative and $a \geq b$? Why or why not?

95. *Banking.* Travis had $257.33 in his checking account. After depositing $152 in the account and writing a check, his account was overdrawn by $42.37. What was the amount of the check?

96. *Sports-Card Values.* The value of a sports card dropped $12 and then rose $17.50 before settling at $61. What was the original value of the card?

Find the missing term or terms.

97. $4x + \underline{\quad} + (-9x) + (-2y) = -5x - 7y$

98. $-3a + 9b + \underline{\quad} + 5a = 2a - 6b$

99. $3m + 2n + \underline{\quad} + (-2m) = 2n + (-6m)$

100. $\underline{\quad} + 9x + (-4y) + x = 10x - 7y$

Aha! **101.** $7t + 23 + \underline{\quad} + \underline{\quad} = 0$

102. *Geometry.* The perimeter of a rectangle is $7x + 10$. If the length of the rectangle is 5, express the width in terms of x.

103. *Golfing.* After five rounds of golf, a golf pro was 3 under par twice, 2 over par once, 2 under par once, and 1 over par once. On average, how far above or below par was the golfer?

YOUR TURN ANSWERS: SECTION 1.5

1. 2   **2.** -3 **3.** -3 **4.** -4 **5.** -6.8 **6.** -1

7. The interest rate dropped 0.08%.   **8.** $4x - 6$

QUICK QUIZ: SECTIONS 1.1–1.5

1. Multiply: $3(6a + 4c + 1)$.   [1.2]

2. Add and, if possible, simplify: $\frac{2}{10} + \frac{6}{5}$.   [1.3]

3. Multiply and, if possible, simplify: $\frac{2}{9} \cdot \frac{3}{8}$.   [1.3]

4. Find the absolute value: $|505|$.   [1.4]

5. Combine like terms: $-12 + 10 + 13x + (-20x)$.   [1.5]

1.6 | Subtraction of Real Numbers

Opposites and Additive Inverses ▪ Subtraction ▪ Problem Solving

In arithmetic, when a number b is subtracted from another number a, the **difference**, $a - b$, is the number that when added to b gives a. For example, $8 - 5 = 3$ because $3 + 5 = 8$. We will use this approach to develop an efficient way of finding the value of $a - b$ for any real numbers a and b.

Opposites and Additive Inverses

Numbers such as 6 and -6 are *opposites*, or *additive inverses*, of each other. Whenever opposites are added, the result is 0; and whenever two numbers add to 0, those numbers are opposites.

EXAMPLE 1   Find the opposite of each number: **(a)** 34; **(b)** -8.3; **(c)** 0.

SOLUTION

a) The opposite of 34 is -34: $34 + (-34) = 0$.

b) The opposite of -8.3 is 8.3: $-8.3 + 8.3 = 0$.

c) The opposite of 0 is 0: $0 + 0 = 0$.

1. Find the opposite of -15.

 YOUR TURN

To write the opposite of a number, we use the symbol $-$, as follows.

> **OPPOSITE**
>
> The *opposite*, or *additive inverse*, of a number a is written $-a$ (read "the opposite of a" or "the additive inverse of a").

Note that if we take a number, say 8, and find its opposite, -8, and then find the opposite of the result, we will have the original number, 8, again.

EXAMPLE 2   Find $-x$ and $-(-x)$ when $x = 16$.

SOLUTION

If $x = 16$, then $-x = -16$.   The opposite of 16 is -16.

If $x = 16$, then $-(-x) = -(-16) = 16$.   The opposite of the opposite of 16 is 16.

2. Find $-x$ and $-(-x)$ when $x = 3.5$.

YOUR TURN

> **THE OPPOSITE OF AN OPPOSITE**
>
> For any real number a,
>
> $$-(-a) = a.$$
>
> (The opposite of the opposite of a is a.)

EXAMPLE 3 Find $-x$ and $-(-x)$ when $x = -3$.

SOLUTION

If $x = -3$, then $-x = -(-3) = 3$.   The opposite of -3 is 3.

Since $-(-x) = x$, it follows that $-(-(-3)) = -3$.   Finding the opposite of an opposite

3. Find $-x$ and $-(-x)$ when $x = -9$.

 YOUR TURN

Note in Example 3 that an extra set of parentheses is used to show that we are substituting the negative number -3 for x. The notation $- -x$ is not used.

A symbol such as -8 is usually read "negative 8." It could be read "the additive inverse of 8," because the additive inverse of 8 is negative 8. It could also be read "the opposite of 8," because the opposite of 8 is -8.

A symbol like $-x$, which has a variable, should be read "the opposite of x" or "the additive inverse of x" and *not* "negative x," since to do so suggests that $-x$ represents a negative number. As we have seen, $-x$ is not always negative.

The symbol "$-$" is read differently depending on where it appears. For example, $-5 - (-x)$ should be read "negative five minus the opposite of x."

Student Notes

As you read mathematics, it is important to verbalize correctly the words and symbols to yourself. Consistently reading the expression $-x$ as "the opposite of x" is a good step in this direction.

EXAMPLE 4 Write each of the following in words.

a) $2 - 8$ **b)** $t - (-4)$ **c)** $-6 - (-x)$

SOLUTION

a) $2 - 8$ is read "two minus eight."

b) $t - (-4)$ is read "t minus negative four."

c) $-6 - (-x)$ is read "negative six minus the opposite of x."

4. Write $-y - 7$ in words.

 YOUR TURN

As we saw in Example 3, $-x$ can represent a positive number. This notation can be used to state the *law of opposites*.

THE LAW OF OPPOSITES

For any two numbers a and $-a$,

$$a + (-a) = 0.$$

(When opposites are added, their sum is 0.)

A negative number is said to have a "negative *sign*." A positive number is said to have a "positive *sign*." If we change a number to its opposite, or additive inverse, we say that we have "changed or reversed its sign."

EXAMPLE 5 Change the sign (find the opposite) of each number: **(a)** -3; **(b)** -10; **(c)** 14.

SOLUTION

a) When we change the sign of -3, we obtain 3.

b) When we change the sign of -10, we obtain 10.

c) When we change the sign of 14, we obtain -14.

5. Change the sign of 12.

 YOUR TURN

Study Skills

If You Must Miss a Class

Occasionally you may know that you will miss a class. It is usually best to alert your instructor to this as soon as possible. He or she may permit you to make up a missed quiz or test *if you provide enough advance notice*. Ask what assignment will be given in your absence and try your best to learn the material on your own. It may be possible to attend another section of the course for the class that you must miss.

Subtraction

Opposites are helpful when subtraction involves negative numbers. To see why, look for a pattern in the following:

Subtracting	*Reasoning*	*Adding the Opposite*
$9 - 5 = 4$	since $4 + 5 = 9$	$9 + (-5) = 4$
$5 - 8 = -3$	since $-3 + 8 = 5$	$5 + (-8) = -3$
$-6 - 4 = -10$	since $-10 + 4 = -6$	$-6 + (-4) = -10$
$-7 - (-10) = 3$	since $3 + (-10) = -7$	$-7 + 10 = 3$
$-7 - (-2) = -5$	since $-5 + (-2) = -7$	$-7 + 2 = -5$

The matching results suggest that we can subtract by adding the opposite of the number being subtracted. This can always be done and often provides the easiest way to subtract real numbers.

SUBTRACTION OF REAL NUMBERS

For any real numbers a and b,

$$a - b = a + (-b).$$

(To subtract, add the opposite, or additive inverse, of the number being subtracted.)

EXAMPLE 6 Subtract each of the following and then check with addition.

a) $2 - 6$ **b)** $4 - (-9)$ **c)** $-4.2 - (-3.6)$

d) $-1.8 - (-7.5)$ **e)** $\frac{1}{5} - \left(-\frac{3}{5}\right)$

SOLUTION

a) $2 - 6 = 2 + (-6) = -4$ The opposite of 6 is -6. We change the subtraction to addition of the opposite. *Check:* $-4 + 6 = 2$.

b) $4 - (-9) = 4 + 9 = 13$ The opposite of -9 is 9. We change the subtraction to addition of the opposite. *Check:* $13 + (-9) = 4$.

c) $-4.2 - (-3.6) = -4.2 + 3.6$ Adding the opposite of -3.6
               $= -0.6$ *Check:* $-0.6 + (-3.6) = -4.2$.

d) $-1.8 - (-7.5) = -1.8 + 7.5$ Adding the opposite
               $= 5.7$ *Check:* $5.7 + (-7.5) = -1.8$.

e) $\dfrac{1}{5} - \left(-\dfrac{3}{5}\right) = \dfrac{1}{5} + \dfrac{3}{5}$ Adding the opposite

            $= \dfrac{1 + 3}{5}$ A common denominator exists so we add in the numerator.

            $= \dfrac{4}{5}$

Check: $\dfrac{4}{5} + \left(-\dfrac{3}{5}\right) = \dfrac{4}{5} + \dfrac{-3}{5} = \dfrac{4 + (-3)}{5} = \dfrac{1}{5}$.

YOUR TURN

Technology Connection

On nearly all graphing calculators, it is essential to distinguish between the key for negation and the key for subtraction. To enter a negative number, we use (-); to subtract, we use (−).

6. Subtract: $-16 - (-20)$.

EXAMPLE 7 Simplify: $8 - (-4) - 2 - (-5) + 3$.

SOLUTION

$$8 - (-4) - 2 - (-5) + 3 = 8 + 4 + (-2) + 5 + 3 \qquad \text{To subtract, we add the opposite.}$$

$$= 18$$

7. Simplify:

$$-3 - (-1) + (-10) - 7.$$

YOUR TURN

The terms of an algebraic expression are separated by plus signs. This means that the terms of $5x - 7y - 9$ are $5x$, $-7y$, and -9, since $5x - 7y - 9 = 5x + (-7y) + (-9)$.

EXAMPLE 8 Identify the terms of $4 - 2ab + 7a - 9$.

SOLUTION We have

$$4 - 2ab + 7a - 9 = 4 + (-2ab) + 7a + (-9), \qquad \text{Rewriting as addition}$$

8. Identify the terms of
$5a - 7x - 10 + y$.

so the terms are 4, $-2ab$, $7a$, and -9.

YOUR TURN

EXAMPLE 9 Combine like terms.

a) $1 + 3x - 7x$ **b)** $-5a - 7b - 4a + 10b$

c) $4 - 3m - 9 + 2m$

SOLUTION

a) $1 + 3x - 7x = 1 + 3x + (-7x)$ Adding the opposite

$$\begin{aligned} &= 1 + (3 + (-7))x \\ &= 1 + (-4)x \end{aligned} \right\}$$ Using the distributive law. Try to do this mentally.

$$= 1 - 4x$$ Rewriting as subtraction to be more concise

b) $-5a - 7b - 4a + 10b = -5a + (-7b) + (-4a) + 10b$ Adding the opposite

$$= -5a + (-4a) + (-7b) + 10b$$ Using the commutative law of addition

$$= -9a + 3b$$ Combining like terms mentally

c) $4 - 3m - 9 + 2m = 4 + (-3m) + (-9) + 2m$ Rewriting as addition

$$= 4 + (-9) + (-3m) + 2m$$ Using the commutative law of addition

$$= -5 + (-1m)$$ We can write $-1m$ as $-m$.

9. Combine like terms:

$$x - 3y + 7y - 2x.$$

$$= -5 - m$$

YOUR TURN

Problem Solving

The words "difference," "minus," and "less than" are examples of key words that translate to subtraction. Since subtraction is not commutative, the order in which we write a translation is important. Unless the context indicates otherwise, "the difference between 5 and 8" translates to $5 - 8$, and "subtract 10 from 3" means to calculate $3 - 10$.

We use subtraction to solve problems involving differences. These include problems that ask "How much more?" or "How much higher?"

EXAMPLE 10 *Record Elevations.* World records for the highest parachute jump and the lowest manned vessel ocean dive were both set in 1960. On August 16 of that year, Captain Joseph Kittinger jumped from a height of 102,800 ft above sea level. Earlier, on January 23, Jacques Piccard and Navy Lieutenant Donald Walsh descended in a bathyscaphe 35,797 ft below sea level. What was the difference in elevation between the highest parachute jump and the lowest ocean dive?

Sources: www.firstflight.org and www.seasky.org

102,800 ft

35,797 ft

10. The lowest elevation in Asia, the Dead Sea, is 1349 ft below sea level. The highest elevation in Asia, Mount Everest, is 29,035 ft. Find the difference in elevation.

Source: National Geographic

SOLUTION To find the difference between two elevations, we always subtract the lower elevation from the higher elevation:

$$\underbrace{\text{Higher elevation}} \quad - \quad \underbrace{\text{Lower elevation}}$$

$$102{,}800 \qquad - \qquad (-35{,}797)$$
$$= 102{,}800 + 35{,}797$$
$$= 138{,}597.$$

The parachute jump began 138,597 ft higher than the ocean dive ended.

YOUR TURN

1.6 EXERCISE SET   FOR EXTRA HELP

MyMathLab® *Math* XL PRACTICE WATCH READ REVIEW

⤷ Vocabulary and Reading Check

Two words appear under each blank in the following sentences. Choose the correct word for each blank.

1. The numbers 5 and -5 are _____
   opposites/reciprocals
   of each other.

2. The number -100 has a negative _____.
   opposite/sign

3. We subtract by adding the _____
   opposite/reciprocal
   of the number being subtracted.

4. The word _____ usually translates to
   difference/quotient
   subtraction.

⤷ **Concept Reinforcement**

In each of Exercises 5–12, match the expression with the appropriate expression from the column on the right.

5. ____ $-x$
6. ____ $12 - x$
7. ____ $12 - (-x)$
8. ____ $x - 12$
9. ____ $x - (-12)$
10. ____ $-x - 12$
11. ____ $-x - x$
12. ____ $-x - (-12)$

a) x minus negative twelve
b) The opposite of x minus x
c) The opposite of x minus twelve
d) The opposite of x
e) The opposite of x minus negative twelve
f) Twelve minus the opposite of x
g) Twelve minus x
h) x minus twelve

Opposites and Additive Inverses

Write each of the following in words.

13. $6 - 10$
14. $5 - 13$
15. $2 - (-12)$
16. $4 - (-1)$
17. $-x - y$
18. $-a - b$
19. $-3 - (-n)$
20. $-7 - (-m)$

Find the opposite, or additive inverse of each number.

21. 51
22. -17
23. $-\frac{11}{3}$
24. $\frac{7}{2}$
25. -3.14
26. 48.2

Find $-x$ when x is each of the following.

27. -45
28. 26
29. $-\frac{14}{3}$
30. $\frac{1}{328}$
31. 0.101
32. 0

Find $-(-x)$ when x is each of the following.

33. 37
34. 29
35. $-\frac{2}{5}$
36. -9.1

Change the sign. (Find the opposite.)

37. -1
38. -7
39. 15
40. 10

Subtraction

Subtract.

41. $7 - 10$
42. $4 - 13$
43. $0 - 6$
44. $0 - 8$
45. $-4 - 3$
46. $-5 - 6$
47. $-9 - (-3)$
48. $-9 - (-5)$
Ahal 49. $-8 - (-8)$
50. $-10 - (-10)$
51. $14 - 19$
52. $12 - 16$

53. $30 - 40$
54. $20 - 27$
55. $-9 - (-9)$
56. $-40 - (-40)$
57. $5 - 5$
58. $7 - 7$
59. $4 - (-4)$
60. $6 - (-6)$
61. $-7 - 4$
62. $-6 - 8$
63. $6 - (-10)$
64. $3 - (-12)$
65. $-4 - 15$
66. $-14 - 2$
67. $-6 - (-5)$
68. $-4 - (-1)$
69. $5 - (-12)$
70. $5 - (-6)$
71. $0 - (-3)$
72. $0 - (-5)$
73. $-5 - (-2)$
74. $-3 - (-1)$
75. $-7 - 14$
76. $-9 - 16$
77. $0 - 11$
78. $0 - 31$
79. $-8 - 0$
80. $-9 - 0$
81. $-52 - 8$
82. $-63 - 11$
83. $2 - 25$
84. $18 - 63$
85. $-4.2 - 3.1$
86. $-10.1 - 2.6$
87. $-1.3 - (-2.4)$
88. $-5.8 - (-7.3)$
89. $3.2 - 8.7$
90. $1.5 - 9.4$
91. $0.072 - 1$
92. $0.825 - 1$
93. $\frac{2}{11} - \frac{9}{11}$
94. $\frac{3}{7} - \frac{5}{7}$
95. $\frac{-1}{5} - \frac{3}{5}$
96. $\frac{-2}{9} - \frac{5}{9}$
97. $-\frac{4}{17} - \left(-\frac{9}{17}\right)$
98. $-\frac{2}{13} - \left(-\frac{5}{13}\right)$

Simplify.

99. $16 - (-12) - 1 - (-2) + 3$
100. $22 - (-18) + 7 + (-42) - 27$
101. $-31 + (-28) - (-14) - 17$
102. $-43 - (-19) - (-21) + 25$
103. $-34 - 28 + (-33) - 44$
104. $39 + (-88) - 29 - (-83)$
Ahal 105. $-93 + (-84) - (-93) - (-84)$
106. $84 + (-99) + 44 - (-18) - 43$

Identify the terms in each expression.

107. $-3y - 8x$
108. $7a - 9b$
109. $9 - 5t - 3st$
110. $-4 - 3x + 2xy$

Combine like terms.

111. $10x - 13x$
112. $3a - 14a$
113. $7a - 12a + 4$
114. $-9x - 13x + 7$

115. $-8n - 9 + 7n$ **116.** $-7 + 9n - 8n$

117. $5 - 3x - 11$ **118.** $2 + 3a - 7$

119. $2 - 6t - 9 - 2t$

120. $-5 + 4b - 7 - 5b$

121. $5y + (-3x) - 9x + 1 - 2y + 8$

122. $14 - (-5x) + 2z - (-32) + 4z - 2x$

123. $13x - (-2x) + 45 - (-21) - 7x$

124. $8t - (-2t) - 14 - (-5t) + 53 - 9t$

Problem Solving

125. Subtract 32 from -8.

126. Subtract 19 from -7.

127. Subtract -25 from 18.

128. Subtract -31 from -5.

In each of Exercises 129–132, translate the phrase to mathematical language and simplify.

129. The difference between 3.8 and -5.2

130. The difference between -2.1 and -5.9

131. The difference between 114 and -79

132. The difference between 23 and -17

133. *Elevation.*   The Jordan River begins in Lebanon at an elevation of 550 m above sea level and empties into the Dead Sea at an elevation of 400 m below sea level. During its 360-km length, by how many meters does it fall?

Source: Brittanica Online

134. *Elevation.*   The elevation of Mount Whitney, the highest peak in California, is 14,497 ft. Death Valley, California, is 282 ft below sea level. What is the difference in elevation?

Sources: mount-whitney.com and infoplease.com

135. *Temperature Extremes.*   The highest temperature ever recorded in the United States is 134°F in Greenland Ranch, California, on July 10, 1913. The lowest temperature ever recorded is -79.8°F in Prospect Creek, Alaska, on January 23, 1971. How much higher was the temperature in Greenland Ranch than that in Prospect Creek?

Source: infoplease.com

136. *Temperature Change.*   In just 12 hr on February 21, 1918, the temperature in Granville, North Dakota, rose from -33°F to 50°F. By how much did the temperature change?

Source: weatherexplained.com

137. *Basketball.*   A team's points differential is the difference between points scored and points allowed. The Chicago Bulls improved their points-per-game differential from -1.6 in 2009–2010 to $+7.3$ in 2010–2011. By how many points did they improve?

Source: espn.go.com

138. *Underwater Elevation.*   The deepest point in the Pacific Ocean is the Marianas Trench, with a depth of 10,911 m. The deepest point in the Atlantic Ocean is the Puerto Rico Trench, with a depth of 8648 m. What is the difference in elevation of the two trenches?

Source: Guinness World Records 2007

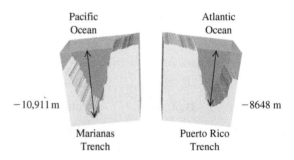

139. Lowell insists that if you can *add* real numbers, then you can also *subtract* real numbers. Do you agree? Why or why not?

140. Are the expressions $-a + b$ and $a + (-b)$ opposites of each other? Why or why not?

Synthesis

141. Explain the different uses of the symbol "$-$". Give examples of each and how they should be read.

142. If a and b are both negative, under what circumstances will $a - b$ be negative?

143. *Power Outages.*   During the Northeast's electrical blackout of August 14, 2003, residents of Bloomfield, New Jersey, lost power at 4:00 P.M. One resident returned from vacation at 3:00 P.M. the following day to find the clocks in her apartment reading 8:00 A.M. At what time, and on what day, was power restored?

Tell whether each statement is true or false for all real numbers m and n. Use various replacements for m and n to support your answer.

144. If $m > n$, then $m - n > 0$.

145. If $m > n$, then $m + n > 0$.

146. If m and n are opposites, then $m - n = 0$.

147. If $m = -n$, then $m + n = 0$.

148. A gambler loses a wager and then loses "double or nothing" (meaning the gambler owes twice as much) twice more. After the three losses, the gambler's assets are $-\$20$. Explain how much the gambler originally bet and how the $20 debt occurred.

149. List the keystrokes needed to compute $-9 - (-7)$.

150. If n is positive and m is negative, what is the sign of $n + (-m)$? Why?

YOUR TURN ANSWERS: SECTION 1.6

1. 15   **2.** $-3.5; 3.5$ **3.** $9; -9$ **4.** The opposite of y minus 7   **5.** -12 **6.** 4   **7.** -19 **8.** $5a, -7x, -10, y$
9. $-x + 4y$ **10.** 30,384 ft

QUICK QUIZ: SECTIONS 1.1–1.6

1. Translate to an equation. Do not solve.

   In the second quarter of 2011, a total of 9.25 million Apple iPad tablets were sold. This was 11% of the total PC sales. How many PCs were sold in all?   [1.1]
   Sources: Apple; *Business Insider*

2. List all the factors of 52.   [1.3]

3. Find the prime factorization of 52.   [1.3]

4. Add: $-10 + (-19)$.   [1.5]

5. Subtract: $-6 - (-11)$.   [1.6]

1.7 Multiplication and Division of Real Numbers

Multiplication ▪ Division

We now develop rules for multiplication and division of real numbers. Because multiplication and division are closely related, the rules are quite similar.

Multiplication

We already know how to multiply two nonnegative numbers. To see how to multiply a positive number and a negative number, consider the following pattern in which multiplication is regarded as repeated addition:

This number decreases by 1 each time.

$$4(-5) = (-5) + (-5) + (-5) + (-5) = -20$$
$$3(-5) = (-5) + (-5) + (-5) = -15$$
$$2(-5) = (-5) + (-5) = -10$$
$$1(-5) = (-5) = -5$$
$$0(-5) = 0 = 0$$

This number increases by 5 each time.

This pattern illustrates that the product of a negative number and a positive number is negative.

Student Notes

The multiplication $2 \cdot (-5)$ can be thought of as starting at 0 and *adding* -5 twice:

$$0 + (-5) + (-5) = -10.$$

> ### THE PRODUCT OF A NEGATIVE NUMBER AND A POSITIVE NUMBER
>
> To multiply a positive number and a negative number, multiply their absolute values. The answer is negative.

EXAMPLE 1   Multiply: **(a)** $8(-5)$; **(b)** $-\frac{1}{3} \cdot \frac{5}{7}$.

SOLUTION   The product of a negative number and a positive number is negative.

a) $8(-5) = -40$ *Think:* $8 \cdot 5 = 40$; make the answer negative.

b) $-\frac{1}{3} \cdot \frac{5}{7} = -\frac{5}{21}$ *Think:* $\frac{1}{3} \cdot \frac{5}{7} = \frac{5}{21}$; make the answer negative.

1. Multiply: $(-3)(10)$.

YOUR TURN

The pattern developed above also illustrates that the product of 0 and any real number is 0.

> ### THE MULTIPLICATIVE PROPERTY OF ZERO
>
> For any real number a,
>
> $$0 \cdot a = a \cdot 0 = 0.$$
>
> (The product of 0 and any real number is 0.)

EXAMPLE 2   Multiply: $173(-452)0$.

SOLUTION   We have

$$173(-452)0 = 173[(-452)0]$$ Because of the associative law of multiplication, we can multiply the last two factors first.

$$= 173[0]$$ Using the multiplicative property of zero

$$= 0.$$ Using the multiplicative property of zero again

2. Multiply: $(-13)(0)(19)$.

Note that whenever 0 appears as a factor, the product is 0.

YOUR TURN

Student Notes

The multiplication $(-2) \cdot (-5)$ can be thought of as starting at 0 and *subtracting* -5 twice:

$$0 - (-5) - (-5) = 0 + 5 + 5$$
$$= 10.$$

An alternative explanation is to write

$$(-2)(-5) = [(-1)(2)](-5)$$
$$= (-1)[(2)(-5)]$$
$$= -[-10]$$
$$= 10.$$

We can extend the above pattern still further to examine the product of two negative numbers.

This number → $2(-5) =$ $(-5) + (-5) = -10$ ← This number

decreases by $1(-5) =$ $(-5) = -5$ increases by 5

1 each time. $0(-5) =$ $0 = 0$ each time.

$-1(-5) =$ $-(-5) = 5$

$-2(-5) = -(-5) - (-5) = 10$

According to the pattern, the product of two negative numbers is positive.

> ### THE PRODUCT OF TWO NEGATIVE NUMBERS
>
> To multiply two negative numbers, multiply their absolute values. The answer is positive.

EXAMPLE 3   Multiply: **(a)** $(-6)(-8)$; **(b)** $(-1.2)(-3)$.

SOLUTION   The product of two negative numbers is positive.

a) The absolute value of -6 is 6 and the absolute value of -8 is 8. Thus,

$$(-6)(-8) = 6 \cdot 8 \qquad \text{Multiplying absolute values. The answer is positive.}$$
$$= 48.$$

3. Multiply: $\left(-\dfrac{1}{2}\right)\left(-\dfrac{1}{3}\right).$

b) $(-1.2)(-3) = (1.2)(3)$ Multiplying absolute values. The answer is positive.
$$\qquad\qquad\qquad = 3.6 \qquad\qquad \text{Try to go directly to this step.}$$

YOUR TURN

When three or more numbers are multiplied, we can order and group the numbers as we please, because of the commutative and associative laws.

EXAMPLE 4   Multiply: **(a)** $-3(-2)(-5)$; **(b)** $-4(-6)(-1)(-2)$.

SOLUTION

a) $-3(-2)(-5) = 6(-5)$ Multiplying the first two numbers. The product of two negatives is positive.
$$\qquad\qquad\qquad = -30 \qquad \text{The product of a positive and a negative is negative.}$$

b) $-4(-6)(-1)(-2) = 24 \cdot 2$ Multiplying the first two numbers and the last two numbers

4. Multiply: $(-1)(-10)(-5)$.

$$\qquad\qquad\qquad\qquad = 48$$

YOUR TURN

We can see the following pattern in the results of Example 4.

The product of an even number of negative numbers is positive.

The product of an odd number of negative numbers is negative.

When a number is multiplied by -1, the result is the opposite of that number. For example, $-1(7) = -7$ and $-1(-5) = 5$.

THE PROPERTY OF -1

For any real number a,

$$-1 \cdot a = -a.$$

(Negative one times a is the opposite of a.)

Division

Note that $a \div b$, or $\dfrac{a}{b}$, is the number, if one exists, that when multiplied by b gives a. For example, to show that $10 \div 2$ is 5, we need only note that $5 \cdot 2 = 10$. Thus division can always be checked with multiplication.

The rules for signs for division are the same as those for multiplication: The quotient of a positive number and a negative number is negative; the quotient of two negative numbers is positive.

> **RULES FOR MULTIPLICATION AND DIVISION**
>
> To multiply or divide two nonzero real numbers:
>
> 1. Using the absolute values, multiply or divide, as indicated.
> 2. If the signs are the same, the answer is positive.
> 3. If the signs are different, the answer is negative.

EXAMPLE 5 Divide, if possible, and check your answer.

a) $14 \div (-7)$

b) $\dfrac{-32}{-4}$

c) $\dfrac{-10}{2}$

d) $\dfrac{-17}{0}$

SOLUTION

a) $14 \div (-7) = -2$ *Think:* $14 \div 7 = 2$; the answer is negative.
Check: $(-2)(-7) = 14$.

b) $\dfrac{-32}{-4} = 8$ *Think:* $32 \div 4 = 8$; the answer is positive.
Check: $8(-4) = -32$.

c) $\dfrac{-10}{2} = -5$ *Think:* $10 \div 2 = 5$; the answer is negative.
Check: $-5(2) = -10$.

d) $\dfrac{-17}{0}$ is **undefined**. We look for a number that when multiplied by 0 gives -17. There is no such number because if 0 is a factor, the product is 0, not -17.

↪ YOUR TURN

Had Example 5(a) been written as $-14 \div 7$ or $-\frac{14}{7}$, rather than $14 \div (-7)$, the result would still have been -2. Thus from Examples 5(a)–5(c), we have the following:

$$\frac{-a}{b} = \frac{a}{-b} = -\frac{a}{b} \quad \text{and} \quad \frac{-a}{-b} = \frac{a}{b}.$$

EXAMPLE 6 Rewrite each of the following in two equivalent forms.

a) $\dfrac{5}{-2}$

b) $-\dfrac{3}{10}$

SOLUTION We use one of the properties just listed.

a) $\dfrac{5}{-2} = \dfrac{-5}{2}$ and $\dfrac{5}{-2} = -\dfrac{5}{2}$ ⎫
⎬ Since $\dfrac{-a}{b} = \dfrac{a}{-b} = -\dfrac{a}{b}$
b) $-\dfrac{3}{10} = \dfrac{-3}{10}$ and $-\dfrac{3}{10} = \dfrac{3}{-10}$ ⎭

↪ YOUR TURN

When a fraction contains a negative sign, it can be helpful to rewrite (or simply visualize) the fraction in an equivalent form.

Student Notes

Try to regard "undefined" as a mathematical way of saying "we do not give any meaning to this expression."

5. Divide, if possible, and check your answer: $(-100) \div 25$.

6. Rewrite in two equivalent forms:

$$\frac{-5}{6}.$$

EXAMPLE 7 Perform the indicated operation: **(a)** $\left(-\frac{4}{5}\right)\left(\frac{-7}{3}\right)$; **(b)** $-\frac{2}{7} + \frac{9}{-7}$.

SOLUTION

a) $\left(-\dfrac{4}{5}\right)\left(\dfrac{-7}{3}\right) = \left(-\dfrac{4}{5}\right)\left(-\dfrac{7}{3}\right)$ Rewriting $\dfrac{-7}{3}$ as $-\dfrac{7}{3}$

$= \dfrac{28}{15}$ Try to go directly to this step.

b) Given a choice, we generally choose a positive denominator:

$-\dfrac{2}{7} + \dfrac{9}{-7} = \dfrac{-2}{7} + \dfrac{-9}{7}$ Rewriting both fractions with a common denominator of 7

$= \dfrac{-11}{7}$, or $-\dfrac{11}{7}$.

7. Perform the indicated operation:

$\dfrac{-3}{4} - \left(\dfrac{7}{-4}\right)$.

YOUR TURN

To divide with fraction notation, it is usually easiest to find a reciprocal and then multiply.

EXAMPLE 8 Find the reciprocal of each number, if it exists.

a) -27 **b)** $\dfrac{-3}{4}$ **c)** $-\dfrac{1}{5}$ **d)** 0

SOLUTION Two numbers are reciprocals of each other if their product is 1.

a) The reciprocal of -27 is $\frac{1}{-27}$. More often, this number is written as $-\frac{1}{27}$. *Check:* $(-27)\left(-\frac{1}{27}\right) = \frac{27}{27} = 1$.

b) The reciprocal of $\frac{-3}{4}$ is $\frac{4}{-3}$, or, equivalently, $-\frac{4}{3}$.   *Check:* $\frac{-3}{4} \cdot \frac{4}{-3} = \frac{-12}{-12} = 1$.

c) The reciprocal of $-\frac{1}{5}$ is -5.   *Check:* $-\frac{1}{5}(-5) = \frac{5}{5} = 1$.

8. Find the reciprocal of $-\frac{10}{9}$, if it exists.

d) The reciprocal of 0 does not exist. To see this, recall that there is no number r for which $0 \cdot r = 1$.

YOUR TURN

EXAMPLE 9 Divide: **(a)** $-\frac{2}{3} \div \left(-\frac{5}{4}\right)$; **(b)** $-\frac{3}{4} \div \frac{3}{10}$.

SOLUTION We divide by multiplying by the reciprocal of the divisor.

a) $-\dfrac{2}{3} \div \left(-\dfrac{5}{4}\right) = -\dfrac{2}{3} \cdot \left(-\dfrac{4}{5}\right) = \dfrac{8}{15}$ Multiplying by the reciprocal

Be careful not to change the sign when taking a reciprocal!

9. Divide: $-\dfrac{5}{9} \div \dfrac{1}{15}$.

b) $-\dfrac{3}{4} \div \dfrac{3}{10} = -\dfrac{3}{4} \cdot \left(\dfrac{10}{3}\right) = -\dfrac{30}{12} = -\dfrac{5}{2} \cdot \dfrac{6}{6} = -\dfrac{5}{2}$ Removing a factor equal to 1: $\frac{6}{6} = 1$

YOUR TURN

To divide negative numbers with decimal notation, it is usually easiest to carry out the division and then focus on the sign.

EXAMPLE 10 Divide: $27.9 \div (-3)$.

SOLUTION

10. Divide: $-96 \div (-0.6)$.

$$27.9 \div (-3) = \frac{27.9}{-3} = -9.3 \qquad \text{Dividing: } 3\overline{)27.9}.^{\;9.3} \\ \text{The answer is negative.}$$

YOUR TURN

In Example 5(d), we explained why we cannot divide -17 by 0. To see why *no* nonzero number b can be divided by 0, remember that $b \div 0$ would have to be the number that when multiplied by 0 gives b. But since the product of 0 and any number is 0, not b, we say that $b \div 0$ is **undefined** for $b \neq 0$. In the special case of $0 \div 0$, we look for a number r such that $0 \div 0 = r$ and $r \cdot 0 = 0$. But, $r \cdot 0 = 0$ for *any* number r. For this reason, we say that $b \div 0$ is undefined for any choice of b.*

Finally, note that $0 \div 7 = 0$ since $0 \cdot 7 = 0$. This can be written $0/7 = 0$. It is important not to confuse division *by* 0 with division *into* 0.

EXAMPLE 11 Divide, if possible: **(a)** $\frac{0}{-2}$; **(b)** $\frac{5}{0}$.

SOLUTION

a) $\dfrac{0}{-2} = 0$ We can divide 0 by a nonzero number. *Check:* $0(-2) = 0$.

11. Divide, if possible:

$0 \div (-12)$.

b) $\dfrac{5}{0}$ is undefined.   We cannot divide by 0.

YOUR TURN

DIVISION INVOLVING ZERO

For any real number a, $\dfrac{a}{0}$ is undefined, and for $a \neq 0$, $\dfrac{0}{a} = 0$.

Study Skills

Organize Your Work

When doing homework, consider using a spiral notebook or collecting your work in a three-ring binder. Because your course will probably include graphing, consider purchasing a notebook filled with graph paper. Write legibly, labeling each section and each exercise and showing all steps. Legible, well-organized work will make it easier for those who read your work to give you constructive feedback and for you to use your work to review for a test.

It is important *not* to confuse *opposite* with *reciprocal*. Keep in mind that the opposite, or additive inverse, of a number is what we add to the number in order to get 0. The reciprocal, or multiplicative inverse, is what we multiply the number by in order to get 1.

Compare the following.

Number	Opposite (Change the sign.)	Reciprocal (Invert but do not change the sign.)
$-\dfrac{3}{8}$	$\dfrac{3}{8}$	$-\dfrac{8}{3}$ $\left(-\dfrac{3}{8}\right)\left(-\dfrac{8}{3}\right) = 1$
19	-19	$\dfrac{1}{19}$ $-\dfrac{3}{8} + \dfrac{3}{8} = 0$
$\dfrac{18}{7}$	$-\dfrac{18}{7}$	$\dfrac{7}{18}$
-7.9	7.9	$-\dfrac{1}{7.9}$, or $-\dfrac{10}{79}$
0	0	Undefined

---

*Sometimes we say that $0 \div 0$ is *indeterminate*.

■ **CONNECTING** **THE CONCEPTS** ■

The rules for multiplication and division of real numbers differ significantly from the rules for addition and subtraction. When simplifying an expression, look at the operation first to determine which set of rules to follow.

Addition

If the signs are the same, add absolute values. *The answer has the same sign as the numbers.*

If the signs are different, subtract absolute values. *The answer has the same sign as the number with the larger absolute value. If the absolute values are the same, the answer is 0.*

Multiplication

If the signs are the same, multiply absolute values. *The answer is positive.*

If the signs are different, multiply absolute values. *The answer is negative.*

Subtraction

Add the opposite of the number being subtracted.

Division

Multiply by the reciprocal of the divisor.

EXERCISES

Perform the indicated operation and, if possible, simplify.

1. $-8 + (-2)$ **2.** $-8 \cdot (-2)$

3. $-8 \div (-2)$ **4.** $-8 - (-2)$

5. $\dfrac{3}{5} - \dfrac{8}{5}$ **6.** $\dfrac{12}{5} + \left(\dfrac{-7}{5}\right)$

7. $(1.3)(-2.9)$ **8.** $-44.1 \div 6.3$

9. $-38 - (-38)$ **10.** $-46 - 46$

1.7 **EXERCISE SET**   FOR EXTRA HELP   MyMathLab® *Math* XL   PRACTICE   WATCH   READ   REVIEW

🖐 **Vocabulary and Reading Check**

Choose from the following list of words to complete each statement. Words may be used more than once or not at all.

even   positive
negative   reciprocal
odd   undefined
opposite   zero

1. The product of two negative numbers is _____.

2. The product of a(n) _____ number of negative numbers is negative.

3. Division by zero is _____.

4. To divide by a fraction, multiply by its _____.

5. The _____ of a negative number is positive.

6. The _____ of a negative number is negative.

🖐 **Concept Reinforcement**

In each of Exercises 7–16, replace the blank with either 0 or 1 to match the description given.

7. The product of two reciprocals ____

8. The sum of a pair of opposites ____

9. The sum of a pair of additive inverses ____

10. The product of two multiplicative inverses ____

11. This number has no reciprocal. ____

12. This number is its own reciprocal. ____

13. This number is the multiplicative identity. ____

14. This number is the additive identity. ____

15. A nonzero number divided by itself ____

16. Division by this number is undefined. ____

Multiplication

Multiply.

17. $-4 \cdot 10$ **18.** $-5 \cdot 6$

19. $-8 \cdot 7$ **20.** $-9 \cdot 2$

21. $4 \cdot (-10)$ **22.** $9 \cdot (-5)$

23. $-9 \cdot (-8)$ **24.** $-10 \cdot (-11)$

25. $-19 \cdot (-10)$ **26.** $-12 \cdot (-10)$

27. $11 \cdot (-12)$ **28.** $15 \cdot (-43)$

29. $4.5 \cdot (-28)$ **30.** $-49 \cdot (-2.1)$

31. $-5 \cdot (-2.3)$ **32.** $-6 \cdot 4.8$

33. $(-25) \cdot 0$ **34.** $0 \cdot (-4.7)$

35. $\frac{2}{5} \cdot \left(-\frac{5}{7}\right)$ **36.** $\frac{5}{7} \cdot \left(-\frac{2}{3}\right)$

37. $-\frac{3}{8} \cdot \left(-\frac{2}{9}\right)$ **38.** $-\frac{5}{8} \cdot \left(-\frac{2}{5}\right)$

39. $(-5.3)(2.1)$ **40.** $(9.5)(-3.7)$

41. $-\frac{5}{9} \cdot \frac{3}{4}$ **42.** $-\frac{8}{3} \cdot \frac{9}{4}$

43. $3 \cdot (-7) \cdot (-2) \cdot 6$ **44.** $9 \cdot (-2) \cdot (-6) \cdot 7$

Aha! **45.** $27 \cdot (-34) \cdot 0$ **46.** $-43 \cdot (-74) \cdot 0$

47. $-\frac{1}{3} \cdot \frac{1}{4} \cdot \left(-\frac{3}{7}\right)$ **48.** $-\frac{1}{2} \cdot \frac{3}{5} \cdot \left(-\frac{2}{7}\right)$

49. $-2 \cdot (-5) \cdot (-3) \cdot (-5)$

50. $-3 \cdot (-5) \cdot (-2) \cdot (-1)$

51. $(-31) \cdot (-27) \cdot 0 \cdot (-13)$

52. $7 \cdot (-6) \cdot 5 \cdot (-4) \cdot 3 \cdot (-2) \cdot 1 \cdot 0$

53. $(-8)(-9)(-10)$

54. $(-7)(-8)(-9)(-10)$

55. $(-6)(-7)(-8)(-9)(-10)$

56. $(-5)(-6)(-7)(-8)(-9)(-10)$

Division

Divide, if possible, and check. If a quotient is undefined, state this.

57. $18 \div (-2)$ **58.** $\frac{24}{-3}$

59. $\frac{36}{-9}$ **60.** $26 \div (-13)$

61. $\frac{-56}{8}$ **62.** $\frac{-35}{-7}$

63. $\frac{-48}{-12}$ **64.** $-63 \div (-9)$

65. $-72 \div 8$ **66.** $\frac{-50}{25}$

67. $-10.2 \div (-2)$ **68.** $-2 \div 0.8$

69. $-100 \div (-11)$ **70.** $\frac{-64}{-7}$

71. $\frac{400}{-50}$ **72.** $-300 \div (-13)$

73. $\frac{48}{0}$ **74.** $\frac{0}{-5}$

75. $-4.8 \div 1.2$ **76.** $-3.9 \div 1.3$

77. $\frac{0}{-9}$ **78.** $0 \div 18$

Aha! **79.** $\frac{9.7(-2.8)0}{4.3}$ **80.** $\frac{(-4.9)(7.2)}{0}$

Write each expression in two equivalent forms, as in Example 6.

81. $\frac{-8}{3}$ **82.** $\frac{-10}{3}$

83. $\frac{29}{-35}$ **84.** $\frac{18}{-7}$

85. $-\frac{7}{3}$ **86.** $-\frac{4}{15}$

87. $\frac{-x}{2}$ **88.** $\frac{9}{-a}$

Find the reciprocal of each number, if it exists.

89. $-\frac{4}{5}$ **90.** $-\frac{13}{11}$

91. $\frac{51}{-10}$ **92.** $\frac{43}{-24}$

93. -10 **94.** 34

95. 4.3 **96.** -1.7

97. $\frac{-1}{4}$ **98.** $\frac{-1}{11}$

99. 0 **100.** -1

Addition, Subtraction, Multiplication, and Division

Perform the indicated operation and, if possible, simplify. If a quotient is undefined, state this.

101. $\left(\frac{-7}{4}\right)\left(-\frac{3}{5}\right)$ **102.** $\left(-\frac{5}{6}\right)\left(\frac{-1}{3}\right)$

103. $\frac{-3}{8} + \frac{-5}{8}$ **104.** $\frac{-4}{5} + \frac{7}{5}$

Aha! **105.** $\left(\frac{-9}{5}\right)\left(\frac{5}{-9}\right)$ **106.** $\left(-\frac{2}{7}\right)\left(\frac{5}{-8}\right)$

107. $\left(-\frac{3}{11}\right) - \left(-\frac{6}{11}\right)$ **108.** $\left(-\frac{4}{7}\right) - \left(-\frac{2}{7}\right)$

109. $\frac{7}{8} \div \left(-\frac{1}{2}\right)$ **110.** $\frac{3}{4} \div \left(-\frac{2}{3}\right)$

111. $\frac{9}{5} \cdot \frac{-20}{3}$ **112.** $\frac{-5}{12} \cdot \frac{7}{15}$

113. $\left(-\frac{18}{7}\right) + \left(\frac{3}{-7}\right)$ **114.** $\left(\frac{12}{-5}\right) + \left(-\frac{3}{5}\right)$

Aha! **115.** $-\frac{5}{9} \div \left(-\frac{5}{9}\right)$ **116.** $\frac{-5}{12} \div \frac{15}{7}$

117. $\frac{-3}{10} + \frac{2}{5}$ **118.** $\frac{-5}{9} + \frac{2}{3}$

119. $\frac{7}{10} \div \left(\frac{-3}{5}\right)$

120. $\left(\frac{-3}{5}\right) \div \frac{6}{15}$

121. $\frac{14}{-9} \div \frac{0}{3}$

122. $\frac{0}{-10} \div \frac{-3}{8}$

123. $\frac{-4}{15} + \frac{2}{-3}$

124. $\frac{3}{-10} + \frac{-1}{5}$

125. Most calculators have a key, often appearing as **1/x**, for finding reciprocals. To use this key, we enter a number and then press **1/x** to find its reciprocal. What should happen if we enter a number and then press the reciprocal key twice? Why?

126. Multiplication can be regarded as repeated addition. Using this idea and the number line, explain why $3 \cdot (-5) = -15$.

Synthesis

127. If two nonzero numbers are opposites of each other, are their reciprocals opposites of each other? Why or why not?

128. If two numbers are reciprocals of each other, are their opposites reciprocals of each other? Why or why not?

Translate to an algebraic expression or equation.

129. The reciprocal of a sum

130. The sum of two reciprocals

131. The opposite of a sum

132. The sum of two opposites

133. A real number is its own opposite.

134. A real number is its own reciprocal.

135. Show that the reciprocal of a sum is *not* the sum of the two reciprocals.

136. Which real numbers are their own reciprocals?

137. Jenna is a meteorologist. On December 10, she notes that the temperature is $-3°F$ at 6:00 A.M. She predicts that the temperature will rise at a rate of $2°$ per hour for 3 hr, and then rise at a rate of $3°$ per hour for 6 hr. She also predicts that the temperature will then fall at a rate of $2°$ per hour for 3 hr, and then fall at a rate of $5°$ per hour for 2 hr. What is Jenna's temperature forecast for 8:00 P.M.?

Tell whether each expression represents a positive number or a negative number when m and n are negative.

138. $\frac{m}{-n}$

139. $\frac{-n}{-m}$

140. $-m \cdot \left(\frac{-n}{m}\right)$

141. $-\left(\frac{n}{-m}\right)$

142. $(m + n) \cdot \frac{m}{n}$

143. $(-n - m)\frac{n}{m}$

144. What must be true of m and n if $-mn$ is to be **(a)** positive? **(b)** zero? **(c)** negative?

145. The following is a proof that a positive number times a negative number is negative. Provide a reason for each step. Assume that $a > 0$ and $b > 0$.

$$a(-b) + ab = a[-b + b]$$
$$= a(0)$$
$$= 0$$

Therefore, $a(-b)$ is the opposite of ab.

146. Is it true that for any numbers a and b, if a is larger than b, then the reciprocal of a is smaller than the reciprocal of b? Why or why not?

147. *Research.* As her airplane was descending, Judy noticed that the onboard monitors indicated an altitude of 20,000 ft and an air temperature of $-15°F$. Find how many degrees air temperature drops for every 1000 ft of altitude. Then predict the temperature on the ground after Judy lands.

YOUR TURN ANSWERS: SECTION 1.7

1. -30 **2.** 0 **3.** $\frac{1}{6}$ **4.** -50 **5.** -4 **6.** $\frac{5}{-6}; -\frac{5}{6}$
7. 1 **8.** $-\frac{9}{10}$ **9.** $-\frac{25}{3}$ **10.** 160 **11.** 0

QUICK QUIZ: SECTIONS 1.1–1.7

1. Factor: $22x + 11 + 33y$. [1.2]

2. Graph on the number line: -3.5. [1.4]

3. Simplify: $-3.1 + 1.5 + (-2.8) + (-1.7)$. [1.5]

4. Combine like terms: $3x - 7m - m - 4x$. [1.6]

5. Divide: $\frac{3}{8} \div \left(-\frac{3}{16}\right)$. [1.7]

1.8   Exponential Notation and Order of Operations

Exponential Notation   ▪   Order of Operations   ▪   Simplifying and the Distributive Law   ▪   The Opposite of a Sum

Algebraic expressions often contain *exponential notation*. In this section, we learn how to use exponential notation as well as rules for the *order of operations* in performing certain algebraic manipulations.

Study Skills

A Journey of 1000 Miles Starts with a Single Step

It is extremely important to include steps when working problems. Doing so allows you and others to follow your thought process. It also helps you to avoid careless errors and to identify specific areas in which you may have made mistakes.

Exponential Notation

A product like $3 \cdot 3 \cdot 3 \cdot 3$, in which the factors are the same, is called a **power.** Powers are often written in **exponential notation**. For

$$\underbrace{3 \cdot 3 \cdot 3 \cdot 3,}_{4 \text{ factors}} \quad \text{we write} \quad 3^4.$$

This is read "three to the fourth power," or simply, "three to the fourth." The number 4 is called an **exponent** and the number 3 a **base**. Because $3^4 = 81$, we say that 81 is a power of 3.

Expressions like s^2 and s^3 are usually read "s squared" and "s cubed," respectively. This comes from the fact that a square with sides of length s has an area A given by $A = s^2$ and a cube with sides of length s has a volume V given by $V = s^3$.

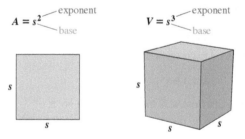

EXAMPLE 1   Write exponential notation for $10 \cdot 10 \cdot 10 \cdot 10 \cdot 10$.

SOLUTION

Exponential notation is 10^5.   5 is the exponent.
10 is the base.

1. Write exponential notation for $(-9)(-9)(-9)$.

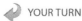 YOUR TURN

EXAMPLE 2   Simplify: **(a)** 5^2; **(b)** $(-5)^3$; **(c)** $(2n)^3$.

SOLUTION

a) $5^2 = 5 \cdot 5 = 25$ The exponent 2 indicates two factors of 5.

b) $(-5)^3 = (-5)(-5)(-5)$ The exponent 3 indicates three factors of -5.

$\qquad = 25(-5)$ Using the associative law of multiplication

$\qquad = -125$

c) $(2n)^3 = (2n)(2n)(2n)$ The exponent 3 indicates three factors of $2n$.

$\qquad = 2 \cdot 2 \cdot 2 \cdot n \cdot n \cdot n$ Using the associative and commutative laws of multiplication

$\qquad = 8n^3$

2. Simplify: $(-2)^4$.

YOUR TURN

Technology Connection

To enter an exponential expression on a graphing calculator, we press ⌃ and then enter the exponent. The x^2 key can be used to enter an exponent of 2.

The following screen shows the calculation

$$\frac{12(9 - 7) + 4 \cdot 5}{2^4 + 3^2}$$

from Example 8 using a calculator with an n/d option.

```
12(9−7)+4∗5
─────────
 2^4+3^2
                44
               ──
                25
```

On calculators without an n/d option, we use parentheses to enclose the numerator and the denominator. The following screen shows the above calculation using parentheses. The number has also been converted to fraction notation.

```
(12(9−7)+4∗5)/(2^4+3^2)
                1.76
Ans▶Frac
               44/25
■
```

Student Notes

Although most scientific and graphing calculators follow the rules for order of operations when evaluating expressions, some do not. Try calculating $4 + 2 \times 5$ on your calculator. If the result shown is 30, your calculator does not follow the rules for order of operations. In this case, you will need to multiply 2×5 first and then add 4.

3. Simplify: $1 - 30 \div 3 + 7$.

 YOUR TURN

To determine what the exponent 1 will mean, look for a pattern in the following:

$$7 \cdot 7 \cdot 7 \cdot 7 = 7^4$$
$$7 \cdot 7 \cdot 7 = 7^3$$
$$7 \cdot 7 = 7^2$$
$$? = 7^1$$

The exponent decreases by 1 each time.

The number of factors decreases by 1 each time. To extend the pattern, we say that

$$7 = 7^1.$$

EXPONENTIAL NOTATION

For any natural number n,

$$b^n \quad \text{means} \quad \overbrace{b \cdot b \cdot b \cdot b \cdots b}^{n \text{ factors}}.$$

Order of Operations

How should $4 + 2 \times 5$ be computed? If we multiply 2 by 5 and then add 4, the result is 14. If we add 2 and 4 first and then multiply by 5, the result is 30. Since these results differ, the order in which we perform operations matters. If grouping symbols such as parentheses ( ), brackets [ ], braces { }, absolute-value symbols | |, or fraction bars appear, they tell us what to do first. For example,

$$(4 + 2) \times 5 \quad \text{indicates} \quad 6 \times 5, \quad \text{resulting in 30},$$

and

$$4 + (2 \times 5) \quad \text{indicates} \quad 4 + 10, \quad \text{resulting in 14}.$$

Besides grouping symbols, the following conventions exist for determining the order in which operations should be performed.

RULES FOR ORDER OF OPERATIONS

1. Simplify, if possible, within the innermost grouping symbols, ( ), [ ], { }, | |, and above or below any fraction bars.
2. Simplify all exponential expressions.
3. Perform all multiplications and divisions, working from left to right.
4. Perform all additions and subtractions, working from left to right.

Thus the correct way to compute $4 + 2 \times 5$ is to first multiply 2 by 5 and then add 4. The result is 14.

EXAMPLE 3   Simplify: $15 - 2 \cdot 5 + 3$.

SOLUTION   When no groupings or exponents appear, we *always* multiply or divide before adding or subtracting:

$$15 - 2 \cdot 5 + 3 = 15 - 10 + 3 \qquad \text{Multiplying}$$
$$= 5 + 3 \qquad \left.\begin{array}{l} \\ \end{array}\right\} \quad \text{Subtracting and adding from}$$
$$= 8. \qquad \qquad \text{left to right}$$

Always calculate within parentheses first. When there are exponents and no parentheses, simplify powers before multiplying or dividing.

EXAMPLE 4 Simplify: **(a)** $(3 \cdot 4)^2$; **(b)** $3 \cdot 4^2$.

SOLUTION

a) $(3 \cdot 4)^2 = (12)^2$ Working within parentheses first
$= 144$

b) $3 \cdot 4^2 = 3 \cdot 16$ Simplifying the power
$= 48$ Multiplying

4. Simplify: $(-5) \cdot 3^2$.

Note that $(3 \cdot 4)^2 \neq 3 \cdot 4^2$.

 YOUR TURN

CAUTION! Example 4 illustrates that, in general, $(ab)^2 \neq ab^2$.

To simplify $-x^2$, it may help to write

$$-x^2 = (-1)x^2.$$

EXAMPLE 5 Evaluate for $x = 5$: **(a)** $(-x)^2$; **(b)** $-x^2$.

SOLUTION

a) $(-x)^2 = (-5)^2 = (-5)(-5) = 25$ We square the opposite of 5.

b) $-x^2 = (-1)x^2 = (-1)(5)^2 = (-1)(25) = -25$ We square 5 and then multiply by -1 (or find the opposite).

5. Evaluate $-x^2$ for $x = 10$.

YOUR TURN

CAUTION! Example 5 illustrates that, in general, $(-x)^2 \neq -x^2$.

Student Notes

When simplifying an expression, it is important to copy the entire expression on each line, not just the parts that have been simplified in a given step. As shown in Examples 6 and 7, each line should be equivalent to the line above it.

6. Evaluate $-2 + 100 \div 2y$ for $y = 10$.

EXAMPLE 6 Evaluate $-15 \div 3(6 - a)^3$ for $a = 4$.

SOLUTION

$$-15 \div 3(6 - a)^3 = -15 \div 3(6 - 4)^3$$ Substituting 4 for a
$$= -15 \div 3(2)^3$$ Working within parentheses first
$$= -15 \div 3 \cdot 8$$ Simplifying the exponential expression
$$\left.\begin{array}{l} = -5 \cdot 8 \\ = -40 \end{array}\right\}$$ Dividing and multiplying from left to right

YOUR TURN

The symbols ( ), [ ], and { } are all used in the same way. Used inside or next to each other, they make it easier to locate the left and right sides of a grouping. When combinations of grouping symbols are used, we begin with the innermost grouping symbols and work to the outside.

EXAMPLE 7 Simplify: $8 \div 4 + 3[9 + 2(3 - 5)^3]$.

SOLUTION

$$8 \div 4 + 3[9 + 2(3 - 5)^3] = 8 \div 4 + 3[9 + 2(-2)^3] \qquad \text{Doing the calculations in the innermost grouping symbols first}$$

$$= 8 \div 4 + 3[9 + 2(-8)] \qquad \begin{matrix} (-2)^3 = (-2)(-2)(-2) \\ = -8 \end{matrix}$$

$$= 8 \div 4 + 3[9 + (-16)]$$

$$= 8 \div 4 + 3[-7] \qquad \text{Completing the calculations within the brackets}$$

$$= 2 + (-21) \qquad \text{Multiplying and dividing from left to right}$$

$$= -19$$

7. Simplify:

$$10 + 5[12 \div (2 - 8)]^2.$$

YOUR TURN

EXAMPLE 8 Calculate: $\dfrac{12(9 - 7) + 4 \cdot 5}{2^4 + 3^2}$.

SOLUTION An equivalent expression with brackets is

$$[12(9 - 7) + 4 \cdot 5] \div [2^4 + 3^2]. \qquad \text{Here the grouping symbols are necessary.}$$

In effect, we need to simplify the numerator, simplify the denominator, and then divide the results:

$$\frac{12(9 - 7) + 4 \cdot 5}{2^4 + 3^2} = \frac{12(2) + 4 \cdot 5}{16 + 9}$$

$$= \frac{24 + 20}{25} = \frac{44}{25}.$$

8. Calculate:

$$\frac{28 \div 14 \cdot 2 - (6 - 1)}{2^2 + 6^2 \div (-3)}.$$

YOUR TURN

Simplifying and the Distributive Law

Sometimes we cannot simplify within grouping symbols. When a sum or a difference is being grouped, we can use the distributive law to remove the grouping symbols.

EXAMPLE 9 Simplify: $5x - 9 + 2(4x + 5)$.

SOLUTION

$$5x - 9 + 2(4x + 5) = 5x - 9 + 8x + 10 \qquad \text{Using the distributive law}$$

$$= 13x + 1 \qquad \text{Combining like terms}$$

9. Simplify:

$$2x + 5(3x - 7) - 20.$$

YOUR TURN

Now that exponents have been introduced, we can make our definition of *like*, or *similar*, *terms* more precise. **Like**, or **similar**, **terms** are either constant terms or terms containing the same variable(s) raised to the same power(s). Thus, 5 and -7, $19xy$ and $2yx$, as well as $4a^3b$ and a^3b are all pairs of like terms.

EXAMPLE 10   Simplify: $7x^2 + 3[x^2 + 2x] - 5x$.

SOLUTION

10. Simplify:

$2a^2 - ab + 10(a^2 + 6ab)$.

$$7x^2 + 3[x^2 + 2x] - 5x = 7x^2 + 3x^2 + 6x - 5x \qquad \text{Using the distributive law}$$
$$= 10x^2 + x \qquad \text{Combining like terms}$$

 YOUR TURN

The Opposite of a Sum

An expression such as $-(x + y)$ indicates the *opposite*, or *additive inverse*, of the sum of x and y. When a sum within grouping symbols is preceded by a "$-$" symbol, we can multiply the sum by -1 and use the distributive law. In this manner, we can find an equivalent expression for the opposite of a sum.

EXAMPLE 11   Write an expression equivalent to $-(3x + 2y + 4)$ without using parentheses.

SOLUTION

11. Write an expression equivalent to $-(2 + 5m + 10n)$ without using parentheses.

$$-(3x + 2y + 4) = -1(3x + 2y + 4) \qquad \text{Using the property of } -1$$
$$= -1(3x) + (-1)(2y) + (-1)4 \qquad \text{Using the distributive law}$$
$$= -3x - 2y - 4 \qquad \text{Using the property of } -1$$

YOUR TURN

> **THE OPPOSITE OF A SUM**
>
> For any real numbers a and b,
>
> $$-(a + b) = (-a) + (-b) = -a - b.$$
>
> (The opposite of a sum is the sum of the opposites.)

To remove parentheses from an expression like $-(x - 7y + 5)$, we can first rewrite the subtraction as addition:

$$-(x - 7y + 5) = -(x + (-7y) + 5) \qquad \text{Rewriting as addition}$$
$$= -x + 7y - 5. \qquad \text{Taking the opposite of a sum}$$

This procedure is generally streamlined to one step in which we find the opposite by "removing parentheses and changing the sign of every term":

$$-(x - 7y + 5) = -x + 7y - 5.$$

EXAMPLE 12   Simplify: $3x - (4x + 2)$.

SOLUTION

$$3x - (4x + 2) = 3x + [-(4x + 2)] \qquad \text{Adding the opposite of } 4x + 2$$
$$= 3x + [-4x - 2] \qquad \text{Taking the opposite of } 4x + 2$$
$$= 3x + (-4x) + (-2)$$
$$= 3x - 4x - 2 \qquad \text{Try to go directly to this step.}$$
$$= -x - 2 \qquad \text{Combining like terms}$$

YOUR TURN

Student Notes

If you prefer, you can simplify expressions like the one in Example 12 using multiplication by -1:

$$3x - (4x + 2) = 3x + [-(4x + 2)]$$
$$= 3x + [-1(4x + 2)]$$
$$= 3x + [-4x - 2].$$

The remaining steps are the same.

12. Simplify: $9 - (5x - 11)$.

In practice, the first three steps of Example 12 are generally skipped.

EXAMPLE 13   Simplify: $5t^2 - 2t - (-4t^2 + 9t)$.

SOLUTION

$$5t^2 - 2t - (-4t^2 + 9t) = 5t^2 - 2t + 4t^2 - 9t$$

Removing parentheses and changing the sign of each term inside

$$= 9t^2 - 11t$$ Combining like terms

13. Simplify:

$$10x - x^2 - (x^2 + 12x).$$

YOUR TURN

Expressions such as $7 - 3(x + 2)$ can be simplified as follows:

$$7 - 3(x + 2) = 7 + [-3(x + 2)]$$ Adding the opposite of $3(x + 2)$

$$= 7 + [-3x - 6]$$ Multiplying $x + 2$ by -3

$$= 7 - 3x - 6$$ Try to go directly to this step.

$$= 1 - 3x.$$ Combining like terms

EXAMPLE 14   Simplify: **(a)** $3n - 2(4n - 5)$; **(b)** $7x^3 + 2 - [5(x^3 - 1) + 8]$.

SOLUTION

a) $3n - 2(4n - 5) = 3n - 8n + 10$ Multiplying each term inside the parentheses by -2; $(-2)(4n) = -8n$, and $(-2)(-5) = 10$

$$= -5n + 10$$ Combining like terms

b) $7x^3 + 2 - [5(x^3 - 1) + 8] = 7x^3 + 2 - [5x^3 - 5 + 8]$ Removing parentheses

$$= 7x^3 + 2 - [5x^3 + 3]$$ Combining like terms

$$= 7x^3 + 2 - 5x^3 - 3$$ Removing brackets

$$= 2x^3 - 1$$ Combining like terms

Chapter Resources:
Collaborative Activity (Select the Symbols), p. 70; Decision Making: Connection, p. 71

14. Simplify:

$$6y^2 - 3(2y^2 - 6y - 7) + 10.$$

YOUR TURN

As we progress through our study of algebra, it is important that we be able to distinguish between the two tasks of **simplifying an expression** and **solving an equation**. In this chapter, we have not solved equations, but we have simplified expressions. This enabled us to write equivalent expressions that were simpler than the given expression.

1.8 EXERCISE SET

Vocabulary and Reading Check

In each of Exercises 1–6, match the expression with the best illustration of that expression from the column on the right.

1. An exponent ____   a) 10^2
2. A base ____   b) The 4 in 4^3
3. The square of a number ____   c) The 6 in x^6
4. The cube of a number ____   d) $-(x + 3) = -x - 3$
5. Like terms ____   e) $3y^4$ and $-y^4$
6. The opposite of a sum ____   f) 8^3

Concept Reinforcement

In each of Exercises 7–12, name the operation that should be performed first. Do not perform the calculations.

7. $4 + 8 \div 2 \cdot 2$
8. $7 - 9 + 15$
9. $5 - 2(3 + 4)$
10. $6 + 7 \cdot 3$
11. $18 - 2[4 + (3 - 2)]$
12. $\dfrac{5 - 6 \cdot 7}{2}$

Exponential Notation

Write exponential notation.

13. $x \cdot x \cdot x \cdot x \cdot x \cdot x$
14. $y \cdot y \cdot y \cdot y \cdot y \cdot y$
15. $(-5)(-5)(-5)$
16. $(-7)(-7)(-7)(-7)$
17. $3t \cdot 3t \cdot 3t \cdot 3t \cdot 3t$
18. $5m \cdot 5m \cdot 5m \cdot 5m \cdot 5m$
19. $2 \cdot n \cdot n \cdot n \cdot n$
20. $8 \cdot a \cdot a \cdot a$

Simplify.

21. 4^2 22. 5^3
23. $(-3)^2$ 24. $(-7)^2$
25. -3^2 26. -7^2
27. 4^3 28. 9^1
29. $(-5)^4$ 30. 5^4
31. 7^1 32. $(-1)^7$
33. $(-2)^5$ 34. -2^5
35. $(3t)^4$ 36. $(5t)^2$
37. $(-7x)^3$ 38. $(-5x)^4$

Order of Operations

Simplify.

39. $5 + 3 \cdot 7$ 40. $3 - 4 \cdot 2$
41. $10 \cdot 5 + 1 \cdot 1$ 42. $19 - 5 \cdot 4 + 3$
43. $5 - 50 \div 5 \cdot 2$ 44. $12 \div 3 + 18 \div 2$
Aha! 45. $14 \cdot 19 \div (19 \cdot 14)$ 46. $18 - 6 \div 3 \cdot 2 + 7$
47. $3(-10)^2 - 8 \div 2^2$ 48. $9 - 3^2 \div 9(-1)$
49. $8 - (2 \cdot 3 - 9)$ 50. $(8 - 2 \cdot 3) - 9$
51. $(8 - 2)(3 - 9)$ 52. $32 \div (-2)^2 \cdot 4$
53. $13(-10)^2 + 45 \div (-5)$ 54. $2^4 + 2^3 - 10 \div (-1)^4$
55. $5 + 3(2 - 9)^2$ 56. $9 - (3 - 5)^3 - 4$
57. $[2 \cdot (5 - 8)]^2 - 12$
58. $2^3 + 2^4 - 5[8 - 4(9 - 10)^2]$
59. $\dfrac{7 + 2}{5^2 - 4^2}$ 60. $\dfrac{(5^2 - 3^2)^2}{2 \cdot 6 - 4}$
61. $8(-7) + |3(-4)|$ 62. $|10(-5)| + 1(-1)$
63. $36 \div (-2)^2 + 4[5 - 3(8 - 9)^5]$
64. $-48 \div (7 - 9)^3 - 2[1 - 5(2 - 6) + 3^2]$
65. $\dfrac{7^2 - (-1)^7}{5 \cdot 7 - 4 \cdot 3^2 - 2^2}$ 66. $\dfrac{(-2)^3 + 4^2}{2 \cdot 3 - 5^2 + 3 \cdot 7}$
67. $\dfrac{-3^3 - 2 \cdot 3^2}{8 \div 2^2 - (6 - |2 - 15|)}$
68. $\dfrac{(-5)^2 - 3 \cdot 5}{3^2 + 4 \cdot |6 - 7| \cdot (-1)^5}$

Evaluate.

69. $9 - 4x$, for $x = 7$
70. $1 + x^3$, for $x = -2$
71. $24 \div t^3$, for $t = -2$
72. $-100 \div a^2$, for $a = -5$
73. $45 \div a \cdot 5$, for $a = -3$
74. $50 \div 2 \cdot t$, for $t = 5$
75. $5x \div 15x^2$, for $x = 3$
76. $6a \div 12a^3$, for $a = 2$

77. $45 \div 3^2 x(x - 1)$, for $x = 3$

78. $-30 \div t(t + 4)^2$, for $t = -6$

79. $-x^2 - 5x$, for $x = -3$

80. $(-x)^2 - 5x$, for $x = -3$

81. $\dfrac{3a - 4a^2}{a^2 - 20}$, for $a = 5$

82. $\dfrac{a^3 - 4a}{a(a - 3)}$, for $a = -2$

Simplifying and the Distributive Law

Simplify.

83. $3x - 2 + 5(2x + 7)$

84. $8n + 3(5n + 2) + 1$

85. $2x^2 + 5(3x^2 - x) - 12x$

86. $6x^2 - x + 4(7x^2 + 3x)$

87. $9t - 7r + 2(3r + 6t)$

88. $4m - 9n + 3(2m - n)$

89. $5t^3 + t + 3(t - 2t^3)$

90. $8n^2 - 3n + 2(n - 4n^2)$

The Opposite of a Sum

Write an equivalent expression without using grouping symbols.

91. $-(9x + 1)$

92. $-(3x + 5)$

93. $-[-7n + 8]$

94. $-(6x - 7)$

95. $-(4a - 3b + 7c)$

96. $-[5n - m - 2p]$

97. $-(3x^2 + 5x - 1)$

98. $-(-9x^3 + 8x + 10)$

Simplify.

99. $8x - (6x + 7)$

100. $2a - (5a - 9)$

101. $2x - 7x - (4x - 6)$

102. $2a + 5a - (6a + 8)$

103. $15x - y - 5(3x - 2y + 5z)$

104. $4a - b - 4(5a - 7b + 8c)$

105. $3x^2 + 11 - (2x^2 + 5)$

106. $5x^4 + 3x - (5x^4 + 3x)$

107. $12a^2 - 3ab + 5b^2 - 5(-5a^2 + 4ab - 6b^2)$

108. $-8a^2 + 5ab - 12b^2 - 6(2a^2 - 4ab - 10b^2)$

109. $-7t^3 - t^2 - 3(5t^3 - 3t)$

110. $9t^4 + 7t - 5(9t^3 - 2t)$

111. $5(2x - 7) - [4(2x - 3) + 2]$

112. $3(6x - 5) - [3(1 - 8x) + 5]$

113. Some students use the mnemonic device PEMDAS to remember the rules for the order of operations. Explain what each letter represents and how the order of the letters in PEMDAS could lead a student to a wrong conclusion about the order of some operations.

114. Jake keys $18/2 \cdot 3$ into his calculator and expects the result to be 3. What mistake is he probably making?

Synthesis

115. Write the sentence $(-x)^2 \neq -x^2$ in words. Explain why $(-x)^2$ and $-x^2$ are not equivalent.

116. Write the sentence $-|x| \neq -x$ in words. Explain why $-|x|$ and $-x$ are not equivalent.

Simplify.

117. $5t - \{7t - [4r - 3(t - 7)] + 6r\} - 4r$

118. $z - \{2z - [3z - (4z - 5z) - 6z] - 7z\} - 8z$

119. $\{x - [f - (f - x)] + [x - f]\} - 3x$

120. Is it true that for all real numbers a and b,
$$ab = (-a)(-b)?$$
Why or why not?

121. Is it true that for all real numbers a, b, and c,
$$a|b - c| = ab - ac?$$
Why or why not?

If $n > 0$, $m > 0$, and $n \neq m$, classify each of the following as either true or false.

122. $-n + m = -(n + m)$

123. $m - n = -(n - m)$

124. $n(-n - m) = -n^2 + nm$

125. $-m(n - m) = -(mn + m^2)$

126. $-n(-n - m) = n(n + m)$

Evaluate.

Aha! **127.** $[x + 3(2 - 5x) \div 7 + x](x - 3)$, for $x = 3$

Aha! **128.** $[x + 2 \div 3x] \div [x + 2 \div 3x]$, for $x = -7$

129. $\dfrac{x^2 + 2^x}{x^2 - 2^x}$, for $x = 3$

130. $\dfrac{x^2 + 2^x}{x^2 - 2^x}$, for $x = 2$

131. In Mexico, between 500 B.C. and 600 A.D., the Mayans represented numbers using powers of 20 and certain symbols. For example, the symbols

represent $4 \cdot 20^3 + 17 \cdot 20^2 + 10 \cdot 20^1 + 0 \cdot 20^0$. Evaluate this number.

Source: National Council of Teachers of Mathematics, 1906 Association Drive, Reston, VA 22091

132. Examine the Mayan symbols and the numbers in Exercise 131. What number does

 , , and

each represent?

133. Calculate the volume of the tower shown below.

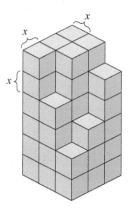

YOUR TURN ANSWERS: SECTION 1.8

1. $(-9)^3$ **2.** 16 **3.** -2 **4.** -45 **5.** -100 **6.** 498

7. 30 **8.** $\dfrac{1}{8}$ **9.** $17x - 55$ **10.** $12a^2 + 59ab$

11. $-2 - 5m - 10n$ **12.** $-5x + 20$

13. $-2x^2 - 2x$ **14.** $18y + 31$

QUICK QUIZ: SECTIONS 1.1–1.8

1. Translate to an algebraic expression: Half of the sum of two numbers. [1.1]

2. Write an inequality with the same meaning as $x > -10$. [1.4]

3. Find decimal notation: $-\dfrac{11}{9}$. [1.4]

4. Multiply: $(-2.1)(-1.4)(-1)$. [1.7]

5. Remove parentheses and simplify:
   $5x - (2y - 3x) - 7y$. [1.8]

1. Twice the difference of a number and 11

2. The product of a number and 11 is 2.

3. Twice the difference of two numbers is 11.

4. The quotient of twice a number and 11

5. The quotient of 11 and the product of two numbers

Translating for Success

Use after Section 1.1.

Translate each phrase or sentence to an expression or an equation and match that translation with one of the choices A–O below. Do not solve.

A. $x = 0.2(11)$

B. $\dfrac{2x}{11}$

C. $2x + 2 = 11$

D. $2(11x + 2)$

E. $11x = 2$

F. $0.2x = 11$

G. $11(2x - y)$

H. $2(x - 11)$

I. $11 + 2x = 2$

J. $2x + y = 11$

K. $2(x - y) = 11$

L. $11(x + 2x)$

M. $2(x + y) = 11$

N. $2 + \dfrac{x}{11}$

O. $\dfrac{11}{xy}$

Answers on page A-3

An additional, animated version of this activity appears in MyMathLab. *To use MyMathLab, you need a course ID and a student access code. Contact your instructor for more information.*

6. Eleven times the sum of a number and twice the number

7. Twice the sum of two numbers is 11.

8. Two more than twice a number is 11.

9. Twice the sum of 11 times a number and 2

10. Twenty percent of some number is 11.

Collaborative Activity   *Teamwork*

Focus: Group problem solving; working collaboratively
Use after: Section 1.1
Time: 15 minutes
Group size: 2

Working and studying as a team often enables students to solve problems that are difficult to solve alone.

Activity

1. The left-hand column below lists the names of 12 colleges. A scrambled list of the names of their sports teams is on the right. As a group, match the names of the colleges to the teams.

   1. University of Texas
   2. Western State College of Colorado
   3. University of North Carolina
   4. University of Massachusetts
   5. Hawaii Pacific University
   6. University of Nebraska
   7. University of California, Santa Cruz
   8. University of Louisiana at Lafayette
   9. Grand Canyon University
   10. Palm Beach Atlantic University
   11. University of Alaska, Anchorage
   12. University of Florida

   a) Antelopes
   b) Banana Slugs
   c) Sea Warriors
   d) Gators
   e) Mountaineers
   f) Sailfish
   g) Longhorns
   h) Tar Heels
   i) Seawolves
   j) Ragin' Cajuns
   k) Cornhuskers
   l) Minutemen

2. After working for 5 min, confer with another group and reach mutual agreement.

3. Does the class agree on all 12 pairs?

4. Do you agree that group collaboration enhances our ability to solve problems?

Collaborative Activity   *Select the Symbols*

Focus: Order of operations
Use after: Section 1.8
Time: 15 minutes
Group size: 2

One way to master the rules for the order of operations is to insert symbols within a display of numbers in order to obtain a predetermined result. For example, the display

$$1 \quad 2 \quad 3 \quad 4 \quad 5$$

can be used to obtain the result 21 as follows:

$$(1 + 2) \div 3 + 4 \cdot 5.$$

Note that without an understanding of the rules for the order of operations, solving a problem of this sort is impossible.

Activity

1. Each group should prepare an exercise similar to the example shown here. (Exponents are not allowed.) To do so, first select five single-digit numbers for display. Then insert operations and grouping symbols and calculate the result.

2. Pair with another group. Each group should give the other its result along with its five-number display, and challenge the other group to insert symbols that will make the display equal the result given.

3. Share with the entire class the various mathematical statements developed by each group.

4. Are the answers always unique for any given set of numbers? Why or why not?

Decision Making & Connection   *(Use after Section 1.8.)*

Calorie Differential.   In order to lose weight, a person must burn more calories than he or she consumes. The difference between one's calorie consumption and one's calorie usage is called the *calorie differential*.

	Calorie Consumption	Calorie Usage	Calorie Differential
Monday	1900	2000	
Tuesday	2600	2100	
Wednesday	2400	2500	

1. The table at left shows Porter's calorie consumption and calorie usage for several days. Calculate the calorie differential for each day. If he is on a diet to lose weight, on which day(s) was he successful? If he is on a diet to gain weight, on which day(s) was he successful?

2. The Basal Metabolic Rate (BMR) is the amount of calories a person uses at rest. One formula uses a person's weight in pounds w, height in inches h, and age in years a. Because of different body composition, there is one formula for women and another for men.

    Women: $\text{BMR} = 655 + 4.35w + 4.7h - 4.7a$

    Men: $\text{BMR} = 66 + 6.23w + 12.7h - 6.8a$

Calorie usage also depends on one's level of activity. To determine your total daily calorie needs to maintain your current weight, you can use the Harris Benedict Formula to multiply your BMR by the appropriate activity factor, as follows.

Activity Level	Daily Calorie Needs to Maintain Weight
Sedentary (little or no exercise)	BMR × 1.2
Lightly active (light exercise/sports 1–3 days/week)	BMR × 1.375
Moderately active (moderate exercise/sports 3–5 days/week)	BMR × 1.55
Very active (hard exercise/sports 6–7 days/week)	BMR × 1.725
Extra active (very hard exercise/sports and physical job)	BMR × 1.9

Source: bmi-calculator.net

If Porter is lightly active, weighs 180 lb, is 70 in. tall, and is 22 years old, what are his daily calorie needs in order to maintain his weight?

 3. *Research.*   The number of calories burned by *extra* exercise can be added to a person's daily calorie needs in order to calculate total calorie usage. How many calories do you burn during exercise? Choose a favorite exercise, and find the number of calories burned per minute during that exercise.

4. Suppose you want to lose one pound. Follow the steps below to estimate how many calories you can consume each day if you exercise 30 min per day.

    1) Use one of the formulas for BMR given above to estimate your Basal Metabolic Rate. Then use the Harris Benedict Formula to estimate your daily calorie needs to maintain your weight.

    2) Calculate how many calories you would burn during 30 min of your favorite extra exercise.

    3) Add the numbers found in steps (1) and (2) to calculate your daily calorie usage.

    4) Divide −3500 by 7 to calculate the calorie differential needed each day in order to lose one pound in one week.

5. Add the number found in step (4) to the number found in step (3) to estimate the daily calorie consumption needed to lose one pound per week, assuming extra exercise.

Study Summary

KEY TERMS AND CONCEPTS	EXAMPLES	PRACTICE EXERCISES

SECTION 1.1: *Introduction to Algebra*

KEY TERMS AND CONCEPTS	EXAMPLES	PRACTICE EXERCISES
To **evaluate** an algebraic expression, substitute a number for each variable and carry out the operations. The result is a **value** of that expression.	Evaluate $\dfrac{x+y}{8}$ for $x = 15$ and $y = 9$. $$\frac{x+y}{8} = \frac{15+9}{8} = \frac{24}{8} = 3$$	**1.** Evaluate $3 + 5c - d$ for $c = 3$ and $d = 10$.
To find the area of a rectangle, a triangle, or a parallelogram, evaluate the appropriate formula for the given values.	Find the area of a triangle with base 3.1 m and height 6 m. $$A = \tfrac{1}{2}bh = \tfrac{1}{2}(3.1\text{ m})(6\text{ m})$$ $$= \tfrac{1}{2}(3.1)(6)(\text{m} \cdot \text{m}) = 9.3\text{ m}^2$$	**2.** Find the area of a rectangle with length 8 ft and width $\tfrac{1}{2}$ ft.
Many problems can be solved by **translating** phrases to algebraic expressions and then forming an equation.	Translate to an equation. Do not solve. When 34 is subtracted from a number, the result is 13. What is the number? Let n represent the number. *Rewording:* 34 subtracted from a number is 13 *Translating:* $n - 34$ $= 13$	**3.** Translate to an equation. Do not solve. 78 is 92 less than some number. What is the number?

SECTION 1.2: *The Commutative, Associative, and Distributive Laws*

KEY TERMS AND CONCEPTS	EXAMPLES	PRACTICE EXERCISES
The Commutative Laws $a + b = b + a$; $ab = ba$	$3 + (-5) = -5 + 3$; $8(10) = 10(8)$	**4.** Use the commutative law of addition to write an expression equivalent to $6 + 10n$.
The Associative Laws $a + (b + c) = (a + b) + c$; $a \cdot (b \cdot c) = (a \cdot b) \cdot c$	$-5 + (5 + 6) = (-5 + 5) + 6$; $2 \cdot (5 \cdot 9) = (2 \cdot 5) \cdot 9$	**5.** Use the associative law of multiplication to write an expression equivalent to $3(ab)$.
The Distributive Law $a(b + c) = ab + ac$	Multiply: $3(2x + 5y)$. $$3(2x + 5y) = 3 \cdot 2x + 3 \cdot 5y = 6x + 15y$$ Factor: $16x + 24y + 8$. $$16x + 24y + 8 = 8(2x + 3y + 1)$$	**6.** Multiply: $$10(5m + 9n + 1).$$ **7.** Factor: $26x + 13$.

SECTION 1.3: *Fraction Notation*

KEY TERMS AND CONCEPTS	EXAMPLES	PRACTICE EXERCISES
A **prime** number has exactly two different factors, the number itself and 1. Natural numbers that have factors other than 1 and the number itself are **composite** numbers.	2, 3, 5, 7, 11, and 13 are the first six prime numbers. 4, 6, 8, 24, and 100 are examples of composite numbers.	**8.** Is 15 prime or composite?

The **prime factorization** of a composite number expresses that number as a product of prime numbers.

The prime factorization of 136 is $2 \cdot 2 \cdot 2 \cdot 17$.

9. Find the prime factorization of 84.

For any nonzero number a,

$$\frac{a}{a} = 1.$$

$\dfrac{15}{15} = 1$ and $\dfrac{2x}{2x} = 1$.   We assume $x \neq 0$.

10. Simplify: $\dfrac{t}{t}$.
Assume $t \neq 0$.

The Identity Property of 1

$$a \cdot 1 = 1 \cdot a = a$$

The number 1 is called the **multiplicative identity.**

$\dfrac{2}{3} = \dfrac{2}{3} \cdot \dfrac{5}{5}$ since $\dfrac{5}{5} = 1$.

11. Simplify: $\dfrac{9}{10} \cdot \dfrac{13}{13}$.

$\dfrac{a}{d} + \dfrac{b}{d} = \dfrac{a+b}{d}$

$\dfrac{a}{d} - \dfrac{b}{d} = \dfrac{a-b}{d}$

$\dfrac{a}{b} \cdot \dfrac{c}{d} = \dfrac{a \cdot c}{b \cdot d}$

$\dfrac{a}{b} \div \dfrac{c}{d} = \dfrac{a}{b} \cdot \dfrac{d}{c}$

$\dfrac{1}{6} + \dfrac{3}{8} = \dfrac{4}{24} + \dfrac{9}{24} = \dfrac{13}{24}$

$\dfrac{5}{12} - \dfrac{1}{6} = \dfrac{5}{12} - \dfrac{2}{12} = \dfrac{3}{12} = \dfrac{1 \cdot 3}{4 \cdot 3} = \dfrac{1}{4} \cdot \dfrac{3}{3} = \dfrac{1}{4} \cdot 1 = \dfrac{1}{4}$

$\dfrac{2}{5} \cdot \dfrac{7}{8} = \dfrac{2 \cdot 7}{5 \cdot 2 \cdot 4} = \dfrac{7}{20}$ Removing a factor equal to 1: $\dfrac{2}{2} = 1$

$\dfrac{10}{9} \div \dfrac{4}{15} = \dfrac{10}{9} \cdot \dfrac{15}{4} = \dfrac{2 \cdot 5 \cdot 3 \cdot 5}{3 \cdot 3 \cdot 2 \cdot 2} = \dfrac{25}{6}$ Removing a factor equal to 1: $\dfrac{2 \cdot 3}{2 \cdot 3} = 1$

Perform the indicated operation and, if possible, simplify.

12. $\dfrac{2}{3} + \dfrac{5}{6}$

13. $\dfrac{3}{4} - \dfrac{3}{10}$

14. $\dfrac{15}{14} \cdot \dfrac{35}{9}$

15. $15 \div \dfrac{3}{5}$

SECTION 1.4:   *Positive and Negative Real Numbers*

Natural numbers:
$$\{1, 2, 3, 4, \dots\}$$

1, 50, and 685 are examples of natural numbers.

16. Which of the following are integers?
$$\frac{9}{10}, \ 0, \ -15, \ \sqrt{2}, \ \frac{30}{3}$$

Whole numbers:
$$\{0, 1, 2, 3, 4, \dots\}$$

0, 37, and 14,615 are examples of whole numbers.

Integers:
$$\{\dots, -3, -2, -1, 0, 1, 2, 3, \dots\}$$

$-25, -2, 0, 1$, and 2000 are examples of integers.

Rational numbers:
$$\left\{\frac{a}{b} \,\middle|\, a \text{ and } b \text{ are}\right.$$
$$\left. \text{integers and } b \neq 0\right\}$$

$\dfrac{1}{6}, \dfrac{-3}{7}, 0, 17, 0.758$, and $9.\overline{608}$ are examples of rational numbers.

The rational numbers and the **irrational numbers** make up the set of **real numbers.**

$\sqrt{7}$ and π are examples of irrational numbers.

Every rational number can be written using fraction notation or decimal notation. When written in decimal notation, a rational number either **repeats** or **terminates.**

$-\dfrac{1}{16} = -0.0625$ This is a terminating decimal.

$\dfrac{5}{6} = 0.8333\ldots = 0.8\overline{3}$ This is a repeating decimal.

17. Find decimal notation:
$$-\frac{10}{9}.$$

Every real number corresponds to a point on the number line. For any two numbers, the one to the left on the number line is less than the one to the right. The symbol $<$ means "**is less than**" and the symbol $>$ means "**is greater than**."	$$\begin{array}{ccccc} -3.1 & -\frac{1}{2} & \sqrt{2} & & 4 \\ \end{array}$$ $-4\ -3\ -2\ -1\ \ 0\ \ 1\ \ 2\ \ 3\ \ 4$ $4 > -3.1 \qquad -\dfrac{1}{2} < \sqrt{2}$	**18.** Write a true sentence using either $<$ or $>$: $-3\ \blacksquare\ -4$.
The **absolute value** of a number is the number of units that number is from 0 on the number line.	$\lvert 3 \rvert = 3$ since 3 is 3 units from 0. $\lvert -3 \rvert = 3$ since -3 is 3 units from 0.	**19.** Find the absolute value: $\lvert -1.5 \rvert$.

SECTION 1.5:   *Addition of Real Numbers*

To **add** two real numbers, use the rules given in Section 1.5.	$-8 + (-3) = -11$; $-8 + 3 = -5$; $8 + (-3) = 5$; $-8 + 8 = 0$	**20.** Add: $-15 + (-10) + 20$.
The Identity Property of 0 $a + 0 = 0 + a = a$ The number 0 is called the **additive identity.**	$-35 + 0 = -35$; $0 + \dfrac{2}{9} = \dfrac{2}{9}$	**21.** Add: $-2.9 + 0$.

SECTION 1.6:   *Subtraction of Real Numbers*

The **opposite**, or **additive inverse,** of a number a is written $-a$. The opposite of the opposite of a is a. $-(-a) = a$	Find $-x$ and $-(-x)$ when $x = -11$. $\qquad -x = -(-11) = 11$; $\qquad -(-x) = -(-(-11)) = -11 \qquad -(-x) = x$	**22.** Find $-(-x)$ when $x = -12$.
To **subtract** two real numbers, add the opposite of the number being subtracted.	$-10 - 12 = -10 + (-12) = -22$; $-10 - (-12) = -10 + 12 = 2$	**23.** Subtract: $6 - (-9)$.
The **terms** of an expression are separated by plus signs. **Like terms** either are constants or have the same variable factors. Like terms can be **combined** using the distributive law.	In the expression $-2x + 3y + 5x - 7y$: $\quad$ The terms are $-2x, 3y, 5x,$ and $-7y$. $\quad$ The like terms are $-2x$ and $5x$, and $3y$ and $-7y$. Combining like terms gives $\quad -2x + 3y + 5x - 7y = -2x + 5x + 3y - 7y$ $\qquad\qquad\qquad\qquad\quad = (-2 + 5)x + (3 - 7)y$ $\qquad\qquad\qquad\qquad\quad = 3x - 4y.$	**24.** Combine like terms: $3c + d - 10c - 2 + 8d$.

SECTION 1.7:   *Multiplication and Division of Real Numbers*

To **multiply** or **divide** two real numbers, use the rules given in Section 1.7. Division by 0 is **undefined**.	$(-5)(-2) = 10$; $30 \div (-6) = -5$; $0 \div (-3) = 0$; $-3 \div 0$ is undefined.	**25.** Multiply: $-3(-7)$. **26.** Divide: $10 \div (-2.5)$.

SECTION 1.8: *Exponential Notation and Order of Operations*

Exponential Notation Exponent n factors $b^n = \overbrace{b \cdot b \cdot b \cdots b}$ Base	$6^2 = 6 \cdot 6 = 36;$ $(-6)^2 = (-6) \cdot (-6) = 36;$ $-6^2 = -(6 \cdot 6) = -36;$ $(6x)^2 = (6x) \cdot (6x) = 36x^2$	**27.** Evaluate: -10^2.
To perform multiple operations, use the rules for **order of operations** given in Section 1.8.	$-3 + (3-5)^3 \div 4(-1) = -3 + (-2)^3 \div 4(-1)$ $= -3 + (-8) \div 4(-1)$ $= -3 + (-2)(-1)$ $= -3 + 2$ $= -1$	**28.** Simplify: $120 \div (-10) \cdot 2$ $- 3(4-5).$
The Opposite of a Sum For any real numbers a and b, $-(a+b) = -a - b.$	$-(2x - 3y) = -(2x) - (-3y) = -2x + 3y$	**29.** Write an equivalent expression without using grouping symbols: $-(-a + 2b - 3c).$
Expressions containing parentheses can be simplified by removing parentheses using the distributive law.	Simplify: $3x^2 - 5(x^2 - 4xy + 2y^2) - 7y^2.$ $3x^2 - 5(x^2 - 4xy + 2y^2) - 7y^2$ $= 3x^2 - 5x^2 + 20xy - 10y^2 - 7y^2$ $= -2x^2 + 20xy - 17y^2$	**30.** Simplify: $2m + n - 3(5 - m - 2n).$

Review Exercises:　Chapter 1

⬡ Concept Reinforcement

In each of Exercises 1–10, classify the statement as either true or false.

1. $4x - 5y$ and $12 - 7a$ are both algebraic expressions containing two terms.   [1.2]*

2. $3t + 1 = 7$ and $8 - 2 = 9$ are both equations. [1.1]

3. The fact that $2 + x$ is equivalent to $x + 2$ is an illustration of the associative law for addition.   [1.2]

4. The statement $4(a + 3) = 4 \cdot a + 4 \cdot 3$ illustrates the distributive law.   [1.2]

5. The number 2 is neither prime nor composite.   [1.3]

6. Every irrational number can be written as a repeating decimal or a terminating decimal.   [1.4]

7. Every natural number is a whole number and every whole number is an integer.   [1.4]

8. The expressions $9r^2s$ and $5rs^2$ are like terms.   [1.8]

9. The opposite of x, written $-x$, never represents a positive number.   [1.6]

10. The number 0 has no reciprocal.   [1.7]

Evaluate.

11. $8t$, for $t = 3$ [1.1]

12. $9 - y^2$, for $y = -5$ [1.8]

13. $-10 + a^2 \div (b + 1)$, for $a = 5$ and $b = -6$ [1.8]

Translate to an algebraic expression.   [1.1]

14. 7 less than y

15. 10 more than the product of x and z

16. 15 times the difference of Brandt's speed and the wind speed

---

*The notation [1.2] refers to Chapter 1, Section 2.

17. Translate to an equation. Do not solve.   [1.1]

Backpacking burns twice as many calories per hour as housecleaning. If Katie burns 237 calories per hour housecleaning, how many calories per hour would she burn backpacking?

Source: www.myoptumhealth.com

18. The following table lists the number of calories that Kim burns when bowling for various lengths of time. Find an equation for the number of calories burned c when Kim bowls for t hours.   [1.1]

Number of Hours Spent Bowling, t	Number of Calories Burned, c
$\frac{1}{2}$	100
2	400
$2\frac{1}{2}$	500

19. Use the commutative law of multiplication to write an expression equivalent to $3t + 5$.   [1.2]

20. Use the associative law of addition to write an expression equivalent to $(2x + y) + z$.   [1.2]

21. Use the commutative and associative laws to write three expressions equivalent to $4(xy)$.   [1.2]

Multiply.   [1.2]

22. $6(3x + 5y)$ **23.** $8(5x + 3y + 2)$

Factor.   [1.2]

24. $21x + 15y$ **25.** $22a + 99b + 11$

26. Find the prime factorization of 56.   [1.3]

Simplify.   [1.3]

27. $\dfrac{20}{48}$ **28.** $\dfrac{18}{8}$

Perform the indicated operation and, if possible, simplify.   [1.3]

29. $\dfrac{5}{12} + \dfrac{3}{8}$ **30.** $\dfrac{9}{16} \div 3$

31. $\dfrac{2}{3} - \dfrac{1}{15}$ **32.** $\dfrac{9}{10} \cdot \dfrac{6}{5}$

33. Tell which integers correspond to this situation. [1.4]

Becky borrowed \$3600 to buy a used car. Clayton has \$1350 in his savings account.

34. Graph on a number line: $\frac{-1}{3}$.   [1.4]

35. Write an inequality with the same meaning as $-3 < x$.   [1.4]

36. Write a true sentence using either $<$ or $>$: $-10 \ \square \ 0$.   [1.4]

37. Find decimal notation: $-\frac{4}{9}$.   [1.4]

38. Find the absolute value: $|-1|$.   [1.4]

39. Find $-(-x)$ when x is -12.   [1.6]

Simplify.

40. $-3 + (-7)$ [1.5]

41. $-\frac{2}{3} + \frac{1}{12}$ [1.5]

42. $-3.8 + 5.1 + (-12) + (-4.3) + 10$ [1.5]

43. $-2 - (-10)$ [1.6]

44. $-\frac{9}{10} - \frac{1}{2}$ [1.6]

45. $-2.7(3.4)$ [1.7]

46. $\frac{2}{3} \cdot \left(-\frac{3}{7}\right)$ [1.7]

47. $2 \cdot (-7) \cdot (-2) \cdot (-5)$ [1.7]

48. $35 \div (-5)$ [1.7]

49. $-5.1 \div 1.7$ [1.7]

50. $-\frac{3}{5} \div \left(-\frac{4}{15}\right)$ [1.7]

51. $120 - 6^2 \div 4 \cdot 8$ [1.8]

52. $(120 - 6^2) \div 4 \cdot 8$ [1.8]

53. $(120 - 6^2) \div (4 \cdot 8)$ [1.8]

54. $16 \div (-2)^3 - 5[3 - 1 + 2(4 - 7)]$ [1.8]

55. $|-3 \cdot 5 - 4 \cdot 8| - 3(-2)$ [1.8]

56. $\dfrac{4(18 - 8) + 7 \cdot 9}{9^2 - 8^2}$ [1.8]

Combine like terms.

57. $11a + 2b + (-4a) + (-3b)$ [1.5]

58. $7x - 3y - 11x + 8y$ [1.6]

59. Find the opposite of -7.   [1.6]

60. Find the reciprocal of -7.   [1.7]

61. Write exponential notation for $2x \cdot 2x \cdot 2x \cdot 2x$.   [1.8]

62. Simplify: $(-5x)^3$.   [1.8]

Remove parentheses and simplify.   [1.8]

63. $2a - (5a - 9)$

64. $11x^4 + 2x + 8(x - x^4)$

65. $2n^2 - 5(-3n^2 + m^2 - 4mn) + 6m^2$

66. $8(x + 4) - 6 - [3(x - 2) + 4]$

Synthesis

67. Explain the difference between a constant and a variable.   [1.1]

68. Explain the difference between a term and a factor.   [1.2]

69. Describe at least three ways in which the distributive law was used in this chapter.   [1.2]

70. Devise a rule for determining the sign of a negative number raised to a power.   [1.8]

71. Evaluate $a^{50} - 20a^{25}b^4 + 100b^8$ for $a = 1$ and $b = 2$.   [1.8]

72. If $0.090909 \ldots = \frac{1}{11}$ and $0.181818 \ldots = \frac{2}{11}$, what rational number is named by each of the following?

   a) $0.272727 \ldots$ [1.4]

   b) $0.909090 \ldots$ [1.4]

Simplify.   [1.8]

73. $-\left|\frac{7}{8} - \left(-\frac{1}{2}\right) - \frac{3}{4}\right|$

74. $(|2.7 - 3| + 3^2 - |-3|) \div (-3)$

Match each phrase in the left column with the most appropriate choice from the right column.

75. _____ A number is nonnegative. [1.4]

76. _____ The product of a number and its reciprocal is 1. [1.7]

77. _____ A number squared   [1.8]

78. _____ A sum of squares   [1.8]

79. _____ The opposite of an opposite is the original number.   [1.6]

80. _____ The order in which numbers are added does not change the result.   [1.2]

81. _____ A number is positive.   [1.4]

82. _____ The absolute value of a product   [1.4]

83. _____ A sum of a number and its reciprocal   [1.7]

84. _____ The square of a sum   [1.8]

85. _____ The absolute value of one number is less than the absolute value of another number.   [1.4]

a) a^2

b) $a + b = b + a$

c) $a > 0$

d) $a + \dfrac{1}{a}$

e) $|ab|$

f) $(a + b)^2$

g) $|a| < |b|$

h) $a^2 + b^2$

i) $a \geq 0$

j) $a \cdot \dfrac{1}{a} = 1$

k) $-(-a) = a$

Test: Chapter 1

 For step-by-step test solutions, access the Chapter Test Prep Videos in MyMathLab®, on YouTube® (search "Bittinger Combo Alg CA" and click on "Channels"), or by scanning the code.

1. Evaluate $\dfrac{2x}{y}$ for $x = 10$ and $y = 5$.

2. Write an algebraic expression: Nine less than the product of two numbers.

3. Find the area of a triangle when the height h is 30 ft and the base b is 16 ft.

4. Use the commutative law of addition to write an expression equivalent to $3p + q$.

5. Use the associative law of multiplication to write an expression equivalent to $x \cdot (4 \cdot y)$.

6. Translate to an equation. Do not solve.

   About 1500 golden lion tamarins, an endangered species of monkey, live in the wild. This is 1050 more than live in zoos worldwide. How many golden lion tamarins live in zoos?

   Source: nationalzoo.si.edu

Multiply.

7. $7(5 + x)$

8. $-5(y - 2)$

Factor.

9. $11 + 44x$

10. $7x + 7 + 49y$

11. Find the prime factorization of 300.

12. Simplify: $\dfrac{24}{56}$.

Write a true sentence using either $<$ or $>$.

13. $-4 \,\square\, 0$ 14. $-3 \,\square\, -8$

Find the absolute value.

15. $\left| \dfrac{9}{4} \right|$ 16. $|-3.8|$

17. Find the opposite of $-\dfrac{2}{3}$.

18. Find the reciprocal of $-\dfrac{4}{7}$.

19. Find $-x$ when x is -10.

20. Write an inequality with the same meaning as $x \le -5$.

Perform the indicated operations and, if possible, simplify.

21. $3.1 - (-4.7)$

22. $-8 + 4 + (-7) + 3$

23. $-\dfrac{1}{8} - \dfrac{3}{4}$

24. $4 \cdot (-12)$

25. $-\dfrac{1}{2} \cdot \left(-\dfrac{4}{9}\right)$

26. $-\dfrac{3}{5} \div \left(-\dfrac{4}{5}\right)$

27. $4.864 \div (-0.5)$

28. $10 - 2(-16) \div 4^2 + |2 - 10|$

29. $9 + 7 - 4 - (-3)$

30. $256 \div (-16) \cdot 4$

31. $2^3 - 10[4 - 3(-2 + 18)]$

32. Combine like terms: $18y + 30a - 9a + 4y$.

33. Simplify: $(-2x)^4$.

Remove parentheses and simplify.

34. $4x - (3x - 7)$

35. $4(2a - 3b) + a - 7$

36. $3[5(y - 3) + 9] - 2(8y - 1)$

Synthesis

37. Find $\dfrac{5y - x}{2}$ when $x = 20$ and y is 4 less than half of x.

38. Insert one pair of parentheses to make the following a true statement:
$$9 - 3 - 4 + 5 = 15.$$

39. Translate to an inequality: A number n is nonnegative.

40. Simplify: $a - \{3a - [4a - (2a - 4a)]\}$.

41. Classify the following as either true or false:
$$a|b - c| = |ab| - |ac|.$$

Equations, Inequalities, and Problem Solving

NUMBER OF IMAGES USED	FEE FOR IMAGES USED
2	$ 65
20	650
24	780

They Say That a Picture Is Worth a Thousand Words.

When you are using a photographer for an event, the number of images you can afford to buy may be limited. If a photographer charges a $125 session fee plus image fees as shown in the table above, how many images could you purchase for $500? (*See Example 3 in Section 2.5.*)

Whether it is the first photograph or the last print, math is used extensively throughout my photography.

Carlton Riffel, owner of Carlton Riffel Photography in Ocala, Florida, uses math when editing images and calculating payments. He is also constantly adjusting camera settings using math to get the right exposure for his photographs.

Solving equations and inequalities is a recurring theme in much of mathematics. In this chapter, we will study some of the principles used to solve equations and inequalities. We will then use equations and inequalities to solve applied problems.

2.1   Solving Equations

Equations and Solutions   ▪   The Addition Principle   ▪   The Multiplication Principle   ▪   Selecting the Correct Approach

Solving equations is an essential part of problem solving in algebra. In this section, we study two of the most important principles used for this task.

Equations and Solutions

An equation is a number sentence stating that the expressions on either side of the equal sign represent the same number. Equations may be true, false, or neither true nor false.

The equation $8 \cdot 4 = 32$ is *true*.

The equation $7 - 2 = 4$ is *false*.

The equation $x + 6 = 13$ is *neither* true nor false, because we do not know what number x represents.

Equations like $x + 6 = 13$ are true for some replacements for x and are false for others.

> **SOLUTION OF AN EQUATION**
>
> Any replacement for a variable that makes an equation true is called a *solution* of the equation. To *solve* an equation means to find all of its solutions.

Student Notes

At the end of each example in this text, you will see ➜ YOUR TURN. This directs you to try an exercise similar to the corresponding example. The answers to those exercises appear at the end of each exercise set.

1. Determine whether 8 is a solution of $12 = 20 - t$.

To determine whether a number is a solution of an equation, we substitute that number for the variable. If the values on both sides of the equal sign are the same, then the number that was substituted is a solution.

EXAMPLE 1   Determine whether 7 is a solution of $x + 6 = 13$.

SOLUTION   We have

$$\begin{array}{r|l} x + 6 = 13 & \text{Writing the equation} \\ \hline 7 + 6 \mid 13 & \text{Substituting 7 for } x \\ 13 \overset{?}{=} 13 \quad \text{\small TRUE} & 13 = 13 \text{ is a true statement.} \end{array}$$

Since the left-hand side and the right-hand side are the same, 7 is a solution.

➜ YOUR TURN

> *CAUTION!*   Note that in Example 1, the solution is 7, not 13.

EXAMPLE 2 Determine whether -1 is a solution of $7x - 2 = 4x + 5$.

SOLUTION We have

$$
\begin{array}{c|c}
\multicolumn{2}{c}{7x - 2 = 4x + 5} \\
\hline
7(-1) - 2 & 4(-1) + 5 \\
-7 - 2 & -4 + 5 \\
-9 \overset{?}{=} 1 &
\end{array}
$$

Writing the equation
Substituting -1 for x
Carrying out calculations on both sides
FALSE   The statement $-9 = 1$ is false.

Since the left-hand and the right-hand sides differ, -1 is not a solution.

YOUR TURN

2. Determine whether -1 is a solution of $5 + 2n = 4 - n$.

The Addition Principle

Consider the equation

$$x = 7.$$

We can easily see that the solution of this equation is 7. Replacing x with 7, we get

$$7 = 7, \quad \text{which is true.}$$

In Example 1, we found that the solution of $x + 6 = 13$ is also 7. Although the solution of $x = 7$ may seem more obvious, because $x + 6 = 13$ and $x = 7$ have identical solutions, the equations are said to be **equivalent**.

EQUIVALENT EQUATIONS

Equations with the same solutions are called *equivalent equations*.

Student Notes

Be sure to remember the difference between an expression and an equation. For example, $5a - 10$ and $5(a - 2)$ are *equivalent expressions* because they represent the same value for all replacements for a. The *equations* $5a = 10$ and $a = 2$ are *equivalent equations* because they have the same solution, 2.

There are principles that enable us to begin with one equation and end up with an equivalent equation, like $x = 7$, for which the solution is obvious. One such principle concerns addition. The equation $a = b$ says that a and b stand for the same number. Suppose this is true, and some number c is added to a. We get the same result if we add c to b, because a and b are the same number.

THE ADDITION PRINCIPLE

For any real numbers a, b, and c,

$$a = b \quad \text{is equivalent to} \quad a + c = b + c.$$

To visualize the addition principle, consider a balance similar to one that a jeweler might use. When the two sides of the balance hold equal weight, the balance is level. If weight is then added or removed, equally, on both sides, the balance will remain level.

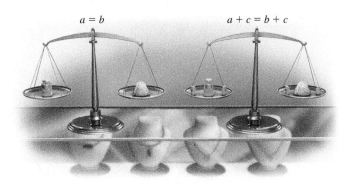

$a = b$ $a + c = b + c$

When using the addition principle, we often say that we "add the same number to both sides of an equation." We can also "subtract the same number from both sides," since subtraction can be regarded as the addition of an opposite.

EXAMPLE 3   Solve: $x + 5 = -7$.

SOLUTION   We can add any number we like to both sides. Since -5 is the opposite, or additive inverse, of 5, we decide to add -5 to each side:

$$x + 5 = -7$$
$$x + 5 - 5 = -7 - 5 \qquad \text{Using the addition principle: adding } -5 \text{ to both sides or subtracting 5 from both sides}$$
$$x + 0 = -12 \qquad \text{Simplifying; } x + 5 - 5 = x + 5 + (-5)$$
$$\qquad\qquad\qquad = x + 0$$
$$x = -12. \qquad \text{Using the identity property of 0}$$

The equation $x = -12$ is equivalent to the equation $x + 5 = -7$ by the addition principle, so the solution of $x = -12$ is the solution of $x + 5 = -7$.

It is obvious that the solution of $x = -12$ is the number -12. To check the answer in the original equation, we substitute.

Check:
$$\begin{array}{c|c} x + 5 = -7 \\ \hline -12 + 5 & -7 \\ -7 \overset{?}{=} -7 & \text{TRUE} \end{array} \qquad -7 = -7 \text{ is true.}$$

3. Solve: $x + 3 = -10$.

The solution of the original equation is -12.

YOUR TURN

In Example 3, note that because we added the *opposite*, or *additive inverse*, of 5, the left-hand side of the equation simplified to x plus the *additive identity*, 0, or simply x. To solve $x + a = b$ for x, we add $-a$ to (or subtract a from) both sides.

EXAMPLE 4   Solve: $-6.5 = y - 8.4$.

SOLUTION   The variable is on the right-hand side this time. We can isolate y by adding 8.4 to each side:

$$-6.5 = y - 8.4 \qquad y - 8.4 \text{ can be regarded as } y + (-8.4).$$
$$-6.5 + 8.4 = y - 8.4 + 8.4 \qquad \text{Using the addition principle: Adding 8.4 to both sides "eliminates" } -8.4 \text{ on the right-hand side.}$$
$$1.9 = y. \qquad y - 8.4 + 8.4 = y + (-8.4) + 8.4$$
$$\qquad\qquad = y + 0 = y$$

Student Notes

We can also think of "undoing" operations in order to isolate a variable. In Example 4, we began with $y - 8.4$ on the right side. To undo the subtraction, we *add* 8.4.

Check:
$$\begin{array}{c|c} -6.5 = y - 8.4 \\ \hline -6.5 & 1.9 - 8.4 \\ -6.5 \overset{?}{=} -6.5 & \text{TRUE} \end{array} \qquad -6.5 = -6.5 \text{ is true.}$$

4. Solve: $-8 = y - 19$.

The solution is 1.9.

YOUR TURN

Note that the equations $a = b$ and $b = a$ have the same meaning. Thus, $-6.5 = y - 8.4$ could have been rewritten as $y - 8.4 = -6.5$.

The Multiplication Principle

A second principle for solving equations concerns multiplying. Suppose a and b are equal. If a and b are multiplied by some number c, then ac and bc will also be equal.

> **THE MULTIPLICATION PRINCIPLE**
>
> For any real numbers a, b, and c, with $c \neq 0$,
>
> $$a = b \quad \text{is equivalent to} \quad a \cdot c = b \cdot c.$$

EXAMPLE 5   Solve: $\frac{5}{4}x = 10$.

SOLUTION   We can multiply both sides by any nonzero number we like. Since $\frac{4}{5}$ is the reciprocal of $\frac{5}{4}$, we decide to multiply both sides by $\frac{4}{5}$:

$$\frac{5}{4}x = 10$$

$\frac{4}{5} \cdot \frac{5}{4}x = \frac{4}{5} \cdot 10$ Using the multiplication principle: Multiplying both sides by $\frac{4}{5}$ "eliminates" the $\frac{5}{4}$ on the left.

$1 \cdot x = 8$ Simplifying

$x = 8.$ Using the identity property of 1

Check:

$$\frac{5}{4}x = 10$$

$$\begin{array}{c|c} \frac{5}{4} \cdot 8 & 10 \\ \hline \frac{40}{4} & \\ 10 \stackrel{?}{=} 10 & \text{TRUE} \end{array}$$ Think of 8 as $\frac{8}{1}$.

$10 = 10$ is true.

5. Solve: $\dfrac{1}{5}x = -3$.

The solution is 8.

YOUR TURN

In Example 5, to get x alone on one side, we multiplied by the *reciprocal*, or *multiplicative inverse* of $\frac{5}{4}$. The simplified left-hand side is x times the *multiplicative identity*, 1, or simply x.

Because division is the same as multiplying by a reciprocal, the multiplication principle also tells us that we can "divide both sides by the same nonzero number." That is,

$$\text{if } a = b, \text{ then } \frac{1}{c} \cdot a = \frac{1}{c} \cdot b \ \text{ and } \ \frac{a}{c} = \frac{b}{c} \quad (\text{provided } c \neq 0).$$

In a product like $3x$, the multiplier 3 is called the **coefficient**. Examining the coefficient of the variable helps us to decide whether to multiply or to divide in order to solve an equation.

- When the coefficient is an integer or a decimal, it is usually easiest to divide on both sides.
- When the coefficient is a fraction, it is usually easiest to multiply by the reciprocal on both sides.

EXAMPLE 6   Solve: **(a)** $-4x = 9$; **(b)** $-x = 5$.

SOLUTION

Student Notes

In Example 6(a), we can think of undoing the multiplication $-4 \cdot x$ by *dividing* by -4.

a) In $-4x = 9$, the coefficient of x is an integer, so we *divide* on both sides:

$$\frac{-4x}{-4} = \frac{9}{-4}$$ Using the multiplication principle: Dividing both sides by -4 is the same as multiplying by $-\frac{1}{4}$.

$$1 \cdot x = -\frac{9}{4}$$ Simplifying

$$x = -\frac{9}{4}.$$ Using the identity property of 1

Check:
$$\frac{-4x = 9}{-4\left(-\frac{9}{4}\right) \mid 9}$$
$$9 \stackrel{?}{=} 9 \quad \text{TRUE} \qquad 9 = 9 \text{ is true.}$$

The solution is $-\frac{9}{4}$.

b) To solve an equation like $-x = 5$, remember that when an expression is multiplied or divided by -1, its sign is changed. Here we divide both sides by -1 to change the sign of $-x$:

$$-x = 5$$ Note that $-x = -1 \cdot x$.

$$\frac{-x}{-1} = \frac{5}{-1}$$ Dividing both sides by -1. (Multiplying by -1 would also work. Note that the reciprocal of -1 is -1.)

$$x = -5.$$ Note that $\frac{-x}{-1}$ is the same as $\frac{x}{1}$.

Check:
$$\frac{-x = 5}{-(-5) \mid 5}$$
$$5 \stackrel{?}{=} 5 \quad \text{TRUE} \qquad 5 = 5 \text{ is true.}$$

6. Solve: $-x = \dfrac{1}{3}$.

The solution is -5.

YOUR TURN

MULTIPLYING AND DIVIDING BY -1

Multiplying a number by -1 changes its sign:

$$(-1)(x) = -x \quad \text{and} \quad (-1)(-x) = x.$$

Dividing a number by -1 changes its sign:

$$\frac{x}{-1} = -x \quad \text{and} \quad \frac{-x}{-1} = x.$$

Study Skills

Seeking Help?

A variety of resources are available to help make studying easier and more enjoyable.

- *Textbook supplements.* See the preface for a description of the supplements for this textbook.
- *Your college or university.* Your own school probably has many resources: a learning lab or tutoring center, study skills workshops or group tutoring sessions tailored for the course you are taking, or a bulletin board or network where you can locate a private tutor.
- *Your instructor.* Find out your instructor's office hours and visit when you need additional help. Many instructors also welcome student e-mail.

---

7. Solve: $\dfrac{4t}{7} = 6$.

EXAMPLE 7   Solve: $\dfrac{2y}{9} = \dfrac{8}{3}$.

SOLUTION   To solve an equation like $\dfrac{2y}{9} = \dfrac{8}{3}$, we can rewrite the left-hand side as $\dfrac{2}{9} \cdot y$ and then use the multiplication principle, multiplying by the reciprocal of $\dfrac{2}{9}$:

$$\frac{2y}{9} = \frac{8}{3}$$

$$\frac{2}{9} \cdot y = \frac{8}{3} \qquad \text{Rewriting } \frac{2y}{9} \text{ as } \frac{2}{9} \cdot y$$

$$\frac{9}{2} \cdot \frac{2}{9} \cdot y = \frac{9}{2} \cdot \frac{8}{3} \qquad \text{Multiplying both sides by } \frac{9}{2}$$

$$1y = \frac{3 \cdot 3 \cdot 2 \cdot 4}{2 \cdot 3} \qquad \text{Removing a factor equal to 1: } \frac{3 \cdot 2}{2 \cdot 3} = 1$$

$$y = 12.$$

Check:

$$\begin{array}{c|c} \dfrac{2y}{9} = \dfrac{8}{3} \\ \hline \dfrac{2 \cdot 12}{9} & \dfrac{8}{3} \\ \dfrac{24}{9} & \\ \dfrac{8}{3} \stackrel{?}{=} \dfrac{8}{3} \text{ TRUE} & \dfrac{8}{3} = \dfrac{8}{3} \text{ is true.} \end{array}$$

The solution is 12.

YOUR TURN

Selecting the Correct Approach

It is important that you be able to determine which principle should be used to solve a particular equation.

EXAMPLE 8   Solve: **(a)** $-8 + x = -3$;   **(b)** $18 = 0.3t$.

SOLUTION

a) To undo addition of -8, we subtract -8 from (or add 8 to) both sides. Note that the opposite of *negative* 8 is *positive* 8.

$$-8 + x = -3$$

$$-8 + x + 8 = -3 + 8 \qquad \text{Using the addition principle}$$

$$x = 5$$

Check:

$$\begin{array}{c|c} -8 + x = -3 \\ \hline -8 + 5 & -3 \\ -3 \stackrel{?}{=} -3 \text{ TRUE} & -3 = -3 \text{ is true.} \end{array}$$

The solution is 5.

b) To undo the multiplication by 0.3, we either divide both sides by 0.3 or multiply both sides by $\dfrac{1}{0.3}$. Note that the reciprocal of *positive* 0.3 is *positive* $\dfrac{1}{0.3}$.

$$18 = 0.3t$$

$$\frac{18}{0.3} = \frac{0.3t}{0.3} \qquad \text{Using the multiplication principle}$$

$$60 = t \qquad \text{Simplifying}$$

Check:

$$\begin{array}{c|c} 18 = 0.3t \\ \hline 18 & 0.3(60) \\ 18 \stackrel{?}{=} 18 & \quad \text{TRUE} \qquad 18 = 18 \text{ is true.} \end{array}$$

The solution is 60.

8. Solve: $2.6 + a = -0.46.$

 YOUR TURN

2.1 EXERCISE SET

FOR EXTRA HELP

MyMathLab® Math XL
PRACTICE   WATCH   READ   REVIEW

⮩ Vocabulary and Reading Check

For each of Exercises 1–6, match the statement with the most appropriate choice from the column on the right.

1. _____ The equations $x + 3 = 7$ and $6x = 24$

2. _____ The expressions $3(x - 2)$ and $3x - 6$

3. _____ A replacement that makes an equation true

4. _____ The role of 9 in $9ab$

5. _____ The principle used to solve $\frac{2}{3} \cdot x = -4$

6. _____ The principle used to solve $\frac{2}{3} + x = -4$

a) A coefficient

b) Equivalent expressions

c) Equivalent equations

d) The multiplication principle

e) The addition principle

f) A solution

⮩ Concept Reinforcement

For each of Exercises 7–10, match the equation with the appropriate step from the column on the right that would be used to most readily solve the equation.

7. _____ $6x = 30$ a) Add 6 to both sides.

8. _____ $x + 6 = 30$ b) Subtract 6 from both sides.

9. _____ $\frac{1}{6}x = 30$ c) Multiply both sides by 6.

10. _____ $x - 6 = 30$ d) Divide both sides by 6.

Equations and Solutions

Determine whether the given number is a solution of the given equation.

11. $6 - x = -2$; 4

12. $6 - x = -2$; 8

13. $\frac{2}{3}t = 12$; 18

14. $\frac{2}{3}t = 12$; 8

15. $x + 7 = 3 - x$; -2

16. $-4 + x = 5x$; -1

17. $4 - \frac{1}{5}n = 8$; -20

18. $-3 = 5 - \dfrac{n}{2}$; 4

The Addition Principle

Solve. Don't forget to check!

19. $x + 10 = 21$

20. $t + 9 = 47$

21. $y + 7 = -18$

22. $x + 12 = -7$

23. $-6 = y + 25$

24. $-5 = x + 8$

25. $x - 18 = 23$

26. $x - 19 = 16$

27. $12 = -7 + y$

28. $15 = -8 + z$

29. $-5 + t = -11$

30. $-6 + y = -21$

31. $r + \frac{1}{3} = \frac{8}{3}$

32. $t + \frac{3}{8} = \frac{5}{8}$

33. $x - \frac{3}{5} = -\frac{7}{10}$

34. $x - \frac{2}{3} = -\frac{5}{6}$

35. $x - \frac{5}{6} = \frac{7}{8}$

36. $y - \frac{3}{4} = \frac{5}{6}$

37. $-\frac{1}{5} + z = -\frac{1}{4}$

38. $-\frac{2}{3} + y = -\frac{3}{4}$

39. $m - 2.8 = 6.3$

40. $y - 5.3 = 8.7$

41. $-9.7 = -4.7 + y$

42. $-7.8 = 2.8 + x$

The Multiplication Principle

Solve. Don't forget to check!

43. $8a = 56$

44. $6x = 72$

45. $84 = 7x$

46. $45 = 9t$

47. $-x = 38$

48. $100 = -x$

Aha! 49. $-t = -8$

50. $-68 = -r$

51. $-7x = 49$

52. $-4x = 36$

53. $-1.3a = -10.4$

54. $-3.4t = -20.4$

55. $\dfrac{y}{8} = 11$

56. $\dfrac{a}{4} = 13$

57. $\dfrac{4}{5}x = 16$

58. $\dfrac{3}{4}x = 27$

59. $\dfrac{-x}{6} = 9$

60. $\dfrac{-t}{4} = 8$

61. $\dfrac{1}{9} = \dfrac{z}{-5}$

62. $\dfrac{2}{7} = \dfrac{x}{-3}$

Aha! **63.** $-\dfrac{3}{5}r = -\dfrac{3}{5}$

64. $-\dfrac{2}{5}y = -\dfrac{4}{15}$

65. $\dfrac{-3r}{2} = -\dfrac{27}{4}$

66. $\dfrac{5x}{7} = -\dfrac{10}{14}$

Selecting the Correct Approach

Solve. The icon ▧ indicates an exercise designed to provide practice using a calculator.

67. $4.5 + t = -3.1$

68. $\frac{3}{4}x = 18$

69. $-8.2x = 20.5$

70. $t - 7.4 = -12.9$

71. $x - 4 = -19$

72. $y - 6 = -14$

73. $t - 3 = -8$

74. $t - 9 = -8$

75. $-12x = 14$

76. $-15x = 20$

77. $48 = -\frac{3}{8}y$

78. $14 = t + 27$

79. $a - \dfrac{1}{6} = -\dfrac{2}{3}$

80. $-\dfrac{x}{6} = \dfrac{2}{9}$

81. $-24 = \dfrac{8x}{5}$

82. $\dfrac{1}{5} + y = -\dfrac{3}{10}$

83. $-\frac{4}{3}t = -12$

84. $\frac{17}{35} = -x$

▧ **85.** $-483.297 = -794.053 + t$

▧ **86.** $-0.2344x = 2028.732$

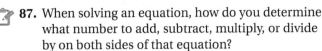 **87.** When solving an equation, how do you determine what number to add, subtract, multiply, or divide by on both sides of that equation?

88. What is the difference between equivalent expressions and equivalent equations?

Skill Review

To the student and the instructor: Skill Review exercises *review skills previously studied in the text. The numbers in brackets immediately following the directions or exercise indicate the section in which the skill was introduced. The answer to all Skill Review exercises appear at the back of the book.*

89. Translate to an algebraic expression:
7 less than one-third of y. [1.1]

90. Multiply: $6(2x + 11)$. [1.2]

91. Factor: $35a + 55c + 5$. [1.2]

92. Graph on the number line: $-\frac{11}{5}$. [1.4]

Synthesis

 93. To solve $-3.5 = 14t$, Anika adds 3.5 to both sides. Will this form an equivalent equation? Will it help solve the equation? Explain.

94. Explain why it is not necessary to state a subtraction principle: For any real numbers a, b, and c, $a = b$ is equivalent to $a - c = b - c$.

Solve for x. Assume $a, c, m \neq 0$.

95. $mx = 11.6m$

96. $x - 4 + a = a$

97. $cx + 5c = 7c$

98. $c \cdot \dfrac{21}{a} = \dfrac{7cx}{2a}$

99. $7 + |x| = 30$

100. $ax - 3a = 5a$

101. If $t - 3590 = 1820$, find $t + 3590$.

102. If $n + 268 = 124$, find $n - 268$.

▦ **103.** La'Toya estimated her monthly business taxes to be \$225. As her last step, she multiplied by 0.3 when she should have divided by 0.3. What should the correct answer be?

104. Are the equations $x = 5$ and $x^2 = 25$ equivalent? Why or why not?

↘ YOUR TURN ANSWERS: SECTION 2.1

1. Yes   **2.** No   **3.** -13 **4.** 11   **5.** -15 **6.** $-\frac{1}{3}$
7. $\frac{21}{2}$ **8.** -3.06

PREPARE TO MOVE ON

Simplify. [1.8]

1. $3 \cdot 4 - 18$

2. $14 - 2(7 - 1)$

3. $4x + 10 - 5x$

4. $x - 2(3x - 7) + 14$

2.2   Using the Principles Together

Applying Both Principles ◾ Combining Like Terms ◾ Clearing Fractions and Decimals ◾ Types of Equations

The addition and multiplication principles, along with the properties and laws concerning real numbers, are our tools for solving equations.

Applying Both Principles

EXAMPLE 1   Solve: $5 + 3x = 17$.

SOLUTION   Were we to evaluate $5 + 3x$, the rules for the order of operations direct us to *first* multiply by 3 and *then* add 5. Because of this, we can isolate $3x$ and then x by reversing these operations: We first subtract 5 from both sides and then divide both sides by 3. Our goal is an equivalent equation of the form $x = a$.

$$5 + 3x = 17$$

$$5 + 3x - 5 = 17 - 5 \qquad \text{Using the addition principle: subtracting 5 from both sides (adding } -5)$$

$$5 + (-5) + 3x = 12 \qquad \text{Using a commutative law. Try to perform this step mentally.}$$

Isolate the x-term.
$$3x = 12 \qquad \text{Simplifying}$$

$$\frac{3x}{3} = \frac{12}{3} \qquad \text{Using the multiplication principle: dividing both sides by 3 (multiplying by } \tfrac{1}{3})$$

Isolate x.
$$x = 4 \qquad \text{Simplifying. This is of the form } x = a.$$

Check:
$$\begin{array}{c|c} 5 + 3x = 17 \\ \hline 5 + 3 \cdot 4 & 17 \\ 5 + 12 & \\ 17 \overset{?}{=} 17 & \text{TRUE} \end{array}$$

We use the rules for order of operations: Find the product, $3 \cdot 4$, and then add.

The solution is 4.

1. Solve: $2x - 5 = 7$.

YOUR TURN

Study Skills

Use the Answer Section Carefully

When using the answers listed at the back of this book, try not to "work backward" from the answer. If you frequently require two or more attempts to answer an exercise correctly, you probably need to work more carefully and/or reread the section preceding the exercise set. Remember that on quizzes and tests you have only one attempt per problem and no answer section to consult.

EXAMPLE 2   Solve: $\frac{4}{3}x - 7 = 1$.

SOLUTION   In $\frac{4}{3}x - 7$, we multiply first and then subtract. To reverse these steps, we first add 7 and then either divide by $\frac{4}{3}$ or multiply by $\frac{3}{4}$.

$$\frac{4}{3}x - 7 = 1$$

$$\frac{4}{3}x - 7 + 7 = 1 + 7 \qquad \text{Adding 7 to both sides}$$

$$\frac{4}{3}x = 8$$

$$\frac{3}{4} \cdot \frac{4}{3}x = \frac{3}{4} \cdot 8 \qquad \text{Multiplying both sides by } \tfrac{3}{4}$$

$$\left. \begin{array}{c} 1 \cdot x = \dfrac{3 \cdot \cancel{4} \cdot 2}{\cancel{4}} \\ x = 6 \end{array} \right\} \quad \text{Simplifying}$$

Check:

$$
\begin{array}{c|c}
\frac{4}{3}x - 7 = 1 \\
\hline
\frac{4}{3} \cdot 6 - 7 & 1 \\
8 - 7 & \\
1 \overset{?}{=} 1 & \text{TRUE}
\end{array}
$$

The solution is 6.

2. Solve: $4 + \frac{2}{3}x = 2$.

YOUR TURN

EXAMPLE 3   Solve: $45 - t = 13$.

SOLUTION   We have

$$45 - t = 13$$

$$45 - t - 45 = 13 - 45 \qquad \text{Subtracting 45 from both sides}$$

$$\left.\begin{array}{r} 45 + (-t) + (-45) = 13 - 45 \\ 45 + (-45) + (-t) = 13 - 45 \end{array}\right\} \quad \text{Try to do these steps mentally.}$$

$$-t = -32 \qquad \text{Try to go directly to this step.}$$

$$(-1)(-t) = (-1)(-32) \qquad \begin{array}{l}\text{Multiplying both sides by } -1. \\ \text{(Dividing by } -1 \text{ would also} \\ \text{work.)}\end{array}$$

$$t = 32.$$

Check:

$$
\begin{array}{c|c}
45 - t = 13 \\
\hline
45 - 32 & 13 \\
13 \overset{?}{=} 13 & \text{TRUE}
\end{array}
$$

The solution is 32.

3. Solve: $-3 - y = 8$.

YOUR TURN

As our skills improve, certain steps can be streamlined.

EXAMPLE 4   Solve: $16.3 - 7.2y = -8.18$.

SOLUTION   We have

$$16.3 - 7.2y = -8.18$$

$$16.3 - 7.2y - 16.3 = -8.18 - 16.3 \qquad \text{Subtracting 16.3 from both sides}$$

$$-7.2y = -24.48 \qquad \text{Simplifying}$$

$$\frac{-7.2y}{-7.2} = \frac{-24.48}{-7.2} \qquad \text{Dividing both sides by } -7.2$$

$$y = 3.4. \qquad \text{Simplifying}$$

Check:

$$
\begin{array}{c|c}
16.3 - 7.2y = -8.18 \\
\hline
16.3 - 7.2(3.4) & -8.18 \\
16.3 - 24.48 & \\
-8.18 \overset{?}{=} -8.18 & \text{TRUE}
\end{array}
$$

The solution is 3.4.

4. Solve: $0.8 = 2.8x + 5$.

YOUR TURN

Technology Connection

A TABLE feature lists the value of a variable expression for different choices of x. For example, to evaluate $6x + 5 - 7x$ for $x = 0, 1, 2, \ldots$, we first use $\boxed{\text{Y=}}$ to enter $6x + 5 - 7x$ as y_1. We then use $\boxed{\text{2ND}}$ $\boxed{\text{TBLSET}}$ to specify TblStart $= 0$, ΔTbl $= 1$, and select AUTO twice. By pressing $\boxed{\text{2ND}}$ $\boxed{\text{TABLE}}$, we can generate a table in which the value of $6x + 5 - 7x$ is listed for values of x starting at 0 and increasing by one's.

X	Y1	
0	5	
1	4	
2	3	
3	2	
4	1	
5	0	
6	−1	
X = 0		

1. Create the above table on your graphing calculator. Scroll up and down to extend the table.
2. Enter $10 - 4x + 7$ as y_2. Your table should now have three columns.
3. For what x-value is y_1 the same as y_2? Compare this with the solution of Example 5(c). Is this a reliable way to solve equations? Why or why not?

Combining Like Terms

If like terms appear on the same side of an equation, we combine them and then solve. Should like terms appear on both sides of an equation, we can use the addition principle to rewrite all like terms on one side.

EXAMPLE 5   Solve.

a) $3x + 4x = -14$
b) $-x + 5 = -8x + 6$
c) $6x + 5 - 7x = 10 - 4x + 7$
d) $2 - 5(x + 5) = 3(x - 2) - 1$

SOLUTION

a) $3x + 4x = -14$

$$
\begin{aligned}
7x &= -14 && \text{Combining like terms} \\
\frac{7x}{7} &= \frac{-14}{7} && \text{Dividing both sides by 7} \\
x &= -2 && \text{Simplifying}
\end{aligned}
$$

The check is left to the student. The solution is -2.

b) To solve $-x + 5 = -8x + 6$, we must first write only variable terms on one side and only constant terms on the other. This can be done by subtracting 5 from both sides, to get all constant terms on the right, and adding $8x$ to both sides, to get all variable terms on the left. These steps can be performed in either order.

> Isolate variable terms on one side and constant terms on the other side.

$$
\begin{aligned}
-x + 5 &= -8x + 6 \\
-x + 8x + 5 &= -8x + 8x + 6 && \text{Adding } 8x \text{ to both sides} \\
7x + 5 &= 6 && \text{Simplifying} \\
7x + 5 - 5 &= 6 - 5 && \text{Subtracting 5 from both sides} \\
7x &= 1 && \text{Combining like terms} \\
\frac{7x}{7} &= \frac{1}{7} && \text{Dividing both sides by 7} \\
x &= \frac{1}{7}
\end{aligned}
$$

The check is left to the student. The solution is $\frac{1}{7}$.

c) $6x + 5 - 7x = 10 - 4x + 7$

$$
\begin{aligned}
-x + 5 &= 17 - 4x && \text{Combining like terms on each side} \\
-x + 5 + 4x &= 17 - 4x + 4x && \text{Adding } 4x \text{ to both sides} \\
5 + 3x &= 17 && \text{Simplifying. This is identical to Example 1.} \\
5 + 3x - 5 &= 17 - 5 && \text{Subtracting 5 from both sides} \\
3x &= 12 && \text{Simplifying} \\
\frac{3x}{3} &= \frac{12}{3} && \text{Dividing both sides by 3} \\
x &= 4
\end{aligned}
$$

Check:

$$
\begin{array}{c|c}
6x + 5 - 7x & = 10 - 4x + 7 \\
\hline
6 \cdot 4 + 5 - 7 \cdot 4 & 10 - 4 \cdot 4 + 7 \\
24 + 5 - 28 & 10 - 16 + 7 \\
1 & \overset{?}{=} 1 \qquad \text{TRUE}
\end{array}
$$

d) $2 - 5(x + 5) = 3(x - 2) - 1$

$2 - 5x - 25 = 3x - 6 - 1$ Using the distributive law. This is now similar to part (c) above.

$-5x - 23 = 3x - 7$ Combining like terms on each side

$-5x - 23 + 7 = 3x - 7 + 7$ Adding 7 to both sides

$-5x - 16 = 3x$ Simplifying

$-5x - 16 + 5x = 3x + 5x$ Adding $5x$ to both sides

$-16 = 8x$

$\dfrac{-16}{8} = \dfrac{8x}{8}$ Dividing both sides by 8

$-2 = x$ This is equivalent to $x = -2$.

The student can confirm that -2 checks and is the solution.

5. Solve:

$2x - (3 - x) = 7x - 1.$

YOUR TURN

Clearing Fractions and Decimals

Equations are generally easier to solve when they do not contain fractions or decimals. The multiplication principle can be used to "clear" fractions or decimals, as shown here.

Clearing Fractions	Clearing Decimals
$\frac{1}{2}x + 5 = \frac{3}{4}$	$2.3x + 7 = 5.4$
$4\left(\frac{1}{2}x + 5\right) = 4 \cdot \frac{3}{4}$	$10(2.3x + 7) = 10 \cdot 5.4$
$2x + 20 = 3$	$23x + 70 = 54$

In each case, the resulting equation is equivalent to the original equation, but easier to solve.

> **AN EQUATION-SOLVING PROCEDURE**
> 1. Use the multiplication principle to clear any fractions or decimals. (This is optional, but can ease computations. See Examples 6 and 7.)
> 2. If necessary, use the distributive law to remove parentheses. Then combine like terms on each side. (See Example 5.)
> 3. Use the addition principle, as needed, to isolate all variable terms on one side. Then combine like terms. (See Examples 1–7.)
> 4. Multiply or divide to solve for the variable, using the multiplication principle. (See Examples 1–7.)
> 5. Check all possible solutions in the original equation. (See Examples 1–4.)

The easiest way to clear an equation of fractions is to multiply *both sides* of the equation by the smallest, or *least*, common denominator of the fractions in the equation.

EXAMPLE 6 Solve: **(a)** $\frac{2}{3}x - \frac{1}{6} = 2x$; **(b)** $\frac{2}{5}(3x + 2) = 8$.

SOLUTION

a) We multiply both sides by 6, the least common denominator of $\frac{2}{3}$ and $\frac{1}{6}$.

$$6\left(\frac{2}{3}x - \frac{1}{6}\right) = 6 \cdot 2x \qquad \text{Multiplying both sides by 6}$$

$$6 \cdot \frac{2}{3}x - 6 \cdot \frac{1}{6} = 6 \cdot 2x \quad \longleftarrow$$

> **CAUTION!**   Be sure the distributive law is used to multiply *all* the terms by 6.

$$4x - 1 = 12x \qquad \text{Simplifying. Note that the fractions are cleared: } 6 \cdot \frac{2}{3} = 4, 6 \cdot \frac{1}{6} = 1, \text{ and } 6 \cdot 2 = 12.$$

$$4x - 1 - 4x = 12x - 4x \qquad \text{Subtracting } 4x \text{ from both sides}$$

$$-1 = 8x$$

$$\frac{-1}{8} = \frac{8x}{8} \qquad \text{Dividing both sides by 8}$$

$$-\frac{1}{8} = x \qquad\qquad \frac{-1}{8} = -\frac{1}{8}$$

The student can confirm that $-\frac{1}{8}$ checks and is the solution.

b) To solve $\frac{2}{5}(3x + 2) = 8$, we can multiply both sides by $\frac{5}{2}$ (or divide by $\frac{2}{5}$) to "undo" the multiplication by $\frac{2}{5}$ on the left side.

$$\frac{5}{2} \cdot \frac{2}{5}(3x + 2) = \frac{5}{2} \cdot 8 \qquad \text{Multiplying both sides by } \frac{5}{2}$$

$$3x + 2 = 20 \qquad \text{Simplifying; } \frac{5}{2} \cdot \frac{2}{5} = 1 \text{ and } \frac{5}{2} \cdot \frac{8}{1} = 20$$

$$3x + 2 - 2 = 20 - 2 \qquad \text{Subtracting 2 from both sides}$$

$$3x = 18$$

$$\frac{3x}{3} = \frac{18}{3} \qquad \text{Dividing both sides by 3}$$

$$x = 6$$

The student can confirm that 6 checks and is the solution.

6. Solve: $\frac{1}{4} - 5x = \frac{2}{3}x$.

⟳ YOUR TURN

Student Notes

Compare the steps of Examples 4 and 7. Note that the two different approaches yield the same solution. Whenever you can use two approaches to solve a problem, try to do so, both as a check and as a valuable learning experience.

To clear an equation of decimals, we count the greatest number of decimal places in any one number. If the greatest number of decimal places is 1, we multiply both sides by 10; if it is 2, we multiply by 100; and so on.

EXAMPLE 7   Solve: $16.3 - 7.2y = -8.18$.

SOLUTION   The greatest number of decimal places in any one number is *two*. Multiplying by 100 will clear all decimals.

$$100(16.3 - 7.2y) = 100(-8.18) \qquad \text{Multiplying both sides by 100}$$

$$100(16.3) - 100(7.2y) = 100(-8.18) \qquad \text{Using the distributive law}$$

$$1630 - 720y = -818 \qquad \text{Simplifying}$$

$$1630 - 720y - 1630 = -818 - 1630 \qquad \text{Subtracting 1630 from both sides}$$

$$-720y = -2448 \qquad \text{Combining like terms}$$

$$\frac{-720y}{-720} = \frac{-2448}{-720} \qquad \text{Dividing both sides by } -720$$

$$y = 3.4$$

In Example 4, the same solution was found without clearing decimals. Finding the same answer in two ways is a good check. The solution is 3.4.

7. Solve: $0.8 = 2.8x + 5$.

⟳ YOUR TURN

Types of Equations

A **linear equation** in one variable—say, x—is an equation equivalent to one of the form $ax = b$ with a and b constants and $a \neq 0$.

We will sometimes refer to the set of solutions, or the **solution set**, of a particular equation. Thus the solution set for Example 7 is $\{3.4\}$. If an equation is true for all replacements, the solution set is $\mathbb{R}$, the set of all real numbers. If an equation is never true, the solution set is the **empty set**, denoted $\varnothing$, or $\{\ \}$. As its name suggests, the empty set is the set containing no elements.

Every equation is either an **identity**, a **contradiction**, or a **conditional equation**.

Type of Equation	Definition	Example	Solution Set
Identity	An equation that is true for all replacements	$x + 5 = 3 + x + 2$	$\mathbb{R}$
Contradiction	An equation that is never true	$n = n + 1$	$\varnothing$, or $\{\ \}$
Conditional equation	An equation that is true for some replacements and false for others	$2x + 5 = 17$	$\{6\}$

EXAMPLE 8   Solve each equation. Then classify the equation as an identity, a contradiction, or a conditional equation.

a) $2x + 7 = 7(x + 1) - 5x$ **b)** $3x - 5 = 3(x - 2)$

c) $3 - 8x = 5 - 7x$

SOLUTION

a) $2x + 7 = 7(x + 1) - 5x$

   $\quad 2x + 7 = 7x + 7 - 5x$ Using the distributive law

   $\quad 2x + 7 = 2x + 7$ Combining like terms

The equation $2x + 7 = 2x + 7$ is true regardless of what x is replaced with, so all real numbers are solutions. Note that $2x + 7 = 2x + 7$ is equivalent to $2x = 2x$, $7 = 7$, or $0 = 0$. The solution set is $\mathbb{R}$, and the equation is an identity.

b) $3x - 5 = 3(x - 2)$

   $\quad\quad\quad 3x - 5 = 3x - 6$ Using the distributive law

   $-3x + 3x - 5 = -3x + 3x - 6$ Using the addition principle

   $\quad\quad\quad\quad -5 = -6$

Since the original equation is equivalent to $-5 = -6$, which is false regardless of the choice of x, the original equation has no solution. The solution set is $\varnothing$, and the equation is a contradiction.

c) $3 - 8x = 5 - 7x$

   $3 - 8x + 7x = 5 - 7x + 7x$ Using the addition principle

   $\quad\quad\quad 3 - x = 5$ Simplifying

   $-3 + 3 - x = -3 + 5$ Using the addition principle

   $\quad\quad\quad\quad -x = 2$ Simplifying

   $\quad\quad\quad\quad x = \dfrac{2}{-1}$, or -2 Dividing both sides by -1 or multiplying both sides by $\frac{1}{-1}$, or -1

There is one solution, -2. For other choices of x, the equation is false. The solution set is $\{-2\}$. This equation is conditional since it can be true or false, depending on the replacement for x.

8. Solve

$\quad y - (2 - y) = 2(y - 1)$.

Then classify the equation as an identity, a contradiction, or a conditional equation.

 YOUR TURN

2.2 EXERCISE SET

FOR EXTRA HELP   MyMathLab® *Math* XL
PRACTICE   WATCH   READ   REVIEW

Vocabulary and Reading Check

Choose the principle or law from the following list that best completes each sentence. Choices will be used more than once.

Addition principle   Distributive law
Multiplication principle

1. To isolate x in $x - 4 = 7$, we would use the
   _____.

2. To isolate x in $5x = 8$, we would use the
   _____.

3. To clear fractions or decimals, we use the
   _____.

4. To remove parentheses, we use the
   _____.

5. To solve $3x - 1 = 8$, we use the _____
   first.

6. To solve $5(x - 1) + 3(x + 7) = 2$, we use the
   _____ first.

Concept Reinforcement

In each of Exercises 7–12, match the equation with an equivalent equation from the column on the right that could be the next step in finding a solution.

7. ____ $3x - 1 = 7$ a) $6x - 6 = 2$

8. ____ $4x + 5x = 12$ b) $4x + 2x = 3$

9. ____ $6(x - 1) = 2$ c) $3x = 7 + 1$

10. ____ $7x = 9$ d) $8x + 2x = 6 + 5$

11. ____ $4x = 3 - 2x$ e) $9x = 12$

12. ____ $8x - 5 = 6 - 2x$ f) $x = \frac{9}{7}$

Applying Both Principles

Solve and check.

13. $2x + 9 = 25$ 14. $5z + 2 = 57$

15. $7t - 8 = 27$ 16. $6x - 5 = 2$

17. $3x - 9 = 1$ 18. $5x - 9 = 41$

19. $8z + 2 = -54$ 20. $4x + 3 = -21$

21. $-37 = 9t + 8$ 22. $-39 = 1 + 5t$

23. $12 - t = 16$ 24. $9 - t = 21$

25. $-6z - 18 = -132$ 26. $-7x - 24 = -129$

27. $5.3 + 1.2n = 1.94$ 28. $6.4 - 2.5n = 2.2$

29. $32 - 7x = 11$ 30. $27 - 6x = 99$

31. $\frac{3}{5}t - 1 = 8$ 32. $\frac{2}{3}t - 1 = 5$

33. $6 + \frac{7}{2}x = -15$ 34. $6 + \frac{5}{4}x = -4$

35. $-\dfrac{4a}{5} - 8 = 2$ 36. $-\dfrac{8a}{7} - 2 = 4$

Combining Like Terms

Solve and check.

37. $6x + 10x = 18$ 38. $-3z + 8z = 45$

39. $4x - 6 = 6x$ 40. $7n = 2n + 4$

41. $2 - 5y = 26 - y$ 42. $6x - 5 = 7 + 2x$

43. $6x + 3 = 2x + 3$ 44. $5y + 3 = 2y + 15$

45. $5 - 2x = 3x - 7x + 25$

46. $10 - 3x = x - 2x + 40$

47. $7 + 3x - 6 = 3x + 5 - x$

48. $5 + 4x - 7 = 4x - 2 - x$

Clearing Fractions and Decimals

Clear fractions or decimals, solve, and check.

49. $\frac{2}{3} + \frac{1}{4}t = 2$ 50. $-\frac{5}{6} + x = -\frac{1}{2} - \frac{2}{3}$

51. $\frac{2}{3} + 4t = 6t - \frac{2}{15}$ 52. $\frac{1}{2} + 4m = 3m - \frac{5}{2}$

53. $\frac{1}{3}x + \frac{2}{5} = \frac{4}{5} + \frac{3}{5}x - \frac{2}{3}$

54. $1 - \frac{2}{3}y = \frac{9}{5} - \frac{1}{5}y + \frac{3}{5}$

55. $2.1x + 45.2 = 3.2 - 8.4x$

56. $0.91 - 0.2z = 1.23 - 0.6z$

57. $0.76 + 0.21t = 0.96t - 0.49$

58. $1.7t + 8 - 1.62t = 0.4t - 0.32 + 8$

59. $\frac{2}{5}x - \frac{3}{2}x = \frac{3}{4}x + 3$ 60. $\frac{5}{16}y + \frac{3}{8}y = 2 + \frac{1}{4}y$

61. $\frac{1}{3}(2x - 1) = 7$ 62. $\frac{1}{5}(4x - 1) = 7$

Solving Linear Equations

Solve and check. Label any contradictions or identities.

63. $7(2a - 1) = 21$ 64. $5(3 - 3t) = 30$

Aha! 65. $11 = 11(x + 1)$ 66. $9 = 3(5x - 2)$

67. $2(3 + 4m) - 6 = 48$ 68. $3(5 + 3m) - 8 = 7$

69. $2x = x + x$

70. $5x - x = x + 3x$

71. $2r + 8 = 6r + 10$

72. $3b - 2 = 7b + 4$

73. $4y - 4 + y + 24 = 6y + 20 - 4y$

74. $5y - 10 + y = 7y + 18 - 5y$

75. $3(x + 4) = 3(x - 1)$

76. $5(x - 7) = 3(x - 2) + 2x$

77. $19 - 3(2x - 1) = 7$

78. $5(d + 4) = 7(d - 2)$

79. $2(3t + 1) - 5 = t - (t + 2)$

80. $4x - (x + 6) = 5(3x - 1) + 8$

81. $19 - (2x + 3) = 2(x + 3) + x$

82. $13 - (2c + 2) = 2(c + 2) + 3c$

83. $4 + 7x = 7(x + 1)$

84. $3(t + 2) + t = 2(3 + 2t)$

85. $\frac{3}{4}(3t - 4) = 15$

86. $\frac{3}{2}(2x + 5) = -\frac{15}{2}$

87. $\frac{1}{6}\left(\frac{3}{4}x - 2\right) = -\frac{1}{5}$

88. $\frac{2}{3}\left(\frac{7}{8} - 4x\right) - \frac{5}{8} = \frac{3}{8}$

89. $0.7(3x + 6) = 1.1 - (x - 3)$

90. $0.9(2x - 8) = 4 - (x + 5)$

91. $2(7 - x) - 20 = 7x - 3(2 + 3x)$

92. $5(x - 7) = 3(x - 2) + 2x$

93. $a + (a - 3) = (a + 2) - (a + 1)$

94. $0.8 - 4(b - 1) = 0.2 + 3(4 - b)$

95. Maggie solves $45 - t = 13$ (Example 3) by adding $t - 13$ to both sides. Is this approach preferable to the one used in Example 3? Why or why not?

96. Why must the rules for the order of operations be understood before solving the equations in this section?

Skill Review

97. Add: $\frac{2}{9} + \frac{1}{6}$. [1.3]

98. Multiply: $\frac{2}{7} \cdot \frac{7}{2}$. [1.3]

99. Find decimal notation: $-\frac{1}{9}$. [1.4]

100. Find the absolute value: $|-16|$. [1.4]

Synthesis

101. What procedure would you use to solve an equation like $0.23x + \frac{17}{3} = -0.8 + \frac{3}{4}x$? Could your procedure be streamlined? If so, how?

102. Ethan is determined to solve $3x + 4 = -11$ by first using the multiplication principle to "eliminate" the 3. How should he proceed and why?

Solve. Label any contradictions or identities.

103. $8.43x - 2.5(3.2 - 0.7x) = -3.455x + 9.04$

104. $0.008 + 9.62x - 42.8 = 0.944x + 0.0083 - x$

105. $-2[3(x - 2) + 4] = 4(5 - x) - 2x$

106. $0 = t - (-6) - (-7t)$

107. $3(x + 5) = 3(5 + x)$

108. $5(x - 7) = 3(x - 2) + 2x$

109. $2x(x + 5) - 3(x^2 + 2x - 1) = 9 - 5x - x^2$

110. $9 - 3x = 2(5 - 2x) - (1 - 5x)$

Aha! **111.** $[7 - 2(8 \div (-2))]x = 0$

112. $\dfrac{5x + 3}{4} + \dfrac{25}{12} = \dfrac{5 + 2x}{3}$

113. Kyle estimates his long-distance driving time, in hours, by multiplying the number of miles he will drive by $\frac{3}{200}$ and then adding $\frac{1}{4}$ for every major city he will drive through. If he estimates that a trip through two major cities will take 8 hr, how many miles will he be driving?

YOUR TURN ANSWERS: SECTION 2.2

1. 6   **2.** −3   **3.** −11   **4.** −1.5   **5.** $-\frac{1}{2}$
6. $\frac{3}{68}$ **7.** −1.5   **8.** $\mathbb{R}$; identity

---

QUICK QUIZ: SECTIONS 2.1–2.2

1. Determine whether −5 is a solution of
$7 - 3x = 22$. [2.1]

Solve and check.

2. $y + 7.5 = 2.1$ [2.1]   **3.** $\dfrac{2x}{5} = 10$ [2.1]

4. $2 - (x - 7) = 13$ [2.2]   **5.** $\dfrac{1}{10}r + \dfrac{1}{5} = \dfrac{1}{2}r$ [2.2]

PREPARE TO MOVE ON

Evaluate. [1.8]

1. $3 - 5a$, for $a = 2$ **2.** $12 \div 4 \cdot t$, for $t = 5$

3. $7x - 2x$, for $x = -3$ **4.** $t(8 - 3t)$, for $t = -2$

2.3   Formulas

Evaluating Formulas ▪ Solving for a Variable

An equation that shows a relationship between variable quantities will use letters and is known as a **formula**. Most of the letters in this book are variables, but some are constants. For example, c in $E = mc^2$ represents the speed of light.

Evaluating Formulas

EXAMPLE 1 *Event Promotion.* Event promoters use the formula

$$p = \frac{1.2x}{s}$$

to determine a ticket price p for an event with x dollars of expenses and anticipated ticket sales of s tickets. Grand Events expects expenses for a concert to be $80,000 and anticipates selling 4000 tickets. What should the ticket price be?

Source: The Indianapolis Star, 2/27/03

SOLUTION We substitute 80,000 for x and 4000 for s and calculate p:

$$p = \frac{1.2x}{s} = \frac{1.2(80,000)}{4000} = 24.$$

The ticket price should be $24.

YOUR TURN

1. Using the formula in Example 1, determine the ticket price when concert expenses are $40,000 and anticipated sales are 2500 tickets.

Technology Connection

Suppose that after calculating $1.2 \cdot 80{,}000 \div 4000$, we want to find $1.2 \cdot 80{,}000 \div 5000$. Pressing **2ND** **ENTRY** gives the following.

```
1.2*80000÷4000
                      24
1.2*80000÷4000 ■
```

Moving the cursor left, we can change 4000 to 5000 and press **ENTER**.

```
1.2*80000÷4000
                      24
1.2*80000÷5000
                    19.2
```

1. Verify the work above and then use **2ND** **ENTRY** to find $1.2 \cdot 60000 \div 5000$.

Solving for a Variable

The **circumference** of a circle is the distance around the circle. The formula $C = 2\pi r$ gives the circumference C of a circle with radius r. For some circles (such as a circular pond), it is easier to measure the circumference than to measure the radius. In order to find the radius of a circle when we know its circumference, we can *solve* the formula for r.

> To **solve** for a variable means to write an equivalent equation with that variable alone on one side of the equation. The letter should not appear at all on the other side of the equation.

EXAMPLE 2 *Circumference of a Circle.* Solve for r: $C = 2\pi r$.

SOLUTION We want r to appear alone on one side of the equation and not to appear at all on the other side.

Given a radius r, we can use this equation to find a circle's circumference C.

$C = 2\pi r$ We want this variable alone.

$\dfrac{C}{2\pi} = \dfrac{2\pi r}{2\pi}$ Dividing both sides by 2π

$\dfrac{C}{2\pi} = r$

Given a circle's circumference C, we can use this equation to find the radius r.

2. Solve for w: $V = lwh$.

YOUR TURN

To see how solving a formula is just like solving an equation, compare the following. In (A), we solve as usual; in (B), we show steps but do not simplify; and in (C), we *cannot* simplify because a, b, and c are unknown.

A. $5x + 2 = 12$
$5x = 12 - 2$
$5x = 10$
$x = \dfrac{10}{5} = 2$

B. $5x + 2 = 12$
$5x = 12 - 2$
$x = \dfrac{12 - 2}{5}$

C. $ax + b = c$
$ax = c - b$
$x = \dfrac{c - b}{a}$

EXAMPLE 3 *Motion.* The rate r at which an object moves is found by dividing distance d traveled by time t, or

$$r = \frac{d}{t}.$$

Solve for t.

Student Notes

When working with formulas, a lowercase letter should not be interchanged with its associated uppercase letter; these letters may represent different quantities. For example, a formula for gravity uses both M and m.

SOLUTION We use the multiplication principle to clear fractions and then solve for t:

$r = \dfrac{d}{t}$ ⟵ We want this variable alone.

$r \cdot t = \dfrac{d}{t} \cdot t$ Multiplying both sides by t

$rt = \dfrac{dt}{t}$ $\dfrac{d}{t} \cdot t = \dfrac{d}{t} \cdot \dfrac{t}{1} = \dfrac{dt}{t}$

$rt = d$ Removing a factor equal to 1: $t/t = 1$.
The equation is cleared of fractions.

$\dfrac{rt}{r} = \dfrac{d}{r}$ Dividing both sides by r

$t = \dfrac{d}{r}.$

3. Solve for x: $y = \dfrac{k}{x}$.

This formula can be used to determine the time spent traveling when the distance and the rate are known.

◀ YOUR TURN

EXAMPLE 4 Solve for y: $3x - 4y = 10$.

SOLUTION There is one term that contains y, so we begin by isolating that term on one side of the equation.

$3x - 4y = 10$ We want this variable alone.
$-4y = 10 - 3x$ Subtracting $3x$ from both sides
$-\frac{1}{4}(-4y) = -\frac{1}{4}(10 - 3x)$ Multiplying both sides by $-\frac{1}{4}$
$y = -\frac{10}{4} + \frac{3}{4}x$ Multiplying using the distributive law
$y = -\frac{5}{2} + \frac{3}{4}x$ Simplifying the fraction

4. Solve for y: $x + 2y = 3$.

◀ YOUR TURN

Study Skills

Pace Yourself

Most instructors agree that it is better for a student to study for one hour four days in a week, than to study once a week for four hours. Of course, the total weekly study time will vary from student to student. It is common to expect an average of two hours of homework for each hour of class time.

5. Solve for p:

$$T = 20(a + p) - 15.$$

EXAMPLE 5   *Nutrition.*   The number of calories K needed each day by a moderately active woman who weighs w pounds, is h inches tall, and is a years old, can be estimated using the formula

$$K = 917 + 6(w + h - a).*$$

Solve for w.

SOLUTION   We undo the operations in the reverse order in which they would be performed on the right side:

$$K = 917 + 6(w + h - a)$$ We want w alone.

$$K - 917 = 6(w + h - a)$$ Subtracting 917 from both sides

$$\frac{K - 917}{6} = w + h - a$$ Dividing both sides by 6

$$\frac{K - 917}{6} + a - h = w.$$ Adding a and subtracting h on both sides

This formula can be used to estimate a woman's weight, if we know her age, height, and caloric needs.

YOUR TURN

The above steps are similar to those used in Section 2.2 to solve equations. We use the addition and multiplication principles just as before. An important difference that we will see in the next example is that we will sometimes need to factor.

> **TO SOLVE A FORMULA FOR A GIVEN VARIABLE**
>
> 1. If the variable for which you are solving appears in a fraction, use the multiplication principle to clear fractions.
> 2. Isolate the term(s), with the variable for which you are solving on one side of the equation.
> 3. If two or more terms contain the variable for which you are solving, factor the variable out.
> 4. Multiply or divide to solve for the variable in question.

We can also solve for a letter that represents a constant.

EXAMPLE 6   *Surface Area of a Right Circular Cylinder.*   The formula $A = 2\pi rh + 2\pi r^2$ gives the surface area A of a right circular cylinder of height h and radius r. Solve for π.

SOLUTION   We have

$$A = 2\pi rh + 2\pi r^2$$ We want this letter alone.

$$A = \pi(2rh + 2r^2)$$ Factoring

$$\frac{A}{2rh + 2r^2} = \pi.$$ Dividing both sides by $2rh + 2r^2$, or multiplying both sides by $1/(2rh + 2r^2)$

We can also write this as

$$\pi = \frac{A}{2rh + 2r^2}.$$

6. Solve for c: $D = 3c + 6cy$.

YOUR TURN

*Based on information from M. Parker (ed.), *She Does Math!* (Washington, D.C.: Mathematical Association of America, 1995), p. 96.

> **CAUTION!** Had we performed the following steps in Example 6, we would *not* have solved for π:
>
> $$A = 2\pi rh + 2\pi r^2 \qquad \text{We want } \pi \text{ alone.}$$
>
> $$A - 2\pi r^2 = 2\pi rh \qquad \text{Subtracting } 2\pi r^2 \text{ from both sides}$$
>
> $$\text{Two occurrences of } \pi$$
>
> $$\frac{A - 2\pi r^2}{2rh} = \pi. \qquad \text{Dividing both sides by } 2rh$$
>
> The mathematics of each step is correct, but because π occurs on both sides of the formula, *we have not solved the formula for π*. Remember that the letter being solved for should be alone on one side of the equation, with no occurrence of that letter on the other side!

2.3 EXERCISE SET

FOR EXTRA HELP

MyMathLab® Math XL
PRACTICE   WATCH   READ   REVIEW

Vocabulary and Reading Check

Classify each of the following statements as either true or false.

1. All letters used in algebra represent variables.

2. If a letter appears on both sides of a formula, that formula is not solved for that letter.

Choose the word that best completes each sentence from the choices listed below the blank.

3. The distance around a circle is its

_____ .
   area/circumference/volume

4. An equation that uses two or more letters to represent a relationship among quantities is a(n)

_____ .
   constant/formula/variable

Evaluating Formulas

Solve.

5. *Outdoor Concerts.* The formula $d = 344t$ can be used to determine how far d, in meters, sound travels through room-temperature air in t seconds. Fans near the back of a large crowd at a concert will experience a time lag between the time they see a note played on stage and the time they hear that note. If the time lag is 0.9 sec, how far are the fans from the stage?

6. *Furnace Output.* Contractors in the Northeast use the formula $B = 30a$ to determine the minimum furnace output B, in British thermal units (Btu's), for a well-insulated house with a square feet of flooring.

Determine the minimum furnace output for an 1800-ft^2 house that is well insulated.

Source: U.S. Department of Energy

7. *College Enrollment.* At many colleges, the number of "full-time-equivalent" students F is given by

$$F = \frac{n}{15},$$

where n is the total number of credits for which students have enrolled in a given semester. Determine the number of full-time-equivalent students on a campus in which students registered for a total of 21,345 credits.

8. *Distance from a Storm.* The formula $M = \frac{1}{5}t$ can be used to determine how far M, in miles, you are from lightning when its thunder takes t seconds to reach your ears. If it takes 10 sec for the sound of thunder to reach you after you have seen the lightning, how far away is the storm?

9. *Federal Funds Rate.* The Federal Reserve Board sets a target f for the federal funds rate, that is, the interest rate that banks charge each other for overnight borrowing of Federal funds. This target rate can be estimated by

$$f = 8.5 + 1.4(I \overset{.}{-} U),$$

where I is the core inflation rate over the previous 12 months and U is the seasonally adjusted unemployment rate. If core inflation is 0.025 and unemployment is 0.044, what should the federal funds rate be?

Source: Greg Mankiw, Harvard University, www.gregmankiw .blogspot.com/2006/06/what-would-alan-do.html

10. *Calorie Density.* The calorie density D, in calories per ounce, of a food that contains c calories and weighs w ounces is given by

$$D = \frac{c}{w}.*$$

Eight ounces of fat-free milk contains 84 calories. Find the calorie density of fat-free milk.

11. *Absorption of Ibuprofen.* When 400 mg of the painkiller ibuprofen is swallowed, the number of milligrams n in the bloodstream t hours later (for $0 \le t \le 6$) is estimated by

$$n = 0.5t^4 + 3.45t^3 - 96.65t^2 + 347.7t.$$

How many milligrams of ibuprofen remain in the blood 1 hr after 400 mg has been swallowed?

12. *Size of a League Schedule.* When all n teams in a league play every other team twice, a total of N games are played, where

$$N = n^2 - n.$$

If a soccer league has 7 teams and all teams play each other twice, how many games are played?

Solving for a Variable

In Exercises 13–52, solve each formula for the indicated letter.

13. $A = bh$, for b
(Area of parallelogram with base b and height h)

14. $A = bh$, for h

Source: Nutrition Action Healthletter, March 2000, p. 9. Center for Science in the Public Interest, Suite 300; 1875 Connecticut Ave NW, Washington, D.C. 20008.

15. $I = Prt$, for P
(Simple-interest formula, where I is interest, P is principal, r is interest rate, and t is time)

16. $I = Prt$, for t

17. $H = 65 - m$, for m
(To determine the number of heating degree days H for a day with m degrees Fahrenheit as the average temperature)

18. $d = h - 64$, for h
(To determine how many inches d above average an h-inch-tall woman is)

19. $P = 2l + 2w$, for l
(Perimeter of a rectangle of length l and width w)

20. $P = 2l + 2w$, for w

21. $A = \pi r^2$, for π
(Area of a circle with radius r)

22. $A = \pi r^2$, for r^2

23. $A = \frac{1}{2}bh$, for h
(Area of a triangle with base b and height h)

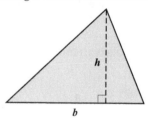

24. $A = \frac{1}{2}bh$, for b

25. $E = mc^2$, for c^2
(A relativity formula from physics)

26. $E = mc^2$, for m

27. $Q = \frac{c + d}{2}$, for d

28. $A = \frac{a + b + c}{3}$, for b

29. $p - q + r = 2$, for q
(Euler's formula from graph theory)

30. $p = \dfrac{r - q}{2}$, for q

31. $w = \dfrac{r}{f}$, for r

(To compute the wavelength w of a musical note with frequency f and speed of sound r)

32. $M = \dfrac{A}{s}$, for A

(To compute the Mach number M for speed A and speed of sound s)

33. $H = \dfrac{TV}{550}$, for T

(To determine the horsepower H of an airplane propeller with thrust T and airplane velocity V)

34. $P = \dfrac{ab}{c}$, for b

35. $F = \frac{9}{5}C + 32$, for C

(To convert the Celsius temperature C to the Fahrenheit temperature F)

36. $M = \frac{5}{9}n + 18$, for n

37. $2x - y = 1$, for y **38.** $3x - y = 7$, for y

39. $2x + 5y = 10$, for y **40.** $3x + 2y = 12$, for y

41. $4x - 3y = 6$, for y **42.** $5x - 4y = 8$, for y

43. $9x + 8y = 4$, for y **44.** $x + 10y = 2$, for y

45. $3x - 5y = 8$, for y **46.** $7x - 6y = 7$, for y

47. $z = 13 + 2(x + y)$, for x

48. $A = 115 + \frac{1}{2}(p + s)$, for s

49. $t = 27 - \frac{1}{4}(w - l)$, for l

50. $m = 19 - 5(x - n)$, for n

51. $A = at + bt$, for t

52. $S = rx + sx$, for x

53. *Area of a Trapezoid.* The formula
$$A = \tfrac{1}{2}ah + \tfrac{1}{2}bh$$
can be used to find the area A of a trapezoid with bases a and b and height h. Solve for h. (*Hint*: First clear fractions.)

54. *Compounding Interest.* The formula
$$A = P + Prt$$
is used to find the amount A in an account when simple interest is added to an investment of P dollars (see Exercise 15). Solve for P.

55. *Chess Rating.* The formula
$$R = r + \dfrac{400(W - L)}{N}$$
is used to establish a chess player's rating R after that player has played N games, won W of them, and lost L of them. Here r is the average rating of the opponents. Solve for L.

Source: The U.S. Chess Federation

56. *Angle Measure.* The angle measure S of a sector of a circle is given by
$$S = \dfrac{360A}{\pi r^2},$$
where r is the radius, A is the area of the sector, and S is in degrees. Solve for r^2.

57. Julia has a formula that allows her to convert Celsius temperatures to Fahrenheit temperatures. She needs a formula for converting Fahrenheit temperatures to Celsius temperatures. What advice can you give her?

58. Under what circumstances would it be useful to solve $I = Prt$ for P? (See Exercise 15.)

Skill Review

Simplify.

59. $-2 + 5 - (-4) - 17$ [1.6]

60. $-98 \div \frac{1}{2}$ [1.7]

Aha! **61.** $4.2(-11.75)(0)$ [1.7]

62. $(-2)^5$ [1.8]

63. $20 \div (-4) \cdot 2 - 3$ [1.8]

64. $5|8 - (2 - 7)|$ [1.8]

Synthesis

65. The equations

$$P = 2l + 2w \quad \text{and} \quad w = \frac{P}{2} - l$$

are equivalent formulas involving the perimeter P, length l, and width w of a rectangle. Write a problem for which the second of the two formulas would be more useful.

66. While solving $2A = ah + bh$ for h, Eva writes

$$\frac{2A - ah}{b} = h.$$

What is her mistake?

67. The Harris–Benedict formula gives the number of calories K needed each day by a moderately active man who weighs w kilograms, is h centimeters tall, and is a years old as

$$K = 21.235w + 7.75h - 10.54a + 102.3.$$

If Janos is moderately active, weighs 80 kg, is 190 cm tall, and needs to consume 2852 calories per day, how old is he?

68. *Altitude and Temperature.* Air temperature drops about 1° Celsius (C) for each 100-m rise above ground level, up to 12 km. If the ground level temperature is t°C, find a formula for the temperature T at an elevation of h meters.

Source: *A Sourcebook of School Mathematics,* Mathematical Association of America, 1980

69. *Surface Area of a Cube.* The surface area A of a cube with side s is given by

$$A = 6s^2.$$

If a cube's surface area is 54 in², find the volume of the cube.

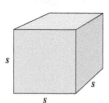

70. *Weight of a Fish.* An ancient fisherman's formula for estimating the weight of a fish is

$$w = \frac{lg^2}{800},$$

where w is the weight, in pounds, l is the length, in inches, and g is the girth (distance around the midsection), in inches. Estimate the girth of a 700-lb yellowfin tuna that is 8 ft long.

71. *Dosage Size.* Clark's rule for determining the size of a particular child's medicine dosage c is

$$c = \frac{w}{a} \cdot d,$$

where w is the child's weight, in pounds, and d is the usual adult dosage for an adult weighing a pounds. Solve for a.

Source: Olsen, June Looby, et al., *Medical Dosage Calculations.* Redwood City, CA: Addison-Wesley, 1995

Solve each formula for the given letter.

72. $\dfrac{y}{z} \div \dfrac{z}{t} = 1$, for y

73. $ac = bc + d$, for c

74. $qt = r(s + t)$, for t

75. $3a = c - a(b + d)$, for a

76. *Furnace Output.* The formula

$$B = 50a$$

is used in New England to estimate the minimum furnace output B, in Btu's, for an old, poorly insulated house with a square feet of flooring. Find an equation for determining the number of Btu's saved by insulating an old house. (*Hint:* See Exercise 6.)

77. Revise the formula in Exercise 67 so that a man's weight in pounds (2.2046 lb = 1 kg) and his height in inches (0.3937 in. = 1 cm) are used.

YOUR TURN ANSWERS: SECTION 2.3

1. $19.20   **2.** $w = \dfrac{V}{lh}$ **3.** $x = \dfrac{k}{y}$ **4.** $y = -\frac{1}{2}x + \frac{3}{2}$

5. $p = \dfrac{T + 15}{20} - a$ **6.** $c = \dfrac{D}{3 + 6y}$

QUICK QUIZ: SECTIONS 2.1–2.3

Solve and check.

1. $-x = -7$ [2.1]

2. $4(n - 7) - n = 36$ [2.2]

3. $1.2t - 0.05 = 3.2t$ [2.2]

4. $3(2x - 4) = 2 - 5(7 - x)$ [2.2]

5. Solve for y: $6x + 2y = 1.$ [2.3]

PREPARE TO MOVE ON

Convert to decimal notation.   [1.4]

1. $\dfrac{1}{4}$ **2.** $\dfrac{9}{8}$ **3.** $\dfrac{2}{3}$ **4.** $\dfrac{5}{6}$

Mid-Chapter Review

We solve equations using the addition and multiplication principles.

For any real numbers a, b, and c:

a) $a = b$ is equivalent to $a + c = b + c$;

b) $a = b$ is equivalent to $ac = bc$, provided $c \neq 0$.

GUIDED SOLUTIONS

Solve. [2.2]*

1. $2x + 3 = 10$

Solution

$$2x + 3 - 3 = 10 - \boxed{} \quad \text{Using the addition principle}$$

$$2x = \boxed{} \quad \text{Simplifying}$$

$$\frac{1}{2} \cdot 2x = \boxed{} \cdot 7 \quad \text{Using the multiplication principle}$$

$$x = \boxed{} \quad \text{Simplifying}$$

2. $\frac{1}{2}(x - 3) = \frac{1}{3}(x - 4)$

Solution

$$6 \cdot \tfrac{1}{2}(x - 3) = \boxed{} \cdot \tfrac{1}{3}(x - 4) \quad \text{Multiplying to clear fractions}$$

$$\boxed{}\,(x - 3) = \boxed{}\,(x - 4) \quad \text{The fractions are cleared.}$$

$$3x - \boxed{} = 2x - \boxed{} \quad \text{Multiplying}$$

$$3x - 9 + 9 = 2x - 8 + \boxed{} \quad \text{Using the addition principle}$$

$$3x = 2x + \boxed{} \quad \text{Simplifying}$$

$$3x - \boxed{} = 2x + 1 - 2x \quad \text{Using the addition principle}$$

$$x = \boxed{} \quad \text{Simplifying}$$

MIXED REVIEW

Solve.

3. $x - 2 = -1$ [2.1]

4. $2 - x = -1$ [2.1]

5. $3t = 5$ [2.1]

6. $-\frac{3}{2}x = 12$ [2.1]

7. $\dfrac{y}{8} = 6$ [2.1]

8. $0.06x = 0.03$ [2.1]

9. $3x - 7x = 20$ [2.2]

10. $9x - 7 = 17$ [2.2]

11. $4(t - 3) - t = 6$ [2.2]

12. $8n - (3n - 5) = 5 - n$ [2.2]

13. $\frac{9}{10}y - \frac{7}{10} = \frac{21}{5}$ [2.2]

14. $2(t - 5) - 3(2t - 7) = 12 - 5(3t + 1)$ [2.2]

15. $\frac{2}{3}(x - 2) - 1 = -\frac{1}{2}(x - 3)$ [2.2]

Solve for the indicated variable. [2.3]

16. $E = wA$, for A

17. $Ax + By = C$, for y

18. $at + ap = m$, for a

19. $m = \dfrac{F}{a}$, for a

20. $v = \dfrac{b - f}{t}$, for b

---

*The notation [2.2] refers to Chapter 2, Section 2.

2.4 Applications with Percent

Converting Between Percent Notation and Decimal Notation   ▪   Solving Percent Problems

Percent problems arise so frequently in everyday life that often we are not even aware of them. In this section, we will solve some real-world percent problems. Before doing so, however, we need to review a few basics.

Converting Between Percent Notation and Decimal Notation

Oceans cover 70% of the earth's surface. This means that of every 100 square miles on the surface of the earth, 70 square miles is ocean. Thus, 70% is a ratio of 70 to 100.

Earth's surface

Ocean
70%

The percent symbol % means "per hundred." We can regard the percent symbol as part of a name for a number. For example,

$$70\% \quad \text{is defined to mean} \quad \frac{70}{100}, \quad \text{or} \quad 70 \times \frac{1}{100}, \quad \text{or} \quad 70 \times 0.01.$$

Study Skills

Do It Again

Continual review of material is a key to success. Not only does review keep the material fresh for a final exam, in many courses (such as math), new concepts are developed using previous concepts. Take advantage of the review exercises built into this text. You may be surprised at the positive results you will see with just a few minutes of review each day.

PERCENT NOTATION

$$n\% \quad \text{means} \quad \frac{n}{100}, \quad \text{or} \quad n \times \frac{1}{100}, \quad \text{or} \quad n \times 0.01.$$

EXAMPLE 1   Convert to decimal notation: **(a)** 78%; **(b)** 1.3%.

SOLUTION

a) $78\% = 78 \times 0.01$ Replacing % with $\times\ 0.01$

$\qquad = 0.78$

b) $1.3\% = 1.3 \times 0.01$ Replacing % with $\times 0.01$

$\qquad = 0.013$

1. Convert to decimal notation: 120%.

YOUR TURN

As shown above, multiplication by 0.01 simply moves the decimal point two places to the left.

To convert from percent notation to decimal notation, move the decimal point two places to the left and drop the percent symbol.

EXAMPLE 2 Convert the percent notation in the following sentence to decimal notation: Only 20% of teenagers get 8 hr of sleep per night.

Source: National Sleep Foundation

SOLUTION

$$20\% = 20.0\% \qquad 0.20.0 \qquad 20\% = 0.20, \text{ or simply } 0.2$$

Move the decimal point two places to the left.

2. Convert to decimal notation: 4%.

YOUR TURN

The procedure used in Examples 1 and 2 can be reversed:

$$0.38 = 38 \times 0.01$$
$$= 38\%. \qquad \text{Replacing } \times 0.01 \text{ with } \%$$

To convert from decimal notation to percent notation, move the decimal point two places to the right and write a percent symbol.

EXAMPLE 3 Convert to percent notation: **(a)** 1.27; **(b)** $\frac{1}{4}$; **(c)** 0.3.

SOLUTION

a) We first move the decimal point two places to the right: 1.27.
and then write a % symbol: 127%   This is the same as multiplying 1.27 by 100 and writing %.

b) Note that $\frac{1}{4} = 0.25$. We move the decimal point two places to the right: 0.25.
and then write a % symbol: 25%   Multiplying by 100 and writing %

c) We first move the decimal point two places to the right (recall that 0.3 = 0.30): 0.30.
and then write a % symbol: 30%   Multiplying by 100 and writing %

3. Convert to percent notation: 0.37.

YOUR TURN

Solving Percent Problems

In solving percent problems, we first *translate* the problem to an equation. Then we *solve* the equation. The key words in the translation are as follows.

KEY WORDS IN PERCENT TRANSLATIONS

"**Of**" translates to " · " or " × ".   "**Is**" or "**Was**" translates to " = ".

"**What**" translates to a variable.   "**%**" translates to "$\times \frac{1}{100}$" or "$\times 0.01$".

Student Notes

A way of checking answers is by estimating as follows:

$11\% \times 49 \approx 10\% \times 50 = 5.$

Since 5 is close to 5.39, our answer is reasonable.

4. What is 6% of 15?

EXAMPLE 4　What is 11% of 49?

SOLUTION

Translate:

What	is	11%	of	49?
↓	↓	↓	↓	↓
a	=	0.11	·	49

"of" means multiply; $11\% = 0.11$

$$a = 5.39$$

Thus, 5.39 is 11% of 49. The answer is 5.39.

⤶ YOUR TURN

EXAMPLE 5　3 is 16 percent of what?

SOLUTION

Translate:

3	is	16 percent	of	what?
↓	↓	↓	↓	↓
3	=	0.16	·	y

$$\frac{3}{0.16} = y \qquad \text{Dividing both sides by 0.16}$$

$$18.75 = y$$

5. 5.2 is 8 percent of what?

Thus, 3 is 16 percent of 18.75. The answer is 18.75.

⤶ YOUR TURN

EXAMPLE 6　What percent of $50 is $34?

SOLUTION

Translate:

What percent	of	$50	is	$34?
↓	↓	↓	↓	
n	·	50	=	34

$$n = \frac{34}{50} \qquad \text{Dividing both sides by 50}$$

$$n = 0.68 = 68\% \qquad \text{Converting to percent notation}$$

6. What percent of 80 is 16?

Thus, $34 is 68% of $50. The answer is 68%.

⤶ YOUR TURN

　　Examples 4–6 represent the three basic types of percent problems. Note that in all the problems, the following quantities are present:

- a percent, expressed in decimal notation in the translation,
- a base amount, referred to by the word "of" in the problem, and
- a percentage of the base, found by multiplying the base times the percent.

Student Notes

Always look for connections between examples. Here you should look for similarities between Examples 4 and 7 as well as between Examples 5 and 8 and between Examples 6 and 9.

7. Alicia presented her line of jewelry to 250 stores, and 25.6% of those stores placed an order. How many stores placed an order?

8. At Valley Heights Community College, 252 freshmen enrolled in a Spanish class. This was 30% of the freshman class. How large was the freshman class?

EXAMPLE 7 *Carpooling.* In 2009, there were 153 million Americans in the work force, and 10.5% of them carpooled to work. How many carpooled to work?

Source: U.S. Census Bureau

SOLUTION We first reword and then translate. We let a = the number of American workers, in millions, who carpooled to work.

Rewording: What is 10.5% of 153?

Translating: $a = 0.105 \times 153$

The letter is by itself on one side of the equation. To solve the equation, we need only multiply:

$$a = 0.105 \times 153 = 16.065.$$

Since 16.065 million is 10.5% of 153 million, we have found that in 2009, about 16.065 million American workers carpooled to work.

YOUR TURN

EXAMPLE 8 *Social Networking.* About 110 million American adults used at least one social-networking website in 2010. This was 47% of all American adults. How many American adults were there in 2010?

Sources: Pew Research Center; U.S. Census Bureau

SOLUTION Before translating the problem to mathematics, we reword and let A represent the total number of American adults, in millions, in 2010.

Rewording: 110 is 47% of A

Translating: $110 = 0.47 \cdot A$

$$\frac{110}{0.47} = A \qquad \text{Dividing both sides by 0.47}$$

$$234 \approx A \qquad \text{The symbol } \approx \text{ means } \textit{is approximately equal to.}$$

There were about 234 million American adults in 2010.

YOUR TURN

EXAMPLE 9 *e-Reader Prices.* During a 2011 promotion, Amazon.com reduced the price of a Kindle e-reader from $139 to $114.

Source: Amazon.com

a) What percent of the regular price does the sale price represent?

b) What is the percent of discount?

SOLUTION

a) We reword and translate, using n for the unknown percent.

Rewording: What percent of 139 is 114?

Translating: $n \cdot 139 = 114$

$$n = \frac{114}{139} \qquad \text{Dividing both sides by 139}$$

$$n \approx 0.82 = 82\% \qquad \text{Converting to percent notation}$$

The sale price is about 82% of the regular price.

b) Since the original price of $139 represents 100% of the regular price, the sale price represents a discount of $(100 - 82)$%, or 18%.

Alternatively, or as a check, we can find the amount of discount and then calculate the percent of discount, using x for the unknown percent.

Amount of discount: $139 - $114 = $25

Rewording: What percent of 139 is 25?

Translating: $x \cdot 139 = 25$

$$x = \frac{25}{139}$$ Dividing both sides by 139

$$x \approx 0.18 = 18\%$$ Converting to percent notation

Chapter Resources:
Collaborative Activity, p. 145;
Decision Making: Connection,
p. 145

9. Recently, Elm Cycles reduced the price of a BMW F 800 Gs motorcycle from $15,000 to $13,500. What is the percent of discount?

We have a check. The percent of discount is 18%.

YOUR TURN

2.4 EXERCISE SET

FOR EXTRA HELP

MyMathLab® MathXL
PRACTICE WATCH READ REVIEW

Vocabulary and Reading Check

Choose from the following list the word that best completes each statement. Not every word will be used.

approximately   not
base   percent
decimal   retail
hundred   right
left   sale

1. To convert from percent notation to decimal notation, move the decimal point two places to the _____ and drop the percent symbol.

2. The percent symbol, %, means "per _____."

3. The expression 1.3% is written in _____ notation.

4. The word "of" in a percent problem generally refers to the _____ amount.

5. The _____ price is the original price minus the discount.

6. The symbol $\approx$ means "is _____ equal to."

Concept Reinforcement

In each of Exercises 7–16, match the question with the most appropriate translation from the following list. Some choices are used more than once.

a) $a = (0.57)23$
b) $57 = 0.23y$
c) $n \cdot 23 = 57$
d) $n \cdot 57 = 23$
e) $23 = 0.57y$
f) $a = (0.23)57$

7. ____ What percent of 57 is 23?

8. ____ What percent of 23 is 57?

9. ____ 23 is 57% of what number?

10. ____ 57 is 23% of what number?

11. ____ 57 is what percent of 23?

12. ____ 23 is what percent of 57?

13. ____ What is 23% of 57?

14. ____ What is 57% of 23?

15. ____ 23% of what number is 57?

16. ____ 57% of what number is 23?

Converting Between Percent Notation and Decimal Notation

Convert the percent notation in each sentence to decimal notation.

17. *Musical Instruments.* Of those who play Guitar Hero and Rock Band but do not currently play an actual musical instrument, 67% indicated that they are likely to begin playing an actual instrument.

Source: Guitar Center Survey, gonintendo.com

18. *Volunteering.* Of all Americans, 55% do volunteer work.

Source: The Nonprofit Almanac in Brief

19. Among American workers, 5% rely on public transportation for their commute.

Source: U.S. Census Bureau

20. If a NASCAR driver loses more than 3% body weight in sweat and does not replace those fluids, the driver's focus and reflexes start declining.
Source: CNN.com

21. Approximately 3.2% of U.S. adults are vegetarians.
Source: Vegetarian Times

22. *Gold.* Gold that is marked 10K is 41.6% gold.

23. *Energy Use.* Using landscape to shade a home's outdoor air-conditioning unit can reduce cooling costs by 10%.
Source: U.S. Department of Energy

24. Semisweet dark chocolate contains about 60% chocolate liquor.

Convert to decimal notation.

25. 6.25%   **26.** 8.375%

27. 0.2%   **28.** 0.8%

29. 175%   **30.** 250%

Convert the decimal notation in each sentence to percent notation.

31. By the end of 2010, about 0.21 of American Internet users had paid to download apps for their cell phones or tablet computers.
Source: Pew Research Center, *Internet and American Life Project*

32. *Baseball Fans.* Baseball is the second most popular sport in the United States, with 0.17 of the adult population saying it is their favorite sport.
Source: Sports Business Daily, 1/25/11

33. In-state tuition at Virginia public colleges and universities cost 0.079 more in 2011–2012 than in 2010–2011.
Source: The State Council of Higher Education for Virginia

34. *Food Security.* The USDA defines food security as access to enough nutritious food for a healthy life. In 2010, approximately 0.057 of U.S. households had very low food security.
Source: USDA

35. *Composition of the Sun.* The sun is 0.7 hydrogen.

36. *Jupiter's Atmosphere.* The atmosphere of Jupiter is 0.1 helium.

Convert to percent notation.

37. 0.0009   **38.** 0.0056

39. 1.06   **40.** 1.08

41. $\frac{3}{5}$ **42.** $\frac{3}{2}$

43. $\frac{8}{25}$ **44.** $\frac{5}{8}$

Solving Percent Problems

Solve.

45. What percent of 76 is 19?

46. What percent of 125 is 30?

47. 14 is 30% of what number?

48. 54 is 24% of what number?

49. 0.3 is 12% of what number?

50. 7 is 175% of what number?

51. What number is 1% of one million?

52. What number is 35% of 240?

53. What percent of 60 is 75?

Aha! **54.** What percent of 70 is 70?

55. What is 2% of 40?

56. What is 40% of 2?

Aha! **57.** 25 is what percent of 50?

58. 0.8 is 2% of what number?

59. What percent of 69 is 23?

60. What percent of 40 is 9?

Renewable Energy. *In 2010, renewable energy sources provided 8 quadrillion Btu's of the U.S. energy consumption. The following circle graph shows the percent provided by each renewable source. In each of Exercises 61–64, determine the amount of Btu's contributed by each source.*

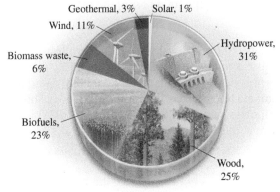

U.S. Renewable Energy

Geothermal, 3%   Solar, 1%
Wind, 11%
Biomass waste, 6%
Hydropower, 31%
Biofuels, 23%
Wood, 25%

Source: U.S. Energy Information Administration

61. Hydropower   **62.** Solar

63. Wind   **64.** Biofuels

65. *College Graduation.* To obtain his bachelor's degree in nursing, Cody must complete 125 credit hours of instruction. If he has completed 60% of his requirement, how many credits did Cody complete?

66. *College Graduation.* To obtain her bachelor's degree in journalism, Addie must complete 125 credit hours of instruction. If 20% of Addie's credit hours remain to be completed, how many credits does she still need to take?

67. *Batting Average.* In the 2011 season, Miguel Cabrera of the Detroit Tigers had 197 hits. His batting average was 0.344, the highest in major league baseball for that season. This means that of the total number of at-bats, 34.4% were hits. How many at-bats did he have?

Source: ESPN

68. *Pass Completions.* In the 2011 season, Drew Brees of the New Orleans Saints completed 468 passes. This was 71.2% of his attempts. How many attempts did he make?

Source: National Football League

69. *Tipping.* Trent left a $4 tip for a meal that cost $25.

a) What percent of the cost of the meal was the tip?
b) What was the total cost of the meal including the tip?

70. *Tipping.* Selena left a $12.76 tip for a meal that cost $58.

a) What percent of the cost of the meal was the tip?
b) What was the total cost of the meal including the tip?

71. *Crude Oil Imports.* In April 2011, crude oil imports to the United States averaged 9.0 million barrels per day. Of this total, 3.0 million came from Canada and Mexico. What percent of crude oil imports came from Canada and Mexico? What percent came from the rest of the world?

Source: U.S. Energy Information Administration

72. *Alternative-Fuel Vehicles.* Of the 1,500,000 alternative-fuel vehicles produced in the United States in 2008, 300,000 were sport utility vehicles. What percent of alternative-fuel vehicles were sport utility vehicles? What percent were other types of vehicles?

Source: U.S. Energy Information Administration

73. *Student Loans.* Glenn takes out a student loan for $2400. After a year, Glenn decides to pay off the interest, which is 6.80% of $2400. How much will he pay?

74. *Student Loans.* To finance her community college education, LaTonya takes out a student loan for $3500. After a year, LaTonya decides to pay off the interest, which is 4.50% of $3500. How much will she pay?

75. *Infant Health.* In a study of 300 pregnant women with "good-to-excellent" diets, 95% had babies in good or excellent health. How many women in this group had babies in good or excellent health?

76. *Infant Health.* In a study of 300 pregnant women with "poor" diets, 8% had babies in good or excellent health. How many women in this group had babies in good or excellent health?

77. *Cost of Self-Employment.* Because of additional taxes and fewer benefits, it has been estimated that a self-employed person must earn 20% more than a non–self-employed person performing the same task(s). If Tia earns $16 per hour working for Village Copy, how much would she need to earn on her own for a comparable income?

78. Refer to Exercise 77. Rik earns $18 per hour working for Round Edge stairbuilders. How much would Rik need to earn on his own for a comparable income?

79. *Budget Overruns.* The "Big Dig" in Boston, also known as the Central Artery/Tunnel Project, has been labeled the most expensive highway project in U.S. history. The original cost estimate for the project was $2.6 billion, and by the time the last major portion of the project was opened to vehicles, the cost was $12 billion over the original estimate. By what percent did the actual cost exceed the initial estimate?

Source: Associated Press, Dec. 20, 2003, cited by msnbc.msn.com: *Boston's "Big Dig" Opens to Public;* Construction Management Schools

80. *Swimming Records.* On December 18, 2009, Cesar Cielo Filho of Brazil set a world record by swimming 50 m on a long course (50-m pool) in 20.91 sec. This record is 0.61 sec longer than the record on the 50-m short course (25-m pool), which was set by Roland Schoeman of South Africa on August 8, 2009. By what percent is the record for a short course faster than the record for a long course?

Source: *Guinness Book of World Records* 2011

81. *Body Fat.* One author of this text exercises regularly at a local YMCA that recently offered a body-fat percentage test to its members. The device used measures the passage of a very low voltage of electricity through the body. The author's body-fat percentage was found to be 16.5%, and he weighs 191 lb. What part of his body weight, in pounds, is fat?

82. *Areas of Alaska and Arizona.* The area of Arizona is 19% of the area of Alaska. The area of Alaska is 586,400 mi². What is the area of Arizona?

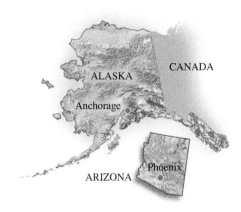

83. *Spam e-Mail.* About 265 billion of the 294 billion e-mails sent each day are spam and viruses. What percent of e-mails are spam and viruses?

Source: Based on information from Radicati Group

84. *Kissing and Colds.* In a medical study, it was determined that if 800 people kiss someone else who has a cold, only 56 will actually catch the cold. What percent is this?

85. *Calorie Content.* An 8-oz serving of Ocean Spray® Cranberry Juice Cocktail contains 120 calories. This is 240% of the number of calories in an 8-oz serving of Ocean Spray® Cranberry Juice Drink. How many calories are in an 8-oz serving of the Cranberry Juice Drink?

86. *Sodium Content.* Each serving of Planters® Lightly Salted Peanuts contains 95 mg of sodium. This is 50% of the sodium content in each serving

of Planters® Dry Roasted Peanuts. How many milligrams of sodium are in a serving of the Dry Roasted Peanuts?

87. How is the use of statistics in the following examples misleading?

  a) A business explaining new restrictions on sick leave cited a recent survey indicating that 40% of all sick days were taken on Monday or Friday.

  b) An advertisement urging summer installation of a security system quoted FBI statistics stating that over 26% of home burglaries occur between Memorial Day and Labor Day.

88. If Julian leaves a $12 tip for a $90 dinner, is he being generous, stingy, or neither? Explain.

Skill Review

89. Find the opposite of $-\frac{1}{3}$. [1.6]

90. Find the reciprocal of $-\frac{1}{3}$. [1.7]

91. Find $-(-x)$ for $x = -12$. [1.6]

92. Simplify: $(-3x)^2$. [1.8]

Synthesis

93. Campus Bookbuyers pays $30 for a book and sells it for $60. Is this a 100% markup or a 50% markup? Explain.

94. Erin is returning a tent that she bought during a 25%-off storewide sale that has ended. She is offered store credit for 125% of what she paid (not to be used on sale items). Is this fair to Erin? Why or why not?

95. The community of Bardville has 1332 left-handed females. If 48% of the community is female and 15% of all females are left-handed, how many people are in the community?

96. It has been determined that at the age of 10, a girl has reached 84.4% of her final adult height. Dana is 4 ft 8 in. at the age of 10. Predict her final adult height.

97. It has been determined that at the age of 15, a boy has reached 96.1% of his final adult height. Jaraan is 6 ft 4 in. at the age of 15. Predict his final adult height.

98. *Dropout Rate.* Between 2007 and 2009, the high school dropout rate in the United States decreased from 87 per thousand to 81 per thousand. Calculate the percent by which the dropout rate decreased and use that percentage to estimate dropout rates for the United States in 2010 and in 2011.

Source: www.childtrendsdatabank.org

99. *Photography.* A 6-in. by 8-in. photo is framed using a mat meant for a 5-in. by 7-in. photo. What percentage of the photo will be hidden by the mat?

100. Would it be better to receive a 5% raise and then, a year later, an 8% raise or the other way around? Why?

Aha!

101. Jorge is in the 30% tax bracket. This means that 30¢ of each dollar earned goes to taxes. Which would cost him the least: contributing $50 that is tax-deductible or contributing $40 that is not tax-deductible? Explain.

102. *Research.* If you have student loans, find the interest rates on those loans, whether the rates are fixed or variable, and how the interest is calculated. How much interest will you owe when the first payment is due?

 YOUR TURN ANSWERS: SECTION 2.4
1. 1.2   **2.** 0.04   **3.** 37%   **4.** 0.9   **5.** 65   **6.** 20%
7. 64 stores   **8.** 840 students   **9.** 10%

QUICK QUIZ: SECTIONS 2.1–2.4
Solve and check.

1. $6x - (5 - x) = 2x - 5$ [2.2]

2. $\dfrac{x}{2} - 10 = \dfrac{1}{3}$ [2.2]

3. Solve for p: $4p + mp = T$.   [2.3]

4. Convert to decimal notation: 1.2%.   [2.4]

5. 5 is 20% of what number?   [2.4]

PREPARE TO MOVE ON
Translate to an algebraic expression or equation.   [1.1]

1. Twice the length plus twice the width

2. 5% of $180

3. The product of 10 and half of a

4. 10 more than three times a number

5. A board's width is 2 in. less than its length.

6. A number is four times as large as a second number.

2.5   Problem Solving

The Five Steps for Problem Solving   •   **Percent Increase and Percent Decrease**

Probably the most important use of algebra is as a tool for problem solving. In this section, we develop a five-step problem-solving approach that is used throughout the remainder of the text.

The Five Steps for Problem Solving

FIVE STEPS FOR PROBLEM SOLVING IN ALGEBRA

1. *Familiarize* yourself with the problem.
2. *Translate* to mathematical language. (This often means writing an equation.)
3. *Carry out* some mathematical manipulation. (This often means *solving* an equation.)
4. *Check* your possible answer in the original problem.
5. *State* the answer clearly, using a complete English sentence.

Of the five steps, the most important is probably the first one: becoming familiar with the problem. Here are some hints for familiarization.

TO BECOME FAMILIAR WITH A PROBLEM

1. Read the problem carefully. Try to visualize the problem.
2. Reread the problem, perhaps aloud. Make sure you understand all words as well as any symbols or abbreviations.
3. List the information given and the question(s) to be answered. Choose a variable (or variables) to represent the unknown and specify exactly what the variable represents. For example, let L = length in centimeters, d = distance in miles, and so on.
4. Look for similarities between the problem and other problems you have already solved. Ask yourself what type of problem this is.
5. Find more information. Look up a formula in a book, at a library, or online. Consult a reference librarian or an expert in the field.
6. Make a table that uses the information you have available. Look for patterns that may help in the translation.
7. Make a drawing and label it with known and unknown information, using specific units if given.
8. Think of a possible answer and check your guess. Note the manner in which your guess is checked.

EXAMPLE 1 *Hiking.* In 1957 at the age of 69, Emma "Grandma" Gatewood became the first woman to hike solo all 2100 mi of the Appalachian trail—from Springer Mountain, Georgia, to Mount Katahdin, Maine. Gatewood repeated the feat in 1960 and again in 1963, becoming the first person to hike the trail three times. When Gatewood stood atop Big Walker Mountain, Virginia, she was three times as far from the northern end of the trail as from the southern end. At that point, how far was she from each end of the trail?

SOLUTION

1. **Familiarize.** It may be helpful to make a drawing.

To gain some familiarity, let's suppose that Gatewood stood 600 mi from Springer Mountain. Three times 600 mi is 1800 mi. Since 600 mi + 1800 mi = 2400 mi and 2400 mi > 2100 mi, we see that our guess is too large. Rather than guess again, we let

s = the distance, in miles, to the southern end

and

$3s$ = the distance, in miles, to the northern end.

(We could also let n = the distance to the northern end and $\frac{1}{3}n$ = the distance to the southern end.)

1. In 2005, Ken Looi of New Zealand set a record by covering 235.3 mi in 24 hr on his unicycle. After 8 hr, he was approximately twice as far from the finish line as he was from the start. How far had he traveled?

Source: *Guinness World Records*

2. **Translate.** From the drawing, we see that the lengths of the two parts of the trail must add up to 2100 mi. This leads to our translation.

Rewording:	Distance to southern end	plus	distance to northern end	is	2100 mi.
Translating:	s	$+$	$3s$	$=$	2100

3. **Carry out.** We solve the equation:

$$s + 3s = 2100$$
$$4s = 2100 \qquad \text{Combining like terms}$$
$$s = 525. \qquad \text{Dividing both sides by 4}$$

4. **Check.** As predicted in the *Familiarize* step, s is less than 600 mi. If $s = 525$ mi, then $3s = 1575$ mi. Since 525 mi + 1575 mi = 2100 mi, we have a check.

5. **State.** Atop Big Walker Mountain, Gatewood stood 525 mi from Springer Mountain and 1575 mi from Mount Katahdin.

YOUR TURN

We can represent several *consecutive integers* using one variable.

	Examples	Algebraic Representation
Consecutive Integers	16, 17, 18, 19, 20; −31, −30, −29, −28	x, $x + 1$, $x + 2$, and so on
Consecutive Even Integers	16, 18, 20, 22, 24; −52, −50, −48, −46	x, $x + 2$, $x + 4$, and so on
Consecutive Odd Integers	21, 23, 25, 27, 29; −71, −69, −67, −65	x, $x + 2$, $x + 4$, and so on

EXAMPLE 2 *Interstate Mile Markers.* U.S. interstate highways post numbered markers at every mile to indicate location in case of an emergency. The sum of two consecutive mile markers on I-70 in Kansas is 559. Find the numbers on the markers.

x	$x + 1$	**Sum of x and $x + 1$**
114	115	229
252	253	505
302	303	605

SOLUTION

1. **Familiarize.** The numbers on the mile markers are consecutive positive integers. Thus if we let $x =$ the smaller number, then $x + 1 =$ the larger number.

   To become familiar with the problem, we can make a table, as shown at left. First, we guess a value for x; then we find $x + 1$. Finally, we add the two numbers and check the sum.

Study Skills

Set Reasonable Expectations

Do not be surprised if your success rate drops some as you work through the exercises in this section. *This is normal.* Your success rate will increase as you gain experience with these types of problems and use some of the study skills already listed.

2. The sum of two consecutive mile markers on I-70 in Indiana is 337. (See Example 2.) Find the numbers on the markers.

From the table, we see that the first marker will be between 252 and 302. We could continue guessing and solve the problem this way, but let's work on developing our algebra skills.

2. **Translate.** We reword the problem and translate as follows.

Rewording: First integer plus next integer is 559.

Translating: x $+$ $(x + 1)$ $=$ 559

3. **Carry out.** We solve the equation:

$$x + (x + 1) = 559$$
$$2x + 1 = 559 \quad \text{Using an associative law and combining like terms}$$
$$2x = 558 \quad \text{Subtracting 1 from both sides}$$
$$x = 279. \quad \text{Dividing both sides by 2}$$

If x is 279, then $x + 1$ is 280.

4. **Check.** Our possible answers are 279 and 280. These are consecutive positive integers and $279 + 280 = 559$, so the answers check.

5. **State.** The mile markers are 279 and 280.

YOUR TURN

EXAMPLE 3 *Photography.* Marissa has a budget of $500 for photographs for her company's new website. Several friends have recommended Fine Taste Photography for the job. Marissa has learned that Fine Taste charges $125 for a day session plus a fee for each image used. From her friends, she has gathered the following data.

Number of Images Used	Fee for Images Used
2	$ 65
20	650
24	780

From the information given, how many images can she buy without exceeding her budget?

SOLUTION

1. **Familiarize.** We can determine how much each image will cost. If we divide each fee by the number of images, we find that the cost is $32.50 per image:

$$\$65 \div 2 = \$32.50,$$
$$\$650 \div 20 = \$32.50,$$
$$\$780 \div 24 = \$32.50.$$

Suppose that Marissa buys 14 images. Then the total cost is the fee for the session plus the fee for the images, or

Session fee plus cost per image times number of images,

$125 $+$ $32.50 $\cdot$ 14

which is $580. Since this amount is greater than the $500 budgeted, we know that our guess of 14 images was too large. However, the process we used to check our guess can be used to translate the problem to mathematical language. We let n = the number of images that Marissa can buy for a total cost of $500.

2. **Translate.** We reword the problem and translate as follows.

Rewording: Session fee plus image fee is $500.

Translating: 125   +   32.50n   =   500

3. **Carry out.** We solve the equation:

$$125 + 32.50n = 500$$
$$32.50n = 375 \qquad \text{Subtracting 125 from both sides}$$
$$n \approx 11.53. \qquad \text{Dividing both sides by 32.50}$$

We need to round the answer to a whole number. In this case, we must round *down* to avoid going over the budget. We have a possible solution of 11 images.

4. **Check.** The fee for 11 images is 11($32.50) = $357.50. The total cost is then $357.50 + $125 = $482.50. If Marissa spends this amount, she will have $17.50 left, which is not enough to buy another image. Also note that our answer is fewer than 14 images, as we expected from the *Familiarize* step.

5. **State.** Marissa can buy 11 images from Fine Taste Photography without exceeding her budget.

3. Refer to Example 3. If Marissa's budget is increased to $1000, how many images can she buy without exceeding her budget?

YOUR TURN

EXAMPLE 4 *Perimeter of an NBA Court.* The perimeter of an NBA basketball court is 288 ft. The length is 44 ft longer than the width. Find the dimensions of the court.

Source: National Basketball Association

SOLUTION

1. **Familiarize.** Recall that the perimeter of a rectangle is twice the length plus twice the width. Suppose the court were 30 ft wide. The length would then be 30 + 44, or 74 ft, and the perimeter would be 2 · 30 ft + 2 · 74 ft, or 208 ft. This shows that in order for the perimeter to be 288 ft, the width must exceed 30 ft. Instead of guessing again, we let w = the width of the court, in feet. Since the court is "44 ft longer than it is wide," we let $w + 44$ = the length of the court, in feet.

Student Notes

Get in the habit of writing what each variable represents before writing an equation. In Example 4, you might write

width (in feet) = w,

length (in feet) = $w + 44$

before translating the problem to an equation. This step becomes more important as problems become more complex.

2. **Translate.** To translate, we use $w + 44$ as the length and 288 as the perimeter. To double the length, $w + 44$, parentheses are essential.

Rewording: Twice the   plus   twice the   is   288 ft.
               length   width

Translating: 2(w + 44)   +   2w   =   288

3. Carry out. We solve the equation:

$$2(w + 44) + 2w = 288$$
$$2w + 88 + 2w = 288 \quad \text{Using the distributive law}$$
$$4w + 88 = 288 \quad \text{Combining like terms}$$
$$4w = 200$$
$$w = 50.$$

The dimensions appear to be $w = 50$ ft, and $l = w + 44 = 94$ ft.

4. Check. If the width is 50 ft and the length is 94 ft, then the court is 44 ft longer than it is wide. The perimeter is $2(50 \text{ ft}) + 2(94 \text{ ft}) = 100 \text{ ft} + 188 \text{ ft}$, or 288 ft, as specified. We have a check.

5. State. An NBA court is 50 ft wide and 94 ft long.

4. The perimeter of a standard high school basketball court is 268 ft. The length is 34 ft longer than the width. Find the dimensions of the court.

Source: Indiana High School Athletic Association

⟲ YOUR TURN

> **CAUTION!** Always be sure to answer the original problem completely. For instance, in Example 1 we needed to find *two* numbers: the distances from the hiker to *each* end of the trail. Similarly, in Example 4 we needed to find two dimensions, not just the width. Be sure to label each answer with the proper unit.

EXAMPLE 5 *Cross Section of a Roof.* In a triangular gable end of a roof, the angle of the peak is twice as large as the angle on the back side of the house. The measure of the angle on the front side is 20° greater than the angle on the back side. How large are the angles?

SOLUTION

1. Familiarize. We make a drawing. We label the measure of the back angle x, the measure of the front angle $x + 20$, and the measure of the peak angle $2x$.

Student Notes

You may be expected to recall material that you have learned in an earlier course. If you have forgotten a formula, refresh your memory by consulting a textbook or a website.

2. Translate. To translate, we need to recall that the sum of the measures of the angles in any triangle is always 180°.

Rewording:	Measure of back angle	+	measure of front angle	+	measure of peak angle	is	180°
Translating:	x	+	$(x + 20)$	+	$2x$	=	180

3. Carry out. We solve:

$$x + (x + 20) + 2x = 180$$

$$4x + 20 = 180 \qquad \text{Combining like terms}$$

$$4x = 160 \qquad \text{Subtracting 20 from both sides}$$

$$x = 40. \qquad \text{Dividing both sides by 4}$$

The measures for the angles appear to be:

Back angle: $x = 40°,$

Front angle: $x + 20 = 40 + 20 = 60°,$

Peak angle: $2x = 2(40) = 80°.$

5. The second angle of a triangle is 30° more than the first. The third angle is half as large as the first. Find the measures of the angles.

4. Check. Consider 40°, 60°, and 80°, as listed above. The measure of the front angle is 20° greater than the measure of the back angle, the measure of the peak angle is twice the measure of the back angle, and the sum is 180°. These numbers check.

5. State. The measures of the angles are 40°, 60°, and 80°.

YOUR TURN

When working with motion problems, we often use tables, as well as the following motion formula.

MOTION FORMULA

$$d = r \cdot t$$

(Distance = Rate × Time)

EXAMPLE 6 *Motion.*   Sharon drove for 3 hr on a highway and then for 1 hr on a side road. Her speed on the highway was 20 mph faster than her speed on the side road. If she traveled a total of 220 mi, how fast did she travel on the side road?

SOLUTION

1. **Familiarize.** After reading the problem carefully, we see that we are asked to find the rate of travel on the side road. We let x = Sharon's speed on the side road, in miles per hour.

   Since we are dealing with motion, we will use the motion formula $d = r \cdot t$. We use the variables in this formula as headings for three columns in a table. The rows of the table correspond to the highway and the side road. We know the times traveled for each type of driving, and we have defined a variable representing the speed on the side road. Thus we can fill in those entries in the table.

Road Type	$d =$	r	$\cdot$	t
Highway				3 hr
Side Road		x mph		1 hr

We want to fill in the remaining entries using the variable x. We know that Sharon's speed on the highway was 20 mph faster than her speed on the side road, or

Highway speed = $(x + 20)$ mph.

Then, since $d = r \cdot t$, we multiply to find each distance:

Highway distance $= (x + 20)(3)$ mi;

Side-road distance $= x(1)$ mi.

Road Type	d	$=$	r	$\cdot$	t
Highway	$(x + 20)(3)$ mi		$(x + 20)$ mph		3 hr
Side Road	$x(1)$ mi		x mph		1 hr

2. Translate. We know that Sharon traveled a total of 220 mi. This gives us the translation to an equation.

Rewording: Highway distance plus side-road distance is total distance.

Translating: $(x + 20)(3)$ $+$ $x(1)$ $=$ 220

3. Carry out. We now have an equation to solve:

$(x + 20)(3) + x(1) = 220$

$3x + 60 + x = 220$ — Using the distributive law

$4x + 60 = 220$ — Combining like terms

$4x = 160$ — Subtracting 60 from both sides

$x = 40.$ — Dividing both sides by 4

4. Check. Since x represents Sharon's speed on the side road, we have the following.

6. Erik drove to his first sales appointment at 60 mph. From there, he drove to his second appointment at 40 mph. It took him twice as long to drive to his first appointment as it did to his second. If he traveled a total of 80 mi, how long did it take him to drive from his first appointment to his second?

	Speed (Rate)	Time	Distance
Highway	$40 + 20 = 60$ mph	3 hr	$60(3) = 180$ mi
Side Road	40 mph	1 hr	$40(1) = 40$ mi

The total distance traveled is 40 mi + 180 mi, or 220 mi. The answer checks.

5. State. Sharon's speed on the side road was 40 mph.

YOUR TURN

> **PROBLEM-SOLVING TIPS**
> 1. The more problems you solve, the more your skills will improve.
> 2. Look for patterns when solving problems.
> 3. Clearly define variables before translating to an equation.
> 4. Consider the dimensions of the variables and constants in the equation. The variables that represent length should all be in the same unit, those that represent money should all be in dollars or all in cents, and so on.
> 5. Make sure that you have completely answered the original problem using the appropriate units.

Percent Increase and Percent Decrease

Whenever a percent of a quantity is calculated and then added to or subtracted from that quantity, the result is a percent increase or a percent decrease. Some examples follow.

Percent Increase	Percent Decrease
Sales tax Salary increase Population growth	Reduction in crimes Lowered sale price Body weight loss

For each example of percent increase or decrease, there are three amounts:

The original amount,

The amount of increase or decrease,

The new amount.

Identifying each amount is important in solving percent increase or decrease problems. The following relationships exist among these amounts.

> The amount of increase is added to the original amount to get the new amount.
>
> The amount of decrease is subtracted from the original amount to get the new amount.
>
> The percent increase or percent decrease is calculated on the basis of the original amount.

EXAMPLE 7 *Fitness.* Through diet and exercise, Gabrielle's weight decreased from 150 lb to 145 lb. What was the percent decrease in her body weight?

SOLUTION We begin by identifying the three amounts. Then we recall that the percent of decrease is calculated on the basis of the original amount.

Original Weight	150 lb
Amount of Weight Lost	5 lb
New Weight	145 lb

Original amount − new amount
= 150 lb − 145 lb

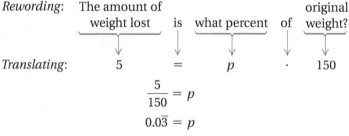

$$\frac{5}{150} = p$$

$$0.0\overline{3} = p$$

The percent of decrease is $3.\overline{3}\%$, or $3\frac{1}{3}\%$.

YOUR TURN

7. After he had recovered from a prolonged illness, Victor's weight increased from 140 lb to 150 lb. What was the percent increase in his body weight?

EXAMPLE 8 *Charitable Organizations.* The tax-exempt Hope Food Pantry received a bill of $242.65 for food storage bags. The bill incorrectly included sales tax of 5.5%. How much does the food bank actually owe?

SOLUTION

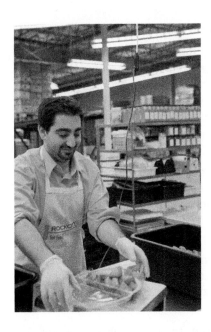

1. **Familiarize.** Sales tax is a percent increase and is calculated on the original price of an item. In this example, we are told the amount after the sales tax has been added, so we let $x =$ the original price of the food storage bags. We can organize the information in a table.

Original Price (in dollars)	x
Amount of Sales Tax	5.5% of x, or 0.055x
Price Including Sales Tax	$242.65

2. **Translate.** We reword the problem and translate as follows.

Rewording: Original price plus sales tax is total price.

Translating: x $+$ $0.055x$ $=$ 242.65

3. **Carry out.** We solve the equation:

$$x + 0.055x = 242.65$$
$$1x + 0.055x = 242.65$$
$$1.055x = 242.65 \quad \text{Combining like terms}$$
$$x = \frac{242.65}{1.055} \quad \text{Dividing both sides by 1.055}$$
$$x = 230.$$

4. **Check.** To check, we first find 5.5% of $230:

5.5% of $230 = 0.055($230) = $12.65.   This is the amount of the sales tax.

Next, we add the sales tax to find the total amount billed:

$230 + $12.65 = $242.65.

Since this is the amount that the food bank was billed, our answer checks.

5. **State.** The food pantry owes $230.

 YOUR TURN

8. Casey is selling his collection of Transformers at an auction. He wants to be left with $1150 after paying a seller's premium of 8% on the final bid (hammer price) for the collection. What must the hammer price be in order for him to clear $1150?

2.5 EXERCISE SET

FOR EXTRA HELP

Vocabulary and Reading Check

1. List the steps in the five-step problem-solving approach in the correct order.

   1) _____ Carry out.

   2) _____ Check.

   3) _____ Familiarize.

   4) _____ State.

   5) _____ Translate.

Each of the following was part of a step in at least one example's solution in this section. In the blank, write the name of the step during which each was done. Select from the five steps listed above.

2. _____ Solve an equation.

3. _____ Write the answer clearly.

4. _____ Make and check a guess.

5. _____ Reword the problem.

6. _____ Make a table.

7. _____ Recall a formula.

8. _____ Compare the answer with a prediction from an earlier step.

The Five Steps for Problem Solving

Solve. Even though you might find the answer quickly in another way, use the five-step process in order to build the skill of problem solving.

9. Three less than twice a number is 19. What is the number?

10. Two fewer than ten times a number is 78. What is the number?

11. Five times the sum of 3 and twice some number is 70. What is the number?

12. Twice the sum of 4 and three times some number is 34. What is the number?

13. *Kayaking.* On May 8, 2010, a team of kayakers set a record time of 5 hr 19 min 17 sec to kayak across the length of Loch Ness, Scotland, UK, a distance of 20.5 mi. If the kayakers were four times as far from the starting point as from the finish, how many miles had they traveled?

Source: *Guinness World Records* 2011

14. *Sled-Dog Racing.* The Iditarod sled-dog race extends for 1049 mi from Anchorage to Nome. If a musher is twice as far from Anchorage as from Nome, how many miles has the musher traveled?

15. *NASCAR Racing.* In February 2011, Trevor Bayne became the youngest winner of the Daytona 500, with a time of 03:59:24 for the 500-mi race. At one point, Bayne was 80 mi closer to the finish than to the start. How far had Bayne traveled at that point?

16. *Indy Car Racing.* In October 2011, Ed Carpenter won the Kentucky Indy 300 with a time of 01:42:02 for the 300-mi race. At one point, Carpenter was 20 mi closer to the finish than to the start. How far had Carpenter traveled at that point?

17. *Apartment Numbers.* The apartments in Erica's apartment house are consecutively numbered on each floor. The sum of her number and her next-door neighbor's number is 2409. What are the two numbers?

18. *Apartment Numbers.* The apartments in Brian's apartment house are numbered consecutively on each floor. The sum of his number and his next-door neighbor's number is 1419. What are the two numbers?

19. *Street Addresses.* The houses on the west side of Lincoln Avenue are consecutive odd numbers. Sam and Colleen are next-door neighbors and the sum of their house numbers is 572. Find their house numbers.

20. *Street Addresses.* The houses on the south side of Elm Street are consecutive even numbers. Wanda and Larry are next-door neighbors and the sum of their house numbers is 794. Find their house numbers.

21. The sum of three consecutive page numbers is 99. Find the numbers.

22. The sum of three consecutive page numbers is 60. Find the numbers.

23. *Longest Marriage.* As half of the world's longest-married couple, the woman was 2 years younger than her husband. Together, their ages totaled 206 years. How old were the man and the woman?

Source: *Guinness World Records* 2011

24. *Oldest Bride.* The world's oldest bride was 19 years older than her groom. Together, their ages totaled 185 years. How old were the bride and the groom?

Source: *Guinness World Records* 2010

25. *e-Mail.* In 2010, approximately 294 billion e-mail messages were sent each day. The number of spam messages was about nine times the number of nonspam messages. How many of each type of message were sent each day in 2010?

Source: Ferris Research

26. *Home Remodeling.* In 2009, Americans spent a total of $286 billion to remodel homes. They spent $178 billion more on owner-occupied homes than on rental units. How much was spent on each?

Source: Joint Center for Housing Studies, Harvard University

27. *Page Numbers.* The sum of the page numbers on the facing pages of a book is 281. What are the page numbers?

28. *Perimeter of a Triangle.* The perimeter of a triangle is 195 mm. If the lengths of the sides are consecutive odd integers, find the length of each side.

29. A rectangular community garden is to be enclosed with 92 m of fencing. In order to allow for compost storage, the garden must be 4 m longer than it is wide. Determine the dimensions of the garden.

30. *Hancock Building Dimensions.* The top of the John Hancock Building in Chicago is a rectangle whose length is 60 ft more than the width. The perimeter is 520 ft. Find the width and the length of the rectangle. Find the area of the rectangle.

31. *Two-by-four.* The perimeter of a cross section of a "two-by-four" piece of lumber is 10 in. The length is 2 in. longer than the width. Find the actual dimensions of the cross section of a two-by-four.

$P = 10$ in.

32. *Standard Billboard Sign.* A standard rectangular highway billboard sign has a perimeter of 124 ft. The length is 6 ft more than three times the width. Find the dimensions of the sign.

33. *Angles of a Triangle.* The second angle of an architect's triangle is three times as large as the first. The third angle is 30° more than the first. Find the measure of each angle.

34. *Angles of a Triangle.* The second angle of a triangular garden is four times as large as the first. The third angle is 45° less than the sum of the other two angles. Find the measure of each angle.

35. *Angles of a Triangle.* The second angle of a triangular kite is four times as large as the first. The third angle is 5° more than the sum of the other two angles. Find the measure of the second angle.

36. *Angles of a Triangle.* The second angle of a triangular building lot is three times as large as the first. The third angle is 10° more than the sum of the other two angles. Find the measure of the third angle.

37. *Rocket Sections.* A rocket is divided into three sections: the payload and navigation section in the top, the fuel section in the middle, and the rocket engine section in the bottom. The top section is one-sixth the length of the bottom section. The middle section is one-half the length of the bottom section. The total length is 240 ft. Find the length of each section.

240 ft

38. *Gourmet Sandwiches.* Jenny, Demi, and Joel buy an 18-in. long gourmet sandwich and take it back to their apartment. Since they have different appetites, Jenny cuts the sandwich so that Demi gets half of what Jenny gets and Joel gets three-fourths of what Jenny gets. Find the length of each person's sandwich.

39. *Boating.* Gaston paddled for 3 hr upstream and then for 2 hr downstream. His speed upstream was 10 mph slower than his speed downstream. If he traveled a total of 30 mi, how fast did he travel downstream?

40. *Commuting.* Bjorn rode for $\frac{1}{2}$ hr on the train and then for $\frac{1}{3}$ hr on the bus. The speed of the train was 50 km/h faster than the speed of the bus. If he traveled a total of 37.5 km, what was the speed of the bus?

Aha! **41.** *Long-Distance Running.* Phoebe runs at 12 km/h and walks at 5 km/h. One afternoon, she ran and walked a total of 17 km. If she ran for the same length of time as she walked, for how long did she run?

42. *Driving.* Theodora drove on the Blue Ridge Parkway at 40 mph and then on an interstate highway at 70 mph. She drove three times as long on the Blue Ridge Parkway as she did on the interstate. If she drove a total of 285 mi, for how long did she drive on the interstate?

Percent Increase and Percent Decrease

43. *Town Budget.* The town of Maxwell increased its annual budget from $1,600,000 to $1,800,000. Find the percent increase in the budget.

44. *Employment.* The number of jobs in a state increased from 1,800,000 to 1,816,200. Find the percent increase in the number of jobs.

45. *Endangered Species.* The number of Yangtze finless porpoises dropped from 2000 in the year 2000 to 1000 in the year 2011. Find the percent decrease in the number of porpoises.

Source: *Scientific American*

46. *Insurance Rates.* In 2011, the average annual premium for GEICO insurance policy owners in California dropped from $1187 to $1060. Find the percent decrease in the annual premium.

Source: California Department of Insurance

47. *Tax-Exempt Organizations.* A tax-exempt hospital received a bill of $1310.75 for linens. The bill incorrectly included sales tax of 7%. How much does the hospital owe?

48. *Automobile Tax.* Miles paid $5824, including 4% sales tax, for an out-of-state purchase of a car. In order to calculate the amount of sales tax he owes in his state, he must first determine the price of the car without sales tax. How much did the car cost before sales tax?

49. *Income Tax Deductions.* Jinney wants to deduct the sales tax that she paid this year on her state income tax return. She spent $4960.80 during the year, including 6% sales tax. How much sales tax did she pay?

50. *State Sales Tax.* The Tea Chest needs to send the sales tax that it has collected to the state. The total sales, including 4% sales tax, are $7115.68. How much in sales tax does the store need to send to the state?

51. *Discount.* Raena paid $224 for a camera during a 30%-off sale. What was the regular price?

52. *Discount.* Raquel paid $68 for a digital picture frame during a 20%-off sale. What was the regular price?

53. *Job Change.* Bradley took a 15% pay cut when he changed jobs. If he makes $30,600 per year at his new job, what was the annual salary for his previous job?

54. *Retirement Account.* The value of Karen's retirement account decreased by 40% to $87,000. How much was her retirement account worth before the decrease?

Aha! **55.** *Couponing.* Through "extreme couponing," Marie saved 85% of her grocery bill. If she paid $15, what was the original amount of the bill?

56. *Couponing.* Elliot had a coupon for 12% off his first meal at a new restaurant. If he was charged $11 for the meal, what was the original price of the meal?

57. *Automobile Sales.* Volkswagen sold 324,402 vehicles in the United States in 2011. This was a 26.3% increase over sales in 2010. How many vehicles did Volkswagen sell in the United States in 2010?

Source: prnewswire.com

58. *Law Enforcement.* During the 2011 holiday season in Sonoma County, California, officials arrested 163 individuals for driving under the influence of alcohol. This was a 29% increase from the number arrested during the same time in 2010. How many were arrested during the holidays in 2010?

Source: Bay City News Service

59. *Selling a Home.* The Brannons are planning to sell their home. If they want to be left with $117,500 after paying 6% of the selling price to a realtor as a commission, for how much must they sell their home?

60. *Law Enforcement.* In Charlotte, North Carolina, the number of annual crashes at targeted intersections fell 43.6% to 2591 crashes after red-light cameras were installed. How many crashes occurred annually before the cameras were installed?

Source: The National Campaign to Stop Red Light Running

Problem Solving

61. *Taxi Fares.* In New York City, taxis charge $3.00 plus $0.40 per one-fifth mile for peak fares. How far can Ralph travel for $17.50 (assuming a peak fare)?

Source: New York City Taxi and Limousine Commission

62. *Taxi Rates.* In Chicago, a taxi ride costs $2.25 plus $1.80 for each mile traveled. Debbie has budgeted $18 for a taxi ride (excluding tip). How far can she travel on her $18 budget?

Source: City of Chicago

63. *Truck Rentals.* Truck-Rite Rentals rents trucks at a daily rate of $49.95 plus 39¢ per mile. Concert Productions has budgeted $100 for renting a truck to haul equipment to an upcoming concert. How far can they travel in one day and stay within their budget?

64. *Truck Rentals.* Fine Line Trucks rents an 18-ft truck for $42 plus 35¢ per mile. Judy needs a truck for one day to deliver a shipment of plants. How far can she drive and stay within a budget of $70?

65. *Complementary Angles.* The sum of the measures of two *complementary* angles is 90°. If one angle measures 15° more than twice the measure of its complement, find the measure of each angle.

66. *Complementary Angles.* Two angles are complementary. (See Exercise 65.) The measure of one angle is $1\frac{1}{2}$ times the measure of the other. Find the measure of each angle.

67. *Supplementary Angles.* The sum of the measures of two *supplementary* angles is 180°. If the measure of one angle is $3\frac{1}{2}$ times the measure of the other, find the measure of each angle.

68. *Supplementary Angles.* Two angles are supplementary. (See Exercise 67.) If one angle measures 45° less than twice the measure of its supplement, find the measure of each angle.

69. *Copier Paper.* The perimeter of standard-size copier paper is 99 cm. The width is 6.3 cm less than the length. Find the length and the width.

70. *Stock Prices.* Sarah's investment in Jet Blue stock grew 28% to $448. How much did she originally invest?

71. *Savings Interest.* Janeka invested money in a savings account at a rate of 6% simple interest. After 1 year, she has $6996 in the account. How much did Janeka originally invest?

72. *Credit Cards.* The balance in Will's Mastercard® account grew 2%, to $870, in one month. What was his balance at the beginning of the month?

73. *Scrabble®.* In a single game on October 12, 2006, Michael Cresta and Wayne Yorra set three North American Scrabble records: the most points in one game by one player, the most total points in the game, and the most points on a single turn. Cresta scored 340 points more than Yorra, and together they scored 1320 points. What was the winning score?

Source: www.slate.com

74. *Bridge Construction.* The San Francisco–Oakland Bay Bridge consists of two spans connected by a tunnel. The East span is 556 ft longer than the West span, and the total length of the two spans is 19,796 ft. How long is the East span?

Source: historicbridges.org

75. *Cost of Food.* The equation $c = 1.2x + 32.94$ can be used to estimate the cost c of a Thanksgiving dinner for 10 people x years after 2000. Determine in what year the cost of a dinner for 10 people will be $50.94.

Source: Based on information from the American Farm Bureau Federation

76. *Teacher Salaries.* The equation $s = 1352x + 44{,}609$ can be used to estimate the average salary s of teachers in public schools x years after 2000. Determine in what year the average salary will be $63,537.

Source: Based on data from the National Center for Education Statistics

77. *Cricket Chirps and Temperature.* The equation $T = \frac{1}{4}N + 40$ can be used to determine the temperature T, in degrees Fahrenheit, given the number of times N a cricket chirps per minute. Determine the number of chirps per minute for a temperature of 80°F.

78. *Race Time.* The equation $R = -0.028t + 20.8$ can be used to predict the world record in the 200-m dash, where R is the record in seconds and t is the number of years since 1920. In what year will the record be 18.0 sec?

79. Marcus claims that he can solve most of the problems in this section by guessing. Is there anything wrong with this approach? Why or why not?

80. When solving Exercise 24, Jamie used a to represent the bride's age and Ben used a to represent the groom's age. Is one of these approaches preferable to the other? Why or why not?

Skill Review

81. Multiply: $4(2n + 8t + 1)$.   [1.8]

82. Factor: $12 + 18x + 21y$.   [1.2]

83. Simplify: $x - 3[2x - 4(x - 1) + 2]$.   [1.8]

84. Find the absolute value: $|0|$.   [1.4]

Synthesis

85. Write a problem for a classmate to solve. Devise it so that the problem can be translated to the equation $x + (x + 2) + (x + 4) = 375$.

86. Write a problem for a classmate to solve. Devise it so that the solution is "Audrey can drive the rental truck for 50 mi without exceeding her budget."

87. *Discounted Dinners.* Kate's "Dining Card" entitles her to $10 off the price of a meal after a 15% tip has been added to the cost of the meal. If, after the discount, the bill is $32.55, how much did the meal originally cost?

88. *Test Scores.* Pam scored 78 on a test that had 4 fill-in questions worth 7 points each and 24 multiple-choice questions worth 3 points each. She had one fill-in question wrong. How many multiple-choice questions did Pam get right?

89. *Gettysburg Address.* Abraham Lincoln's 1863 Gettysburg Address refers to the year 1776 as "four *score* and seven years ago." Determine what a score is.

90. One number is 25% of another. The larger number is 12 more than the smaller. What are the numbers?

91. A storekeeper goes to the bank to get $10 worth of change. She requests twice as many quarters as half dollars, twice as many dimes as quarters, three times as many nickels as dimes, and no pennies or dollars. How many of each coin did the storekeeper get?

92. *Perimeter of a Rectangle.* The width of a rectangle is three-fourths of the length. The perimeter of the rectangle becomes 50 cm when the length and the width are each increased by 2 cm. Find the length and the width.

93. *Discounts.* In exchange for opening a new credit account, Macy's Department Stores® subtracts 10% from all purchases made the day the account is established. Julio is opening an account and has a coupon for which he receives 10% off the first day's reduced price of a camera. If Julio's final price is $77.75, what was the price of the camera before the two discounts?

94. *Sharing Fruit.* Apples are collected in a basket for six people. One-third, one-fourth, one-eighth, and one-fifth of the apples are given to four people, respectively. The fifth person gets ten apples, and one apple remains for the sixth person. Find the original number of apples in the basket.

95. *eBay Purchases.* An eBay seller charges $9.99 for the first DVD purchased and $6.99 for all others. For shipping and handling, he charges the full shipping fee of $3 for the first DVD, one-half of the shipping charge for the second item, and one-third of the shipping charge per item for all remaining items. The total cost of a shipment (excluding tax) was $45.45. How many DVDs were in the shipment?

96. *Winning Percentage.* In a basketball league, the Falcons won 15 of their first 20 games. In order to win 60% of the total number of games, how many more games will they have to play, assuming they win only half of the remaining games?

97. *Taxi Fares.* In New York City, an off-peak taxi ride costs $2.50 plus 40¢ per $\frac{1}{5}$ mile and 40¢ per minute stopped in traffic. Due to traffic, Glenda's taxi took 20 min to complete what is usually a 10-min drive. If she is charged $18.50 for the ride, how far did Glenda travel?

Source: New York City Taxi and Limousine Commission

98. *Test Scores.*   Ella has an average score of 82 on three tests. Her average score on the first two tests is 85. What was the score on the third test?

 99. A school purchases a piano and must choose between paying $2000 at the time of purchase or $2150 at the end of one year. Which option should the school select and why?

100. Annette claims the following problem has no solution: "The sum of the page numbers on facing pages is 191. Find the page numbers." Is she correct? Why or why not?

Aha!

101. The perimeter of a rectangle is 101.74 cm. If the length is 4.25 cm longer than the width, find the dimensions of the rectangle.

102. The second side of a triangle is 3.25 cm longer than the first side. The third side is 4.35 cm longer than the second side. If the perimeter of the triangle is 26.87 cm, find the length of each side.

YOUR TURN ANSWERS: SECTION 2.5

1. About 78.4 mi   **2.** 168 and 169   **3.** 26 images
4. Width: 50 ft; length: 84 ft   **5.** 60°, 90°, 30°   **6.** $\frac{1}{2}$ hr
7. Approximately 7.1%, or $7\frac{1}{7}$%   **8.** $1250

QUICK QUIZ: SECTIONS 2.1–2.5
Solve and check. Label any contradictions or identities.

1. $-\frac{2}{5}x = -\frac{5}{3}$ [2.1]

2. $3t - 8 - (9 - t) = 2(5t + 4) - 7$ [2.2]

3. Solve for v: $B = \dfrac{3}{v}$.   [2.3]

4. Caitlan has $500 in a savings account that is paying 2.1% interest per year. How much will she earn in a year?   [2.4]

5. One day Jordan spent a total of 4 hr studying American Literature, College Algebra, and Non-Verbal Communication. He spent twice as much time studying algebra as he did studying literature, and he spent 30 min longer studying communication than he did studying literature. For how long did he study literature?   [2.5]

PREPARE TO MOVE ON
Write a true sentence using either $<$ or $>$.   [1.4]

1. $-8 \,\square\, 1$ **2.** $-2 \,\square\, -5$

Write a second inequality with the same meaning.   [1.4]

3. $x \geq -4$ **4.** $5 > y$

2.6   **Solving Inequalities**

Solutions of Inequalities   ▪   Graphs of Inequalities   ▪   Set-Builder Notation and Interval Notation   ▪   Solving Inequalities Using the Addition Principle   ▪   Solving Inequalities Using the Multiplication Principle   ▪   Using the Principles Together

Many real-world situations translate to *inequalities*. For example, a student might need to register for *at least* 12 credits; an elevator might be designed to hold *at most* 2000 pounds; a tax credit might be allowable for families with incomes of *less than* $25,000; and so on. Before solving applications, we must adapt our equation-solving principles to the solving of inequalities.

Solutions of Inequalities

An inequality is a number sentence containing $>$ (is greater than), $<$ (is less than), $\geq$ (is greater than or equal to), $\leq$ (is less than or equal to), or $\neq$ (is not equal to). Inequalities may be true or false. For example,

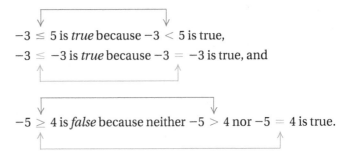

$-3 \leq 5$ is *true* because $-3 < 5$ is true,

$-3 \leq -3$ is *true* because $-3 = -3$ is true, and

$-5 \geq 4$ is *false* because neither $-5 > 4$ nor $-5 = 4$ is true.

Inequalities like

$$-7 > x, \quad t < 5, \quad 5x - 2 \geq 9, \quad \text{and} \quad -3y + 8 \leq -7$$

are true for some replacements of the variable and false for others.

Any value for the variable that makes an inequality true is called a **solution**. The set of all solutions is called the **solution set**. When all solutions of an inequality have been found, we say that we have **solved** the inequality.

EXAMPLE 1   Determine whether the given number is a solution of $y \geq 6$: **(a)** 6; **(b)** −4.

SOLUTION

a) Since $6 \geq 6$ is true, 6 is a solution.

b) Since $-4 \geq 6$ is false, −4 is not a solution.

1. Determine whether −1 is a solution of $x > -3$.

YOUR TURN

Graphs of Inequalities

Because the solutions of inequalities like $x < 2$ are too numerous to list, it is helpful to make a drawing, or **graph**, that represents all the solutions. Graphs of inequalities in one variable can be drawn on the number line by shading all points that are solutions. Parentheses are used to indicate endpoints that *are not* solutions and brackets to indicate endpoints that *are* solutions.*

EXAMPLE 2   Graph each inequality: **(a)** $x < 2$; **(b)** $y \geq -3$; **(c)** $-2 < x \leq 3$.

SOLUTION

a) The solutions of $x < 2$ are those numbers less than 2. They are shown on the graph by shading all points to the left of 2. The parenthesis at 2 and the shading to its left indicate that 2 *is not* part of the graph, but numbers like 1.2 and 1.99 are.

b) The solutions of $y \geq -3$ are shown on the number line by shading the point for −3 and all points to the right of −3. The bracket at −3 indicates that −3 *is* part of the graph.

Student Notes

Note that $-2 < x < 3$ means $-2 < x$ *and* $x < 3$. Because of this, statements like $2 < x < 1$ make no sense—no number is both greater than 2 and less than 1.

c) The inequality $-2 < x \leq 3$ is read "−2 is less than x *and* x is less than or equal to 3," or "x is greater than −2 *and* less than or equal to 3." To be a solution of $-2 < x \leq 3$, a number must be a solution of both $-2 < x$ *and* $x \leq 3$. The number 1 is a solution, as are −0.5, 1.9, and 3. The parenthesis indicates that −2 *is not* a solution, whereas the bracket indicates that 3 *is* a solution. The other solutions are shaded.

2. Graph the inequality:

$$0 \leq t < 5.$$

YOUR TURN

---

*An alternative notation uses open dots to indicate endpoints that are not solutions and closed dots to indicate endpoints that are solutions. Using this notation, the solutions of $x < 2$ are graphed as ⟨——————◦——⟩ and the solutions of $y \geq -3$ are graphed as ⟨——•————————⟩.

━━━━━ **EXPLORING** **THE CONCEPT** ━━━━━

Consider the inequality and the graph in Example 2(a). Match each change in the inequality described in the left-hand column with the corresponding change in the graph described in the right-hand column.

Inequality

$$x < 2$$

1. Replace $<$ with $\leq$.
2. Replace $<$ with $>$.
3. Replace 2 with -1.

Graph

a) The) changes to a (and the shading moves to the right of the (.
b) The) changes to a].
c) The) moves to the left.

ANSWERS

1. (b)   2. (a)   3. (c)

Set-Builder Notation and Interval Notation

To write the solution set of $x < 3$, we can use **set-builder notation:**

$$\{x \,|\, x < 3\}.$$

This is read "The set of all x such that x is less than 3."

Another way to write solutions of an inequality in one variable is to use **interval notation.** Interval notation uses parentheses, ( ), and brackets, [ ].

If a and b are real numbers with $a < b$, we define the **open interval (a, b)** as the set of all numbers x for which $a < x < b$. This means that x can be any number between a and b, but it cannot be either a or b.

The **closed interval $[a, b]$** is defined as the set of all numbers x for which $a \leq x \leq b$. **Half-open intervals $(a, b]$** and **$[a, b)$** contain one endpoint and not the other.

We use the symbols ∞ and $-\infty$ to represent positive infinity and negative infinity, respectively. Thus the notation (a, ∞) represents the set of all real numbers greater than a, and $(-\infty, a)$ represents the set of all real numbers less than a.

Interval notation for a set of numbers corresponds to its graph.

> **CAUTION!** Do not confuse the *interval* (a, b) with the *ordered pair* (a, b). The context in which the notation appears should make the meaning clear.

Student Notes

You may have noticed which inequality signs in set-builder notation correspond to brackets and which correspond to parentheses. The relationship could be written informally as

$$\geq \quad \leq \quad [\,]$$
$$> \quad < \quad (\,).$$

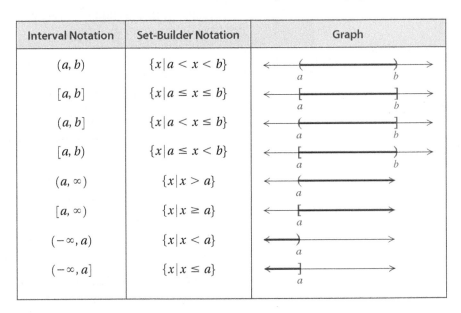

Interval Notation	Set-Builder Notation	Graph
(a, b)	$\{x \,|\, a < x < b\}$	
$[a, b]$	$\{x \,|\, a \leq x \leq b\}$	
$(a, b]$	$\{x \,|\, a < x \leq b\}$	
$[a, b)$	$\{x \,|\, a \leq x < b\}$	
(a, ∞)	$\{x \,|\, x > a\}$	
$[a, \infty)$	$\{x \,|\, x \geq a\}$	
$(-\infty, a)$	$\{x \,|\, x < a\}$	
$(-\infty, a]$	$\{x \,|\, x \leq a\}$	

EXAMPLE 3   Graph $t \geq -2$ on the number line and write the solution set using both set-builder notation and interval notation.

SOLUTION   Using set-builder notation, we write the solution set as $\{t \,|\, t \geq -2\}$.

Using interval notation, we write $[-2, \infty)$.

To graph the solution, we shade all numbers to the right of -2 and use a bracket to indicate that -2 is also a solution.

3. Graph $y < 1$ on the number line and write the solution set using both set-builder notation and interval notation.

YOUR TURN

Study Skills

Sleep Well

Being well rested, alert, and focused is very important when studying math. Often, problems that may seem confusing to a sleepy person are easily understood after a good night's sleep. Using your time efficiently is always important, so you should be aware that an alert, wide-awake student can often accomplish more in 10 minutes than a sleepy student can accomplish in 30 minutes.

Solving Inequalities Using the Addition Principle

Consider a balance similar to one that appears in Section 2.1. When one side of the balance holds more weight than the other, the balance tips in that direction. If equal amounts of weight are then added to or subtracted from both sides of the balance, the balance remains tipped in the same direction.

The balance illustrates the idea that when a number, such as 2, is added to (or subtracted from) both sides of a true inequality, such as $3 < 7$, we get another true inequality:

$$3 + 2 < 7 + 2, \quad \text{or} \quad 5 < 9.$$

Similarly, if we add -4 to both sides of $x + 4 < 10$, we get an *equivalent* inequality:

$$x + 4 + (-4) < 10 + (-4), \quad \text{or} \quad x < 6.$$

We say that $x + 4 < 10$ and $x < 6$ are **equivalent**, which means that both inequalities have the same solution set.

> **THE ADDITION PRINCIPLE FOR INEQUALITIES**
>
> For any real numbers a, b, and c:
>
> $a < b$ is equivalent to $a + c < b + c$;
>
> $a \leq b$ is equivalent to $a + c \leq b + c$;
>
> $a > b$ is equivalent to $a + c > b + c$;
>
> $a \geq b$ is equivalent to $a + c \geq b + c$.

As with equations, our goal is to isolate the variable on one side.

EXAMPLE 4   Solve $x + 2 > 8$ and then graph the solution.

SOLUTION   We use the addition principle, subtracting 2 from both sides:

$$x + 2 - 2 > 8 - 2 \qquad \text{Subtracting 2 from, or adding } -2 \text{ to, both sides}$$
$$x > 6.$$

Any number greater than 6 makes $x > 6$ true and is a solution of both that inequality and $x + 2 > 8$. Using set-builder notation, we write the solution set as $\{x \mid x > 6\}$. Using interval notation, we write the solution set as $(6, \infty)$. The graph is as follows:

Because most inequalities have an infinite number of solutions, we cannot possibly check them all. A partial check can be made using one of the possible solutions. For this example, we can substitute any number greater than 6—say, 6.1—into the original inequality:

$$\frac{x + 2 > 8}{6.1 + 2 \overset{?}{\mid} 8}$$
$$8.1 \overset{?}{>} 8 \quad \text{TRUE} \qquad 8.1 > 8 \text{ is a true statement.}$$

Since $8.1 > 8$ is true, 6.1 is a solution. Any number greater than 6 is a solution.

4. Solve $t - 4 < 1$ and then graph the solution.

 YOUR TURN

Technology Connection

As a partial check of Example 5, we can let $y_1 = 3x - 1$ and $y_2 = 2x - 5$. We set TblStart $= -5$ and ΔTbl $= 1$ in the TBLSET menu to get the following table. By scrolling up or down, you can note that for $x \leq -4$, we have $y_1 \leq y_2$.

X	Y₁	Y₂
-5	-16	-15
-4	-13	-13
-3	-10	-11
-2	-7	-9
-1	-4	-7
0	-1	-5
1	2	-3

X = -5

5. Solve $4 + 5n \geq 4n - 1$ and then graph the solution.

 YOUR TURN

EXAMPLE 5 Solve $3x - 1 \leq 2x - 5$ and then graph the solution.

SOLUTION We have

$$\begin{aligned}
3x - 1 &\leq 2x - 5 \\
3x - 1 + 1 &\leq 2x - 5 + 1 && \text{Adding 1 to both sides} \\
3x &\leq 2x - 4 && \text{Simplifying} \\
3x - 2x &\leq 2x - 4 - 2x && \text{Subtracting } 2x \text{ from both sides} \\
x &\leq -4. && \text{Simplifying}
\end{aligned}$$

The graph is as follows:

The student should check that any number less than or equal to -4 is a solution. The solution set is $\{x \mid x \leq -4\}$, or $(-\infty, -4]$.

Solving Inequalities Using the Multiplication Principle

There is a multiplication principle for inequalities similar to that for equations, but it must be modified when multiplying both sides by a negative number. Consider the true inequality

$$3 < 7.$$

If we multiply both sides by a *positive* number—say, 2—we get another true inequality:

$$3 \cdot 2 < 7 \cdot 2, \quad \text{or} \quad 6 < 14. \qquad \text{TRUE}$$

If we multiply both sides by a negative number—say, -2—we get a *false* inequality:

$$3 \cdot (-2) < 7 \cdot (-2), \quad \text{or} \quad -6 < -14. \qquad \text{FALSE}$$

The fact that $6 < 14$ is true, but $-6 < -14$ is false, stems from the fact that the negative numbers, in a sense, *mirror* the positive numbers. Whereas 14 is to the *right* of 6 on the number line, the number -14 is to the *left* of -6. Thus if we reverse the inequality symbol in $-6 < -14$, we get a true inequality:

$$-6 > -14. \quad \text{TRUE}$$

THE MULTIPLICATION PRINCIPLE FOR INEQUALITIES

For any real numbers a and b,
when c is a *positive* number,

$a < b$ is equivalent to $ac < bc$, and
$a > b$ is equivalent to $ac > bc$;

when c is a *negative* number,

$a < b$ is equivalent to $ac > bc$, and
$a > b$ is equivalent to $ac < bc$.

Similar statements hold for $\leq$ and $\geq$.

CAUTION! When multiplying or dividing both sides of an inequality by a negative number, don't forget to reverse the inequality symbol!

EXAMPLE 6 Solve and graph each inequality: **(a)** $\frac{1}{4}x < 7$; **(b)** $-2y \leq 18$.

SOLUTION

a) $\frac{1}{4}x < 7$

$4 \cdot \frac{1}{4}x < 4 \cdot 7$ Multiplying both sides by 4, the reciprocal of $\frac{1}{4}$

The symbol stays the same, since 4 is positive.

$x < 28$ Simplifying

The solution set is $\{x \mid x < 28\}$, or $(-\infty, 28)$. The graph is shown at left.

b) $-2y \leq 18$

$\dfrac{-2y}{-2} \geq \dfrac{18}{-2}$ Multiplying both sides by $-\frac{1}{2}$, or dividing both sides by -2

At this step, we reverse the inequality, because $-\frac{1}{2}$ is negative.

$y \geq -9$ Simplifying

As a partial check, we substitute a number greater than -9, say -8, into the original inequality:

$$
\begin{array}{c|c}
-2y & \leq 18 \\
\hline
-2(-8) & 18 \\
16 \stackrel{?}{\leq} 18 & \text{TRUE} \quad 16 \leq 18 \text{ is a true statement.}
\end{array}
$$

The solution set is $\{y \mid y \geq -9\}$, or $[-9, \infty)$. The graph is shown at left.

6. Solve and graph: $10 > -5x$.

YOUR TURN

Using the Principles Together

We use the addition and multiplication principles together to solve inequalities much as we did when solving equations.

EXAMPLE 7 Solve: $6 - 5y > 7$.

SOLUTION We have

$$6 - 5y > 7$$
$$-6 + 6 - 5y > -6 + 7 \qquad \text{Adding } -6 \text{ to both sides}$$
$$-5y > 1 \qquad \text{Simplifying}$$
$$-\tfrac{1}{5} \cdot (-5y) < -\tfrac{1}{5} \cdot 1 \qquad \text{Multiplying both sides by } -\tfrac{1}{5}, \text{ or dividing both sides by } -5$$

Remember to reverse the inequality symbol!

$$y < -\tfrac{1}{5}. \qquad \text{Simplifying}$$

As a partial check, we substitute a number smaller than $-\tfrac{1}{5}$, say -1, into the original inequality:

$$\begin{array}{c|c} 6 - 5y > 7 \\ \hline 6 - 5(-1) & 7 \\ 6 - (-5) & \\ 11 \overset{?}{>} 7 & \text{TRUE} \qquad 11 > 7 \text{ is a true statement.} \end{array}$$

The solution set is $\left\{ y \mid y < -\tfrac{1}{5} \right\}$, or $\left(-\infty, -\tfrac{1}{5} \right)$. The graph is shown at left.

7. Solve: $12 - y \le 3$.

YOUR TURN

EXAMPLE 8 Solve: **(a)** $16.3 - 7.2p \le -8.18$; **(b)** $1 - 3(x - 9) < 5(x + 6) - 2$.

SOLUTION

a) The greatest number of decimal places in any one number is *two*. Multiplying both sides by 100 will clear decimals. Then we proceed as before.

$$16.3 - 7.2p \le -8.18$$
$$100(16.3 - 7.2p) \le 100(-8.18) \qquad \text{Multiplying both sides by 100}$$
$$100(16.3) - 100(7.2p) \le 100(-8.18) \qquad \text{Using the distributive law}$$
$$1630 - 720p \le -818 \qquad \text{Simplifying}$$
$$1630 - 720p - 1630 \le -818 - 1630 \qquad \text{Subtracting 1630 from both sides}$$
$$-720p \le -2448 \qquad \text{Simplifying;} \quad -818 - 1630 = -2448$$
$$\frac{-720p}{-720} \ge \frac{-2448}{-720} \qquad \text{Dividing both sides by } -720$$

Remember to reverse the symbol!

$$p \ge 3.4$$

The solution set is $\{ p \mid p \ge 3.4 \}$, or $[3.4, \infty)$.

b)
$$1 - 3(x - 9) < 5(x + 6) - 2$$
$$1 - 3x + 27 < 5x + 30 - 2 \qquad \text{Using the distributive law to remove parentheses}$$
$$-3x + 28 < 5x + 28 \qquad \text{Simplifying}$$
$$-3x + 28 - 28 < 5x + 28 - 28 \qquad \text{Subtracting 28 from both sides}$$
$$-3x < 5x$$
$$-3x + 3x < 5x + 3x \qquad \text{Adding } 3x \text{ to both sides}$$
$$0 < 8x$$
$$0 < x \qquad \text{Dividing both sides by 8}$$

The solution set is $\{ x \mid 0 < x \}$, or $\{ x \mid x > 0 \}$, or $(0, \infty)$.

8. Solve: $\tfrac{1}{4} - \tfrac{2}{3}n \ge -\tfrac{1}{2}$.

YOUR TURN

CONNECTING 🔗 THE CONCEPTS

The procedure for solving inequalities is very similar to that used to solve equations. There are, however, two important differences.

- The multiplication principle for inequalities differs from the multiplication principle for equations: When we multiply or divide on both sides of an inequality by a *negative* number, we must *reverse* the direction of the inequality.

- The solution set of an equation like those solved in this chapter typically consists of one number. The solution set of an inequality typically consists of a set of numbers and is written using either set-builder notation or interval notation.

Compare the following solutions.

Solve: $2 - 3x = x + 10$.

SOLUTION

$$2 - 3x = x + 10$$

$-3x = x + 8$ Subtracting 2 from both sides

$-4x = 8$ Subtracting x from both sides

$x = -2$ Dividing both sides by -4

The solution is -2.

Solve: $2 - 3x > x + 10$.

SOLUTION

$$2 - 3x > x + 10$$

$-3x > x + 8$ Subtracting 2 from both sides

$-4x > 8$ Subtracting x from both sides

$x < -2$ Dividing both sides by -4 and reversing the direction of the inequality symbol

The solution is $\{x \mid x < -2\}$, or $(-\infty, -2)$.

EXERCISES

Solve.

1. $x - 6 = 15$

2. $x - 6 \leq 15$

3. $3x = -18$

4. $3x > -18$

5. $7 - 3x \geq 8$

6. $7 - 3x = 8$

7. $\dfrac{n}{6} - 6 = 5$

8. $\dfrac{n}{6} - 6 < 5$

9. $10 \geq -2(a - 5)$

10. $10 = -2(a - 5)$

2.6   EXERCISE SET

FOR EXTRA HELP   MyMathLab® Math XL

PRACTICE   WATCH   READ   REVIEW

👉 Vocabulary and Reading Check

Choose the word from the following list that best completes each sentence. Not every word will be used.

bracket	infinity	parenthesis
closed	interval	set-builder
half-open	open	solution

1. The number -2 is one _____ of the inequality $x < 0$.

2. The solution set $\{x \mid x \geq 10\}$ is an example of _____ notation.

3. The interval $[6, 10]$ is an example of a(n) _____ interval.

4. When graphing the solution of the inequality $-3 \leq x \leq 2$, place a(n) _____ at both ends of the interval.

👉 Concept Reinforcement

Insert the symbol $<$, $>$, $\leq$, or $\geq$ to make each pair of inequalities equivalent.

5. $-5x \leq 30$; $x \;\underline{\quad}\; -6$

6. $-7t \geq 56$; $t \;\underline{\quad}\; -8$

7. $-2t > -14$; $t \;\underline{\quad}\; 7$

8. $-3x < -15$; $x \;\underline{\quad}\; 5$

Classify each pair of inequalities as "equivalent" or "not equivalent."

9. $x < -2$; $-2 > x$

10. $t > -1$; $-1 < t$

11. $-4x - 1 \leq 15$; $-4x \leq 16$

12. $-2t + 3 \geq 11$; $-2t \geq 14$

Solutions of Inequalities

Determine whether each number is a solution of the given inequality.

13. $x > -4$
   a) 4
   b) -6
   c) -4

14. $t < 3$
   a) -3
   b) 3
   c) $2\frac{19}{20}$

15. $y \leq 19$
   a) 18.99
   b) 19.01
   c) 19

16. $n \geq -4$
   a) 0
   b) -4.1
   c) -3.9

17. $c \geq -7$
   a) 0
   b) $-5\frac{4}{5}$
   c) $1\frac{1}{3}$

18. $m \leq -2$
   a) $-1\frac{9}{10}$
   b) 0
   c) $-2\frac{1}{3}$

Graphs of Inequalities

Graph on the number line.

19. $y < 2$

20. $x \leq 7$

21. $x \geq -1$

22. $t > -2$

23. $0 \leq t$

24. $1 \leq m$

25. $-5 \leq x < 2$

26. $-3 < x \leq 5$

27. $-4 < x < 0$

28. $0 \leq x \leq 5$

Set-Builder Notation and Interval Notation

Graph each inequality, and write the solution set using both set-builder notation and interval notation.

29. $y < 6$

30. $x > 4$

31. $x \geq -4$

32. $t \leq 6$

33. $t > -3$

34. $y < -3$

35. $x \leq -7$

36. $x \geq -6$

Describe each graph using both set-builder notation and interval notation.

37.

38.

39.

40.

41.

42.

43.

44.

Solving Inequalities Using the Addition Principle

Solve. Graph and write both set-builder notation and interval notation for each answer.

45. $y + 6 > 9$

46. $x + 8 \leq -10$

47. $n - 6 < 11$

48. $n - 4 > -3$

49. $2x \leq x - 9$

50. $3x \leq 2x + 7$

51. $5 \geq t + 8$

52. $4 < t + 9$

53. $t - \frac{1}{8} > \frac{1}{2}$

54. $y - \frac{1}{3} > \frac{1}{4}$

55. $-9x + 17 > 17 - 8x$

56. $-8n + 12 > 12 - 7n$

Aha! 57. $-23 < -t$

58. $19 < -x$

Solving Inequalities Using the Multiplication Principle

Solve. Graph and write both set-builder notation and interval notation for each answer.

59. $4x < 28$

60. $3x \geq 24$

61. $-24 > 8t$

62. $-16x < -64$

63. $1.8 \geq -1.2n$

64. $9 \leq -2.5a$

65. $-2y \leq \frac{1}{5}$

66. $-2x \geq \frac{1}{5}$

67. $-\frac{8}{5} > 2x$

68. $-\frac{5}{8} < -10y$

Using the Principles Together

Solve.

69. $2 + 3x < 20$

70. $7 + 4y < 31$

71. $4t - 5 \leq 23$

72. $15x - 7 \leq -7$

73. $39 > 3 - 9x$

74. $5 > 5 - 7y$

75. $5 - 6y > 25$

76. $8 - 2y > 9$

77. $-3 < 8x + 7 - 7x$

78. $-5 < 9x + 8 - 8x$

79. $6 - 4y > 6 - 3y$

80. $7 - 8y > 5 - 7y$

81. $2.1x + 43.2 > 1.2 - 8.4x$

82. $0.96y - 0.79 \leq 0.21y + 0.46$

83. $1.7t + 8 - 1.62t < 0.4t - 0.32 + 8$

84. $0.7n - 15 + n \geq 2n - 8 - 0.4n$

85. $\frac{x}{3} + 4 \leq 1$

86. $\frac{2}{3} - \frac{x}{5} < \frac{4}{15}$

87. $3 < 5 - \dfrac{t}{7}$

88. $2 > 9 - \dfrac{x}{5}$

89. $4(2y - 3) \leq -44$

90. $3(2y - 3) > 21$

91. $8(2t + 1) > 4(7t + 7)$

92. $3(t - 2) \geq 9(t + 2)$

93. $3(r - 6) + 2 < 4(r + 2) - 21$

94. $5(t + 3) + 9 \geq 3(t - 2) - 10$

95. $\frac{4}{5}(3x + 4) \leq 20$

96. $\frac{2}{3}(2x - 1) \geq 10$

97. $\frac{2}{3}\left(\frac{7}{8} - 4x\right) - \frac{5}{8} < \frac{3}{8}$

98. $\frac{3}{4}\left(3x - \frac{1}{2}\right) - \frac{2}{3} < \frac{1}{3}$

99. Are the inequalities $x > -3$ and $x \geq -2$ equivalent? Why or why not?

100. Are the inequalities $t < -7$ and $t \leq -8$ equivalent? Why or why not?

Skill Review

Simplify. [1.8]

101. $5x - 2(3 - 6x)$

102. $8m - n - 3(2m + 5n)$

103. $x - 2[4y + 3(8 - x) - 1]$

104. $9x - 2\{4 - 5[6 - 2(x + 1) - x]\}$

Synthesis

105. Explain how it is possible for the graph of an inequality to consist of just one number. (*Hint*: See Example 2c.)

106. The statements of the addition and multiplication principles begin with *conditions* described for the variables. Explain the conditions given for each principle.

Solve.

107. $x < x + 1$

108. $6[4 - 2(6 + 3t)] > 5[3(7 - t) - 4(8 + 2t)] - 20$

109. $27 - 4[2(4x - 3) + 7] \geq 2[4 - 2(3 - x)] - 3$

Solve for x.

110. $\frac{1}{2}(2x + 2b) > \frac{1}{3}(21 + 3b)$

111. $-(x + 5) \geq 4a - 5$

112. $y < ax + b$ (Assume $a < 0$.)

113. $y < ax + b$ (Assume $a > 0$.)

114. Graph the solutions of $|x| < 3$ on the number line.

115. Determine the solution set of $|x| > -3$.

116. Determine the solution set of $|x| < 0$.

117. In order for a meal to be labeled "lowfat," it must have fewer than 3 g of fat per serving *and* the number of calories from fat must be 30% or fewer of the food's total calories.

   a) Each Chik Patties Breaded Veggie Pattie contains 150 calories per serving, and 54 of those calories come from fat. Can these patties be labeled "lowfat"?

   b) Cabot's 50% Reduced Fat Cheddar contains, as the name implies, 50% less fat than Cabot's regular cheddar cheese, but still cannot be labeled lowfat. What can you conclude about the fat content of a serving of Cabot's regular cheddar cheese?

YOUR TURN ANSWERS: SECTION 2.6

1. Yes   **2.**   [number line graph, 0 to 5]

3.   [number line graph, 0 to 1] $\{y \mid y < 1\}$, or $(-\infty, 1)$

4. $\{t \mid t < 5\}$, or $(-\infty, 5)$ [number line graph, 0 to 5]

5. $\{n \mid n \geq -5\}$, or $[-5, \infty)$ [number line graph, -5 to 0]

6. $\{x \mid x > -2\}$, or $(-2, \infty)$ [number line graph, -2 to 0]

7. $\{y \mid y \geq 9\}$, or $[9, \infty)$ **8.** $\left\{n \mid n \leq \frac{9}{8}\right\}$, or $\left(-\infty, \frac{9}{8}\right]$

QUICK QUIZ: SECTIONS 2.1–2.6

Solve.

1. $1 - (d - 7) = 6d - 2(5d + 10)$ [2.2]

2. $3x - 7x > 10 - x$ [2.6]

3. Pernell left an 18% tip for his lunch service. If the tip was $2.70, what was the price of the lunch before the tip? [2.4]

4. Melissa's dinner cost $20.89, including 8% sales tax. What was the price of the dinner before the tax was added? [2.5]

5. Solve for c: $X = 12 - 5(d - c)$.   [2.3]

PREPARE TO MOVE ON

Translate to an equation. Do not solve.   [1.1]

1. The area of a triangle is 5 m². The base is 3 m long. What is the height?

2. The perimeter of a triangle is 12 ft. One side is 1 ft longer than the shortest side. The third side is $\frac{1}{2}$ ft longer than the shortest side. How long is the shortest side of the triangle?

2.7 Solving Applications with Inequalities

Translating to Inequalities ▪ Solving Problems

The five steps for problem solving can be used for problems involving inequalities.

Translating to Inequalities

Before solving problems that involve inequalities, we list some important phrases to look for. Sample translations are listed as well.

Important Words	Sample Sentence	Definition of Variables	Translation
is at least	Kelby walks at least 1.5 mi a day.	Let k represent the length of Kelby's walk, in miles.	$k \geq 1.5$
is at most	At most 5 students dropped the course.	Let n represent the number of students who dropped the course.	$n \leq 5$
cannot exceed	The cost cannot exceed $12,000.	Let c represent the cost, in dollars.	$c \leq 12{,}000$
must exceed	The speed must exceed 40 mph.	Let s represent the speed, in miles per hour.	$s > 40$
is less than	Hamid's weight is less than 130 lb.	Let w represent Hamid's weight, in pounds.	$w < 130$
is more than	Boston is more than 200 mi away.	Let d represent the distance to Boston, in miles.	$d > 200$
is between	The film is between 90 min and 100 min long.	Let t represent the length of the film, in minutes.	$90 < t < 100$
minimum	Ned drank a minimum of 5 glasses of water a day.	Let w represent the number of glasses of water Ned drank.	$w \geq 5$
maximum	The maximum penalty is $100.	Let p represent the penalty, in dollars.	$p \leq 100$
no more than	Alan consumes no more than 1500 calories.	Let c represent the number of calories Alan consumes.	$c \leq 1500$
no less than	Patty scored no less than 80.	Let s represent Patty's score.	$s \geq 80$

The following phrases deserve special attention.

> **TRANSLATING "AT LEAST" AND "AT MOST"**
>
> The quantity x is at least some amount q: $x \geq q$.
> (If x is *at least* q, it cannot be less than q.)
>
> The quantity x is at most some amount q: $x \leq q$.
> (If x is *at most* q, it cannot be more than q.)

Solving Problems

EXAMPLE 1 *Catering Costs.* To cater a party, Papa Roux charges a $50 setup fee plus $15 per person. The cost of Hotel Pharmacy's end-of-season softball party cannot exceed $450. How many people can attend the party?

SOLUTION

1. **Familiarize.** Suppose that 20 people were to attend the party. The cost would then be $50 + $15 · 20, or $350. This shows that more than 20 people could attend without exceeding $450. Instead of making another guess, we let n = the number of people in attendance.

2. Translate. The cost of the party will be $50 for the setup fee plus $15 times the number of people attending. We can reword as follows:

Rewording:	The setup fee	plus	the cost of the meals	cannot exceed	$450.
Translating:	50	+	$15 \cdot n$	$\leq$	450

3. Carry out. We solve for n:

$$50 + 15n \leq 450$$

$$15n \leq 400 \qquad \text{Subtracting 50 from both sides}$$

$$n \leq \frac{400}{15} \qquad \text{Dividing both sides by 15}$$

$$n \leq 26\frac{2}{3}. \qquad \text{Simplifying}$$

1. Refer to Example 1. Suppose that Hotel Pharmacy decides to use a different caterer. This caterer charges a $100 setup fee plus $12 per person. How many people can attend the party?

4. Check. The solution set is all numbers less than or equal to $26\frac{2}{3}$. Since n represents the number of people in attendance, we round to a whole number. Since the nearest whole number, 27, is not part of the solution set, we round *down* to 26. If 26 people attend, the cost will be $50 + $15 \cdot 26$, or $440, and if 27 attend, the cost will exceed $450.

5. State. At most 26 people can attend the party.

 YOUR TURN

Study Skills

Avoiding Temptation

Make the most of your study time by choosing the right location. For example, sit in a comfortable chair in a well-lit location, but stay away from a coffee shop where friends may stop by. Once you begin studying, let any calls go to voice mail, and avoid text messages and e-mail.

> *CAUTION!* Solutions of problems should always be checked using the original wording of the problem. In some cases, answers might need to be whole numbers or integers or rounded off in a particular direction.

Some applications with inequalities involve *averages*, or *means*.

> **AVERAGE, OR MEAN**
>
> To find the **average**, or **mean**, of a set of numbers, add the numbers and then divide by the number of addends.

EXAMPLE 2 *Financial Aid.* Full-time students in a health-care education program can receive financial aid and employee benefits from Covenant Health System by working at Covenant while attending school and also agreeing to work there after graduation. Students who work an average of at least 16 hr per week receive extra pay and part-time employee benefits. For the first three weeks of September, Dina worked 20 hr, 12 hr, and 14 hr. How many hours must she work during the fourth week in order to average at least 16 hr per week for the month?

Source: Covenant Health Systems

SOLUTION

1. Familiarize. Suppose Dina works 10 hr during the fourth week. Her average for the month would be

$$\frac{20\,\text{hr} + 12\,\text{hr} + 14\,\text{hr} + 10\,\text{hr}}{4} = 14\,\text{hr}. \qquad \text{There are 4 addends, so we divide by 4.}$$

This shows that Dina must work more than 10 hr during the fourth week, if she is to average at least 16 hr of work per week. We let $x =$ the number of hours Dina works during the fourth week.

2. **Translate.** We reword the problem and translate as follows:

Rewording: The average number of hours Dina worked / should be at least / 16 hr.

Translating: $\dfrac{20 + 12 + 14 + x}{4} \geq 16$

3. **Carry out.** Because of the fraction, it is convenient to use the multiplication principle first:

$$\frac{20 + 12 + 14 + x}{4} \geq 16$$

$$4\left(\frac{20 + 12 + 14 + x}{4}\right) \geq 4 \cdot 16 \quad \text{Multiplying both sides by 4}$$

$$20 + 12 + 14 + x \geq 64$$

$$46 + x \geq 64 \quad \text{Simplifying}$$

$$x \geq 18. \quad \text{Subtracting 46 from both sides}$$

Chapter Resource:
Translating for Success, p. 144

2. Refer to Example 2. Suppose that for the first three weeks of October, Dina worked 12 hr, 14 hr, and 18 hr. How many hours must she work during the fourth week in order to average at least 16 hr per week for the month?

4. **Check.** As a partial check, we show that if Dina works 18 hr, she will average at least 16 hr per week:

$$\frac{20 + 12 + 14 + 18}{4} = \frac{64}{4} = 16. \quad \text{Note that 16 is at least 16.}$$

5. **State.** Dina will average at least 16 hr of work per week for September if she works at least 18 hr during the fourth week.

 YOUR TURN

2.7 EXERCISE SET   FOR EXTRA HELP

   MyMathLab® MathXL
PRACTICE   WATCH   READ   REVIEW

Vocabulary and Reading Check

Choose the phrase that best completes the sentence from the phrases listed below each blank.

1. If Matt's income is always $500 per week or more, then his income _____ $500.
   is at least/is at most

2. If Amy's entertainment budget for each month is $250, then her entertainment expenses _____ $250.
   must exceed/cannot exceed

3. If Lori works out 30 min or more every day, then her exercise time is _____ 30 min.
   no less than/no more than

4. If Marco must pay $20 or more toward his credit-card loan each month, then $20 is his _____ monthly payment.
   maximum/minimum

Concept Reinforcement

In each of Exercises 5–12, match the sentence with one of the following:

$$a < b; \quad a \leq b; \quad b < a; \quad b \leq a.$$

5. a is at least b.

6. a exceeds b.

7. a is at most b.

8. a is exceeded by b.

9. b is no more than a.

10. b is no less than a.

11. b is less than a.

12. b is more than a.

Translating to Inequalities

Translate to an inequality.

13. A number is less than 10.

14. A number is greater than or equal to 4.

15. The temperature is at most −3°C.

16. A full-time student must take at least 12 credits of classes.

17. To rent a car, a driver must have a minimum of 5 years driving experience.

18. Normandale Community College is no more than 15 mi away.

19. The age of the Mayan altar exceeds 1200 years.

20. The maximum safe exposure limit of formaldehyde is 2 parts per million.

21. Bianca earns no less than $12 per hour.

22. The cost of production of software cannot exceed $12,500.

23. Ireland gets between 1100 and 1600 hours of sunshine per year.

24. The cost of gasoline was at most $4 per gallon.

Solving Problems

Use an inequality and the five-step process to solve each problem.

25. *Furnace Repairs.*   RJ's Plumbing and Heating charges $55 plus $40 per hour for emergency service. Gary remembers being billed over $150 for an emergency call. How long was RJ's there?

26. *College Tuition.*   Vanessa's financial aid stipulates that her tuition not exceed $2500. If her local community college charges a $95 registration fee plus $675 per course, what is the greatest number of courses for which Vanessa can register?

27. *Graduate School.*   An unconditional acceptance into the Master of Business Administration (MBA) program at Arkansas State University will be given to students whose GMAT score plus 200 times the undergraduate grade point average is at least 950. Robbin's GMAT score was 500. What must her grade point average be in order to be unconditionally accepted into the program?

Source: graduateschool.astate.edu

28. *Car Payments.*   As a rule of thumb, debt payments (other than mortgages) should be less than 8% of a consumer's monthly gross income. Oliver makes $54,000 per year and has a $100 student-loan payment every month. What size car payment can he afford?

Source: money.cnn.com

29. *Quiz Average.*   Rod's quiz grades are 73, 75, 89, and 91. What scores on a fifth quiz will make his average quiz grade at least 85?

30. *Nutrition.*   Following the guidelines of the U.S. Department of Agriculture, Dale tries to eat at least 5 half-cup servings of vegetables each day. For the first six days of one week, she had 4, 6, 7, 4, 6, and 4 servings. How many servings of vegetables should Dale eat on Saturday, in order to average at least 5 servings per day for the week?

31. *College Course Load.*   To remain on financial aid, Millie needs to complete an average of at least 7 credits per quarter each year. In the first three quarters of 2012, Millie completed 5, 7, and 8 credits. How many credits of course work must Millie complete in the fourth quarter if she is to remain on financial aid?

32. *Music Lessons.*   Band members at Colchester Middle School are expected to average at least 20 min of practice time per day. One week Monroe practiced 15 min, 28 min, 30 min, 0 min, 15 min, and 25 min. How long must he practice on the seventh day if he is to meet expectations?

33. *Baseball.*   In order to qualify for a batting title, a major league baseball player must average at least 3.1 plate appearances per game. For the first nine games of the season, a player had 5, 1, 4, 2, 3, 4, 4, 3, and 2 plate appearances. How many plate appearances must the player have in the tenth game in order to average at least 3.1 per game?

Source: Major League Baseball

34. *Education.*   The Mecklenberg County Public Schools stipulate that a standard school day will average at least $5\frac{1}{2}$ hr, excluding meal breaks. For the first four days of one school week, bad weather resulted in school days of 4 hr, $6\frac{1}{2}$ hr, $3\frac{1}{2}$ hr, and $6\frac{1}{2}$ hr. How long must the Friday school day be in order to average at least $5\frac{1}{2}$ hr for the week?

Source: www.meck.k12.va.us

35. *Perimeter of a Triangle.*   One side of a triangle is 2 cm shorter than the base. The other side is 3 cm longer than the base. What lengths of the base will allow the perimeter to be greater than 19 cm?

36. *Perimeter of a Sign.*   The perimeter of a rectangular sign is not to exceed 50 ft. The length is to be twice the width. What widths will meet these conditions?

37. *Well Drilling.*   All Seasons Well Drilling offers two plans. Under the "pay-as-you-go" plan, they charge $500 plus $8 per foot for a well of any depth. Under their "guaranteed-water" plan, they charge a flat fee of $4000 for a well that is guaranteed to provide adequate water for a household. For what depths would it save a customer money to use the pay-as-you-go plan?

38. *Cost of Road Service.*   Rick's Automotive charges $50 plus $15 for each quarter hour when making a road call. Twin City Repair charges $70 plus $10 for each quarter hour. Under what circumstances would it be more economical for a motorist to call Rick's?

39. *Insurance-Covered Repairs.*   Most insurance companies will replace a vehicle if an estimated repair exceeds 80% of the "blue-book" value of the vehicle. Michele's insurance company paid $8500 for repairs to her Subaru after an accident. What can be concluded about the blue-book value of the car?

40. *Insurance-Covered Repairs.*   Following an accident, Jeff's Ford pickup was replaced by his insurance company because the damage was so extensive. Before the damage, the blue-book value of the truck was $21,000. How much would it have cost to repair the truck? (See Exercise 39.)

41. *Sizes of Packages.*   The U.S. Postal Service defines a "package" as a parcel for which the sum of the length and the girth is less than 84 in. (Length is the longest side of a package and girth is the distance around the other two sides of the package.) A box has a fixed girth of 29 in. Determine (in terms of an inequality) those lengths for which the box is considered a "package."

Girth = 29 in.

L

42. *Sizes of Envelopes.*   Rhetoric Advertising is a direct-mail company. It determines that for a particular campaign, it can use any envelope with a fixed width of $3\frac{1}{2}$ in. and an area of at least $17\frac{1}{2}$ in². Determine (in terms of an inequality) those lengths that will satisfy the company constraints.

$3\frac{1}{2}$ in. $17\frac{1}{2}$ in²

L

43. *Body Temperature.*   A person is considered to be feverish when his or her temperature is higher than 98.6°F. The formula $F = \frac{9}{5}C + 32$ can be used to convert Celsius temperatures C to Fahrenheit temperatures F. For which Celsius temperatures is a person considered feverish?

44. *Gold Temperatures.*   Gold stays solid at Fahrenheit temperatures below 1945.4°. Determine (in terms of an inequality) those Celsius temperatures for which gold stays solid. Use the formula given in Exercise 43.

45. *Area of a Triangular Sign.*   Zoning laws in Harrington prohibit displaying signs with areas exceeding 12 ft². If Flo's Marina is ordering a triangular sign with an 8-ft base, how tall can the sign be?

46. *Area of a Triangular Flag.*   As part of an outdoor education course, Trisha needs to make a bright-colored triangular flag with an area of at least 3 ft². What lengths can the triangle be if the base is $1\frac{1}{2}$ ft?

47. *Fat Content in Foods.*   Reduced Fat Sargento colby cheese contains 5 g of fat per serving. In order for a food to be labeled "reduced fat," it must have at least 25% less fat than the regular item. What can you conclude about the number of grams of fat in a serving of the regular Sargento colby cheese?

Source: Nutrition facts label

48. *Fat Content in Foods.*   Reduced Fat Wheat Thins crackers contain 3.5 g of fat per serving. What can you conclude about the number of grams of fat in a serving of regular Wheat Thins crackers? (See Exercise 47.)

Source: Nutrition facts label

49. *Weight Gain.*   In the last weeks before the yearly Topsfield Weigh In, heavyweight pumpkins gain about 26 lb per day. Charlotte's heaviest pumpkin weighs 532 lb on September 5. For what dates will its weight exceed 818 lb?

Source: Based on a story in the *Burlington Free Press*

50. *Pond Depth.*   On July 1, Garrett's Pond was 25 ft deep. Since that date, the water level has dropped $\frac{2}{3}$ ft per week. For what dates will the water level not exceed 21 ft?

51. *Cell-Phone Budget.*   Liam has budgeted $60 per month for his cell phone. For his service, he pays a monthly fee of $39.95, plus taxes of $6.65, plus 10¢ for each text message sent or received. How many text messages can he send or receive and not exceed his budget?

52. *Banquet Costs.*   The women's volleyball team can spend at most $700 for its awards banquet at a local restaurant. If the restaurant charges a $100 setup fee plus $24 per person, at most how many can attend?

53. *World Records in the Mile Run.*   The formula
$$R = -0.0065t + 4.3259$$
can be used to predict the world record, in minutes, for the 1-mi run t years after 1900. Determine (in terms of an inequality) those years for which the world record will be less than 3.6 min.

Source: Based on information from Information Please Database, Pearson Education, Inc.

54. *World Records in the Women's 1500-m Run.* The formula
$$R = -0.0026t + 4.0807$$
can be used to predict the world record, in minutes, for the 1500-m run t years after 1900. Determine (in terms of an inequality) those years for which the world record will be less than 3.7 min.

Source: Based on information from *Track and Field*

55. *Toll Charges.*   The equation
$$y = 0.078x + 3.13$$
can be used to estimate the cost y, in dollars, of driving x miles on the Pennsylvania Turnpike. For what mileages x will the cost be at most $14?

56. *Price of a Movie Ticket.*   The average price of a movie ticket can be estimated by the equation
$$P = 0.237Y - 468.87,$$
where Y is the year and P is the average price, in dollars. For what years will the average price of a movie ticket be at least $9? (Include the year in which the $9 ticket first occurs.)

Source: Based on data from National Association of Theatre Owners

57. If f represents Fran's age and t represents Todd's age, write a sentence that would translate to $t + 3 < f$.

58. Explain how the meanings of "Five more than a number" and "Five is more than a number" differ.

Skill Review

59. Use the commutative law of addition to write an expression equivalent to $xy + 7$.   [1.2]

60. Find the prime factorization of 225.   [1.3]

61. Change the sign of 18.   [1.6]

62. Find $-(-x)$ for $x = -5$.   [1.6]

Synthesis

63. Write a problem for a classmate to solve. Devise the problem so the answer is "At most 18 passengers can go on the boat." Design the problem so that at least one number in the solution must be rounded down.

64. Write a problem for a classmate to solve. Devise the problem so the answer is "The Rothmans can drive 90 mi without exceeding their truck rental budget."

65. *Ski Wax.*   Green ski wax works best between 5° and 15° Fahrenheit. Determine those Celsius temperatures for which green ski wax works best. (See Exercise 43.)

66. *Parking Fees.*   Mack's Parking Garage charges $4.00 for the first hour and $2.50 for each additional hour. For how long has a car been parked when the charge exceeds $16.50?

67. The area of a square can be no more than 64 cm². What lengths of a side will allow this?

68. The sum of two consecutive odd integers is less than 100. What is the largest pair of such integers?

69. *Frequent Buyer Bonus.*   Alice's Books allows customers to select one free book for every 10 books purchased. The price of that book cannot exceed the average cost of the 10 books. Neoma has bought 9 books whose average cost is $12 per book. How much should her tenth book cost if she wants to select a $15 book for free?

70. *Parking Fees.*   When asked how much the parking charge is for a certain car (see Exercise 66), Mack replies, "between 14 and 24 dollars." For how long has the car been parked?

71. *Grading.*   After 9 quizzes, Blythe's average is 84. Is it possible for Blythe to improve her average by two points with the next quiz? Why or why not?

72. *Discount Card.*   Barnes & Noble offers a member card for $25 per year. This card entitles a customer to a 40% discount off list price on hardcover bestsellers, a 10% discount on other eligible purchases, and $15 off the price of a Nook™ device. Describe two sets of circumstances for which an individual would save money by paying for a membership.

Source: Barnes & Noble

73. *Research.*   Find a formula for the maximum mortgage payment, sometimes called front-end ratio, based on annual income. Using this formula, determine what annual salaries qualify for a $1000 monthly mortgage payment.

QUICK QUIZ: SECTIONS 2.1–2.7
Solve.

1. $3 - x \geq 1 - 2(5 - x)$ [2.6]

2. $0.03t - 2.1 = 10$ [2.2]

3. Kenneth saved $13.75 on a pair of running shoes that originally were priced at $68.75. What percent of the original price did he save?   [2.4]

4. Two hours into a 72-km bicycle race, Jeannette realized that she had twice as far to ride as she had already ridden. At this point, how far was Jeannette from the finish line?   [2.5]

5. On her first three history papers, Nara received scores of 88, 86, and 74. What scores on the fourth paper will make her average grade at least 80?   [2.7]

PREPARE TO MOVE ON
Graph on the number line.   [1.4]

1. -12 **2.** 26

Simplify.   [1.8]

3. $\dfrac{286 - 127}{6 - 4}$ **4.** $\dfrac{1.3 - 9.8}{1 - 2}$

YOUR TURN ANSWERS: SECTION 2.7

1. At most 29 people   **2.** At least 20 hr

1. *Consecutive Integers.* The sum of two consecutive even integers is 102. Find the integers.

2. *Salary Increase.* After Susanna earned a 5% raise, her new salary was $25,750. What was her former salary?

3. *Dimensions of a Rectangle.* The length of a rectangle is 6 in. more than the width. The perimeter of the rectangle is 102 in. Find the length and the width.

4. *Population.* The population of Kelling Point is decreasing at a rate of 5% per year. The current population is 25,750. What was the population the previous year?

5. *Reading Assignment.* Quinn has 6 days to complete a 150-page reading assignment. How many pages must he read the first day so that he has no more than 102 pages left to read on the 5 remaining days?

Translating for Success

Use after Section 2.7.

Translate each word problem to an equation or an inequality and select a correct translation from A–O.

A. $0.05(25,750) = x$

B. $x + 2x = 102$

C. $2x + 2(x + 6) = 102$

D. $150 - x \leq 102$

E. $x - 0.05x = 25,750$

F. $x + (x + 2) = 102$

G. $x + (x + 6) > 102$

H. $x + 5x = 150$

I. $x + 0.05x = 25,750$

J. $x + (2x + 6) = 102$

K. $x + (x + 1) = 102$

L. $102 + x > 150$

M. $0.05x = 25,750$

N. $102 + 5x > 150$

O. $x + (x + 6) = 102$

Answers on page A-6

An additional, animated version of this activity appears in MyMathLab. *To use MyMathLab, you need a course ID and a student access code. Contact your instructor for more information.*

6. *Numerical Relationship.* One number is 6 more than twice another. The sum of the numbers is 102. Find the numbers.

7. *DVD Collections.* Together Mindy and Ken have 102 DVDs. If Ken has 6 more than Mindy, how many does each have?

8. *Sales Commissions.* Kirk earns a commission of 5% on his sales. One year, he earned commissions totaling $25,750. What were his total sales for the year?

9. *Fencing.* Jess has 102 ft of fencing that he plans to use to enclose dog runs at two houses. The perimeter of one run is to be twice the perimeter of the other. Into what lengths should the fencing be cut?

10. *Quiz Scores.* Lupe has a total of 102 points on the first 6 quizzes in her sociology class. How many total points must she earn on the 5 remaining quizzes in order to have more than 150 points for the semester?

Collaborative Activity   *Sales and Discounts*

Focus: Applications and models using percent
Time: 15 minutes
Use after: Section 2.4
Group size: 3
Materials: Calculators are optional.

Often a store will reduce the price of an item by a fixed percentage. When the sale ends, the items are returned to their original prices. Suppose a department store reduces all sporting goods 20%, all clothing 25%, and all electronics 10%.

Activity

1. Each group member should select one of the following items: a $50 basketball, an $80 jacket, or a $200 television. Fill in the first three columns of the first three rows of the chart below.

2. Apply the appropriate discount and determine the sale price of your item. Fill in the fourth column of the chart.

3. Next, find a multiplier that can be used to convert the sale price back to the original price and fill in the remaining column of the chart. Does this multiplier depend on the price of the item?

4. Working as a group, compare the results of part (3) for all three items. Then develop a formula for a multiplier that will restore a sale price to its original price, p, after a discount r has been applied. Complete the fourth row of the table and check that your formula will duplicate the results of part (3).

5. Use the formula from part (4) to find the multiplier that a store would use to return an item to its original price after a "30% off" sale expires. Fill in the last line on the chart.

6. Inspect the last column of your chart. How can these multipliers be used to determine the percentage by which a sale price is increased when a sale ends?

Original Price, p	Discount, r	$1 - r$	Sale Price	Multiplier to convert back to p
p	r	$1 - r$		
	0.30			

Decision Making & Connection   (*Use after Section 2.4.*)

Cost of Self-Employment.   Because of additional taxes and fewer benefits, it has been estimated that a self-employed person must earn 20% more than a non–self-employed person performing the same work.

1. Barry is considering starting his own lawn-care business. He currently earns $16 per hour as a crew manager working for a large lawn-care company. He estimates that he can earn $18 per hour if he starts his own business, but he will lose his benefits. On the basis of these hourly rates alone, which option should Barry choose?

2. Develop a formula that gives the minimum amount A that a self-employed person must earn in order to make a salary equivalent to that of a non–self-employed person making x dollars.

 3. *Research.*   Determine the extra costs that a self-employed person has. Consider self-employment taxes, insurance and vacation benefits, retirement benefits, and other costs. Based on your research, does the 20% rule seem accurate?

Study Summary

KEY TERMS AND CONCEPTS	EXAMPLES	PRACTICE EXERCISES

SECTION 2.1: *Solving Equations*

The Addition Principle for Equations

$a = b$ is equivalent to $a + c = b + c$.

Solve: $x + 5 = -2$.

$$x + 5 = -2$$
$$x + 5 + (-5) = -2 + (-5) \qquad \text{Adding } -5 \text{ to both sides}$$
$$x = -7$$

1. Solve: $x - 8 = -3$.

The Multiplication Principle for Equations

$a = b$ is equivalent to $ac = bc$, for $c \neq 0$.

Solve: $-\frac{1}{3}x = 7$.

$$-\frac{1}{3}x = 7$$
$$(-3)\left(-\frac{1}{3}x\right) = (-3)(7) \qquad \text{Multiplying both sides by } -3$$
$$x = -21$$

2. Solve: $\frac{1}{4}x = 1.2$.

SECTION 2.2: *Using the Principles Together*

When solving equations, we usually work in the reverse order of the order of operations.

Solve: $-3x - 7 = -8$.

$$-3x - 7 + 7 = -8 + 7 \qquad \text{Adding 7 to both sides}$$
$$-3x = -1$$
$$\frac{-3x}{-3} = \frac{-1}{-3} \qquad \text{Dividing both sides by } -3$$
$$x = \frac{1}{3}$$

3. Solve: $4 - 3x = 7$.

We can **clear fractions** by multiplying both sides of an equation by the least common multiple of the denominators in the equation.

We can **clear decimals** by multiplying both sides by a power of 10. If there is at most one decimal place in any one number, we multiply by 10. If there are at most two decimal places, we multiply by 100, and so on.

Solve: $\frac{1}{2}x - \frac{1}{3} = \frac{1}{6}x + \frac{2}{3}$.

$$6\left(\tfrac{1}{2}x - \tfrac{1}{3}\right) = 6\left(\tfrac{1}{6}x + \tfrac{2}{3}\right) \qquad \text{Multiplying by 6, the least common denominator}$$
$$6 \cdot \tfrac{1}{2}x - 6 \cdot \tfrac{1}{3} = 6 \cdot \tfrac{1}{6}x + 6 \cdot \tfrac{2}{3} \qquad \text{Using the distributive law}$$
$$3x - 2 = x + 4 \qquad \text{Simplifying}$$
$$2x = 6 \qquad \text{Subtracting } x \text{ from and adding 2 to both sides}$$
$$x = 3$$

4. Solve: $\frac{1}{6}t - \frac{3}{4} = t - \frac{2}{3}$.

SECTION 2.3: *Formulas*

A **formula** uses letters to show a relationship among two or more quantities. Formulas can be solved for a given letter using the addition and multiplication principles.

Solve for y: $x = \frac{2}{5}y + 7$.

$$x = \tfrac{2}{5}y + 7 \qquad \text{We are solving for } y.$$
$$x - 7 = \tfrac{2}{5}y \qquad \text{Isolating the term containing } y$$
$$\tfrac{5}{2}(x - 7) = \tfrac{5}{2} \cdot \tfrac{2}{5}y \qquad \text{Multiplying both sides by } \tfrac{5}{2}$$
$$\tfrac{5}{2}x - \tfrac{5}{2} \cdot 7 = 1 \cdot y \qquad \text{Using the distributive law}$$
$$\tfrac{5}{2}x - \tfrac{35}{2} = y \qquad \text{We have solved for } y.$$

5. Solve for c: $ac - bc = d$.

SECTION 2.4: *Applications with Percent*

Key Words in Percent Translations

"Of" translates to " $\cdot$ " or "$\times$"

"What" translates to a variable

"Is" or "Was" translates to "$=$"

"%" translates to "$\times \frac{1}{100}$" or "$\times 0.01$"

What percent   of   60   is   7.2?

$$n \quad \cdot \quad 60 = 7.2$$

$$n = \frac{7.2}{60}$$

$$n = 0.12$$

Thus, 7.2 is 12% of 60.

6. 12 is 15% of what number?

SECTION 2.5: *Problem Solving*

Five Steps for Problem Solving in Algebra

1. *Familiarize* yourself with the problem.
2. *Translate* to mathematical language. (This often means writing an equation or an inequality.)
3. *Carry out* some mathematical manipulation. (This often means *solving* an equation or an inequality.)
4. *Check* your possible answer in the original problem.
5. *State* the answer clearly.

The perimeter of a rectangle is 70 cm. The width is 5 cm longer than half the length. Find the length and the width.

1. **Familiarize.** The formula for the perimeter of a rectangle is $P = 2l + 2w$. We can describe the width in terms of the length: $w = \frac{1}{2}l + 5$.

2. **Translate.**

Rewording: Twice the length plus twice the width is the perimeter.

Translating: $\quad 2l \quad + \quad 2\left(\frac{1}{2}l + 5\right) = \quad 70$

3. **Carry out.** Solve the equation:

$$2l + 2\left(\tfrac{1}{2}l + 5\right) = 70$$

$$2l + l + 10 = 70 \qquad \text{Using the distributive law}$$

$$3l + 10 = 70 \qquad \text{Combining like terms}$$

$$3l = 60 \qquad \text{Subtracting 10 from both sides}$$

$$l = 20. \qquad \text{Dividing both sides by 3}$$

If $l = 20$, then $w = \frac{1}{2}l + 5 = \frac{1}{2} \cdot 20 + 5 = 10 + 5 = 15$.

4. **Check.** The width should be 5 cm longer than half the length. Since half the length is 10 cm, and 15 cm is 5 cm longer, this statement checks. The perimeter should be 70 cm. Since $2l + 2w = 2(20) + 2(15) = 40 + 30 = 70$, this statement also checks.

5. **State.** The length is 20 cm and the width is 15 cm.

7. Deborah rode a total of 120 mi in two bicycle fundraisers. One ride was 25 mi longer than the other. How long was each fundraiser?

SECTION 2.6:   *Solving Inequalities*

An **inequality** is any sentence containing $<, >, \leq, \geq,$ or $\neq$. Solution sets of inequalities can be **graphed** and written in **set-builder notation** or **interval notation**.

Interval Notation	Set-Builder Notation	Graph
(a, b)	$\{x \mid a < x < b\}$	
$[a, b]$	$\{x \mid a \leq x \leq b\}$	
$[a, b)$	$\{x \mid a \leq x < b\}$	
$(a, b]$	$\{x \mid a < x \leq b\}$	
(a, ∞)	$\{x \mid a < x\}$	
$(-\infty, a)$	$\{x \mid x < a\}$	

8. Write using interval notation:

$$\{x \mid x \leq 0\}.$$

The Addition Principle for Inequalities

For any real numbers a, b, and c,

$a < b$ is equivalent to $a + c < b + c$;

$a > b$ is equivalent to $a + c > b + c$.

Similar statements hold for $\leq$ and $\geq$.

Solve: $x + 3 \leq 5$.

$$x + 3 \leq 5$$
$$x + 3 - 3 \leq 5 - 3 \quad \text{Subtracting 3 from both sides}$$
$$x \leq 2$$

The solution is $\{x \mid x \leq 2\}$, or $(-\infty, 2]$.

9. Solve: $x - 11 > -4$.

The Multiplication Principle for Inequalities

For any real numbers a and b, and for any *positive* number c,

$a < b$ is equivalent to $ac < bc$;

$a > b$ is equivalent to $ac > bc$.

For any real numbers a and b, and for any *negative* number c,

$a < b$ is equivalent to $ac > bc$;

$a > b$ is equivalent to $ac < bc$.

Similar statements hold for $\leq$ and $\geq$.

Solve: $3x > 9$.

$$3x > 9$$
$$\tfrac{1}{3} \cdot 3x > \tfrac{1}{3} \cdot 9 \quad \text{The inequality symbol does not change because } \tfrac{1}{3} \text{ is positive.}$$
$$x > 3$$

The solution is $\{x \mid x > 3\}$, or $(3, \infty)$.

Solve: $-3x > 9$.

$$-3x > 9$$
$$-\tfrac{1}{3} \cdot -3x < -\tfrac{1}{3} \cdot 9 \quad \text{The inequality symbol is reversed because } -\tfrac{1}{3} \text{ is negative.}$$
$$x < -3$$

The solution is $\{x \mid x < -3\}$, or $(-\infty, -3)$.

10. Solve: $-8x \leq 2$.

SECTION 2.7:   *Solving Applications with Inequalities*

Many real-world problems can be solved by translating the problem to an inequality and applying the five-step problem-solving strategy.

Translate to an inequality.

The test score must exceed 85.	$s > 85$
At most 15 volunteers greeted visitors.	$v \leq 15$
Ona makes no more than $100 per week.	$w \leq 100$
Herbs need at least 4 hr of sun per day.	$h \geq 4$

11. Translate to an inequality:

Luke runs no less than 3 mi per day.

Review Exercises: Chapter 2

⭢ Concept Reinforcement

Classify each of the following statements as either true or false.

1. $5x - 4 = 2x$ and $3x = 4$ are equivalent equations. [2.1]

2. $5 - 2t < 9$ and $t > 6$ are equivalent inequalities. [2.6]

3. Some equations have no solution. [2.1]

4. Consecutive odd integers are 2 units apart. [2.5]

5. For any number a, $a \le a$. [2.6]

6. The addition principle is always used before the multiplication principle. [2.2]

7. A 10% discount results in a sale price that is 90% of the original price. [2.4]

8. Often it is impossible to list all solutions of an inequality number by number. [2.6]

Solve. Label any contradictions or identities.

9. $x + 9 = -16$ [2.1]

10. $-8x = -56$ [2.1]

11. $-\dfrac{x}{5} = 13$ [2.1]

12. $x - 0.1 = 1.01$ [2.1]

13. $-\frac{2}{3} + x = -\frac{1}{6}$ [2.1]

14. $4y + 11 = 5$ [2.2]

15. $5 - x = 13$ [2.2]

16. $3t + 7 = t - 1$ [2.2]

17. $7x - 6 = 25x$ [2.2]

18. $\frac{1}{4}x - \frac{5}{8} = \frac{3}{8}$ [2.2]

19. $14y = 23y - 17 - 9y$ [2.2]

20. $0.22y - 0.6 = 0.12y + 3 - 0.8y$ [2.2]

21. $\frac{1}{4}x - \frac{1}{8}x = 3 - \frac{1}{16}x$ [2.2]

22. $6(4 - n) = 18$ [2.2]

23. $4(5x - 7) = -56$ [2.2]

24. $8(x - 2) = 4(x - 4)$ [2.2]

25. $3(x - 4) + 2 = x + 2(x - 5)$ [2.2]

Solve each formula for the given letter. [2.3]

26. $C = \pi d$, for d

27. $V = \frac{1}{3}Bh$, for B

28. $5x - 2y = 10$, for y

29. $tx = ax + b$, for x

30. Find decimal notation for 1.2%. [2.4]

31. Find percent notation for $\frac{11}{25}$. [2.4]

32. What percent of 60 is 42? [2.4]

33. 49 is 35% of what number? [2.4]

Determine whether each number is a solution of $x \le -5$. [2.6]

34. -3

35. -7

36. 0

Graph on the number line. [2.6]

37. $5x - 6 < 2x + 3$

38. $-2 < x \le 5$

39. $t > 0$

Solve. Write the answers in set-builder notation and interval notation. [2.6]

40. $t + \frac{2}{3} \ge \frac{1}{6}$

41. $2 + 6y > 20$

42. $7 - 3y \ge 27 + 2y$

43. $-4y < 28$

44. $3 - 4x < 27$

45. $4 - 8x < 13 + 3x$

46. $13 \le -\frac{2}{3}t + 5$

47. $7 \le 1 - \frac{3}{4}x$

Solve.

48. Between January 2010 and October 2010, 3.2 million students graduated from high school. Of these, 2.2 million were enrolled in college in October 2010. What percent of the high school graduates were enrolled in college? [2.4]

    Source: U.S. Bureau of Labor Statistics

49. An 18-ft beam is cut into two pieces. One piece is 2 ft longer than the other. How long are the pieces? [2.5]

50. In 2011, a total of 262,000 students from China and India enrolled in U.S. colleges and universities. The number of Chinese students was 2000 more than one and one-half times the number of Indian students. How many Chinese students and how many Indian students enrolled in the United States in 2011? [2.5]

Source: Institute of International Education

51. From 2007 to 2011, the number of new international students increased by 37 percent to 215,000. How many new international students were there in 2007? [2.4]

Source: Institute of International Education

52. The sum of two consecutive odd integers is 116. Find the integers. [2.5]

53. The perimeter of a rectangle is 56 cm. The width is 6 cm less than the length. Find the width and the length. [2.5]

54. After a 25% reduction, a picnic table is on sale for $120. What was the regular price? [2.5]

55. The measure of the second angle of a triangle is 50° more than that of the first. The measure of the third angle is 10° less than twice the first. Find the measures of the angles. [2.5]

56. Kathleen has budgeted an average of $95 per month for entertainment. For the first five months of the year, she has spent $98, $89, $110, $85, and $83. How much can Kathleen spend in the sixth month without exceeding her average entertainment budget? [2.7]

57. To make copies of blueprints, Vantage Reprographics charges a $6 setup fee plus $4 per copy. Myra can spend no more than $65 for the copying. What number of copies will allow her to stay within budget? [2.7]

Synthesis

 58. How does the multiplication principle for equations differ from the multiplication principle for inequalities? [2.1], [2.6]

 59. Explain how checking the solutions of an equation differs from checking the solutions of an inequality. [2.1], [2.6]

60. A study of sixth- and seventh-graders in Boston revealed that, on average, the students spent 3 hr 20 min per day watching TV or playing video and computer games. This represents 108% more than the average time spent reading or doing homework. How much time each day was spent, on average, reading or doing homework? [2.4]

Source: Harvard School of Public Health

61. In June 2007, a team of Brazilian scientists exploring the Amazon measured its length as 65 mi longer than the Nile. If the combined length of both rivers is 8385 mi, how long is each river? [2.5]

Source: news.nationalgeographic.com

Solve.

62. $2|n| + 4 = 50$ [1.4], [2.2]

63. $|3n| = 60$ [1.4], [2.1]

64. $y = 2a - ab + 3$, for a [2.3]

65. The Maryland Heart Center gives the following steps to calculate the number of fat grams needed daily by a moderately active woman. Write the steps as one formula relating the number of fat grams F to a woman's weight w, in pounds. [2.3]

1. Calculate the total number of calories per day.
____ pounds × 12 calories = ____ total calories per day

2. Take the total number of calories and multiply by 30 percent.
____ calories per day × 0.30 = ____ calories from fat per day.

3. Take the number of calories from fat per day and divide by 9 (there are 9 calories per gram of fat).
____ calories from fat per day divided by 9 = ____ fat grams per day

Test: Chapter 2

For step-by-step test solutions, access the Chapter Test Prep Videos in MyMathLab®, on YouTube® (search "Bittinger Combo Alg CA" and click on "Channels"), or by scanning the code.

Solve. Label any contradictions or identities.

1. $t + 7 = 16$

2. $6x = -18$

3. $-\frac{4}{7}x = -28$

4. $3t + 7 = 2t - 5$

5. $\frac{1}{2}x - \frac{3}{5} = \frac{2}{5}$

6. $8 - y = 16$

7. $4.2x + 3.5 = 1.2 - 2.5x$

8. $4(x + 2) = 36$

9. $\frac{5}{6}(3x + 1) = 20$

10. $13t - (5 - 2t) = 5(3t - 1)$

Solve. Write the answers in both set-builder notation and interval notation.

11. $x + 6 > 1$

12. $14x + 9 > 13x - 4$

13. $-5y \geq 65$

14. $4n + 3 < -17$

15. $3 - 5x > 38$

16. $\frac{1}{2}t - \frac{1}{4} \leq \frac{3}{4}t$

17. $5 - 9x \geq 19 + 5x$

Solve each formula for the given letter.

18. $A = 2\pi rh$, for r

19. $w = \dfrac{P + l}{2}$, for l

20. Find decimal notation for 230%.

21. Find percent notation for 0.003.

22. What number is 18.5% of 80?

23. What percent of 75 is 33?

Graph on the number line.

24. $y < 4$

25. $-2 \leq x \leq 2$

Solve.

26. The perimeter of a rectangular calculator is 36 cm. The length is 4 cm greater than the width. Find the width and the length.

27. In January 2009, Jenny Foster ran the 165-mi Ozark Highlands Trail in 2 days, 14 hr, 25 min. When she reached the top of Hare Mountain, the highest point on the trail, she was three times as far from Buffalo River at one end of the trail as she was from Lake Ft. Smith State Park at the other end of the trail. At that point, how far was she from each end of the trail?

Source: Ozark Highlands Trail Association

28. The perimeter of a triangle is 249 mm. If the sides are consecutive odd integers, find the length of each side.

29. By lowering the temperature of their electric hot-water heater from 140°F to 120°F, the Kellys' average electric bill dropped by 7% to $60.45. What was their electric bill before they lowered the temperature of their hot water?

30. Local light rail service in Denver, Colorado, costs $2.25 per trip (one way). A monthly pass costs $79. Gail is a student at Community College of Denver. Express as an inequality the number of trips per month that Gail should make if the pass is to save her money.

Source: rtd-denver.com

Synthesis

Solve.

31. $c = \dfrac{2cd}{a - d}$, for d

32. $3|w| - 8 = 37$

33. Translate to an inequality.

A plant marked "partial sun" needs at least 4 hr but no more than 6 hr of sun each day.

Source: www.yardsmarts.com

34. A concert promoter had a certain number of tickets to give away. Five people got the tickets. The first got one-third of the tickets, the second got one-fourth of the tickets, and the third got one-fifth of the tickets. The fourth person got eight tickets, and there were five tickets left for the fifth person. Find the total number of tickets given away.

Cumulative Review: Chapters 1–2

Simplify.

1. $18 + (-30)$ [1.5]

2. $\frac{1}{2} - \left(-\frac{1}{4}\right)$ [1.6]

3. $-1.2(3.5)$ [1.7]

4. $-5 \div \left(-\frac{1}{2}\right)$ [1.7]

5. $150 - 10^2 \div 25 \cdot 4$ [1.8]

6. $(150 - 10^2) \div (25 \cdot 4)$ [1.8]

Remove parentheses and simplify.   [1.8]

7. $5x - (3x - 1)$

8. $3[4n - 5(2n - 1)] - 3(n - 7)$

9. Graph on the number line: $-\frac{5}{2}$.   [1.4]

10. Factor: $6x + 4y + 8z$.   [1.2]

Solve.

11. $4x - 7 = 3x + 9$ [2.1]

12. $\frac{2}{3}t + 7 = 13$ [2.2]

13. $9(2a - 1) = 4$ [2.2]

14. $12 - 3(5x - 1) = x - 1$ [2.2]

15. $3(x + 1) - 2 = 8 - 5(x + 7)$ [2.2]

Solve each formula for the given letter.   [2.3]

16. $\frac{1}{2}x = 2yz$, for z

17. $4x - 9y = 1$, for y

18. $an = p - rn$, for n

19. Find decimal notation for 183%.   [2.4]

20. Find percent notation for $\frac{3}{8}$.   [2.4]

21. Graph on the number line: $t > -\frac{5}{2}$.   [2.6]

Solve. Write the answer in both set-builder notation and interval notation.   [2.6]

22. $4t + 10 \leq 2$

23. $8 - t > 5$

24. $4 < 10 - \dfrac{x}{5}$

25. $4(2n - 3) \leq 2(5n - 8)$

Solve.

26. The total attendance at NCAA basketball games for the 2009–2010 school year was 33 million. This was 31.25% less than the total attendance at NCAA football games during that year. What was the total attendance at NCAA football games during the 2009–2010 school year?   [2.4]

Source: NCAA

27. The wavelength w, in meters per cycle, of a musical note is given by

$$w = \frac{r}{f},$$

where r is the speed of the sound, in meters per second, and f is the frequency, in cycles per second. The speed of sound in air is 344 m/sec. What is the wavelength of a note whose frequency in air is 24 cycles per second?   [2.3]

28. A 24-ft ribbon is cut into two pieces. One piece is 6 ft longer than the other. How long are the pieces?   [2.5]

29. Ariel has budgeted an average of $65 per month for bus fares. For the first five months of the year, she has spent $88, $15, $125, $50, and $60. How much can Ariel spend in the sixth month without exceeding her average bus-fare budget?   [2.7]

30. In 2010, about 285 million people had diabetes. The International Diabetes Foundation predicts that by 2030, 438 million people may have the disease. By what percent would the number of people with diabetes increase?   [2.5]

31. The second angle of a triangle is twice as large as the first. The third angle is 5° more than four times the first. Find the measure of the largest angle.   [2.5]

32. The length of a rectangular frame is 53 cm. For what widths would the perimeter be greater than 160 cm?   [2.7]

Synthesis

33. Simplify:

$$t - \{t - [3t - (2t - t) - t] - 4t\} - t.$$ [1.8]

34. Solve: $3|n| + 10 = 25$.   [2.2]

35. Lindy sold her Fender acoustic guitar on eBay using iSold It™. The iSold It™ location she used charges 35% of the first $500 of the selling price and 20% of the amount over $500. After these charges were deducted from the selling price, she received $745. For how much did her guitar sell?   [2.4], [2.5]

Introduction to Graphing

MONTH	NUMBER OF APPS DOWNLOADED PER DEVICE
October 2008	10
April 2009	25
October 2009	33
April 2010	45
October 2010	55
January 2011	63

Source: Based on data from www.asymco.com

We Love Our Apps!

In only 454 days, developers uploaded 100,000 iPad apps. And users are downloading the apps even faster. Only 31 months after the iTunes store began selling apps, users had downloaded 10 billion of them. Although the data in the table above shows only apps sold in the iTunes store, apps for other devices are also being downloaded at an increasing rate. Since the number of devices owned is also increasing, industry analysts have asked whether the increase in the sales of apps is merely due to more people buying them. As the data above indicate, this is not the case. The actual number of apps *per device* is increasing as well. We can use these data to predict the number of apps downloaded per device in the future. (*See Example 8 in Section 3.7.*)

Source: PadGadget Apps Tracker and Apple App Store

I have always had a deep interest in mathematics, and this interest has helped me to become an effective software developer.

Krishnan, a computer programmer in both Dallas, Texas, and Hyderabad, India, uses math ranging from percentages and fractions to trigonometry and statistics when writing software and developing responsive, high-performance websites.

We now begin our study of graphing. First we examine graphs as they commonly appear in newspapers or magazines and develop terminology. Following that, we graph certain equations and study the connection between rate and slope. We will also learn how graphs are used as a problem-solving tool in many applications.

Our work in this chapter centers on equations that contain two variables.

3.1 | Reading Graphs, Plotting Points, and Scaling Graphs

Problem Solving with Bar Graphs and Line Graphs   •   Points and Ordered Pairs   •   Numbering the Axes Appropriately

Today's print and electronic media make almost constant use of graphs. In this section, we consider problem solving with bar graphs and line graphs. Then we examine graphs that use a coordinate system.

Problem Solving with Bar Graphs and Line Graphs

A *bar graph* is a convenient way of showing comparisons. In every bar graph, certain categories, such as levels of education in the example below, are paired with certain numbers.

Study Skills

To Err Is Human
Most students who are successful in this course work in pencil. We all make mistakes and by using pencil and eraser we are more willing to admit to ourselves that something needs to be rewritten. Try working with a pencil and eraser if you aren't doing so already.

EXAMPLE 1 *Earnings.* The bar graph below shows median weekly earnings for full-time wage and salary workers ages 25 and older.
Source: U.S. Census Bureau

Studying Can Pay

Source: U.S. Bureau of Labor Statistics

a) Keagan plans to earn an associate's degree. What is the median income for workers with that level of education?

b) Isabella would like to make at least $1000 per week. What level of education should she pursue?

SOLUTION

a) Level of education is shown on the horizontal scale of the graph. We locate "associate's degree" and go to the top of that bar. Then we move horizontally from the top of the bar to the vertical scale, which shows earnings. We read there that Keagan can expect to make about $750 per week.

1. Use the bar graph in Example 1 to estimate by how much the median weekly earnings of a high school graduate exceeds that of a person who did not earn a high school diploma.

b) By moving up the vertical scale to $1000 and then moving horizontally, we see that the first bar to reach a height of $1000 or higher corresponds to a bachelor's degree. Thus Isabella should pursue a bachelor's, master's, doctoral, or professional degree in order to make at least $1000 per week.

YOUR TURN

EXAMPLE 2 *Exercise and Pulse Rate.* The following *line graph* shows the relationship between a person's resting pulse rate and the number of months of regular exercise.* Note that the symbol ⌇ is used to indicate that counting on the vertical scale begins at 50.

Since there are no points on the graph for pulse rates less than 50, that portion of the graph has been omitted. This is indicated by the symbol ⌇.

a) How many months of regular exercise are required to lower the pulse rate as much as possible?

b) How many months of regular exercise are needed to achieve a pulse rate of 65 beats per minute?

SOLUTION

a) The lowest point on the graph occurs above the number 6. Thus, after 6 months of regular exercise, the pulse rate is lowered as much as possible.

b) To determine how many months of exercise are needed to lower a person's resting pulse rate to 65, we locate 65 midway between 60 and 70 on the vertical scale. From that location, we move right until the line is reached. At that point, we move down to the horizontal scale and read the number of months required, as shown.

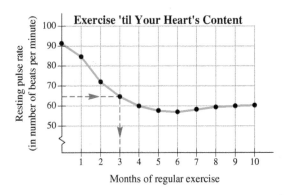

2. Use the graph in Example 2 to determine how many months of regular exercise are required before the resting pulse rate begins to rise.

The pulse rate is 65 beats per minute after 3 months of regular exercise.

YOUR TURN

*Data from *Body Clock* by Dr. Martin Hughes (New York: Facts on File, Inc.), p. 60.

Points and Ordered Pairs

The line graph in Example 2 contains a collection of points. Each point pairs up a number of months of exercise with a pulse rate. To create such a graph, we **graph**, or **plot**, pairs of numbers on a plane. This is done using two perpendicular number lines called **axes** (pronounced "ak-sēz"; singular, **axis**). The point at which the axes cross is called the **origin**. Arrows on the axes indicate the positive directions.

Consider the pair $(3, 4)$. The numbers in such a pair are called **coordinates**. The **first coordinate** in this case is 3 and the **second coordinate** is 4.* To plot, or graph, $(3, 4)$, we start at the origin, move horizontally to the 3, move up vertically 4 units, and then make a "dot." Thus, $(3, 4)$ is located above 3 on the first axis and to the right of 4 on the second axis.

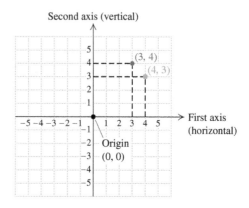

The point $(4, 3)$ is also plotted in the figure above. Note that $(3, 4)$ and $(4, 3)$ are different points. For this reason, coordinate pairs are called **ordered pairs**— the order in which the numbers appear is important.

EXAMPLE 3   Plot the point $(-3, 4)$.

SOLUTION   The first number, -3, is negative. Starting at the origin, we move 3 units in the negative horizontal direction (3 units to the left). The second number, 4, is positive, so we move 4 units in the positive vertical direction (up). The point $(-3, 4)$ is above -3 on the first axis and to the left of 4 on the second axis.

3. Plot the point $(-2, -4)$.

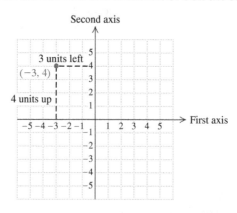

YOUR TURN

To find the coordinates of a point, we see how far to the right or left of the origin the point is and how far above or below the origin it is. Note that the coordinates of the origin itself are $(0, 0)$.

---

*The first coordinate is called the *abscissa* and the second coordinate is called the *ordinate*. The plane is called the *Cartesian coordinate plane* after the French mathematician René Descartes (1595–1650).

EXAMPLE 4   Find the coordinates of points A, B, C, D, E, F, and G.

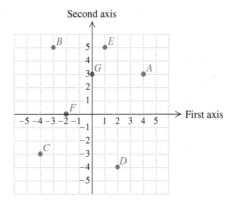

4. Find the coordinates of point P.

SOLUTION   Point A is 4 units to the right of the origin and 3 units above the origin. Its coordinates are $(4, 3)$. The coordinates of the other points are as follows:

B: $(-3, 5)$; C: $(-4, -3)$; D: $(2, -4)$;

E: $(1, 5)$; F: $(-2, 0)$; G: $(0, 3)$.

YOUR TURN

The variables x and y are commonly used when graphing on a plane. Coordinates of ordered pairs are often labeled

(x-coordinate, y-coordinate).

The first, or horizontal, axis is labeled the x-axis, and the second, or vertical, axis is labeled the y-axis.

The horizontal axis and the vertical axis divide the plane into four regions, or **quadrants**, as indicated by Roman numerals in the figure below. Note that the point $(-4, 5)$ is in the second quadrant and the point $(5, -5)$ is in the fourth quadrant. The points $(3, 0)$ and $(0, 1)$ are on the axes and are not considered to be in any quadrant.

Second quadrant:
First coordinate negative, second coordinate positive:
$(-, +)$

First quadrant:
Both coordinates positive:
$(+, +)$

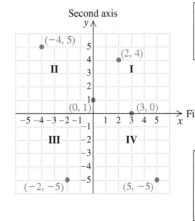

Third quadrant:
Both coordinates negative:
$(-, -)$

Fourth quadrant:
First coordinate positive, second coordinate negative:
$(+, -)$

Student Notes

The scale on the horizontal axis may be different from the scale on the vertical axis. Within each axis, however, the number of units each mark represents must be constant.

Numbering the Axes Appropriately

We draw only part of the plane when we create a graph. Although it is standard to show the origin and parts of all quadrants, as in the graphs in Examples 3 and 4, for some applications it may be more practical to show a different portion of the plane. Note, too, that on the graphs in Examples 3 and 4, the marks on the axes are one unit apart. In this case, we say that the **scale** of each axis is 1. Often it is necessary to use a different scale on one or both of the axes.

Technology Connection

The portion of the coordinate plane shown by a graphing calculator is called a **viewing window**. We indicate the **dimensions** of the window by setting a minimum x-value, a maximum x-value, a minimum y-value, and a maximum y-value. The **scale** by which we count must also be chosen. Window settings are often abbreviated in the form [L, R, B, T], with the letters representing **L**eft, **R**ight, **B**ottom, and **T**op endpoints. The window $[-10, 10, -10, 10]$ is called the **standard viewing window**. On most graphing calculators, a standard viewing window can be set using an option in the ZOOM menu.

To set up a $[-100, 100, -5, 5]$ window, we press WINDOW and use the following settings. A scale of 10 for the x-axis is large enough for the marks on the x-axis to be distinct.

```
WINDOW
  Xmin=-100
  Xmax=100
  Xscl=10
  Ymin=-5
  Ymax=5
  Yscl=1
  Xres=1
```

When GRAPH is pressed, a graph extending from -100 to 100 along the x-axis (counted by 10's) and from -5 to 5 along the y-axis appears. When the arrow keys are pressed, a cursor can be moved, its coordinates appearing at the bottom of the window.

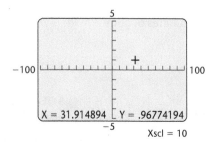

Set up the following viewing windows, choosing an appropriate scale for each axis. Then move the cursor and practice reading coordinates.

1. $[-10, 10, -10, 10]$
2. $[-5, 5, 0, 100]$
3. $[-1, 1, -0.1, 0.1]$

EXAMPLE 5   Use a grid 10 squares wide and 10 squares high to plot $(-34, 450)$, $(48, 95)$ and $(10, -200)$.

SOLUTION   Since x-coordinates vary from a low of -34 to a high of 48, the 10 horizontal squares must span $48 - (-34)$, or 82 units. Because 82 is not a multiple of 10, we round *up* to the next multiple of 10, which is 90. Dividing 90 by 10, we find that if each square is 9 units wide (has a scale of 9), we could represent all the x-values. However, since it is more convenient to count by 10's, we will instead use a scale of 10. Starting at 0, we count backward to -40 and forward to 60.

This is how we will arrange the x-axis.

There is more than one correct way to cover the values from -34 to 48 using 10 increments. For instance, we could have counted from -60 to 90, using a scale of 15. In general, we try to use the smallest range and scale that will cover the given coordinates. Scales that are multiples of 2, 5, or 10 are especially convenient. The numbering always begins at the origin.

Since we must be able to show y-values from -200 to 450, the 10 vertical squares must span $450 - (-200)$, or 650 units. For convenience, we round 650 *up* to 700 and then divide by 10: $700 \div 10 = 70$. Using 70 as the scale, we count *down* from 0 until we pass -200 and *up* from 0 until we pass 450, as shown at left.

Next, we combine our work to draw a graph in which the x-axis extends from -40 to 60 with a scale of 10 and the y-axis extends from -210 to 490 with a scale of 70. To correctly locate the axes on the grid, we must see that the two 0's coincide

This is how we will arrange the y-axis.

Chapter Resource:
Collaborative Activity, p. 222

where the axes cross. Finally, once the graph is numbered, we plot the points as shown.

5. Use a grid 10 squares wide and 10 squares high to plot $(15, -2)$, $(3, 60)$, and $(-20, 12)$. Scales may vary.

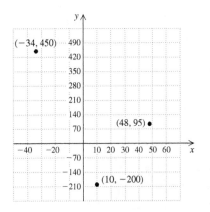

Each axis can have its own scale, as shown here.

YOUR TURN

3.1 EXERCISE SET

FOR EXTRA HELP

MyMathLab® Math XL
PRACTICE   WATCH   READ   REVIEW

Vocabulary and Reading Check

Match the letter from the graph with the most appropriate term. Not all letters will be used.

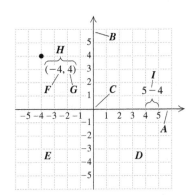

1. ____ Third quadrant

2. ____ Origin

3. ____ Second coordinate

4. ____ y-axis

5. ____ Ordered pair

6. ____ Scale

Concept Reinforcement

In each of Exercises 7–10, match the set of coordinates with the graph below that would be the best for plotting the points.

7. ____ $(-9, 3)$, $(-2, -1)$, $(4, 5)$

8. ____ $(-2, -1)$, $(1, 5)$, $(7, 3)$

9. ____ $(-2, -9)$, $(2, 1)$, $(4, -6)$

10. ____ $(-2, -1)$, $(-9, 3)$, $(-4, -6)$

a)

b)

c)

d)

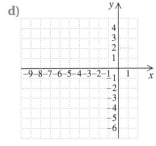

Problem Solving with Bar Graphs and Line Graphs

Driving under the Influence. *A blood-alcohol level of 0.08% or higher makes driving illegal in the United States. The following bar graph shows how many drinks a person of a certain weight would need to consume in 1 hr in order to achieve a blood-alcohol level of 0.08%. Note that a 12-oz beer, a 5-oz glass of wine, or a cocktail containing $1\frac{1}{2}$ oz of distilled liquor all count as one drink.*

Source: Adapted from soberup.com and vsa.vassar.edu/~source/drugs/alcohol.html

Friends Don't Let Friends Drive Drunk

11. Approximately how many drinks would a 100-lb person have consumed in 1 hr to reach a blood-alcohol level of 0.08%?

12. Approximately how many drinks would a 160-lb person have consumed in 1 hr to reach a blood-alcohol level of 0.08%?

13. What can you conclude about the weight of someone who has consumed 3 drinks in 1 hr without reaching a blood-alcohol level of 0.08%?

14. What can you conclude about the weight of someone who has consumed 4 drinks in 1 hr without reaching a blood-alcohol level of 0.08%?

DVD Spending. *The following line graph shows U.S. consumer spending on the rental and purchase of DVDs.*

Home Entertainment

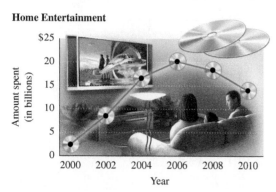

Source: The Digital Entertainment Group

15. Approximately how much was spent on DVDs in 2004?

16. Approximately how much was spent on DVDs in 2010?

17. In what year was approximately $2.5 billion spent on DVDs?

18. In what two years was approximately $14 billion spent on DVDs?

19. In what year was the most money spent on DVDs?

20. In what year or years did consumers spend less than $10 billion on DVDs?

Points and Ordered Pairs

Plot each group of points.

21. $(1, 2)$, $(-2, 3)$, $(4, -1)$, $(-5, -3)$, $(4, 0)$, $(0, -2)$

22. $(-2, -4)$, $(4, -3)$, $(5, 4)$, $(-1, 0)$, $(-4, 4)$, $(0, 5)$

23. $(4, 4)$, $(-2, 4)$, $(5, -3)$, $(-5, -5)$, $(0, 4)$, $(0, -4)$, $(-4, 0)$, $(0, 0)$

24. $(2, 5)$, $(-1, 3)$, $(3, -2)$, $(-2, -4)$, $(0, 0)$, $(0, -5)$, $(5, 0)$, $(-5, 0)$

25. *Text Messaging.* Listed below are estimates of the number of text messages sent in the United States. Make a line graph of the data.

Year	Number of Monthly Text Messages (in billions)
2005	7
2006	8
2007	30
2008	107
2009	153
2010	188

Source: CTIA—The Wireless Association®

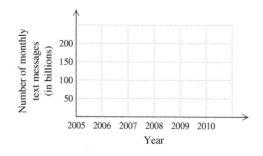

26. *Telephone Bill.* Listed below is the average local monthly wireless phone bill in the United States for various years. Make a line graph of the data, listing years on the horizontal scale.

Year	Average Local Monthly Wireless Bill
1990	$80.90
1994	56.21
1998	39.43
2002	48.40
2006	50.56
2010	47.21

Source: CTIA—The Wireless Association®

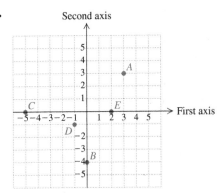

In Exercises 27–30, find the coordinates of points A, B, C, D, and E.

27.

28.

29.

30.

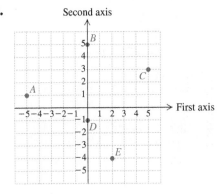

In which quadrant or on which axis is each point located?

31. $(7, -2)$ **32.** $(-1, -4)$ **33.** $(-4, -3)$

34. $(1, -5)$ **35.** $(0, -3)$ **36.** $(6, 0)$

37. $(-4.9, 8.3)$ **38.** $(7.5, 2.9)$ **39.** $\left(-\frac{5}{2}, 0\right)$

40. $(0, 2.8)$ **41.** $(160, 2)$ **42.** $\left(-\frac{1}{2}, 2000\right)$

43. In which quadrants are the first coordinates positive?

44. In which quadrants are the second coordinates negative?

45. In which quadrants do both coordinates have the same sign?

46. In which quadrants do the first and second coordinates have opposite signs?

Numbering the Axes Appropriately

In Exercises 47–56, use a grid 10 squares wide and 10 squares tall to plot the given coordinates. Choose your scale carefully. Scales may vary.

47. $(-75, 5), (-18, -2), (9, -4)$

48. $(-13, 3), (48, -1), (62, -4)$

49. $(-1, 83), (-5, -14), (5, 37)$

50. $(2, -79), (4, -25), (-4, 12)$

51. $(-10, -4), (-16, 7), (3, 15)$

52. $(5, -16), (-7, -4), (12, 3)$

53. $(-100, -5), (350, 20), (800, 37)$

54. $(750, -8), (-150, 17), (400, 32)$

55. $(-83, 491), (-124, -95), (54, -238)$

56. $(738, -89), (-49, -6), (-165, 53)$

57. The following graph was included in a mailing sent by Agway® to their oil customers in 2000. What information is missing from the graph and why is the graph misleading?

Residential Fuel Oil and Natural Gas Prices

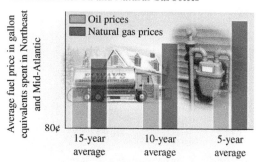

Source: Energy Research Center Inc. *3/1/99–2/29/00

58. What do all points plotted on the vertical axis of a graph have in common?

Skill Review

Simplify.

59. $-\frac{1}{2} + \frac{1}{3}$ [1.5]

60. $-2.6 - 9.1$ [1.6]

61. $3(-40)$ [1.7]

62. $-100 \div (-20)$ [1.7]

63. $(-1)(-2)(-3)(-4)$ [1.7]

64. $3 + (-4) + (-6) + 10$ [1.5]

Synthesis

65. Describe what the result would be if the first and second coordinates of every point in the following graph of an arrow were interchanged.

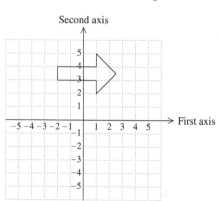

66. The graph accompanying Example 2 flattens out. Why do you think this occurs?

67. In which quadrant(s) could a point be located if its coordinates are opposites of each other?

68. In which quadrant(s) could a point be located if its coordinates are reciprocals of each other?

69. The points $(-1, 1), (4, 1),$ and $(4, -5)$ are three vertices of a rectangle. Find the coordinates of the fourth vertex.

70. The pairs $(-2, -3), (-1, 2),$ and $(4, -3)$ can serve as three (of four) vertices for three different parallelograms. Find the fourth vertex of each parallelogram.

71. Graph eight points such that the sum of the coordinates in each pair is 7. Answers may vary.

72. Find the perimeter of a rectangle if three of its vertices are $(5, -2), (-3, -2),$ and $(-3, 3)$.

73. Find the area of a triangle whose vertices have coordinates $(0, 9), (0, -4),$ and $(5, -4)$.

Sorting Solid Waste. Circle graphs, or pie charts, are often used to show what percent of the whole each item in a group represents. Use the following pie chart to answer Exercises 74–77.

Sorting Solid Waste

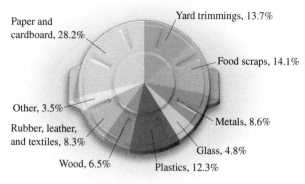

Source: U.S. Environmental Protection Agency

74. In 2009, Americans generated 243 million tons of waste. How much of the waste was plastic?

75. In 2009, the average American generated 4.3 lb of waste per day. How much of that was paper and cardboard?

76. Americans are recycling about 25.5% of all glass that is in the waste stream. How much glass did Americans recycle in 2009? (See Exercise 74.)

77. Americans are recycling about 59.9% of all yard trimmings. What amount of yard trimmings did the average American recycle per day in 2009? (Use the information in Exercise 75.)

Coordinates on the Globe. *Coordinates can also be used to describe the location on a sphere: 0° latitude is the equator and 0° longitude is a line from the North Pole to the South Pole through France and Algeria. In the following figure, hurricane Clara is at a point about 260 mi northwest of Bermuda near latitude 36.0° North, longitude 69.0° West.*

78. Approximate the latitude and the longitude of Bermuda.

79. Approximate the latitude and the longitude of Lake Okeechobee.

80. In the *Star Trek* science-fiction series, a three-dimensional coordinate system is used to locate objects in space. If the center of a planet is used as the origin, how many "quadrants" will exist? Why? If possible, sketch a three-dimensional coordinate system and label each "quadrant."

 81. *Research.* Find the average monthly wireless phone bill in the United States for the most recent year. (See Exercise 26.) Extend the line graph in Exercise 26 to include this information. How would you describe the trends shown by this graph?

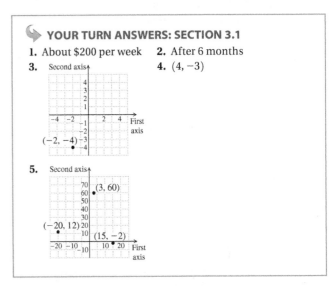

YOUR TURN ANSWERS: SECTION 3.1

1. About $200 per week   **2.** After 6 months
3. (graph)   **4.** $(4, -3)$
5. (graph)

PREPARE TO MOVE ON

Solve for y. [2.3]

1. $5y = 2x$ **2.** $2y = -3x$

3. $x - y = 8$ **4.** $2x + 5y = 10$

5. $5x - 8y = 1$

3.2 Graphing Linear Equations

Solutions of Equations   ▪   Graphing Linear Equations   ▪   Applications

Not only do graphs help us to visualize data, but they can also be used to represent solutions of equations.

Solutions of Equations

When an equation contains two variables, solutions are ordered pairs. Each number in the pair replaces a letter in the equation. Unless stated otherwise, the first number in each pair replaces the variable that occurs first alphabetically.

EXAMPLE 1 Determine whether each of the following pairs is a solution of $4b - 3a = 22$: **(a)** $(2, 7)$; **(b)** $(1, 6)$.

Student Notes

It is sometimes—but not always—necessary to use parentheses when substituting for a variable. It is always safe to do so, and developing the habit of using parentheses when substituting may reduce errors.

1. Determine whether the ordered pair $(2, -3)$ is a solution of $6c - d = 15$.

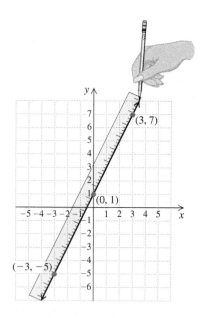

2. Show that the pairs $(2, -3)$ and $(0, -5)$ are solutions of $x - y = 5$. Then graph the two points to find another pair that is a solution.

SOLUTION

a) We substitute 2 for a and 7 for b (alphabetical order of variables):

$$\begin{array}{c|c} 4b - 3a = 22 \\ \hline 4(7) - 3(2) & 22 \\ 28 - 6 & \\ 22 \stackrel{?}{=} 22 & \text{TRUE} \end{array}$$

Since $22 = 22$ is *true*, the pair $(2, 7)$ *is* a solution.

b) In this case, we replace a with 1 and b with 6:

$$\begin{array}{c|c} 4b - 3a = 22 \\ \hline 4(6) - 3(1) & 22 \\ 24 - 3 & \\ 21 \stackrel{?}{=} 22 & \text{FALSE} \qquad 21 \neq 22 \end{array}$$

Since $21 = 22$ is *false*, the pair $(1, 6)$ is *not* a solution.

YOUR TURN

EXAMPLE 2 Show that the pairs $(3, 7)$, $(0, 1)$, and $(-3, -5)$ are solutions of $y = 2x + 1$. Then graph the three points to find another pair that is a solution.

SOLUTION To show that a pair is a solution, we substitute, replacing x with the first coordinate and y with the second coordinate of each pair:

$$\begin{array}{c|c} y = 2x + 1 \\ \hline 7 & 2 \cdot 3 + 1 \\ & 6 + 1 \\ 7 \stackrel{?}{=} 7 & \text{TRUE} \end{array} \qquad \begin{array}{c|c} y = 2x + 1 \\ \hline 1 & 2 \cdot 0 + 1 \\ & 0 + 1 \\ 1 \stackrel{?}{=} 1 & \text{TRUE} \end{array} \qquad \begin{array}{c|c} y = 2x + 1 \\ \hline -5 & 2(-3) + 1 \\ & -6 + 1 \\ -5 \stackrel{?}{=} -5 & \text{TRUE} \end{array}$$

In each of the three cases, the substitution results in a true equation. Thus the pairs $(3, 7)$, $(0, 1)$, and $(-3, -5)$ are all solutions. We graph them as shown at left.

Note that the three points appear to "line up." Will other points that line up with these points also represent solutions of $y = 2x + 1$? To find out, we use a ruler and draw a line passing through $(-3, -5)$, $(0, 1)$, and $(3, 7)$.

The line appears to pass through $(2, 5)$. Let's check to see if this pair is a solution of $y = 2x + 1$:

$$\begin{array}{c|c} y = 2x + 1 \\ \hline 5 & 2 \cdot 2 + 1 \\ & 4 + 1 \\ 5 \stackrel{?}{=} 5 & \text{TRUE} \end{array}$$

We see that $(2, 5)$ *is* a solution. In fact, any point on this line represents a solution of $y = 2x + 1$. The line is called the *graph* of the equation and it represents *all* solutions of the equation.

YOUR TURN

SOLUTIONS OF EQUATIONS IN TWO VARIABLES

- Solutions of equations in two variables are ordered pairs.
- Numbers in ordered pairs replace variables in equations in alphabetical order (unless stated otherwise).
- To graph an equation is to make a drawing that represents its solutions.
- Every solution of an equation is represented by a point on its graph, and every point on the graph of an equation represents a solution.

Graphing Linear Equations

Equations like $y = 2x + 1$ or $4b - 3a = 22$ are said to be **linear** because the **graph** of each equation is a line. In general, any equation that can be written in the form $y = mx + b$ or $Ax + By = C$ (where m, b, A, B, and C are constants and A and B are not both 0) is linear.

Linear equations can be graphed as follows.

TO GRAPH A LINEAR EQUATION

1. Select a value for one coordinate and calculate the corresponding value of the other coordinate. Form an ordered pair. This pair is one solution of the equation.
2. Repeat step (1) to find a second ordered pair. A third ordered pair should be found to use as a check.
3. Plot the ordered pairs and draw a straight line passing through the points. The line represents all solutions of the equation.

EXAMPLE 3   Graph: $y = -3x + 1$.

SOLUTION   Since $y = -3x + 1$ is in the form $y = mx + b$, the equation is linear and the graph is a straight line. We select a convenient value for x, compute y, and form an ordered pair. Then we repeat the process for other choices of x.

If $x = 2$,   then $y = -3 \cdot 2 + 1 = -5$,   and $(2, -5)$ is a solution.

If $x = 0$,   then $y = -3 \cdot 0 + 1 = 1$,   and $(0, 1)$ is a solution.

If $x = -1$,   then $y = -3(-1) + 1 = 4$,   and $(-1, 4)$ is a solution.

Results are often listed in a table, as shown below. The points corresponding to each pair are then plotted.

Calculate ordered pairs.

$$y = -3x + 1$$

x	y	(x, y)
2	−5	(2, −5)
0	1	(0, 1)
−1	4	(−1, 4)

(1) Choose x.
(2) Compute y.
(3) Form the pair (x, y).
(4) Plot the points.

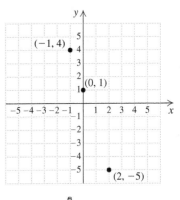

Plot the points.

Note that all three points line up. If they didn't, we would know that we had made a mistake, because the equation is linear. When only two points are plotted, an error is more difficult to detect.

Draw the graph.

Finally, we use a ruler or other straight-edge to draw a line. We add arrowheads to the ends of the line to indicate that it extends indefinitely beyond the edge of the grid drawn. Every point on the line represents a solution of $y = -3x + 1$.

3. Graph: $y = -2x + 3$.

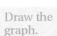 YOUR TURN

EXPLORING 🔍 THE CONCEPT

In Example 4, we graphed $y = 2x - 3$. Try graphing it again using different values for x.

1. Complete the table below.
2. Plot the points on graph paper and draw the graph.
3. Does the choice of x-values affect the graph?

x	y	(x, y)
-1		
2		
3		

ANSWERS

1. y: $-5, 1, 3$; (x, y): $(-1, -5), (2, 1), (3, 3)$
2. Same graph as in Example 4
3. No

4. Graph: $y = 3x - 1$.

_____ 🔁 YOUR TURN

EXAMPLE 4 Graph: $y = 2x - 3$.

SOLUTION We select some convenient x-values and compute y-values.

If $x = 0$, then $y = 2 \cdot 0 - 3 = -3$, and $(0, -3)$ is a solution.
If $x = 1$, then $y = 2 \cdot 1 - 3 = -1$, and $(1, -1)$ is a solution.
If $x = 4$, then $y = 2 \cdot 4 - 3 = 5$, and $(4, 5)$ is a solution.

$$y = 2x - 3$$

x	y	(x, y)
0	-3	$(0, -3)$
1	-1	$(1, -1)$
4	5	$(4, 5)$

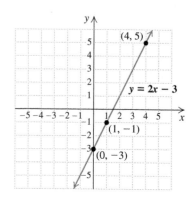

EXAMPLE 5 Graph: $4x + 2y = 12$.

SOLUTION To form ordered pairs, we can replace either variable with a number and then calculate the other coordinate:

If $y = 0$, we have
$$4x + 2 \cdot 0 = 12$$
$$4x = 12$$
$$x = 3,$$

so $(3, 0)$ is a solution.

If $x = 0$, we have
$$4 \cdot 0 + 2y = 12$$
$$2y = 12$$
$$y = 6,$$

so $(0, 6)$ is a solution.

If $y = 2$, we have
$$4x + 2 \cdot 2 = 12$$
$$4x + 4 = 12$$
$$4x = 8$$
$$x = 2,$$

so $(2, 2)$ is a solution.

$$4x + 2y = 12$$

x	y	(x, y)
3	0	$(3, 0)$
0	6	$(0, 6)$
2	2	$(2, 2)$

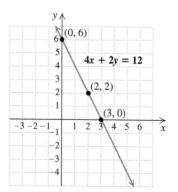

5. Graph: $2x + 3y = 6$.

_____ 🔁 YOUR TURN

Note that in Examples 3 and 4 the variable y is isolated on one side of the equation. This generally simplifies calculations, so it is important to be able to solve for y before graphing.

EXAMPLE 6 Graph $3y = 2x$ by first solving for y.

SOLUTION To isolate y, we divide both sides by 3, or multiply both sides by $\frac{1}{3}$:

$$3y = 2x$$

$$\tfrac{1}{3} \cdot 3y = \tfrac{1}{3} \cdot 2x \qquad \text{Using the multiplication principle to}$$
$$\text{multiply both sides by } \tfrac{1}{3}$$

$$\left.\begin{array}{l} 1y = \tfrac{2}{3} \cdot x \\ y = \tfrac{2}{3}x. \end{array}\right\} \quad \text{Simplifying}$$

Because all the equations above are equivalent, we can use $y = \frac{2}{3}x$ to draw the graph of $3y = 2x$.

To graph $y = \frac{2}{3}x$, we can select x-values that are multiples of 3. This allows us to avoid fractions when corresponding y-values are computed.

$$\left.\begin{array}{ll} \text{If } x = 3, & \text{then } y = \tfrac{2}{3} \cdot 3 = 2. \\ \text{If } x = -3, & \text{then } y = \tfrac{2}{3}(-3) = -2. \\ \text{If } x = 6, & \text{then } y = \tfrac{2}{3} \cdot 6 = 4. \end{array}\right\} \quad \begin{array}{l} \text{Note that when multiples of 3 are} \\ \text{substituted for } x, \text{ the } y\text{-coordinates} \\ \text{are not fractions.} \end{array}$$

The following table lists these solutions. Next, we plot the points and see that they form a line. Finally, we draw and label the line.

$3y = 2x$, or $y = \frac{2}{3}x$

x	y	(x, y)
3	2	$(3, 2)$
-3	-2	$(-3, -2)$
6	4	$(6, 4)$

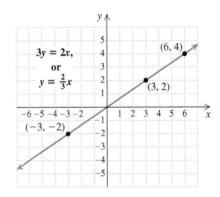

6. Graph $3y = 5x$ by first solving for y.

 YOUR TURN

EXAMPLE 7 Graph $x + 5y = -10$ by first solving for y.

SOLUTION We have

$$x + 5y = -10$$

$$5y = -x - 10 \qquad \text{Adding } -x \text{ to both sides}$$

$$y = \tfrac{1}{5}(-x - 10) \qquad \text{Multiplying both sides by } \tfrac{1}{5}$$

$$y = -\tfrac{1}{5}x - 2. \qquad \text{Using the distributive law}$$

CAUTION! It is very important to multiply *both* $-x$ and -10 by $\frac{1}{5}$.

Study Skills

Talk It Out

If you are finding it difficult to master a particular topic or concept, talk about it with a classmate. Verbalizing your questions about the material might help clarify it for you. If your classmate is also finding the material difficult, ask your instructor, a tutor, or another classmate for help.

Thus, $x + 5y = -10$ is equivalent to $y = -\frac{1}{5}x - 2$. If we now choose x-values that are multiples of 5, we can avoid fractions when calculating the corresponding y-values.

If $x = 5$,   then $y = -\frac{1}{5} \cdot 5 - 2 = -1 - 2 = -3$.

If $x = 0$,   then $y = -\frac{1}{5} \cdot 0 - 2 = 0 - 2 = -2$.

If $x = -5$, then $y = -\frac{1}{5}(-5) - 2 = 1 - 2 = -1$.

$x + 5y = -10$, or $y = -\frac{1}{5}x - 2$

x	y	(x, y)
5	−3	(5, −3)
0	−2	(0, −2)
−5	−1	(−5, −1)

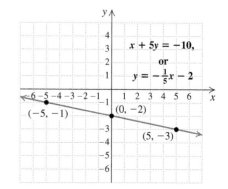

7. Graph $x + 2y = -6$ by first solving for y.

YOUR TURN

Applications

Linear equations appear in many real-life situations.

Engine Size (in liters)	Annual Idling Cost
1.8	$ 30
2.0	34
3.5	62
4.3	75
5.7	109
6.2	112

Source: U.S. Department of Energy, quoted in www.greenenergytimes.org, October 15, 2011

EXAMPLE 8   *Fuel Cost.*   The amount of fuel that an engine burns while idling depends on the size of the engine. The table at left lists the annual cost of idling for 5 min per day for various engine sizes. These costs are based on a gasoline price of $3.75 per gallon. The annual idling cost can be approximated by

$$c = 19a - 4,$$

where c is the annual cost of idling 5 min per day and a is the engine size, in liters. Graph the equation and then use the graph to estimate the annual idling cost for a 5.3-L engine.

SOLUTION   We graph the equation by selecting values for a and then calculating the associated values of c.

If $a = 2$,   then $c = 19(2) - 4 = 34$.

If $a = 4$,   then $c = 19(4) - 4 = 72$.

If $a = 6$,   then $c = 19(6) - 4 = 110$.

a	c
2	34
4	72
6	110

Because we are *selecting* values for a and *calculating* values for c, we represent a on the horizontal axis and c on the vertical axis. Counting by 0.5 horizontally and by 10 vertically will allow us to plot all three pairs, as shown on the left below.

8. Use the graph in Example 8 to estimate the annual cost of idling for 5 min per day for a 2.5-L engine.

Since the three points line up, our calculations are probably correct. We draw a line, as shown on the right above. We begin the line at $a = 1.8$, since that is the smallest engine size given in the table above. To estimate the idling cost for a 5.3-L engine, we locate the point on the line that is above 5.3 and then find the value on the c-axis that corresponds to that point. The idling cost for a 5.3-L engine is about $97.

YOUR TURN

CAUTION! When the coordinates of a point are read from a graph, as in Example 8, values should not be considered exact.

Many equations in two variables have graphs that are not straight lines. Three such *nonlinear* graphs are shown below. As before, each graph represents the solutions of the given equation.

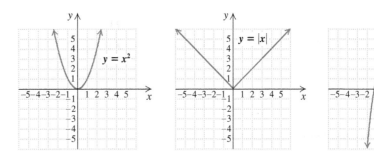

Technology Connection

Most graphing calculators require that y be alone on one side before the equation is entered. For example, to graph $5y + 4x = 13$, we would first solve for y. The student can check that solving for y yields $y = -\frac{4}{5}x + \frac{13}{5}$.

We press ⟨ Y= ⟩, enter $-\frac{4}{5}x + \frac{13}{5}$ as Y1, and press ⟨ GRAPH ⟩. The graph is shown here in the standard viewing window $[-10, 10, -10, 10]$.

$$y_1 = -\frac{4}{5}x + \frac{13}{5}$$

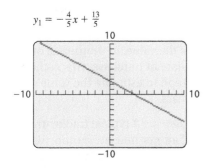

Using a graphing calculator, graph each of the following. Select the "standard" $[-10, 10, -10, 10]$ window.

1. $y = -5x + 6.5$
2. $y = 3x + 4.5$
3. $7y - 4x = 22$
4. $5y + 11x = -20$
5. $2y - x^2 = 0$
6. $y + x^2 = 8$

There are many graphing calculator apps available for mobile devices. These can also be used to graph equations and to study characteristics of graphs. The graph of $y = -\frac{4}{5}x + \frac{13}{5}$ is shown below in such an app.

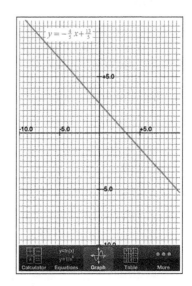

3.2 EXERCISE SET

FOR EXTRA HELP

MyMathLab® Math XL

PRACTICE   WATCH   READ   REVIEW

Vocabulary and Reading Check

Classify each of the following statements as either true or false.

1. A linear equation in two variables has at most one solution.

2. Every solution of $y = 3x - 7$ is an ordered pair.

3. The graph of $y = 3x - 7$ represents all solutions of the equation.

4. If a point is on the graph of $y = 3x - 7$, the corresponding ordered pair is a solution of the equation.

5. To find a solution of $y = 3x - 7$, we can choose any value for x and calculate the corresponding y-value.

6. The graph of every equation is a straight line.

Solutions of Equations

Determine whether each equation has the given ordered pair as a solution.

7. $y = 4x - 7$; $(2, 1)$

8. $y = 5x + 8$; $(0, 8)$

9. $3y + 4x = 19$; $(5, 1)$

10. $5x - 3y = 15$; $(0, 5)$

11. $4m - 5n = 7$; $(3, -1)$

12. $3q - 2p = -8$; $(1, -2)$

In Exercises 13–20, an equation and two ordered pairs are given. Show that each pair is a solution and graph the two pairs to find another solution. Answers may vary.

13. $y = x + 3$; $(-1, 2), (4, 7)$

14. $y = x - 2$; $(3, 1), (-2, -4)$

15. $y = \frac{1}{2}x + 3$; $(4, 5), (-2, 2)$

16. $y = \frac{1}{2}x - 1$; $(6, 2), (0, -1)$

17. $y + 3x = 7$; $(2, 1), (4, -5)$

18. $2y + x = 5$; $(-1, 3), (7, -1)$

19. $4x - 2y = 10$; $(0, -5), (4, 3)$

20. $6x - 3y = 3$; $(1, 1), (-1, -3)$

Graphing Linear Equations

Graph each equation.

21. $y = x + 1$

22. $y = x - 1$

23. $y = -x$

24. $y = x$

25. $y = 2x$

26. $y = -3x$

27. $y = 2x + 2$

28. $y = 3x - 2$

29. $y = -\frac{1}{2}x$

30. $y = \frac{1}{4}x$

31. $y = \frac{1}{3}x - 4$

32. $y = \frac{1}{2}x + 1$

33. $x + y = 4$

34. $x + y = -5$

35. $x - y = -2$

36. $y - x = 3$

37. $x + 2y = -6$

38. $x + 2y = 8$

39. $y = -\frac{2}{3}x + 4$

40. $y = \frac{3}{2}x + 1$

41. $4x = 3y$

42. $2x = 5y$

43. $5x - y = 0$

44. $3x - 5y = 0$

45. $6x - 3y = 9$

46. $8x - 4y = 12$

47. $6y + 2x = 8$

48. $8y + 2x = -4$

Applications

49. *Student Aid.* The average amount of financial aid a per undergraduate student can be approximated by
$$a = 0.2t + 3.1,$$
where a is in thousands of constant 2010 dollars and t is the number of years since 1996. Graph the equation and use the graph to estimate the average amount of financial aid per undergraduate student in 2012.

Source: Based on data from Trends in Student Aid 2011, College Board Advocacy and Policy Center

50. *Value of a Color Copier.* The value of Duplio-graphic's color copier is given by
$$v = -0.68t + 3.4,$$
where v is the value, in thousands of dollars, t years from the date of purchase. Graph the equation and use the graph to estimate the value of the copier after $2\frac{1}{2}$ years.

51. *Fuel Efficiency.* A typical tractor-trailer will move 18 tons of air per mile at 55 mph. Air resistance increases with speed, causing fuel efficiency to decrease at higher speeds. At highway speeds, a certain truck's fuel efficiency t, in miles per gallon (mpg), can be approximated by
$$t = -0.1s + 13.1,$$
where s is the speed of the truck, in miles per hour (mph). Graph the equation and then use the graph to estimate the fuel efficiency at 66 mph.

Source: Based on data from Kenworth Truck Co.

52. *Increasing Life Expectancy.* A smoker is 15 times more likely to die of lung cancer than a nonsmoker. An ex-smoker who stopped smoking t years ago is w times more likely to die of lung cancer than a nonsmoker, where

$$w = 15 - t.$$

Graph the equation and use the graph to estimate how much more likely it is for Sandy to die of lung cancer than Polly, if Polly never smoked and Sandy quit $2\frac{1}{2}$ years ago.

Source: Data from *Body Clock* by Dr. Martin Hughes, p. 60. New York: Facts on File, Inc.

53. *Photobook Pricing.* The price p, in dollars, of an 8-in. by 8-in. hardcover photobook is given by

$$p = 0.7n + 16,$$

where n is the number of pages in the photobook. Graph the equation and use the graph to estimate the price of a photobook containing 25 pages.

Source: www.shutterfly.com

54. *Value of Computer Software.* The value v of a shopkeeper's inventory software program, in hundreds of dollars, is given by

$$v = -\tfrac{3}{4}t + 6,$$

where t is the number of years since the shopkeeper first bought the program. Graph the equation and use the graph to estimate what the program is worth 4 years after it was first purchased.

55. *Apps.* In the first two years after the iPad was launched, the number of apps available for that device could be estimated by

$$a = 0.23d - 7,$$

where a is the number of apps, in thousands, and d is the number of days after the iPad was launched. Graph the equation and use the graph to estimate the number of apps available 400 days after the iPad was launched.

Source: Based on data from PadGadget Apps Tracker and Apple App Store

56. *Record Temperature Drop.* On January 22, 1943, the temperature T, in degrees Fahrenheit, in Spearfish, South Dakota, could be approximated by

$$T = -2m + 54,$$

where m is the number of minutes since 9:00 A.M. that morning. Graph the equation and use the graph to estimate the temperature at 9:15 A.M.

Source: Based on information from the National Oceanic Atmospheric Administration

57. *Cost of College.* The cost T, in hundreds of dollars, of tuition and fees at many community colleges can be approximated by

$$T = \tfrac{5}{4}c + 2,$$

where c is the number of credits for which a student registers. Graph the equation and use the graph to estimate the cost of tuition and fees when a student registers for 4 three-credit courses.

58. *Cost of College.* The total cost C, in thousands of constant 2011 dollars, of a year at a public two-year college can be approximated by

$$C = \tfrac{1}{8}t + 8.5,$$

where t is the number of years since 1997. Graph the equation and use the graph to predict the cost of a year at a public two-year college in 2014.

Source: Based on information in *Trends in College Pricing 2011*, College Board Advocacy and Policy Center

59. The equations $3x + 4y = 8$ and $y = -\tfrac{3}{4}x + 2$ are equivalent. Which equation would be easier to graph and why?

60. Suppose that a linear equation is graphed by plotting three points and that the three points line up. Does this *guarantee* that the equation is being correctly graphed? Why or why not?

Skill Review

Solve and check. [2.2]

61. $5x + 3(2 - x) = 12$

62. $3(y - 5) - 8y = 6$

Solve. [2.3]

63. $A = \dfrac{T + Q}{2}$, for Q

64. $pq + p = w$, for p

65. $Ax + By = C$, for y

66. $\dfrac{y - k}{m} = x - h$, for y

Synthesis

67. Janice consistently makes the mistake of plotting the x-coordinate of an ordered pair using the y-axis, and the y-coordinate using the x-axis. How will Janice's incorrect graph compare with the correct graph?

68. Explain how the graph in Example 8 can be used to determine the engine size for which the annual idling cost is $100.

69. *Bicycling.*   Long Beach Island in New Jersey is a long, narrow, flat island. For exercise, Laura routinely bikes to the northern tip of the island and back. Because of the steady wind, she uses one gear going north and another for her return. Laura's bike has 21 gears and the sum of the two gears used on her ride is always 24. Write and graph an equation that represents the different pairings of gears that Laura uses. Note that there are no fraction gears on a bicycle.

In Exercises 70–73, find an equation for each graph shown.

70.

71.

72.

73.

74. Translate to an equation:

   d dimes and n nickels total $1.75.

Then graph the equation and use the graph to determine three different combinations of dimes and nickels that total $1.75 (see also Exercise 87).

75. Translate to an equation:

   d $25 dinners and l $5 lunches total $225.

Then graph the equation and use the graph to determine three different combinations of lunches and dinners that total $225 (see also Exercise 87).

Use the suggested x-values $-3, -2, -1, 0, 1, 2,$ *and 3 to graph each equation.*

76. $y = |x|$ Aha! **77.** $y = -|x|$

Aha! **78.** $y = |x| - 2$ **79.** $y = x^2$

80. $y = x^2 + 1$

For Exercises 81–86, use a graphing calculator to graph the equation. Use a $[-10, 10, -10, 10]$ *window.*

81. $y = -2.8x + 3.5$

82. $y = 4.5x + 2.1$

83. $y = 2.8x - 3.5$

84. $y = -4.5x - 2.1$

85. $y = x^2 + 4x + 1$

86. $y = -x^2 + 4x - 7$

87. Study the graph in Exercises 74 and 75. Does *every* point on the graph represent a solution of the associated problem? Why or why not?

88. *Research.*   Find the size of the engine in your car or a friend's car. (See Example 8.)

   a) Use the results of Example 8 to estimate the annual cost of idling this engine for 5 min per day.

   b) The data in Example 8 were based on a gasoline price of $3.75 per gallon. Estimate the annual idling cost of this engine at current gasoline prices using the formula

   $x = c \cdot p \div 3.75,$

   where x is the current idling cost, c is the cost calculated in part (a), and p is the current gasoline price per gallon.

YOUR TURN ANSWERS: SECTION 3.2

1. Yes

2.

$x - y = 5$		$x - y = 5$	$(1, -4)$
$2 - (-3)$	5	$0 - (-5)$	5
$5 \overset{?}{=} 5$ TRUE		$5 \overset{?}{=} 5$ TRUE	

3.

4.

5.

6.

7.

8. About $44

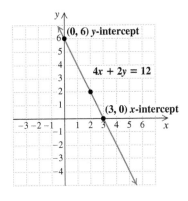

QUICK QUIZ: SECTIONS 3.1–3.2

1. Plot the points $(3, -2)$ and $(0, 4)$.   [3.1]

2. In which quadrant or on which axis is $(5, -9)$ located?   [3.1]

3. Determine whether the ordered pair $(-2, 4)$ is a solution of the equation $y = 2 - 2x$.   [3.2]

Graph each equation.   [3.2]

4. $y = 3x$ **5.** $4x - y = 1$

PREPARE TO MOVE ON

Solve and check.   [2.2]

1. $5x + 3 \cdot 0 = 12$ **2.** $3 \cdot 0 - 8y = 6$

3. $2 \cdot 5 + 8y = 3$ **4.** $-6x + 8 \cdot 1 = 1$

3.3   Graphing and Intercepts

Intercepts • Using Intercepts to Graph • Graphing Horizontal Lines or Vertical Lines

Unless a line is horizontal or vertical, it will cross both axes. Often, finding the points where a line crosses the axes provides a quick way of graphing linear equations.

Intercepts

To graph $4x + 2y = 12$, we can plot the points $(3, 0)$, $(0, 6)$, and $(2, 2)$ and then draw the line.

- The point at which a graph crosses the y-axis is called the **y-intercept**. In the figure shown here, the y-intercept is $(0, 6)$. **The x-coordinate of a y-intercept is always 0.**

- The point at which a graph crosses the x-axis is called the **x-intercept**. In the figure shown here, the x-intercept is $(3, 0)$. **The y-coordinate of an x-intercept is always 0.**

Some curves have more than one y-intercept or more than one x-intercept.

EXAMPLE 1   For the graph shown below, **(a)** give the coordinates of any x-intercepts and **(b)** give the coordinates of any y-intercepts.

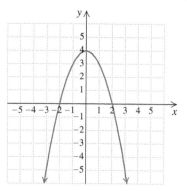

1. For the graph shown below, **(a)** give the coordinates of any x-intercepts and **(b)** give the coordinates of any y-intercepts.

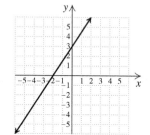

SOLUTION

a) The x-intercepts are the points at which the graph crosses the x-axis. For the graph shown, the x-intercepts are $(-2, 0)$ and $(2, 0)$.

b) The y-intercept is the point at which the graph crosses the y-axis. For the graph shown, the y-intercept is $(0, 4)$.

YOUR TURN

Using Intercepts to Graph

It is important to know how to locate the intercepts of a graph from the equation being graphed.

> **TO FIND INTERCEPTS**
>
> To find the y-intercept(s) of an equation's graph, replace x with 0 and solve for y.
>
> To find the x-intercept(s) of an equation's graph, replace y with 0 and solve for x.

EXAMPLE 2   Find the y-intercept and the x-intercept of the graph of $2x + 4y = 20$.

SOLUTION   To find the y-intercept, we let $x = 0$ and solve for y:

$$2 \cdot 0 + 4y = 20 \qquad \text{Replacing } x \text{ with } 0$$
$$4y = 20$$
$$y = 5.$$

Thus the y-intercept is $(0, 5)$.

To find the x-intercept, we let $y = 0$ and solve for x:

$$2x + 4 \cdot 0 = 20 \qquad \text{Replacing } y \text{ with } 0$$
$$2x = 20$$
$$x = 10.$$

2. Find the y-intercept and the x-intercept of the graph of $x + 3y = 6$.

Thus the x-intercept is $(10, 0)$.

YOUR TURN

Since two points are sufficient to graph a line, intercepts can be used to graph linear equations.

EXAMPLE 3 Graph $2x + 4y = 20$ using intercepts. Find a third point as a check.

SOLUTION In Example 2, we showed that the y-intercept is $(0, 5)$ and the x-intercept is $(10, 0)$. Before drawing a line, we plot a third point as a check. We substitute any convenient value for x and solve for y.

If we let $x = 5$, then

$$2 \cdot 5 + 4y = 20 \qquad \text{Substituting 5 for } x$$
$$10 + 4y = 20$$
$$4y = 10 \qquad \text{Subtracting 10 from both sides}$$
$$y = \tfrac{10}{4}, \text{ or } 2\tfrac{1}{2}. \qquad \text{Solving for } y; \left(5, 2\tfrac{1}{2}\right) \text{ must be on the graph.}$$

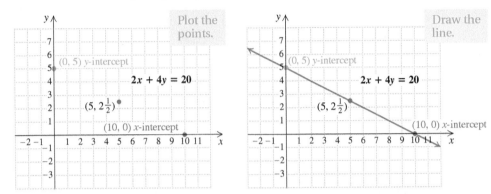

3. Graph $3x + 5y = 15$ using intercepts.

The point $\left(5, 2\tfrac{1}{2}\right)$ appears to line up with the intercepts, so our work is probably correct. To finish, we draw and label the line.

YOUR TURN

Note that when we solved for the y-intercept, we replaced x with 0 and simplified $2x + 4y = 20$ to $4y = 20$. Thus, to find the y-intercept, we can momentarily ignore the x-term and solve the remaining equation.

In a similar manner, when we solved for the x-intercept, we simplified $2x + 4y = 20$ to $2x = 20$. Thus, to find the x-intercept, we can momentarily ignore the y-term and then solve this remaining equation.

EXAMPLE 4 Graph $3x - 2y = 60$ using intercepts. Find a third point as a check.

SOLUTION To find the y-intercept, we let $x = 0$. This amounts to temporarily ignoring the x-term and then solving:

$$-2y = 60 \qquad \text{For } x = 0, \text{ we have } 3 \cdot 0 - 2y, \text{ or simply } -2y.$$
$$y = -30.$$

The y-intercept is $(0, -30)$.

To find the x-intercept, we let $y = 0$. This amounts to temporarily disregarding the y-term and then solving:

$$3x = 60 \qquad \text{For } y = 0, \text{ we have } 3x - 2 \cdot 0, \text{ or simply } 3x.$$
$$x = 20.$$

The x-intercept is $(20, 0)$.

To find a third point, we can replace x with 4 and solve for y:

$$3 \cdot 4 - 2y = 60 \qquad \text{Numbers other than 4 can be used for } x.$$
$$12 - 2y = 60$$
$$-2y = 48$$
$$y = -24. \qquad \text{This means that } (4, -24) \text{ is on the graph.}$$

Study Skills

Create Your Own Glossary
Understanding terminology is essential for success in any math course. Try writing your own glossary toward the back of your notebook. Often, just the act of writing out a word's definition can help you remember what the word means.

In order for us to graph all three points, the y-axis of our graph must go down to at least -30 and the x-axis must go up to at least 20. Using a scale of 5 units per square allows us to display both intercepts and $(4, -24)$, as well as the origin.

The point $(4, -24)$ appears to line up with the intercepts, so we draw and label the line, as shown below.

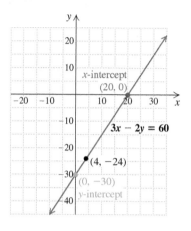

4. Graph $2x - 5y = 30$ using intercepts.

YOUR TURN

Technology Connection

When an equation is graphed using a graphing calculator, we may not always see both intercepts. For example, if $y = -0.8x + 17$ is graphed in the window $[-10, 10, -10, 10]$, neither intercept is visible, as shown in the graph on the left below.

To better view intercepts, we can change the window dimensions or we can zoom out. On many graphing calculator apps, we can zoom in or out using the touch screen. On a graphing calculator without a touch screen, the ZOOM feature allows us to reduce or magnify a graph or a portion of a graph. Before zooming, we must set the ZOOM *factors* in the memory of the ZOOM key. If we zoom out with factors set at 5, both intercepts are visible but the axes are heavily drawn, as shown in the graph in the middle below.

This suggests that the *scales* of the axes should be changed. To do this, we use the WINDOW menu and set Xscl to 5 and Yscl to 5. The resulting graph has tick marks 5 units apart and clearly shows both intercepts, as shown in the graph on the right below. Other choices for Xscl and Yscl can also be made.

Graph each equation so that both intercepts can be easily viewed. Zoom or adjust the window settings so that tick marks can be clearly seen on both axes.

1. $y = -0.72x - 15$ **2.** $y - 2.13x = 27$
3. $5x + 6y = 84$ **4.** $2x - 7y = 150$
5. $19x - 17y = 200$ **6.** $6x + 5y = 159$

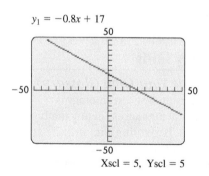

Graphing Horizontal Lines or Vertical Lines

The equations graphed in Examples 3 and 4 are in the form $Ax + By = C$. We have already stated that any equation in the form $Ax + By = C$ is linear, provided A and B are not both zero. What if A or B (but not both) is zero? We will find that when A is zero, there is no x-term and the graph is a horizontal line. We will also find that when B is zero, there is no y-term and the graph is a vertical line.

EXAMPLE 5 Graph: $y = 3$.

SOLUTION We can regard the equation $y = 3$ as $0 \cdot x + y = 3$. No matter what number we choose for x, we find that y must be 3 if the equation is to be solved. Consider the following table.

$$y = 3$$

Choose any number for x. ⟶

x	y	(x, y)
-2	3	$(-2, 3)$
0	3	$(0, 3)$
4	3	$(4, 3)$

y must be 3.

All pairs will have 3 as the y-coordinate.

When we plot $(-2, 3)$, $(0, 3)$, and $(4, 3)$ and connect the points, we obtain a horizontal line. Any pair of the form $(x, 3)$ is a solution, so the line is parallel to the x-axis with y-intercept $(0, 3)$. Note that the graph of $y = 3$ has no x-intercept.

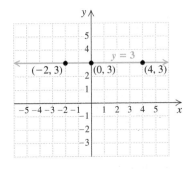

5. Graph: $y = 2$.

_____ ⟵ YOUR TURN

EXAMPLE 6 Graph: $x = -4$.

SOLUTION We can regard the equation $x = -4$ as $x + 0 \cdot y = -4$. We create a table with all -4's in the x-column.

Student Notes

Sometimes students draw horizontal lines when they should be drawing vertical lines and vice versa. To avoid this mistake, first locate the correct number on the axis whose label is given. Thus, to graph $x = 2$, we locate 2 on the x-axis and then draw a line perpendicular to that axis at that point. Note that the graph of $x = 2$ on a plane is a line, whereas the graph of $x = 2$ on a number line is a point.

$$x = -4$$

x must be -4. ⟶

x	y	(x, y)
-4	-5	$(-4, -5)$
-4	1	$(-4, 1)$
-4	3	$(-4, 3)$

Any number can be used for y.

All pairs will have -4 as the x-coordinate.

When we plot $(-4, -5)$, $(-4, 1)$, and $(-4, 3)$ and connect the points, we obtain a vertical line. Any ordered pair of the form $(-4, y)$ is a solution. The line is parallel to the y-axis with x-intercept $(-4, 0)$. Note that the graph of $x = -4$ has no y-intercept.

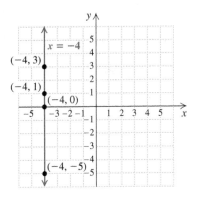

6. Graph: $x = -2$.

_____ YOUR TURN

LINEAR EQUATIONS IN ONE VARIABLE

The graph of $y = b$ is a horizontal line, with y-intercept $(0, b)$.

The graph of $x = a$ is a vertical line, with x-intercept $(a, 0)$.

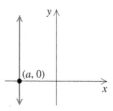

EXAMPLE 7   Write an equation for each graph.

a)

b)

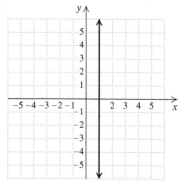

7. Write an equation for the following graph.

SOLUTION

a) Note that every point on the horizontal line passing through $(0, -2)$ has -2 as the y-coordinate. Thus the equation of the line is $y = -2$.

b) Note that every point on the vertical line passing through $(1, 0)$ has 1 as the x-coordinate. Thus the equation of the line is $x = 1$.

 YOUR TURN

3.3   EXERCISE SET

FOR EXTRA HELP

MyMathLab® Math XL

PRACTICE   WATCH   READ   REVIEW

Vocabulary and Reading Check

Choose the word from the following list that best completes each sentence. Words will be used more than once.

x-intercept
y-intercept

1. A horizontal line has a(n) _____.

2. A vertical line has a(n) _____.

3. To find a(n) _____, replace x with 0 and solve for y.

4. To find a(n) _____, replace y with 0 and solve for x.

5. The point $(-3, 0)$ could be a(n) _____ of a graph.

6. The point $(0, 7)$ could be a(n) _____ of a graph.

Concept Reinforcement

In each of Exercises 7–12, match the phrase with the most appropriate choice from the column on the right.

7. _____ A vertical line

8. _____ A horizontal line

9. _____ A y-intercept

10. _____ An x-intercept

11. _____ A third point as a check

12. _____ Use a scale of 10 units per square.

a) $2x + 5y = 100$

b) $(3, -2)$

c) $(1, 0)$

d) $(0, 2)$

e) $y = 3$

f) $x = -4$

Intercepts

*For Exercises 13–20, list **(a)** the coordinates of the y-intercept and **(b)** the coordinates of all x-intercepts.*

13.

14.

15.

16.

17.

18.

19.

20.

*For Exercises 21–30, list **(a)** the coordinates of any y-intercept and **(b)** the coordinates of any x-intercept. Do not graph.*

21. $3x + 5y = 15$

22. $2x + 7y = 14$

23. $9x - 2y = 36$

24. $10x - 3y = 60$

25. $-4x + 5y = 80$

26. $-5x + 6y = 100$

Aha! 27. $x = 12$

28. $y = 10$

29. $y = -9$

30. $x = -5$

Using Intercepts to Graph

Find the intercepts. Then graph.

31. $3x + 5y = 15$

32. $2x + y = 6$

33. $x + 2y = 4$

34. $2x + 5y = 10$

35. $-x + 2y = 8$

36. $-x + 3y = 9$

37. $3x + y = 9$

38. $2x - y = 8$

39. $y = 2x - 6$

40. $y = -3x + 6$

41. $5x - 10 = 5y$

42. $3x - 9 = 3y$

43. $2x - 5y = 10$

44. $2x - 3y = 6$

45. $6x + 2y = 12$

46. $4x + 5y = 20$

47. $4x + 3y = 16$

48. $3x + 2y = 8$

49. $2x + 4y = 1$

50. $3x - 6y = 1$

51. $5x - 3y = 180$

52. $10x + 7y = 210$

53. $y = -30 + 3x$

54. $y = -40 + 5x$

55. $-4x = 20y + 80$

56. $60 = 20x - 3y$

57. $y - 3x = 0$

58. $x + 2y = 0$

Graphing Horizontal Lines or Vertical Lines

Graph.

59. $y = 1$

60. $y = 4$

61. $x = 3$

62. $x = 6$

63. $y = -2$ **64.** $y = -4$

65. $x = -1$ **66.** $x = -6$

67. $y = -15$ **68.** $x = 20$

69. $y = 0$ **70.** $y = \frac{3}{2}$

71. $x = -\frac{5}{2}$ **72.** $x = 0$

73. $-4x = -100$ **74.** $12y = -360$

75. $35 + 7y = 0$ **76.** $-3x - 24 = 0$

Write an equation for each graph.

77.   **78.**

79.   **80.**

81.   **82.**

 83. Explain in your own words why the graph of $y = 8$ is a horizontal line.

84. Explain in your own words why the graph of $x = -4$ is a vertical line.

Skill Review

Translate to an algebraic expression.   [1.1]

85. 7 less than d

86. 5 more than w

87. The sum of 7 and four times a number

88. The product of 3 and a number

89. Twice the sum of two numbers

90. Half of the sum of two numbers

Synthesis

91. Describe what the graph of $x + y = C$ will look like for any choice of C.

92. If the graph of a linear equation has one point that is both the x-intercept and the y-intercept, what is that point? Why?

93. Write an equation for the x-axis.

94. Write an equation of the line parallel to the x-axis and passing through $(3, 5)$.

95. Write an equation of the line parallel to the y-axis and passing through $(-2, 7)$.

96. Find the coordinates of the point of intersection of the graphs of $y = x$ and $y = 6$.

97. Find the coordinates of the point of intersection of the graphs of the equations $x = -3$ and $y = 4$.

98. Write an equation of the line shown in Exercise 13.

99. Write an equation of the line shown in Exercise 16.

100. Find the value of C such that the graph of $3x + C = 5y$ has an x-intercept of $(-4, 0)$.

101. Find the value of C such that the graph of $4x = C - 3y$ has a y-intercept of $(0, -8)$.

102. For A and B nonzero, the graphs of $Ax + D = C$ and $By + D = C$ will be parallel to an axis. Explain why.

103. Find the x-intercept of the graph of $Ax + D = C$.

In Exercises 104–109, find the intercepts of each equation algebraically. Then adjust the window and scale so that the intercepts can be checked graphically with no further window adjustments.

104. $3x + 2y = 50$

105. $2x - 7y = 80$

106. $y = 1.3x - 15$

107. $y = 0.2x - 9$

108. $25x - 20y = 1$

109. $50x + 25y = 1$

110. Draw a graph illustrating the following data. What portion of the graph is horizontal? How is this reflected in the data?

Month	President's Approval Rating
February	60%
March	50
April	40
May	40
June	40
July	40
August	60

YOUR TURN ANSWERS: SECTION 3.3

1. (a) $(-2, 0)$; (b) $(0, 3)$ **2.** y-intercept: $(0, 2)$; x-intercept: $(6, 0)$

3.   **4.**

5.   **6.**

7. $y = 4$

QUICK QUIZ: SECTIONS 3.1–3.3

Graph.

1. $y = 2x - 5$ [3.2]   **2.** $y = 4$ [3.3]

3. $x = -1$ [3.3]   **4.** $3x - 4y = 12$ [3.3]

5. *Ozone Layer.* Listed below are estimates of the ozone level. Make a line graph of the data.   [3.1]

Year	Minimum Ozone Level (in Dobson units)
2005	113.8
2006	98.2
2007	116.2
2008	114.1
2009	107.5
2010	128.0

Source: NASA Ozone Watch

PREPARE TO MOVE ON

Simplify.   [1.8]

1. $\dfrac{870 - 630}{12 - 6}$ **2.** $\dfrac{7360 - 2180}{21 - 11}$

3. $\dfrac{25{,}360 - 18{,}480}{722 - 310}$ **4.** $\dfrac{3.67 - 1.8376}{6 - 3}$

3.4 Rates

Rates of Change • Visualizing Rates

Rates of Change

Because graphs make use of two axes, they allow us to visualize how two quantities change with respect to each other. A number accompanied by a ratio of two units is used to represent this type of change and is referred to as a *rate*.

> **RATE**
>
> A *rate* is a ratio that indicates how two quantities change with respect to each other.

Study Skills

Find a Study Buddy

It is not always a simple matter to find a study partner. Friendships can become strained and tension can develop if one of the study partners feels that he or she is working too much or too little. Try to find a partner with whom you feel compatible and don't take it personally if your first partner is not a good match. With some effort you will be able to locate a suitable partner. Often tutor centers or learning labs are good places to look for one.

Rates occur often in everyday life:

A website that grows by 10,000 visitors over a period of 2 months has an average *growth rate* of $\frac{10,000}{2}$, or 5000, visitors per month.

A vehicle traveling 150 mi in 3 hr is moving at a *rate* of $\frac{150}{3}$, or 50, mph (miles per hour).

A class of 25 students pays a total of $93.75 to visit a museum. The *rate* is $\frac{\$93.75}{25}$, or $3.75, per student.

> **CAUTION!**   To calculate a rate, it is important to keep track of the units being used.

EXAMPLE 1   *Car Rental.*   On January 3, Alisha rented a Chevrolet Cruze with a full tank of gas and 9312 mi on the odometer. On January 7, she returned the car with 9630 mi on the odometer.* If the rental agency charged Alisha $108 for the rental and needed 12 gal of gas to fill up the gas tank, find the following rates.

a) The car's rate of gas mileage, in miles per gallon

b) The average cost of the rental, in dollars per day

c) The car's rate of travel, in miles per day

SOLUTION

a) The rate of gas mileage, in miles per gallon, is found by dividing the number of miles traveled by the number of gallons used for that amount of driving:

$$\text{Rate, in miles per gallon} = \frac{9630 \text{ mi} - 9312 \text{ mi}}{12 \text{ gal}}$$

The word "per" indicates division.

$$= \frac{318 \text{ mi}}{12 \text{ gal}}$$

$$= 26.5 \text{ mi/gal} \qquad \text{Dividing}$$

$$= 26.5 \text{ miles per gallon.}$$

b) The average cost of the rental, in dollars per day, is found by dividing the cost of the rental by the number of days:

$$\text{Rate, in dollars per day} = \frac{108 \text{ dollars}}{4 \text{ days}}$$

From January 3 to January 7 is $7 - 3 = 4$ days.

$$= 27 \text{ dollars/day}$$

$$= \$27 \text{ per day.}$$

c) The car's rate of travel, in miles per day, is found by dividing the number of miles traveled by the number of days:

$$\text{Rate, in miles per day} = \frac{318 \text{ mi}}{4 \text{ days}}$$

$9630 \text{ mi} - 9312 \text{ mi} = 318 \text{ mi}$; From January 3 to January 7 is $7 - 3 = 4$ days.

$$= 79.5 \text{ mi/day}$$

$$= 79.5 \text{ mi per day.}$$

1. Refer to Exercise 1. Find the average daily rate of gas consumption, in gallons per day.

 YOUR TURN

*For all problems concerning rentals, assume that the pickup time was later in the day than the return time so that no late fees were applied.

CAUTION! Units are a vital part of real-world problems. They must be considered in the translation of a problem and included in the answer to a problem.

Many problems involve a rate of travel, or *speed*. The **speed** of an object is found by dividing the distance traveled by the time required to travel that distance.

EXAMPLE 2 *Transportation.* An Atlantic City Express bus makes regular trips between Paramus and Atlantic City, New Jersey. At 6:00 P.M., the bus is at mileage marker 40 on the Garden State Parkway, and at 8:00 P.M. it is at marker 170. Find the average speed of the bus.

SOLUTION Speed is the distance traveled divided by the time spent traveling:

$$\text{Bus speed} = \frac{\text{Distance traveled}}{\text{Time spent traveling}}$$

$$= \frac{\text{Change in mileage}}{\text{Change in time}}$$

$$= \frac{130 \text{ mi}}{2 \text{ hr}} \qquad \begin{array}{l} 170 \text{ mi} - 40 \text{ mi} = 130 \text{ mi};\\ 8\text{:}00 \text{ P.M.} - 6\text{:}00 \text{ P.M.} = 2 \text{ hr} \end{array}$$

$$= 65 \frac{\text{mi}}{\text{hr}}$$

$$= 65 \text{ miles per hour.} \quad \begin{array}{l} \textit{This average speed does not}\\ \textit{indicate by how much the bus}\\ \textit{speed may vary along the route.} \end{array}$$

2. A hummingbird flew across Shannon's yard, a distance of 250 ft, in 5 sec. Find the average speed of the hummingbird.

YOUR TURN

Visualizing Rates

Graphs allow us to visualize a rate of change. As a rule, the quantity listed in the numerator appears on the vertical axis and the quantity listed in the denominator appears on the horizontal axis.

EXAMPLE 3 *Rain Forests.* Between 2004 and 2010, the additional yearly amount of Brazilian rain forest that was deforested decreased by 1250 mi² per year. During 2004, approximately 10,000 mi² of rain forest was deforested. Draw a graph to represent this information.

Source: Based on information from National Institute of Space Research

SOLUTION To label the axes, note that the rate is given as 1250 mi² per year, or

$$1250 \frac{\text{mi}^2}{\text{year}}. \qquad \begin{array}{l} \leftarrow \text{ Numerator: vertical axis}\\ \leftarrow \text{ Denominator: horizontal axis} \end{array}$$

We list *square miles of rain forest deforested* on the vertical axis and *Year* on the horizontal axis. (See the figure on the left at the top of the following page.)

Next, we select a scale for each axis that allows us to plot the information. If we count by increments of 2000 on the vertical axis, we can show 10,000 mi² for 2004 and decreasing amounts for later years. On the horizontal axis, we can count by increments of 1 year. (See the figure in the middle at the top of the following page.)

Label the axes.

Select the scale.

Draw the graph.

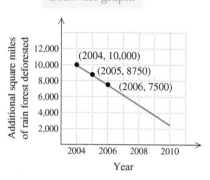

We are given that 10,000 mi² of rain forest was deforested during 2004. This gives us one point on the graph: (2004, 10,000).

We use the rate of change to find more points on the graph. Since the amount of yearly deforestation is decreasing, the rate of change is negative:

Deforestation during 2004: 10,000 mi²;

Deforestation during 2005: 10,000 − 1250 = 8750 mi²;

Deforestation during 2006: 8750 − 1250 = 7500 mi².

3. Refer to Example 3. Between 1997 and 2003, the amount of Brazilian rain forest that was deforested each year *increased* at a rate of approximately 700 mi² per year. In 1997, approximately 5100 mi² of rain forest was deforested. Draw a graph to represent this information.

These calculations give us two more points on the graph: (2005, 8750) and (2006, 7500). After plotting the three points, we draw a line through them, as shown in the figure on the right above. This gives us the graph.

YOUR TURN

EXAMPLE 4 *Banking.* Nadia prepared the following graph from data collected on a recent day at a local bank.

a) What rate can be determined from the graph?

b) What is that rate?

SOLUTION

a) Because the vertical axis shows the number of transactions and the horizontal axis lists the time in hour-long increments, we can find the rate *Number of transactions per hour.*

4. Refer to Example 4. Nadia prepared the following graph for data at a different bank location. What is the rate?

b) The points (9:00, 75) and (11:00, 225) are both on the graph. This tells us that in the 2 hours between 9:00 and 11:00, there were 225 − 75 = 150 transactions. Thus the average rate is

$$\frac{225 \text{ transactions} - 75 \text{ transactions}}{11:00 - 9:00} = \frac{150 \text{ transactions}}{2 \text{ hours}}$$

$$= 75 \text{ transactions per hour.}$$

YOUR TURN

3.4 EXERCISE SET

FOR EXTRA HELP

MyMathLab®

PRACTICE   WATCH   READ   REVIEW

Vocabulary and Reading Check

Classify each of the following statements as either true or false.

1. A rate is a ratio.

2. In the phrase "meters per second," the word "per" indicates division.

3. To find the speed of an object, divide the time by the distance traveled.

4. A quantity appearing on the vertical axis of a graph should be used in the numerator of the associated rate of change.

Concept Reinforcement

For each of Exercises 5–8, fill in the missing units for each rate.

5. If Eva biked 100 miles in 5 hours, her average rate was 20 _____.

6. If it took Lauren 18 hours to read 6 chapters, her average rate was 3 _____.

7. If Denny's ticket cost $300 for a 150-mile flight, his average rate was 2 _____.

8. If Marc made 8 cakes using 20 cups of flour, his average rate was $2\frac{1}{2}$ _____.

Rates of Change

Solve. For Exercises 9–16, round answers to the nearest cent, where appropriate.

9. *Car Rentals.* Late on June 5, Gaya rented a Ford Focus with a full tank of gas and 13,741 mi on the odometer. On June 8, she returned the car with 14,131 mi on the odometer. The rental agency charged Gaya $118 for the rental and needed 13 gal of gas to fill up the tank.

   a) Find the car's rate of gas consumption, in miles per gallon.

   b) Find the average cost of the rental, in dollars per day.

   c) Find the average rate of travel, in miles per day.

   d) Find the rental rate, in cents per mile.

10. *SUV Rentals.* On February 10, Oscar rented a Chevy Trailblazer with a full tank of gas and 13,091 mi on the odometer. On February 12, he returned the vehicle with 13,322 mi on the

odometer. The rental agency charged $92 for the rental and needed 14 gal of gas to fill the tank.

   a) Find the SUV's rate of gas consumption, in miles per gallon.

   b) Find the average cost of the rental, in dollars per day.

   c) Find the average rate of travel, in miles per day.

   d) Find the rental rate, in cents per mile.

11. *Bicycle Rentals.* At 9:00, Jodi rented a mountain bike from The Bike Rack. She returned the bicycle at 11:00, after cycling 14 mi. Jodi paid $15 for the rental.

   a) Find Jodi's average speed, in miles per hour.

   b) Find the rental rate, in dollars per hour.

   c) Find the rental rate, in dollars per mile.

12. *Bicycle Rentals.* At 2:00, Braden rented a mountain bike from Slickrock Cycles. He returned the bike at 5:00, after cycling 18 mi. Braden paid $24 for the rental.

   a) Find Braden's average speed, in miles per hour.

   b) Find the rental rate, in dollars per hour.

   c) Find the rental rate, in dollars per mile.

13. *Proofreading.* Sergei began proofreading at 9:00 A.M., starting at the top of page 93. He worked until 2:00 P.M. that day and finished page 195. He billed the publishers $110 for the day's work.

   a) Find the rate of pay, in dollars per hour.

   b) Find the average proofreading rate, in number of pages per hour.

   c) Find the rate of pay, in dollars per page.

14. *Temporary Help.* A typist for Kelly Services reports to 3E's Properties for work at 10:00 A.M. and leaves at 6:00 P.M. after having typed from the end of page 8 to the end of page 50 of a proposal. 3E's pays $120 for the typist's services.

   a) Find the rate of pay, in dollars per hour.

   b) Find the average typing rate, in number of pages per hour.

   c) Find the rate of pay, in dollars per page.

15. *National Debt.* The U.S. federal budget debt was $8612 billion in 2006 and $15,041 billion in 2011. Find the average rate at which the debt was increasing.

   Source: U.S. Office of Management and Budget

16. *Four-Year-College Tuition.* The average amount of room, board, and tuition at a public four-year college was $17,447 in 2006 and $21,189 in 2010. Find the average rate at which room, board, and tuition are increasing.

Source: U.S. National Center for Education Statistics

17. *Elevators.* At 2:38, Lara entered an elevator on the 34th floor of the Regency Hotel. At 2:40, she stepped off at the 5th floor.

a) Find the elevator's average rate of travel, in number of floors per minute.

b) Find the elevator's average rate of travel, in seconds per floor.

18. *Snow Removal.* By 1:00 P.M., Shani had already shoveled 2 driveways, and by 6:00 P.M. that day, the number was up to 7.

a) Find Shani's average shoveling rate, in number of driveways per hour.

b) Find Shani's average shoveling rate, in hours per driveway.

19. *Mountaineering.* The fastest ascent of Mt. Everest was accomplished by the Sherpa guide Pemba Dorje of Nepal in 2004. Pemba Dorje climbed from base camp, elevation 17,700 ft, to the summit, elevation 29,029 ft, in 8 hr 10 min.

Source: *Guinness Book of World Records* 2012

a) Find Pemba Dorje's average rate of ascent, in feet per minute.

b) Find Pemba Dorje's average rate of ascent, in minutes per foot.

20. *Pottery.* Master potter Mark Byles holds the record for the most clay pots thrown in 1 hr. He made 150 clay flower pots during the allotted hour.

Source: *Guinness Book of World Records* 2012

a) Find Mark's average pot-throwing rate, in pots per minute.

b) Find Mark's average pot-throwing rate, in minutes per pot.

Visualizing Rates

In Exercises 21–30, draw a linear graph to represent the given information. Be sure to label and number the axes appropriately (see Example 3).

21. *Recycling.* Between 2001 and 2010, the amount of steel recycled in the United States increased at an average rate of approximately 125,000 tons per year. In 2001, approximately 4,600,000 tons of steel was recycled. Draw a graph to represent this information.

Source: U.S. Environmental Protection Agency

22. *Health Insurance.* In 2008, the average cost for health insurance for a family was about $12,700, and the figure was rising at a rate of about $700 per year.

Source: Based on data from Kaiser/HRET Survey of Health Benefits

23. *Prescription Drug Sales.* In 2009, there were sales of approximately $4 billion of anti-Alzheimer's prescription drug products in the United States, and the figure was increasing at a rate of about $0.5 billion per year.

Source: IMS National Sales Perspectives

24. *Violent Crimes.* In 2009, there were approximately 17.1 violent crimes per 1000 Americans, and the figure was dropping at a rate of about 1.9 violent crimes per 1000 per year.

Source: U.S. Bureau of Justice Statistics

25. *Train Travel.* At 3:00 P.M., the Boston–Washington Metroliner had traveled 230 mi and was cruising at a rate of 90 miles per hour.

26. *Plane Travel.* At 4:00 P.M., the Seattle–Los Angeles shuttle had traveled 400 mi and was cruising at a rate of 300 miles per hour.

27. *Wages.* By 2:00 P.M., Diane had earned $50. She continued earning money at a rate of $15 per hour.

28. *Wages.* By 3:00 P.M., Arnie had earned $70. He continued earning money at a rate of $12 per hour.

29. *Telephone Bills.* Roberta's phone bill was already $7.50 when she made a call for which she was charged at a rate of $0.10 per minute.

30. *Telephone Bills.* At 3:00 P.M., Theo's phone bill was $6.50 and increasing at a rate of 7¢ per minute.

In Exercises 31–40, use the graph provided to calculate a rate of change in which the units of the horizontal axis are used in the denominator.

31. *Call Center.* The following graph shows data from a technical assistance call center. At what rate are calls being handled?

32. *Hairdresser.* Eve's Custom Cuts has a graph displaying data from a recent day of work. At what rate does Eve work?

33. *Train Travel.* The following graph shows data from a recent train ride from Chicago to St. Louis. At what rate did the train travel?

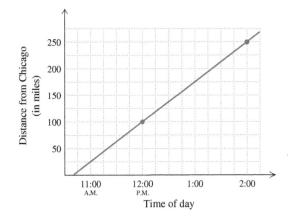

34. *Train Travel.* The following graph shows data from a recent train ride from Denver to Kansas City. At what rate did the train travel?

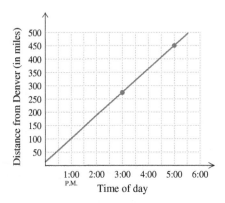

35. *Cost of a Telephone Call.* The following graph shows data from a recent phone call between the United States and Uruguay. At what rate was the customer being billed?

36. *Cost of a Telephone Call.* The following graph shows data from a recent phone call between the United States and China. At what rate was the customer being billed?

37. *Population.* The following graph shows data regarding the population of Cleveland, Ohio. At what rate was the population changing?

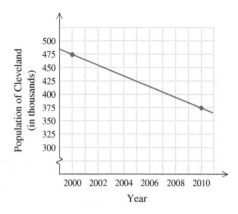

38. *Depreciation of an Office Machine.* Data regarding the value of a particular color copier is represented in the following graph. At what rate is the value changing?

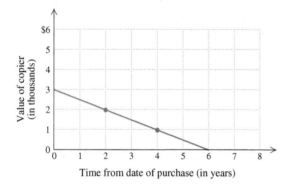

39. *Gas Mileage.* The following graph shows data for a 2012 Honda Civic Hybrid driven on interstate highways. At what rate was the vehicle consuming gas?

Source: www.fueleconomy.gov

40. *Gas Mileage.* The following graph shows data for a 2012 Ford Escape Hybrid AWD driven on city streets. At what rate was the vehicle consuming gas?

Source: www.fueleconomy.gov

In Exercises 41–46, match each description with the most appropriate graph from the choices below. Scales are intentionally omitted. Assume that of the three sports listed, swimming is the slowest and biking is the fastest.

41. ____ Robin trains for triathlons by running, biking, and then swimming every Saturday.

42. ____ Gene trains for triathlons by biking, running, and then swimming every Sunday.

43. ____ Shirley trains for triathlons by swimming, biking, and then running every Sunday.

44. ____ Evan trains for triathlons by swimming, running, and then biking every Saturday.

45. ____ Angie trains for triathlons by biking, swimming, and then running every Sunday.

46. ____ Mick trains for triathlons by running, swimming, and then biking every Saturday.

e) 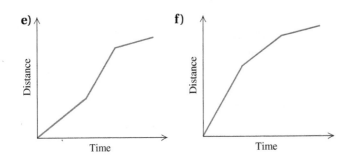 **f)**

Distance / *Time* (graphs)

---

47. What does a negative rate of travel indicate? Explain.

48. Explain how to convert from kilometers per hour to meters per second.

Skill Review

49. Find the prime factorization of 150. [1.3]

50. Graph on the number line: -3.5. [1.4]

51. Find decimal notation: $-\dfrac{11}{8}$. [1.4]

52. Find the absolute value: $\left|-\dfrac{1}{3}\right|$. [1.4]

53. Find the opposite of $\dfrac{3}{2}$. [1.6]

54. Find the reciprocal of $\dfrac{3}{2}$. [1.7]

Synthesis

55. How would the graphs of Jon's and Jenny's total earnings compare in each of the following situations?

　a) Jon earns twice as much per hour as Jenny.
　b) Jon and Jenny earn the same hourly rate, but Jenny received a bonus for a cost-saving suggestion.
　c) Jon is paid by the hour, and Jenny is paid a weekly salary.

56. Write an exercise similar to those in Exercises 9–20 for a classmate to solve. Design the problem so that the solution is "The motorcycle's rate of gas consumption was 65 miles per gallon."

57. *Aviation.* A Boeing 737 airplane climbs from sea level to a cruising altitude of 31,500 ft at a rate of 6300 ft/min. After cruising for 3 min, the jet is forced to land, descending at a rate of 3500 ft/min. Represent the flight with a graph in which altitude is measured on the vertical axis and time on the horizontal axis.

58. *Wages with Commissions.* Each salesperson at Mike's Bikes is paid $140 per week plus 13% of all sales up to $2000, and then 20% on any sales in excess of $2000. Draw a graph in which sales are measured on the horizontal axis and wages on the vertical axis. Then use the graph to estimate the wages paid when a salesperson sells $2700 in merchandise in one week.

59. *Taxi Fares.* The driver of a New York City Yellow Cab recently charged $3.00 plus 40¢ for each fifth of a mile traveled for night service. Draw a graph that could be used to determine the cost of a fare.

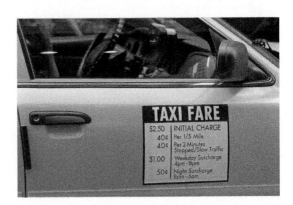

60. *Gas Mileage.* A particular Kawasaki motorcycle travels three times as far as a Ford Escape Hybrid on the same amount of gas (see Exercise 40). Draw a graph that reflects this information.

61. *Aviation.* Tim's F-16 jet is moving forward at a deck speed of 95 mph aboard an aircraft carrier that is traveling 39 mph in the same direction. How fast is the jet traveling, in minutes per mile, with respect to the sea?

62. *Navigation.* In 3 sec, Penny walks 24 ft to the bow (front) of a tugboat. The boat is cruising at a rate of 5 ft/sec. What is Penny's rate of travel with respect to land?

63. *Running.* Anne ran from the 4-km mark to the 7-km mark of a 10-km race in 15.5 min. At this rate, how long would it take Anne to run a 5-mi race?

64. *Running.* Jerod ran from the 2-mi marker to the finish line of a 5-mi race in 25 min. At this rate, how long would it take Jerod to run a 10-km race?

65. Trevor picks apples twice as fast as Doug. By 4:30, Doug had already picked 4 bushels of apples. Fifty minutes later, his total reached $5\frac{1}{2}$ bushels. Find Trevor's picking rate. Give your answer in bushels per hour.

66. At 3:00 P.M., Carrie and Chad had already made 46 candles. By 5:00 P.M., the total had reached 100 candles. Assuming a constant production rate, at what time did they make their 82nd candle?

 YOUR TURN ANSWERS: SECTION 3.4

1. 3 gal per day   **2.** 50 ft per sec

3.

4. 200 transactions per hour

QUICK QUIZ: SECTIONS 3.1–3.4

1. In which quadrant or on which axis is $(0, -15)$ located?   [3.1]

2. Determine whether the ordered pair $(-3, -1)$ is a solution of the equation $2a - 3b = -9$.   [3.2]

3. Graph: $y = -3$.   [3.3]

4. Graph: $y = -3x$.   [3.2]

5. In 2008, there were about 39,200 commercial pilots in the United States. The number of pilots is expected to increase to 46,500 by 2018. Find the rate of increase, in number of pilots per year.   [3.4]

   Source: U.S. Department of Labor, Bureau of Labor Statistics

---

PREPARE TO MOVE ON

Simplify.

1. $-2 - (-7)$ [1.6]   **2.** $-9 - (-3)$ [1.6]

3. $\dfrac{5 - (-4)}{-2 - 7}$ [1.8]   **4.** $\dfrac{8 - (-4)}{2 - 11}$ [1.8]

5. $\dfrac{-4 - 8}{11 - 2}$ [1.8]   **6.** $\dfrac{-5 - (-3)}{4 - 6}$ [1.8]

7. $\dfrac{-6 - (-6)}{-2 - 7}$ [1.8]   **8.** $\dfrac{-3 - 5}{-1 - (-1)}$ [1.8]

3.5 Slope

Rate and Slope ▪ Horizontal Lines and Vertical Lines ▪ Applications

Study Skills

Add Your Voice to the Author's

If you own your text, consider using it as a notebook. Since many instructors' work closely parallels the book, it is often useful to make notes on the appropriate page as he or she is lecturing.

A *rate* is a measure of how two quantities change with respect to each other. In this section, we will discuss how rate is related to the slope of a line.

Rate and Slope

Gary currently replaces his employees' laptop computers every two years. For a new program, he is considering changing this policy to replacing them every three years with a more durable model. The following tables list the costs of replacing the computers using both programs.

Two-Year Replacement	
Years Since Start of Program	Cost of Computers
0	$ 0
2	3,000
4	6,000
6	9,000
8	12,000

Three-Year Replacement	
Years Since Start of Program	Cost of Computers
0	$ 0
3	4,000
6	8,000
9	12,000
12	16,000

We now graph the pairs of numbers listed in the tables, using the horizontal axis for the number of years since the start of the program and the vertical axis for the cost of the computers.

Two-Year Replacement

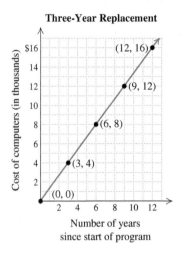

Three-Year Replacement

By comparing the cost of the computers over a specified period of time, we can compare the two rates. Note that the rate of the two-year replacement program is greater so its graph is steeper.

Replacement Program	Cost of Computers	Rate
Two-year	$3000 every 2 years	$\dfrac{3\text{ thousand dollars}}{2\text{ years}} = \dfrac{3}{2}$ thousand dollars per year, or $1500/year
Three-year	$4000 every 3 years	$\dfrac{4\text{ thousand dollars}}{3\text{ years}} = \dfrac{4}{3}$ thousand dollars per year, or $1333.33/year

The rates $\frac{3}{2}$ and $\frac{4}{3}$ can also be found using the coordinates of any two points that are on each line.

EXAMPLE 1 Use the graph of the Two-Year Replacement program above to find the cost of computers per year.

SOLUTION We can use the points $(6, 9)$ and $(8, 12)$ to find the rate for the two-year program. To do so, remember that these coordinates tell us that after 6 years, the computer cost is $9 thousand, and after 8 years, the computer cost is $12 thousand. In the 2 years between the 6-year and 8-year points, $12 − $9, or $3 thousand, was spent. Thus we have

$$\text{Two-year rate} = \frac{\text{change in cost of computers}}{\text{corresponding change in time}}$$

$$= \frac{12 - 9 \text{ thousand dollars}}{8 - 6 \text{ years}}$$

$$= \frac{3 \text{ thousand dollars}}{2 \text{ years}}$$

$$= \frac{3}{2} \text{ thousand dollars per year, or } \$1500/\text{year.}$$

Because the line is straight, the same rate is found using *any* pair of points on the line. For example, using $(0, 0)$ and $(4, 6)$, we have

$$\text{Two-year rate} = \frac{6 - 0 \text{ thousand dollars}}{4 - 0 \text{ years}} = \frac{6 \text{ thousand dollars}}{4 \text{ years}}$$

$$= \frac{3}{2} \text{ thousand dollars per year, or } \$1500/\text{year}.$$

1. Use the graph of the Three-Year Replacement program to find the cost of computers per year.

YOUR TURN

Note that the rate is always the vertical change divided by the corresponding horizontal change.

When the axes of a graph are simply labeled x and y, the ratio of vertical change to horizontal change is the rate at which y is changing with respect to x. This ratio is a measure of a line's slant, or **slope**.

Consider a line passing through $(2, 3)$ and $(6, 5)$, as shown below. We find the ratio of vertical change, or *rise*, to horizontal change, or *run*, as follows:

$$\begin{array}{l}\text{Ratio of vertical change} \\ \text{to horizontal change}\end{array} = \frac{\text{change in } y}{\text{change in } x} = \frac{\text{rise}}{\text{run}}$$

$$= \left. \begin{array}{l} \dfrac{5 - 3}{6 - 2} \\[2mm] = \dfrac{2}{4}, \text{ or } \dfrac{1}{2}. \end{array} \right\}$$

Note that these calculations can be performed without viewing a graph.

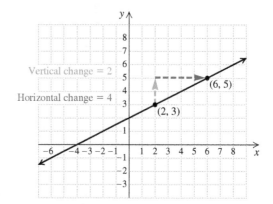

Thus the y-coordinates of points on this line increase at a rate of 2 units for every 4-unit increase in x, which is 1 unit for every 2-unit increase in x, or $\frac{1}{2}$ unit for every 1-unit increase in x. The slope of the line is $\frac{1}{2}$.

In the definition of *slope* below, the *subscripts* 1 and 2 are used to distinguish point 1 and point 2 from each other. The slightly lowered 1's and 2's are not exponents but are used to denote x-values (and y-values) for different points.

Student Notes

The notation x_1 is read "x sub one."

SLOPE

The *slope* of the line containing points (x_1, y_1) and (x_2, y_2) is given by

$$m = \frac{\text{change in } y}{\text{change in } x} = \frac{\text{rise}}{\text{run}} = \frac{y_2 - y_1}{x_2 - x_1}.$$

EXAMPLE 2 Find the slope of the line containing the points $(-4, 3)$ and $(2, -6)$.

SOLUTION From $(-4, 3)$ to $(2, -6)$, the change in y, or rise, is $-6 - 3$, or -9. The change in x, or run, is $2 - (-4)$, or 6. Thus,

$$\begin{aligned}
\text{Slope} &= \frac{\text{change in } y}{\text{change in } x} \\
&= \frac{\text{rise}}{\text{run}} \\
&= \frac{-6 - 3}{2 - (-4)} \\
&= \frac{-9}{6} \\
&= -\frac{9}{6}, \text{ or } -\frac{3}{2}.
\end{aligned}$$

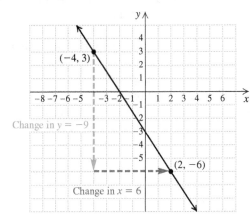

The graph of the line is shown above for reference.

2. Find the slope of the line containing the points $(2, 7)$ and $(-6, 0)$.

YOUR TURN

Student Notes

You may wonder which point should be regarded as (x_1, y_1) and which should be (x_2, y_2). To see that the math works out the same either way, perform both calculations on your own.

CAUTION! When we use the formula

$$m = \frac{y_2 - y_1}{x_2 - x_1},$$

it makes no difference which point is considered (x_1, y_1). What matters is that we subtract the y-coordinates in the same order that we subtract the x-coordinates.

To illustrate, we reverse *both* of the subtractions in Example 2. The slope is still $-\frac{3}{2}$:

$$\text{Slope} = \frac{\text{change in } y}{\text{change in } x} = \frac{3 - (-6)}{-4 - 2} = \frac{9}{-6} = -\frac{3}{2}.$$

═══════════════ EXPLORING 🔍 THE CONCEPT ═══════════════

The *sign* of the slope of a line indicates whether the line slants up or down from left to right. The *absolute value* of the slope indicates the steepness of the slope.

A.

$m = \frac{3}{7}$

B.

$m = 2$, or $\frac{2}{1}$

C.

$m = -2$, or $\frac{-2}{1}$

D.

$m = -\frac{3}{7}$

1. Which of the graphs shown have a negative slope?
2. Which of the graphs shown have a positive slope?
3. On the basis of the graphs shown, choose the word that makes each statement true:
   a) A line with a positive slope slants _____ from left to right.
      up/down
   b) A line with a negative slope slants _____ from left to right.
      up/down
4. Which is larger: $\left|\frac{3}{7}\right|$ or $|2|$?
5. Which is larger: $\left|-\frac{3}{7}\right|$ or $|-2|$?
6. On the basis of the graphs shown, choose the word that makes the statement true:
   The _____ the absolute value of the slope, the steeper the line.
      larger/smaller

ANSWERS
1. C, D   2. A, B   3. (a) Up; (b) down   4. |2| 5. |−2| 6. Larger

---

> A line with positive slope slants up from left to right, and a line with negative slope slants down from left to right. The larger the absolute value of the slope, the steeper the line.

Horizontal Lines and Vertical Lines

What about the slope of a horizontal line or a vertical line?

EXAMPLE 3   Find the slope of the line $y = 4$.

SOLUTION   Consider the points $(2, 4)$ and $(-3, 4)$, which are on the line. The change in y, or the rise, is $4 - 4$, or 0. The change in x, or the run, is $-3 - 2$, or -5. Thus,

$$m = \frac{4 - 4}{-3 - 2}$$

$$= \frac{0}{-5}$$

$$= 0.$$

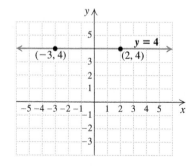

3. Find the slope of the line $y = 2$.

_____

Any two points on a horizontal line have the same y-coordinate. Thus the change in y is 0, so the slope is 0.

YOUR TURN

A horizontal line has slope 0.

EXAMPLE 4   Find the slope of the line $x = -3$.

SOLUTION   Consider the points $(-3, 4)$ and $(-3, -2)$, which are on the line. The change in y, or the rise, is $-2 - 4$, or -6. The change in x, or the run, is $-3 - (-3)$, or 0. Thus,

$$m = \frac{-2 - 4}{-3 - (-3)}$$

$$= \frac{-6}{0}. \quad \text{(undefined)}$$

Since division by 0 is not defined, the slope of this line is not defined. The answer to a problem of this type is "The slope of this line is undefined."

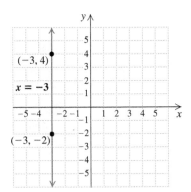

4. Find the slope of the line $x = -1$.

_____

YOUR TURN

The slope of a vertical line is undefined.

Applications

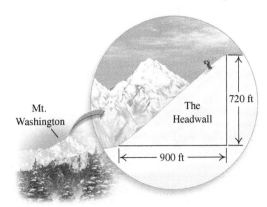

y ↑   Road grade $\frac{a}{b}$ (expressed as a percent)

a

b x

Slope has many real-world applications, ranging from car speed to production rate. Slope can also measure steepness. For example, numbers like 2%, 3%, and 6% are often used to represent the **grade** of a road, a measure of a road's steepness. That is, since $3\% = \frac{3}{100}$, a 3% grade means that for every horizontal distance of 100 ft, the road rises or drops 3 ft. The concept of grade also occurs in skiing or snowboarding, where a 7% grade is considered very tame, but a 70% grade is considered steep.

EXAMPLE 5   _Skiing._   Among the steepest skiable terrain in North America, the Headwall on Mount Washington, in New Hampshire, drops 720 ft over a horizontal distance of 900 ft. Find the grade of the Headwall.

Mt. Washington

The Headwall

720 ft

900 ft

5. A mountain road rises 250 ft over a horizontal distance of 4000 ft. Find the grade of the road.

SOLUTION The grade of the Headwall is its slope, expressed as a percent:

$$m = \frac{720}{900} = \frac{8}{10} = 80\%.$$ Grade is slope expressed as a percent.

 YOUR TURN

Carpenters use slope when designing stairs, ramps, or roof pitches. Another application occurs in the engineering of a dam—the force or strength of a river depends on how much the river drops over a specified distance.

3.5 EXERCISE SET

FOR EXTRA HELP

 MyMathLab® Math XL PRACTICE WATCH READ REVIEW

Vocabulary and Reading Check

Choose the expression or word from the list below that best completes each statement.

x	negative
y	positive
$x_2 - x_1$	rise
$y_2 - y_1$	run
change in x	undefined
change in y	zero

1. Slope is the rate at which ____ is changing with respect to ____.

2. The slope of a line can be expressed in terms of change as follows: ――――――.

3. The slope of a line can be expressed using *rise* and *run* as follows: ――――.

4. The slope of the line containing (x_1, y_1) and (x_2, y_2) is given by ――――.

5. If a line slants up from left to right, the sign of its slope is _____, and if a line slants down from left to right, the sign of its slope is _____.

6. The slope of a horizontal line is _____, and the slope of a vertical line is _____.

Concept Reinforcement

In each of Exercises 7–14, state whether the rate is positive, negative, or zero.

7. The rate at which a teenager's height changes

8. The rate at which an elderly person's height changes

9. The rate at which a pond's water level changes during a drought

10. The rate at which a pond's water level changes during the rainy season

11. The rate at which a person's I.Q. changes during his or her sleep

12. The rate at which the number of people in attendance at a basketball game changes in the moments before the opening tipoff

13. The rate at which the number of people in attendance at a basketball game changes in the moments after the final buzzer sounds

14. The rate at which the number of U.S. Senators changes

Rate and Slope

15. *Blogging.* Find the rate at which a professional blogger is paid.

Source: Based on information from readwriteweb.com

16. *Fitness.* Find the rate at which a runner burns calories.

17. *Laptop Computer Prices.* Find the rate of change in the average price of a new laptop computer.

Source: Based on information from PriceGrabber.com Market Reporter Database

18. *Employment.* Find the rate of change in the number of news reporters and correspondents employed in the United States.

Source: Based on information from the U.S. Department of Labor, Bureau of Labor Statistics

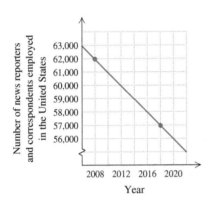

19. *College Admission Tests.* Find the rate of change in SAT critical reading scores with respect to family income.

Source: The College Board, College-Bound Seniors 2011 Total Group Profile Report

20. *Long-Term Care.* Find the rate of change in the daily cost of a private room in a nursing home.

Source: Based on data from MetLife Market Survey of Nursing Home, Assisted Living, Adult Day Services, and Home Care Costs, 2009–2011

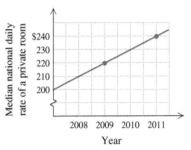

21. *Meteorology.* Find the rate of change in the temperature in Spearfish, Montana, on January 22, 1943, as shown below.

Source: National Oceanic Atmospheric Administration

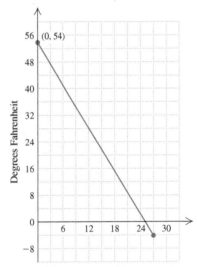

22. *Credit Unions.* Find the rate of change in the number of federal credit unions.

Source: National Credit Union Association

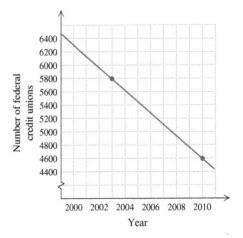

Find the slope, if it is defined, of each line. If the slope is undefined, state this.

23.

24.

25.

26.

27.

28.

29.

30.

31.

32.

33.

34.

35.

36.

37.

38.

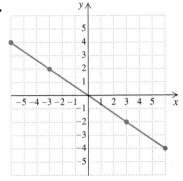

Find the slope of the line containing each given pair of points. If the slope is undefined, state this.

39. $(1, 3)$ and $(5, 8)$ **40.** $(1, 8)$ and $(6, 9)$

41. $(-2, 4)$ and $(3, 0)$ **42.** $(-4, 2)$ and $(2, -3)$

43. $(-4, 0)$ and $(5, 6)$ **44.** $(3, 0)$ and $(6, 9)$

45. $(0, 7)$ and $(-3, 10)$ **46.** $(0, 9)$ and $(-5, 0)$

47. $(-2, 3)$ and $(-6, 5)$ **48.** $(-1, 4)$ and $(5, -8)$

Aha! **49.** $\left(-2, \frac{1}{2}\right)$ and $\left(-5, \frac{1}{2}\right)$ **50.** $(-5, -1)$ and $(2, -3)$

51. $(5, -4)$ and $(2, -7)$ **52.** $(-10, 3)$ and $(-10, 4)$

53. $(6, -4)$ and $(6, 5)$ **54.** $(5, -2)$ and $(-4, -2)$

Horizontal Lines and Vertical Lines

Find the slope of each line whose equation is given. If the slope is undefined, state this.

55. $y = 5$ **56.** $y = 13$

57. $x = -8$ **58.** $x = 18$

59. $x = 9$ **60.** $x = -7$

61. $y = -10$ **62.** $y = -4$

Applications

63. *Surveying.*   Lick Skillet Road, near Boulder, Colorado, climbs 230 m over a horizontal distance of 1600 m. What is the grade of the road?

64. *Navigation.*   Capital Rapids drops 54 ft vertically over a horizontal distance of 1080 ft. What is the slope of the rapids?

65. *Construction.*   Part of New Valley rises 28 ft over a horizontal distance of 80 ft, and is too steep to build on. What is the slope of the land?

66. *Engineering.*   At one point, Yellowstone's Beartooth Highway rises 315 ft over a horizontal distance of 4500 ft. Find the grade of the road.

67. *Carpentry.*   Find the slope (or pitch) of the roof.

2 ft 5 in.

8 ft 2 in.

68. *Exercise.*   Find the slope (or grade) of the treadmill.

0.4 ft

5 ft

69. *Bicycling.*   To qualify as a rated climb on the Tour de France, a grade must average at least 4%. The ascent of Dooley Mountain, Oregon, part of the Elkhorn Classic, begins at 3500 ft and climbs to 5400 ft over a horizontal distance of 37,000 ft. What is the grade of the road? Would it qualify as a rated climb if it were part of the Tour de France?

Source: barkercityherald.com

70. *Construction.*   Public buildings regularly include steps with 7-in. risers and 11-in. treads. Find the grade of such a stairway.

11 in.

7 in.

71. Explain why the order in which coordinates are subtracted to find slope does not matter so long as y-coordinates and x-coordinates are subtracted in the same order.

72. If one line has a slope of -3 and another has a slope of 2, which line is steeper? Why?

Skill Review

73. Multiply: $3(4 + a)$. [1.2]

74. Factor: $14 + 35x$. [1.2]

75. Find $-x$ when x is -15. [1.6]

76. Write another inequality with the same meaning as $x \geq 3$. [1.4]

77. Write exponential notation for $5t \cdot 5t \cdot 5t$. [1.8]

78. Simplify: $(-2y)^4$. [1.8]

Synthesis

79. The points $(-4, -3)$, $(1, 4)$, $(4, 2)$, and $(-1, -5)$ are vertices of a quadrilateral. Use slopes to explain why the quadrilateral is a parallelogram.

80. Which is steeper and why: a ski slope that is 50° or one with a grade of 100%?

81. The plans below are for a skateboard "Fun Box." For the ramps labeled A, find the slope or grade.

Source: www.heckler.com

82. A line passes through $(4, -7)$ and never enters the first quadrant. What numbers could the line have for its slope?

83. A line passes through $(2, 5)$ and never enters the second quadrant. What numbers could the line have for its slope?

84. *Architecture.* Architects often use the equation $x + y = 18$ to determine the height y, in inches, of the riser of a step when the tread is x inches wide. Express the slope of stairs designed with this equation without using the variable y.

In Exercises 85 and 86, the slope of the line is $-\frac{2}{3}$, but the numbering on one axis is missing. How many units should each tick mark on that unnumbered axis represent?

85.

86.

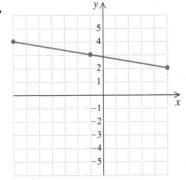

YOUR TURN ANSWERS: SECTION 3.5

1. $\frac{4}{3}$ thousand dollars per year, or $1333.33 per year **2.** $\frac{7}{8}$
3. 0 **4.** Undefined **5.** 6.25%

QUICK QUIZ: SECTIONS 3.1– 3.5

Graph.

1. $x = -2$ [3.3]   **2.** $3x - y = 3$ [3.3]

3. $y = 2x - 4$ [3.2]

4. Find the slope of the line containing $(9, -4)$ and $(10, -5)$. [3.5]

5. Find the slope of the line given by $y = 21$. If the slope is undefined, state this. [3.5]

PREPARE TO MOVE ON

Solve for y. [2.3]

1. $2x + 3y = 7$ **2.** $3x - 4y = 8$

3. $ax + by = c$ **4.** $ax - by = c$

Mid-Chapter Review

We can plot points and graph equations on a *Cartesian coordinate plane*.

- A point is represented by an *ordered pair*.
- The graph of an equation represents all of its solutions.
- Equations can be *linear* or *nonlinear*.
- The *slope* of a line represents a rate of change: Slope $= m = \dfrac{\text{change in } y}{\text{change in } x} = \dfrac{y_2 - y_1}{x_2 - x_1}$.

GUIDED SOLUTIONS

1. Find the y-intercept and the x-intercept of the graph of $y - 3x = 6$.   [3.3]

Solution

y-intercept: $y - 3 \cdot \boxed{} = 6$

$y = \boxed{}$

The y-intercept is $(\boxed{}, \boxed{})$.

x-intercept: $\boxed{} - 3x = 6$

$-3x = 6$

$x = \boxed{}$

The x-intercept is $(\boxed{}, \boxed{})$.

2. Find the slope of the line containing the points $(1, 5)$ and $(3, -1)$.   [3.5]

Solution

$m = \dfrac{y_2 - y_1}{x_2 - x_1} = \dfrac{-1 - \boxed{}}{3 - \boxed{}}$

$= \dfrac{\boxed{}}{2}$

$= \boxed{}$

MIXED REVIEW

3. Plot the point $(0, -3)$.   [3.1]

4. In which quadrant is the point $(4, -15)$ located? [3.1]

5. Determine whether the ordered pair $(-2, -3)$ is a solution of the equation $y = 5 - x$.   [3.2]

Graph by hand.

6. $y = x - 3$ [3.2]

7. $y = -3x$ [3.2]

8. $3x - y = 2$ [3.2]

9. $4x - 5y = 20$ [3.3]

10. $y = -2$ [3.3]

11. $x = 1$ [3.3]

12. By the end of June, Construction Builders had winterized 10 homes. By the end of August, they had winterized a total of 38 homes. Find the rate at which the company was winterizing homes.   [3.4]

13. From a base elevation of 9600 ft, Longs Peak, Colorado, rises to a summit elevation of 14,255 ft over a horizontal distance of 15,840 ft. Find the average grade of Longs Peak.   [3.5]

Find the slope of the line containing the given pair of points. If the slope is undefined, state this.   [3.5]

14. $(-5, -2)$ and $(1, 8)$

15. $(1, 2)$ and $(4, -7)$

16. $(0, 0)$ and $(0, -2)$

17. $(6, -3)$ and $(2, -3)$

18. What is the slope of the line $y = 4$?   [3.5]

19. What is the slope of the line $x = -7$?   [3.5]

20. Find the x-intercept and the y-intercept of the line given by $2y - 3x = 12$.   [3.3]

3.6 Slope–Intercept Form

Using the *y*-intercept and the Slope to Graph a Line • Equations in Slope–Intercept Form •
Graphing and Slope–Intercept Form • Parallel Lines and Perpendicular Lines

If we know the slope and the *y*-intercept of a line, it is possible to graph the line. In this section, we will discover that a line's slope and its *y*-intercept can be determined directly from the line's equation, provided the equation is written in a certain form.

Using the *y*-intercept and the Slope to Graph a Line

Last year, Gary spent $4000 upgrading the local area network (LAN) for his company's computer system. Now he plans to spend $3000 every two years to update his employees' laptop computers. We can make a table and draw a graph showing his costs.

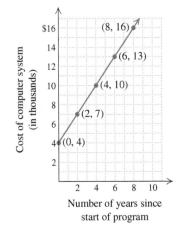

Years Since Start of Program	Cost of Computers (in thousands)
0	$ 4
2	7
4	10
6	13
8	16

The slope of the line is the rate of change in computer cost per year;

$$\text{Slope} = \frac{\text{change in } y}{\text{change in } x} = \frac{\text{rise}}{\text{run}} = \frac{y_2 - y_1}{x_2 - x_1},$$

where (x_1, y_1) and (x_2, y_2) are any two points on the graphed line. Here we select $(0, 4)$ and $(2, 7)$:

$$\text{Slope} = \frac{\text{change in } y}{\text{change in } x} = \frac{7 - 4}{2 - 0} = \frac{3}{2}.$$ The rate of change is $\frac{3}{2}$ thousand dollars per year, or $1500/year

Knowing that the slope is $\frac{3}{2}$, we could have drawn the graph by plotting $(0, 4)$ and from there moving 3 units *up* and 2 units *to the right*. This would have located the point $(2, 7)$. Using $(0, 4)$ and $(2, 7)$, we can then draw the line. This is the method used in the next example.

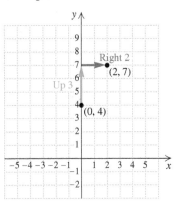

Study Skills

When One Just Isn't Enough

When an exercise gives you difficulty, it is usually wise to practice solving some other exercises that are very similar to the one that gave you trouble. Usually, if the troubling exercise is odd-numbered, the next (even-numbered) exercise is quite similar. You may also be able to practice similar problems in an online tutorial program.

EXAMPLE 1   Draw a line that has slope $\frac{1}{4}$ and y-intercept $(0, 2)$.

SOLUTION   We plot $(0, 2)$ and from there move 1 unit *up* and 4 units *to the right*. This locates the point $(4, 3)$. We plot $(4, 3)$ and draw a line passing through $(0, 2)$ and $(4, 3)$, as shown on the right below.

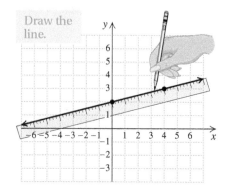

1. Draw a line that has slope $\frac{2}{3}$ and y-intercept $(0, -1)$.

YOUR TURN

Equations in Slope–Intercept Form

It is possible to read the slope and the y-intercept of a line directly from its equation. To find the y-intercept of an equation's graph, we replace x with 0 and solve the resulting equation for y. Compare the following.

$$y = 2x + 3 \qquad\qquad\qquad y = mx + b$$
$$\;\;= 2 \cdot 0 + 3 = 0 + 3 = 3 \qquad\qquad = m \cdot 0 + b = 0 + b = b$$

The y-intercept of the graph of $y = 2x + 3$ is $(0, 3)$.

The y-intercept of the graph of $y = mx + b$ is $(0, b)$.

To calculate the slope of the graph of $y = 2x + 3$, we need two ordered pairs that are solutions of the equation. The y-intercept $(0, 3)$ is one pair; a second pair, $(1, 5)$, can be found by substituting 1 for x. We then have

$$\text{Slope} = \frac{\text{change in } y}{\text{change in } x} = \frac{5 - 3}{1 - 0} = \frac{2}{1} = 2.$$

Note that the slope, 2, is also the x-coefficient in $y = 2x + 3$. It can be similarly shown that the graph of any equation of the form $y = mx + b$ has slope m (see Exercise 83).

THE SLOPE–INTERCEPT EQUATION

The equation $y = mx + b$ is called the *slope–intercept equation*. The graph of $y = mx + b$ has slope m and y-intercept $(0, b)$.

The equation of any nonvertical line can be written in this form. The use of the letter m for slope is derived from the French verb *monter*, to climb.

EXAMPLE 2   Find the slope and the y-intercept of each line whose equation is given.

a) $y = \frac{4}{5}x - 8$ **b)** $2x + y = 5$ **c)** $3x - 4y = 7$

Student Notes

To write an equation "in the form $y = mx + b$" means to solve the equation for y, so that "$y = $" is followed by the term containing x and then the constant term. It may help to write your equation below the general form and align the y, the $=$, and the x. For Example 2(b), you could write

$$y = \quad mx + b$$
$$y = -2x + 5.$$

From this form, you can see that $m = -2$ and $b = 5$.

SOLUTION

a) We rewrite $y = \frac{4}{5}x - 8$ as $y = \frac{4}{5}x + (-8)$. Now we simply read the slope and the y-intercept from the equation:

$$y = \frac{4}{5}x + (-8).$$

The slope is $\frac{4}{5}$. The y-intercept is $(0, -8)$.

b) We first solve for y to find an equivalent equation in the form $y = mx + b$:

$$2x + y = 5$$
$$y = -2x + 5. \qquad \text{Adding } -2x \text{ to both sides}$$

The slope is -2. The y-intercept is $(0, 5)$.

c) We rewrite the equation in the form $y = mx + b$:

$$3x - 4y = 7$$
$$-4y = -3x + 7 \qquad \text{Adding } -3x \text{ to both sides}$$
$$y = -\tfrac{1}{4}(-3x + 7) \qquad \text{Multiplying both sides by } -\tfrac{1}{4}$$
$$y = \tfrac{3}{4}x - \tfrac{7}{4}. \qquad \text{Using the distributive law}$$

The slope is $\frac{3}{4}$. The y-intercept is $\left(0, -\frac{7}{4}\right)$.

2. Find the slope and the y-intercept of the line given by $y = -\frac{1}{3}x - 7$.

YOUR TURN

EXAMPLE 3 A line has slope $-\frac{12}{5}$ and y-intercept $(0, 11)$. Find an equation of the line.

SOLUTION We use the slope–intercept equation, substituting $-\frac{12}{5}$ for m and 11 for b:

$$y = mx + b = -\frac{12}{5}x + 11.$$

The desired equation is $y = -\frac{12}{5}x + 11$.

3. A line has slope 4 and y-intercept $(0, -1)$. Find an equation of the line.

YOUR TURN

EXAMPLE 4 *Fast-Food Menus.* The following graph shows the number of items on a McDonald's® lunch menu for various years. Determine an equation for the graph.

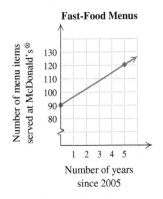

Fast-Food Menus

Source: Based on information from Technomic MenuMonitor

4. Determine an equation for the following graph.

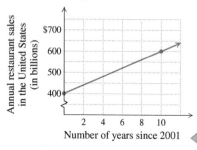

Source: Based on information from the National Restaurant Association

SOLUTION   If we know the y-intercept and the slope, we can use slope–intercept form to write an equation for the line. From the graph, we see that $(0, 90)$ is the y-intercept and that the line passes through $(5, 120)$. We calculate the slope:

$$m = \frac{\text{change in } y}{\text{change in } x} = \frac{120 - 90}{5 - 0} = \frac{30}{5} = 6.$$

The desired equation is

$$y = 6x + 90, \qquad \text{Using 6 for } m \text{ and 90 for } b$$

where y is the number of menu items x years after 2005.

YOUR TURN

Graphing and Slope–Intercept Form

In Example 1, we drew a graph, knowing only the slope and the y-intercept. In Example 2, we determined the slope and the y-intercept of a line by examining its equation. We now combine the two procedures to develop a quick way to graph a linear equation.

EXAMPLE 5   Graph: **(a)** $y = \frac{3}{4}x + 5$; **(b)** $2x + 3y = 3$.

SOLUTION   To graph each equation, we plot the y-intercept and find additional points using the slope.

a) We can read the slope and the y-intercept from the equation $y = \frac{3}{4}x + 5$:

> Slope: $\frac{3}{4}$; y-intercept: $(0, 5)$.

We plot the y-intercept $(0, 5)$. This gives us one point on the line.
   Starting at $(0, 5)$, we use the slope $\frac{3}{4}$ to find another point.

> Determine the slope and the y-intercept.

> Plot the y-intercept.

> We move 3 units *up* since the numerator (change in y) is *positive*.

> Use the slope to find a second point.

> We move 4 units *to the right* since the denominator (change in x) is *positive*.

This gives us a second point on the line, $(4, 8)$.
   We can find a third point on the line by rewriting the slope $\frac{3}{4}$ as $\frac{-3}{-4}$, since these fractions are equivalent. Now, starting again at $(0, 5)$, we use the slope $\frac{-3}{-4}$ to find another point.

> We move 3 units *down* since the numerator (change in y) is *negative*.

> Use the slope to find a third point.

> We move 4 units *to the left* since the denominator (change in x) is *negative*.

This gives us a third point on the line, $(-4, 2)$.
   Finally, we draw the line.

> Draw the line.

Student Notes

Recall the following:

$$\frac{3}{4} = \frac{-3}{-4};$$

$$-\frac{3}{4} = \frac{-3}{4} = \frac{3}{-4};$$

$$2 = \frac{2}{1} \quad \text{and} \quad -2 = \frac{-2}{1}.$$

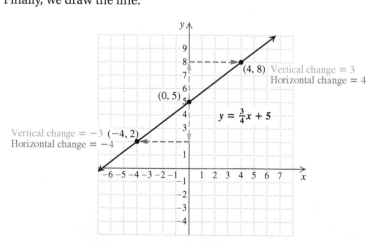

b) To graph $2x + 3y = 3$, we first rewrite it to find the slope and the y-intercept:

$$2x + 3y = 3$$
$$3y = -2x + 3 \qquad \text{Adding } -2x \text{ to both sides}$$
$$y = \tfrac{1}{3}(-2x + 3) \qquad \text{Multiplying both sides by } \tfrac{1}{3}$$
$$y = -\tfrac{2}{3}x + 1. \qquad \text{Using the distributive law}$$

We plot the y-intercept, $(0, 1)$.

The slope is $-\tfrac{2}{3}$. For graphing, we think of this slope as $\tfrac{-2}{3}$ or $\tfrac{2}{-3}$. Starting at $(0, 1)$, we use the slope $\tfrac{-2}{3}$ to find a second point.

We move 2 units *down* since the numerator is *negative*.

We move 3 units *to the right* since the denominator is *positive*.

We plot the new point, $(3, -1)$.

Now, starting at $(3, -1)$ and again using the slope $\tfrac{-2}{3}$, we move to a third point, $(6, -3)$.

Alternatively, we can start at $(0, 1)$ and use the slope $\tfrac{2}{-3}$.

We move 2 units *up* since the numerator is *positive*.

We move 3 units *to the left* since the denominator is *negative*.

This leads to another point on the graph, $(-3, 3)$.

Student Notes

The signs of the numerator and the denominator of the slope indicate whether to move up, down, left, or right. Compare the following slopes.

$\dfrac{1}{2} \begin{array}{l}\leftarrow 1 \text{ unit up} \\ \leftarrow 2 \text{ units right}\end{array}$

$\dfrac{-1}{-2} \begin{array}{l}\leftarrow 1 \text{ unit down} \\ \leftarrow 2 \text{ units left}\end{array}$

$\dfrac{-1}{2} \begin{array}{l}\leftarrow 1 \text{ unit down} \\ \leftarrow 2 \text{ units right}\end{array}$

$\dfrac{1}{-2} \begin{array}{l}\leftarrow 1 \text{ unit up} \\ \leftarrow 2 \text{ units left}\end{array}$

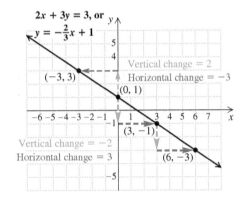

$2x + 3y = 3$, or $y = -\tfrac{2}{3}x + 1$

(−3, 3)   Vertical change = 2   Horizontal change = −3   (0, 1)

Vertical change = −2   Horizontal change = 3   (3, −1)   (6, −3)

It is important to be able to use both $\tfrac{2}{-3}$ and $\tfrac{-2}{3}$ to draw the graph.

5. Graph: $y = -\tfrac{1}{2}x - 2$.

 YOUR TURN

Parallel Lines and Perpendicular Lines

Two lines are parallel if they lie in the same plane and do not intersect no matter how far they are extended. If two lines are vertical, they are parallel. How can we tell if nonvertical lines are parallel? The answer is simple: We look at their slopes.

> **SLOPE AND PARALLEL LINES**
>
> Two lines are parallel if they have the same slope or if both lines are vertical.

EXAMPLE 6   Determine whether the line given by $y = -3x + 4.2$ is parallel to the line given by $6x + 2y = 1$.

SOLUTION   If the slopes of the lines are the same, the lines are parallel.
The slope of $f(x) = -3x + 4.2$ is -3.
To find the slope of $6x + 2y = 1$, we write the equation in slope–intercept form:

$$6x + 2y = 1$$
$$2y = -6x + 1 \qquad \text{Subtracting } 6x \text{ from both sides}$$
$$y = -3x + \tfrac{1}{2}. \qquad \text{Dividing both sides by 2}$$

The slope of the second line is -3. Since the slopes are equal, the lines are parallel.

6. Determine whether the line given by $8x + y = 2$ is parallel to the line given by $y = 8x + 7$.

YOUR TURN

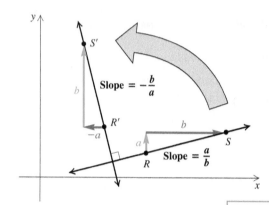

Slope $= -\dfrac{b}{a}$

Slope $= \dfrac{a}{b}$

Two lines are perpendicular if they intersect at a right angle. If one line is vertical and another is horizontal, they are perpendicular. There are other instances in which two lines are perpendicular.

Consider a line $\overleftrightarrow{RS}$ as shown at left, with slope a/b. Then think of rotating the figure 90° to get a line $\overleftrightarrow{R'S'}$ perpendicular to $\overleftrightarrow{RS}$. For the new line, the rise and the run are interchanged, but the run is now negative. Thus the slope of the new line is $-b/a$. Let's multiply the slopes:

$$\frac{a}{b}\left(-\frac{b}{a}\right) = -1.$$

This can help us determine which lines are perpendicular.

> **SLOPE AND PERPENDICULAR LINES**
>
> Two lines are perpendicular if the product of their slopes is -1 or if one line is vertical and the other line is horizontal.

Thus, if one line has slope m ($m \neq 0$), the slope of any line perpendicular to it is $-1/m$. That is, we take the reciprocal of m ($m \neq 0$) and change the sign.

EXAMPLE 7   Determine whether the graphs of $2x + y = 8$ and $y = \tfrac{1}{2}x + 7$ are perpendicular.

SOLUTION   The second equation is given in slope–intercept form:

$$y = \tfrac{1}{2}x + 7. \qquad \text{The slope is } \tfrac{1}{2}.$$

To find the slope of the other line, we solve for y:

$$2x + y = 8$$
$$y = -2x + 8. \qquad \text{Adding } -2x \text{ to both sides}$$
$$\text{The slope is } -2.$$

The lines are perpendicular if the product of their slopes is -1. Since

$$\tfrac{1}{2}(-2) = -1,$$

7. Determine whether the graphs of $x + y = 3$ and $x - y = 8$ are perpendicular.

the graphs are perpendicular. The graphs of both equations are shown at left, and they do appear to be perpendicular.

YOUR TURN

3.6 EXERCISE SET

FOR EXTRA HELP MyMathLab® Math XL PRACTICE WATCH

 Vocabulary and Reading Check

Classify each of the following as either "slope" or "y-intercept."

1. m for $y = mx + b$

2. $(0, b)$ for $y = mx + b$

3. The point at which a graph crosses the y-axis

4. A value that is the same for parallel lines

5. $(0, 5)$ for $y = x + 5$

6. 1 for $y = x + 5$

Concept Reinforcement

In each of Exercises 7–12, match the phrase with the most appropriate choice from the following list.

a) $\left(0, \frac{3}{4}\right)$ b) 2

c) $(0, -3)$ d) $\frac{2}{3}$

e) $(0, -2)$ f) 3

7. ____ The slope of the graph of $y = 3x - 2$

8. ____ The slope of the graph of $y = 2x - 3$

9. ____ The slope of the graph of $y = \frac{2}{3}x + 3$

10. ____ The y-intercept of the graph of $y = 2x - 3$

11. ____ The y-intercept of the graph of $y = 3x - 2$

12. ____ The y-intercept of the graph of $y = \frac{2}{3}x + \frac{3}{4}$

Using the y-intercept and the Slope to Graph a Line

Draw a line that has the given slope and y-intercept.

13. Slope $\frac{2}{3}$; y-intercept $(0, 1)$

14. Slope $\frac{3}{5}$; y-intercept $(0, -1)$

15. Slope $\frac{5}{3}$; y-intercept $(0, -2)$

16. Slope $\frac{1}{2}$; y-intercept $(0, 0)$

17. Slope $-\frac{1}{3}$; y-intercept $(0, 5)$

18. Slope $-\frac{4}{5}$; y-intercept $(0, 6)$

19. Slope 2; y-intercept $(0, 0)$

20. Slope -2; y-intercept $(0, -3)$

21. Slope -3; y-intercept $(0, 2)$

22. Slope 3; y-intercept $(0, 4)$

Aha! 23. Slope 0; y-intercept $(0, -5)$

24. Slope 0; y-intercept $(0, 1)$

Equations in Slope–Intercept Form

Find the slope and the y-intercept of each line from the given equation.

25. $y = -\frac{2}{7}x + 5$ 26. $y = -\frac{3}{8}x + 4$

27. $y = \frac{1}{3}x + 7$ 28. $y = \frac{4}{5}x + 1$

29. $y = \frac{9}{5}x - 4$ 30. $y = -\frac{9}{10}x - 5$

31. $-3x + y = 7$ 32. $-4x + y = 7$

33. $4x + 2y = 8$ 34. $3x + 4y = 12$

Aha! 35. $y = 3$ 36. $y - 3 = 5$

37. $2x - 5y = -8$ 38. $12x - 6y = 9$

39. $9x - 8y = 0$ 40. $7x = 5y$

Find the slope–intercept equation of the line with the indicated slope and y-intercept.

41. Slope 5; y-intercept $(0, 7)$

42. Slope -4; y-intercept $\left(0, -\frac{3}{5}\right)$

43. Slope $\frac{7}{8}$; y-intercept $(0, -1)$

44. Slope $\frac{5}{7}$; y-intercept $(0, 4)$

45. Slope $-\frac{5}{3}$; y-intercept $(0, -8)$

46. Slope $\frac{3}{4}$; y-intercept $(0, -35)$

Aha! 47. Slope 0; y-intercept $\left(0, \frac{1}{3}\right)$

48. Slope 7; y-intercept $(0, 0)$

Determine an equation for each graph shown.

49.

Federal Credit Union Members

Source: Based on information from the National Credit Union Association

50.

Cost of an Overseas Internet Call

51.

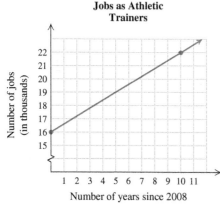

Jobs as Athletic Trainers

Source: Based on data from the U.S. Bureau of Labor Statistics

52.

Average Hourly Earnings for Home Health Aides

Source: Based on data from the U.S. Bureau of Labor Statistics

Graphing and Slope–Intercept Form

Graph.

53. $y = \frac{2}{3}x + 2$

54. $y = -\frac{2}{3}x - 3$

55. $y = -\frac{2}{3}x + 3$

56. $y = \frac{2}{3}x - 2$

57. $y = \frac{3}{2}x + 3$

58. $y = \frac{3}{2}x - 2$

59. $y = -\frac{4}{3}x + 3$

60. $y = -\frac{3}{2}x - 2$

61. $2x + y = 1$

62. $3x + y = 2$

63. $3x + y = 0$

64. $2x + y = 0$

65. $4x + 5y = 15$

66. $2x + 3y = 9$

67. $x - 4y = 12$

68. $x + 5y = 20$

Parallel Lines and Perpendicular Lines

Without graphing, tell whether the graphs of each pair of equations are parallel.

69. $x + 2 = y$,
   $y - x = -2$

70. $2x - 1 = y$,
   $2y - 4x = 7$

71. $y + 9 = 3x$,
   $3x - y = -2$

72. $y + 8 = -6x$,
   $-2x + y = 5$

73. $y = 3x + 9$,
   $2y = 8x - 2$

74. $y = -7x - 9$,
   $-3y = 21x + 7$

Without graphing, tell whether the graphs of each pair of equations are perpendicular.

75. $x - 2y = 3$,
   $4x + 2y = 1$

76. $2x - 5y = -3$,
   $2x + 5y = 4$

77. $y = 3x + 1$,
   $6x + 2y = 5$

78. $y = -x + 7$,
   $y = x + 3$

79. Can a horizontal line be graphed using the method of Example 5? Why or why not?

80. Can a vertical line be graphed using the method of Example 5? Why or why not?

Skill Review

Solve.

81. Mr. and Mrs. Sturgis left a $3 tip for a meal that cost $25. What percent of the cost of the meal was the tip? [2.4]

82. Irniq is writing a 1000-word essay. He has three times as many words to write as he has already written. How many words has he written? [2.5]

83. In December, the balance in Dalila's college savings account grew 15%, to $2760. What was her balance at the beginning of the month? [2.5]

84. The perimeter of a hospital's rectangular flower garden is 140 ft. The width is 30 ft less than the length. Find the width and the length. [2.5]

Synthesis

85. Explain how it is possible for an incorrect graph to be drawn, even after plotting three points that line up.

86. Which would you prefer, and why: graphing an equation of the form $y = mx + b$ or graphing an equation of the form $Ax + By = C$?

87. Show that the slope of the line given by $y = mx + b$ is m. (*Hint*: Substitute both 0 and 1 for x to find two pairs of coordinates. Then use the formula, Slope = change in y/change in x.)

88. Write an equation of the line with the same slope as the line given by $5x + 2y = 8$ and the same y-intercept as the line given by $3x - 7y = 10$.

89. Write an equation of the line parallel to the line given by $-4x + 8y = 5$ and having the same y-intercept as the line given by $4x - 3y = 0$.

90. Write an equation of the line parallel to the line given by $3x - 2y = 8$ and having the same y-intercept as the line given by $2y + 3x = -4$.

91. Write an equation of the line parallel to the line given by $4x + 5y = 9$ and having the same y-intercept as the line given by $2x + 3y = 12$.

92. Write an equation of the line perpendicular to the line given by $2x + 3y = 7$ and having the same y-intercept as the line given by $5x + 2y = 10$.

93. Write an equation of the line perpendicular to the line given by $3x - 5y = 8$ and having the same y-intercept as the line given by $2x + 4y = 12$.

94. Write an equation of the line perpendicular to the line given by $3x - 2y = 9$ and having the same y-intercept as the line given by $2x + 5y = 0$.

95. Write an equation of the line perpendicular to the line given by $2x + 5y = 6$ that passes through $(2, 6)$. (*Hint*: Draw a graph.)

96. Graph $y_1 = -\frac{3}{4}x - 2$, $y_2 = -\frac{1}{5}x - 2$, $y_3 = -\frac{3}{4}x - 5$, and $y_4 = -\frac{1}{5}x - 5$ using the SIMULTANEOUS mode. Then match each line with the corresponding equation. Check using TRACE.

YOUR TURN ANSWERS: SECTION 3.6

1. **2.** Slope: $-\frac{1}{3}$; y-intercept: $(0, -7)$

3. $y = 4x - 1$ **4.** $y = 20x + 400$, where y is the amount of U.S. restaurant sales, in billions of dollars, and x is the number of years since 2001

5. $y = -\frac{1}{2}x - 2$ **6.** No **7.** Yes

QUICK QUIZ: SECTIONS 3.1–3.6
Graph.

1. $y = 3$ [3.3] **2.** $y = \frac{1}{2}x - 4$ [3.6]

3. In which quadrant or on which axis is $(-12, -0.02)$ located? [3.1]

4. List the coordinates of the x- and y-intercepts of the graph of $y - x = 7$. [3.3]

5. Find the slope of the graph of $y - x = 7$. [3.6]

PREPARE TO MOVE ON
Solve. [2.3]

1. $y - k = m(x - h)$, for y

2. $y - 9 = -2(x + 4)$, for y

Simplify. [1.6]

3. $-10 - (-3)$ **4.** $8 - (-5)$

5. $-4 - 5$

3.7 Point–Slope Form and Equations of Lines

Point–Slope Form ▪ Finding the Equation of a Line ▪ Estimations and Predictions Using Two Points

If we know the slope of a line and a point through which the line passes, then we can draw the line. With this information, we can also write an equation of the line.

Point–Slope Form

Suppose that a line of slope m passes through the point (x_1, y_1). For any other point (x, y) to lie on this line, we must have

$$\frac{y - y_1}{x - x_1} = m.$$

Note that if (x_1, y_1) itself replaces (x, y), the denominator is 0. To address this concern, we multiply both sides by $x - x_1$:

$$(x - x_1)\frac{y - y_1}{x - x_1} = m(x - x_1)$$

$$y - y_1 = m(x - x_1). \qquad \text{This equation } is \text{ true for } (x, y) = (x_1, y_1).$$

Every point on the line is a solution of this equation. This is the **point–slope form** of a linear equation.

> **POINT–SLOPE FORM**
>
> Any equation of the form $y - y_1 = m(x - x_1)$ is said to be written in *point–slope* form and has a graph that is a straight line.
>
> The slope of the line is m.
>
> The line passes through (x_1, y_1).

EXAMPLE 1   Graph: $(y + 4) = -\frac{1}{2}(x - 3)$.

SOLUTION   We first write the equation in point–slope form:

$$y - y_1 = m(x - x_1)$$

$$y - (-4) = -\tfrac{1}{2}(x - 3). \qquad y + 4 = y - (-4)$$

From the equation, we see that $m = -\frac{1}{2}$, $x_1 = 3$, and $y_1 = -4$. We plot $(3, -4)$, count off a slope of $-\frac{1}{2}$, and draw the line.

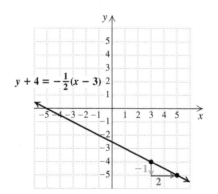

$y + 4 = -\frac{1}{2}(x - 3)$

1. Graph: $y - 1 = 3(x + 2)$.

 YOUR TURN

We can use point–slope form to find an equation of the line.

EXAMPLE 2   Use point–slope form to find an equation of the line with slope 3 that passes through $(-7, 8)$.

SOLUTION   We substitute into the point–slope form:

$$y - y_1 = m(x - x_1)$$
$$y - 8 = 3(x - (-7)). \quad \text{Substituting 3 for } m, -7 \text{ for } x_1, \text{ and } 8 \text{ for } y_1$$

This is an equation of the line. If desired, we can solve for y to write it in slope–intercept form.

YOUR TURN

2. Use point–slope form to find an equation of the line with slope -5 that passes through $(1, -6)$.

The point–slope form can be used to find the equation of any line given the slope and a point. Other forms of linear equations can also be used and may be more convenient in some situations.

Finding the Equation of a Line

GIVEN THE SLOPE AND THE y-INTERCEPT

If we know the slope m and the y-intercept $(0, b)$ of a line, we can find an equation of the line by substituting into slope–intercept form, $y = mx + b$.

EXAMPLE 3   Find an equation for the line parallel to $8y = 7x - 24$ with y-intercept $(0, -6)$.

SOLUTION   We first find slope–intercept form of the given line:

$$8y = 7x - 24$$
$$y = \tfrac{7}{8}x - 3. \quad \text{Multiplying both sides by } \tfrac{1}{8}$$
$$\underline{} \text{ The slope is } \tfrac{7}{8}.$$

The slope of any line parallel to the line given by $8y = 7x - 24$ is $\tfrac{7}{8}$. For a y-intercept of $(0, -6)$, we must have

$$y = mx + b$$
$$y = \tfrac{7}{8}x - 6. \quad \text{Substituting } \tfrac{7}{8} \text{ for } m \text{ and } -6 \text{ for } b$$

3. Find an equation for the line parallel to $3y = 3x + 12$ with y-intercept $(0, 5)$.

YOUR TURN

GIVEN THE SLOPE AND A POINT OR GIVEN TWO POINTS

When we know the slope m of a line and any point on the line, we can find the equation of the line either by using slope–intercept form, $y = mx + b$, and solving for b or by substituting directly into point–slope form, $y - y_1 = m(x - x_1)$.

EXAMPLE 4   Find an equation for the line perpendicular to $2x + y = 5$ that passes through $(1, -3)$.

SOLUTION   We first find slope–intercept form of the given line:

$$2x + y = 5$$
$$y = -2x + 5. \quad \text{Subtracting } 2x \text{ from both sides}$$
$$\underline{} \text{ The slope is } -2.$$

Study Skills

Understand Your Mistakes

When your instructor returns a graded quiz, test, or assignment, it is important that you review and understand what your mistakes were. Take advantage of the opportunity to learn from your mistakes.

4. Find an equation in point–slope form for the line perpendicular to $3x - 4y = 7$ that passes through $(8, 2)$.

The slope of any line perpendicular to the line given by $2x + y = 5$ is the opposite of the reciprocal of -2, or $\frac{1}{2}$. Substituting into the point–slope form, we have

$$y - y_1 = m(x - x_1)$$
$$y - (-3) = \tfrac{1}{2}(x - 1). \qquad \text{Substituting } \tfrac{1}{2} \text{ for } m, 1 \text{ for } x_1, \text{ and } -3 \text{ for } y_1$$

YOUR TURN

EXAMPLE 5 Use slope–intercept form to find an equation of the line with slope 4 that passes through $(6, -5)$.

SOLUTION Since the slope of the line is 4, we have

$$y = mx + b$$
$$y = 4x + b. \qquad \text{Substituting 4 for } m$$

To find b, we use the fact that if $(6, -5)$ is a point on the line, then that ordered pair is a solution of the equation of the line.

$$y = 4x + b \qquad \text{We know that } m \text{ is 4.}$$
$$-5 = 4(6) + b \qquad \text{Substituting 6 for } x \text{ and } -5 \text{ for } y$$
$$-5 = 24 + b$$
$$-29 = b \qquad \text{Solving for } b$$

5. Use slope–intercept form to find an equation of the line with slope $\frac{1}{2}$ that passes through $(8, -3)$.

Now we know that $b = -29$, so the equation of the line is

$$y = 4x - 29. \qquad m = 4 \text{ and } b = -29$$

YOUR TURN

We can also find the equation of a line if we know two points on the line.

EXAMPLE 6 Find the slope–intercept equation of the line passing through $(-1, -5)$ and $(3, -2)$.

SOLUTION We first determine the slope of the line and then write an equation in point–slope form. (We could also use slope–intercept form as in Example 5.) Note that

Find the slope.

$$m = \frac{-5 - (-2)}{-1 - 3} = \frac{-3}{-4} = \frac{3}{4}.$$

Since the line passes through $(3, -2)$, we have

Substitute the point and the slope in the point–slope form.

$$y - (-2) = \tfrac{3}{4}(x - 3) \qquad \text{Substituting into } y - y_1 = m(x - x_1)$$
$$y + 2 = \tfrac{3}{4}x - \tfrac{9}{4} \qquad \text{Using the distributive law}$$

Write in slope–intercept form.

$$y = \tfrac{3}{4}x - \tfrac{9}{4} - 2 \qquad \text{Subtracting 2 from both sides}$$
$$y = \tfrac{3}{4}x - \tfrac{17}{4}. \qquad -\tfrac{9}{4} - \tfrac{8}{4} = -\tfrac{17}{4}$$

6. Find the slope–intercept equation of the line passing through $(6, -1)$ and $(-2, -3)$.

You can check that using $(-1, -5)$ as (x_1, y_1) in $y - y_1 = \tfrac{3}{4}(x - x_1)$ yields the same slope–intercept equation of the line.

YOUR TURN

HORIZONTAL LINES OR VERTICAL LINES

If we know that a line is horizontal or vertical and we know one point on the line, we can find an equation for the line.

EXAMPLE 7 Find **(a)** the equation of the horizontal line that passes through $(1, -4)$, and **(b)** the equation of the vertical line that passes through $(1, -4)$.

SOLUTION

a) An equation of a horizontal line is of the form $y = b$. In order for $(1, -4)$ to be a solution of $y = b$, we must have $b = -4$. Thus the equation of the line is $y = -4$.

b) An equation of a vertical line is of the form $x = a$. In order for $(1, -4)$ to be a solution of $x = a$, we must have $a = 1$. Thus the equation of the line is $x = 1$.

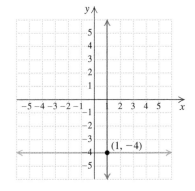

7. Find the equation of the vertical line that passes through $(2, 8)$.

 YOUR TURN

Estimations and Predictions Using Two Points

We can estimate real-life quantities that are not already known by using two points with known coordinates. When the unknown point is located *between* the two points, this process is called **interpolation**. If a graph passing through the known points is *extended* to predict future values, the process is called **extrapolation**. In statistics, methods exist for using a set of several points to interpolate or extrapolate values using lines and other curves.

Month	Total Number of Apps Downloaded from the iTunes Store per iOS Device
October 2008	10
April 2009	25
October 2009	33
April 2010	45
October 2010	55
January 2011	63

Source: Based on data from www.asymco.com

EXAMPLE 8 *Apps.* The number of apps downloaded to mobile devices has increased rapidly in recent years. This increase is not due entirely to the fact that more mobile devices have been purchased. As the data in the table at left indicate, the number of apps downloaded per iOS device (iPhone, iPad, and iPod) has increased.

a) Graph the data from October 2009 and January 2011. Let x represent the number of months since October 2008 and y the number of apps downloaded per device. Then use the two points to determine an equation for the line.

b) Estimate the number of apps downloaded per device in July 2010 and the number of apps downloaded per device in January 2012.

SOLUTION

a) We first draw and label a horizontal axis to display the month and a vertical axis to display the number of apps downloaded per device. Next, we number the axes, choosing scales that include both the given values and the values to be estimated.

Since $x =$ the number of months since October 2008, we plot $(12, 33)$ and $(27, 63)$ and draw a line passing through both points.

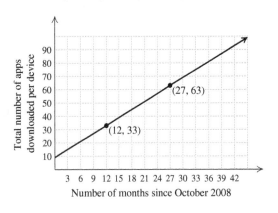

To find an equation for the line, we first calculate its slope:

$$m = \frac{\text{change in } y}{\text{change in } x} = \frac{63 - 33}{27 - 12} = \frac{30}{15} = 2.$$

The number of total apps downloaded per device purchased increased at a rate of 2 apps per month. We can use either of the given points to write a point–slope equation for the line. Choosing $(12, 33)$, we write an equivalent equation in slope–intercept form:

Chapter Resources:
Visualizing for Success, p. 221;
Decision Making: Connection,
p. 222

$y - y_1 = m(x - x_1)$	Writing the general point–slope equation
$y - 33 = 2(x - 12)$	Substituting. This is a point–slope equation.
$y - 33 = 2x - 24$	Using the distributive law
$y = 2x + 9.$	Adding 33 to both sides. This is slope–intercept form.

b) To estimate the total number of apps downloaded per device in July 2010, we substitute 21 for x in the slope–intercept equation:

$$y = 2 \cdot 21 + 9 = 51. \qquad \text{July 2010 is 21 months after October 2008.}$$

In July 2010, there were about 51 apps downloaded per device purchased. Because July 2010 is *between* October 2009 and January 2011, we are *interpolating* here.

To estimate the total number of apps downloaded per device purchased in January 2012, we substitute 39 for x in the slope–intercept equation:

$$y = 2 \cdot 39 + 9 = 87. \qquad \text{January 2012 is 39 months after October 2008.}$$

In January 2012, there were about 87 apps downloaded per device purchased. Because January 2012 is *beyond* January 2011, we are *extrapolating* here. This prediction assumes that the trend indicated by the data continues.

The following graph confirms the estimates found above.

8. The data used for Example 8 do not all lie on a straight line. Thus a different pair of points may yield a different equation for the line used to model the application.

a) The data from April 2009 and October 2010 correspond to the points $(6, 25)$ and $(24, 55)$. Find an equation for the line containing these points and then rewrite it in slope–intercept form.

b) Use the equation found in part (a) to estimate the number of apps downloaded per device in July 2010 and to estimate the number of apps downloaded per device in January 2012.

 YOUR TURN

CONNECTING THE CONCEPTS

Any line can be described by a number of equivalent equations. We write the equation in the form that is most useful for us. For example, all four of the equations shown at right describe the same line.

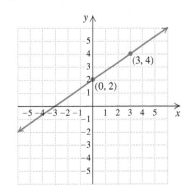

$2x - 3y = -6;$

$y = \frac{2}{3}x + 2;$

$y - 4 = \frac{2}{3}(x - 3);$

$2x + 6 = 3y$

Form of a Linear Equation	Example	Uses
Standard form: $Ax + By = C$	$2x - 3y = -6$	Finding x- and y-intercepts; Graphing using intercepts
Slope–intercept form: $y = mx + b$	$y = \frac{2}{3}x + 2$	Finding slope and y-intercept; Graphing using slope and y-intercept; Writing an equation given slope and y-intercept
Point–slope form: $y - y_1 = m(x - x_1)$	$y - 4 = \frac{2}{3}(x - 3)$	Finding slope and a point on the line; Graphing using slope and a point on the line; Writing an equation given slope and a point on the line

EXERCISES

Tell whether each equation is in standard form, slope–intercept form, point–slope form, or none of these.

1. $y = -\frac{1}{2}x - 7$

2. $5x - 8y = 10$

3. $x = y + 2$

4. $\frac{1}{2}x + \frac{1}{3}y = 5$

5. $y - 2 = 5(x - (-1))$

6. $3y + 7 = x$

Write each equation in standard form.

7. $2x = 5y + 10$

8. $y = 2x + 7$

Write each equation in slope–intercept form.

9. $2x - 7y = 8$

10. $y + 5 = -(x + 3)$

3.7 EXERCISE SET

FOR EXTRA HELP

MyMathLab® MathXL

PRACTICE   WATCH   READ   REVIEW

Vocabulary and Reading Check

Classify each of the following statements as either true or false.

1. The equation $y = -3x - 1$ is written in point–slope form.

2. The equation $y - 4 = -3(x - 1)$ is written in point–slope form.

3. Knowing the coordinates of just one point on a line is enough to write an equation of the line.

4. Knowing coordinates of just one point on a line and the slope of the line is enough to write an equation of the line.

5. Knowing the coordinates of just two points on a line is enough to write an equation of the line.

6. Point–slope form can be used with any point that is used to calculate the slope of that line.

Point–Slope Form

For each point–slope equation listed, state the slope and a point on the graph.

7. $y - 3 = \frac{1}{4}(x - 5)$

8. $y - 5 = 6(x - 1)$

9. $y + 1 = -7(x - 2)$

10. $y - 4 = -\frac{2}{3}(x + 8)$

11. $y - 6 = -\frac{10}{3}(x + 4)$

12. $y + 1 = -9(x - 7)$

Aha! 13. $y = 5x$

14. $y = \frac{4}{5}x$

Graph.

15. $y - 2 = 3(x - 5)$

16. $y - 4 = 2(x - 3)$

17. $y - 2 = -4(x - 1)$

18. $y - 4 = -5(x - 1)$

19. $y + 4 = \frac{1}{2}(x + 2)$

20. $y + 7 = \frac{1}{3}(x + 5)$

21. $y = -(x - 8)$

22. $y = -3(x + 2)$

Finding the Equation of a Line

Find an equation for each line. Write your final answer in slope–intercept form.

23. Parallel to $y = 3x - 7$; y-intercept $(0, 4)$

24. Parallel to $y = \frac{1}{2}x + 6$; y-intercept $(0, -1)$

25. Perpendicular to $y = -\frac{3}{4}x + 1$; y-intercept $(0, -12)$

26. Perpendicular to $y = \frac{5}{8}x - 2$; y-intercept $(0, 9)$

27. Parallel to $2x - 3y = 4$; y-intercept $\left(0, \frac{1}{2}\right)$

28. Perpendicular to $4x + 7y = 1$; y-intercept $(0, -4.2)$

29. Perpendicular to $x + y = 18$; y-intercept $(0, -32)$

30. Parallel to $x - y = 6$; y-intercept $(0, 27)$

Find an equation in point–slope form for the line having the specified slope and containing the point indicated.

31. $m = 6$, $(7, 1)$

32. $m = 4$, $(3, 8)$

33. $m = -5$, $(3, 4)$

34. $m = -7$, $(1, 2)$

35. $m = \frac{1}{2}$, $(-2, -5)$

36. $m = 1$, $(-4, -6)$

37. $m = -1$, $(9, 0)$

38. $m = -\frac{2}{3}$, $(5, 0)$

Find an equation of the line having the specified slope and containing the indicated point. Write your final answer in slope–intercept form.

39. $m = 2$, $(1, -4)$

40. $m = -4$, $(-1, 5)$

41. $m = -\frac{3}{5}$, $(-4, 8)$

42. $m = -\frac{1}{5}$, $(-2, 1)$

43. $m = -0.6$, $(-3, -4)$

44. $m = 2.3$, $(4, -5)$

Aha! 45. $m = \frac{2}{7}$, $(0, -6)$

46. $m = \frac{1}{4}$, $(0, 3)$

47. $m = \frac{3}{5}$, $(-4, 6)$

48. $m = -\frac{2}{7}$, $(6, -5)$

Write an equation of the line containing the specified point and parallel to the indicated line.

49. $(2, 5)$, $x - 2y = 3$

50. $(1, 4)$, $3x + y = 5$

51. $(-3, 2)$, $x + y = 7$

52. $(-1, -6)$, $x - 5y = 1$

53. $(-2, -3)$, $2x + 3y = -7$

54. $(3, -4)$, $5x - 6y = 4$

Aha! 55. $(5, -4)$, $x = 2$

56. $(-3, 6)$, $y = 7$

Write an equation of the line containing the specified point and perpendicular to the indicated line.

57. $(3, 1)$, $2x - 3y = 4$

58. $(6, 0)$, $5x + 4y = 1$

59. $(-4, 2)$, $x + y = 6$

60. $(-2, -5)$, $x - 2y = 3$

61. $(1, -3)$, $3x - y = 2$

62. $(-5, 6)$, $4x - y = 3$

63. $(-4, -7)$, $3x - 5y = 6$

64. $(-4, 5)$, $7x - 2y = 1$

65. $(-3, 7)$, $y = 5$

66. $(4, -2)$, $x = 1$

Find an equation of the line containing each pair of points. Write your final answer in slope–intercept form.

67. $(2, 3)$ and $(3, 7)$ **68.** $(3, 8)$ and $(1, 4)$

69. $(1.2, -4)$ and $(3.2, 5)$

70. $(-1, -2.5)$ and $(4, 8.5)$

Aha! **71.** $(2, -5)$ and $(0, -1)$ **72.** $(-2, 0)$ and $(0, -7)$

73. $(-6, -10)$ and $(-3, -5)$

74. $(-1, -3)$ and $(-4, -9)$

Find an equation of each line.

75. Horizontal line through $(2, -6)$

76. Horizontal line through $(-1, 8)$

77. Vertical line through $(-10, -9)$

78. Vertical line through $(4, 12)$

Estimations and Predictions Using Two Points

In Exercises 79–84, assume the data is linear.

79. *Volunteering.* The number of volunteers from the Millennial generation (those born in 1982 or later) has increased from 6.1 million in 2003 to 11.6 million in 2010.

    Source: www.volunteeringinamerica.gov

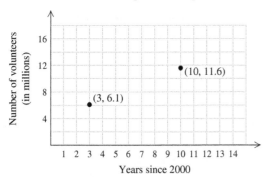

a) Find an equation for the line containing the given points. Let x represent the number of years after 2000 and y the number of volunteers, in millions.

b) Estimate the number of volunteers from the Millennial generation in 2008 and in 2014.

80. *Volunteering.* The average annual number of volunteer hours per United States resident has decreased from 37.9 hr in 2004 to 33.9 hr in 2010.

    Source: www.volunteeringinamerica.gov

a) Find an equation for the line representing the given data. Let x represent the number of years after 2000 and y the average annual number of volunteer hours.

b) Estimate the average annual number of volunteer hours in 2008 and in 2014.

81. *College Enrollment.* The number of students who completed high school and enrolled in college that same year increased from 1.8 million in 2005 to 2.1 million in 2009.

    Source: Digest of Education Statistics, National Center for Education Statistics

a) Find an equation for the line including the given data points. Let x represent the number of years after 2000 and y the number of recent high school graduates (or the equivalent) who enrolled in college that year.

b) Estimate the number of high school graduates (or the equivalent) who enrolled in college in 2007 and in 2015.

82. *Nursery School Enrollment.* The percent of children ages 3 and 4 who are enrolled in nursery school has decreased from 54.5% in 2007 to 52.4% in 2009.

    Source: Digest of Education Statistics, National Center for Education Statistics

a) Find an equation for the line containing the given data points. Let x represent the number of years after 2000 and y the percent of children ages 3 and 4 who are enrolled in nursery school.

b) Estimate the percent of children ages 3 and 4 enrolled in nursery school in 2008 and in 2012.

83. *Urban Population.* The percent of the U.S. population that lives in metropolitan areas was approximately 79% in 2000 and 76.5% in 2009.

    Sources: Census 2000 and 2009 American Community Survey

a) Define variables x and y and find an equation for the line containing the given data points. Answers may vary.

b) Estimate the percent of the U.S. population that lived in metropolitan areas in 2005, and predict the percent living in metropolitan areas in 2012.

84. *Aging Population.* The number of U.S. residents over the age of 65 was approximately 36.3 million in 2004 and 40.1 million in 2010.

    Source: U.S. Census Bureau

a) Define variables x and y and find an equation for the line containing the given data points. Answers may vary.

b) Estimate the number of U.S. residents over the age of 65 in 2006 and in 2016.

85. Can equations for horizontal or vertical lines be written in point–slope form? Why or why not?

86. Describe a situation in which it is easier to graph the equation of a line in point–slope form than in slope–intercept form.

Skill Review

Solve.

87. $\frac{3}{8}x = -24$ [2.1]

88. $6 - x = -3$ [2.2]

89. $\frac{t}{3} = 6$ [2.1]

90. $\frac{1}{2}n - \frac{1}{3} = \frac{1}{6}n + \frac{3}{2}$ [2.2]

91. $2(x - 7) > 5x + 3$ [2.6] **92.** $10 - x \le 12$ [2.6]

Synthesis

 93. Describe a procedure that can be used to write the slope–intercept equation for any nonvertical line passing through two given points.

94. Any nonvertical line has many equations in point–slope form, but only one in slope–intercept form. Why is this?

Graph.

Aha! **95.** $y - 3 = 0(x - 52)$ **96.** $y + 4 = 0(x + 93)$

Write the slope–intercept equation for each line shown.

97.

98.

99. Write the slope–intercept equation of the line that has the same y-intercept as the line $x - 3y = 6$ and contains the point $(5, -1)$.

100. Write the slope–intercept equation of the line that contains the point $(-1, 5)$ and is parallel to the line passing through $(2, 7)$ and $(-1, -3)$.

101. Write the slope–intercept equation of the line that has x-intercept $(-2, 0)$ and is parallel to $4x - 8y = 12$.

102. Find k so that the graph of $5y - kx = 7$ and the line containing $(7, -3)$ and $(-2, 5)$ are parallel.

103. Find k so that the graph of $7y - kx = 9$ and the line containing the points $(2, -1)$ and $(-4, 5)$ are perpendicular.

Another form of a linear equation is the double-intercept form: $\frac{x}{a} + \frac{y}{b} = 1$. *From this form, we can read the x-intercept* $(a, 0)$ *and the y-intercept* $(0, b)$ *directly.*

104. Find the x-intercept and the y-intercept of the graph of $\frac{x}{2} + \frac{y}{5} = 1$.

105. Find the x-intercept and the y-intercept of the graph of $\frac{x}{10} - \frac{y}{3} = 1$.

106. Write the equation $6x + 5y = 30$ in double-intercept form and find the intercepts.

107. If data do not lie exactly on a straight line, more than one equation can be used to model the data. This situation is illustrated in Example 7 and Your Turn Exercise 7. A line of "best fit" can be found using methods not discussed in this section. The most common method used is *linear regression*. To use the linear regression fea-ture of a graphing calculator, use the **STAT** key. Under the STAT EDIT menu, enter x-coordinates in L_1 and y-coordinates in L_2. Then in the STAT CALC menu, choose the Lin Reg option. Use linear regression to find an equation that fits the data in the table in Example 8.

YOUR TURN ANSWERS: SECTION 3.7

1.

2. $y - (-6) = -5(x - 1)$

3. $y = x + 5$

4. $y - 2 = -\frac{4}{3}(x - 8)$

5. $y = \frac{1}{2}x - 7$

6. $y = \frac{1}{4}x - \frac{5}{2}$

$y - 1 = 3(x + 2)$

7. $x = 2$

8. (a) $y = \frac{5}{3}x + 15$, where x is the number of months since October 2008 and y is the number of apps downloaded per device; **(b)** 50 apps per device; 80 apps per device

---

QUICK QUIZ: SECTIONS 3.1–3.7

Graph.

1. $y - 3 = 2x$ [3.2]   **2.** $x + 7 = 8$ [3.3]

3. $y = -3x + 2$ [3.6]   **4.** $3x - 6y = 6$ [3.3]

5. $y - 1 = 2(x + 1)$ [3.7]

PREPARE TO MOVE ON

Simplify. [1.8]

1. $(-5)^3$ **2.** $(-2)^6$

3. -2^6 **4.** $3 \cdot 2^4 - 5 \cdot 2^3$

5. $(5 - 7)^2(3 - 2 \cdot 2)$

A

B

C

D

E

Visualizing for Success

Use after Section 3.7.

Match each equation with its graph.

1. $y = x + 4$

2. $y = 2x$

3. $y = 3$

4. $x = 3$

5. $y = -\frac{1}{2}x$

6. $2x - 3y = 6$

7. $y = -3x - 2$

8. $3x + 2y = 6$

9. $y - 3 = 2(x - 1)$

10. $y + 2 = \frac{1}{2}(x + 1)$

Answers on page A-15

An additional, animated version of this activity appears in MyMathLab. *To use MyMathLab, you need a course ID and a student access code. Contact your instructor for more information.*

F

G

H

I

J

Collaborative Activity   *You Sank My Battleship!*

Focus: Graphing points; logical questioning
Use after: Section 3.1
Time: 15–25 minutes
Group size: 3–5
Materials: Graph paper

In the game Battleship®, a player places a miniature ship on a grid that only that player can see. An opponent guesses at coordinates that might "hit" the "hidden" ship. The following activity is similar to this game.

Activity

1. Using only integers from −10 to 10 (inclusive), one group member should secretly record the coordinates of a point on a slip of paper. (This point is the hidden "battleship.")

2. The other group members can then ask up to 10 "yes/no" questions in an effort to determine the coordinates of the secret point. Be sure to phrase each question mathematically (for example, "Is the *x*-coordinate negative?").

3. The group member who selected the point should answer each question. On the basis of the answer given, another group member should cross out the points no longer under consideration. All group members should check that this is done correctly.

4. If the hidden point has not been determined after 10 questions have been answered, the secret coordinates should be revealed to all group members.

5. Repeat parts (1)–(4) until each group member has had the opportunity to select the hidden point and answer questions.

Decision Making *&* Connection

Depreciation.   From the minute a new car is driven out of a dealership, it *depreciates*, or drops in value with the passing of time. The Kelley Blue Book Market Report is a periodic listing of the values of used cars. The following data are taken from two such reports from the 2011 and the 2012 Central Editions.

Car	Lending Value, November 2011	Lending Value, March 2012
2006 Saturn Ion	$4725	$4650
2006 Mitsubishi Lancer	5800	5525
2006 Kia Rio	5125	4500

1. Assuming that the values are dropping linearly, draw a line representing the value of each car. Draw all three lines on the same graph, using different colored pens or pencils if possible. Let the horizontal axis represent the time, in years, since

(***Use after Section 3.7.***)

January 2011, and the vertical axis the value of each car.

2. At what rate is each car depreciating and how are the different rates illustrated in the graph of part (1)?

3. Find a linear equation that models the value of each car. Let *x* represent the number of years since January 2011, and *y* the value.

4. Use the equations found in part (3) to estimate the value of each car in January 2013.

5. If you had planned to buy one of the three cars in November 2011 and sell it in January 2013, which one would you have purchased, and why?

6. *Research.*   Find the trade-in value of your car or of that of a friend. Use the trade-in value and the price originally paid for the car to estimate the rate of depreciation. Then find a linear equation that models the value of the car and use it to estimate its value one year from now.

Study Summary

KEY TERMS AND CONCEPTS	EXAMPLES	PRACTICE EXERCISES

SECTION 3.1: *Reading Graphs, Plotting Points, and Scaling Graphs*

Ordered pairs can be plotted or **graphed** using a **coordinate system** that uses two **axes**, which are most often labeled x and y. The axes intersect at the **origin**, $(0, 0)$, and divide a plane into four **quadrants**.

1. Plot the points $(0, -5)$ and $(2, -3)$.

2. In which quadrant is the point $(-10, -20)$ located?

SECTION 3.2: *Graphing Linear Equations*

To **graph** an equation means to make a drawing that represents all of its solutions.

A **linear equation**, such as $y = 2x - 7$ or $2x + 3y = 12$, has a graph that is a straight line.

$$3x = y + 1$$

x	y	(x, y)
1	2	$(1, 2)$
0	-1	$(0, -1)$
-1	-4	$(-1, -4)$

3. Graph: $y = 2x + 1$.

SECTION 3.3: *Graphing and Intercepts*

To find a y-intercept $(0, b)$, let $x = 0$ and solve for y.

To find an x-intercept $(a, 0)$, let $y = 0$ and solve for x.

4. Find the x-intercept and the y-intercept of the line given by $10x - y = 10$.

Horizontal Lines
The graph of $y = b$ is a horizontal line, with y-intercept $(0, b)$.

Vertical Lines
The graph of $x = a$ is a vertical line, with x-intercept $(a, 0)$.

5. Graph: $y = -2$.

6. Graph: $x = 3$.

SECTION 3.4: *Rates*

A **rate** is a ratio that indicates how two quantities change with respect to each other.

Tara had \$1500 in her savings account at the beginning of February, and \$2400 at the beginning of May. Find the rate at which Tara is saving.

$$\text{Savings rate} = \frac{\text{Amount saved}}{\text{Number of months}} = \frac{\$2400 - \$1500}{3 \text{ months}}$$

$$= \frac{\$900}{3 \text{ months}} = \$300 \text{ per month}$$

7. At 8:30 A.M., a high school had served 47 people at their pancake breakfast. By 9:15 A.M., the total served had reached 67. Find the serving rate, in number of meals per minute.

SECTION 3.5:   *Slope*

Slope

$$\text{Slope} = m = \frac{\text{change in } y}{\text{change in } x}$$

$$= \frac{\text{rise}}{\text{run}} = \frac{y_2 - y_1}{x_2 - x_1}$$

The slope of a horizontal line is 0.

The slope of a vertical line is undefined.

The slope of the line containing the points $(-1, -4)$ and $(2, -6)$ is

$$m = \frac{-6 - (-4)}{2 - (-1)} = \frac{-2}{3} = -\frac{2}{3}.$$

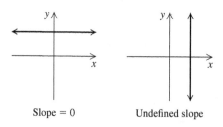

Slope $= 0$ Undefined slope

8. Find the slope of the line containing the points $(1, 4)$ and $(-9, 3)$.

9. Find the slope of the line given by $y = 10$.

SECTION 3.6:   *Slope–Intercept Form*

Slope–Intercept Form

$$y = mx + b$$

The slope of the line is m. The y-intercept of the line is $(0, b)$.

For the line given by $y = \frac{2}{3}x - 8$:

The slope is $\frac{2}{3}$ and the y-intercept is $(0, -8)$.

10. Find the slope and the y-intercept of the line given by $y = -4x + \frac{2}{5}$.

To graph a line written in slope–intercept form, plot the y-intercept, count off the slope to locate a second point, and draw the line.

11. Graph: $y = \frac{1}{2}x + 2$.

Parallel Lines
Two lines are parallel if they have the same slope or if both are vertical.

Determine whether the graphs of $y = \frac{2}{3}x - 5$ and $3y - 2x = 7$ are parallel.

$$y = \frac{2}{3}x - 5 \qquad 3y - 2x = 7$$

The slope is $\frac{2}{3}$. $3y = 2x + 7$

$$y = \frac{2}{3}x + \frac{7}{3}$$

The slope is $\frac{2}{3}$.

Since the slopes are the same, the graphs are parallel.

12. Determine whether the graphs of $y = 4x - 12$ and $4y = x - 9$ are parallel.

SECTION 3.7:   *Point–Slope Form and Equations of Lines*

Point–Slope Form

$$y - y_1 = m(x - x_1)$$

The slope of the line is m. The line passes through (x_1, y_1).

Write a point–slope equation for the line with slope -2 that contains the point $(3, -5)$.

$$y - y_1 = m(x - x_1)$$

$$y - (-5) = -2(x - 3)$$

13. Write a point–slope equation for the line with slope $\frac{1}{4}$ and containing the point $(-1, 6)$.

Review Exercises: Chapter 3

⤵ Concept Reinforcement

Classify each of the following statements as either true or false.

1. Not every ordered pair lies in one of the four quadrants. [3.1]

2. The equation of a vertical line cannot be written in slope–intercept form. [3.6]

3. Equations for lines written in slope–intercept form appear in the form $Ax + By = C$. [3.6]

4. Every horizontal line has an x-intercept. [3.3]

5. A line's slope is a measure of rate. [3.5]

6. A positive rate of ascent means that an airplane is flying increasingly higher above the earth. [3.4]

7. Any two points on a line can be used to determine the slope of a nonvertical line. [3.5]

8. Knowing a line's slope is enough to write the equation of the line. [3.6]

9. Knowing two points on a line is enough to write the equation of the line. [3.7]

10. Parallel lines that are not vertical have the same slope. [3.6]

The following bar graph shows the number of volunteers in the United States in 2010 by age group. [3.1]

Source: U.S. Department of Labor, Bureau of Labor Statistics

Volunteering in America

11. Approximately how many more people ages 35 to 44 volunteered than those ages 25 to 34?

12. About 2% of the volunteers ages 16 to 19 volunteered in environmental organizations. How many people ages 16 to 19 volunteered in environmental organizations?

Plot each point. [3.1]

13. $(5, -1)$ 14. $(2, 3)$ 15. $(-4, 0)$

In which quadrant is each point located? [3.1]

16. $(-8, -7)$ 17. $(15.3, -13.8)$ 18. $\left(-\frac{1}{2}, \frac{1}{10}\right)$

Find the coordinates of each point in the figure. [3.1]

19. A 20. B 21. C

22. Use a grid 10 squares wide and 10 squares high to plot $(-65, -2)$, $(-10, 6)$, and $(25, 7)$. Choose the scale carefully. [3.1]

23. Determine whether the equation $y = 2x + 7$ has the given ordered pair as a solution: **(a)** $(3, 1)$; **(b)** $(-3, 1)$. [3.2]

24. Show that the ordered pairs $(0, -3)$ and $(2, 1)$ are solutions of the equation $2x - y = 3$. Then use the graph of the two points to determine another solution. Answers may vary. [3.2]

Graph.

25. $y = x - 5$ [3.2]   26. $y = -\frac{1}{4}x$ [3.2]

27. $y = -x + 4$ [3.2]   28. $4x + y = 3$ [3.2]

29. $4x + 5 = 3$ [3.3]   30. $5x - 2y = 10$ [3.3]

31. $y = 6$ [3.3]   32. $y = \frac{2}{3}x - 5$ [3.6]

33. $2x + y = 4$ [3.3]

34. $y + 2 = -\frac{1}{2}(x - 3)$ [3.7]

35. *Automobiles.* The average age of vehicles currently driven in the United States is given by $a = 0.2t + 8.8$, where t is the number of years since 2000. Graph the equation with t on the horizontal axis and use the graph to estimate the average age of an American vehicle in 2012. [3.2]

Source: Based on data from R. L. Polk & Co.

36. At 4:00 P.M., Jesse's Honda Civic was at mile marker 17 of Interstate 290 in Chicago. At 4:45 P.M., Jesse was at mile marker 23. [3.4]

a) Find Jesse's driving rate, in number of miles per minute.

b) Find Jesse's driving rate, in number of minutes per mile.

37. *Gas Mileage.* The following graph shows data for the gas consumption of a 4-cylinder Ford Explorer driven on city streets. At what rate was the vehicle consuming gas? [3.4]

Find the slope of each line. [3.5]

38.

39.

40.

Find the slope of the line containing the given pair of points. If it is undefined, state this. [3.5]

41. $(-2, 5)$ and $(3, -1)$

42. $(6, 5)$ and $(-2, 5)$

43. $(-3, 0)$ and $(-3, 5)$

44. $(-8.3, 4.6)$ and $(-9.9, 1.4)$

45. Find the x-intercept and the y-intercept of the line given by $5x - 8y = 80$. [3.3]

46. Find the slope and the y-intercept of the line given by $3x + 5y = 45$. [3.6]

47. *Architecture.* To meet federal standards, a wheelchair ramp cannot rise more than 1 ft over a horizontal distance of 12 ft. Express this slope as a grade. [3.5]

Determine whether each pair of lines is parallel, perpendicular, or neither. [3.6]

48. $y + 5 = -x,$
$x - y = 2$

49. $3x - 5 = 7y,$
$7y - 3x = 7$

50. Write the slope–intercept equation of the line with slope $\frac{3}{8}$ and y-intercept $(0, 7)$. [3.6]

51. Write a point–slope equation for the line with slope $-\frac{1}{3}$ that contains the point $(-2, 9)$. [3.7]

52. Write the slope–intercept equation for the line containing the points $(-2, 5)$ and $(3, 10)$. [3.7]

53. Write the slope–intercept equation for the line that is perpendicular to the line $3x - 5y = 9$ and that contains the point $(2, -5)$. [3.7]

54. The average in-state tuition at a public two-year college was \$1847 in 2005 and \$2713 in 2011.

a) Graph the data points and determine an equation for the related line.

b) Calculate the average in-state tuition at a public two-year college in 2010 and estimate the average in-state tuition at a public two-year college in 2013. [3.7]

Sources: U.S. National Center for Education Statistics, College Board, Trends in College Pricing 2010

Synthesis

55. Can two perpendicular lines share the same y-intercept? Why or why not? [3.3]

56. Is it possible for a graph to have only one intercept? Why or why not? [3.3]

57. Find the value of m in $y = mx + 3$ such that $(-2, 5)$ is on the graph. [3.2]

58. Find the area and the perimeter of a rectangle for which $(-2, 2)$, $(7, 2)$, and $(7, -3)$ are three of the vertices. [3.1]

59. Find three solutions of $y = 4 - |x|$. [3.2]

Test: Chapter 3

For step-by-step test solutions, access the Chapter Test Prep Videos in MyMathLab®, on YouTube® (search "Bittinger Combo Alg CA" and click on "Channels"), or by scanning the code.

Income. *The following line graph shows data for median household income in the United States, adjusted for inflation.*

Source: U.S. Census Bureau

1. By how much did median household income decrease from 2007 to 2010?

2. In which year or years shown was median household income the highest?

In which quadrant is each point located?

3. $(-2, -10)$

4. $(-1.6, 2.3)$

Find the coordinates of each point in the figure.

5. *A*

6. *B*

7. *C*

Graph.

8. $y = 2x - 1$

9. $2x - 4y = -8$

10. $y + 1 = 6$

11. $y = \frac{3}{4}x$

12. $2x - y = 3$

13. $x = -1$

14. $y + 4 = -\frac{1}{2}(x - 3)$

Find the slope of the line containing each pair of points. If it is undefined, state this.

15. $(3, -2)$ and $(4, 3)$

16. $(-5, 6)$ and $(-1, -3)$

17. $(4, 7)$ and $(4, -8)$

18. *Running.* Jon reached the 3-km mark of a race at 2:15 P.M. and the 6-km mark at 2:24 P.M. What was his running rate?

19. At one point Filbert Street, the steepest street in San Francisco, drops 63 ft over a horizontal distance of 200 ft. Find the road grade.

20. Find the x-intercept and the y-intercept of the line given by $5x - y = 30$.

21. Find the slope and the y-intercept of the line given by $y - 8x = 10$.

22. Write the slope–intercept equation of the line with slope $-\frac{1}{3}$ and y-intercept $(0, -11)$.

Determine without graphing whether each pair of lines is parallel, perpendicular, or neither.

23. $4y + 2 = 3x,$
$-3x + 4y = -12$

24. $y = -2x + 5,$
$2y - x = 6$

25. Write the slope–intercept equation of the line that is perpendicular to the line $2x - 5y = 8$ and that contains the point $(-3, 2)$.

26. *Aerobic Exercise.* A person's target heart rate is the number of beats per minute that brings the most aerobic benefit to his or her heart. The target heart rate for a 20-year-old is 150 beats per minute; for a 60-year-old, it is 120 beats per minute.

a) Graph the data and determine an equation for the related line. Let a = age and r = target heart rate, in number of beats per minute.

b) Calculate the target heart rate for a 36-year-old.

Synthesis

27. Write an equation of the line that is parallel to the graph of $2x - 5y = 6$ and has the same y-intercept as the graph of $3x + y = 9$.

28. A diagonal of a square connects the points $(-3, -1)$ and $(2, 4)$. Find the area and the perimeter of the square.

29. List the coordinates of three other points that are on the same line as $(-2, 14)$ and $(17, -5)$. Answers may vary.

Cumulative Review: Chapters 1–3

1. Evaluate $\dfrac{x}{5y}$ for $x = 70$ and $y = 2$. [1.1]

2. Multiply: $6(2a - b + 3)$. [1.2]

3. Factor: $8x - 4y + 2$. [1.2]

4. Find the prime factorization of 54. [1.3]

5. Find decimal notation: $-\frac{3}{20}$. [1.4]

6. Find decimal notation: 36.7%. [2.4]

Simplify.

7. $\frac{3}{5} - \frac{5}{12}$ [1.3]

8. $3.4 + (-0.8)$ [1.5]

9. $(-2)(-1.4)(2.6)$ [1.7]

10. $\frac{3}{8} \div \left(-\frac{9}{10}\right)$ [1.7]

11. $1 - [32 \div (4 + 2^2)]$ [1.8]

12. $3(x - 1) - 2[x - (2x + 7)]$ [1.8]

Solve.

13. $\frac{5}{3}x = -45$ [2.1]

14. $3x - 7 = 41$ [2.2]

15. $\dfrac{3}{4} = \dfrac{-n}{8}$ [2.1]

16. $14 - 5x = 2x$ [2.2]

17. $3(5 - x) = 2(3x + 4)$ [2.2]

18. $\frac{1}{4}x - \frac{2}{3} = \frac{3}{4} + \frac{1}{3}x$ [2.2]

19. $x - 28 < 20 - 2x$ [2.6]

20. Solve $A = 2\pi rh + \pi r^2$ for h. [2.3]

21. In which quadrant is the point $(3, -1)$ located? [3.1]

22. Graph on the number line: $-1 < x \le 2$. [2.6]

23. Use a grid 10 squares wide and 10 squares high to plot $(-150, -40)$, $(40, -7)$, and $(0, 6)$. Choose the scale carefully. [3.1]

Graph.

24. $x = 3$ [3.3]

25. $2x - 5y = 10$ [3.3]

26. $y = -2x + 1$ [3.2]

27. $y = \frac{2}{3}x$ [3.2]

28. $2y - 5 = 3$ [3.3]

29. Find the slope and the y-intercept of the line given by $3x - y = 2$. [3.6]

30. Find the slope of the line containing the points $(-4, 1)$ and $(2, -1)$. [3.5]

31. Write an equation of the line with slope $\frac{2}{7}$ and y-intercept $(0, -4)$. [3.6]

32. Write a point–slope equation of the line with slope $-\frac{3}{8}$ that contains the point $(-6, 4)$. [3.7]

33. A 150-lb person will burn 240 calories per hour when riding a bicycle at 6 mph. The same person will burn 410 calories per hour when cycling at 12 mph. [3.7]

    Source: American Heart Association

    a) Graph the data and determine an equation for the related line. Let $r =$ the rate at which the person is cycling and $c =$ the number of calories burned per hour. Use the horizontal axis for r.

    b) Use the equation of part (a) to estimate the number of calories burned per hour by a 150-lb person cycling at 10 mph.

34. In 2010, the mean earnings of individuals with a high school diploma was $31,003. This was about 54% of the mean earnings of those with a bachelor's degree. What were the mean earnings of individuals with a bachelor's degree in 2010? [2.4]

    Source: U.S. Census Bureau

35. In order to qualify for availability pay, a criminal investigator must average at least 2 hr of unscheduled duty per workday. For the first four days of one week, Alayna worked 1, 0, 3, and 2 unscheduled hours. How many unscheduled hours must she work on Friday in order to qualify for availability pay? [2.7]

    Source: U.S. Department of Justice

Synthesis

36. Anya's salary at the end of a year is $26,780. This reflects a 4% salary increase in February and then a 3% cost-of-living increase in June. What was her salary at the beginning of the year? [2.5]

Solve. If no solution exists, state this.

37. $4|x| - 13 = 3$ [1.4], [2.2]

38. $\dfrac{2 + 5x}{4} = \dfrac{11}{28} + \dfrac{8x + 3}{7}$ [2.2]

39. $5(7 + x) = (x + 6)5$ [2.2]

Polynomials

ELEPHANT	GIRTH (in centimeters)	LENGTH (in centimeters)	FOOTPAD CIRCUMFERENCE (in centimeters)
Male, age 3 years	244	140	86
Female, age 3 years	231	135	86
Male, age 25 years	404	229	130
Female, age 25 years	366	226	117

It's Not Easy to Weigh an Elephant.

That's why wildlife experts have developed formulas for estimating the weight of an elephant using measurements that are much easier to obtain. One such formula uses the girth of the elephant, measured at the heart, the length of the elephant, and the circumference of the footpad of the elephant to estimate the elephant's weight. We can use that formula to estimate the weight of the elephants described in the table above. (*See Exercises 15 and 16 in Exercise Set 4.7.*)

Source: "How Much Does That Elephant Weigh?" by Mark MacAllister on fieldtripearth.org

As a field biologist, having mathematical skill is incredibly important in order for me to translate the ordinary behavior of animals into a scientific story.

Shermin de Silva, Director of Uda Walawe Elephant Research Project, uses a variety of aspects of math, including algebra, geometry, and calculus, to study how elephants behave and move in their environment, as well as to keep track of changes in their population size for conservation.

Algebraic expressions such as $16t^2$, $5a^2 - 3ab$, and $3x^2 - 7x + 5$ are called polynomials. Polynomials occur frequently in applications and appear in most branches of mathematics. Thus learning to add, subtract, multiply, and divide polynomials is an important part of nearly every course in elementary algebra. The focus of this chapter is finding equivalent expressions, not solving equations.

4.1 Exponents and Their Properties

Multiplying Powers with Like Bases ▪ Dividing Powers with Like Bases ▪ Zero as an Exponent ▪
Raising a Power to a Power ▪ Raising a Product or a Quotient to a Power

Before beginning our study of polynomials, we must develop some rules for working with exponents.

Multiplying Powers with Like Bases

An expression like a^3 means $a \cdot a \cdot a$. We can use this fact to find the product of two expressions that have the same base:

$a^3 \cdot a^2 = (a \cdot a \cdot a)(a \cdot a)$ There are three factors in a^3 and two factors in a^2.

$a^3 \cdot a^2 = a \cdot a \cdot a \cdot a \cdot a$ Using an associative law

$a^3 \cdot a^2 = a^5$.

Note that the exponent in a^5 is the sum of the exponents in $a^3 \cdot a^2$. That is, $3 + 2 = 5$. Similarly,

$b^4 \cdot b^3 = (b \cdot b \cdot b \cdot b)(b \cdot b \cdot b)$

$b^4 \cdot b^3 = b^7$,   where $4 + 3 = 7$.

Adding the exponents gives the correct result.

> **THE PRODUCT RULE**
>
> For any number a and any positive integers m and n,
>
> $$a^m \cdot a^n = a^{m+n}.$$
>
> (To multiply powers with the same base, keep the base and add the exponents.)

Study Skills

Helping Yourself by Helping Others

When you feel confident in your command of a topic, don't hesitate to help classmates experiencing trouble. Your understanding and retention of a concept will deepen when you explain it to someone else and your classmate will appreciate your help.

EXAMPLE 1 Multiply and simplify each of the following. (Here "simplify" means express the product as one base to a power whenever possible.)

a) $2^3 \cdot 2^8$

b) $5^3 \cdot 5^8 \cdot 5$

c) $(r + s)^7(r + s)^6$

d) $(a^3 b^2)(a^3 b^5)$

SOLUTION

a) $2^3 \cdot 2^8 = 2^{3+8}$ Adding exponents: $a^m \cdot a^n = a^{m+n}$

$\quad\quad = 2^{11}$

> **CAUTION!** The base is unchanged: $2^3 \cdot 2^8 \neq 4^{11}$.

b) $5^3 \cdot 5^8 \cdot 5 = 5^3 \cdot 5^8 \cdot 5^1$ Recall that $x^1 = x$ for any number x.

$\quad\quad\quad\quad = 5^{3+8+1}$ Adding exponents

$\quad\quad\quad\quad = 5^{12}$

> **CAUTION!** $5^{12} \neq 5 \cdot 12$.

c) $(r+s)^7(r+s)^6 = (r+s)^{7+6}$ The base here is $r+s$.

$\quad\quad\quad\quad\quad = (r+s)^{13}$

> **CAUTION!** $(r+s)^{13} \neq r^{13} + s^{13}$.

d) $(a^3b^2)(a^3b^5) = a^3b^2a^3b^5$ Using an associative law

$\quad\quad\quad\quad = a^3a^3b^2b^5$ Using a commutative law

$\quad\quad\quad\quad = a^6b^7$ Adding exponents

1. Multiply and simplify:

$\quad x^5 \cdot x \cdot x^4.$

YOUR TURN

Dividing Powers with Like Bases

Recall that any expression that is divided or multiplied by 1 is unchanged. This, together with the fact that any nonzero number divided by itself is 1, leads to a rule for division:

$$\frac{a^5}{a^2} = \frac{a \cdot a \cdot a \cdot a \cdot a}{a \cdot a} = \frac{a \cdot a \cdot a}{1} \cdot \frac{a \cdot a}{a \cdot a}$$

$$\frac{a^5}{a^2} = \frac{a \cdot a \cdot a}{1} \cdot 1$$

$$\frac{a^5}{a^2} = a \cdot a \cdot a = a^3.$$

Note that the exponent in a^3 is the difference of the exponents in a^5/a^2. Similarly,

$$\frac{x^4}{x^3} = \frac{x \cdot x \cdot x \cdot x}{x \cdot x \cdot x} = \frac{x}{1} \cdot \frac{x \cdot x \cdot x}{x \cdot x \cdot x} = \frac{x}{1} \cdot 1 = x = x^1.$$

Subtracting the exponents gives the correct result.

> **THE QUOTIENT RULE**
>
> For any nonzero number a and any positive integers m and n for which $m > n$,
>
> $$\frac{a^m}{a^n} = a^{m-n}.$$
>
> (To divide powers with the same base, subtract the exponent of the denominator from the exponent of the numerator.)

EXAMPLE 2   Divide and simplify. (Here "simplify" means express the quotient as one base to a power whenever possible.)

a) $\dfrac{7^9}{7^4}$ **b)** $\dfrac{(5a)^{12}}{(5a)^4}$ **c)** $\dfrac{4p^5q^7}{6p^2q}$

SOLUTION

a) $\dfrac{7^9}{7^4} = 7^{9-4}$ Subtracting exponents: $\dfrac{a^m}{a^n} = a^{m-n}$

$\qquad = 7^5$

> **CAUTION!** The base is unchanged: $\dfrac{7^9}{7^4} \neq 1^5$.

b) $\dfrac{(5a)^{12}}{(5a)^4} = (5a)^{12-4} = (5a)^8$

> **CAUTION!** The base is $5a$, so the parentheses are essential.

2. Divide and simplify:

$$\dfrac{(x+p)^6}{(x+p)}.$$

c) $\dfrac{4p^5q^7}{6p^2q} = \dfrac{4}{6} \cdot \dfrac{p^5}{p^2} \cdot \dfrac{q^7}{q^1}$ Note that the 4 and the 6 are factors, not exponents!

$\qquad = \dfrac{2}{3} \cdot p^{5-2} \cdot q^{7-1} = \dfrac{2}{3}p^3q^6$ Using the quotient rule twice; simplifying

YOUR TURN

Zero as an Exponent

The quotient rule can be used to help determine what 0 means when it appears as an exponent. Consider a^4/a^4, where a is nonzero. Since the numerator and the denominator are the same,

$$\dfrac{a^4}{a^4} = 1.$$ We assume $a \neq 0$.

On the other hand, using the quotient rule would give us

$$\dfrac{a^4}{a^4} = a^{4-4} = a^0.$$ Subtracting exponents

Since $a^0 = a^4/a^4 = 1$, this suggests that $a^0 = 1$ for any nonzero value of a.

> **THE EXPONENT ZERO**
>
> For any real number a, with $a \neq 0$,
>
> $$a^0 = 1.$$
>
> (Any nonzero number raised to the 0 power is 1.)

Note that in the above box, 0^0 is not defined. For this text, we will assume that expressions like a^m do not represent 0^0.

EXAMPLE 3 Simplify: **(a)** 1948^0;   **(b)** $(-9)^0$;   **(c)** $(3x)^0$;   **(d)** $3x^0$;   **(e)** $(-1)9^0$; **(f)** -9^0.

SOLUTION

a) $1948^0 = 1$ Any nonzero number raised to the 0 power is 1.

b) $(-9)^0 = 1$ Any nonzero number raised to the 0 power is 1. The base here is -9.

c) $(3x)^0 = 1$, for any $x \neq 0$.   The parentheses indicate that the base is $3x$.

d) Since $3x^0$ means $3 \cdot x^0$, the base is x. Recall that simplifying exponential expressions is done before multiplication in the rules for order of operations:

$$3x^0 = 3 \cdot 1 = 3, \quad \text{for any } x \neq 0.$$

e) $(-1)9^0 = (-1)1 = -1$ The base here is 9.

f) -9^0 is read "the opposite of 9^0" and is equivalent to $(-1)9^0$:

$$-9^0 = (-1)9^0 = (-1)1 = -1.$$

3. Simplify: 99^0.

Note from parts (b), (e), and (f) that $-9^0 = (-1)9^0$ and $-9^0 \neq (-9)^0$.

↩ YOUR TURN

Raising a Power to a Power

Consider an expression like $(7^2)^4$:

$$(7^2)^4 = (7^2)(7^2)(7^2)(7^2) \qquad \text{There are four factors of } 7^2.$$
$$(7^2)^4 = (7 \cdot 7)(7 \cdot 7)(7 \cdot 7)(7 \cdot 7) \qquad \text{We could also use the product rule.}$$
$$(7^2)^4 = 7 \cdot 7 \cdot 7 \cdot 7 \cdot 7 \cdot 7 \cdot 7 \cdot 7 \qquad \text{Using an associative law}$$
$$(7^2)^4 = 7^8.$$

Note that the exponent in 7^8 is the product of the exponents in $(7^2)^4$. Similarly,

$$(y^5)^3 = y^5 \cdot y^5 \cdot y^5 \qquad \text{There are three factors of } y^5.$$
$$(y^5)^3 = (y \cdot y \cdot y \cdot y \cdot y)(y \cdot y \cdot y \cdot y \cdot y)(y \cdot y \cdot y \cdot y \cdot y)$$
$$(y^5)^3 = y^{15}.$$

Once again, we get the same result if we multiply exponents:

$$(y^5)^3 = y^{5 \cdot 3} = y^{15}.$$

> **THE POWER RULE**
>
> For any number a and any whole numbers m and n,
>
> $$(a^m)^n = a^{mn}.$$
>
> (To raise a power to a power, multiply the exponents and leave the base unchanged.)

Remember that for this text we assume that 0^0 is not considered.

EXAMPLE 4 Simplify: $(m^2)^5$.

SOLUTION

$$(m^2)^5 = m^{2 \cdot 5} \qquad \text{Multiplying exponents: } (a^m)^n = a^{mn}$$
$$= m^{10}$$

4. Simplify: $(3^8)^{10}$.

↩ YOUR TURN

Raising a Product or a Quotient to a Power

When an expression inside parentheses is raised to a power, the inside expression is the base. Let's compare $2a^3$ and $(2a)^3$:

$2a^3 = 2 \cdot a \cdot a \cdot a;$ The base is a.

$(2a)^3 = (2a)(2a)(2a)$ The base is $2a$.
$(2a)^3 = (2 \cdot 2 \cdot 2)(a \cdot a \cdot a)$
$(2a)^3 = 2^3 a^3$
$(2a)^3 = 8a^3.$

We see that $2a^3$ and $(2a)^3$ are *not* equivalent. Note too that $(2a)^3$ can be simplified by cubing each factor in $2a$. This leads to the following rule for raising a product to a power.

> **RAISING A PRODUCT TO A POWER**
>
> For any numbers a and b and any whole number n,
>
> $$(ab)^n = a^n b^n.$$
>
> (To raise a product to a power, raise each factor to that power.)

EXAMPLE 5   Simplify: **(a)** $(4a)^3$; **(b)** $(-5x^4)^2$; **(c)** $(a^7 b)^2 (a^3 b^4)$.

SOLUTION

a) $(4a)^3 = 4^3 a^3 = 64a^3$ Raising each factor to the third power and simplifying

b) $(-5x^4)^2 = (-5)^2 (x^4)^2$ Raising each factor to the second power. Parentheses are important here.

$ = 25x^8$ Simplifying $(-5)^2$ and using the power rule

c) $(a^7 b)^2 (a^3 b^4) = (a^7)^2 b^2 a^3 b^4$ Raising a product to a power

$ = a^{14} b^2 a^3 b^4$ Multiplying exponents

$ = a^{17} b^6$ Adding exponents

5. Simplify: $(-2y^4)^3$.

↪ YOUR TURN

> **CAUTION!**   The rule $(ab)^n = a^n b^n$ applies only to *products* raised to a power, not to sums or differences. For example, $(3 + 4)^2 \neq 3^2 + 4^2$ since $49 \neq 9 + 16$. Similarly, $(5 + x)^2 \neq 5^2 + x^2$.

There is a similar rule for raising a quotient to a power.

> **RAISING A QUOTIENT TO A POWER**
>
> For any numbers a and b, $b \neq 0$, and any whole number n,
>
> $$\left(\frac{a}{b}\right)^n = \frac{a^n}{b^n}.$$
>
> (To raise a quotient to a power, raise the numerator to the power and divide by the denominator to the power.)

EXAMPLE 6   Simplify: **(a)** $\left(\dfrac{x}{5}\right)^2$; **(b)** $\left(\dfrac{5}{a^4}\right)^3$; **(c)** $\left(\dfrac{3a^4}{b^3}\right)^2$.

SOLUTION

a) $\left(\dfrac{x}{5}\right)^2 = \dfrac{x^2}{5^2} = \dfrac{x^2}{25}$ Squaring the numerator and the denominator

b) $\left(\dfrac{5}{a^4}\right)^3 = \dfrac{5^3}{(a^4)^3}$ Raising a quotient to a power

$\phantom{\left(\dfrac{5}{a^4}\right)^3} = \dfrac{125}{a^{4 \cdot 3}} = \dfrac{125}{a^{12}}$ Using the power rule and simplifying

c) $\left(\dfrac{3a^4}{b^3}\right)^2 = \dfrac{(3a^4)^2}{(b^3)^2}$ Raising a quotient to a power

6. Simplify: $\left(\dfrac{-3}{a^3}\right)^2$.

$\phantom{\left(\dfrac{3a^4}{b^3}\right)^2} = \dfrac{3^2 (a^4)^2}{b^{3 \cdot 2}} = \dfrac{9a^8}{b^6}$ Raising a product to a power and using the power rule

↪ YOUR TURN

In the following summary of definitions and rules, we assume that no denominators are 0 and that 0^0 is not considered.

DEFINITIONS AND PROPERTIES OF EXPONENTS

For any whole numbers m and n,

1 as an exponent:	$a^1 = a$
0 as an exponent:	$a^0 = 1$
The Product Rule:	$a^m \cdot a^n = a^{m+n}$
The Quotient Rule:	$\dfrac{a^m}{a^n} = a^{m-n}$
The Power Rule:	$(a^m)^n = a^{mn}$
Raising a product to a power:	$(ab)^n = a^n b^n$
Raising a quotient to a power:	$\left(\dfrac{a}{b}\right)^n = \dfrac{a^n}{b^n}$

4.1 EXERCISE SET

FOR EXTRA HELP   MyMathLab® Math
PRACTICE   WATCH   READ   REVIEW

Vocabulary and Reading Check

Complete the sentence using the most appropriate phrase from the column on the right. Each phrase is used once.

1. To raise a product to a power, ____
2. To raise a quotient to a power, ____
3. To raise a power to a power, ____
4. To divide powers with the same base, ____
5. Any nonzero number raised to the 0 power ____
6. To multiply powers with the same base, ____
7. To square a fraction, ____
8. To square a product, ____

a) keep the base and add the exponents.
b) multiply the exponents and leave the base unchanged.
c) square the numerator and square the denominator.
d) square each factor.
e) raise each factor to that power.
f) raise the numerator to the power and divide by the denominator to the power.
g) is one.
h) subtract the exponent of the denominator from the exponent of the numerator.

Concept Reinforcement

Identify the base and the exponent in each expression.

9. $(2x)^5$
10. $(x + 1)^0$
11. $2x^3$
12. $-y^6$
13. $\left(\dfrac{4}{y}\right)^7$
14. $(-5x)^4$

Multiplying Powers with Like Bases

Simplify.

15. $d^3 \cdot d^{10}$
16. $8^4 \cdot 8^3$
17. $a^6 \cdot a$
18. $y^7 \cdot y^9$
19. $6^5 \cdot 6^{10}$
20. $t^0 \cdot t^{16}$
21. $(3y)^4(3y)^8$
22. $(2t)^8(2t)^{17}$

23. $(5p)^0(5p)^1$
24. $(8n)(8n)^9$
25. $(x + 3)^5(x + 3)^8$
26. $(m - 3)^4(m - 3)^5$
27. $(a^2b^7)(a^3b^2)$
28. $(a^8b^3)(a^4b)$
29. $r^3 \cdot r^7 \cdot r^0$
30. $s^4 \cdot s^5 \cdot s^2$
31. $(mn^5)(m^3n^4)$
32. $(a^3b)(ab)^4$

Dividing Powers with Like Bases

Simplify. Assume that no denominator is 0 and that 0^0 is not considered.

33. $\dfrac{7^5}{7^2}$
34. $\dfrac{4^7}{4^3}$

35. $\dfrac{t^8}{t}$

36. $\dfrac{x^7}{x}$

37. $\dfrac{(5a)^7}{(5a)^6}$

38. $\dfrac{(3m)^9}{(3m)^8}$

Aha! **39.** $\dfrac{(x+y)^8}{(x+y)^8}$

40. $\dfrac{(9x)^{10}}{(9x)^2}$

41. $\dfrac{(r+s)^{12}}{(r+s)^4}$

42. $\dfrac{(a-b)^4}{(a-b)^3}$

43. $\dfrac{12d^9}{15d^2}$

44. $\dfrac{10n^7}{15n^3}$

45. $\dfrac{8a^9b^7}{2a^2b}$

46. $\dfrac{12r^{10}s^7}{4r^2s}$

47. $\dfrac{x^{12}y^9}{x^0y^2}$

48. $\dfrac{a^{10}b^{12}}{a^2b^0}$

Zero as an Exponent

Simplify.

49. t^0 when $t = 15$

50. y^0 when $y = 38$

51. $5x^0$ when $x = -22$

52. $7m^0$ when $m = 1.7$

53. $7^0 + 4^0$

54. $(8 + 5)^0$

55. $(-3)^1 - (-3)^0$

56. $(-4)^0 - (-4)^1$

Raising a Power to a Power

Simplify.

57. $(x^3)^{11}$

58. $(a^5)^8$

59. $(5^8)^4$

60. $(2^5)^2$

61. $(t^{20})^4$

62. $(x^{25})^6$

Raising a Product or a Quotient to a Power

Simplify. Assume that no denominator is 0 and that 0^0 is not considered.

63. $(10x)^2$

64. $(5a)^2$

65. $(-2a)^3$

66. $(-3x)^3$

67. $(-5n^7)^2$

68. $(-4m^4)^2$

69. $(a^2b)^7$

70. $(xy^4)^9$

71. $(r^5t)^3(r^2t^8)$

72. $(a^4b^6)(a^2b)^5$

73. $(2x^5)^3(3x^4)$

74. $(5x^3)^2(2x^7)$

75. $\left(\dfrac{x}{5}\right)^3$

76. $\left(\dfrac{2}{a}\right)^4$

77. $\left(\dfrac{7}{6n}\right)^2$

78. $\left(\dfrac{4x}{3}\right)^3$

79. $\left(\dfrac{a^3}{b^8}\right)^6$

80. $\left(\dfrac{x^5}{y^2}\right)^7$

81. $\left(\dfrac{x^2y}{z^3}\right)^4$

82. $\left(\dfrac{a^4}{b^2c}\right)^5$

83. $\left(\dfrac{a^3}{-2b^5}\right)^4$

84. $\left(\dfrac{x^5}{-3y^3}\right)^4$

85. $\left(\dfrac{5x^7y}{-2z^4}\right)^3$

86. $\left(\dfrac{-4p^5}{3m^2n^3}\right)^3$

Aha! **87.** $\left(\dfrac{4x^3y^5}{3z^7}\right)^0$

88. $\left(\dfrac{5a^7}{2b^5c}\right)^0$

89. Explain in your own words why $-5^2 \neq (-5)^2$.

90. Under what circumstances should exponents be added?

Skill Review

Solve.

91. $-\dfrac{x}{7} = 3$　[2.1]

92. $3x - 2 \le 5 - x$　[2.6]

93. $\frac{1}{2}x + \frac{1}{3} = \frac{1}{6}x$　[2.2]

94. $6(x - 10) = 3[4(x - 5)]$　[2.2]

95. $8 - 2(n - 7) > 9 - (3 - n)$　[2.6]

96. $8(5 - y) = 32$　[2.2]

Synthesis

97. Under what conditions does a^n represent a negative number? Why?

98. Using the quotient rule, explain why 9^0 is 1.

99. Suppose that the width of a square is three times the width of a second square. How do the areas of the squares compare? Why?

100. Suppose that the width of a cube is twice the width of a second cube. How do the volumes of the cubes compare? Why?

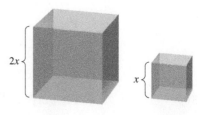

Find a value of the variable that shows that the two expressions are not equivalent. Answers may vary.

101. $3x^2$; $(3x)^2$

102. $(a + 5)^2$; $a^2 + 5^2$

103. $\dfrac{t^6}{t^2}$; t^3

104. $\dfrac{a + 7}{7}$; a

Simplify.

105. $y^{4x} \cdot y^{2x}$

106. $a^{10k} \div a^{2k}$

107. $\dfrac{x^{5t}(x^t)^2}{(x^{3t})^2}$

108. $\dfrac{\left(\frac{1}{2}\right)^3\left(\frac{2}{3}\right)^4}{\left(\frac{5}{6}\right)^3}$

109. Solve for x:

$$\frac{t^{26}}{t^x} = t^x.$$

Replace ▨ with $>$, $<$, or $=$ to write a true sentence.

110. 3^5 ▨ 3^4

111. 4^2 ▨ 4^3

112. 4^3 ▨ 5^3

113. 4^3 ▨ 3^4

114. 9^7 ▨ 3^{13}

115. 25^8 ▨ 125^5

▨ *Use the fact that $10^3 \approx 2^{10}$ to estimate each of the following powers of 2. Then compute the power of 2 with a calculator and find the difference between the exact value and the approximation.*

116. 2^{14}

117. 2^{22}

118. 2^{26}

119. 2^{31}

▨ *In computer science, 1 KB of memory refers to 1 kilobyte, or 1×10^3 bytes, of memory. This is really an approximation of 1×2^{10} bytes (since computer memory actually uses powers of 2).*

120. The TI-84 Plus graphing calculator has 480 KB of "FLASH ROM." How many bytes is this?

121. The TI-84 Plus Silver Edition graphing calculator has 1.5 MB (megabytes) of FLASH ROM, where 1 MB is 1000 KB (see Exercise 120). How many bytes of FLASH ROM does this calculator have?

↘ **YOUR TURN ANSWERS: SECTION 4.1**

1. x^{10} **2.** $(x + p)^5$ **3.** 1 **4.** 3^{80} **5.** $-8y^{12}$ **6.** $\dfrac{9}{a^6}$

PREPARE TO MOVE ON

Perform the indicated operations.

1. $-10 - 14$ [1.6]

2. $-3(5)$ [1.7]

3. $-16 + 5$ [1.5]

4. $12 - (-4)$ [1.6]

5. $-3 + (-11)$ [1.5]

6. $-8 - (-12)$ [1.6]

4.2 Negative Exponents and Scientific Notation

Negative Integers as Exponents ▪ Scientific Notation ▪ Multiplying and Dividing Using Scientific Notation

We now attach a meaning to negative exponents. Once we understand both positive exponents and negative exponents, we can study a method for writing numbers known as *scientific notation*.

Negative Integers as Exponents

Let's define negative exponents so that the rules that apply to whole-number exponents will hold for all integer exponents. To do so, consider a^{-5} and the rule for adding exponents:

$$a^{-5} = a^{-5} \cdot 1 \qquad \text{Using the identity property of 1}$$

$$= \frac{a^{-5}}{1} \cdot \frac{a^5}{a^5} \qquad \text{Writing 1 as } \frac{a^5}{a^5} \text{ and } a^{-5} \text{ as } \frac{a^{-5}}{1}$$

$$= \frac{a^{-5+5}}{a^5} \qquad \text{Adding exponents}$$

$$= \frac{1}{a^5}. \qquad -5 + 5 = 0 \text{ and } a^0 = 1$$

This leads to our definition of negative exponents.

> **NEGATIVE EXPONENTS**
>
> For any real number a that is nonzero and any integer n,
>
> $$a^{-n} = \frac{1}{a^n}.$$
>
> (The numbers a^{-n} and a^n are reciprocals of each other.)

Study Skills

Connect the Dots

Whenever possible, look for connections between concepts covered in different sections or chapters. For example, two sections may both discuss exponents, or two chapters may both cover polynomials.

1. Express using positive exponents and, if possible, simplify: $7x^{-2}$.

EXAMPLE 1 Express using positive exponents and, if possible, simplify.

a) m^{-3} **b)** 4^{-2} **c)** $(-3)^{-2}$ **d)** ab^{-1}

SOLUTION

a) $m^{-3} = \dfrac{1}{m^3}$ m^{-3} is the reciprocal of m^3.

b) $4^{-2} = \dfrac{1}{4^2} = \dfrac{1}{16}$ 4^{-2} is the reciprocal of 4^2. Note that $4^{-2} \neq 4(-2)$.

c) $(-3)^{-2} = \dfrac{1}{(-3)^2} = \dfrac{1}{(-3)(-3)} = \dfrac{1}{9}$ $(-3)^{-2}$ is the reciprocal of $(-3)^2$. Note that $(-3)^{-2} \neq -\dfrac{1}{3^2}$.

d) $ab^{-1} = a\left(\dfrac{1}{b^1}\right) = a\left(\dfrac{1}{b}\right) = \dfrac{a}{b}$ b^{-1} is the reciprocal of b^1. Note that the base is b, not ab.

YOUR TURN

> **CAUTION!** A negative exponent does not, in itself, indicate that an expression is negative. As shown in Example 1,
>
> $$4^{-2} \neq 4(-2) \quad \text{and} \quad (-3)^{-2} \neq -\frac{1}{3^2}.$$

The following is another way to illustrate why negative exponents are defined as they are.

On this side, we divide by 5 at each step.	$125 = 5^3$	On this side, the exponents decrease by 1.
	$25 = 5^2$	
	$5 = 5^1$	
	$1 = 5^0$	
	$\dfrac{1}{5} = 5^?$	
	$\dfrac{1}{25} = 5^?$	

To continue the pattern, it follows that

$$\frac{1}{5} = \frac{1}{5^1} = 5^{-1}, \qquad \frac{1}{25} = \frac{1}{5^2} = 5^{-2}, \quad \text{and, in general,} \quad \frac{1}{a^n} = a^{-n}.$$

EXAMPLE 2 Express $\dfrac{1}{x^7}$ using negative exponents.

2. Express $\dfrac{1}{10^7}$ using negative exponents.

SOLUTION We know that $\dfrac{1}{a^n} = a^{-n}$. Thus, $\dfrac{1}{x^7} = x^{-7}$.

YOUR TURN

The rules for exponents still hold when exponents are negative.

EXAMPLE 3   Simplify. Do not use negative exponents in the answer.

a) $t^5 \cdot t^{-2}$

b) $(5x^2 y^{-3})^4$

c) $\dfrac{x^{-4}}{x^{-5}}$

d) $\dfrac{1}{t^{-5}}$

e) $\dfrac{s^{-3}}{t^{-5}}$

f) $\dfrac{-10x^{-3}y}{5x^2 y^5}$

SOLUTION

a) $t^5 \cdot t^{-2} = t^{5+(-2)} = t^3$ Adding exponents

b) $(5x^2 y^{-3})^4 = 5^4 (x^2)^4 (y^{-3})^4$ Raising each factor to the fourth power

$$= 625x^8 y^{-12} = \dfrac{625x^8}{y^{12}}$$

c) $\dfrac{x^{-4}}{x^{-5}} = x^{-4-(-5)} = x^1 = x$ We subtract exponents even if the exponent in the denominator is negative.

d) Since $\dfrac{1}{a^n} = a^{-n}$, we have $\dfrac{1}{t^{-5}} = t^{-(-5)} = t^5$.

e) $\dfrac{s^{-3}}{t^{-5}} = s^{-3} \cdot \dfrac{1}{t^{-5}}$

$$= \dfrac{1}{s^3} \cdot t^5 = \dfrac{t^5}{s^3}$$ Using the result from part (d) above

f) $\dfrac{-10x^{-3}y}{5x^2 y^5} = \dfrac{-10}{5} \cdot \dfrac{x^{-3}}{x^2} \cdot \dfrac{y^1}{y^5}$ Note that the -10 and 5 are factors.

$$= -2 \cdot x^{-3-2} \cdot y^{1-5}$$ Using the quotient rule twice; simplifying

$$= -2x^{-5} y^{-4} = \dfrac{-2}{x^5 y^4}$$

3. Simplify:

$$\dfrac{3x^{-2}}{x^{10}}.$$

Do not use negative exponents in the answer.

 YOUR TURN

The result from Example 3(e) can be generalized.

FACTORS AND NEGATIVE EXPONENTS

For any nonzero real numbers a and b and any integers m and n,

$$\dfrac{a^{-n}}{b^{-m}} = \dfrac{b^m}{a^n}.$$

(A factor can be moved to the other side of the fraction bar if the sign of the exponent is changed.)

EXAMPLE 4   Simplify: $\dfrac{-15x^{-7}}{5y^2 z^{-4}}$.

SOLUTION   We can move the factors x^{-7} and z^{-4} to the other side of the fraction bar if we change the sign of each exponent:

$$\dfrac{-15x^{-7}}{5y^2 z^{-4}} = \dfrac{-15}{5} \cdot \dfrac{x^{-7}}{y^2 z^{-4}}$$ We can simply divide the constant factors.

$$= -3 \cdot \dfrac{z^4}{y^2 x^7}$$

$$= \dfrac{-3z^4}{x^7 y^2}.$$

4. Simplify: $\dfrac{12a^{-1}}{4bc^{-3}}$.

 YOUR TURN

Another way to change the sign of the exponent is to take the reciprocal of the base. To understand why this is true, note that

$$\left(\frac{s}{t}\right)^{-5} = \frac{s^{-5}}{t^{-5}} = \frac{t^5}{s^5} = \left(\frac{t}{s}\right)^5.$$

This often provides the easiest way to simplify an expression containing a negative exponent.

RECIPROCALS AND NEGATIVE EXPONENTS

For any nonzero real numbers a and b and any integer n,

$$\left(\frac{a}{b}\right)^{-n} = \left(\frac{b}{a}\right)^{n}.$$

(A base to a power is equal to the reciprocal of the base raised to the opposite power.)

EXAMPLE 5   Simplify: $\left(\dfrac{x^4}{2y}\right)^{-3}$.

SOLUTION

$$\left(\frac{x^4}{2y}\right)^{-3} = \left(\frac{2y}{x^4}\right)^3 \qquad \text{Taking the reciprocal of the base and changing the sign of the exponent}$$

$$= \frac{(2y)^3}{(x^4)^3} \qquad \text{Raising a quotient to a power by raising both the numerator and the denominator to the power}$$

$$= \frac{2^3 y^3}{x^{12}} \qquad \text{Raising a product to a power; using the power rule in the denominator}$$

$$= \frac{8y^3}{x^{12}} \qquad \text{Cubing 2}$$

5. Simplify: $\left(\dfrac{3x}{y^5}\right)^{-2}$.

YOUR TURN

Scientific Notation

Scientific notation provides a useful way of writing the very large or very small numbers that occur in science. The following are examples of scientific notation.

The mass of the earth:

6.0×10^{24} kilograms (kg) = 6,000,000,000,000,000,000,000,000 kg

The mass of a hydrogen atom:

1.7×10^{-24} g = 0.0000000000000000000000017 g

Student Notes

Definitions are usually written as concisely as possible, so that every phrase included is important. The definition for scientific notation states that $1 \le N < 10$. Thus, 2.68×10^5 is written in scientific notation, but 26.8×10^5 and 0.268×10^5 are *not* written in scientific notation.

SCIENTIFIC NOTATION

Scientific notation for a number is an expression of the type

$$N \times 10^m,$$

where N is at least 1 but less than 10 (that is, $1 \le N < 10$), N is expressed in decimal notation, and m is an integer.

Converting from scientific notation to decimal notation involves multiplying by a power of 10. Consider the following.

Scientific Notation	*Multiplication*	*Decimal Notation*
4.52×10^2	4.52×100	452.
4.52×10^1	4.52×10	45.2
4.52×10^0	4.52×1	4.52
4.52×10^{-1}	4.52×0.1	0.452
4.52×10^{-2}	4.52×0.01	0.0452

We generally perform this multiplication mentally. Thus to convert $N \times 10^m$ to decimal notation, we move the decimal point.

- When m is positive, we move the decimal point m places to the right.
- When m is negative, we move the decimal point $|m|$ places to the left.

EXAMPLE 6   Convert to decimal notation: **(a)** 7.893×10^5; **(b)** 4.7×10^{-8}.

SOLUTION

a) Since the exponent is positive, the decimal point moves to the right:

7.89300. $7.893 \times 10^5 = 789{,}300$ The decimal point moves 5 places to the right.

5 places

b) Since the exponent is negative, the decimal point moves to the left:

0.00000004.7 $4.7 \times 10^{-8} = 0.000000047$ The decimal point moves 8 places to the left.

8 places

6. Convert to decimal notation:

8.04×10^{-3}.

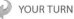 YOUR TURN

To convert from decimal notation to scientific notation, this procedure is reversed.

EXAMPLE 7   Write in scientific notation: **(a)** 83,000; **(b)** 0.0327.

SOLUTION

a) We need to find m such that $83{,}000 = 8.3 \times 10^m$. To change 8.3 to 83,000 requires moving the decimal point 4 places to the right. This can be accomplished by multiplying by 10^4. Thus,

$83{,}000 = 8.3 \times 10^4$.   This is scientific notation.

b) We need to find m such that $0.0327 = 3.27 \times 10^m$. To change 3.27 to 0.0327 requires moving the decimal point 2 places to the left. This can be accomplished by multiplying by 10^{-2}. Thus,

$0.0327 = 3.27 \times 10^{-2}$.   This is scientific notation.

7. Write in scientific notation:

600,000.

YOUR TURN

In scientific notation, positive exponents are used to represent large numbers and negative exponents are used to represent small numbers between 0 and 1.

Multiplying and Dividing Using Scientific Notation

Products and quotients of numbers written in scientific notation are found using the rules for exponents.

EXAMPLE 8 Simplify.

a) $(1.8 \times 10^9) \cdot (2.3 \times 10^{-4})$ **b)** $(3.41 \times 10^5) \div (1.1 \times 10^{-3})$

SOLUTION

a) $(1.8 \times 10^9) \cdot (2.3 \times 10^{-4})$

$= 1.8 \times 2.3 \times 10^9 \times 10^{-4}$ Using the associative and commutative laws

$= 4.14 \times 10^{9+(-4)}$ Adding exponents

$= 4.14 \times 10^5$

b) $(3.41 \times 10^5) \div (1.1 \times 10^{-3})$

$$= \frac{3.41 \times 10^5}{1.1 \times 10^{-3}}$$

$$= \frac{3.41}{1.1} \times \frac{10^5}{10^{-3}}$$

$= 3.1 \times 10^{5-(-3)}$ Subtracting exponents

$= 3.1 \times 10^8$

Chapter Resource:
Decision Making: Connection, p. 294

8. Simplify:

$(2.2 \times 10^{-8}) \times (2.5 \times 10^{-10})$.

 YOUR TURN

When a problem is stated using scientific notation, we generally use scientific notation for the answer. This often requires an additional conversion.

EXAMPLE 9 Simplify.

a) $(3.1 \times 10^5) \cdot (4.5 \times 10^{-3})$
b) $(7.2 \times 10^{-7}) \div (8.0 \times 10^6)$

SOLUTION

a) We have

$$(3.1 \times 10^5) \cdot (4.5 \times 10^{-3}) = 3.1 \times 4.5 \times 10^5 \times 10^{-3}$$
$$= 13.95 \times 10^2.$$

Our answer is not yet in scientific notation because 13.95 is not between 1 and 10. We convert to scientific notation as follows:

$13.95 \times 10^2 = 1.395 \times 10^1 \times 10^2$ Substituting 1.395×10^1 for 13.95

$= 1.395 \times 10^3.$ Adding exponents

Technology Connection

A key labeled $\boxed{10^x}$, $\boxed{\wedge}$, or $\boxed{EE}$ is used to enter scientific notation into a calculator. Sometimes this is a secondary function, meaning that another key—often labeled SHIFT or $\boxed{2ND}$ —must be pressed first.

To check Example 9(a), we press

· 3.1 $\boxed{EE}$ 5 $\boxed{\times}$ 4.5 $\boxed{EE}$ $\boxed{(-)}$ 3 $\boxed{ENTER}$.

The result that appears represents 1.395×10^3. On some calculators, the MODE SCI must be selected in order to display scientific notation.

```
3.1E5*4.5E−3
                    1.395E3
```

Calculate each of the following.

1. $(3.8 \times 10^9) \cdot (4.5 \times 10^7)$
2. $(2.9 \times 10^{-8}) \div (5.4 \times 10^6)$
3. $(9.2 \times 10^7) \div (2.5 \times 10^{-9})$

b) $(7.2 \times 10^{-7}) \div (8.0 \times 10^6) = \dfrac{7.2 \times 10^{-7}}{8.0 \times 10^6} = \dfrac{7.2}{8.0} \times \dfrac{10^{-7}}{10^6}$

$= 0.9 \times 10^{-13}$

$= 9.0 \times 10^{-1} \times 10^{-13}$ Substituting 9.0×10^{-1} for 0.9

9. Simplify: $\dfrac{1.2 \times 10^6}{3.0 \times 10^{-11}}$.

$= 9.0 \times 10^{-14}$ Adding exponents

YOUR TURN

CONNECTING THE CONCEPTS

DEFINITIONS AND PROPERTIES OF EXPONENTS

The following summary assumes that no denominators are 0 and that 0^0 is not considered. For any integers m and n,

1 as an exponent:	$a^1 = a$
0 as an exponent:	$a^0 = 1$
Negative exponents:	$a^{-n} = \dfrac{1}{a^n}$,
	$\dfrac{a^{-n}}{b^{-m}} = \dfrac{b^m}{a^n}$,
	$\left(\dfrac{a}{b}\right)^{-n} = \left(\dfrac{b}{a}\right)^n$

The Product Rule: $a^m \cdot a^n = a^{m+n}$

The Quotient Rule: $\dfrac{a^m}{a^n} = a^{m-n}$

The Power Rule: $(a^m)^n = a^{mn}$

Raising a product to a power: $(ab)^n = a^n b^n$

Raising a quotient to a power: $\left(\dfrac{a}{b}\right)^n = \dfrac{a^n}{b^n}$

EXERCISES

Simplify. Do not use negative exponents in the answer.

1. $x^4 x^{10}$

2. $x^{-4} x^{-10}$

3. $\dfrac{x^{-4}}{x^{10}}$

4. $\dfrac{x^4}{x^{-10}}$

5. $(x^{-4})^{-10}$

6. $(x^4)^{10}$

7. $\dfrac{1}{c^{-8}}$

8. c^{-8}

9. $\left(\dfrac{a^3}{b^4}\right)^5$

10. $\left(\dfrac{a^3}{b^4}\right)^{-5}$

4.2 EXERCISE SET

FOR EXTRA HELP

MyMathLab® *Math* XL
PRACTICE WATCH READ REVIEW

 Vocabulary and Reading Check

Classify each of the following statements as either true or false.

1. A negative exponent indicates a reciprocal.

2. The expressions 3^{-2} and -3^2 are equivalent.

3. A positive exponent of the base 10 in scientific notation indicates a number greater than or equal to 10.

4. The number 18.68×10^{12} is written in scientific notation.

⟜ **Concept Reinforcement**

Match each expression with an equivalent expression from the column on the right.

5. ____ $\left(\dfrac{x^3}{y^2}\right)^{-2}$ a) $\dfrac{y^6}{x^9}$

6. ____ $\left(\dfrac{y^2}{x^3}\right)^{-2}$ b) $\dfrac{x^9}{y^6}$

7. ____ $\left(\dfrac{y^{-2}}{x^{-3}}\right)^{-3}$ c) $\dfrac{y^4}{x^6}$

8. ____ $\left(\dfrac{x^{-3}}{y^{-2}}\right)^{-3}$ d) $\dfrac{x^6}{y^4}$

State whether scientific notation for each of the following numbers would include a positive power of 10 or a negative power of 10.

9. The length of an Olympic marathon, in centimeters

10. The thickness of a cat's whisker, in meters

11. The mass of a hydrogen atom, in grams

12. The mass of a pickup truck, in grams

13. The time between leap years, in seconds

14. The time between a bird's heartbeats, in hours

Negative Integers as Exponents

Express using positive exponents. Then, if possible, simplify.

15. 2^{-3}
16. 10^{-5}
17. $(-2)^{-6}$
18. $(-3)^{-4}$
19. t^{-9}
20. x^{-7}
21. $8x^{-3}$
22. xy^{-9}
23. $\dfrac{1}{a^{-8}}$
24. $\dfrac{1}{z^{-6}}$
25. 7^{-1}
26. 3^{-1}
27. $3a^8b^{-6}$
28. $5a^{-7}b^4$
29. $\left(\dfrac{x}{2}\right)^{-5}$
30. $\left(\dfrac{a}{2}\right)^{-4}$
31. $\dfrac{z^{-4}}{3x^5}$
32. $\dfrac{y^{-5}}{x^{-3}}$

Express using negative exponents.

33. $\dfrac{1}{9^2}$
34. $\dfrac{1}{5^2}$
35. $\dfrac{1}{y^3}$
36. $\dfrac{1}{t^4}$
37. $\dfrac{1}{t}$
38. $\dfrac{1}{8}$

Simplify. Do not use negative exponents in the answer.

39. $2^{-5} \cdot 2^8$
40. $5^{-8} \cdot 5^{10}$
41. $x^{-3} \cdot x^{-9}$
42. $x^{-4} \cdot x^{-7}$
43. $t^{-3} \cdot t$
44. $y^{-5} \cdot y$
45. $(5a^{-2}b^{-3})(2a^{-4}b)$
46. $(3a^{-5}b^{-7})(2ab^{-2})$
47. $(n^{-5})^3$
48. $(m^{-5})^{10}$
49. $(t^{-3})^{-6}$
50. $(a^{-4})^{-7}$
51. $(mn)^{-7}$
52. $(ab)^{-9}$
53. $(3x^{-4})^2$
54. $(2a^{-5})^3$
55. $(5r^{-4}t^3)^2$
56. $(4x^5y^{-6})^3$
57. $\dfrac{t^{12}}{t^{-2}}$
58. $\dfrac{x^7}{x^{-2}}$
59. $\dfrac{y^{-7}}{y^{-3}}$
60. $\dfrac{z^{-6}}{z^{-2}}$
61. $\dfrac{15y^{-7}}{3y^{-10}}$
62. $\dfrac{-12a^{-5}}{2a^{-8}}$
63. $\dfrac{2x^6}{x}$
64. $\dfrac{3x}{x^{-1}}$
65. $\dfrac{-15a^{-7}}{10b^{-9}}$
66. $\dfrac{12x^{-6}}{8y^{-10}}$

Aha! 67. $\dfrac{t^{-7}}{t^{-7}}$
68. $\dfrac{a^{-5}}{b^{-7}}$
69. $\dfrac{3t^4}{s^{-2}u^{-4}}$
70. $\dfrac{5x^{-8}}{y^{-3}z^2}$
71. $(x^4y^5)^{-3}$
72. $(t^5x^3)^{-4}$
73. $(3m^{-5}n^{-3})^{-2}$
74. $(2y^{-4}z^{-2})^{-3}$
75. $(a^{-5}b^7c^{-2})(a^{-3}b^{-2}c^6)$
76. $(x^3y^{-4}z^{-5})(x^{-4}y^{-2}z^9)$
77. $\left(\dfrac{a^4}{3}\right)^{-2}$
78. $\left(\dfrac{y^2}{2}\right)^{-2}$
79. $\left(\dfrac{m^{-1}}{n^{-4}}\right)^3$
80. $\left(\dfrac{x^2y}{z^{-5}}\right)^3$
81. $\left(\dfrac{2a^2}{3b^4}\right)^{-3}$
82. $\left(\dfrac{a^2b}{2d^3}\right)^{-5}$

Aha! 83. $\left(\dfrac{5x^{-2}}{3y^{-2}z}\right)^0$
84. $\left(\dfrac{4a^3b^{-2}}{5c^{-3}}\right)^1$
85. $\dfrac{-6a^3b^{-5}}{-3a^7b^{-8}}$
86. $\dfrac{12x^{-2}y^4}{-3xy^{-7}}$
87. $\dfrac{10x^{-4}yz^7}{8x^7y^{-3}z^{-3}}$
88. $\dfrac{9a^6b^{-4}c^7}{27a^{-4}b^5c^9}$

Scientific Notation

Convert to decimal notation.

89. 4.92×10^3

90. 8.13×10^4

91. 8.92×10^{-3}

92. 7.26×10^{-4}

93. 9.04×10^8

94. 1.35×10^7

95. 3.497×10^{-6}

96. 9.043×10^{-3}

Convert to scientific notation.

97. 36,000,000

98. 27,400

99. 0.00583

100. 0.0814

101. 78,000,000,000

102. 3,700,000,000,000

103. 0.000001032

104. 0.00000008

Multiplying and Dividing Using Scientific Notation

Multiply or divide, as indicated, and write scientific notation for the result.

105. $(3 \times 10^5)(2 \times 10^8)$

106. $(3.1 \times 10^7)(2.1 \times 10^{-4})$

107. $(3.8 \times 10^9)(6.5 \times 10^{-2})$

108. $(7.1 \times 10^{-7})(8.6 \times 10^{-5})$

109. $(8.7 \times 10^{-12})(4.5 \times 10^{-5})$

110. $(4.7 \times 10^5)(6.2 \times 10^{-12})$

111. $\dfrac{8.5 \times 10^8}{3.4 \times 10^{-5}}$

112. $\dfrac{5.6 \times 10^{-2}}{2.5 \times 10^5}$

113. $(4.0 \times 10^3) \div (8.0 \times 10^8)$

114. $(1.5 \times 10^{-3}) \div (1.6 \times 10^{-6})$

115. $\dfrac{7.5 \times 10^{-9}}{2.5 \times 10^{12}}$

116. $\dfrac{3.0 \times 10^{-2}}{6.0 \times 10^{10}}$

117. Without performing actual computations, explain why 3^{-29} is smaller than 2^{-29}.

118. Explain why each of the following is not scientific notation: 12.6×10^8; $4.8 \times 10^{1.7}$; 0.207×10^{-5}.

Skill Review

Simplify.

119. $\frac{1}{6} - \frac{1}{3}$ [1.6]

120. $x - (x - 7)$ [1.8]

121. $(-2a)^5$ [1.8]

122. $|7 - 8|$ [1.8]

123. $24 \div 6 \cdot 2 - 3[4(3 - 1) - 7]$ [1.8]

124. $(-3)(-1)(-5)(-1)(-1)$ [1.7]

Synthesis

125. Explain why $(-17)^{-8}$ is positive.

126. Explain what requirements must be met in order for x^{-n} to represent a negative integer.

127. Explain why scientific notation cannot be used without an understanding of the rules for exponents.

128. Write the reciprocal of 1.25×10^{-6} in scientific notation.

129. Write $8^{-3} \cdot 32 \div 16^2$ as a power of 2.

130. Write $81^3 \div 27 \cdot 9^2$ as a power of 3.

Simplify each of the following. Do not use a calculator.

Aha! **131.** $\dfrac{125^{-4}(25^2)^4}{125}$

132. $(13^{-12})^2 \cdot 13^{25}$

133. $[(5^{-3})^2]^{-1}$

134. $5^0 - 5^{-1}$

135. $3^{-1} + 4^{-1}$

136. Determine whether each of the following is true for all pairs of integers m and n and all positive numbers x and y.
a) $x^m \cdot y^n = (xy)^{mn}$
b) $x^m \cdot y^m = (xy)^{2m}$
c) $(x - y)^m = x^m - y^m$

Solve. Write scientific notation for each answer.

137. *Ecology.* In one year, a large tree can remove from the air the same amount of carbon dioxide produced by a car traveling 500 mi. If New York City contains approximately 600,000 trees, how many miles of car traffic can those trees clean in a year?

Sources: Colorado Tree Coalition; New York City Department of Parks and Recreations

138. *Computer Technology.* One gigabyte is 1 billion bytes of information, and a terabyte is 1000 gigabytes. Intel Corp. has developed silicon-based connections that use lasers to move data at a rate of 50 gigabytes per second. The printed collection of the U.S. Library of Congress contains 10 terabytes of information. How long would it take to copy the Library of Congress using these connections?

Sources: spie.org; newworldencyclopedia.org

139. *Hotel Management.* The Four Seasons Hotel in Seattle contains 110,000 ft^2 of condominium space. If these condos sold for about \$2100 per ft^2, how much money did the hotel make selling the condominiums?

Source: seattletimes.nwsource.com

140. *Coral Reefs.*   There are 10 million bacteria per square centimeter of coral in a coral reef. The coral reefs near the Hawaiian Islands cover 14,000 km². How many bacteria are there in Hawaii's coral reefs?

Sources: livescience.com; U.S. Geological Survey

141. *Biology.*   A human hair is about 4×10^{-5} m in diameter. A strand of DNA is 2 nanometers in diameter. How many strands of DNA laid side by side would it take to equal the width of a human hair?

 YOUR TURN ANSWERS: SECTION 4.2

1. $\dfrac{7}{x^2}$ **2.** 10^{-7} **3.** $\dfrac{3}{x^{12}}$ **4.** $\dfrac{3c^3}{ab}$ **5.** $\dfrac{y^{10}}{9x^2}$

6. 0.00804 **7.** 6×10^5 **8.** 5.5×10^{-18} **9.** 4.0×10^{16}

QUICK QUIZ: SECTIONS 4.1–4.2

Simplify.

1. $(2n^2m)^3(5nm^4)^2$ [4.1]   **2.** $6^{-12} \cdot 6$ [4.2]

3. $(2x^2y^{-1})^{-3}$ [4.2]   **4.** 289^0 [4.1]

5. Convert $30,070,000$ to scientific notation.   [4.2]

PREPARE TO MOVE ON

Combine like terms.   [1.6]

1. $9x + 2y - x - 2y$ **2.** $5a - 7b - 8a + b$

3. $-3x + (-2) - 5 - (-x)$ **4.** $2 - t - 3t - r - 7$

Evaluate.   [1.8]

5. $4 + x^3$, for $x = 10$

6. $-x^2 - 5x + 3$, for $x = -2$

4.3   Polynomials

Terms ▪ Types of Polynomials ▪ Degree and Coefficients ▪ Combining Like Terms ▪
Evaluating Polynomials and Applications

We now examine an important algebraic expression known as a *polynomial*. Certain polynomials have appeared earlier in this text so you already have some experience working with them.

Terms

At this point, we have seen a variety of algebraic expressions like

$$3a^2b^4, \quad 2l + 2w, \quad \text{and} \quad 5x^2 + x - 2.$$

Within these expressions, $3a^2b^4$, $2l$, $2w$, $5x^2$, x, and -2 are examples of *terms*. A **term** can be a number (like -2), a variable (like x), a product of numbers and/or variables (like $3a^2b^4$), or a quotient of numbers and/or variables (like $7/t$).

 If a term is a product of constants and/or variables, it is called a **monomial**. A term, but not a monomial, can include division by a variable. A **polynomial** is a monomial or a sum of monomials.

Study Skills

A Text Is Not Light Reading
Do not expect a math text to read like a magazine or novel. On one hand, most assigned readings in a math text consist of only a few pages. On the other hand, every sentence and word is important and should make sense. If they don't, ask for help as soon as possible.

Examples of monomials: $7, \quad t, \quad 2l, \quad 2w, \quad 5x^3y, \quad \frac{3}{7}a^5$

Examples of polynomials: $4x - 7, \quad \frac{2}{3}t^2, \quad -5n^2 + m - 1, \quad x, \quad 0$

Note that $4x - 7$ is a polynomial because it can be written as $4x + (-7)$. When a polynomial is written as a sum of monomials, each monomial is called a *term of the polynomial*.

EXAMPLE 1   Identify the terms of the polynomial $3t^4 - 5t^6 - 4t + 2$.

SOLUTION   The terms are $3t^4, -5t^6, -4t$, and 2. We can see this by rewriting all subtractions as additions of opposites:

$$3t^4 - 5t^6 - 4t + 2 = 3t^4 + (-5t^6) + (-4t) + 2.$$

These are the terms of the polynomial.

1. Identify the terms of the polynomial $3x - 6 + 5x^4$.

YOUR TURN

Types of Polynomials

A polynomial with two terms is called a **binomial**, and one with three terms is called a **trinomial**. Polynomials with four or more terms have no special name.

Monomials	Binomials	Trinomials	No Special Name
$4x^2$	$2x + 4$	$3t^3 + 4t + 7$	$4x^3 - 5x^2 + xy - 8$
9	$3a^5 + 6bc$	$6x^7 - 8z^2 + 4$	$z^5 + 2z^4 - z^3 + 7z + 3$
$-7a^{19}b^5$	$-9x^7 - 6$	$4x^2 - 6x - \frac{1}{2}$	$4x^6 - 3x^5 + x^4 - x^3 + 2x - 1$

The following algebraic expressions are *not* polynomials:

(1) $\dfrac{x + 3}{x - 4},$ **(2)** $5x^3 - 2x^2 + \dfrac{1}{x},$ **(3)** $\dfrac{1}{x^3 - 2}.$

Expressions (1) and (3) are not polynomials because they represent quotients, not sums. Expression (2) is not a polynomial because $1/x$ is not a monomial.

Degree and Coefficients

The **degree of a monomial** is the number of variable factors in the monomial. Thus the degree of $7t^2$ is 2 because $7t^2$ has two variable factors: $7t^2 = 7 \cdot t \cdot t$. When there is only one variable, the degree is the exponent of that variable.

EXAMPLE 2   Determine the degree of each monomial: **(a)** $8x^4$;   **(b)** $3x$;   **(c)** 7.

SOLUTION

a) The degree of $8x^4$ is 4. x^4 represents 4 variable factors: $x \cdot x \cdot x \cdot x$.

b) The degree of $3x$ is 1.   There is 1 variable factor.

c) The degree of 7 is 0.   There is no variable factor.

2. Determine the degree of the term $12t$.

YOUR TURN

The degree of a constant, such as 7, is 0 since there are no variable factors. The monomial 0 is an exception, since $0 = 0x = 0x^2 = 0x^3$ and so on. We say that the monomial 0 has *no* degree. Note that a term of a polynomial is a monomial, so that we can also refer to the degree of a term.

The part of a term that is a constant factor is the **coefficient** of that term. Thus the coefficient of $3x$ is 3, and the coefficient for the term 7 is simply 7.

EXAMPLE 3   Identify the coefficient of each term in the polynomial

$$4x^3 - 7x^2 + x - 8.$$

SOLUTION

The coefficient of $4x^3$ is 4.

The coefficient of $-7x^2$ is -7.

The coefficient of the third term is 1, since $x = 1x$.

The coefficient of -8 is simply -8.

3. Identify the coefficient of each term in the polynomial $y^5 - y^2 + 12y - 9$.

 YOUR TURN

The **leading term** of a polynomial is the term of highest degree. Its coefficient is called the **leading coefficient**, and its degree is referred to as the **degree of the polynomial**. To see how this terminology is used, consider the polynomial

$$3x^2 - 8x^3 + 5x^4 + 7x - 6.$$

The *terms* are $3x^2, -8x^3, 5x^4, 7x,$ and -6.

The *coefficients* are $3, -8, 5, 7,$ and -6.

The *degree of each term* is $2, 3, 4, 1,$ and 0.

The *leading term* is $5x^4$ and the *leading coefficient* is 5.

The *degree of the polynomial* is 4.

Combining Like Terms

Like, or *similar, terms* are either constant terms or terms containing the same variable(s) raised to the same power(s). For example, the like terms in

$$4x^3 + 5x - 7x^2 + 2x^3 + x^2$$

are $4x^3$ and $2x^3$ as well as $-7x^2$ and x^2.

Often we can simplify polynomials by *combining,* or *collecting,* like terms.

EXAMPLE 4   Write an equivalent expression by combining like terms.

a) $2x^3 + 6x^3$ **b)** $5x^2 + 7 + 2x^4 - 6x^2 - 11 - 2x^4$

c) $7a^3 - 5a^2 + 9a^3 + a^2$ **d)** $\frac{2}{3}x^4 - x^3 - \frac{1}{6}x^4 + \frac{2}{5}x^3 - \frac{3}{10}x^3$

SOLUTION

a) $2x^3 + 6x^3 = (2 + 6)x^3$ Using the distributive law

$\qquad\qquad\quad = 8x^3$

b) $5x^2 + 7 + 2x^4 - 6x^2 - 11 - 2x^4$

$\qquad = 5x^2 - 6x^2 + 2x^4 - 2x^4 + 7 - 11$

$\qquad = (5 - 6)x^2 + (2 - 2)x^4 + (7 - 11)$ ⎱

$\qquad = -1x^2 + 0x^4 + (-4)$ ⎰ These steps are often done mentally.

$\qquad = -x^2 - 4$

c) $7a^3 - 5a^2 + 9a^3 + a^2 = 7a^3 - 5a^2 + 9a^3 + 1a^2$ $a^2 = 1 \cdot a^2 = 1a^2$

$\qquad\qquad\qquad\qquad\qquad = 16a^3 - 4a^2$

d) $\frac{2}{3}x^4 - x^3 - \frac{1}{6}x^4 + \frac{2}{5}x^3 - \frac{3}{10}x^3 = \left(\frac{2}{3} - \frac{1}{6}\right)x^4 + \left(-1 + \frac{2}{5} - \frac{3}{10}\right)x^3$

$\qquad\qquad\qquad = \left(\frac{4}{6} - \frac{1}{6}\right)x^4 + \left(-\frac{10}{10} + \frac{4}{10} - \frac{3}{10}\right)x^3$

$\qquad\qquad\qquad = \frac{3}{6}x^4 - \frac{9}{10}x^3$

$\qquad\qquad\qquad = \frac{1}{2}x^4 - \frac{9}{10}x^3$ There are no like terms, so we are done.

Student Notes

Remember that when we combine like terms, we are not solving equations, but are forming equivalent expressions.

4. Write an equivalent expression by combining like terms:

$2n^2 - 6n + n^2 + 6n$.

 YOUR TURN

Note in Example 4 that the solutions are written so that the term of highest degree appears first, followed by the term of next highest degree, and so on. This is known as **descending order** and is the form in which answers will normally appear.

Evaluating Polynomials and Applications

When each variable in a polynomial is replaced with a number, the polynomial then represents a number, or *value*, that can be calculated using the rules for order of operations.

EXAMPLE 5 Evaluate $-x^2 + 3x + 9$ for $x = -2$.

SOLUTION For $x = -2$, we have

Substitute.

$$-x^2 + 3x + 9 = -(-2)^2 + 3(-2) + 9 \qquad \text{The negative sign in front of } x^2 \text{ remains.}$$

$$= -(4) + 3(-2) + 9 \qquad \text{Evaluating the exponential expression}$$

Simplify.

$$= -4 + (-6) + 9 \qquad \text{Multiplying}$$

5. Evaluate $t^3 - 5t^2 - 10t + 1$ for $t = -1$.

$$= -10 + 9 = -1. \qquad \text{Adding}$$

YOUR TURN

6. Use the polynomial given in Example 6 to estimate the power generated by a 20-mph wind.

EXAMPLE 6 *Renewable Energy Sources.* The number of watts of power P generated by a particular wind turbine at a wind speed of x miles per hour can be approximated by the polynomial

$$P = 0.0157x^3 + 0.1163x^2 - 1.3396x + 3.7063.$$

Estimate the power generated by a 10-mph wind.

Source: Based on data from QST, November 2006

SOLUTION To find the power generated by a 10-mph wind, we evaluate the polynomial for $x = 10$:

$$P = 0.0157x^3 + 0.1163x^2 - 1.3396x + 3.7063$$

$$= 0.0157(10)^3 + 0.1163(10)^2 - 1.3396(10) + 3.7063$$

$$= 15.7 + 11.63 - 13.396 + 3.7063$$

$$= 17.6403.$$

Since this value is approximate, we round the answer. A 10-mph wind will generate about 17.6 watts.

YOUR TURN

Sometimes, a graph can be used to estimate the value of a polynomial visually.

EXAMPLE 7 *Renewable Energy Sources.* In the following figure, the polynomial from Example 6 has been graphed by evaluating it for several choices of x. Use the graph to estimate the power generated by a 30-mph wind.

SOLUTION To estimate the power generated by a 30-mph wind, we locate 30 on the horizontal axis of the graph. From there, we move vertically until we meet the curve. From that point, we move horizontally to the P-axis.

7. Use the graph given in Example 7 to estimate the power generated by a 15-mph wind.

We see that the power generated by a 30-mph wind is approximately 490 watts. (For $x = 30$, the value of $0.0157x^3 + 0.1163x^2 - 1.3396x + 3.7063$ is approximately 490.)

↻ YOUR TURN

Technology Connection

One way to evaluate a polynomial is to use the TRACE key. For example, to evaluate $0.0157x^3 + 0.1163x^2 - 1.3396x + 3.7063$ in Example 7 for $x = 30$, we can graph the polynomial $y = 0.0157x^3 + 0.1163x^2 - 1.3396x + 3.7063$. We then use TRACE and enter an x-value of 30.

The value of the polynomial appears as y, and the cursor appears at $(30, 492.0883)$. The VALUE option of the CALC menu works in a similar way.

Xscl = 10, Yscl = 100

1. Use TRACE or CALC VALUE to find the value of $0.0157x^3 + 0.1163x^2 - 1.3396x + 3.7063$ for $x = 40$.

4.3 EXERCISE SET

FOR EXTRA HELP

MyMathLab® *MathXL*
PRACTICE   WATCH   READ   REVIEW

Vocabulary and Reading Check

Match the description in the left-hand column with the most appropriate algebraic expression from the column on the right.

1. _____ A polynomial with four terms
2. _____ A polynomial with 7 as its leading coefficient
3. _____ A trinomial written in descending order
4. _____ A polynomial with degree 5
5. _____ A binomial with degree 7
6. _____ A monomial of degree 0
7. _____ An expression with two terms that is not a binomial
8. _____ An expression with three terms that is not a trinomial

a) $8x^3 + \dfrac{2}{x^2}$

b) $5x^4 + 3x^3 - 4x + 7$

c) $\dfrac{3}{x} - 6x^2 + 9$

d) $8t - 4t^5$

e) 5

f) $6x^2 + 7x^4 - 2x^3$

g) $4t - 2t^7$

h) $3t^2 + 4t + 7$

Concept Reinforcement

Determine whether each expression is a polynomial.

9. $3x - 7$

10. $-2x^5 + 9 - 7x^2$

11. $\dfrac{x^2 + x + 1}{x^3 - 7}$

12. -10

13. $\frac{1}{4}x^{10} - 8.6$

14. $\dfrac{3}{x^4} - \dfrac{1}{x} + 13$

Terms

Identify the terms of each polynomial.

15. $8x^3 - 11x^2 + 6x + 1$
16. $5a^3 + 4a^2 - a - 7$
17. $-t^6 - 3t^3 + 9t - 4$
18. $n^5 - 4n^3 + 2n - 8$

Types of Polynomials

Classify each polynomial as a monomial, a binomial, a trinomial, or a polynomial with no special name.

19. $x^2 - 23x + 17$
20. $-9x^2$
21. $x^3 - 7x + 2x^2 - 4$
22. $t^3 + 4$
23. $y + 8$
24. $3x^8 + 12x^3 - 9$
25. 17
26. $2x^4 - 7x^3 + x^2 + x - 6$

Degree and Coefficients

27. Complete the following table for the polynomial
$7x^2 + 8x^5 - 4x^3 + 6 - \frac{1}{2}x^4$.

Term	Coefficient	Degree of the Term	Degree of the Polynomial
		5	
$-\frac{1}{2}x^4$			
	-4		
		2	
	6		

28. Complete the following table for the polynomial
$-3x^4 + 6x^3 - 2x^2 + 8x + 7$.

Term	Coefficient	Degree of the Term	Degree of the Polynomial
	-3		
$6x^3$			
		2	
		1	
	7		

Determine the coefficient and the degree of each term in each polynomial.

29. $8x^4 + 2x$
30. $9a^3 - 4a^2$
31. $9t^2 - 3t + 4$
32. $7x^4 + 5x - 3$
33. $x^4 - x^3 + 4x - 3$
34. $2a^5 + a^2 + 8a + 10$

For each of the following polynomials, (a) list the degree of each term; (b) determine the leading term and the leading coefficient; and (c) determine the degree of the polynomial.

35. $5t + t^3 + 8t^4$
36. $1 + 6n + 4n^2$
37. $3a^2 - 7 + 2a^4$
38. $9x^4 + x^2 + x^7 - 12$
39. $8 + 6x^2 - 3x - x^5$
40. $9a - a^4 + 3 + 2a^3$

Combining Like Terms

Combine like terms. Write all answers in descending order.

41. $5n^2 + n + 6n^2$ **42.** $5a + 7a^2 + 3a$

43. $3a^4 - 2a + 2a + a^4$

44. $9b^5 + 3b^2 - 2b^5 - 3b^2$

45. $4b^3 + 5b + 7b^3 + b^2 - 6b$

46. $6x^2 + 2x^4 - 2x^2 - x^4 - 4x^2 + x$

47. $10x^2 + 2x^3 - 3x^3 - 4x^2 - 6x^2 - x^4$

48. $12t^6 - t^3 + 8t^6 + 4t^3 - t^7 - 3t^3$

49. $\frac{1}{5}x^4 + 7 - 2x^2 + 3 - \frac{2}{15}x^4 + 2x^2$

50. $\frac{1}{6}x^3 + 3x^2 - \frac{1}{3}x^3 + 7 + x^2 - 10$

51. $8.3a^2 + 3.7a - 8 - 9.4a^2 + 1.6a + 0.5$

52. $1.4y^3 + 2.9 - 7.7y - 1.3y - 4.1 + 9.6y^3$

Evaluating Polynomials and Applications

Evaluate each polynomial for $x = 3$ and for $x = -3$.

53. $-4x + 9$ **54.** $-6x + 5$

55. $2x^2 - 3x + 7$ **56.** $4x^2 - 6x + 9$

57. $-3x^3 + 7x^2 - 4x - 8$

58. $-2x^3 - 3x^2 + 4x + 2$

59. $2x^4 - \frac{1}{9}x^3$ **60.** $\frac{1}{3}x^4 - 2x^3$

61. *Skydiving.* During the first 13 sec of a jump, the number of feet that a skydiver falls in t seconds is approximated by the polynomial

$$11.12t^2.$$

In 2009, 108 U.S. skydivers fell headfirst in formation from a height of 18,000 ft. How far had they fallen 10 sec after having jumped from the plane?

Source: www.telegraph.co.uk

62. *Skydiving.* For jumps that exceed 13 sec, the polynomial $173t - 369$ can be used to approximate the distance, in feet, that a skydiver has fallen in t seconds. Approximately how far has a skydiver fallen 20 sec after having jumped from a plane?

Circumference. The circumference of a circle of radius r is given by the polynomial $2\pi r$, where π is an irrational number. For an approximation of π, use 3.14.

63. Find the circumference of a circle with radius 10 cm.

64. Find the circumference of a circle with radius 5 ft.

Area of a Circle. The area of a circle of radius r is given by the polynomial πr^2. Use 3.14 for π.

65. Find the area of a circle with radius 7 m.

66. Find the area of a circle with radius 6 ft.

67. *Kayaking.* The distance $s(t)$, in feet, traveled by a body falling freely from rest in t seconds is approximated by $s(t) = 16t^2$. On March 4, 2009, Brazilian kayaker Pedro Olivia set a world record waterfall descent on the Rio Sacre in Brazil. He was airborne for 2.9 sec. How far did he drop?

Source: www.telegraph.co.uk

68. *SCAD Diving.* The SCAD thrill ride is a 2.5-sec free fall into a net. How far does the diver fall? (See Exercise 67.)

Source: "What is SCAD?", www.scadfreefall.co.uk

69. *Stacking Spheres.* In 2004, the journal *Annals of Mathematics* accepted a proof of the so-called Kepler Conjecture: that the most efficient way to pack spheres is in the shape of a square pyramid. The number N of balls in the stack is given by the polynomial function

$$N(x) = \tfrac{1}{3}x^3 + \tfrac{1}{2}x^2 + \tfrac{1}{6}x,$$

where x is the number of layers. Use both the function and the figure to find $N(3)$. Then calculate the number of oranges in a pyramid with 5 layers.

Source: *The New York Times* 4/6/04

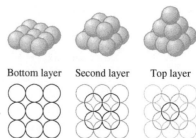

Bottom layer   Second layer   Top layer

70. *Stacking Cannonballs.* The function in Exercise 69 was discovered by Thomas Harriot, assistant to Sir Walter Raleigh, when preparing for an expedition at sea. How many cannonballs did they pack if there were 10 layers to their pyramid?

Source: *The New York Times* 4/7/04

Veterinary Science. *Gentamicin is an antibiotic frequently used by veterinarians. The concentration, in micrograms per milliliter* (mcg/mL), *of Gentamicin in a horse's bloodstream t hours after injection can be approximated by the polynomial*

$$C = -0.005t^4 + 0.003t^3 + 0.35t^2 + 0.5t.$$

Use the following graph for Exercises 71 and 72.

Source: Michele Tulis, DVM, telephone interview

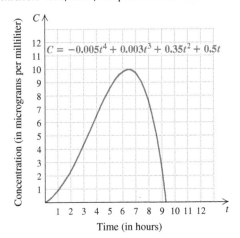

71. Estimate the concentration, in mcg/mL, of Gentamicin in the bloodstream 2 hr after injection.

72. Estimate the concentration, in mcg/mL, of Gentamicin in the bloodstream 4 hr after injection.

73. Explain how it is possible for a term to not be a monomial.

74. Why is it important to understand the rules for order of operations when evaluating polynomials?

Skill Review

Graph.

75. $y = 3x$ [3.2]

76. $y = \frac{1}{2}x - 5$ [3.6]

77. $3x - y = 3$ [3.3]

78. $y = -1$ [3.3]

79. $x = 2$ [3.3]

80. $y + 2 = -2(x - 1)$ [3.7]

Synthesis

81. Suppose that the coefficients of a polynomial are all integers and the polynomial is evaluated for some integer. Must the value of the polynomial then also be an integer? Why or why not?

82. Is it easier to evaluate a polynomial before or after like terms have been combined? Why?

83. Construct a polynomial in x (meaning that x is the variable) of degree 5 with four terms, with coefficients that are consecutive even integers. Write in descending order.

Revenue, Cost, and Profit. *Gigabytes Electronics is selling a new type of computer monitor. Total revenue is the total amount of money taken in and total cost is the total amount paid for producing the items. The firm estimates that for the monitor's first year, revenue from the sale of x monitors is*

$$250x - 0.5x^2 \text{ dollars,}$$

and the total cost is given by

$$4000 + 0.6x^2 \text{ dollars.}$$

Profit *is the difference between revenue and cost.*

84. Find the profit when 20 monitors are produced and sold.

85. Find the profit when 30 monitors are produced and sold.

Simplify.

86. $\frac{9}{2}x^8 + \frac{1}{9}x^2 + \frac{1}{2}x^9 + \frac{9}{2}x + \frac{9}{2}x^9 + \frac{8}{9}x^2 + \frac{1}{2}x - \frac{1}{2}x^8$

87. $(3x^2)^3 + 4x^2 \cdot 4x^4 - x^4(2x)^2 + ((2x)^2)^3 - 100x^2(x^2)^2$

88. A polynomial in x has degree 3. The coefficient of x^2 is 3 less than the coefficient of x^3. The coefficient of x is three times the coefficient of x^2. The remaining constant is 2 more than the coefficient of x^3. The sum of the coefficients is -4. Find the polynomial.

89. Use the graph for Exercises 71 and 72 to determine the times for which the concentration of Gentamicin is 5 mcg/mL.

90. *Path of the Olympic Arrow.* The Olympic flame at the 1992 Summer Olympics in Spain was lit by a flaming arrow. As the arrow moved d meters horizontally from the archer, its height h, in meters, was approximated by the polynomial

$$-0.0064d^2 + 0.8d + 2.$$

Complete the table for the choices of d given. Then plot the points and draw a graph representing the path of the arrow.

d	$-0.0064d^2 + 0.8d + 2$
0	
30	
60	
90	
120	

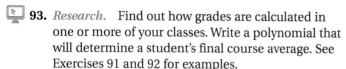 *Semester Averages.* Professor Sakima calculates a student's average for her course using

$$A = 0.3q + 0.4t + 0.2f + 0.1h,$$

with q, t, f, and h representing a student's quiz average, test average, final exam score, and homework average, respectively. In Exercises 91 and 92, find the given student's course average rounded to the nearest tenth.

91. Beth: quizzes: 60, 85, 72, 91; final exam: 84; tests: 89, 93, 90; homework: 88

92. Cameron: quizzes: 95, 99, 72, 79; final exam: 91; tests: 68, 76, 92; homework: 86

93. *Research.* Find out how grades are calculated in one or more of your classes. Write a polynomial that will determine a student's final course average. See Exercises 91 and 92 for examples.

In Exercises 94 and 95, complete the table for the given choices of t. Then plot the points and connect them with a smooth curve representing the graph of the polynomial.

94.

t	$-t^2 + 6t - 4$
1	
2	
3	
4	
5	

95.

t	$-t^2 + 10t - 18$
3	
4	
5	
6	
7	

YOUR TURN ANSWERS: SECTION 4.3

1. $3x, -6, 5x^4$ **2.** 1   **3.** $1, -1, 12, -9$ **4.** $3n^2$
5. 5   **6.** Approximately 149 watts   **7.** Approximately 60 watts

QUICK QUIZ: SECTIONS 4.1–4.3
Simplify.

1. $(-3x^5 y^4)^2$ [4.1]   **2.** $\dfrac{48a^5 b}{-3ab}$ [4.1]

3. List the coefficients of the polynomial $x^6 - 6x + \frac{1}{2}$.   [4.3]

4. Evaluate $-x - 3x^2 + x^3$ for $x = -10$.   [4.3]

5. Evaluate t^0 for $t = -12.5$.   [4.1]

PREPARE TO MOVE ON
Simplify. [1.8]

1. $2x + 5 - (x + 8)$ **2.** $3x - 7 - (5x - 1)$

3. $4a + 3 - (-2a + 6)$ **4.** $\frac{1}{2}t - \frac{1}{4} - \left(\frac{3}{2}t + \frac{3}{4}\right)$

5. $4t^4 + 8t - (5t^4 - 9t)$

6. $0.1a^2 + 5 - (-0.3a^2 + a - 6)$

4.4 Addition and Subtraction of Polynomials

Addition of Polynomials ▪ Opposites of Polynomials ▪ Subtraction of Polynomials ▪ Problem Solving

Addition of Polynomials

To add two polynomials, we write a plus sign between them and combine like terms.

EXAMPLE 1 Write an equivalent expression by adding.

a) $(-5x^3 + 6x - 1) + (4x^3 + 3x^2 + 2)$

b) $\left(\frac{2}{3}x^4 + 3x^2 - 7x + \frac{1}{2}\right) + \left(-\frac{1}{3}x^4 + 5x^3 - 3x^2 + 3x - \frac{1}{2}\right)$

SOLUTION

a) $(-5x^3 + 6x - 1) + (4x^3 + 3x^2 + 2)$

$= -5x^3 + 6x - 1 + 4x^3 + 3x^2 + 2$ Writing without parentheses

$= -5x^3 + 4x^3 + 3x^2 + 6x - 1 + 2$ Using the commutative and associative laws to write like terms together

$= (-5 + 4)x^3 + 3x^2 + 6x + (-1 + 2)$ Combining like terms; using the distributive law

$= -x^3 + 3x^2 + 6x + 1$ Note that $-1x^3 = -x^3$.

b) $\left(\frac{2}{3}x^4 + 3x^2 - 7x + \frac{1}{2}\right) + \left(-\frac{1}{3}x^4 + 5x^3 - 3x^2 + 3x - \frac{1}{2}\right)$

$= \left(\frac{2}{3} - \frac{1}{3}\right)x^4 + 5x^3 + (3 - 3)x^2 + (-7 + 3)x + \left(\frac{1}{2} - \frac{1}{2}\right)$ Combining like terms

$= \frac{1}{3}x^4 + 5x^3 - 4x$

YOUR TURN

> **CAUTION!** Note that equations like those in Examples 1 and 2 are written to show how one expression can be rewritten in an equivalent form. This is very different from solving an equation.

1. Write an equivalent expression by adding:

$(-y^3 + 6y^2 - 4y) + (y^2 + 2y)$.

After some practice, polynomial addition is often performed mentally.

EXAMPLE 2 Add: $(2 - 3x + x^2) + (-5 + 7x - 3x^2 + x^3)$.

SOLUTION We have

$(2 - 3x + x^2) + (-5 + 7x - 3x^2 + x^3)$

$= (2 - 5) + (-3 + 7)x + (1 - 3)x^2 + x^3$ You might do this step mentally.

$= -3 + 4x - 2x^2 + x^3$.   Then you would write only this.

YOUR TURN

2. Add:

$(-1 - 4n + n^2) + (7 + 10n + 3n^2)$.

In the polynomials of the last example, the terms are arranged according to degree, from least to greatest. Such an arrangement is called *ascending order*. As a rule, answers are written in ascending order when the polynomials in the original problem are given in ascending order. If the polynomials in the original problem are given in descending order, the answer is usually written in descending order.

To add using columns, we write the polynomials one under the other, listing like terms under one another and leaving space for any missing terms.

EXAMPLE 3 Add:

$9x^5 - 2x^3 + 6x^2 + 3$ and $5x^4 - 7x^2 + 6$ and $3x^6 - 5x^5 + x^2 + 5$.

SOLUTION We arrange the polynomials with like terms in columns.

$$
\begin{array}{l}
9x^5 \qquad\quad - 2x^3 + 6x^2 + 3 \\
\qquad\quad 5x^4 \qquad\quad - 7x^2 + 6 \qquad\text{We leave spaces for missing terms.}\\
\underline{3x^6 - 5x^5 \qquad\qquad\qquad + 1x^2 + 5} \qquad\text{Writing } x^2 \text{ as } 1x^2 \\
3x^6 + 4x^5 + 5x^4 - 2x^3 \qquad\qquad + 14 \qquad\text{Adding}
\end{array}
$$

The answer is $3x^6 + 4x^5 + 5x^4 - 2x^3 + 14$.

YOUR TURN

3. Add using columns:

$12x^3 + 6x - 7$ and

$x^3 - 5x^2 + 6x - 1$.

Opposites of Polynomials

The opposite of the polynomial $x^2 - 3x + 5$ is written $-(x^2 - 3x + 5)$. We can remove the parentheses and the negative sign by changing the sign of every term within the parentheses.

> **THE OPPOSITE OF A POLYNOMIAL**
>
> To find an equivalent polynomial for the *opposite*, or *additive inverse*, of a polynomial, change the sign of every term. This is the same as multiplying the polynomial by -1.

EXAMPLE 4 Write two equivalent expressions for the opposite of $4x^5 - 7x^3 - 8x + \frac{5}{6}$.

SOLUTION

i) $-\left(4x^5 - 7x^3 - 8x + \frac{5}{6}\right)$ This is one way to write the opposite of $4x^5 - 7x^3 - 8x + \frac{5}{6}$.

ii) $-4x^5 + 7x^3 + 8x - \frac{5}{6}$ Changing the sign of every term

4. Write two equivalent expressions for the opposite of $-a^4 - 5a^2 + 10$.

Thus, $-\left(4x^5 - 7x^3 - 8x + \frac{5}{6}\right)$ and $-4x^5 + 7x^3 + 8x - \frac{5}{6}$ are equivalent. Both expressions represent the opposite of $4x^5 - 7x^3 - 8x + \frac{5}{6}$.

YOUR TURN

EXAMPLE 5 Simplify: $-\left(-7x^4 - \frac{5}{9}x^3 + 8x^2 - x + 67\right)$.

SOLUTION We have

$$-\left(-7x^4 - \frac{5}{9}x^3 + 8x^2 - x + 67\right) = 7x^4 + \frac{5}{9}x^3 - 8x^2 + x - 67.$$

The same result can be found by multiplying by -1:

$$-(-7x^4 - \frac{5}{9}x^3 + 8x^2 - x + 67)$$
$$= -1(-7x^4) + (-1)\left(-\frac{5}{9}x^3\right) + (-1)(8x^2) + (-1)(-x) + (-1)67$$
$$= 7x^4 + \frac{5}{9}x^3 - 8x^2 + x - 67.$$

5. Simplify:

$-(3.5a^4 - \frac{2}{3}a^3 - 7a + 9)$.

YOUR TURN

Subtraction of Polynomials

We can now subtract one polynomial from another by adding the opposite of the polynomial being subtracted. Recall that $5 - 3 = 5 + (-3)$ and, as a rule, $a - b = a + (-b)$.

EXAMPLE 6 Write an equivalent expression by subtracting.

a) $(9x^5 + x^3 - 2x^2 + 4) - (-2x^5 + x^4 - 4x^3 - 3x^2)$

b) $(7x^5 + x^3 - 9x) - (3x^5 - 4x^3 + 5)$

SOLUTION

a) $(9x^5 + x^3 - 2x^2 + 4) - (-2x^5 + x^4 - 4x^3 - 3x^2)$
$= 9x^5 + x^3 - 2x^2 + 4 + 2x^5 - x^4 + 4x^3 + 3x^2$ Adding the opposite
$= 11x^5 - x^4 + 5x^3 + x^2 + 4$ Combining like terms

6. Write an equivalent expression by subtracting:

$(y^3 - 7y^2 - 9) - (-3y^3 - y^2 + 11)$.

b) $(7x^5 + x^3 - 9x) - (3x^5 - 4x^3 + 5)$
$= 7x^5 + x^3 - 9x + (-3x^5) + 4x^3 - 5$ Adding the opposite
$= 7x^5 + x^3 - 9x - 3x^5 + 4x^3 - 5$ Try to go directly to this step.
$= 4x^5 + 5x^3 - 9x - 5$ Combining like terms

YOUR TURN

To subtract using columns, we first replace the coefficients in the polynomial being subtracted with their opposites. We then add as before.

EXAMPLE 7 Write in columns and subtract:

$$(5x^2 - 3x + 6) - (9x^2 - 5x - 3).$$

SOLUTION

i) $\quad 5x^2 - 3x + 6$ Writing like terms in columns
$\quad -(9x^2 - 5x - 3)$

7. Write in columns and subtract:

$(12x^2 + x - 1) -$
$(4x^2 + 10x - 8).$

ii) $\quad 5x^2 - 3x + 6$ Changing signs and removing parentheses
$\quad -9x^2 + 5x + 3$ You might start with this step.

iii) $\quad 5x^2 - 3x + 6$
$\quad -9x^2 + 5x + 3$
$\quad \overline{-4x^2 + 2x + 9}$ Adding

YOUR TURN

If you can do so without error, you can mentally find the opposite of each term being subtracted, and write the answer. Lining up like terms is important and may require leaving some blank space.

EXAMPLE 8 Write in columns and subtract:

$$(x^3 + x^2 - 12) - (-2x^3 + x^2 - 3x + 6).$$

SOLUTION We have

8. Write in columns and subtract:

$(5x^4 - 3x^3 - x^2 + 6) -$
$(-4x^3 + 9x - 2).$

$$\begin{array}{r} x^3 + x^2 \quad\quad - 12 \\ -(-2x^3 + x^2 - 3x + \ 6) \\ \hline 3x^3 \quad\quad + 3x - 18 \end{array}$$

Leaving a blank space for the missing term

YOUR TURN

Problem Solving

EXAMPLE 9 Find a polynomial for the sum of the areas of rectangles $A, B, C,$ and D.

Study Skills

Aim for Mastery
In each exercise set, you may encounter one or more exercises that give you trouble. Do not ignore these problems, but instead work to master them. These are the problems (not the "easy" problems) that you will need to revisit as you progress through the course. Consider marking these exercises so that you can easily locate them when studying or reviewing for a quiz or a test.

SOLUTION

1. **Familiarize.** Recall that the area of a rectangle is the product of its length and width.

2. **Translate.** We translate the problem to mathematical language. The sum of the areas is a sum of products. We find each product and then add:

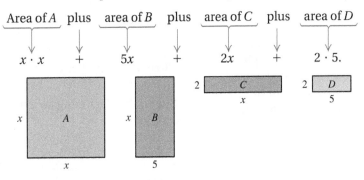

$$\underset{x \cdot x}{\text{Area of } A} \underset{+}{\text{plus}} \underset{5x}{\text{area of } B} \underset{+}{\text{plus}} \underset{2x}{\text{area of } C} \underset{+}{\text{plus}} \underset{2 \cdot 5.}{\text{area of } D}$$

3. **Carry out.** We simplify $x \cdot x$ and $2 \cdot 5$ and combine like terms:

$$x^2 + 5x + 2x + 10 = x^2 + 7x + 10.$$

4. **Check.** A partial check is to replace x with a number—say, 3. Then we evaluate $x^2 + 7x + 10$ and compare that result with an alternative calculation:

$$3^2 + 7 \cdot 3 + 10 = 9 + 21 + 10 = 40.$$

When we substitute 3 for x and calculate the total area by regarding the figure as one large rectangle, we should also get 40:

$$\text{Total area} = (x + 5)(x + 2) = (3 + 5)(3 + 2) = 8 \cdot 5 = 40.$$

Our check is only partial, since it is possible for an incorrect answer to equal 40 when evaluated for $x = 3$. This would be unlikely, especially if a second choice of x—say, $x = 5$—also checks. We leave that check to the student.

5. **State.** A polynomial for the sum of the areas is $x^2 + 7x + 10$.

9. Find a polynomial for the sum of the areas of rectangles A, B, C, and D.

YOUR TURN

EXAMPLE 10 A 16-ft wide round fountain is built in a square city park that measures x ft by x ft. Find a polynomial for the remaining area of the park.

SOLUTION

1. **Familiarize.** We make a drawing of the square park and the circular fountain, and let x represent the length of a side of the park.

The area of a square of side s is given by $A = s^2$, and the area of a circle of radius r is given by $A = \pi r^2$. Note that a circle with a diameter of 16 ft has a radius of 8 ft.

2. **Translate.** We reword the problem and translate as follows.

Rewording: Area of park minus area of fountain is area left over.

Translating: x ft $\cdot$ x ft $-$ $\pi \cdot 8$ ft $\cdot$ 8 ft $=$ Area left over

3. **Carry out.** We carry out the multiplication:

$$x^2 \text{ ft}^2 - 64\pi \text{ ft}^2 = (x^2 - 64\pi) \text{ ft}^2 = \text{Area left over.}$$

4. **Check.** As a partial check, note that the units in the answer are square feet (ft^2), a measure of area, as expected.

5. **State.** The remaining area of the park is $(x^2 - 64\pi) \text{ ft}^2$.

10. Consider the fountain and park described in Example 10. If the fountain is 20 ft wide, find a polynomial for the remaining area of the park.

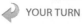 YOUR TURN

Technology Connection

To check polynomial addition or subtraction, we can let y_1 = the expression before the addition or subtraction has been performed and y_2 = the simplified sum or difference. If the addition or subtraction is correct, y_1 will equal y_2 and $y_2 - y_1$ will be 0. We enter $y_2 - y_1$ as y_3, using **VARS**. Below is a check of Example 6(b) in which

$$y_1 = (7x^5 + x^3 - 9x) - (3x^5 - 4x^3 + 5),$$
$$y_2 = 4x^5 + 5x^3 - 9x - 5,$$

and

$$y_3 = y_2 - y_1.$$

We graph only y_3. If indeed y_1 and y_2 are equivalent, then y_3 should equal 0. This means its graph should coincide with the x-axis. The TRACE or TABLE features can confirm

that y_3 is always 0, or we can select y_3 to be drawn bold at the ⟨ Y= ⟩ window.

$$y_3 = y_2 - y_1$$

X = 2.5531915   Y = 0

1. Use a graphing calculator to check Examples 1, 2, and 6.

4.4 EXERCISE SET

FOR EXTRA HELP

MyMathLab® Math XL
PRACTICE   WATCH   READ   REVIEW

Vocabulary and Reading Check

Choose the word or words from the following list to complete each sentence. Words may be used more than once or not at all.

ascending	missing
descending	opposite
like	sign

1. To subtract a polynomial, add the _____ of the polynomial.

2. When the terms of a polynomial are arranged according to degree, from least to greatest, the polynomial is written in _____ order.

3. To write an equivalent expression for the _____ of a polynomial, we change the _____ of every term.

4. To add or subtract polynomials using columns, we write _____ terms in columns and leave spaces for _____ terms.

Concept Reinforcement

For each of Exercises 5–8, replace ▨ with the correct expression or operation sign.

5. $(3x^2 + 2) + (6x^2 + 7) = (3 + 6)▨ + (2 + 7)$

6. $(5t - 6) + (4t + 3) = (5 + 4)t + (▨ + 3)$

7. $(9x^3 - x^2) - (3x^3 + x^2) = 9x^3 - x^2 - 3x^3 ▨ x^2$

8. $(-2n^3 + 5) - (n^2 - 2) = -2n^3 + 5 - n^2 ▨ 2$

Addition of Polynomials

Add.

9. $(3x + 2) + (x + 7)$

10. $(x + 1) + (12x + 10)$

11. $(2t + 7) + (-8t + 1)$

12. $(4t - 3) + (-11t + 2)$

13. $(x^2 + 6x + 3) + (-4x^2 - 5)$

14. $(x^2 - 5x + 4) + (8x - 9)$

15. $(7t^2 - 3t - 6) + (2t^2 + 4t + 9)$

16. $(8a^2 + 4a - 7) + (6a^2 - 3a - 1)$

17. $(4m^3 - 7m^2 + m - 5) + (4m^3 + 7m^2 - 4m - 2)$

18. $(5n^3 - n^2 + 4n + 11) + (2n^3 - 4n^2 + n - 11)$

19. $(3 + 6a + 7a^2 + a^3) + (4 + 7a - 8a^2 + 6a^3)$

20. $(7 + 4t - 5t^2 + 6t^3) + (2 + t + 6t^2 - 4t^3)$

21. $(3x^6 + 2x^4 - x^3 + 5x) + (-x^6 + 3x^3 - 4x^2 + 7x^4)$

22. $(4x^5 - 6x^3 - 9x + 1) + (3x^4 + 6x^3 + 9x^2 + x)$

23. $\left(\frac{3}{5}x^4 + \frac{1}{2}x^3 - \frac{2}{3}x + 3\right) + \left(\frac{2}{5}x^4 - \frac{1}{4}x^3 - \frac{3}{4}x^2 - \frac{1}{6}x\right)$

24. $\left(\frac{1}{3}x^9 + \frac{1}{5}x^5 - \frac{1}{2}x^2 + 7\right) + \left(-\frac{1}{5}x^9 + \frac{1}{4}x^4 - \frac{3}{5}x^5\right)$

25. $(5.3t^2 - 6.4t - 9.1) + (4.2t^3 - 1.8t^2 + 7.3)$

26. $(4.9a^3 + 3.2a^2 - 5.1a) + (2.1a^2 - 3.7a + 4.6)$

27. $-4x^3 + 8x^2 + 3x - 2$
    $\underline{\quad\quad - 4x^2 + 3x + 2}$

28. $-3x^4 + 6x^2 + 2x - 4$
$ - 3x^2 + 2x + 4$

29. $0.05x^4 + 0.12x^3 - 0.5x^2$
$ - 0.02x^3 + 0.02x^2 + 2x$
$1.5x^4 + 0.01x^2 + 0.15$
$0.25x^3 + 0.85$
$-0.25x^4 + 10x^2 - 0.04$

30. $0.15x^4 + 0.10x^3 - 0.9x^2$
$ - 0.01x^3 + 0.01x^2 + x$
$1.25x^4 + 0.11x^2 + 0.01$
$0.27x^3 + 0.99$
$-0.35x^4 + 15x^2 - 0.03$

Opposites of Polynomials

Write two equivalent expressions for the opposite of each polynomial, as in Example 4.

31. $-3t^3 + 4t^2 - 7$

32. $-x^3 - 5x^2 + 2x$

33. $x^4 - 8x^3 + 6x$

34. $5a^3 + 2a - 17$

Simplify.

35. $-(3a^4 - 5a^2 + 1.2)$

36. $-(-6a^3 + 0.2a^2 - 7)$

37. $-(-4x^4 + 6x^2 + \frac{3}{4}x - 8)$

38. $-(3x^5 - 2x^3 - \frac{3}{5}x^2 + 16)$

Subtraction of Polynomials

Subtract.

39. $(3x + 1) - (5x + 8)$

40. $(7x + 3) - (3x + 2)$

41. $(-9t + 12) - (t^2 + 3t - 1)$

42. $(a^2 - 3a - 2) - (2a^2 - 6a - 2)$

43. $(4a^2 + a - 7) - (3 - 8a^3 - 4a^2)$

44. $(-4x^2 + 2x) - (-5x^2 + 2x^3 + 3)$

Aha! **45.** $(7x^3 - 2x^2 + 6) - (6 - 2x^2 + 7x^3)$

46. $(8x^5 + 3x^4 + x - 1) - (8x^5 + 3x^4 - 1)$

47. $(3 + 5a + 3a^2 - a^3) - (2 + 4a - 9a^2 + 2a^3)$

48. $(7 + t - 5t^2 + 2t^3) - (1 + 2t - 4t^2 + 5t^3)$

49. $(\frac{5}{8}x^3 - \frac{1}{4}x - \frac{1}{3}) - (-\frac{1}{2}x^3 + \frac{1}{4}x - \frac{1}{3})$

50. $(\frac{1}{5}x^3 + 2x^2 - \frac{3}{10}) - (-\frac{2}{5}x^3 + 2x^2 + \frac{7}{1000})$

51. $(0.07t^3 - 0.03t^2 + 0.01t) - (0.02t^3 + 0.04t^2 - 1)$

52. $(0.9a^3 + 0.2a - 5) - (0.7a^4 - 0.3a - 0.1)$

53. $x^3 + 3x^2 + 1$
$-(x^3 + x^2 - 5)$

54. $x^2 + 5x + 6$
$-(x^2 + 2x + 1)$

55. $4x^4 - 2x^3$
$-(7x^4 + 6x^3 + 7x^2)$

56. $5x^4 + 6x^3 - 9x^2$
$-(-6x^4 + x^2)$

Problem Solving

57. Solve.

a) Find a polynomial for the sum of the areas of the rectangles shown in the figure.

b) Find the sum of the areas when $x = 5$ and $x = 7$.

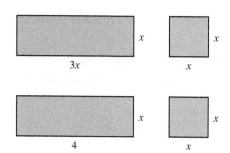

58. Solve. Leave the answers in terms of π.

a) Find a polynomial for the sum of the areas of the circles shown in the figure.

b) Find the sum of the areas when $r = 5$ and $r = 11.3$.

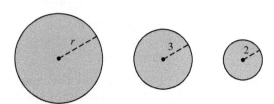

In each of Exercises 59 and 60, find a polynomial for the perimeter of the figure.

59.

60.

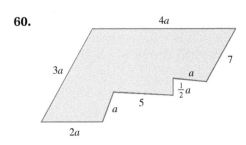

Find two algebraic expressions for the area of each figure. First, regard the figure as one large rectangle, and then regard the figure as a sum of four smaller rectangles.

61.

62.

63.

64.

In each of Exercises 65–68, find a polynomial for the shaded area of the figure.

65.

66.

67.

68.

69. A 2-ft by 6-ft bath enclosure is installed in a new bathroom measuring x ft by x ft. Find a polynomial for the remaining floor area.

70. A 5-ft by 7-ft Jacuzzi™ is installed on an outdoor deck measuring y ft by y ft. Find a polynomial for the remaining area of the deck.

71. A 12-ft wide round patio is laid in a garden measuring z ft by z ft. Find a polynomial for the remaining area of the garden.

72. A 10-ft wide round water trampoline is floating in a pool measuring x ft by x ft. Find a polynomial for the remaining surface area of the pool.

73. A 12-m by 12-m mat includes a circle of diameter d meters for wrestling. Find a polynomial for the area of the mat outside the wrestling circle.

74. A 2-m by 3-m rug is spread inside a tepee that has a diameter of x meters. Find a polynomial for the area of the tepee's floor that is not covered.

75. Explain why parentheses are used in the statement of the solution of Example 10: $(x^2 - 64\pi)$ ft².

76. Is the sum of two trinomials always a trinomial? Why or why not?

Skill Review

Find the slope–intercept equation for each line described.

77. Slope $\frac{1}{3}$; y-intercept $(0, 2)$ [3.6]

78. Slope 4; contains the point $(-6, 0)$ [3.7]

79. Slope 0; contains the point $(4, 10)$ [3.7]

80. Slope -3; contains the point $(1, 5)$ [3.7]

81. Slope $-\frac{4}{7}$; contains the point $(0, -4)$ [3.6]

82. Contains the points $(-2, 0)$ and $(4, -8)$ [3.7]

Synthesis

83. What can be concluded about two polynomials whose sum is zero?

84. Which, if any, of the commutative, associative, and distributive laws are needed for adding polynomials? Why?

Simplify.

85. $(6t^2 - 7t) + (3t^2 - 4t + 5) - (9t - 6)$

86. $(3x^2 - 4x + 6) - (-2x^2 + 4) + (-5x - 3)$

87. $4(x^2 - x + 3) - 2(2x^2 + x - 1)$

88. $3(2y^2 - y - 1) - (6y^2 - 3y - 3)$

89. $(345.099x^3 - 6.178x) - (94.508x^3 - 8.99x)$

In each of Exercises 90–93, find a polynomial for the surface area of the right rectangular solid.

90.

91.

92.

93.

94. Find a polynomial for the total length of all edges in the figure appearing in Exercise 93.

95. *Total Profit.*   Hadley Electronics is marketing a new digital camera. Total revenue is the total amount of money taken in. The firm determines that when it sells x cameras, its total revenue is given by

$$R = 175x - 0.4x^2.$$

Total cost is the total cost of producing x cameras. Hadley Electronics determines that the total cost of producing x cameras is given by

$$C = 5000 + 0.6x^2.$$

The total profit P is

$$(\text{Total Revenue}) - (\text{Total Cost}) = R - C.$$

a) Find a polynomial for total profit.

b) What is the total profit on the production and sale of 75 cameras?

c) What is the total profit on the production and sale of 120 cameras?

 96. Does replacing each occurrence of the variable x in $4x^7 - 6x^3 + 2x$ with its opposite result in the opposite of the polynomial? Why or why not?

 YOUR TURN ANSWERS: SECTION 4.4

1. $-y^3 + 7y^2 - 2y$ **2.** $6 + 6n + 4n^2$
3. $13x^3 - 5x^2 + 12x - 8$
4. $-(-a^4 - 5a^2 + 10); a^4 + 5a^2 - 10$
5. $-3.5a^4 + \frac{2}{3}a^3 + 7a - 9$ **6.** $4y^3 - 6y^2 - 20$
7. $8x^2 - 9x + 7$ **8.** $5x^4 + x^3 - x^2 - 9x + 8$
9. $x^2 + 4x + 3$ **10.** $(x^2 - 100\pi)\,\text{ft}^2$

QUICK QUIZ: SECTIONS 4.1–4.4

Simplify.

1. $\left(\dfrac{-2x^3}{3y^5}\right)^{-2}$ [4.1]   **2.** $(y + 3)^5(y + 3)^7$ [4.1]

3. Determine the degree of $5n - n^4 + 7 + 6n^2$.   [4.3]

4. Combine like terms and write in descending order: $2y - 7y^2 - y^3 + y^2$.   [4.3]

5. Subtract: $(5y^2 - y + 7) - (-y - 3)$.   [4.4]

PREPARE TO MOVE ON

Simplify.

1. $2(x^2 - x + 3)$ [1.8]

2. $-5(3x^2 - 2x - 7)$ [1.8]

3. $x^2 \cdot x^6$ [4.1]   **4.** $y^6 \cdot y$ [4.1]

5. $2n \cdot n^2$ [4.1]   **6.** $-6n^4 \cdot n^8$ [4.1]

Mid-Chapter Review

Properties of exponents allow us to simplify exponential expressions and to work with polynomials.

$$a^1 = a \qquad a^m \cdot a^n = a^{m+n}$$

$$a^0 = 1 \qquad (a^m)^n = a^{mn}$$

$$a^{-n} = \frac{1}{a^n} \qquad \frac{a^m}{a^n} = a^{m-n}$$

GUIDED SOLUTIONS

1. Simplify: $\dfrac{x^{-3}y}{x^{-4}y^7}$.   [4.2]

   Solution

   $$\frac{x^{-3}y}{x^{-4}y^7} = x^{-3-(\boxed{})}y^{\boxed{}-7} = x^{\boxed{}}y^{\boxed{}} = \frac{\boxed{}}{\boxed{}}$$

2. Subtract: $(x^2 + 7x - 12) - (3x^2 - 6x - 1)$.   [4.4]

   Solution

   $(x^2 + 7x - 12) - (3x^2 - 6x - 1) = x^2 + 7x - 12 \,\boxed{}\, 3x^2 \,\boxed{}\, 6x \,\boxed{}\, 1$ Adding the opposite

   $\qquad\qquad\qquad\qquad\qquad = \boxed{}\, x^2 + \boxed{}\, x - \boxed{}$ Combining like terms

MIXED REVIEW

Simplify. Do not use negative exponents in the answer.

3. $(x^2 y^5)^8$ [4.1]

4. $(4x)^0$ [4.1]

5. $\dfrac{3a^{11}}{12a}$ [4.1]

6. $\dfrac{-48ab^7}{18ab^6}$ [4.1]

7. $5x^{-2}$ [4.2]

8. $(a^{-2}bc^3)^{-1}$ [4.2]

9. $\left(\dfrac{2a^2}{3}\right)^{-3}$ [4.2]

10. $\dfrac{8m^{-2}n^3}{12m^4n^7}$ [4.2]

11. Convert to decimal notation: 1.89×10^{-6}.
    [4.2]

12. Convert to scientific notation: 27,000,000,000.
    [4.2]

13. Determine the degree of $8t^2 - t^3 + 5$.   [4.3]

14. Combine like terms:
    $$3a^2 - 6a - a^2 + 7 + a - 10.$$ [4.3]

Perform the indicated operation and simplify.

15. $(3x^2 - 2x + 6) + (5x - 3)$ [4.4]

16. $(9x + 6) - (2x - 1)$ [4.4]

17. $(4x^2 - x - 7) - (10x^2 - 3x + 5)$ [4.4]

18. $(t^9 + 3t^6 - 8t^2) + (5t^7 - 3t^6 + 8t^2)$ [4.4]

19. $(3a^4 - 9a^3 - 7) - (4a^3 + 13a^2 - 3)$ [4.4]

20. $(x^4 - 2x^2 - \tfrac{1}{2}x) - (x^5 - x^4 + \tfrac{1}{2}x)$ [4.4]

4.5 Multiplication of Polynomials

Multiplying Monomials   ■   Multiplying a Monomial and a Polynomial   ■   Multiplying Any Two Polynomials

We now multiply polynomials using techniques based on the distributive, associative, and commutative laws and the rules for exponents.

Multiplying Monomials

Consider $(3x)(4x)$. We multiply as follows:

$$(3x)(4x) = 3 \cdot x \cdot 4 \cdot x \qquad \text{Using an associative law}$$
$$= 3 \cdot 4 \cdot x \cdot x \qquad \text{Using a commutative law}$$
$$= (3 \cdot 4) \cdot x \cdot x \qquad \text{Using an associative law}$$
$$= 12x^2.$$

Student Notes

Remember that when we compute $(3 \cdot 5)(2 \cdot 4)$, each factor is used only once, even if we change the order:

$$(3 \cdot 5)(2 \cdot 4) = (5 \cdot 2)(3 \cdot 4)$$
$$= 10 \cdot 12 = 120.$$

In the same way,

$$(3 \cdot x)(2 \cdot x) = (3 \cdot 2)(x \cdot x)$$
$$= 6x^2.$$

Some students mistakenly "reuse" a factor.

---

1. Multiply to form an equivalent expression: $(-6t^3)(9t)$.

> **TO MULTIPLY MONOMIALS**
>
> To find an equivalent expression for the product of two monomials, multiply the coefficients and then multiply any variables using the product rule for exponents.

EXAMPLE 1   Multiply to form an equivalent expression.

a) $(5x)(6x)$ **b)** $(-a)(3a)$ **c)** $(7x^5)(-4x^3)$

SOLUTION

a) $(5x)(6x) = (5 \cdot 6)(x \cdot x)$ Multiplying the coefficients; multiplying the variables
$$= 30x^2 \qquad \text{Simplifying}$$

b) $(-a)(3a) = (-1a)(3a)$ Writing $-a$ as $-1a$ can ease calculations.
$$= (-1 \cdot 3)(a \cdot a) \qquad \text{Using an associative law and a commutative law}$$
$$= -3a^2$$

c) $(7x^5)(-4x^3) = 7(-4)(x^5 \cdot x^3)$
$$\left. \begin{array}{l} = -28x^{5+3} \\ = -28x^8 \end{array} \right\} \quad \text{Using the product rule for exponents}$$

YOUR TURN

Multiplying a Monomial and a Polynomial

To find an equivalent expression for the product of a monomial, such as $5x$, and a polynomial, such as $2x^2 - 3x + 4$, we use the distributive law.

EXAMPLE 2   Multiply: **(a)** $x(x + 3)$; **(b)** $5x(2x^2 - 3x + 4)$.

SOLUTION

a) $x(x + 3) = x \cdot x + x \cdot 3$ Using the distributive law
$$= x^2 + 3x$$

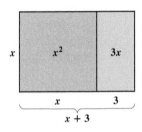

b) $5x(2x^2 - 3x + 4) = (5x)(2x^2) - (5x)(3x) + (5x)(4)$ Using the distributive law

$$= 10x^3 - 15x^2 + 20x$$ Performing the three multiplications

2. Multiply: $3a(5a^3 - a + 11)$.

 YOUR TURN

The product in Example 2(a) can be visualized as the area of a rectangle with width x and length $x + 3$. Note that the total area can be expressed as $x(x + 3)$ or, by adding the two smaller areas, $x^2 + 3x$.

> **THE PRODUCT OF A MONOMIAL AND A POLYNOMIAL**
>
> To multiply a monomial and a polynomial, multiply each term of the polynomial by the monomial.

Try to do this mentally, when possible. Remember that we multiply coefficients and, when the bases match, add exponents.

EXAMPLE 3   Multiply: $2x^2(x^3 - 7x^2 + 10x - 4)$.

SOLUTION

Think: $2x^2 \cdot x^3 - 2x^2 \cdot 7x^2 + 2x^2 \cdot 10x - 2x^2 \cdot 4$

3. Multiply:

$5y^3(2y^3 - 8y^2 + y - 5)$.

$$2x^2(x^3 - 7x^2 + 10x - 4) = 2x^5 \quad - \quad 14x^4 \quad + \quad 20x^3 \quad - \quad 8x^2$$

YOUR TURN

Multiplying Any Two Polynomials

Before considering the product of *any* two polynomials, let's look at products when both polynomials are binomials. To multiply, we again begin by using the distributive law. This time, however, it is a *binomial* rather than a monomial that is being distributed.

EXAMPLE 4   Multiply each pair of binomials.

a) $x + 5$ and $x + 4$ **b)** $4x - 3$ and $x - 2$

SOLUTION

a) $(x + 5)(x + 4) = (x + 5)x + (x + 5)4$ Using the distributive law

$$= x(x + 5) + 4(x + 5)$$ Using the commutative law for multiplication

$$= x \cdot x + x \cdot 5 + 4 \cdot x + 4 \cdot 5$$ Using the distributive law (twice)

$$= x^2 + 5x + 4x + 20$$ Multiplying the monomials

$$= x^2 + 9x + 20$$ Combining like terms

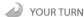

b) $(4x - 3)(x - 2) = (4x - 3)x - (4x - 3)2$ Using the distributive law

$$= x(4x - 3) - 2(4x - 3)$$ Using the commutative law for multiplication. This step is often omitted.

$$= x \cdot 4x - x \cdot 3 - 2 \cdot 4x - 2(-3)$$ Using the distributive law (twice)

$$= 4x^2 - 3x - 8x + 6$$ Multiplying the monomials

$$= 4x^2 - 11x + 6$$ Combining like terms

4. Multiply $x + 3$ and $5x - 1$.

⟵ YOUR TURN

To visualize the product in Example 4(a), consider a rectangle of length $x + 5$ and width $x + 4$. The total area can be expressed as $(x + 5)(x + 4)$ or, by adding the four smaller areas, $x^2 + 5x + 4x + 20$.

Study Skills

Take a Peek Ahead

Try to at least glance at the next section of material that will be covered in class. This will make it easier to concentrate on your instructor's lecture instead of trying to write to everything down.

Let's consider the product of a binomial and a trinomial. Again we make repeated use of the distributive law.

EXAMPLE 5 Multiply: $(x^2 + 2x - 3)(x + 4)$.

SOLUTION

$$(x^2 + 2x - 3)(x + 4)$$

$$= (x^2 + 2x - 3)x + (x^2 + 2x - 3)4$$ Using the distributive law

$$= x(x^2 + 2x - 3) + 4(x^2 + 2x - 3)$$ Using the commutative law

$$= x \cdot x^2 + x \cdot 2x - x \cdot 3 + 4 \cdot x^2 + 4 \cdot 2x - 4 \cdot 3$$ Using the distributive law (twice)

5. Multiply:

$(2t^2 - t + 5)(t + 3)$.

$$= x^3 + 2x^2 - 3x + 4x^2 + 8x - 12$$ Multiplying the monomials

$$= x^3 + 6x^2 + 5x - 12$$ Combining like terms

⟵ YOUR TURN

To use columns for long multiplication, multiply each term in the top row by every term in the bottom row. We write like terms in columns, and then add the results. Such multiplication is similar to multiplying whole numbers.

321	300 + 20 + 1	
× 12	× 10 + 2	
642	600 + 40 + 2	Multiplying the top row by 2
321	3000 + 200 + 10	Multiplying the top row by 10
3852	3000 + 800 + 50 + 2	Adding

> **THE PRODUCT OF TWO POLYNOMIALS**
>
> To multiply two polynomials P and Q, select one of the polynomials—say, P. Then multiply each term of P by every term of Q and combine like terms.

EXAMPLE 6   Multiply: $(5x^4 - 2x^2 + 3x)(x^2 + 2x)$.

SOLUTION

$$
\begin{array}{r}
5x^4 - 2x^2 + 3x \\
x^2 + 2x \\
\hline
10x^5 \qquad - 4x^3 + 6x^2 \\
5x^6 \qquad - 2x^4 + 3x^3 \\
\hline
5x^6 + 10x^5 - 2x^4 - x^3 + 6x^2
\end{array}
$$

Note that each polynomial is written in descending order.

Multiplying the top row by $2x$

Multiplying the top row by x^2

Combining like terms

Line up like terms in columns.

6. Multiply using columns:

$(3x^3 - x^2 + 5)(x - 4)$.

 YOUR TURN

Sometimes we multiply horizontally, while still aligning like terms as we write the product.

EXAMPLE 7   Multiply: $(2x^3 + 3x^2 - 4x + 6)(3x + 5)$.

SOLUTION

$$
\begin{aligned}
(2x^3 + 3x^2 - 4x + 6)(3x + 5) &= \overbrace{6x^4 + 9x^3 - 12x^2 + 18x}^{\text{Multiplying by } 3x} \\
&\quad + \underbrace{10x^3 + 15x^2 - 20x + 30}_{\text{Multiplying by } 5} \\
&= 6x^4 + 19x^3 + 3x^2 - 2x + 30
\end{aligned}
$$

7. Multiply:

$(5y^3 - 4y^2 + y + 2)(3y + 1)$.

 YOUR TURN

CHECKING BY EVALUATING

How can we be certain that our multiplication (or addition or subtraction) of polynomials is correct? One check is to simply review our calculations. A different type of check makes use of the fact that equivalent expressions have the same value when evaluated for the same replacement. Thus a quick, partial, check of Example 7 can be made by selecting a convenient replacement for x (say, 1) and comparing the values of the expressions $(2x^3 + 3x^2 - 4x + 6)(3x + 5)$ and $6x^4 + 19x^3 + 3x^2 - 2x + 30$:

$$
\begin{aligned}
(2x^3 + 3x^2 - 4x + 6)(3x + 5) &= (2 \cdot 1^3 + 3 \cdot 1^2 - 4 \cdot 1 + 6)(3 \cdot 1 + 5) \\
&= (2 + 3 - 4 + 6)(3 + 5) \\
&= 7 \cdot 8 = 56;
\end{aligned}
$$

$$
\begin{aligned}
6x^4 + 19x^3 + 3x^2 - 2x + 30 &= 6 \cdot 1^4 + 19 \cdot 1^3 + 3 \cdot 1^2 - 2 \cdot 1 + 30 \\
&= 6 + 19 + 3 - 2 + 30 \\
&= 28 - 2 + 30 = 56.
\end{aligned}
$$

Since the value of both expressions is 56, the multiplication in Example 7 is very likely correct.

It is possible, by chance, for two expressions that are not equivalent to share the same value when evaluated. For this reason, checking by evaluating is only a partial check. Consult your instructor for the checking approach that he or she prefers.

Technology Connection

Tables can also be used to check polynomial multiplication. To illustrate, we can check Example 7 by entering $y_1 = (2x^3 + 3x^2 - 4x + 6)(3x + 5)$ and $y_2 = 6x^4 + 19x^3 + 3x^2 - 2x + 30$.

When TABLE is then pressed, we are shown two columns of values—one for y_1 and one for y_2. If our multiplication is correct, the columns of values will match.

X	Y1	Y2
−3	36	36
−2	−10	−10
−1	22	22
0	30	30
1	56	56
2	286	286
3	1050	1050

X = −3

1. Form a table and scroll up and down to check Example 6.
2. Check Example 7 by letting

$$y_1 = (2x^3 + 3x^2 - 4x + 6)(3x + 5),$$
$$y_2 = 6x^4 + 19x^3 + 3x^2 - 2x + 30,$$

and

$$y_3 = y_2 - y_1.$$

Then check that y_3 is always 0.

4.5 EXERCISE SET

FOR EXTRA HELP

MyMathLab® Math XL
PRACTICE   WATCH   READ   REVIEW

⬥ Vocabulary and Reading Check

For each step, write the letter that gives an explanation of what was done on that step.

a) Combining like terms
b) Multiplying monomials
c) Using the commutative law for multiplication
d) Using the distributive law

$(2x + 3)(5x - 4)$

$= (2x + 3)(5x) - (2x + 3)(4)$ (d)

$= (5x)(2x + 3) - 4(2x + 3)$ 1. ____

$= (5x)(2x) + (5x)(3) - 4(2x) - 4(3)$ 2. ____

$= 10x^2 + 15x - 8x - 12$ 3. ____

$= 10x^2 + 7x - 12$ 4. ____

⬥ Concept Reinforcement

In each of Exercises 5–10, match the expression with the correct result from the column on the right. Choices may be used more than once.

5. ____ $3x^2 \cdot 2x^4$ a) $6x^8$

6. ____ $3x^8 + 5x^8$ b) $8x^6$

7. ____ $4x^3 \cdot 2x^5$ c) $6x^6$

8. ____ $3x^5 \cdot 2x^3$ d) $8x^8$

9. ____ $4x^6 + 2x^6$

10. ____ $4x^4 \cdot 2x^2$

Multiplying Monomials

Multiply.

11. $(3x^5)7$ **12.** $2x^3 \cdot 11$

13. $(-x^3)(x^4)$ **14.** $(-x^2)(-x)$

15. $(-x^6)(-x^2)$ **16.** $(-x^5)(x^3)$

17. $4t^2(9t^2)$ **18.** $(6a^8)(3a^2)$

19. $(0.3x^3)(-0.4x^6)$ **20.** $(-0.1x^6)(0.2x^4)$

21. $\left(-\frac{1}{4}x^4\right)\left(\frac{1}{5}x^8\right)$ **22.** $\left(-\frac{1}{5}x^3\right)\left(-\frac{1}{3}x\right)$

23. $(-5n^3)(-1)$ **24.** $19t^2 \cdot 0$

25. $(-4y^5)(6y^2)(-3y^3)$ **26.** $7x^2(-2x^3)(2x^6)$

Multiplying a Monomial and a Polynomial

Multiply.

27. $5x(4x + 1)$ **28.** $3x(2x - 7)$

29. $(a - 9)3a$ **30.** $(a - 7)4a$

31. $x^2(x^3 + 1)$ **32.** $-2x^3(x^2 - 1)$

33. $-3n(2n^2 - 8n + 1)$

34. $4n(3n^3 - 4n^2 - 5n + 10)$

35. $-5t^2(3t + 6)$ **36.** $7t^2(2t + 1)$

37. $\frac{2}{3}a^4\left(6a^5 - 12a^3 - \frac{5}{8}\right)$ **38.** $\frac{3}{4}t^5\left(8t^6 - 12t^4 + \frac{12}{7}\right)$

Multiplying Any Two Polynomials

Multiply.

39. $(x + 3)(x + 4)$

40. $(x + 7)(x + 3)$

41. $(t + 7)(t - 3)$

42. $(t - 4)(t + 3)$

43. $(a - 0.6)(a - 0.7)$

44. $(a - 0.4)(a - 0.8)$

45. $(x + 3)(x - 3)$

46. $(x + 6)(x - 6)$

47. $(4 - x)(7 - 2x)$

48. $(5 + x)(5 + 2x)$

49. $\left(t + \frac{3}{2}\right)\left(t + \frac{4}{3}\right)$

50. $\left(a - \frac{2}{5}\right)\left(a + \frac{5}{2}\right)$

51. $\left(\frac{1}{4}a + 2\right)\left(\frac{3}{4}a - 1\right)$

52. $\left(\frac{2}{5}t - 1\right)\left(\frac{3}{5}t + 1\right)$

Draw and label rectangles similar to those following Examples 2 and 4 to illustrate each product.

53. $x(x + 5)$ **54.** $x(x + 2)$

55. $(x + 1)(x + 2)$ **56.** $(x + 3)(x + 1)$

57. $(x + 5)(x + 3)$ **58.** $(x + 4)(x + 6)$

Multiply and check. Write the answer in descending order.

59. $(x^2 - x + 3)(x + 1)$

60. $(x^2 + x - 7)(x + 2)$

61. $(2a + 5)(a^2 - 3a + 2)$

62. $(3t - 4)(t^2 - 5t + 1)$

63. $(y^2 - 7)(3y^4 + y + 2)$

64. $(a^2 + 4)(5a^3 - 3a - 1)$

Aha! **65.** $(3x + 2)(7x + 4x + 1)$

66. $(4x - 5x - 3)(1 + 2x^2)$

67. $(x^2 + 5x - 1)(x^2 - x + 3)$

68. $(x^2 - 3x + 2)(x^2 + x + 1)$

69. $\left(5t^2 - t + \frac{1}{2}\right)(2t^2 + t - 4)$

70. $(2t^2 - 5t - 4)\left(3t^2 - t + \frac{1}{2}\right)$

71. $(x + 1)(x^3 + 7x^2 + 5x + 4)$

72. $(x + 2)(x^3 + 5x^2 + 9x + 3)$

73. Is it possible to understand polynomial multiplication without understanding the distributive law? Why or why not?

74. The polynomials
$$(a + b + c + d) \quad \text{and} \quad (r + s + m + p)$$
are multiplied. Without performing the multiplication, determine how many terms the product will contain. Provide a justification for your answer.

Skill Review

75. Solve $A = \dfrac{b + c}{2}$ for c.   [2.3]

76. What percent of 30 is 24?   [2.4]

77. Graph $t \geq -3$ on the number line.   [2.6]

78. In which quadrant or on what axis is the point $\left(-\frac{1}{2}, 0\right)$ located?   [3.1]

79. Find the slope of the line containing the points $(2, 3)$ and $(5, -1)$.   [3.5]

80. Find the slope and the y-intercept of the line given by $x - 3y = 5$.   [3.6]

Synthesis

81. Under what conditions will the product of two binomials be a trinomial?

82. Explain how the following figure can be used to show that $(x + 3)^2 \neq x^2 + 9$.

Find a polynomial for the shaded area of each figure.

83.

14y − 5 ; 3y ; 6y ; 3y + 5

84.

21t + 8 ; 3t − 4 ; 4t ; 2t

For each figure, determine what the missing number must be in order for the figure to have the given area.

85. Area is $x^2 + 8x + 15$ **86.** Area is $x^2 + 7x + 10$

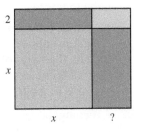

? ; x ; x ; 3 ; 2 ; x ; x ; ?

87. A box with a square bottom and no top is to be made from a 12-in.–square piece of cardboard. Squares with side x are cut out of the corners and the sides are folded up. Find the polynomials for the volume and the outside surface area of the box.

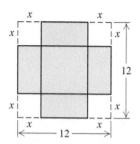

88. Find a polynomial for the volume of the solid shown below.

89. An open wooden box is a cube with side x cm. The box, including its bottom, is made of wood that is 1 cm thick. Find a polynomial for the interior volume of the cube.

90. A side of a cube is $(x + 2)$ cm long. Find a polynomial for the volume of the cube.

91. A sphere of radius x is enclosed in a plastic cube that is just large enough for the sphere.
   a) Find a polynomial for the amount of air that is in the cube outside the sphere.
   b) The diameter of a baseball is 2.9 in. If a baseball is enclosed in the plastic cube, how much air is in the box?

92. A rectangular garden is twice as long as it is wide and is surrounded by a sidewalk that is 4 ft wide. The area of the sidewalk is 256 ft². Find the dimensions of the garden.

Compute and simplify.

93. $(x + 3)(x + 6) + (x + 3)(x + 6)$

Aha! **94.** $(x - 2)(x - 7) - (x - 7)(x - 2)$

95. $(x + 5)^2 - (x - 3)^2$

96. $(x + 2)(x + 4)(x - 5)$

97. $(x - 3)^3$

Aha! **98.** Extend the pattern and simplify
$$(x - a)(x - b)(x - c)(x - d) \cdots (x - z).$$

99. Use a graphing calculator to check your answers to Exercises 27, 47, and 59. Use graphs, tables, or both, as directed by your instructor.

YOUR TURN ANSWERS: SECTION 4.5

1. $-54t^4$ **2.** $15a^4 - 3a^2 + 33a$
3. $10y^6 - 40y^5 + 5y^4 - 25y^3$ **4.** $5x^2 + 14x - 3$
5. $2t^3 + 5t^2 + 2t + 15$ **6.** $3x^4 - 13x^3 + 4x^2 + 5x - 20$
7. $15y^4 - 7y^3 - y^2 + 7y + 2$

QUICK QUIZ: SECTIONS 4.1–4.5

1. Multiply: $-2x^4(3x^5 - 8x + 12)$.   [4.5]

2. Add: $(2x^4 + 7x^2 - 10x) + (8x^4 - 7x^2 - 5x + 1)$.   [4.4]

3. Subtract: $(6a^2 - 8a - 3) - (-a^2 + 2a - 1)$.   [4.4]

4. Simplify: $(x^2y)(5xy)^3$.   [4.1]

5. Classify $x^7 + x - 3$ as a monomial, a binomial, a trinomial, or a polynomial with no special name.   [4.3]

PREPARE TO MOVE ON
Simplify.

1. 0.7^2 [1.8]   2. $(7x^3)^2$ [4.1]

3. $\left(-\dfrac{3}{2}\right)^2$ [1.8]   4. $2(3x)\left(\dfrac{1}{4}\right)$ [1.8]

5. $2 \cdot 5a \cdot 0.2$ [1.8]   6. $\left(\dfrac{1}{3}t^4\right)^2$ [4.1]

4.6 Special Products

Products of Two Binomials • Multiplying Sums and Differences of Two Terms • Squaring Binomials • Multiplications of Various Types

Study Skills

Two Books Are Better Than One

Many students find it helpful to use a second book as a reference when studying. Perhaps you or a friend own a text from a previous math course that can serve as a resource. Often professors have older texts that they will happily give away. Library book sales and thrift shops can also be excellent sources for extra books. Saving your text when you finish a math course can provide you with an excellent aid for your next course.

Patterns that we observe in certain polynomial products allow us to compute such products quickly.

Products of Two Binomials

We can find the product $(x + 5)(x + 4)$ by using the distributive law a total of three times. Note that each term in $x + 5$ is multiplied by each term in $x + 4$:

$$(x + 5)(x + 4) = x \cdot x + x \cdot 4 + 5 \cdot x + 5 \cdot 4$$
$$= x^2 + 4x + 5x + 20$$
$$= x^2 + 9x + 20.$$

Note that $x \cdot x$ is found by multiplying the *First* terms of each binomial, $x \cdot 4$ is found by multiplying the *Outer* terms of the two binomials, $5 \cdot x$ is the product of the *Inner* terms of the two binomials, and $5 \cdot 4$ is the product of the *Last* terms of each binomial:

$$\begin{array}{cccc} \text{First} & \text{Outer} & \text{Inner} & \text{Last} \\ \text{terms} & \text{terms} & \text{terms} & \text{terms} \end{array}$$

$$(x + 5)(x + 4) = x \cdot x + 4 \cdot x + 5 \cdot x + 5 \cdot 4.$$

To remember this shortcut for multiplying, we use the initials **FOIL**.

THE FOIL METHOD

To multiply two binomials, $A + B$ and $C + D$, multiply the First terms AC, the Outer terms AD, the Inner terms BC, and then the Last terms BD. Then combine like terms, if possible.

$$(A + B)(C + D) = AC + AD + BC + BD$$

1. Multiply First terms: AC.
2. Multiply Outer terms: AD.
3. Multiply Inner terms: BC.
4. Multiply Last terms: BD.

$$\downarrow$$
FOIL

Because addition is commutative, the individual multiplications can be performed in any order. Both FLOI and FIOL yield the same result as FOIL, but FOIL is most easily remembered and most widely used.

EXAMPLE 1   Form an equivalent expression by multiplying: $(x + 8)(x^2 + 5)$.

SOLUTION

$$(x + 8)(x^2 + 5) = x^3 + 5x + 8x^2 + 40$$ There are no like terms.
$$= x^3 + 8x^2 + 5x + 40$$ Writing in descending order

1. Form an equivalent expression by multiplying:

$(t + 3)(t^2 - 5)$.

YOUR TURN

After multiplying, remember to combine any like terms.

EXAMPLE 2   Multiply to form an equivalent expression.

a) $(x + 7)(x + 4)$ b) $(y + 3)(y - 2)$
c) $(4t^3 + 5t)(3t^2 - 2)$ d) $(3 - 4x)(7 - 5x^3)$

SOLUTION

a) $(x + 7)(x + 4) = x^2 + 4x + 7x + 28$ Using FOIL
$$= x^2 + 11x + 28$$ Combining like terms

b) $(y + 3)(y - 2) = y^2 - 2y + 3y - 6$ Using FOIL
$$= y^2 + y - 6$$

c) $(4t^3 + 5t)(3t^2 - 2) = 12t^5 - 8t^3 + 15t^3 - 10t$ Using FOIL and the rules for exponents

$$= 12t^5 + 7t^3 - 10t$$

d) $(3 - 4x)(7 - 5x^3) = 21 - 15x^3 - 28x + 20x^4$
$$= 21 - 28x - 15x^3 + 20x^4$$

2. Multiply to form an equivalent expression: $(x - 1)(x - 9)$.

In general, if the original binomials are written in *ascending* order, the answer is also written that way.

YOUR TURN

Multiplying Sums and Differences of Two Terms

Consider the product of the sum and the difference of the same two terms, such as

$$(x + 5)(x - 5).$$

Since this is the product of two binomials, we can use FOIL. In doing so, we find that the "outer" and "inner" products are opposites:

$$(x + 5)(x - 5) = x^2 - 5x + 5x - 25$$ The "outer" and "inner" terms "drop out." Their sum is zero.

$$= x^2 - 25.$$

Because opposites always add to zero, for products like $(x + 5)(x - 5)$ we can use a shortcut that is faster than FOIL.

THE PRODUCT OF A SUM AND A DIFFERENCE

The product of the sum and the difference of the same two terms is the square of the first term minus the square of the second term:

$$(A + B)(A - B) = \underbrace{A^2 - B^2}.$$

This is called a *difference of squares*.

EXAMPLE 3 Multiply.

a) $(x + 4)(x - 4)$ **b)** $(5 + 2w)(5 - 2w)$ **c)** $(3a^4 - 5)(3a^4 + 5)$

SOLUTION

$$(A + B)(A - B) = A^2 - B^2$$

a) $(x + 4)(x - 4) = x^2 - 4^2$ Saying the words can help: "The square of the first term, x^2, minus the square of the second, 4^2"

$\qquad\qquad\qquad\quad = x^2 - 16$ Simplifying

b) $(5 + 2w)(5 - 2w) = 5^2 - (2w)^2$

$\qquad\qquad\qquad\qquad = 25 - 4w^2$ Squaring both 5 and $2w$

c) $(3a^4 - 5)(3a^4 + 5) = (3a^4)^2 - 5^2$

$\qquad\qquad\qquad\qquad\quad = 9a^8 - 25$ $(3a^4)^2 = 3^2 \cdot (a^4)^2 = 9 \cdot a^{4 \cdot 2} = 9a^8$

3. Multiply: $(y - 10)(y + 10)$.

 YOUR TURN

Squaring Binomials

Consider the square of a binomial, such as $(x + 3)^2$. This can be expressed as $(x + 3)(x + 3)$. Since this is the product of two binomials, we can use FOIL. But again, this type of product occurs so often that a faster method has been developed. Look for a pattern in the following:

a) $(x + 3)^2 = (x + 3)(x + 3)$

$\qquad\qquad = x^2 + 3x + 3x + 9$

$\qquad\qquad = x^2 + 6x + 9;$

b) $(a - 7)^2 = (a - 7)(a - 7)$

$\qquad\qquad = a^2 - 7a - 7a + 49$

$\qquad\qquad = a^2 - 14a + 49.$

Perhaps you noticed that in each product the "outer" product and the "inner" product are identical. The other two terms, the "first" product and the "last" product, are squares.

THE SQUARE OF A BINOMIAL

The square of a binomial is the square of the first term, plus twice the product of the two terms, plus the square of the last term:

$$(A + B)^2 = A^2 + 2AB + B^2;$$
$$(A - B)^2 = A^2 - 2AB + B^2.$$

These are called *perfect-square trinomials.**

EXAMPLE 4 Write an equivalent expression for each square of a binomial.

a) $(x + 7)^2$ **b)** $(t - 5)^2$

c) $(3a + 0.4)^2$ **d)** $(5x - 3x^4)^2$

---

*Another name for these is *trinomial squares.*

SOLUTION

$$(A + B)^2 = A^2 + 2 \cdot A \cdot B + B^2$$
$$\downarrow \quad \downarrow \qquad \downarrow \quad \downarrow \quad \downarrow \qquad \downarrow$$

a) $(x + 7)^2 = x^2 + 2 \cdot x \cdot 7 + 7^2$

Saying the words can help: "The square of the first term, x^2, plus twice the product of the terms, $2 \cdot 7x$, plus the square of the second term, 7^2"

$$= x^2 + 14x + 49$$

b) $(t - 5)^2 = t^2 - 2 \cdot t \cdot 5 + 5^2$
$$= t^2 - 10t + 25$$

c) $(3a + 0.4)^2 = (3a)^2 + 2 \cdot 3a \cdot 0.4 + 0.4^2$
$$= 9a^2 + 2.4a + 0.16$$

d) $(5x - 3x^4)^2 = (5x)^2 - 2 \cdot 5x \cdot 3x^4 + (3x^4)^2$
$$= 25x^2 - 30x^5 + 9x^8 \qquad \text{Using the rules for exponents}$$

4. Multiply: $(x^2 - 3)^2$.

YOUR TURN

CAUTION!   Although the square of a product is the product of the squares, the square of a sum is *not* the sum of the squares. That is, $(AB)^2 = A^2B^2$, but

The term $2AB$ is missing.

$$(A + B)^2 \ne A^2 + B^2.$$

To confirm this inequality, note that

$$(7 + 5)^2 = 12^2 = 144,$$

whereas

$$7^2 + 5^2 = 49 + 25 = 74, \quad \text{and} \quad 74 \ne 144.$$

Geometrically, $(A + B)^2$ can be viewed as the area of a square with sides of length $A + B$:

$$(A + B)(A + B) = (A + B)^2.$$

This is equal to the sum of the areas of the four smaller regions:

$$A^2 + AB + AB + B^2 = A^2 + 2AB + B^2.$$

Thus,

$$(A + B)^2 = A^2 + 2AB + B^2.$$

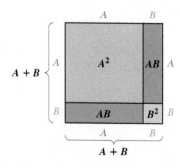

Note that the areas A^2 and B^2 do not fill the area $(A + B)^2$. Two additional areas, AB and AB, are needed.

===== EXPLORING 🔍 THE CONCEPT =====

Match each of the following squares with the appropriate square of a binomial and perfect-square trinomial.

1.

2.

3.

4.

Squared binomial

a) $(x + 2)^2$
b) $(x + 1)^2$
c) $(4 + x)^2$
d) $(3 + x)^2$

Perfect-square trinomial

A) $x^2 + 2x + 1$
B) $x^2 + 4x + 4$
C) $x^2 + 6x + 9$
D) $x^2 + 8x + 16$

ANSWERS

1. (b), (A)   2. (d), (C)
3. (a), (B)   4. (c), (D)

Multiplications of Various Types

Recognizing patterns often helps when new problems are encountered. To simplify a new multiplication problem, always examine what type of product it is so that the best method for finding that product can be used. To do this, ask yourself questions similar to the following.

MULTIPLYING TWO POLYNOMIALS

1. Is the multiplication the product of a monomial and a polynomial? If so, multiply each term of the polynomial by the monomial.

2. Is the multiplication the product of two binomials? If so:

   a) Is it the product of the sum and the difference of the *same* two terms? If so, use the pattern

   $$(A + B)(A - B) = A^2 - B^2.$$

   b) Is the product the square of a binomial? If so, use the pattern

   $$(A + B)(A + B) = (A + B)^2 = A^2 + 2AB + B^2$$

   or

   $$(A - B)(A - B) = (A - B)^2 = A^2 - 2AB + B^2.$$

   c) If neither (a) nor (b) applies, use FOIL.

3. Is the multiplication the product of two polynomials other than those above? If so, multiply each term of one by every term of the other. Use columns if you wish.

EXAMPLE 5   Multiply.

a) $(x + 3)(x - 3)$ b) $(t + 7)(t - 5)$

c) $(x + 7)(x + 7)$ d) $2x^3(9x^2 + x - 7)$

e) $(p + 3)(p^2 + 2p - 1)$ f) $(3x - \frac{1}{4})^2$

SOLUTION

a) $(x + 3)(x - 3) = x^2 - 9$ This is the product of the sum and the difference of the same two terms.

b) $(t + 7)(t - 5) = t^2 - 5t + 7t - 35$ Using FOIL
$$= t^2 + 2t - 35$$

c) $(x + 7)(x + 7) = x^2 + 14x + 49$ This is the square of a binomial, $(x + 7)^2$.

d) $2x^3(9x^2 + x - 7) = 18x^5 + 2x^4 - 14x^3$ Multiplying each term of the trinomial by the monomial

> **Chapter Resource:**
> Visualizing for Success, p. 293

e) We multiply each term of $p^2 + 2p - 1$ by every term of $p + 3$:

$$(p + 3)(p^2 + 2p - 1) = p^3 + 2p^2 - \ p \qquad \text{Multiplying by } p$$
$$+ \ 3p^2 + 6p - 3 \qquad \text{Multiplying by 3}$$
$$= p^3 + 5p^2 + 5p - 3. \qquad \text{Combining like terms}$$

f) $(3x - \frac{1}{4})^2 = 9x^2 - 2(3x)(\frac{1}{4}) + \frac{1}{16}$ Squaring a binomial
$$= 9x^2 - \frac{3}{2}x + \frac{1}{16}$$

5. Multiply: $(4x + 7)(4x - 7)$.

 YOUR TURN

4.6   EXERCISE SET

FOR EXTRA HELP

MyMathLab® Math XL
PRACTICE   WATCH   READ   REVIEW

Vocabulary and Reading Check

Classify each of the following statements as either true or false.

1. FOIL is simply a memory device for finding the product of two binomials.

2. The polynomial $x^2 + 49$ is an example of a perfect-square trinomial.

3. Once FOIL is used, it is always possible to combine like terms.

4. The square of $A + B$ is not the sum of the squares of A and B.

Products of Two Binomials

Multiply.

5. $(x^2 + 2)(x + 3)$ 6. $(x - 5)(x^2 - 6)$

7. $(t^4 - 2)(t + 7)$ 8. $(n^3 + 8)(n - 4)$

9. $(y + 2)(y - 3)$ 10. $(a + 2)(a + 2)$

11. $(3x + 2)(3x + 5)$ 12. $(4x + 1)(2x + 7)$

13. $(5x - 3)(x + 4)$ 14. $(4x - 5)(4x + 5)$

15. $(3 - 2t)(5 - t)$ 16. $(7 - a)(4 - 3a)$

17. $(x^2 + 3)(x^2 - 7)$ 18. $(x^2 + 2)(x^2 - 8)$

Multiplying Sums and Differences of Two Terms

Multiply.

19. $(p - \frac{1}{4})(p + \frac{1}{4})$ 20. $(q + \frac{3}{4})(q + \frac{3}{4})$

21. $(x + 0.3)(x - 0.3)$ 22. $(x - 0.1)(x + 0.1)$

23. $(10x^2 + 3)(10x^2 - 3)$ 24. $(5 - 4x^5)(5 + 4x^5)$

25. $(1 - 5t^3)(1 + 5t^3)$ 26. $(x^{10} + 3)(x^{10} - 3)$

Squaring Binomials

Find an equivalent expression for the following squares of binomials.

27. $(t - 2)^2$ 28. $(a - 10)^2$

29. $(x + 10)(x + 10)$ 30. $(x + 12)(x + 12)$

31. $(3x + 2)^2$ 32. $(5x + 1)^2$

33. $(1 - 10a)^2$ 34. $(7 - 6p)^2$

35. $(x^3 + 12)^2$ 36. $(x^5 - 4)^2$

Multiplications of Various Types

Multiply. Try to recognize the type of product before multiplying.

37. $(x^2 + 3)(x^3 - 1)$ 38. $(x^4 - 3)(2x + 1)$

39. $(x + 8)(x - 8)$ 40. $(x + 1)(x - 1)$

41. $(-3n + 2)(n + 7)$

42. $(-m + 5)(2m - 9)$

43. $(x + 3)^2$

44. $(2x - 1)^2$

45. $(7x^3 - 1)^2$

46. $(5x^3 + 2)^2$

47. $(9a^3 + 1)(9a^3 - 1)$

48. $(t^2 - 0.2)(t^2 + 0.2)$

49. $(x^4 + 0.1)(x^4 - 0.1)$

50. $(a^3 + 5)(a^3 - 5)$

51. $\left(t - \frac{3}{4}\right)\left(t + \frac{3}{4}\right)$

52. $\left(m - \frac{2}{3}\right)\left(m + \frac{2}{3}\right)$

53. $(1 - 3t)(1 + 5t^2)$

54. $(1 + 2t)(1 - 3t^2)$

55. $\left(a - \frac{2}{5}\right)^2$

56. $\left(t - \frac{1}{5}\right)^2$

57. $(t^4 + 3)^2$

58. $(a^3 + 6)^2$

59. $(5x - 9)(9x + 5)$

60. $(7x - 2)(2x - 7)$

61. $7n^3(2n^2 - 1)$

62. $5m^3(4 - 3m^2)$

63. $(a - 3)(a^2 + 2a - 4)$

64. $(x^2 - 5)(x^2 + x - 1)$

65. $(7 - 3x^4)(7 - 3x^4)$

66. $(x - 4x^3)^2$

67. $(2 - 3x^4)^2$

68. $(5 - 2t^3)^2$

69. $(5t + 6t^2)^2$

70. $(3p^2 - p)^2$

71. $5x(x^2 + 6x - 2)$

72. $6x(-x^5 + 6x^2 + 9)$

73. $(q^5 + 1)(q^5 - 1)$

74. $(p^4 + 2)(p^4 - 2)$

75. $3t^2(5t^3 - t^2 + t)$

76. $-5x^3(x^2 + 8x - 9)$

77. $(6x^4 - 3x)^2$

78. $(8a^3 + 5)(8a^3 - 5)$

79. $(9a + 0.4)(2a^3 + 0.5)$

80. $(2a - 0.7)(8a^3 - 0.5)$

81. $\left(\frac{1}{5} - 6x^4\right)\left(\frac{1}{5} + 6x^4\right)$

82. $\left(3 + \frac{1}{2}t^5\right)\left(3 + \frac{1}{2}t^5\right)$

83. $(a + 1)(a^2 - a + 1)$

84. $(x - 5)(x^2 + 5x + 25)$

Find the total area of all shaded rectangles.

85.

86.

87.

88.

89.

90.

91.

92.

Draw and label rectangles similar to those in Exercises 85–92 to illustrate each of the following.

93. $(x + 5)^2$

94. $(x + 8)^2$

95. $(3 + x)^2$

96. $(7 + t)^2$

97. $(2t + 1)^2$

98. $(3a + 2)^2$

99. Kristi feels that since she can find the product of any two binomials using FOIL, she needn't study the other special products. What advice would you give her?

100. Under what conditions is the product of two binomials a binomial?

Skill Review

Solve.

101. *Energy Use.* Bailey's refrigerator, upright freezer, and washing machine together use 1200 kilowatt-hours per year (kWh/year) of electricity. Her refrigerator uses three times as much energy as her washing machine, and her freezer uses six times as much energy as her washing machine. How much energy is used by each appliance? [2.5]

Source: Based on data from ftc.gov/appliancedata

102. *Energy Credit.* During some years, U.S. tax law allowed a tax credit of 30% of the price of a geothermal heat pump, with a maximum credit of $2000. For what prices of a heat pump could a 30% credit be taken? [2.7]

Solve. [2.3]

103. $3ab = c$, for a

104. $ax - by = c$, for x

Synthesis

105. By writing $19 \cdot 21$ as $(20 - 1)(20 + 1)$, Blair can find the product mentally. How do you think he does this?

106. The product $(A + B)^2$ can be regarded as the sum of the areas of four regions (as shown following Example 4). How might one visually represent $(A + B)^3$? Why?

Multiply.

Aha! **107.** $(4x^2 + 9)(2x + 3)(2x - 3)$

108. $(9a^2 + 1)(3a - 1)(3a + 1)$

Aha! **109.** $(3t - 2)^2(3t + 2)^2$

110. $(5a + 1)^2(5a - 1)^2$

111. $(t^3 - 1)^4(t^3 + 1)^4$

112. $(32.41x + 5.37)^2$

Calculate as the difference of squares.

113. 18×22 [*Hint:* $(20 - 2)(20 + 2)$.]

114. 93×107

Solve.

115. $(x + 2)(x - 5) = (x + 1)(x - 3)$

116. $(2x + 5)(x - 4) = (x + 5)(2x - 4)$

Find a polynomial for the total shaded area in each figure.

117.

118.

119.

120. Find $(10 - 2x)^2$ by subtracting the white areas from 10^2.

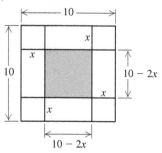

121. Find $(y - 2)^2$ by subtracting the white areas from y^2.

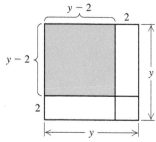

122. Find three consecutive integers for which the sum of the squares is 65 more than three times the square of the smallest integer.

123. Use a graphing calculator and the method developed in Section 4.5 to check your answers to Exercises 22, 47, and 83.

YOUR TURN ANSWERS: SECTION 4.6

1. $t^3 + 3t^2 - 5t - 15$ **2.** $x^2 - 10x + 9$ **3.** $y^2 - 100$
4. $x^4 - 6x^2 + 9$ **5.** $16x^2 - 49$

QUICK QUIZ: SECTIONS 4.1–4.6

Multiply.

1. $(10a^3 b^{10})(-2ab^2)$ [4.1]   **2.** $n \cdot n^{13} \cdot n^0$ [4.1]

3. $(x - 3)(4x^2 - x + 2)$ [4.5]

4. $(10x^5 + 1)(10x^5 - 1)$ [4.6]

5. $(3a + 4)^2$ [4.6]

PREPARE TO MOVE ON

Evaluate.   [1.1]

1. $\dfrac{2m}{n}$, for $m = 10$ and $n = 5$

2. $x - y$, for $x = 37$ and $y = 18$

Combine like terms.   [1.6]

3. $2a - 6c - c + 10a$ **4.** $4y + 7y + 2y - w$

4.7 Polynomials in Several Variables

Evaluating Polynomials ▪ Like Terms and Degree ▪ Addition and Subtraction ▪ Multiplication

Thus far, the polynomials that we have studied have had only one variable. Polynomials such as

$$5x + x^2y - 3y + 7, \quad 9ab^2c - 2a^3b^2 + 8a^2b^3, \quad \text{and} \quad 4m^2 - 9n^2$$

contain two or more variables. In this section, we will add, subtract, multiply, and evaluate such **polynomials in several variables**.

Evaluating Polynomials

To evaluate a polynomial in two or more variables, we substitute numbers for the variables. Then we compute, using the rules for order of operations.

EXAMPLE 1 Evaluate the polynomial $4 + 3x + xy^2 + 8x^3y^3$ for $x = -2$ and $y = 5$.

SOLUTION We substitute -2 for x and 5 for y:

$$4 + 3x + xy^2 + 8x^3y^3 = 4 + 3(-2) + (-2) \cdot 5^2 + 8(-2)^3 \cdot 5^3$$
$$= 4 - 6 - 50 - 8000 = -8052.$$

YOUR TURN

1. Evaluate the polynomial $x^2y - 3y^2 - 2xy$ for $x = 4$ and $y = -3$.

EXAMPLE 2 *Surface Area of a Right Circular Cylinder.* The surface area of a right circular cylinder is given by the polynomial

$$2\pi rh + 2\pi r^2,$$

where h is the height and r is the radius of the base. A 12-oz can has a height of 4.7 in. and a radius of 1.2 in. Approximate its surface area to the nearest tenth of a square inch.

SOLUTION We evaluate the polynomial for $h = 4.7$ in. and $r = 1.2$ in. If 3.14 is used to approximate π, we have

$$2\pi rh + 2\pi r^2 \approx 2(3.14)(1.2 \text{ in.})(4.7 \text{ in.}) + 2(3.14)(1.2 \text{ in.})^2$$
$$= 2(3.14)(1.2 \text{ in.})(4.7 \text{ in.}) + 2(3.14)(1.44 \text{ in}^2)$$
$$= 35.4192 \text{ in}^2 + 9.0432 \text{ in}^2 = 44.4624 \text{ in}^2.$$

If the π key of a calculator is used, we have

$$2\pi rh + 2\pi r^2 \approx 2(3.141592654)(1.2 \text{ in.})(4.7 \text{ in.})$$
$$+ 2(3.141592654)(1.2 \text{ in.})^2$$
$$\approx 44.48495197 \text{ in}^2.$$

Note that the unit in the answer (square inches) is a unit of area. The surface area is about 44.5 in^2 (square inches).

YOUR TURN

2. Use the formula given in Example 2 to find the surface area of a right circular cylinder with a height of 10 cm and a radius of 3 cm. Round to the nearest tenth of a square centimeter.

Study Skills

Use Your Voice

Don't be hesitant to ask questions in class at appropriate times. Most instructors welcome questions and encourage students to ask them. Other students probably have the same questions you do, so asking questions can help others as well as you.

Like Terms and Degree

Recall that the degree of a monomial is the number of variable factors in the term. For example, the degree of $5x^2$ is 2 because there are two variable factors in $5 \cdot x \cdot x$. Similarly, the degree of $5a^2b^4$ is 6 because there are 6 variable factors in $5 \cdot a \cdot a \cdot b \cdot b \cdot b \cdot b$. Note that 6 can be found by adding the exponents 2 and 4. The degree of a polynomial is the degree of the term of highest degree.

EXAMPLE 3   Identify the degree of each term and the degree of the polynomial

$$9x^2y^3 - 14xy^2z^3 + xy + 4y + 5x^2 + 7.$$

SOLUTION

Term	Degree	Degree of the Polynomial
$9x^2y^3$	5	
$-14xy^2z^3$	6	
xy	2	
$4y$	1	6
$5x^2$	2	
7	0	

3. Identify the degree of each term and the degree of the polynomial $2x^2y + 9y - 6 + 4x^3y^5$.

YOUR TURN

Note in Example 3 that although both xy and $5x^2$ have degree 2, they are *not* like terms. *Like*, or *similar, terms* either have exactly the same variables with exactly the same exponents or are constants. For example,

$8a^4b^7$ and $5b^7a^4$ are like terms

and

-17 and 3 are like terms,

but

$-2x^2y$ and $9xy^2$ are *not* like terms.

As always, combining like terms is based on the distributive law.

EXAMPLE 4   Combine like terms to form equivalent expressions.

a) $9x^2y + 3xy^2 - 5x^2y - xy^2$

b) $7ab - 5ab^2 + 3ab^2 + 6a^3 + 9ab - 11a^3 + b - 1$

SOLUTION

a) $9x^2y + 3xy^2 - 5x^2y - xy^2 = (9 - 5)x^2y + (3 - 1)xy^2$

$\qquad\qquad\qquad\qquad\qquad = 4x^2y + 2xy^2$ Try to go directly to this step.

b) $7ab - 5ab^2 + 3ab^2 + 6a^3 + 9ab - 11a^3 + b - 1$

$\qquad = -5a^3 - 2ab^2 + 16ab + b - 1$ We choose to write descending powers of a. Other, equivalent, forms can also be used.

4. Combine like terms:

$$2p^2x - x^2 + 9px^2 - 5p^2x.$$

YOUR TURN

Student Notes

Always read the problem carefully. The difference between

$$(-5x^3 - 3y) + (8x^3 + 4x^2)$$

and

$$(-5x^3 - 3y)(8x^3 + 4x^2)$$

is enormous. To avoid wasting time working on an incorrectly copied exercise, be sure to double-check that you have written the correct problem in your notebook.

5. Add: $(3a^2b - b^2 + 7ab) +$ $(4ab - 7a^2b)$.

6. Subtract:

$(12x^3 - 3xy^2 - xy) -$ $(-4xy^2 + xy - 5x^3)$.

7. Multiply:

$(ab - 2a)(5a^2 + 3ab^2 + b^3)$.

Addition and Subtraction

The same procedures used for adding or subtracting polynomials in one variable are used to add or subtract polynomials in several variables.

EXAMPLE 5   Add.

a) $(-5x^3 + 3y - 5y^2) + (8x^3 + 4x^2 + 7y^2)$
b) $(5ab^2 - 4a^2b + 5a^3 + 2) + (3ab^2 - 2a^2b + 3a^3b - 5)$

SOLUTION

a) $(-5x^3 + 3y - 5y^2) + (8x^3 + 4x^2 + 7y^2)$
$= (-5 + 8)x^3 + 4x^2 + 3y + (-5 + 7)y^2$ Try to do this step mentally.
$= 3x^3 + 4x^2 + 3y + 2y^2$

b) $(5ab^2 - 4a^2b + 5a^3 + 2) + (3ab^2 - 2a^2b + 3a^3b - 5)$
$= 8ab^2 - 6a^2b + 5a^3 + 3a^3b - 3$

YOUR TURN

EXAMPLE 6   Subtract:

$$(4x^2y + x^3y^2 + 3x^2y^3 + 6y) - (4x^2y - 6x^3y^2 + x^2y^2 - 5y).$$

SOLUTION   We find the opposite of $4x^2y - 6x^3y^2 + x^2y^2 - 5y$ and then add.

$(4x^2y + x^3y^2 + 3x^2y^3 + 6y) - (4x^2y - 6x^3y^2 + x^2y^2 - 5y)$
$= 4x^2y + x^3y^2 + 3x^2y^3 + 6y - 4x^2y + 6x^3y^2 - x^2y^2 + 5y$
$= 7x^3y^2 + 3x^2y^3 - x^2y^2 + 11y$ Combining like terms

YOUR TURN

Multiplication

To multiply polynomials in several variables, multiply each term of one polynomial by every term of the other.

EXAMPLE 7   Multiply: $(3x^2y - 2xy + 3y)(xy + 2y)$.

SOLUTION

$$3x^2y - 2xy + 3y$$
$$\underline{\hspace{2cm} xy + 2y}$$
$$6x^2y^2 - 4xy^2 + 6y^2 \qquad \text{Multiplying by } 2y$$
$$\underline{3x^3y^2 - 2x^2y^2 + 3xy^2 \qquad \text{Multiplying by } xy}$$
$$3x^3y^2 + 4x^2y^2 - \ xy^2 + 6y^2 \qquad \text{Adding}$$

YOUR TURN

Using patterns for special products, such as the square of a binomial, can speed up our work.

EXAMPLE 8   Multiply.

a) $(p + 5w)(2p - 3w)$ **b)** $(3x + 2y)^2$

c) $(a^3 - 7a^2b)^2$ **d)** $(3x^2y + 2y)(3x^2y - 2y)$

e) $(-2x^3y^2 + 5t)(2x^3y^2 + 5t)$ **f)** $(2x + 3 - 2y)(2x + 3 + 2y)$

SOLUTION

$$\overset{\text{F}}{} \qquad \overset{\text{O}}{} \qquad \overset{\text{I}}{} \qquad \overset{\text{L}}{}$$

a) $(p + 5w)(2p - 3w) = 2p^2 - 3pw + 10pw - 15w^2$

$\qquad\qquad\qquad\qquad = 2p^2 + 7pw - 15w^2$ Combining like terms

$$(A + B)^2 = A^2 + 2 \cdot A \cdot B + B^2$$

b) $(3x + 2y)^2 = (3x)^2 + 2(3x)(2y) + (2y)^2$ Squaring a binomial

$\qquad\qquad = 9x^2 + 12xy + 4y^2$

$$(A - B)^2 = A^2 - 2 \cdot A \cdot B + B^2$$

c) $(a^3 - 7a^2b)^2 = (a^3)^2 - 2(a^3)(7a^2b) + (7a^2b)^2$ Squaring a binomial

$\qquad\qquad = a^6 - 14a^5b + 49a^4b^2$ Using the rules for exponents

$$(A + B)(A - B) = A^2 - B^2$$

d) $(3x^2y + 2y)(3x^2y - 2y) = (3x^2y)^2 - (2y)^2$ Multiplying the sum and the difference of two terms

$\qquad\qquad\qquad = 9x^4y^2 - 4y^2$ Using the rules for exponents

e) $(-2x^3y^2 + 5t)(2x^3y^2 + 5t) = (5t - 2x^3y^2)(5t + 2x^3y^2)$ Using the commutative law for addition twice

$\qquad\qquad\qquad = (5t)^2 - (2x^3y^2)^2$ Multiplying the sum and the difference of two terms

$\qquad\qquad\qquad = 25t^2 - 4x^6y^4$

$$(A - B)(A + B) = A^2 - B^2$$

f) $(2x + 3 - 2y)(2x + 3 + 2y) = (2x + 3)^2 - (2y)^2$ Multiplying a sum and a difference

$\qquad\qquad\qquad = 4x^2 + 12x + 9 - 4y^2$ Squaring a binomial

---

CAUTION!

$(3x + 2y)^2 \neq (3x)^2 + (2y)^2$

Technology Connection

One way to evaluate the polynomial in Example 1 for $x = -2$ and $y = 5$ is to store -2 to X and 5 to Y and enter the polynomial.

```
-2 → X
                    -2
5 → Y
                     5
4+3X+XY²+8X³Y³
                  -8052
■
```

Evaluate.

1. $3x^2 - 2y^2 + 4xy + x$, for $x = -6$ and $y = 2.3$
2. $a^2b^2 - 8c^2 + 4abc + 9a$, for $a = 11$, $b = 15$, and $c = -7$

---

8. Multiply:

$(5x - 2xy)(x^2 - 2y).$

 YOUR TURN

In Example 8, we recognized patterns that might not be obvious, particularly in parts (e) and (f). In part (e), we *can* use FOIL, and in part (f), we *can* use long multiplication, but doing so is slower. By carefully inspecting a problem before "jumping in," we can save ourselves considerable work. At least one instructor refers to this as "working smart" instead of "working hard."*

Chapter Resource:
Collaborative Activity, p. 294

---

*Thanks to Pauline Kirkpatrick of Wharton County Junior College for this language.

4.7 EXERCISE SET

FOR EXTRA HELP

MyMathLab® MathXL
PRACTICE   WATCH   READ   REVIEW

Vocabulary and Reading Check

Consider the polynomial $2x^2y + 7xy^3 + 5x^2y$. *Choose the phrase from the list on the right that describes the expression on the left as it relates to the polynomial.*

1. ____ $2x^2y$ and $5x^2y$
2. ____ x, y
3. ____ 4
4. ____ 3

a) The degree of the polynomial
b) Like terms
c) The number of terms in the polynomial
d) The variables in the polynomial

Concept Reinforcement

Each of the expressions in Exercises 5–10 can be regarded as either (**a**) *the square of a binomial,* (**b**) *the product of the sum and the difference of the same two terms, or* (**c**) *neither of the above. Select the appropriate choice for each expression.*

5. $(3x + 5y)^2$
6. $(4x - 9y)(4x + 9y)$
7. $(5a + 6b)(-6b + 5a)$
8. $(4a - 3b)(4a - 3b)$
9. $(r - 3s)(5r + 3s)$
10. $(2x - 7y)(7y - 2x)$

Evaluating Polynomials

Evaluate each polynomial for $x = 5$ *and* $y = -2$.

11. $x^2 - 2y^2 + 3xy$

12. $x^2 + 5y^2 - 4xy$

Evaluate each polynomial for $x = 2, y = -3,$ *and* $z = -4$.

13. $xy^2z - z$

14. $xy - x^2z + yz^2$

Zoology. *The polynomial* $11.5g + 7.55l + 12.5c - 4016$ *can be used to estimate the weight of an elephant, in kilograms, given the girth g of the elephant at the heart, the length l of the elephant, and the circumference c of the elephant's footpad. Use the formula and the data from the following table for Exercises 15 and 16.*

Elephant	Girth, g (in centimeters)	Length, l (in centimeters)	Footpad Circumference, c (in centimeters)
Male, age 3 yr	244	140	86
Female, age 3 yr	231	135	86
Male, age 25 yr	404	229	130
Female, age 25 yr	366	226	117

Source: "How Much Does That Elephant Weigh?" by Mark MacAllister on fieldtripearth.org

15. Estimate the weight of the 3-year-old female elephant described in the table.

16. Estimate the weight of the 25-year-old male elephant described in the table.

Surface Area of a Silo. *A silo is a structure that is shaped like a right circular cylinder with a half sphere on top. The surface area of a silo of height h and radius r (including the area of the base) is given by the polynomial* $2\pi rh + \pi r^2$.

17. A coffee grinder is shaped like a silo, with a height of 7 in. and a radius of $1\frac{1}{2}$ in. Find the surface area of the coffee grinder. Use 3.14 for π.

18. A $1\frac{1}{2}$-oz bottle of roll-on deodorant has a height of 4 in. and a radius of $\frac{3}{4}$ in. Find the surface area of the bottle if the bottle is shaped like a silo. Use 3.14 for π.

Altitude of a Launched Object. *The altitude of an object, in meters, is given by the polynomial*

$$h + vt - 4.9t^2,$$

where h is the height, in meters, at which the launch occurs, v is the initial upward speed (or velocity), in meters per second, and t is the number of seconds for which the object is airborne.

19. A bocce ball is thrown upward with an initial speed of 18 m/sec by a person atop the Leaning Tower of Pisa, which is 50 m above the ground. How high will the ball be 2 sec after it has been thrown?

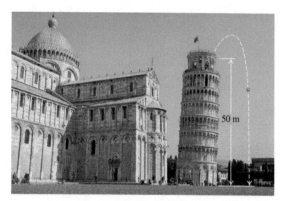

50 m

20. A golf ball is launched upward with an initial speed of 30 m/sec by a golfer on the third level of The Golf Club at Chelsea Piers, Manhattan, which is 10 m above the ground. How high above the ground will the ball be after 3 sec?

Like Terms and Degree

Identify the degree of each term of each polynomial. Then find the degree of the polynomial.

21. $3x^2y - 5xy + 2y^2 - 11$

22. $xy^3 + 7x^3y^2 - 6xy^4 + 2$

23. $7 - abc + a^2b + 9ab^2$

24. $3p - pq - 7p^2q^3 - 8pq^6$

Combine like terms.

25. $3r + s - r - 7s$

26. $9a + b - 8a - 5b$

27. $5xy^2 - 2x^2y + x + 3x^2$

28. $m^3 + 2m^2n - 3m^2 + 3mn^2$

29. $6u^2v - 9uv^2 + 3vu^2 - 2v^2u + 11u^2$

30. $3x^2 + 6xy + 3y^2 - 5x^2 - 10xy$

31. $5a^2c - 2ab^2 + a^2b - 3ab^2 + a^2c - 2ab^2$

32. $3s^2t + r^2t - 9ts^2 - st^2 + 5t^2s - 7tr^2$

Addition and Subtraction

Add or subtract, as indicated.

33. $(6x^2 - 2xy + y^2) + (5x^2 - 8xy - 2y^2)$

34. $(7r^3 + rs - 5r^2) - (2r^3 - 3rs + r^2)$

35. $(3a^4 - 5ab + 6ab^2) - (9a^4 + 3ab - ab^2)$

36. $(2r^2t - 5rt + rt^2) - (7r^2t + rt - 5rt^2)$

Aha! **37.** $(5r^2 - 4rt + t^2) + (-6r^2 - 5rt - t^2) + (-5r^2 + 4rt - t^2)$

38. $(2x^2 - 3xy + y^2) + (-4x^2 - 6xy - y^2) + (4x^2 + 6xy + y^2)$

39. $(x^3 - y^3) - (-2x^3 + x^2y - xy^2 + 2y^3)$

40. $(a^3 + b^3) - (-5a^3 + 2a^2b - ab^2 + 3b^3)$

41. $(2y^4x^3 - 3y^3x) + (5y^4x^3 - y^3x) - (9y^4x^3 - y^3x)$

42. $(5a^2b - 7ab^2) - (3a^2b + ab^2) + (a^2b - 2ab^2)$

43. Subtract $7x + 3y$ from the sum of $4x + 5y$ and $-5x + 6y$.

44. Subtract $5a + 2b$ from the sum of $2a + b$ and $3a - 4b$.

Multiplication

Multiply.

45. $(4c - d)(3c + 2d)$

46. $(5x + y)(2x - 3y)$

47. $(xy - 1)(xy + 5)$

48. $(ab + 3)(ab - 5)$

49. $(2a - b)(2a + b)$

50. $(a - 3b)(a + 3b)$

51. $(5rt - 2)(4rt - 3)$

52. $(3xy - 1)(4xy + 2)$

53. $(m^3n + 8)(m^3n - 6)$

54. $(9 - u^2v^2)(2 - u^2v^2)$

55. $(6x - 2y)(5x - 3y)$

56. $(7a - 6b)(5a + 4b)$

57. $(pq + 0.1)(-pq + 0.1)$

58. $(rt + 0.2)(-rt + 0.2)$

59. $(x + h)^2$

60. $(a - r)^2$

61. $(4a - 5b)^2$

62. $(2x + 5y)^2$

63. $(ab + cd^2)(ab - cd^2)$

64. $(p^3 - 5q)(p^3 + 5q)$

65. $(2xy + x^2y + 3)(xy + y^2)$

66. $(5cd - c^2 - d^2)(2c - c^2d)$

Aha! **67.** $(a + b - c)(a + b + c)$

68. $(x + y + 2z)(x + y - 2z)$

69. $[a + b + c][a - (b + c)]$

70. $(a + b + c)(a - b - c)$

Find the total area of each figure.

71.

72.

73.

74.

75.

76.

77.

78.
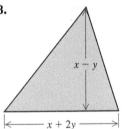

Draw and label rectangles similar to those in Exercises 71, 72, 75, and 76 to illustrate each product.

79. $(r + s)(u + v)$ **80.** $(m + r)(n + v)$

81. $(a + b + c)(a + d + f)$ **82.** $(r + s + t)^2$

83. Is it possible for a polynomial in 4 variables to have a degree less than 4? Why or why not?

84. A fourth-degree monomial is multiplied by a third-degree monomial. What is the degree of the product? Explain your reasoning.

Skill Review

Simplify. [1.8]

85. $-16 + 20 \div 2^2 \cdot 5 - 3$

86. $2 - (3 - 8)^2 \div (-5)$

87. $2[3 - 4(5 - 6)^2 - 1] + 10$

88. $-6|-2 - (-1)| + 3(-5)$

89. $2a - 3(-x - 5a + 7)$

90. $4(y + 7) - (y - 2) + (2y - 9)$

Synthesis

91. The concept of "leading term" was intentionally not discussed in this section. Why not?

92. Explain how it is possible for the sum of two trinomials in several variables to be a binomial in one variable.

Find a polynomial for the shaded area in each figure. (Leave results in terms of π where appropriate.)

93.

94.

95.

96.

97. Find a polynomial for the total volume of the following figure.

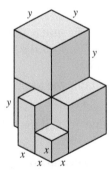

98. Find the shaded area in the following figure using each of the approaches given below. Then check that both answers match.

a) Find the shaded area by subtracting the area of the unshaded square from the total area of the figure.

b) Find the shaded area by adding the areas of the three shaded rectangles.

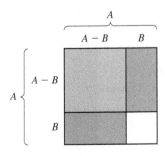

Find a polynomial for the surface area of each solid object shown. (Leave results in terms of π.)

99.

100.

101. The observatory at Danville University is shaped like a silo that is 40 ft high and 30 ft wide (see Exercise 17). The Heavenly Bodies Astronomy Club is to paint the exterior of the observatory using paint that covers 250 ft² per gallon. How many gallons should they purchase? Explain your reasoning.

102. Multiply: $(x + a)(x - b)(x - a)(x + b)$.

Spreadsheet applications allow values for cells to be calculated from values in other cells. For example, if the cell C1 contains the formula

$$= A1 + 2 * B1,$$

the value in C1 will be the sum of the value in A1 and twice the value in B1. This formula is a polynomial in the two variables A1 and B1.

103. The cell D4 contains the formula

$$= 2 * A4 + 3 * B4.$$

What is the value in D4 if the value in A4 is 5 and the value in B4 is 10?

104. The cell D6 contains the formula

$$= A1 - 0.2 * B1 + 0.3 * C1.$$

What is the value in D6 if the value in A1 is 10, the value in B1 is −3, and the value in C1 is 30?

105. *Interest Compounded Annually.* An amount of money P that is invested at the yearly interest rate r grows to the amount $P(1 + r)^t$ after t years. Find a polynomial that can be used to determine the amount to which P will grow after 2 years.

106. *Yearly Depreciation.* An investment P that drops in value at the yearly rate r drops in value to

$$P(1 - r)^t$$

after t years. Find a polynomial that can be used to determine the value to which P has dropped after 2 years.

107. Suppose that $10,400 is invested at 4.5%, compounded annually. How much is in the account at the end of 5 years? (See Exercise 105.)

108. A $90,000 investment in computer hardware is depreciating at a yearly rate of 12.5%. How much is the investment worth after 4 years? (See Exercise 106.)

109. *Research.* Find the interest rates on several accounts offered by your bank or another local bank.

   a) Suppose $10,000 is invested in each account. Compare the amounts in each account at the end of 10 years if the interest were compounded annually. (See Exercise 105.)

   b) Find the formula used to calculate the amount in an account if the interest is compounded more often than once a year. Use the compounding period from the bank you chose to compare amounts in each account after 10 years.

YOUR TURN ANSWERS: SECTION 4.7

1. −51   **2.** 245.0 cm²
3. Degrees of terms: 3, 1, 0, 8; degree of polynomial: 8
4. $-3p^2x - x^2 + 9px^2$ **5.** $-4a^2b - b^2 + 11ab$
6. $17x^3 + xy^2 - 2xy$
7. $5a^3b + 3a^2b^3 + ab^4 - 10a^3 - 6a^2b^2 - 2ab^3$
8. $5x^3 - 10xy - 2x^3y + 4xy^2$

QUICK QUIZ: SECTIONS 4.1–4.7

1. Evaluate $-2x^3 - 3x^2 - 5x + 17$ for $x = -2$.   [4.3]

2. Subtract:

$$(3.1x^2 + 2.7x - 1.1) - (-x^2 + 5.6x - 7.2).$$ [4.4]

3. Multiply: $(x + 3)(5x^3 - x + 4)$.   [4.5]

4. Multiply: $(a^2 + 10)(a^2 - 10)$.   [4.6]

5. Evaluate $xz - z^2 - 2y$ for $x = -2$, $y = 3$, and $z = -5$.   [4.7]

PREPARE TO MOVE ON

Subtract.   [4.4]

1. $\quad x^2 - 3x - 7$
$\underline{-(\quad\quad 5x - 3)}$

2. $\quad 2x^3 \quad\quad - x + 3$
$\underline{-(\quad\quad x^2 \quad\quad - 1)}$

3. $\quad 3x^2 + \ x + 5$
$\underline{-(3x^2 + 3x)}$

4. $\quad 4x^3 - 3x^2 + x$
$\underline{-(4x^3 - 8x^2)}$

4.8 Division of Polynomials

Dividing by a Monomial ▪ Dividing by a Binomial

Study Skills

Anticipate the Future

It is never too soon to begin reviewing for an exam. Make time each week to review important problems, formulas, and properties. Take advantage of the Quick Quizzes following most exercise sets, as well as the Mid-Chapter Reviews. There is also at least one Connecting the Concepts in each chapter. Spend time reviewing the information in this special feature as a way of keeping the "big picture" in focus.

In this section, we study division of polynomials. We will find that polynomial division is similar to division in arithmetic.

Dividing by a Monomial

We first consider division by a monomial. When dividing a monomial by a monomial, we subtract exponents when bases are the same. For example,

$$\frac{42a^2b^5}{-3ab^2} = \frac{42}{-3}a^{2-1}b^{5-2} \qquad \text{Recall that } a^m/a^n = a^{m-n}.$$
$$= -14ab^3.$$

> **CAUTION!** The coefficients are divided but the exponents are subtracted.

To divide a polynomial by a monomial, we note that since

$$\frac{A}{C} + \frac{B}{C} = \frac{A + B}{C},$$

it follows that

$$\frac{A + B}{C} = \frac{A}{C} + \frac{B}{C}. \qquad \text{Switching the left side and the right side of the equation}$$

This is actually how we perform divisions like $86 \div 2$:

$$\frac{86}{2} = \frac{80 + 6}{2} = \frac{80}{2} + \frac{6}{2} = 40 + 3.$$

Similarly, to divide a polynomial by a monomial, we divide each term by the monomial:

$$\frac{80x^5 + 6x^7}{2x^3} = \frac{80x^5}{2x^3} + \frac{6x^7}{2x^3}$$
$$= \frac{80}{2}x^{5-3} + \frac{6}{2}x^{7-3} \qquad \text{Dividing coefficients and subtracting exponents}$$
$$= 40x^2 + 3x^4.$$

EXAMPLE 1 Divide $x^4 + 15x^3 - 6x^2$ by $3x$.

SOLUTION We divide each term of $x^4 + 15x^3 - 6x^2$ by $3x$:

$$\frac{x^4 + 15x^3 - 6x^2}{3x} = \frac{x^4}{3x} + \frac{15x^3}{3x} - \frac{6x^2}{3x}$$
$$= \frac{1}{3}x^{4-1} + \frac{15}{3}x^{3-1} - \frac{6}{3}x^{2-1} \qquad \text{Dividing coefficients and subtracting exponents}$$
$$= \frac{1}{3}x^3 + 5x^2 - 2x. \qquad \text{This is the quotient.}$$

To check, we multiply our answer by $3x$, using the distributive law:

$$3x\left(\frac{1}{3}x^3 + 5x^2 - 2x\right) = 3x \cdot \frac{1}{3}x^3 + 3x \cdot 5x^2 - 3x \cdot 2x$$

$$= x^4 + 15x^3 - 6x^2.$$

This is the polynomial that was being divided, so our answer, $\frac{1}{3}x^3 + 5x^2 - 2x$, checks.

1. Divide $t^3 - 4t^2 + 12t$ by $4t$.

YOUR TURN

EXAMPLE 2   Divide and check: $(10a^5b^4 - 2a^3b^2 + 6a^2b) \div (-2a^2b)$.

SOLUTION   We have

$$\frac{10a^5b^4 - 2a^3b^2 + 6a^2b}{-2a^2b} = \frac{10a^5b^4}{-2a^2b} - \frac{2a^3b^2}{-2a^2b} + \frac{6a^2b}{-2a^2b}$$

> We divide coefficients and subtract exponents.

$$= -\frac{10}{2}a^{5-2}b^{4-1} - \left(-\frac{2}{2}\right)a^{3-2}b^{2-1} + \left(-\frac{6}{2}\right)$$

$$= -5a^3b^3 + ab - 3.$$

2. Divide and check:

$$(-3x^2y + 9x^3y^2 - 6x^2y^2)$$
$$\div (3x^2y).$$

Check: $-2a^2b(-5a^3b^3 + ab - 3)$

$$= -2a^2b(-5a^3b^3) + (-2a^2b)(ab) + (-2a^2b)(-3)$$
$$= 10a^5b^4 - 2a^3b^2 + 6a^2b$$

Our answer, $-5a^3b^3 + ab - 3$, checks.

YOUR TURN

Dividing by a Binomial

The divisors in Examples 1 and 2 have just one term. For divisors with more than one term, we use long division, much as we do in arithmetic.

EXAMPLE 3   Divide $x^2 + 5x + 6$ by $x + 3$.

SOLUTION   We begin by dividing x^2 by x:

> Divide   the first term, x^2, by the first term in the divisor: $x^2/x = x$. Ignore the term 3 for the moment.

$$\begin{array}{r} x \\ x + 3 \overline{) x^2 + 5x + 6} \\ -(x^2 + 3x) \\ \hline 2x. \end{array}$$

Multiply: $x(x + 3) = x^2 + 3x$.

Subtract   both x^2 and $3x$: $x^2 + 5x - (x^2 + 3x) = 2x$.

Now we "bring down" the next term—in this case, 6. The current remainder, $2x + 6$, now becomes the focus of our division. We divide $2x$ by x.

$$\begin{array}{r} x + 2 \\ x + 3 \overline{) x^2 + 5x + 6} \\ -(x^2 + 3x) \\ \hline 2x + 6 \\ -(2x + 6) \\ \hline 0 \end{array}$$

Divide $2x$ by x: $2x/x = 2$.

Multiply: $2(x + 3) = 2x + 6$.

Subtract: $(2x + 6) - (2x + 6) = 0$.

Student Notes

Since long division of polynomials requires many steps, we recommend that you double-check each step of your work as you move forward.

The quotient is $x + 2$. The notation R 0 indicates a remainder of 0, although a remainder of 0 is generally not listed in an answer.

Check: To check, we multiply the quotient by the divisor and add any remainder to see if we get the dividend:

$$\overbrace{(x + 3)}^{\text{Divisor}} \overbrace{(x + 2)}^{\text{Quotient}} + \overbrace{0}^{\text{Remainder}} = \overbrace{x^2 + 5x + 6}^{\text{Dividend}}.$$

Our answer, $x + 2$, checks.

3. Divide $x^2 - 3x - 10$ by $x - 5$.

YOUR TURN

EXAMPLE 4   Divide: $(2x^2 + 5x - 1) \div (2x - 1)$.

SOLUTION   We begin by dividing $2x^2$ by $2x$:

Divide the first term by the first term: $2x^2/(2x) = x$.

$$
\begin{array}{r}
x \\
2x - 1 \overline{)2x^2 + 5x - 1} \\
-(2x^2 - x) \\
\hline
6x
\end{array}
$$

Multiply: $x(2x - 1) = 2x^2 - x$.

Subtract by changing signs and adding: $(2x^2 + 5x) - (2x^2 - x) = 6x$.

> **CAUTION!** Write the parentheses around the polynomial being subtracted to remind you to subtract all its terms.

Now, we bring down the -1 and divide $6x - 1$ by $2x - 1$, focusing on the $6x$ and the $2x$.

$$
\begin{array}{r}
x + 3 \\
2x - 1 \overline{)2x^2 + 5x - 1} \\
-(2x^2 - x) \\
\hline
6x - 1 \\
-(6x - 3) \\
\hline
2
\end{array}
$$

Divide $6x$ by $2x$: $6x/(2x) = 3$.

Multiply: $3(2x - 1) = 6x - 3$.

Subtract. Note that $-1 - (-3) = -1 + 3 = 2$.

The answer is $x + 3$ with R 2.
Another way to write $x + 3$ R 2 is as

$$\underbrace{x + 3}_{\text{Quotient}} + \frac{\overset{\text{Remainder}}{2}}{\underset{\text{Divisor}}{2x - 1}}.$$

(This is the way answers will be given at the back of the book.)

Check: To check, we multiply the divisor by the quotient and add the remainder:

$$(2x - 1)(x + 3) + 2 = 2x^2 + 5x - 3 + 2$$
$$= 2x^2 + 5x - 1. \quad \text{Our answer checks.}$$

4. Divide:

$(2x^2 - 3x + 5) \div (2x + 3)$.

YOUR TURN

Our division procedure ends when the degree of the remainder is less than that of the divisor. Check that this was indeed the case in Example 4.

When we are dividing polynomials, it is important that both the divisor and the dividend are written in descending order. Any missing terms in the dividend should be written in, using 0 for the coefficients.

EXAMPLE 5   Divide each of the following.

a) $(x^3 + 1) \div (x + 1)$ **b)** $(9a^2 + a^3 - 5) \div (a^2 - 1)$

SOLUTION

a)
$$
\begin{array}{r}
x^2 - x + 1 \\
x + 1 \overline{)x^3 + 0x^2 + 0x + 1} \\
\end{array}
$$
$\leftarrow$ Writing in the missing terms

$-(x^3 + x^2)$

$-x^2 + 0x$ $\longleftarrow$ Subtracting $x^3 + x^2$ from $x^3 + 0x^2$ and bringing down the $0x$

$-(-x^2 - x)$

$x + 1 \leftarrow$ Subtracting $-x^2 - x$ from $-x^2 + 0x$ and bringing down the 1

$-(x + 1)$

0

The answer is $x^2 - x + 1$.

Check: $(x + 1)(x^2 - x + 1) = x^3 - x^2 + x + x^2 - x + 1$
$$= x^3 + 1.$$

b) We rewrite the problem in descending order.

$$(a^3 + 9a^2 - 5) \div (a^2 - 1).$$

Thus,

$$
\begin{array}{r}
a + 9 \\
a^2 - 1 \overline{)a^3 + 9a^2 + 0a - 5} \\
\end{array}
$$
$\leftarrow$ Writing in the missing term

$-(a^3 - a)$

$9a^2 + a - 5$ $\longleftarrow$ Subtracting $a^3 - a$ from $a^3 + 9a^2 + 0a$ and bringing down the -5

$-(9a^2 - 9)$

$a + 4$ The degree of the remainder is less than the degree of the divisor, so we are finished.

The answer is $a + 9 + \dfrac{a + 4}{a^2 - 1}$.

Check: $(a^2 - 1)(a + 9) + a + 4 = a^3 + 9a^2 - a - 9 + a + 4$
$$= a^3 + 9a^2 - 5.$$

5. Divide: $(2x^2 - 5) \div (x - 1)$.

YOUR TURN

4.8 EXERCISE SET

FOR EXTRA HELP

MyMathLab® Math XL

PRACTICE   WATCH   READ   REVIEW

Vocabulary and Reading Check

Use the words from the following list to label the numbered expressions from the division shown.

dividend, divisor, quotient, remainder

$$
\begin{array}{r}
②\,x + 2 \\
①\,x - 3 \overline{)x^2 - x + 9}\,③ \\
-(x^2 - 3x) \\
\hline
2x + 9 \\
-(2x - 6) \\
\hline
15 \;④
\end{array}
$$

1. _____

2. _____

3. _____

4. _____

Dividing by a Monomial

Divide and check.

5. $\dfrac{40x^6 - 25x^3}{5}$

6. $\dfrac{16a^5 - 24a^2}{8}$

7. $\dfrac{u - 2u^2 + u^7}{u}$

8. $\dfrac{50x^5 - 7x^4 + 2x}{x}$

9. $(18t^3 - 24t^2 + 6t) \div (3t)$

10. $(20t^3 - 15t^2 + 30t) \div (5t)$

11. $(42x^5 - 36x^3 + 9x^2) \div (6x^2)$

12. $(24x^6 + 18x^4 + 8x^3) \div (4x^3)$

13. $(32t^5 + 16t^4 - 8t^3) \div (-8t^3)$

14. $(36t^6 - 27t^5 - 9t^2) \div (-9t^2)$

15. $\dfrac{8x^2 - 10x + 1}{2x}$

16. $\dfrac{9x^2 + 3x - 2}{3x}$

17. $\dfrac{5x^3y + 10x^5y^2 + 15x^2y}{5x^2y}$

18. $\dfrac{12a^3b^2 + 4a^4b^5 + 16ab^2}{4ab^2}$

19. $\dfrac{9r^2s^2 + 3r^2s - 6rs^2}{-3rs}$

20. $\dfrac{4x^4y - 8x^6y^2 + 12x^8y^6}{4x^4y}$

Dividing by a Binomial

Divide.

21. $(x^2 - 8x + 12) \div (x - 2)$

22. $(x^2 + 2x - 15) \div (x + 5)$

23. $(t^2 - 10t - 20) \div (t - 5)$

24. $(t^2 + 8t - 15) \div (t + 4)$

25. $(2x^2 + 11x - 5) \div (x + 6)$

26. $(3x^2 - 2x - 13) \div (x - 2)$

27. $\dfrac{t^3 + 27}{t + 3}$

28. $\dfrac{a^3 + 8}{a + 2}$

29. $\dfrac{a^2 - 21}{a - 5}$

30. $\dfrac{t^2 - 13}{t - 4}$

31. $(5x^2 - 16x) \div (5x - 1)$

32. $(3x^2 - 7x + 1) \div (3x - 1)$

33. $(6a^2 + 17a + 8) \div (2a + 5)$

34. $(10a^2 + 19a + 9) \div (2a + 3)$

35. $\dfrac{2t^3 - 9t^2 + 11t - 3}{2t - 3}$

36. $\dfrac{8t^3 - 22t^2 - 5t + 12}{4t + 3}$

37. $(x^3 - x^2 + x - 1) \div (x - 1)$

38. $(t^3 - t^2 + t - 1) \div (t + 1)$

39. $(t^4 + 4t^2 + 3t - 6) \div (t^2 + 5)$

40. $(t^4 - 2t^2 + 4t - 5) \div (t^2 - 3)$

41. $(4x^4 - 3 - x - 4x^2) \div (2x^2 - 3)$

42. $(x + 6x^4 - 4 - 3x^2) \div (1 + 2x^2)$

43. How is the distributive law used when dividing a polynomial by a binomial?

44. On an assignment, Emmy Lou *incorrectly* writes

$$\dfrac{12x^3 - 6x}{3x} = 4x^2 - 6x.$$

What mistake do you think she is making and how might you convince her that a mistake has been made?

Skill Review

Graph.

45. $y = -\frac{2}{3}x + 4$ [3.6]

46. $8x = 4y$ [3.2]

47. Find the slope and the y-intercept of the line given by $2y = 8x + 7$.   [3.6]

48. Find the slope–intercept form of the line containing the points $(6, 3)$ and $(-2, -7)$.   [3.7]

Synthesis

49. Explain how to form trinomials for which division by $x - 5$ results in a remainder of 3.

50. Under what circumstances will the quotient of two binomials have more than two terms?

Divide.

51. $(10x^{9k} - 32x^{6k} + 28x^{3k}) \div (2x^{3k})$

52. $(45a^{8k} + 30a^{6k} - 60a^{4k}) \div (3a^{2k})$

53. $(6t^{3h} + 13t^{2h} - 4t^h - 15) \div (2t^h + 3)$

54. $(x^4 + a^2) \div (x + a)$

55. $(5a^3 + 8a^2 - 23a - 1) \div (5a^2 - 7a - 2)$

56. $(15y^3 - 30y + 7 - 19y^2) \div (3y^2 - 2 - 5y)$

57. Divide the sum of $4x^5 - 14x^3 - x^2 + 3$ and $2x^5 + 3x^4 + x^3 - 3x^2 + 5x$ by $3x^3 - 2x - 1$.

58. Divide $5x^7 - 3x^4 + 2x^2 - 10x + 2$ by the sum of $(x - 3)^2$ and $5x - 8$.

If the remainder is 0 when one polynomial is divided by another, the divisor is a factor *of the dividend. Find the value(s) of c for which x − 1 is a factor of each polynomial.*

59. $x^2 - 4x + c$

60. $2x^2 - 3cx - 8$

61. $c^2x^2 + 2cx + 1$

62. *Business.* A company's **revenue** R from an item is defined as the price paid per item times the quantity of items sold.

  a) Easy on the Eyes sells high-quality reproductions of original watercolors. Find an expression for the price paid per reproduction if the revenue from the sale of q reproductions is $(80q - q^2)$ dollars.

  b) Find an expression for the price paid per reproduction if one more reproduction is sold but the revenue remains $(80q - q^2)$ dollars.

63. The volume of a cube is $(a^3 + 3a^2 + 3a + 1)$ cm³.

  a) Find the length of one side of the cube.

  b) Find the area of one side of the cube.

 YOUR TURN ANSWERS: SECTION 4.8

1. $\frac{1}{4}t^2 - t + 3$ **2.** $-1 + 3xy - 2y$ **3.** $x + 2$

4. $x - 3 + \dfrac{14}{2x + 3}$ **5.** $2x + 2 + \dfrac{-3}{x - 1}$

QUICK QUIZ: SECTIONS 4.1–4.8

1. Determine the leading term of the polynomial $3t^2 - t^5 + 10 + 2t^4$.   [4.3]

2. Multiply: $3x^4(-5x^2 - 6x + 1)$.   [4.5]

3. Multiply: $\left(\frac{1}{3}a^2 + 6\right)^2$.   [4.6]

4. Add: $(a^2b - 2ab + 5ab^2) + (3ab^2 - a^2b - 8ab)$.   [4.7]

5. Divide: $(16n^4 - 8n^3 + 4n) \div (4n)$.   [4.8]

PREPARE TO MOVE ON

List the factors in each expression.   [1.2]

1. $3(x + 7)$ **2.** $(x - 3)(x + 10)$

3. $x(x + 1)(2x - 5)$

Factor.   [1.2]

4. $9x + 15y$ **5.** $14a + 7c + 7$

1

2

3

4

5

Visualizing for Success

Use after Section 4.6.

In each of Exercises 1–10, find two algebraic expressions for the shaded area of the figure from the list below.

A. $9 - 4x^2$

B. $x^2 - (x - 6)^2$

C. $(x + 3)(x - 3)$

D. $10^2 + 2^2$

E. $8x + 15$

F. $(x + 5)(x + 3) - x^2$

G. $x^2 - 6x + 9$

H. $(3 - 2x)^2 + 4x(3 - 2x)$

I. $(x + 3)^2$

J. $(5x + 3)^2 - 25x^2$

K. $(5 - 2x)^2 + 4x(5 - 2x)$

L. $x^2 - 9$

M. 104

N. $x^2 - 15$

O. $12x - 36$

P. $30x + 9$

Q. $(x - 5)(x - 3) + 3(x - 5)$ $+ 5(x - 3)$

R. $(x - 3)^2$

S. $25 - 4x^2$

T. $x^2 + 6x + 9$

Answers on page A-22

An additional, animated version of this activity appears in MyMathLab. *To use MyMathLab, you need a course ID and a student access code. Contact your instructor for more information.*

6

7

8

9

10

Collaborative Activity   *Finding the Magic Number*

Focus: Evaluating polynomials in several
        variables
Use after: Section 4.7
Time: 15–25 minutes
Group size: 3
Materials: A coin for each person

Can you determine the requirements for your
baseball team to clinch first place?

  A team's *magic number* is the combined number of wins by that team and losses by the second-
place team that guarantee the leading team a
first-place finish. For example, if the Cubs' magic
number is 3 over the Reds, any combination of
Cubs wins and Reds losses that totals 3 will guarantee a first-place finish for the Cubs. A team's
magic number is computed using the polynomial

$$G - P - L + 1,$$

where G is the length of the season, in games,
P is the number of games that the leading team has
played, and L is the total number of games that the
second-place team has lost minus the total number of games that the leading team has lost.

Activity

1. The standings below are from a fictitious
   league. Each group should calculate the
   Jaguars' magic number with respect to the
   Catamounts as well as the Jaguars' magic
   number with respect to the Wildcats. (Assume
   that the schedule is 162 games long.)

	W	L
Jaguars	92	64
Catamounts	90	66
Wildcats	89	66

2. Each group member should play the role of
   one of the teams, using coin tosses to simu-
   late the remaining games. If a group member
   correctly predicts the side (heads or tails) that
   comes up, the coin toss represents a win for
   that team. Should the other side appear, the
   toss represents a loss. Assume that these games
   are against other (unlisted) teams in the league.
   Each group member should perform three coin
   tosses and then update the standings.

3. Recalculate the two magic numbers, using
   the updated standings from part (2).

4. Slowly—one coin toss at a time—play out the
   remainder of the season. Record all wins and
   losses, update the standings, and recalculate the
   magic numbers each time all three group members have completed a round of coin tosses.

5. Examine the work in part (4) and explain why
   a magic number of 0 indicates that a team
   has been eliminated from contention.

Decision Making & Connection   (*Use after Section 4.2.*)

Buying a Smartphone.   One decision to make when
purchasing a smartphone is the amount of memory
you need. In order to determine that, you need to
know what kind of files you plan to store on the phone.
For these exercises, use the following equivalents:
1 megabyte = 1 million bytes and 1 gigabyte (GB) =
1 billion bytes.

1. Anna is considering a smartphone with 64 GB of
   memory. She plans to use the phone primarily for
   viewing movies. The average size of the movies she
   wants to download is 800 megabytes. How many
   movies could she store on the device?

2. Nate has a collection of 2000 songs. The average
   size of each song is 10 megabytes. The smartphone
   he is considering can be purchased with 16 GB,
   32 GB, or 64 GB. What size phone should he buy?

3. *Research.* Determine the average size of a game
   file. If Nate instead had a collection of 2000 games,
   what size phone should he buy?

4. On the basis of your own use of media, estimate the
   amount of memory you would need to purchase.

Study Summary

KEY TERMS AND CONCEPTS	EXAMPLES	PRACTICE EXERCISES

SECTION 4.1: *Exponents and Their Properties*

1 as an exponent: $a^1 = a$

0 as an exponent: $a^0 = 1$

The Product Rule: $a^m \cdot a^n = a^{m+n}$

The Quotient Rule: $\dfrac{a^m}{a^n} = a^{m-n}$

The Power Rule: $(a^m)^n = a^{mn}$

Raising a product to a power: $(ab)^n = a^n b^n$

Raising a quotient to a power: $\left(\dfrac{a}{b}\right)^n = \dfrac{a^n}{b^n}$

$3^1 = 3$

$3^0 = 1$

$3^5 \cdot 3^9 = 3^{5+9} = 3^{14}$

$\dfrac{3^7}{3} = 3^{7-1} = 3^6$

$(3^4)^2 = 3^{4\cdot2} = 3^8$

$(3x^5)^4 = 3^4(x^5)^4 = 81x^{20}$

$\left(\dfrac{3}{x}\right)^6 = \dfrac{3^6}{x^6}$

Simplify.

1. 6^1

2. $(-5)^0$

3. $x^5 x^{11}$

4. $\dfrac{8^9}{8^2}$

5. $(y^5)^3$

6. $(x^3 y)^{10}$

7. $\left(\dfrac{x^2}{7}\right)^5$

SECTION 4.2: *Negative Exponents and Scientific Notation*

$a^{-n} = \dfrac{1}{a^n}$;

$\dfrac{a^{-n}}{b^{-m}} = \dfrac{b^m}{a^n}$

Scientific notation:
$N \times 10^m, 1 \le N < 10$.

$3^{-2} = \dfrac{1}{3^2} = \dfrac{1}{9}$;

$\dfrac{3^{-7}}{x^{-5}} = \dfrac{x^5}{3^7}$

$4100 = 4.1 \times 10^3$;

$5 \times 10^{-3} = 0.005$

Write without negative exponents.

8. 10^{-1} 9. $\dfrac{x^{-1}}{y^{-3}}$

---

10. Convert to scientific notation: 0.000904.

11. Convert to decimal notation: 6.9×10^5.

SECTION 4.3: *Polynomials*

A **polynomial** is a monomial or a sum of monomials.

When a polynomial is written as a sum of monomials, each monomial is a **term** of the polynomial.

The **degree of a term** of a polynomial is the number of variable factors in that term.

The **coefficient** of a term is the part of the term that is a constant factor.

The **leading term** of a polynomial is the term of highest degree.

The **leading coefficient** is the coefficient of the leading term.

The **degree of the polynomial** is the degree of the leading term.

Polynomial: $10x - x^3 + 4x^5 + 7$

Term	$10x$	$-x^3$	$4x^5$	7
Degree of Term	1	3	5	0
Coefficient of Term	10	−1	4	7
Leading Term	$4x^5$			
Leading Coefficient	4			
Degree of Polynomial	5			

For Exercises 12–17, consider the polynomial $x^2 - 10 + 5x - 8x^6$.

12. List the terms of the polynomial.

13. What is the degree of the term $5x$?

14. What is the coefficient of the term x^2?

15. What is the leading term of the polynomial?

16. What is the leading coefficient of the polynomial?

17. What is the degree of the polynomial?

A **monomial** has one term.
A **binomial** has two terms.
A **trinomial** has three terms.

Monomial: $4x^3$
Binomial: $x^2 - 5$
Trinomial: $3t^3 + 2t - 10$

18. Classify the polynomial
$$8x - 3 - x^4$$
as a monomial, a binomial, or a trinomial.

Like terms, or **similar terms,** are either constant terms or terms containing the same variable(s) raised to the same power(s). These can be **combined** within a polynomial.

Combine like terms:
$$3y^4 + 6y^2 - 7 - y^4 - 6y^2 + 8.$$
$3y^4 + 6y^2 - 7 - y^4 - 6y^2 + 8$
$= \underbrace{3y^4 - y^4}_{} + \underbrace{6y^2 - 6y^2}_{} - \underbrace{7 + 8}_{}$
$= \quad 2y^4 \quad + \quad 0 \quad + \quad 1$
$= 2y^4 + 1$

19. Combine like terms:
$$3x^2 + 5x - 10x + x.$$

To **evaluate** a polynomial, replace the variable with a number. The **value** is calculated using the rules for order of operations.

Evaluate $t^3 - 2t^2 - 5t + 1$ for $t = -2$.
$t^3 - 2t^2 - 5t + 1$
$= (-2)^3 - 2(-2)^2 - 5(-2) + 1$
$= -8 - 2(4) - (-10) + 1$
$= -8 - 8 + 10 + 1$
$= -5$

20. Evaluate $2 - 3x - x^2$ for $x = -1$.

SECTION 4.4: *Addition and Subtraction of Polynomials*

Add polynomials by combining like terms.

$(2x^2 - 3x + 7) + (5x^3 + 3x - 9)$
$= 2x^2 + (-3x) + 7 + 5x^3 + 3x + (-9)$
$= 5x^3 + 2x^2 - 2$

21. Add: $(9x^2 - 3x) + (4x - x^2)$.

Subtract polynomials by adding the opposite of the polynomial being subtracted.

$(2x^2 - 3x + 7) - (5x^3 + 3x - 9)$
$= 2x^2 - 3x + 7 + (-5x^3 - 3x + 9)$
$= 2x^2 - 3x + 7 - 5x^3 - 3x + 9$
$= -5x^3 + 2x^2 - 6x + 16$

22. Subtract: $(9x^2 - 3x) - (4x - x^2)$.

SECTION 4.5: *Multiplication of Polynomials*

Multiply polynomials by multiplying each term of one polynomial by each term of the other.

$(x + 2)(x^2 - x - 1)$
$= x \cdot x^2 - x \cdot x - x \cdot 1 + 2 \cdot x^2$
$\quad - 2 \cdot x - 2 \cdot 1$
$= x^3 - x^2 - x + 2x^2 - 2x - 2$
$= x^3 + x^2 - 3x - 2$

23. Multiply:
$$(x - 1)(x^2 - x - 2).$$

SECTION 4.6: *Special Products*

FOIL (First, Outer, Inner, Last):
$(A + B)(C + D) = AC + AD + BC + BD$

$(x + 3)(x - 2) = x^2 - 2x + 3x - 6$
$\qquad\qquad\quad = x^2 + x - 6$

24. Multiply:
$$(x + 4)(2x + 3).$$

The product of a sum and a difference: $\quad (A + B)(A - B) = A^2 - B^2$ $A^2 - B^2$ is called a **difference of squares.**	$(t^3 + 5)(t^3 - 5) = (t^3)^2 - 5^2$ $\qquad\qquad\qquad = t^6 - 25$	**25.** Multiply: $\quad (5 + 3x)(5 - 3x)$.
The square of a binomial: $\quad (A + B)^2 = A^2 + 2AB + B^2;$ $\quad (A - B)^2 = A^2 - 2AB + B^2$ $A^2 + 2AB + B^2$ and $A^2 - 2AB + B^2$ are called **perfect-square trinomials.**	$(5x + 3)^2 = (5x)^2 + 2(5x)(3) + 3^2$ $\qquad\quad = 25x^2 + 30x + 9;$ $(5x - 3)^2 = (5x)^2 - 2(5x)(3) + 3^2$ $\qquad\quad = 25x^2 - 30x + 9$	*Multiply.* **26.** $(x + 9)^2$ **27.** $(8x - 1)^2$

SECTION 4.7: *Polynomials in Several Variables*

To **evaluate** a polynomial, replace each variable with a number and simplify.	Evaluate $4 - 3xy + x^2y$ for $x = 5$ and $y = -1$. $4 - 3xy + x^2y = 4 - 3(5)(-1)$ $\qquad\qquad\qquad\quad + (5)^2(-1)$ $\qquad\qquad\quad = 4 - (-15) + (-25)$ $\qquad\qquad\quad = -6$	**28.** Evaluate $xy - y^2 - 4x$ for $x = -2$ and $y = 3$.
The **degree** of a term is the number of variable factors in the term or the sum of the exponents of the variables.	The degree of $-19x^3yz^2$ is 6.	**29.** What is the degree of $4mn^5$?
Add, subtract, and multiply polynomials in several variables in the same way as polynomials in one variable.	$(3xy^2 - 4x^2y + 5xy) + (xy - 6x^2y)$ $\quad = 3xy^2 - 10x^2y + 6xy;$ $(3xy^2 - 4x^2y + 5xy) - (xy - 6x^2y)$ $\quad = 3xy^2 + 2x^2y + 4xy;$ $(2a^2b + 3a)(5a^2b - a)$ $\quad = 10a^4b^2 + 13a^3b - 3a^2$	**30.** Add: $(3cd^2 + 2c) + (4cd - 9c)$. **31.** Subtract: $(8pw - p^2w) - (p^2w + 8pw)$. **32.** Multiply: $(7xy - x^2)^2$.

SECTION 4.8: *Division of Polynomials*

To divide a polynomial by a monomial, divide each term by the monomial. Divide coefficients and subtract exponents.	$\dfrac{3t^5 - 6t^4 + 4t^2 + 9t}{3t} = \dfrac{3t^5}{3t} - \dfrac{6t^4}{3t} + \dfrac{4t^2}{3t} + \dfrac{9t}{3t}$ $\qquad\qquad\qquad\qquad = t^4 - 2t^3 + \tfrac{4}{3}t + 3$	**33.** Divide: $\dfrac{4y^5 - 8y^3 + 16y^2}{4y^2}$.
To divide a polynomial by a binomial, use long division.	Divide: $(x^2 + 5x - 2) \div (x - 3)$. $\qquad\qquad\quad\; x\; + 8$ $x - 3\overline{)x^2 + 5x\; -\; 2}$ $\qquad\; \underline{-(x^2 - 3x)}$ $\qquad\qquad\quad 8x\; -\; 2$ $\qquad\qquad\; \underline{-(8x - 24)}$ $\qquad\qquad\qquad\qquad 22$ $(x^2 + 5x - 2) \div (x - 3)$ $\qquad = x + 8 + \dfrac{22}{x - 3}$	**34.** Divide: $(x^2 - x + 4) \div (x + 1)$.

Review Exercises: Chapter 4

Concept Reinforcement

Classify each of the following statements as either true or false.

1. When two polynomials that are written in descending order are added, the result is generally written in descending order. [4.4]

2. The product of the sum and the difference of the same two terms is a difference of squares. [4.6]

3. When a binomial is squared, the result is a perfect-square trinomial. [4.6]

4. FOIL can be used whenever two polynomials are being multiplied. [4.6]

5. The degree of a polynomial cannot exceed the value of the polynomial's leading coefficient. [4.3]

6. Scientific notation is used only for extremely large numbers. [4.2]

7. FOIL can be used with polynomials in several variables. [4.7]

8. A positive number raised to a negative exponent can never represent a negative number. [4.2]

Simplify. [4.1]

9. $n^3 \cdot n^8 \cdot n$

10. $(7x)^8 \cdot (7x)^2$

11. $t^6 \cdot t^0$

12. $\dfrac{4^5}{4^2}$

13. $\dfrac{(a+b)^4}{(a+b)^4}$

14. $\dfrac{-18c^9d^3}{2c^5d}$

15. $(-2xy^2)^3$

16. $(2x^3)(-3x)^2$

17. $(a^2b)(ab)^5$

18. $\left(\dfrac{2t^5}{3s^4}\right)^2$

19. Express using a positive exponent: 8^{-6}. [4.2]

20. Express using a negative exponent: $\dfrac{1}{a^9}$. [4.2]

Simplify. Do not use negative exponents in the answer. [4.2]

21. $4^5 \cdot 4^{-7}$

22. $\dfrac{6a^{-5}b}{3a^8b^{-8}}$

23. $(w^3)^{-5}$

24. $(2x^{-3}y)^{-2}$

25. $\left(\dfrac{2x}{y}\right)^{-3}$

26. Convert to decimal notation: 4.7×10^8. [4.2]

27. Convert to scientific notation: 0.0000109. [4.2]

Multiply or divide and write scientific notation for the result. [4.2]

28. $(3.8 \times 10^4)(5.5 \times 10^{-1})$

29. $\dfrac{1.28 \times 10^{-8}}{2.5 \times 10^{-4}}$

30. Identify the terms of the polynomial:
$$-4y^5 + 7y^2 - 3y - 2.$$ [4.3]

31. List the coefficients of the terms in the polynomial:
$$7n^4 - \tfrac{5}{6}n^2 - 4n + 10.$$ [4.3]

For each polynomial, (a) *list the degree of each term;* (b) *determine the leading term and the leading coefficient; and* (c) *determine the degree of the polynomial.* [4.3]

32. $4t^2 + 6 + 15t^5$

33. $-2x^5 + 7 - 3x^2 + x$

Classify each polynomial as a monomial, a binomial, a trinomial, or a polynomial with no special name. [4.3]

34. $4x^3 - 5x + 3$

35. $4 - 9t^3 - 7t^4 + 10t^2$

36. $7y^2$

Combine like terms and write in descending order. [4.3]

37. $-4t^3 + 2t + 4t^3 + 8 - t - 9$

38. $-a + \tfrac{1}{3} + 20a^5 - 1 - 6a^5 - 2a^2$

Evaluate each polynomial for $x = -2$. [4.3]

39. $9x - 6$

40. $x^2 - 3x + 6$

Add or subtract, as indicated. [4.4]

41. $(8x^4 - x^3 + x - 4) + (x^5 + 7x^3 - 3x - 5)$

42. $(5a^5 - 2a^3 - 9a^2) + (2a^5 + a^3) + (-a^5 - 3a^2)$

43. $(3x^5 - 4x^4 + 2x^2 + 3) - (2x^5 - 4x^4 + 3x^3 + 4x^2 - 5)$

44. $\begin{aligned} -\tfrac{3}{4}x^4 + \tfrac{1}{2}x^3 \qquad\qquad\quad + \tfrac{7}{8} \\ -\tfrac{1}{4}x^3 - x^2 - \tfrac{7}{4}x \quad \\ +\tfrac{3}{2}x^4 \qquad\quad + \tfrac{2}{3}x^2 \qquad\quad - \tfrac{1}{2} \end{aligned}$

45. $\begin{aligned} 2x^5 \qquad - x^3 \qquad + x + 3 \\ -(3x^5 - x^4 + 4x^3 + 2x^2 - x + 3) \end{aligned}$

46. The length of a rectangle is 3 m greater than its width.

w + 3

w

a) Find a polynomial for the perimeter.   [4.4]
b) Find a polynomial for the area.   [4.5]

Multiply.

47. $5x^2(-6x^3)$ [4.5]

48. $(7x + 1)^2$ [4.6]

49. $(a - 7)(a + 4)$ [4.6]

50. $(d - 8)(d + 8)$ [4.6]

51. $(4x^2 - 5x + 1)(3x - 2)$ [4.5]

52. $3t^2(5t^3 - 2t^2 + 4t)$ [4.5]

53. $(2a + 9)(2a - 9)$ [4.6]

54. $(x - 0.8)(x - 0.5)$ [4.6]

55. $(x^4 - 2x + 3)(x^3 + x - 1)$ [4.5]

56. $(4y^3 - 5)^2$ [4.6]

57. $(2t^2 + 3)(t^2 - 7)$ [4.6]

58. $\left(a - \frac{1}{2}\right)\left(a + \frac{2}{3}\right)$ [4.6]

59. $(-7 + 2n)(7 + 2n)$ [4.6]

60. Evaluate $2 - 5xy + y^2 - 4xy^3 + x^6$ for $x = -1$ and $y = 2$.   [4.7]

Identify the coefficient and the degree of each term of each polynomial. Then find the degree of the polynomial.   [4.7]

61. $x^5y - 7xy + 9x^2 - 8$

62. $a^3b^8c^2 - c^{22} + a^5c^{10}$

Combine like terms.   [4.7]

65. $u + 3v - 5u + v - 7$

64. $6m^3 + 3m^2n + 4mn^2 + m^2n - 5mn^2$

Add or subtract, as indicated.   [4.7]

65. $(4a^2 - 10ab - b^2) + (-2a^2 - 6ab + b^2)$

66. $(6x^3y^2 - 4x^2y - 6x) - (-5x^3y^2 + 4x^2y + 6x^2 - 6)$

Multiply.   [4.7]

67. $(2x + 5y)(x - 3y)$

68. $(5ab - cd^2)^2$

69. Find a polynomial for the shaded area.   [4.7]

x − y

x + y

Divide.   [4.8]

70. $(3y^5 - y^2 + 12y) \div (3y)$

71. $(6x^3 - 5x^2 - 13x + 13) \div (2x + 3)$

72. $\dfrac{t^4 + t^3 + 2t^2 - t - 3}{t + 1}$

Synthesis

73. Explain why $5x^3$ and $(5x)^3$ are not equivalent expressions.   [4.1]

74. A binomial is squared and the result, written in descending order, is $x^2 - 6x + 9$. Is it possible to determine what binomial was squared? Why or why not?   [4.6]

75. Determine, without performing the multiplications, the degree of each product.   [4.5]
a) $(x^5 - 6x^2 + 3)(x^4 + 3x^3 + 7)$
b) $(x^7 - 4)^4$

76. Simplify:
$(-3x^5 \cdot 3x^3 - x^6(2x)^2 + (3x^4)^2 + (2x^2)^4 - 20x^2(x^3)^2)^2$.   [4.1], [4.3]

77. A polynomial has degree 4. There is no x^2-term. The coefficient of x^4 is two times the coefficient of x^3. The coefficient of x is 3 less than the coefficient of x^4. The remaining coefficient is 7 less than the coefficient of x. The sum of the coefficients is 15. Find the polynomial.   [4.3]

Aha! **78.** Multiply: $[(x - 5) - 4x^3][(x - 5) + 4x^3]$.   [4.6]

79. Solve: $(x - 7)(x + 10) = (x - 4)(x - 6)$.   [2.2], [4.6]

80. *Blood Donors.*   Every 4–6 weeks, Jordan donates 1.14×10^6 cubic millimeters (two pints) of whole blood, from which platelets are removed and the blood returned to his body. In one cubic millimeter of blood, there are about 2×10^5 platelets. Approximate the number of platelets in Jordan's typical donation.   [4.2]

Test: Chapter 4

For step-by-step test solutions, access the Chapter Test Prep Videos in MyMathLab®, on YouTube (search "Bittinger Combo Alg CA" and click on "Channels"), or by scanning the code.

Simplify.

1. $x^7 \cdot x \cdot x^5$

2. $\dfrac{3^8}{3^7}$

3. $\dfrac{(3m)^4}{(3m)^4}$

4. $(t^5)^9$

5. $(-3y^2)^3$

6. $(5x^4y)(-2x^5y)^3$

7. $\dfrac{24a^7b^4}{20a^2b}$

8. $\left(\dfrac{4p}{5q^3}\right)^2$

9. Express using a positive exponent: y^{-7}.

10. Express using a negative exponent: $\dfrac{1}{5^6}$.

Simplify.

11. $t^{-4} \cdot t^{-5}$

12. $\dfrac{9x^3y^2}{3x^8y^{-3}}$

13. $(2a^3b^{-1})^{-4}$

14. $\left(\dfrac{ab}{c}\right)^{-3}$

15. Convert to scientific notation: 3,060,000,000.

16. Convert to decimal notation: 5×10^{-8}.

Multiply or divide, as indicated, and write scientific notation for the result.

17. $\dfrac{5.6 \times 10^6}{3.2 \times 10^{-11}}$

18. $(2.4 \times 10^5)(5.4 \times 10^{16})$

19. Classify $4x^2y - 7y^3$ as a monomial, a binomial, a trinomial, or a polynomial with no special name.

20. Identify the coefficient of each term of the polynomial:
$$3x^5 - x + \tfrac{1}{9}.$$

21. Determine the degree of each term, the leading term and the leading coefficient, and the degree of the polynomial:
$$2t^3 - t + 7t^5 + 4.$$

22. Evaluate $x^2 + 5x - 1$ for $x = -3$.

Combine like terms and write in descending order.

23. $y^2 - 3y - y + \tfrac{3}{4}y^2$

24. $3 - x^2 + 8x + 5x^2 - 6x - 2x + 4x^3$

Add or subtract, as indicated.

25. $(3x^5 + 5x^3 - 5x^2 - 3) + (x^5 + x^4 - 3x^2 + 2x - 4)$

26. $\left(x^4 + \tfrac{2}{3}x + 5\right) + \left(4x^4 + 5x^2 + \tfrac{1}{3}x\right)$

27. $(5a^4 + 3a^3 - a^2 - 2a - 1) - (7a^4 - a^2 - a + 6)$

28. $(t^3 - 0.3t^2 - 20) - (t^4 - 1.5t^3 + 0.3t^2 - 11)$

Multiply.

29. $-2x^2(3x^2 - 3x - 5)$

30. $\left(x - \tfrac{1}{3}\right)^2$

31. $(5t - 7)(5t + 7)$

32. $(3b + 5)(2b - 1)$

33. $(x^6 - 4)(x^8 + 4)$

34. $(8 - y)(6 + 5y)$

35. $(2x + 1)(3x^2 - 5x - 3)$

36. $(8a^3 + 3)^2$

37. Evaluate $2x^2y - 3y^2$ for $x = -3$ and $y = 2$.

38. Combine like terms:
$$2x^3y - y^3 + xy^3 + 8 - 6x^3y - x^2y^2 + 11.$$

39. Subtract:
$$(8a^2b^2 - ab + b^3) - (-6ab^2 - 7ab - ab^3 + 5b^3).$$

40. Multiply: $(3x^5 - y)(3x^5 + y)$.

Divide.

41. $(12x^4 + 9x^3 - 15x^2) \div (3x^2)$

42. $(6x^3 - 8x^2 - 14x + 13) \div (x + 2)$

Synthesis

43. The height of a box is 1 less than its length, and the length is 2 more than its width. Express the volume in terms of the length.

44. Simplify: $2^{-1} - 4^{-1}$.

45. Every day about 265 billion spam e-mails are sent. If each spam e-mail wastes 4 sec of the recipient's time, how many hours are wasted each day due to spam?

Source: Based on data from Radicati Group

Cumulative Review: Chapters 1–4

1. Evaluate $\dfrac{2x + y}{5}$ for $x = 12$ and $y = 6$. [1.1]

2. Evaluate $5x^2y - xy + y^2$ for $x = -1$ and $y = -2$. [4.7]

Simplify.

3. $\frac{1}{15} - \frac{2}{9}$ [1.6]

4. $2 - [10 - (5 + 12 \div 2^2 \cdot 3)]$ [1.8]

5. $2y - (y - 7) + 3$ [1.8]

6. $t^4 \cdot t^7 \cdot t$ [4.1]

7. $\dfrac{-100x^6y^8}{25xy^5}$ [4.1]

8. $(2a^2b)(5ab^3)^2$ [4.1]

9. Factor: $10a - 6b + 12$. [1.2]

10. Determine the degree of the polynomial
$-x^4 + 5x^3 + 3x^6 - 1$. [4.3]

11. In which quadrant is $(-2, 5)$ located? [3.1]

Graph.

12. $3y + 2x = 0$ [3.2]   **13.** $3y - 2x = 12$ [3.3]

14. $3y = 2$ [3.3]   **15.** $3y = 2x + 9$ [3.6]

16. Find the slope and the y-intercept of the line given by $y = \frac{1}{10}x + \frac{3}{8}$. [3.6]

17. Find the slope of the line containing the points $(2, 3)$ and $(-6, 8)$. [3.5]

18. Write an equation of the line with slope $-\frac{2}{3}$ and y-intercept $(0, -10)$. [3.6]

Solve.

19. $\frac{1}{6}n = -\frac{2}{3}$ [2.1]

20. $5y + 7 = 8y - 1$ [2.2]

21. $2 - (x - 7) = 8 - 4(x + 5)$ [2.2]

22. $-\frac{1}{2}t \le 4$ [2.6]

23. $3x - 5 > 9x - 8$ [2.6]

24. Solve $c = \dfrac{5pq}{2t}$ for t. [2.3]

Add or subtract, as indicated.

25. $(2u^2v - uv^2 + uv) + (3u^2 - v^2u + 5vu^2)$ [4.7]

26. $(2x^5 - x^4 - x) - (x^5 - x^4 + x)$ [4.4]

Multiply.

27. $8x^3(-2x^2 - 6x + 7)$ [4.5]

28. $(x - 2)(x^2 + x - 5)$ [4.5]

29. $(4t^2 + 3)^2$ [4.6]

30. $\left(\frac{1}{2}x + 1\right)\left(\frac{1}{2}x - 1\right)$ [4.6]

31. $(2r^2 + s)(3r^2 - 4s)$ [4.7]

32. Divide: $(x^2 - x + 3) \div (x - 1)$. [4.8]

Simplify. Do not use negative exponents in the answer. [4.2]

33. 7^{-10} **34.** $(3x^{-7}y^{-2})^{-1}$

35. In 2011, China and the United States together had installed wind turbines capable of producing about 95 thousand megawatts of electricity. China's wind-turbine capacity was 11 thousand megawatts greater than that of the United States. What was China's wind-turbine capacity? [2.5]
Source: World Wind Energy Association

36. In 2010, U.S. electric utilities used coal to generate 1.8 trillion kilowatt hours (kWh) of electricity. This was 45% of the total amount of electricity generated. How much electricity was generated in 2010? [2.4]
Source: U.S. Energy Information Administration

37. While studying in the United States under a student visa, Ana can work on campus no more than 20 hr per week. For the first 4 days of one week, she worked 3, 2, 5, and 6 hr. How many hours can she work on the fifth day without violating this restriction? [2.7]

38. U.S. retail losses due to employee theft have increased from \$15.9 billion in 2008 to \$16.2 billion in 2011. Find the rate of change of retail losses due to employee theft. [3.4]
Source: National Retail Federation

Synthesis

Solve. If no solution exists, state this.

39. $3x - 2(x + 6) = 4(x - 3)$ [2.2]

40. $x - (2x - 1) = 3x - 4(x + 1) + 10$ [2.2]

Simplify.

41. $7^{-1} + 8^0$ [4.2]

42. $-2x^5(x^7) + (x^3)^4 - (4x^5)^2(-x^2)$ [4.1], [4.3]

Polynomials and Factoring

NUMBER OF MINUTES t AFTER INJECTION	NUMBER OF MICROGRAMS N OF EPINEPHRINE IN THE BLOODSTREAM
2	160
5	250
8	160

An Epinephrine Shot Could Save Your Life.

An injection of the drug epinephrine (adrenaline) can slow down or stop an extreme allergic reaction. Because the drug is injected directly into the bloodstream, it is carried quickly throughout the body. The table above lists the number of micrograms of epinephrine in an adult's bloodstream t minutes after 250 micrograms have been injected. As the data in the table seem to indicate, the effect wears off quickly as well. We can use a *quadratic equation* to model these data and predict the concentration of epinephrine in the bloodstream for other values of t.

(*See Example 4 in Section 5.8.*)

Math is critical when calculating dosages of medication.

Neil Kao, M.D., F.A.C.P., an allergist and clinical immunologist in Greenville, South Carolina, says that prior to prescribing an antibiotic, a physician should be aware of the patient's age, mass, in kilograms, coexistent medical diseases, other medications taken, and the suspected organism. These factors are used in calculating the correct dosage.

F actoring is multiplying reversed. Thus factoring polynomials requires a solid understanding of how to multiply polynomials. Factoring is an important skill that will be used to solve equations and simplify other types of expressions found later in the study of algebra.

5.1 Introduction to Factoring

Factoring Monomials ▪ Factoring When Terms Have a Common Factor ▪ Factoring by Grouping ▪ Checking by Evaluating

Just as a number like 15 can be factored as $3 \cdot 5$, a polynomial like $x^2 + 7x$ can be factored as $x(x + 7)$. In both cases, we ask ourselves, "What was multiplied to obtain the given result?" The situation is much like a popular television game show in which an "answer" is given and participants must find the "question" to which the answer corresponds.

Study Skills

You've Got Mail

Many students overlook an excellent opportunity to get questions answered—e-mail. If your instructor makes his or her e-mail address available, consider using it to get help. Often, just the act of writing out your question brings some clarity. If you do use e-mail, allow some time for your instructor to reply.

> **FACTORING**
>
> To *factor* a polynomial is to find an equivalent expression that is a product. An equivalent expression of this type is called a *factorization* of the polynomial.

Factoring Monomials

To factor a monomial, we find monomials whose product is equivalent to the original monomial. For example, $20x^2$ can be factored as $2 \cdot 10x^2$, $4x \cdot 5x$, or $10x \cdot 2x$, as well as several other ways. To check, we multiply.

EXAMPLE 1   Find three factorizations of $15x^3$.

SOLUTION

a) $15x^3 = (3 \cdot 5)(x \cdot x^2)$ Thinking of how 15 and x^3 can each be factored
$ = (3x)(5x^2)$ The factors are $3x$ and $5x^2$. *Check*: $3x \cdot 5x^2 = 15x^3$.

b) $15x^3 = (3 \cdot 5)(x^2 \cdot x)$
$ = (3x^2)(5x)$ The factors are $3x^2$ and $5x$. *Check*: $3x^2 \cdot 5x = 15x^3$.

c) $15x^3 = ((-5)(-3))x^3$
$ = (-5)(-3x^3)$ The factors are -5 and $-3x^3$.
 *Check*: $(-5)(-3x^3) = 15x^3$.

1. Find three factorizations of $30a^3$.

We see that $(3x)(5x^2)$, $(3x^2)(5x)$, and $(-5)(-3x^3)$ are all factorizations of $15x^3$. Other factorizations exist as well.

↪ YOUR TURN

Factoring When Terms Have a Common Factor

To factor a polynomial with two or more terms, we use the distributive law with the sides of the equation switched.

Multiply: $3(x + 2y - z) = 3 \cdot x + 3 \cdot 2y - 3 \cdot z$
$ = 3x + 6y - 3z$

Factor: $3x + 6y - 3z = 3 \cdot x + 3 \cdot 2y - 3 \cdot z$
$ = 3(x + 2y - z)$

In the factorization above, note that since 3 appears as a factor of $3x$, $6y$, and $-3z$, it is a *common factor* for all the terms of $3x + 6y - 3z$.

We generally factor out the *largest* common factor.

EXAMPLE 2 Factor to form an equivalent expression: $8a - 12$.

SOLUTION We write the prime factorization of both terms, lining up common factors in columns:

The prime factorization of $8a$ is $2 \cdot 2 \cdot 2 \cdot a$;

The prime factorization of 12 is $2 \cdot 2 \cdot \qquad 3$.

Since both factorizations include two factors of 2, the largest common factor is $2 \cdot 2$, or 4:

$$8a - 12 = 4 \cdot 2a - 4 \cdot 3 \qquad \text{4 is a factor of } 8a \text{ and of 12.}$$
$$8a - 12 = 4(2a - 3). \qquad \text{Try to go directly to this step.}$$

Check: $4(2a - 3) = 4 \cdot 2a - 4 \cdot 3 = 8a - 12$, as expected.

2. Factor to form an equivalent expression: $12x - 30$.

The factorization of $8a - 12$ is $4(2a - 3)$.

YOUR TURN

> **CAUTION!** $2 \cdot 2 \cdot 2 \cdot a - 2 \cdot 2 \cdot 3$ is a factorization of the *terms* of $8a - 12$ but not of the polynomial itself. The factorization of $8a - 12$ is $4(2a - 3)$.

A common factor may contain a variable.

EXAMPLE 3 Factor: $24x^5 + 30x^2$.

SOLUTION

The prime factorization of $24x^5$ is $2 \cdot 2 \cdot 2 \cdot 3 \cdot \qquad x \cdot x \cdot x \cdot x \cdot x.$

The prime factorization of $30x^2$ is $2 \cdot \qquad 3 \cdot 5 \cdot x \cdot x.$

The largest common factor is $2 \cdot 3 \cdot x \cdot x$, or $6x^2$.

$$24x^5 + 30x^2 = 6x^2 \cdot 4x^3 + 6x^2 \cdot 5 \qquad \text{Factoring each term}$$
$$= 6x^2(4x^3 + 5) \qquad \text{Factoring out } 6x^2$$

Check: $6x^2(4x^3 + 5) = 6x^2 \cdot 4x^3 + 6x^2 \cdot 5 = 24x^5 + 30x^2$, as expected.

3. Factor: $30x^4 + 40x^3$.

The factorization of $24x^5 + 30x^2$ is $6x^2(4x^3 + 5)$.

YOUR TURN

The largest common factor of a polynomial is the largest common factor of the coefficients times the largest common factor of the variable(s) in all the terms. Suppose in Example 3 that you did not recognize the *largest* common factor, and removed only part of it, as follows:

$$24x^5 + 30x^2 = 2x^2 \cdot 12x^3 + 2x^2 \cdot 15 \qquad 2x^2 \text{ is a common factor.}$$
$$= 2x^2(12x^3 + 15). \qquad 12x^3 + 15 \text{ itself contains a common factor, 3.}$$

Note that $12x^3 + 15$ still has a common factor, 3. To find the largest common factor, we extend the above factoring, as follows, until no more common factors exist:

$$24x^5 + 30x^2 = 2x^2[3(4x^3 + 5)] \qquad \text{Factoring } 12x^3 + 15. \text{ Remember to rewrite the first common factor, } 2x^2.$$
$$= 6x^2(4x^3 + 5). \qquad \text{Using an associative law; } 2x^2 \cdot 3 = 6x^2$$

Since $4x^3 + 5$ cannot be factored any further, we say that we have factored *completely*. **When we are directed simply to factor, it is understood that we should always factor completely.**

EXAMPLE 4   Factor: $12x^5 - 15x^4 + 27x^3$.

SOLUTION

The prime factorization of $12x^5$ is $2 \cdot 2 \cdot 3 \cdot \qquad x \cdot x \cdot x \cdot x \cdot x.$
The prime factorization of $15x^4$ is $\qquad 3 \cdot \qquad 5 \cdot x \cdot x \cdot x \cdot x.$
The prime factorization of $27x^3$ is $\qquad 3 \cdot 3 \cdot 3 \cdot \qquad x \cdot x \cdot x.$

The largest common factor is $3 \cdot x \cdot x \cdot x$, or $3x^3$.

$$12x^5 - 15x^4 + 27x^3 = 3x^3 \cdot 4x^2 - 3x^3 \cdot 5x + 3x^3 \cdot 9$$
$$= 3x^3(4x^2 - 5x + 9)$$

Since $4x^2 - 5x + 9$ has no common factor, we are done, except for a check:

$$3x^3(4x^2 - 5x + 9) = 3x^3 \cdot 4x^2 - 3x^3 \cdot 5x + 3x^3 \cdot 9$$
$$= 12x^5 - 15x^4 + 27x^3,$$

4. Factor: $8a^5 + 12a^3 - 6a^2$.

as expected. The factorization of $12x^5 - 15x^4 + 27x^3$ is $3x^3(4x^2 - 5x + 9)$.

YOUR TURN

Note in Examples 3 and 4 that the *largest* common variable factor is the *smallest* power of x in the original polynomial.

With practice, we can determine the largest common factor without writing the prime factorization of each term. Then, to factor, we write the largest common factor and parentheses and then fill in the parentheses. It is customary for the leading coefficient of the polynomial inside the parentheses to be positive.

EXAMPLE 5   Factor: **(a)** $8r^5s^2 + 16rs^5$; **(b)** $-3xy + 6xz - 3x$.

SOLUTION

a) $8r^5s^2 + 16rs^5 = 8rs^2(r^4 + 2s^3)$ Try to go directly to this step.

The largest common factor is $8rs^2$. $\longleftarrow \begin{cases} 8r^5s^2 = 2 \cdot 2 \cdot 2 \cdot \qquad r \cdot r^4 \cdot s^2 \\ 16rs^5 = 2 \cdot 2 \cdot 2 \cdot 2 \cdot r \cdot \qquad s^2 \cdot s^3 \end{cases}$

Check: $8rs^2(r^4 + 2s^3) = 8r^5s^2 + 16rs^5.$

b) $-3xy + 6xz - 3x = -3x(y - 2z + 1)$ Note that either $-3x$ or $3x$ can be the largest common factor.

Student Notes

The 1 in $(y - 2z + 1)$ plays an important role in Example 5(b). Without the 1, the term $-3x$ would not appear in the check.

We generally factor out a negative when the first coefficient is negative. The way we factor can depend on the situation in which we are working. We might also factor as follows:

$$-3xy + 6xz - 3x = 3x(-y + 2z - 1).$$

The checks are left to the student.

5. Factor: $12a^2b^4 - 8a^3b^3$.

YOUR TURN

In some texts, the largest common factor is referred to as the *greatest* common factor. We have avoided this language because, as shown in Example 5(b), the largest common factor may represent a negative value that is actually *less* than other common factors.

TIPS FOR FACTORING

1. Factor out the largest common factor, if one exists.
2. The common factor multiplies a polynomial with the same number of terms as the original polynomial.
3. Factoring can always be checked by multiplying. Multiplication should yield the original polynomial.

Factoring by Grouping

Sometimes algebraic expressions contain a common factor with two or more terms.

EXAMPLE 6 Factor: $x^2(x + 1) + 2(x + 1)$.

SOLUTION The binomial $x + 1$ is a factor of both $x^2(x + 1)$ and $2(x + 1)$. Thus, $x + 1$ is a common factor:

$$x^2(x + 1) + 2(x + 1) = (x + 1)x^2 + (x + 1)2 \quad \text{Using a commutative law twice. Try to do this step mentally.}$$

$$= (x + 1)(x^2 + 2). \quad \text{Factoring out the common factor, } x + 1$$

To check, we could simply reverse the above steps.
   The factorization is $(x + 1)(x^2 + 2)$.

6. Factor: $x(x - 5) + 3(x - 5)$.

YOUR TURN

Some polynomials with four terms have a common binomial factor. In order to identify that factor, we regroup into two groups of two terms each.

EXAMPLE 7 Factor: $5x^3 - x^2 + 15x - 3$.

SOLUTION

$$5x^3 - x^2 + 15x - 3 = (5x^3 - x^2) + (15x - 3) \quad \text{Grouping as two binomials}$$

$$= x^2(5x - 1) + 3(5x - 1) \quad \text{Factoring each binomial}$$

$$= (5x - 1)(x^2 + 3) \quad \text{Factoring out the common factor, } 5x - 1$$

Check: $(5x - 1)(x^2 + 3) = 5x \cdot x^2 + 5x \cdot 3 - 1 \cdot x^2 - 1 \cdot 3 \quad \text{Using FOIL}$
$$= 5x^3 - x^2 + 15x - 3.$$

7. Factor: $x^3 + 3x^2 + 4x + 12$.

YOUR TURN

If a polynomial can be split into groups of terms and the groups share a common factor, then the original polynomial can be factored. This method, known as **factoring by grouping**, can be tried on any polynomial with four or more terms.

EXAMPLE 8   Factor by grouping.

a) $2x^3 + 8x^2 + x + 4$ **b)** $4t^3 - 15 + 20t^2 - 3t$

SOLUTION

a) $2x^3 + 8x^2 + x + 4 = (2x^3 + 8x^2) + (x + 4)$

$\qquad\qquad\qquad\quad = 2x^2(x + 4) + 1(x + 4)$ Factoring $2x^3 + 8x^2$ to find a common binomial factor. Writing the 1 helps with the next step.

> *CAUTION!*   Be sure to include the term 1.

$\qquad\qquad\qquad\quad = (x + 4)(2x^2 + 1)$ Factoring out the common factor, $x + 4$. The 1 is essential in the factor $2x^2 + 1$.

$\quad$ *Check:* $(x + 4)(2x^2 + 1) = x \cdot 2x^2 + x \cdot 1 + 4 \cdot 2x^2 + 4 \cdot 1$ Using FOIL

$\qquad\qquad\qquad\qquad\qquad\quad = 2x^3 + x + 8x^2 + 4$

$\qquad\qquad\qquad\qquad\qquad\quad = 2x^3 + 8x^2 + x + 4.$ Using a commutative law

The factorization is $(x + 4)(2x^2 + 1)$.

b) When we try grouping $4t^3 - 15 + 20t^2 - 3t$ as

$\qquad (4t^3 - 15) + (20t^2 - 3t),$

we are unable to factor $4t^3 - 15$. When this happens, we can rearrange the polynomial and try a different grouping:

$\qquad 4t^3 - 15 + 20t^2 - 3t = 4t^3 + 20t^2 - 3t - 15$ Using the commutative law to rearrange the terms

$\qquad\qquad\qquad\qquad\qquad\quad = 4t^2(t + 5) - 3(t + 5)$ By factoring out -3, we see that $t + 5$ is a common factor.

$\qquad\qquad\qquad\qquad\qquad\quad = (t + 5)(4t^2 - 3).$ To check, we use FOIL.

8. Factor by grouping:

$\qquad 3x^3 - 3x^2 + 2x - 2.$

 YOUR TURN

To reverse the order of subtraction, we can factor out -1.

> **FACTORING OUT -1 TO REVERSE SUBTRACTION**
> $\qquad b - a = -1(a - b) = -(a - b)$

EXAMPLE 9   Factor: $t^5 - 5t^4 + 10 - 2t$.

SOLUTION

$\qquad t^5 - 5t^4 + 10 - 2t = (t^5 - 5t^4) + (10 - 2t)$ Grouping

$\qquad\qquad\qquad\qquad\quad = t^4(t - 5) + 2(5 - t)$ Factoring each binomial

$\qquad\qquad\qquad\qquad\quad = t^4(t - 5) + 2(-1)(t - 5)$ Factoring out -1 to reverse $5 - t$

$\qquad\qquad\qquad\qquad\quad = t^4(t - 5) - 2(t - 5)$ Simplifying

$\qquad\qquad\qquad\qquad\quad = (t - 5)(t^4 - 2)$ Factoring out $t - 5$

9. Factor: $2x^3 - 16x^2 + 8 - x$.

The check is left to the student.

YOUR TURN

Checking by Evaluating

One way to check a factorization is to multiply. A second type of check uses the fact that equivalent expressions have the same value when evaluated for the same replacement. Thus a quick, partial check of Example 8(a) can be made by using a convenient replacement for x (say, 1) and evaluating both $2x^3 + 8x^2 + x + 4$ and $(x + 4)(2x^2 + 1)$:

$$2 \cdot 1^3 + 8 \cdot 1^2 + 1 + 4 = 2 + 8 + 1 + 4 = 15;$$
$$(1 + 4)(2 \cdot 1^2 + 1) = 5 \cdot 3 = 15.$$

Since the value of both expressions is the same, the factorization is probably correct. Evaluating for several values will make the check more certain.

Chapter Resource:
Decision Making: Connection, p. 366

Technology Connection

A partial check of a factorization can be performed using a table or a graph. To check Example 8(a), we let

$$y_1 = 2x^3 + 8x^2 + x + 4 \quad \text{and} \quad y_2 = (x + 4)(2x^2 + 1).$$

Then we set up a table in AUTO mode. If the factorization is correct, the values of y_1 and y_2 will be the same regardless of the table settings used.

ΔTBL = 1

X	Y1	Y2
0	4	4
1	15	15
2	54	54
3	133	133
4	264	264
5	459	459
6	730	730

X = 0

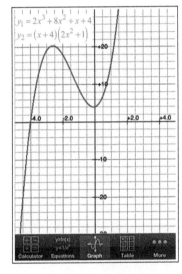

We can also graph $y_1 = 2x^3 + 8x^2 + x + 4$ and $y_2 = (x + 4)(2x^2 + 1)$. If the graphs appear to coincide, the factorization is probably correct. The TRACE feature can be used to confirm this. This approach is illustrated using a graphing calculator app.

Use a table or a graph to determine whether each of the following factorizations is correct.

1. $x^2 - 7x - 8 = (x - 8)(x + 1)$
2. $4x^2 - 5x - 6 = (4x + 3)(x - 2)$
3. $5x^2 + 17x - 12 = (5x + 3)(x - 4)$
4. $10x^2 + 37x + 7 = (5x - 1)(2x + 7)$
5. $12x^2 - 17x - 5 = (6x + 1)(2x - 5)$
6. $12x^2 - 17x - 5 = (4x + 1)(3x - 5)$
7. $x^2 - 4 = (x - 2)(x - 2)$
8. $x^2 - 4 = (x + 2)(x - 2)$

5.1 EXERCISE SET

FOR EXTRA HELP   MyMathLab® Math
PRACTICE   WATCH   READ   REVIEW

Vocabulary and Reading Check

Classify each of the following statements as either true or false.

1. The largest common factor of a polynomial always has the same degree as the polynomial itself.

2. When the leading coefficient of a polynomial is negative, we generally factor out a common factor with a negative coefficient.

3. A polynomial is not prime if it contains a common factor other than 1 or -1.

4. All polynomials with four terms can be factored by grouping.

Concept Reinforcement

In each of Exercises 5–12, match the phrase with the most appropriate choice from the column on the right.

5. ____ A factorization of $35a^2b$

6. ____ A factor of $35a^2b$

7. ____ A common factor of $5x + 10$ and $4x + 8$

8. ____ A factorization of $3x^4 - 9x^2$

9. ____ A factorization of $9x^4 - 3x^2$

10. ____ A common factor of $2x + 10$ and $4x + 8$

11. ____ A factor of $3a + 6a^2$

12. ____ A factorization of $3a + 6a^2$

a) $3a(1 + 2a)$

b) $x + 2$

c) $3x^2(3x^2 - 1)$

d) $1 + 2a$

e) $3x^2(x^2 - 3)$

f) $5a^2$

g) 2

h) $7a \cdot 5ab$

Factoring Monomials

Find three factorizations for each monomial. Answers may vary.

13. $14x^3$

14. $22x^3$

15. $-15a^4$

16. $-8t^5$

17. $25t^5$

18. $9a^4$

Factoring When Terms Have a Common Factor

Factor. Remember to use the largest common factor and to check by multiplying. Factor out a negative factor if the first coefficient is negative.

19. $8x + 24$

20. $10x + 50$

21. $2x^2 + 2x - 8$

22. $6x^2 + 3x - 15$

23. $3t^2 + t$

24. $2t^2 + t$

25. $-5y^2 - 10y$

26. $-4y^2 - 12y$

27. $x^3 + 6x^2$

28. $5x^4 - x^2$

29. $16a^4 - 24a^2$

30. $25a^5 + 10a^3$

31. $-6t^6 + 9t^4 - 4t^2$

32. $-10t^5 + 15t^4 + 9t^3$

33. $6x^8 + 12x^6 - 24x^4 + 30x^2$

34. $10x^4 - 30x^3 - 50x - 20$

35. $x^5y^5 + x^4y^3 + x^3y^3 - x^2y^2$

36. $x^9y^6 - x^7y^5 + x^4y^4 + x^3y^3$

37. $-35a^3b^4 + 10a^2b^3 - 15a^3b^2$

38. $-21r^5t^4 - 14r^4t^6 + 21r^3t^6$

Factoring by Grouping

Factor.

39. $n(n - 6) + 3(n - 6)$

40. $b(b + 5) + 3(b + 5)$

41. $x^2(x + 3) - 7(x + 3)$

42. $3z^2(2z + 9) + (2z + 9)$

43. $y^2(2y - 9) + (2y - 9)$

44. $x^2(x - 7) - 3(x - 7)$

Factor by grouping, if possible, and check.

45. $x^3 + 2x^2 + 5x + 10$

46. $z^3 + 3z^2 + 7z + 21$

47. $9n^3 - 6n^2 + 3n - 2$

48. $10x^3 - 25x^2 + 2x - 5$

49. $4t^3 - 20t^2 + 3t - 15$

50. $8a^3 - 2a^2 + 12a - 3$

51. $7x^3 + 5x^2 - 21x - 15$

52. $5x^3 + 4x^2 - 10x - 8$

53. $6a^3 + 7a^2 + 6a + 7$

54. $7t^3 - 5t^2 + 7t - 5$

55. $2x^3 - 12x^2 - x + 6$

56. $x^3 - x^2 - 2x + 5$

57. $p^3 + p^2 - 3p + 10$

58. $a^3 - 3a^2 + 6 - 2a$

59. $y^3 + 8y^2 - 2y - 16$

60. $3x^3 + 18x^2 - 5x - 25$

61. $2x^3 + 36 - 8x^2 - 9x$

62. $20g^3 + 5 - 4g^2 - 25g$

63. In answering a factoring problem, Taylor says the largest common factor is $-5x^2$ and Kimber says the largest common factor is $5x^2$. Can they both be correct? Why or why not?

64. Write a two-sentence paragraph in which the word "factor" is used at least once as a noun and once as a verb.

Skill Review

Simplify.

65. $\frac{2}{5} \div \frac{10}{3}$ [1.3]

66. $-1 + 20 \div 2^2 \cdot 5$ [1.8]

67. $(2xy^{-4})^{-1}$ [4.2]

68. $(a^2b^3c)(a^5b^4c^2)$ [4.1]

69. $(3x^2 - x - 3) - (-x^2 - 6x + 10)$ [4.4]

70. $(w^2y + yz - w^2) + (w^2 - 2w^2y + wz)$ [4.7]

Synthesis

71. Suresh factors $12x^2y - 18xy^2$ as $6xy \cdot 2x - 6xy \cdot 3y$. Is this the factorization of the polynomial? Why or why not?

72. Azrah recognizes that evaluating usually provides only a partial check of her factoring. Because of this, she often performs a second check with a different replacement value. Is this a good idea? Why or why not?

Factor, if possible.

73. $4x^5 + 6x^2 + 6x^3 + 9$

74. $x^6 + x^2 + x^4 + 1$

75. $2x^4 + 2x^3 - 4x^2 - 4x$

76. $x^3 + x^2 - 2x + 2$

Aha! **77.** $5x^5 - 5x^4 + x^3 - x^2 + 3x - 3$

Aha! **78.** $ax^2 + 2ax + 3a + x^2 + 2x + 3$

79. Write a trinomial of degree 7 for which $8x^2y^3$ is the largest common factor. Answers may vary.

80. Kris and Tina are each calculating the amount of sheet metal needed to form a circular canister with a radius of 5 in. and a height of 20 in. Kris uses the formula $A = 2\pi rh + 2\pi r^2$. Tina adds $5 + 20$, and then multiplies that sum by 10 and then by π. Do the methods give the same result? Which seems easier?

YOUR TURN ANSWERS: SECTION 5.1

1. $(3a)(10a^2), (6a^2)(5a), (-3)(-10a^3)$; answers may vary
2. $6(2x - 5)$ **3.** $10x^3(3x + 4)$ **4.** $2a^2(4a^3 + 6a - 3)$
5. $4a^2b^3(3b - 2a)$ **6.** $(x - 5)(x + 3)$ **7.** $(x + 3)(x^2 + 4)$
8. $(x - 1)(3x^2 + 2)$ **9.** $(x - 8)(2x^2 - 1)$

PREPARE TO MOVE ON

Multiply. [4.6]

1. $(x + 2)(x + 7)$ 2. $(x - 2)(x - 7)$

3. $(x + 2)(x - 7)$ 4. $(x - 2)(x + 7)$

List all factors of each number. [1.3]

5. 60   6. 18

5.2 | Factoring Trinomials of the Type $x^2 + bx + c$

When the Constant Term Is Positive ▪ When the Constant Term Is Negative ▪ Prime Polynomials ▪ Factoring Completely

We now learn how to factor trinomials like

$$x^2 + 5x + 4 \quad \text{or} \quad x^2 + 3x - 10,$$

for which no common factor exists and the leading coefficient is 1. Recall that when factoring, we are writing an equivalent expression that is a product. For these trinomials, the factors will be binomials.

Study Skills

Leave a Trail

Students sometimes make the mistake of viewing their support-ing work as "scrap" work. Most instructors regard your reasoning as extremely important. Try to organize your supporting work so that your instructor (and you as well) can follow your steps. If you abandon a line of work, a simple $\times$ through it will allow you and others to review it if desired.

Compare the following multiplications:

$$
\begin{array}{cccc}
F & O & I & L \\
\downarrow & \downarrow & \downarrow & \downarrow
\end{array}
$$

$$(x + 2)(x + 5) = x^2 + 5x + 2x + 2 \cdot 5$$
$$= x^2 + 7x + 10;$$

$$(x - 2)(x - 5) = x^2 - 5x - 2x + (-2)(-5)$$
$$= x^2 - 7x + 10;$$

$$(x + 3)(x - 7) = x^2 - 7x + 3x + 3(-7)$$
$$= x^2 - 4x - 21;$$

$$(x - 3)(x + 7) = x^2 + 7x - 3x + (-3)7$$
$$= x^2 + 4x - 21.$$

Note that for all four products:

- The product of the two binomials is a trinomial.
- The coefficient of x in the trinomial is the sum of the constant terms in the binomials.
- The constant term in the trinomial is the product of the constant terms in the binomials.

These observations lead to a method for factoring certain trinomials. We first consider those with a positive constant term, as in the first two products above.

When the Constant Term Is Positive

To factor a polynomial like $x^2 + 7x + 10$, we think of FOIL in reverse. The x^2 suggests that the first term of each bino-mial factor is x. Next, we look for numbers p and q such that

$$x^2 + 7x + 10 = (x + p)(x + q).$$

To get the middle term and the last term of the trinomial, we need two numbers, p and q, whose product is 10 and whose sum is 7. Those numbers are 2 and 5. Thus the fac-torization is

$$(x + 2)(x + 5).$$

Check: $(x + 2)(x + 5) = x^2 + 5x + 2x + 10$
$$= x^2 + 7x + 10.$$

EXAMPLE 1 Factor to form an equivalent expression:

$$x^2 + 5x + 6.$$

SOLUTION Think of FOIL in reverse. The first term of each factor is x:

$$(x +)(x +).$$

To complete the factorization, we need a constant term for each binomial. The constants must have a product of 6 and a sum of 5. We list some pairs of numbers that multiply to 6 and then check the sum of each pair of factors.

A GEOMETRIC APPROACH TO EXAMPLE 1

The product of two binomials can be regarded as the sum of the areas of four rectangles. Thus we can regard the factoring of $x^2 + 5x + 6$ as a search for p and q so that the sum of areas A, B, C, and D is $x^2 + 5x + 6$.

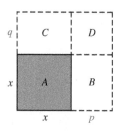

Note that area D is the product of p and q. In order for area D to be 6, p and q must be either 1 and 6 or 2 and 3. We illustrate both below.

When p and q are 1 and 6, the total area is $x^2 + 7x + 6$, but when p and q are 2 and 3, as shown on the right, the total area is $x^2 + 5x + 6$, as desired. Thus the factorization of $x^2 + 5x + 6$ is $(x + 2)(x + 3)$.

Pairs of Factors of 6	Sums of Factors
1, 6	7
2, 3	5 ← The numbers we seek are 2 and 3.
−1, −6	−7
−2, −3	−5

Every pair has a product of 6.   *One* pair has a sum of 5.

Since

$$2 \cdot 3 = 6 \quad \text{and} \quad 2 + 3 = 5,$$

the factorization of $x^2 + 5x + 6$ is $(x + 2)(x + 3)$.

Check: $(x + 2)(x + 3) = x^2 + 3x + 2x + 6 = x^2 + 5x + 6.$

Thus, $(x + 2)(x + 3)$ is a product that is equivalent to $x^2 + 5x + 6$.

Note that since 5 and 6 are both positive, when factoring $x^2 + 5x + 6$ we need not have listed negative factors of 6. Note too that changing the signs of the factors changes only the sign of the sum (see the table above).

1. Factor to form an equivalent expression: $x^2 + 6x + 8$.

YOUR TURN

At the beginning of this section, we considered the multiplication $(x - 2)(x - 5)$. For this product, the resulting trinomial, $x^2 - 7x + 10$, has a positive constant term but a negative coefficient of x. This is because the *product* of two negative numbers is always positive, whereas the *sum* of two negative numbers is always negative.

TO FACTOR $x^2 + bx + c$ WHEN c IS POSITIVE

When the constant term c of a trinomial is positive, look for two numbers with the same sign. Select pairs of numbers with the sign of b, the coefficient of the middle term.

$x^2 - 7x + 10 = (x - 2)(x - 5);$ b is negative; c is positive.

$x^2 + 7x + 10 = (x + 2)(x + 5)$ b is positive; c is positive.

EXAMPLE 2 Factor: $y^2 - 8y + 12$.

SOLUTION Since the constant term is positive and the coefficient of the middle term is negative, we look for a factorization of 12 in which both factors are negative. Their sum must be −8.

Pairs of Factors of 12	Sums of Factors
−1, −12	−13
−2, −6	−8 ← We need a sum of −8. The numbers we need are −2 and −6.
−3, −4	−7

The factorization of $y^2 - 8y + 12$ is $(y - 2)(y - 6)$. The check is left to the student.

2. Factor: $a^2 - 8a + 15$.

YOUR TURN

When the Constant Term Is Negative

As we saw in two of the multiplications at the beginning of this section, the product of two binomials can have a negative constant term:

$$(x + 3)(x - 7) = x^2 - 4x - 21$$

and

$$(x - 3)(x + 7) = x^2 + 4x - 21.$$

It is important to note that when the signs of the constants in the binomials are reversed, only the sign of the middle term of the trinomial changes.

EXAMPLE 3 Factor: $x^2 - 8x - 20$.

SOLUTION The constant term, -20, must be expressed as the product of a negative number and a positive number. Since the sum of these two numbers must be negative (specifically, -8), the negative number must have the greater absolute value.

Pairs of Factors of − 20	Sums of Factors
1, −20	−19
2, −10	−8 ← The numbers we need are 2 and −10.
4, −5	−1

The numbers that we are looking for are 2 and -10.

Check: $(x + 2)(x - 10) = x^2 - 10x + 2x - 20$
$$= x^2 - 8x - 20.$$

3. Factor: $t^2 - 2t - 15$.

The factorization of $x^2 - 8x - 20$ is $(x + 2)(x - 10)$.

YOUR TURN

TO FACTOR $x^2 + bx + c$ WHEN c IS NEGATIVE

When the constant term c is negative, look for a positive number and a negative number that multiply to c. Consider only pairs of numbers for which the number with the larger absolute value has the sign of b.

$x^2 - 4x - 21 = (x + 3)(x - 7);$ b is negative; c is negative.

$x^2 + 4x - 21 = (x - 3)(x + 7)$ b is positive; c is negative.

Student Notes

Writing a trinomial in descending order will help you to identify b and c.

EXAMPLE 4   Factor: $t^2 - 24 + 5t$.

SOLUTION   We first write the trinomial in descending order: $t^2 + 5t - 24$. The factorization of the constant term, -24, must have one positive factor and one negative factor. The sum must be 5, so the positive factor must have the larger absolute value. Thus we consider only pairs of factors in which the positive factor has the larger absolute value.

Pairs of Factors of -24	Sums of Factors
$-1, 24$	23
$-2, 12$	10
$-3, \ 8$	5 ←——— The numbers we need are -3 and 8.
$-4, \ 6$	2

4. Factor: $t^2 - 28 + 3t$.

The factorization is $(t - 3)(t + 8)$. The check is left to the student.

YOUR TURN

Polynomials in two or more variables, such as $a^2 + 4ab - 21b^2$, are factored in a similar manner.

EXAMPLE 5   Factor: $a^2 + 4ab - 21b^2$.

SOLUTION   We look for numbers p and q such that

$$a^2 + 4ab - 21b^2 = (a + pb)(a + qb).$$

Our thinking is much the same as if we were factoring $x^2 + 4x - 21$. We look for factors of -21 whose sum is 4. Those factors are -3 and 7. Thus,

$$a^2 + 4ab - 21b^2 = (a - 3b)(a + 7b).$$

Check: $(a - 3b)(a + 7b) = a^2 + 7ab - 3ba - 21b^2$
$$= a^2 + 4ab - 21b^2.$$

5. Factor: $x^2 - 3xy - 18y^2$.

The factorization of $a^2 + 4ab - 21b^2$ is $(a - 3b)(a + 7b)$.

YOUR TURN

Prime Polynomials

EXAMPLE 6   Factor: $x^2 - x + 5$.

SOLUTION   Since 5 has very few factors, we can easily check all possibilities.

Pairs of Factors of 5	Sums of Factors
$5, \ 1$	6
$-5, -1$	-6

6. Factor: $x^2 + x + 1$.

Since there are no factors whose sum is -1, the polynomial is *not* factorable into binomials.

 YOUR TURN

In this text, a polynomial like $x^2 - x + 5$ that cannot be factored using rational numbers is said to be **prime**. In more advanced courses, other types of numbers are considered. There, polynomials like $x^2 - x + 5$ can be factored and are not considered prime.

Factoring Completely

Often factoring requires two or more steps. Remember, when told to factor, we should *factor completely*. This means that the final factorization should contain only prime polynomials.

EXAMPLE 7   Factor: $-2x^3 + 20x^2 - 50x$.

SOLUTION   *Always* look first for a common factor. This time there is one. Since the leading coefficient is negative, we begin by factoring out $-2x$:

$$-2x^3 + 20x^2 - 50x = -2x(x^2 - 10x + 25).$$

Now consider $x^2 - 10x + 25$. Since the constant term is positive and the coefficient of the middle term is negative, we look for a factorization of 25 in which both factors are negative. Their sum must be -10.

Pairs of Factors of 25	Sums of Factors
$-25, -1$	-26
$-5, -5$	-10 ← The numbers we need are -5 and -5.

The factorization of $x^2 - 10x + 25$ is $(x - 5)(x - 5)$, or $(x - 5)^2$. The factorization of the original polynomial also includes the factor $-2x$.

> **CAUTION!** When factoring involves more than one step, be careful to write out the *entire* factorization.

Check: $-2x(x - 5)(x - 5) = -2x[x^2 - 10x + 25]$ Multiplying binomials
$$= -2x^3 + 20x^2 - 50x.$$ Using the distributive law

The factorization of $-2x^3 + 20x^2 - 50x$ is $-2x(x - 5)(x - 5)$, or $-2x(x - 5)^2$.

YOUR TURN

Once any common factors have been factored out, the following summary can be used to factor $x^2 + bx + c$.

> **TO FACTOR $x^2 + bx + c$**
>
> 1. Find a pair of factors that have c as their product and b as their sum.
>   a) When c is positive, both factors will have the same sign as b.
>   b) When c is negative, one factor will be positive and the other will be negative. Select the factors such that the factor with the larger absolute value has the same sign as b.
> 2. Check by multiplying.

Note that each polynomial has a unique factorization (except for the order in which the factors are written).

Student Notes

Whenever a new set of parentheses is created while factoring, check the expression inside the parentheses to see if it can be factored further.

---

7. Factor: $3x^3 + 30x^2 + 27x$.

  Chapter Resource:
Collaborative Activity (Visualizing Factoring), p. 365

5.2 EXERCISE SET

FOR EXTRA HELP

MyMathLab® *MathXL*

PRACTICE WATCH READ REVIEW

Vocabulary and Reading Check

Classify each of the following statements as either true or false.

1. Whenever the product of a pair of factors is negative, the factors have the same sign.

2. Anytime the sum of a negative number and a positive number is negative, the negative number has the greater absolute value.

3. When factoring any polynomial, it is always best to look first for a common factor.

4. When we factor a trinomial such as $x^2 + 6x + 5$, we try to write it as the product of two binomials.

Concept Reinforcement

For Exercises 5–10, assume that $x^2 + bx + c$ can be factored as $(x + p)(x + q)$. Complete each sentence by replacing each blank with either "positive" or "negative."

5. If b is positive and c is positive, then p will be _____ and q will be _____.

6. If b is negative and c is positive, then p will be _____ and q will be _____.

7. If p is negative and q is negative, then b must be _____ and c must be _____.

8. If p is positive and q is positive, then b must be _____ and c must be _____.

9. If b, c, and p are all negative, then q must be _____.

10. If b and c are negative and p is positive, then q must be _____.

Factoring $x^2 + bx + c$

Factor completely. Remember to look first for a common factor. Check by multiplying. If a polynomial is prime, state this.

11. $x^2 + 8x + 16$

12. $x^2 + 9x + 20$

13. $x^2 + 11x + 10$

14. $y^2 + 8y + 7$

15. $t^2 - 9t + 14$

16. $a^2 - 9a + 20$

17. $b^2 - 5b + 4$

18. $z^2 - 8z + 7$

19. $d^2 - 7d + 10$

20. $x^2 - 8x + 15$

21. $x^2 - 2x - 15$

22. $x^2 - x - 42$

23. $x^2 + 2x - 15$

24. $x^2 + x - 42$

25. $2x^2 - 14x - 36$

26. $3y^2 - 9y - 84$

27. $-x^3 + 6x^2 + 16x$

28. $-x^3 + x^2 + 42x$

29. $4y - 45 + y^2$

30. $7x - 60 + x^2$

31. $x^2 - 72 + 6x$

32. $-2x - 99 + x^2$

33. $-5b^2 - 35b + 150$

34. $-c^4 - c^3 + 56c^2$

35. $x^5 - x^4 - 2x^3$

36. $2a^2 - 4a - 70$

37. $x^2 + 5x + 10$

38. $x^2 + 11x + 18$

39. $32 + 12t + t^2$

40. $y^2 - y + 1$

41. $x^2 + 20x + 99$

42. $x^2 + 20x + 100$

43. $3x^3 - 63x^2 - 300x$

44. $2x^3 - 40x^2 + 192x$

45. $-4x^2 - 40x - 100$

46. $-2x^2 + 42x + 144$

47. $y^2 - 20y + 96$

48. $144 - 25t + t^2$

49. $-a^6 - 9a^5 + 90a^4$

50. $-a^4 - a^3 + 132a^2$

51. $t^2 + \frac{2}{3}t + \frac{1}{9}$

52. $x^2 - \frac{2}{5}x + \frac{1}{25}$

53. $11 + w^2 - 4w$

54. $6 + p^2 + 2p$

55. $p^2 - 7pq + 10q^2$

56. $a^2 - 2ab - 3b^2$

57. $m^2 + 5mn + 5n^2$

58. $x^2 - 11xy + 24y^2$

59. $s^2 - 4st - 12t^2$

60. $b^2 + 8bc - 20c^2$

61. $6a^{10} + 30a^9 - 84a^8$

62. $5a^8 - 20a^7 - 25a^6$

63. Without multiplying $(x - 17)(x - 18)$, explain why it cannot possibly be a factorization of $x^2 + 35x + 306$.

64. Shari factors $x^3 - 8x^2 + 15x$ as $(x^2 - 5x)(x - 3)$. Is she wrong? Why or why not? What advice would you offer?

Skill Review

Solve.

65. $\frac{y}{2} = -5$ [2.1]

66. $x - 0.05 = 1.08$ [2.1]

67. $3x + 7 = 12$ [2.2]

68. $9 - 5x = 4 - 3x$ [2.2]

69. $x - (2x - 5) = 16$ [2.2]

70. $\frac{1}{3}x - \frac{1}{6} = \frac{1}{2}$ [2.2]

Synthesis

71. When searching for a factorization, why do we list pairs of numbers with the correct *product* instead of pairs of numbers with the correct *sum*?

72. When factoring $x^2 + bx + c$ with a large value of c, Riley begins by writing out the prime factorization of c. What is the advantage of doing this?

73. Find all integers b for which $a^2 + ba - 50$ can be factored.

74. Find all integers m for which $y^2 + my + 50$ can be factored.

Factor completely.

75. $y^2 - 0.2y - 0.08$

76. $x^2 + \frac{1}{2}x - \frac{3}{16}$

77. $-\frac{1}{3}a^3 + \frac{1}{3}a^2 + 2a$

78. $-a^7 + \frac{25}{7}a^5 + \frac{30}{7}a^6$

79. $x^{2m} + 11x^m + 28$

80. $-t^{2n} + 7t^n - 10$

Aha! **81.** $(a + 1)x^2 + (a + 1)3x + (a + 1)2$

82. $ax^2 - 5x^2 + 8ax - 40x - (a - 5)9$
(*Hint*: See Exercise 81.)

83. Find the volume of a cube if its surface area is $(6x^2 + 36x + 54)$ square meters.

Find a polynomial in factored form for the shaded area in each figure. (Use π in your answers where appropriate.)

84.

85.

86.

87.

88.

89.

90. A census taker asks a woman, "How many children do you have?"

"Three," she answers.

"What are their ages?"

She responds, "The product of their ages is 36. The sum of their ages is the house number next door."

The math-savvy census taker walks next door, reads the house number, appears puzzled, and returns to the woman, asking, "Is there something you forgot to tell me?"

"Oh yes," says the woman. "I'm sorry. The oldest child is playing a video game."

The census taker records the three ages, thanks the woman for her time, and leaves.

How old is each child? Explain how you reached this conclusion. (*Hint*: Consider factorizations.)

YOUR TURN ANSWERS: SECTION 5.2

1. $(x + 2)(x + 4)$ **2.** $(a - 3)(a - 5)$ **3.** $(t + 3)(t - 5)$
4. $(t + 7)(t - 4)$ **5.** $(x - 6y)(x + 3y)$ **6.** Not factorable, or prime   **7.** $3x(x + 9)(x + 1)$

QUICK QUIZ: SECTIONS 5.1–5.2

Factor.

1. $12x^4 - 30x^3 + 6x^2$ [5.1]

2. $3x^3 - 12x^2 + 5x - 20$ [5.1]

3. $x^2 - 3x + 2$ [5.2]

4. $a^2 + 2ab - 8b^2$ [5.2]

5. $3x^2 + 15x + 18$ [5.2]

PREPARE TO MOVE ON

Multiply.   [4.6]

1. $(2x + 3)(3x + 4)$ 2. $(2x + 3)(3x - 4)$

3. $(2x - 3)(3x + 4)$ 4. $(2x - 3)(3x - 4)$

5. $(5x - 1)(x - 7)$ 6. $(x + 6)(3x - 5)$

5.3 Factoring Trinomials of the Type $ax^2 + bx + c$

Factoring with FOIL ● The Grouping Method

In this section, we learn to factor trinomials in which the leading, or x^2, coefficient is not 1. First, we will use another FOIL-based method and then we will use an alternative method that involves factoring by grouping. Use the method that you prefer or the one recommended by your instructor.

Factoring with FOIL

Before factoring trinomials of the type $ax^2 + bx + c$, consider the following:

$$\begin{array}{ccccc} \text{F} & \text{O} & \text{I} & \text{L} & \\ (2x + 5)(3x + 4) = 6x^2 & + & 8x & + & 15x + 20 \\ & = 6x^2 & + & 23x & + 20. \end{array}$$

To factor $6x^2 + 23x + 20$, we could reverse the multiplication and look for two binomials whose product is this trinomial. We see from above that:

- the product of the First terms must be $6x^2$;
- the product of the Outer terms plus the product of the Inner terms must be $23x$; and
- the product of the Last terms must be 20.

How can such a factorization be found without first seeing the corresponding multiplication? Our first approach relies on trial and error and FOIL.

Study Skills

Read the Instructions First

Take the time to carefully read the instructions before beginning an exercise or a series of exercises. Not only will this give you direction in your work, it may also help you in your problem solving. For example, you may be asked to supply more than one answer, or you may be told that answers may vary.

TO FACTOR $ax^2 + bx + c$ USING FOIL

1. Make certain that all common factors have been removed. If any remain, factor out the largest common factor.
2. Find two First terms whose product is ax^2:

   $$(\blacksquare x + \quad)(\blacksquare x + \quad) = ax^2 + bx + c.$$
   FOIL

3. Find two Last terms whose product is c:

   $$(\blacksquare x + \blacksquare)(\blacksquare x + \blacksquare) = ax^2 + bx + c.$$
   FOIL

4. Check by multiplying to see if the sum of the Outer and Inner products is bx. If it is not, repeat steps (2) and (3) until the correct combination is found.

   $$(\blacksquare x + \blacksquare)(\blacksquare x + \blacksquare) = ax^2 + bx + c.$$
   I
   O
   FOIL

If no correct combination exists, state that the polynomial is prime.

EXAMPLE 1   Factor: $3x^2 - 10x - 8$.

SOLUTION

1. First, check for a common factor. In this case, there is none (other than 1 or -1).

2. Find two **First** terms whose product is $3x^2$. The only possibilities for the **First** terms are $3x$ and x:

   $(3x +\ \ )(x +\ \ )$.

3. Find two **Last** terms whose product is -8. There are four pairs of factors of -8 and each can be listed in two ways:

$$
\begin{array}{cc}
-1, \ \ 8 & \quad 8, -1 \\
1, -8 & \quad -8, \ \ 1 \\
-2, \ \ 4 & \quad 4, -2 \\
2, -4 & \quad -4, \ \ 2.
\end{array}
$$

   and

   Important! Since the First terms are not identical, changing the order of the factors of -8 in the binomial factors results in a different product.

4. Knowing that all **First** and **Last** products will check, systematically inspect the **O**uter and **I**nner products resulting from steps (2) and (3). Look for the combination in which the sum of the products is the middle term, $-10x$.

Pair of Factors	*Corresponding Trial*	*Product*	
$-1, \ \ 8$	$(3x - 1)(x + 8)$	$3x^2 + 24x - x - 8$	
		$= 3x^2 + 23x - 8$	Wrong middle term
$1, -8$	$(3x + 1)(x - 8)$	$3x^2 - 24x + x - 8$	
		$= 3x^2 - 23x - 8$	Wrong middle term
$-2, \ \ 4$	$(3x - 2)(x + 4)$	$3x^2 + 12x - 2x - 8$	
		$= 3x^2 + 10x - 8$	Wrong middle term
$2, -4$	$(3x + 2)(x - 4)$	$3x^2 - 12x + 2x - 8$	
		$= 3x^2 - 10x - 8$	Correct middle term!—
$8, -1$	$(3x + 8)(x - 1)$	$3x^2 - 3x + 8x - 8$	
		$= 3x^2 + 5x - 8$	Wrong middle term
$-8, \ \ 1$	$(3x - 8)(x + 1)$	$3x^2 + 3x - 8x - 8$	
		$= 3x^2 - 5x - 8$	Wrong middle term
$4, -2$	$(3x + 4)(x - 2)$	$3x^2 - 6x + 4x - 8$	
		$= 3x^2 - 2x - 8$	Wrong middle term
$-4, \ \ 2$	$(3x - 4)(x + 2)$	$3x^2 + 6x - 4x - 8$	
		$= 3x^2 + 2x - 8$	Wrong middle term

1. Factor: $3x^2 - 13x - 10$.

The correct factorization is $(3x + 2)(x - 4)$.   ←

YOUR TURN

Two observations can be made from Example 1. First, we listed all possible trials even though we generally stop after finding the correct factorization. We did this to show that **each trial differs only in the middle term of the product**. Second, note that **only the sign of the middle term changes when the signs in the binomials are reversed**.

A GEOMETRIC APPROACH TO **EXAMPLE 2**

The factoring of $10x^2 + 37x + 7$ can be regarded as a search for r and s so that the sum of areas A, B, C, and D is $10x^2 + 37x + 7$.

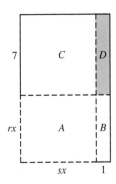

Because A must be $10x^2$, the product rs must be 10. Only when r is 2 and s is 5 will the sum of areas B and C be $37x$ (see below).

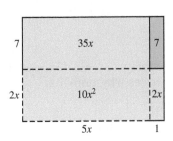

EXAMPLE 2   Factor: $10x^2 + 37x + 7$.

SOLUTION

1. There is no factor (other than 1 or −1) common to all three terms.

2. Because $10x^2$ factors as $10x \cdot x$ or $5x \cdot 2x$, we have two possibilities:

$$(10x +)(x +) \quad \text{or} \quad (5x +)(2x +).$$

3. There are two pairs of factors of 7 and each can be listed in two ways:

$$\begin{matrix} 1, & 7 \\ -1, & -7 \end{matrix} \quad \text{and} \quad \begin{matrix} 7, & 1 \\ -7, & -1 \end{matrix}.$$

4. Look for **O**uter and **I**nner products for which the sum is the middle term. Because all coefficients in $10x^2 + 37x + 7$ are positive, we need consider only those combinations involving positive factors of 7.

Trial	*Product*	
$(10x + 1)(x + 7)$	$10x^2 + 70x + 1x + 7$	
	$= 10x^2 + 71x + 7$	Wrong middle term
$(10x + 7)(x + 1)$	$10x^2 + 10x + 7x + 7$	
	$= 10x^2 + 17x + 7$	Wrong middle term
$(5x + 7)(2x + 1)$	$10x^2 + 5x + 14x + 7$	
	$= 10x^2 + 19x + 7$	Wrong middle term
$(5x + 1)(2x + 7)$	$10x^2 + 35x + 2x + 7$	
	$= 10x^2 + 37x + 7$	Correct middle term!

The correct factorization is $(5x + 1)(2x + 7)$.

2. Factor: $14x^2 + 13x + 3$.

 YOUR TURN

EXAMPLE 3   Factor: $24x^3 - 76x^2 + 40x$.

SOLUTION

1. First, we factor out the largest common factor, $4x$:

$$4x(6x^2 - 19x + 10).$$

2. Next, we factor $6x^2 - 19x + 10$. Since $6x^2$ can be factored as $3x \cdot 2x$ or $6x \cdot x$, we have two possibilities:

$$(3x +)(2x +) \quad \text{or} \quad (6x +)(x +).$$

3. The constant term, 10, can be factored as $1 \cdot 10, 2 \cdot 5, (-1)(-10)$, and $(-2)(-5)$. Since the middle term is negative, we need consider only the factorizations with negative factors:

$$\begin{matrix} -1, & -10 \\ & \text{and} \\ -2, & -5 \end{matrix} \qquad \begin{matrix} -10, & -1 \\ \\ -5, & -2. \end{matrix}$$

4. The two possibilities from step (2) and the four possibilities from step (3) give $2 \cdot 4$, or 8, possible factorizations to consider.

We first try these factors with $(3x + \quad)(2x + \quad)$, looking for **O**uter and **I**nner products for which the sum is $-19x$. If none gives the correct factorization, then we will consider $(6x + \quad)(x + \quad)$.

Trial	*Product*	
$(3x - 1)(2x - 10)$	$6x^2 - 30x - 2x + 10$	
	$= 6x^2 - 32x + 10$	Wrong middle term
$(3x - 10)(2x - 1)$	$6x^2 - 3x - 20x + 10$	
	$= 6x^2 - 23x + 10$	Wrong middle term
$(3x - 2)(2x - 5)$	$6x^2 - 15x - 4x + 10$	
	$= 6x^2 - 19x + 10$	Correct middle term!
$(3x - 5)(2x - 2)$	$6x^2 - 6x - 10x + 10$	
	$= 6x^2 - 16x + 10$	Wrong middle term

The factorization of $6x^2 - 19x + 10$ is $(3x - 2)(2x - 5)$, but do not forget the common factor! The factorization of $24x^3 - 76x^2 + 40x$ is

$$4x(3x - 2)(2x - 5).$$

3. Factor: $12n^4 + 10n^3 - 12n^2$.

↰ YOUR TURN

Student Notes

Keep your work organized so that you can see what you have already considered. For example, when factoring $6x^2 - 19x + 10$, we can list all possibilities and cross out those in which a common factor appears:

$(3x - 1)(2x - 10)$
$(3x - 10)(2x - 1)$
$(3x - 2)(2x - 5)$
$(3x - 5)(2x - 2)$
$(6x - 1)(x - 10)$
$(6x - 10)(x - 1)$
$(6x - 2)(x - 5)$
$(6x - 5)(x - 2)$

By being organized and not erasing, we can see that there are only four possible factorizations.

In Example 3, look again at the possibility $(3x - 5)(2x - 2)$. Without multiplying, we can reject such a possibility. To see why, note that

$$(3x - 5)(2x - 2) = (3x - 5)2(x - 1).$$

The expression $2x - 2$ has a common factor, 2. But we removed the *largest* common factor in step (1). If $2x - 2$ were one of the factors, then 2 would be *another* common factor in addition to the original, $4x$. Thus, $(2x - 2)$ cannot be part of the factorization of $6x^2 - 19x + 10$. Similar reasoning can be used to reject $(3x - 1)(2x - 10)$ as a possible factorization.

Once the largest common factor is factored out, none of the remaining factors can have a common factor.

TIPS FOR FACTORING $ax^2 + bx + c$

To factor $ax^2 + bx + c \, (a > 0)$:

- Make sure that any common factor has been factored out.
- Once the largest common factor has been factored out of the original trinomial, no binomial factor can contain a common factor (other than 1 or -1).
- If c is positive, then the signs in both binomial factors must match the sign of b.
- Reversing the signs in the binomials reverses the sign of the middle term of their product.
- Organize your work so that you can keep track of which possibilities you have checked.
- Remember to include the largest common factor—if there is one—in the final factorization.
- Check by multiplying.

EXAMPLE 4   Factor: $10x + 8 - 3x^2$.

SOLUTION   An important problem-solving strategy is to find a way to make new problems look like problems we already know how to solve. The factoring tips above apply only to trinomials of the form $ax^2 + bx + c$, with $a > 0$. This leads us to rewrite $10x + 8 - 3x^2$ in descending order:

$$10x + 8 - 3x^2 = -3x^2 + 10x + 8. \qquad \text{Using the commutative law to write descending order}$$

Although $-3x^2 + 10x + 8$ looks similar to the trinomials we have factored, the tips above require a positive leading coefficient. This can be found by factoring out -1:

$$-3x^2 + 10x + 8 = -1(3x^2 - 10x - 8) \qquad \text{Factoring out } -1 \text{ changes the signs of the coefficients.}$$
$$= -1(3x + 2)(x - 4). \qquad \text{Using the result from Example 1}$$

The factorization of $10x + 8 - 3x^2$ is $-1(3x + 2)(x - 4)$.

4. Factor: $9y - 10 - 2y^2$.

YOUR TURN

EXAMPLE 5   Factor: $6r^2 - 13rs - 28s^2$.

SOLUTION   In order for the product of the first terms to be $6r^2$ and the product of the last terms to be $-28s^2$, the binomial factors will be of the form

$$(\blacksquare r + \blacksquare s)(\blacksquare r + \blacksquare s).$$

We verify that no common factor exists and then examine the first term, $6r^2$. There are two possibilities:

$$(2r + \quad)(3r + \quad) \quad \text{or} \quad (6r + \quad)(r + \quad).$$

The last term, $-28s^2$, has the following pairs of factors:

$$
\begin{array}{ccc}
s, -28s & & -28s, \quad s \\
-s, \quad 28s & & 28s, \quad -s \\
2s, -14s & \text{and} & -14s, \quad 2s \\
-2s, \quad 14s & & 14s, -2s \\
4s, \quad -7s & & -7s, \quad 4s \\
-4s, \quad 7s & & 7s, -4s.
\end{array}
$$

Note that listing the pairs of factors of $-28s^2$ is just like listing the pairs of factors of -28, except that each factor also contains a factor of s.

Some trials, like $(2r + 28s)(3r - s)$ and $(2r + 14s)(3r - 2s)$, cannot be correct because both $(2r + 28s)$ and $(2r + 14s)$ contain a common factor, 2. We try $(2r + 7s)(3r - 4s)$:

$$(2r + 7s)(3r - 4s) = 6r^2 - 8rs + 21rs - 28s^2$$
$$= 6r^2 + 13rs - 28s^2.$$

Our trial is incorrect, but only because of the sign of the middle term. To correctly factor $6r^2 - 13rs - 28s^2$, we simply change the signs in the binomials:

$$(2r - 7s)(3r + 4s) = 6r^2 + 8rs - 21rs - 28s^2$$
$$= 6r^2 - 13rs - 28s^2.$$

The correct factorization of $6r^2 - 13rs - 28s^2$ is $(2r - 7s)(3r + 4s)$.

5. Factor: $12x^2 - 8xy - 15y^2$.

YOUR TURN

The Grouping Method

Another method of factoring trinomials of the type $ax^2 + bx + c$ is known as the *grouping method*. The grouping method relies on rewriting $ax^2 + bx + c$ in the form $ax^2 + px + qx + c$ and then factoring by grouping. To develop this method, consider the following*:

$$(2x + 5)(3x + 4) = 2x \cdot 3x + 2x \cdot 4 + 5 \cdot 3x + 5 \cdot 4 \qquad \text{Using FOIL}$$

$$= 2 \cdot 3 \cdot x^2 + 2 \cdot 4x + 5 \cdot 3x + 5 \cdot 4$$

$$= 2 \cdot 3 \cdot x^2 + (2 \cdot 4 + 5 \cdot 3)x + 5 \cdot 4$$

$$\underset{a}{\big\updownarrow} \qquad\qquad \underset{b}{\big\updownarrow} \qquad \underset{c}{\big\updownarrow}$$

$$= 6x^2 \quad + \quad 23x \quad + \quad 20.$$

Note that reversing these steps shows that $6x^2 + 23x + 20$ can be rewritten as $6x^2 + 8x + 15x + 20$ and then factored by grouping. Note that the numbers that add to b (in this case, $2 \cdot 4$ and $5 \cdot 3$) also multiply to ac (in this case, $2 \cdot 3 \cdot 5 \cdot 4$).

TO FACTOR $ax^2 + bx + c$ USING THE GROUPING METHOD

1. Factor out the largest common factor, if one exists.
2. Multiply the leading coefficient a and the constant c.
3. Find a pair of factors of ac whose sum is b.
4. Rewrite the middle term, bx, as a sum or a difference using the factors found in step (3).
5. Factor by grouping.
6. Include any common factor from step (1) and check by multiplying.

EXAMPLE 6   Factor: $3x^2 - 10x - 8$.

SOLUTION

1. First, we note that there is no common factor (other than 1 or -1).
2. We multiply the leading coefficient, 3, and the constant, -8:

   $$3(-8) = -24.$$

3. We next look for a factorization of -24 in which the sum of the factors is the coefficient of the middle term, -10.

Pairs of Factors of -24	Sums of Factors
1, -24	-23
-1, 24	23
2, -12	-10 $\longleftarrow$ $2 + (-12) = -10$
-2, 12	10
3, -8	-5
-3, 8	5
4, -6	-2
-4, 6	2

We normally stop listing pairs of factors once we have found the one we need.

---

*This discussion was inspired by a lecture given by Irene Doo at Austin Community College.

4. Next, we express the middle term as a sum or a difference using the factors found in step (3):

$$-10x = 2x - 12x.$$

5. We now factor by grouping as follows:

$$3x^2 - 10x - 8 = 3x^2 + 2x - 12x - 8$$

Substituting $2x - 12x$ for $-10x$. We could also use $-12x + 2x$.

$$= x(3x + 2) - 4(3x + 2)$$
$$= (3x + 2)(x - 4).$$

Factoring by grouping

6. *Check:* $(3x + 2)(x - 4) = 3x^2 - 12x + 2x - 8 = 3x^2 - 10x - 8.$

The factorization of $3x^2 - 10x - 8$ is $(3x + 2)(x - 4)$.

6. Factor: $2x^2 - 3x - 20$.

YOUR TURN

EXAMPLE 7 Factor: $8x^3 + 22x^2 - 6x$.

SOLUTION

1. We factor out the largest common factor, $2x$:

$$8x^3 + 22x^2 - 6x = 2x(4x^2 + 11x - 3).$$

2. To factor $4x^2 + 11x - 3$ by grouping, we multiply the leading coefficient, 4, and the constant term, -3:

$$4(-3) = -12.$$

3. We next look for factors of -12 that add to 11.

Pairs of Factors of -12	Sums of Factors
1, -12	-11
-1, 12	11 ←
.	.
.	.
.	.

Since $-1 + 12 = 11$, there is no need to list other pairs of factors.

4. We then rewrite the $11x$ in $4x^2 + 11x - 3$ using the results of step (3):

$$11x = -1x + 12x, \quad \text{or} \quad 11x = 12x - 1x.$$

5. Next, we factor by grouping:

$$4x^2 + 11x - 3 = 4x^2 - 1x + 12x - 3$$

Rewriting the middle term; $12x - 1x$ could also be used.

$$= x(4x - 1) + 3(4x - 1)$$
$$= (4x - 1)(x + 3).$$

Factoring by grouping

6. The factorization of $4x^2 + 11x - 3$ is $(4x - 1)(x + 3)$. But don't forget the common factor, $2x$. The factorization of the original trinomial is

$$2x(4x - 1)(x + 3).$$

7. Factor: $30n^3 + 5n^2 - 60n$.

YOUR TURN

5.3 EXERCISE SET

FOR EXTRA HELP   MyMathLab® Math XL
PRACTICE   WATCH   READ   REVIEW

Vocabulary and Reading Check

Match each polynomial in Exercises 1–4 with the statement that is true when factoring that polynomial.

a) Factor out a common factor first.

b) The only possibilities for the first terms of the binomial factors are $5x$ and x.

c) Both of the constants in the binomial factors must be negative.

d) The polynomial is prime.

1. ____ $11x^2 + 3x + 1$

2. ____ $12x^2 + 18x + 21$

3. ____ $5x^2 - 14x - 3$

4. ____ $2x^2 - 7x + 5$

Factoring Trinomials of the Type $ax^2 + bx + c$

Factor completely. If a polynomial is prime, state this.

5. $2x^2 + 7x - 4$

6. $3x^2 + x - 4$

7. $3x^2 - 17x - 6$

8. $5x^2 - 19x - 4$

9. $4t^2 + 12t + 5$

10. $6t^2 + 17t + 7$

11. $15a^2 - 14a + 3$

12. $10a^2 - 11a + 3$

13. $6x^2 + 17x + 12$

14. $6x^2 + 19x + 10$

15. $6x^2 - 10x - 4$

16. $5t^3 - 21t^2 + 18t$

17. $7t^3 + 15t^2 + 2t$

18. $15t^2 + 20t - 75$

19. $10 - 23x + 12x^2$

20. $-20 + 31x - 12x^2$

21. $-35x^2 - 34x - 8$

22. $28x^2 + 38x - 6$

23. $4 + 6t^2 - 13t$

24. $9 + 8t^2 - 18t$

25. $25x^2 + 40x + 16$

26. $49t^2 + 42t + 9$

27. $20y^2 + 59y - 3$

28. $25a^2 - 23a - 2$

29. $14x^2 + 73x + 45$

30. $35x^2 - 57x - 44$

31. $-2x^2 + 15 + x$

32. $2t^2 - 19 - 6t$

33. $-6x^2 - 33x - 15$

34. $-12x^2 - 28x + 24$

35. $10a^2 - 8a - 18$

36. $20y^2 - 25y + 5$

37. $12x^2 + 68x - 24$

38. $6x^2 + 21x + 15$

39. $4x + 1 + 3x^2$

40. $-9 + 18x^2 + 21x$

Factor. Use factoring by grouping even though it may seem reasonable to first combine like terms.

41. $x^2 + 3x - 2x - 6$

42. $x^2 + 4x - 2x - 8$

43. $8t^2 - 6t - 28t + 21$

44. $35t^2 - 40t + 21t - 24$

45. $6x^2 + 4x + 15x + 10$

46. $3x^2 - 2x + 3x - 2$

47. $2y^2 + 8y - y - 4$

48. $7n^2 + 35n - n - 5$

49. $6a^2 - 8a - 3a + 4$

50. $10a^2 - 4a - 5a + 2$

Factor completely. If a polynomial is prime, state this.

51. $16t^2 + 23t + 7$

52. $9t^2 + 14t + 5$

53. $-9x^2 - 18x - 5$

54. $-16x^2 - 32x - 7$

55. $10x^2 + 30x - 70$

56. $10a^2 + 25a - 15$

57. $18x^3 + 21x^2 - 9x$

58. $6x^3 - 4x^2 - 10x$

59. $89x + 64 + 25x^2$

60. $47 - 42y + 9y^2$

61. $168x^3 + 45x^2 + 3x$

62. $144x^5 - 168x^4 + 48x^3$

63. $-14t^4 + 19t^3 + 3t^2$

64. $-70a^4 + 68a^3 - 16a^2$

65. $132y + 32y^2 - 54$

66. $220y + 60y^2 - 225$

67. $2a^2 - 5ab + 2b^2$

68. $3p^2 - 16pq - 12q^2$

69. $8s^2 + 22st + 14t^2$

70. $10s^2 + 4st - 6t^2$

71. $27x^2 - 72xy + 48y^2$

72. $-30a^2 - 87ab - 30b^2$

73. $-24a^2 + 34ab - 12b^2$

74. $15a^2 - 5ab - 20b^2$

75. $19x^3 - 3x^2 + 14x^4$

76. $10x^5 - 2x^4 + 22x^3$

77. $18a^7 + 8a^6 + 9a^8$

78. $40a^8 + 16a^7 + 25a^9$

79. Asked to factor $2x^2 - 18x + 36$, Juan *incorrectly* answers

$$2x^2 - 18x + 36 = 2(x^2 + 9x + 18)$$
$$= 2(x + 3)(x + 6).$$

If this were a 10-point quiz question, how many points would you take off? Why?

80. Asked to factor $4x^2 + 28x + 48$, Therese *incorrectly* answers

$$4x^2 + 28x + 48 = (2x + 6)(2x + 8)$$
$$= 2(x + 3)(x + 4).$$

If this were a 10-point quiz question, how many points would you take off? Why?

Skill Review

Graph.

81. $2x - 5y = 10$ [3.3]

82. $-5x = 10$ [3.3]

83. $y = \frac{2}{3}x - 1$ [3.6]

84. $y - 2 = -2(x + 4)$ [3.7]

85. $\frac{1}{2}y = 1$ [3.3]

86. $x = -y$ [3.2]

Synthesis

 87. Explain how you would prove to a fellow student that a given trinomial is prime.

88. For the trinomial $ax^2 + bx + c$, suppose that a is the product of three different prime factors and c is the product of another two prime factors. How many possible factorizations (like those in Example 1) exist? Explain your reasoning.

Factor. If a polynomial is prime, state this.

89. $18x^2y^2 - 3xy - 10$

90. $8x^2y^3 + 10xy^2 + 2y$

91. $9a^2b^3 + 25ab^2 + 16$

92. $-9t^{10} - 12t^5 - 4$

93. $16t^{10} - 8t^5 + 1$

94. $9a^2b^2 - 15ab - 2$

95. $-15x^{2m} + 26x^m - 8$

96. $-20x^{2n} - 16x^n - 3$

97. $3a^{6n} - 2a^{3n} - 1$

98. $a^{2n+1} - 2a^{n+1} + a$

99. $7(t - 3)^{2n} + 5(t - 3)^n - 2$

100. $3(a + 1)^{n+1}(a + 3)^2 - 5(a + 1)^n(a + 3)^3$

101. Kara bought a number of sections of decorative fencing, all of equal length, to fence in a rectangular 1500-ft^2 yard. For each of the shorter sides of the rectangle, she used 4 sections plus 2 ft cut from another section. For each of the longer sides, she used 7 sections plus 1 ft cut from another section. How long was each section of fencing?

> **YOUR TURN ANSWERS: SECTION 5.3**
> **1.** $(3x + 2)(x - 5)$ **2.** $(2x + 1)(7x + 3)$
> **3.** $2n^2(2n + 3)(3n - 2)$ **4.** $-1(2y - 5)(y - 2)$
> **5.** $(2x - 3y)(6x + 5y)$ **6.** $(2x + 5)(x - 4)$
> **7.** $5n(2n + 3)(3n - 4)$

QUICK QUIZ: SECTIONS 5.1–5.3

Factor completely. If a polynomial is prime, state this.

1. $6a^2b^3 - 9ab^4 + 15a^3b^5$ [5.1]

2. $x^3 - 7x^2 + 12x$ [5.2]

3. $p^2 + p - 7$ [5.2]

4. $4a^2 + 16a + 15$ [5.3]

5. $6x^2 - x - 5$ [5.3]

PREPARE TO MOVE ON

Multiply.   [4.6]

1. $(x - 2)^2$ 2. $(x + 2)^2$

3. $(x + 2)(x - 2)$ 4. $(5t - 3)^2$

5. $(4a + 1)^2$ 6. $(2n + 7)(2n - 7)$

5.4 Factoring Perfect-Square Trinomials and Differences of Squares

Recognizing Perfect-Square Trinomials ▪ Factoring Perfect-Square Trinomials ▪ Recognizing Differences of Squares ▪ Factoring Differences of Squares ▪ Factoring Completely

Reversing the rules for special products provides us with shortcuts for factoring certain polynomials.

Recognizing Perfect-Square Trinomials

Some trinomials are squares of binomials. For example, $x^2 + 10x + 25$ is the square of the binomial $x + 5$, because

$$(x + 5)^2 = x^2 + 2 \cdot x \cdot 5 + 5^2 = x^2 + 10x + 25.$$

A trinomial that is the square of a binomial is called a **perfect-square trinomial**.

We can square binomials using the following special-product rule:

$$(A + B)^2 = A^2 + 2AB + B^2;$$
$$(A - B)^2 = A^2 - 2AB + B^2.$$

Reading the right-hand sides first, we can use these equations to factor perfect-square trinomials. In order for a trinomial to be the square of a binomial, it must have the following:

1. Two expressions, A^2 and B^2, must be squares, such as

   $4, \quad x^2, \quad 81m^2, \quad 16t^2.$

2. Neither A^2 nor B^2 is being subtracted.

3. The remaining term is either $2 \cdot A \cdot B$ or $-2 \cdot A \cdot B$, where A and B are the **square roots** of A^2 and B^2.

Because $3^2 = 9$, we say that 3 is the *square root* of 9. Also, 2 is the square root of 4, 4 is the square root of 16, and so on.

Note that in order for an expression to be a square, its coefficient must be a perfect square and the power(s) of the variable(s) must be even.

EXAMPLE 1 Determine whether each of the following is a perfect-square trinomial.

a) $x^2 + 6x + 9$ **b)** $t^2 - 8t - 9$ **c)** $16x^2 + 49 - 56x$

SOLUTION

a) **1.** Two expressions, x^2 and 9, are squares.

   2. Neither x^2 nor 9 is being subtracted.

   3. The remaining term, $6x$, is $2 \cdot x \cdot 3$, where x and 3 are the square roots of x^2 and 9.

   Thus, $x^2 + 6x + 9$ *is* a perfect-square trinomial.

b) Both t^2 and 9 are squares. However, since 9 is being subtracted, $t^2 - 8t - 9$ *is not* a perfect-square trinomial.

c) To see if $16x^2 + 49 - 56x$ is a perfect-square trinomial, it helps to first write it in descending order:

   $16x^2 - 56x + 49.$

Student Notes

If you're not already quick to recognize the squares that represent $1^2, 2^2, 3^2, \ldots, 12^2$, this would be a good time to memorize these numbers.

Study Skills

Fill in Your Blanks

Don't hesitate to write out any missing steps that you'd like to see included. For instance, in Example 1(c), we state (in red) that $16x^2$ is a square. To solidify your understanding, you may want to write $4x \cdot 4x = 16x^2$ in the margin of your text.

Next, note that:

1. Two expressions, $16x^2$ and 49, are squares.

2. Neither $16x^2$ nor 49 is being subtracted.

3. Twice the product of the square roots, $2 \cdot 4x \cdot 7$, is $56x$. The remaining term, $-56x$, is the opposite of this product.

Thus, $16x^2 + 49 - 56x$ *is* a perfect-square trinomial.

1. Determine whether $100 - 20x + x^2$ is a perfect-square trinomial.

YOUR TURN

Factoring Perfect-Square Trinomials

To factor perfect-square trinomials, we recognize the following patterns.

> **FACTORING A PERFECT-SQUARE TRINOMIAL**
> $$A^2 + 2AB + B^2 = (A + B)^2;$$
> $$A^2 - 2AB + B^2 = (A - B)^2$$

Each factorization uses the square roots of the squared terms and the sign of the remaining term. To verify these equations, you should compute $(A + B)(A + B)$ and $(A - B)(A - B)$.

EXAMPLE 2   Factor.

a) $x^2 + 6x + 9$ **b)** $t^2 + 49 - 14t$ **c)** $100x^2 - 180x + 81$

SOLUTION

a) $x^2 + 6x + 9 = x^2 + 2 \cdot x \cdot 3 + 3^2 = (x + 3)^2$ The sign of the middle term is positive.

$$\underset{A^2\ +\ 2\ \ A\ \ B\ +\ B^2}{} = \underset{(A\ +\ B)^2}{}$$

b) $t^2 + 49 - 14t = t^2 - 14t + 49$ Using a commutative law to write in descending order

$$= t^2 - 2 \cdot t \cdot 7 + 7^2 = (t - 7)^2$$
$$\underset{A^2\ -\ 2\ \ A\ \ B\ +\ B^2}{} = \underset{(A\ -\ B)^2}{}$$

2. Factor: $x^2 + 2x + 1$.

c) $100x^2 - 180x + 81 = (10x)^2 - 2 \cdot 10x \cdot 9 + 9^2 = (10x - 9)^2$ Recall that $(10x)^2 = 100x^2$.

$$\underset{A^2\ \ -\ 2\ \ A\ \ \ B\ +\ B^2}{} = \underset{(A\ -\ B)^2}{}$$

The checks are left to the student.

YOUR TURN

Polynomials in more than one variable can also be perfect-square trinomials.

EXAMPLE 3   Factor: $4p^2 - 12pt + 9t^2$.

SOLUTION   We have

$$4p^2 - 12pt + 9t^2 = (2p)^2 - 2(2p)(3t) + (3t)^2 \quad 4p^2 \text{ and } 9t^2 \text{ are squares.}$$
$$= (2p - 3t)^2. \quad \text{The sign of the middle term is negative.}$$

Check: $(2p - 3t)(2p - 3t) = 4p^2 - 12pt + 9t^2.$

3. Factor: $100a^2 + 20ab + b^2$.

The factorization is $(2p - 3t)^2$.

YOUR TURN

EXAMPLE 4 Factor: $-75m^3 - 60m^2 - 12m$.

SOLUTION *Always* look first for a common factor. This time there is one. We factor out $-3m$ so that the leading coefficient of the polynomial inside the parentheses is positive:

Factor out the common factor.

Factor the perfect-square trinomial.

$$-75m^3 - 60m^2 - 12m = -3m[25m^2 + 20m + 4] \qquad 25m^2 = (5m)^2$$
$$= -3m[(5m)^2 + 2(5m)(2) + 2^2]$$
$$= -3m(5m + 2)^2.$$

Check: $-3m(5m + 2)^2 = -3m(5m + 2)(5m + 2)$
$$= -3m(25m^2 + 20m + 4)$$
$$= -75m^3 - 60m^2 - 12m.$$

4. Factor: $-4n^3 + 12n^2 - 9n$.

The factorization is $-3m(5m + 2)^2$.

YOUR TURN

Recognizing Differences of Squares

Any expression that can be written in the form $A^2 - B^2$, like $x^2 - 9$, is called a **difference of squares**. In order for a binomial to be a difference of squares, it must have the following.

1. There must be two expressions, both squares, such as

$$25, \quad t^2, \quad 4x^2, \quad 1, \quad x^6, \quad 49y^8, \quad 100x^2y^2.$$

2. The terms in the binomial must have different signs.

EXAMPLE 5 Determine whether each of the following is a difference of squares.
a) $9x^2 - 64$ **b)** $25 - t^3$ **c)** $-4x^{10} + 36$

SOLUTION

a) **1.** The first expression is a square: $9x^2 = (3x)^2$.
The second expression is a square: $64 = 8^2$.

  2. The terms have different signs.

Thus, $9x^2 - 64$ is a difference of squares, $(3x)^2 - 8^2$.

b) **1.** The expression t^3 is not a square.

Thus, $25 - t^3$ is not a difference of squares.

c) **1.** The expressions $4x^{10}$ and 36 are squares: $4x^{10} = (2x^5)^2$ and $36 = 6^2$.

  2. The terms have different signs.

5. Determine whether $-x^2 + 49$ is a difference of squares.

Thus, $-4x^{10} + 36$ is a difference of squares, $6^2 - (2x^5)^2$. It is helpful to rewrite $-4x^{10} + 36$ in the equivalent form $36 - 4x^{10}$ before factoring.

YOUR TURN

Factoring Differences of Squares

To factor a difference of squares, we reverse the special product

$$(A + B)(A - B) = A^2 - AB + AB - B^2 = A^2 - B^2.$$

FACTORING A DIFFERENCE OF SQUARES

$$A^2 - B^2 = (A + B)(A - B)$$

Once we have identified the expressions that are playing the roles of A and B, the factorization can be written directly.

EXAMPLE 6 Factor: **(a)** $x^2 - 4$; **(b)** $1 - 9p^2$; **(c)** $s^6 - 16t^{10}$; **(d)** $50x^2 - 8x^8$.

SOLUTION

a) $x^2 - 4 = x^2 - 2^2 = (x + 2)(x - 2)$

$$A^2 - B^2 = (A + B)(A - B)$$

b) $1 - 9p^2 = 1^2 - (3p)^2 = (1 + 3p)(1 - 3p)$

$$A^2 - B^2 = (A + B)(A - B)$$

c) $s^6 - 16t^{10} = (s^3)^2 - (4t^5)^2$ Using the rules for powers

$$A^2 - B^2$$

$$= (s^3 + 4t^5)(s^3 - 4t^5)$$ Try to go directly to this step.

$$(A + B)(A - B)$$

d) *Always* look first for a common factor. This time there is one, $2x^2$:

Factor out the common factor.

$$50x^2 - 8x^8 = 2x^2(25 - 4x^6)$$

$$= 2x^2[5^2 - (2x^3)^2]$$ Recognizing $A^2 - B^2$.
Try to do this mentally.

Factor the difference of squares.

$$= 2x^2(5 + 2x^3)(5 - 2x^3).$$

Check: $2x^2(5 + 2x^3)(5 - 2x^3) = 2x^2(25 - 4x^6)$
$$= 50x^2 - 8x^8.$$

The factorization of $50x^2 - 8x^8$ is $2x^2(5 + 2x^3)(5 - 2x^3)$.

6. Factor: $a^4 - 9b^2$.

 YOUR TURN

> **CAUTION!** A difference of squares is *not* the square of the difference; that is,
>
> $$A^2 - B^2 \neq (A - B)^2.$$ To see this, note that
> $$(A - B)^2 = A^2 - 2AB + B^2.$$

Factoring Completely

Sometimes, as in Examples 4 and 6(d), a *complete* factorization requires two or more steps. Factoring is complete only when no factor can be factored further.

EXAMPLE 7 Factor: $y^4 - 16$.

SOLUTION   We have

Factor a difference of squares.

$$y^4 - 16 = (y^2)^2 - 4^2$$ Recognizing $A^2 - B^2$

$$= (y^2 + 4)(y^2 - 4)$$ Note that $y^2 - 4$ is not prime.

Factor another difference of squares.

$$= (y^2 + 4)(y + 2)(y - 2).$$ Note that $y^2 - 4$ is itself a difference of squares.

Check: $(y^2 + 4)(y + 2)(y - 2) = (y^2 + 4)(y^2 - 4)$
$$= y^4 - 16.$$

7. Factor: $t^4 - 81$.

The factorization is $(y^2 + 4)(y + 2)(y - 2)$.

YOUR TURN

Note in Example 7 that the factor $y^2 + 4$ is a *sum* of squares that cannot be factored further.

CAUTION!   There is no general formula for factoring a sum of squares. In particular,

$$A^2 + B^2 \neq (A + B)^2 \quad \text{and} \quad A^2 + B^2 \neq (A + B)(A - B).$$

As you proceed through the exercises, these suggestions may prove helpful.

TIPS FOR FACTORING

1. *Always* look first for a common factor! If there is one, factor it out.
2. Be alert for perfect-square trinomials and for binomials that are differences of squares. Once recognized, they can be factored without trial and error.
3. Always factor completely.
4. Check by multiplying.

5.4   EXERCISE SET

FOR EXTRA HELP

MyMathLab® Math XL
PRACTICE   WATCH   READ   REVIEW

Vocabulary and Reading Check

Identify each of the following as a perfect-square trinomial, a difference of squares, a prime polynomial, or none of these.

1. $4x^2 + 49$
2. $x^2 - 64$
3. $t^2 - 100$
4. $x^2 - 5x + 4$
5. $9x^2 + 6x + 1$
6. $a^2 - 8a + 16$
7. $2t^2 + 10t + 6$
8. $-25x^2 - 9$
9. $16t^2 - 25$
10. $4r^2 + 20r + 25$

Recognizing Perfect-Square Trinomials

Determine whether each of the following is a perfect-square trinomial.

11. $x^2 + 18x + 81$
12. $x^2 - 16x + 64$
13. $x^2 - 10x - 25$
14. $x^2 - 14x - 49$
15. $x^2 - 3x + 9$
16. $x^2 + 4x + 4$
17. $9x^2 + 25 - 30x$
18. $36x^2 + 16 - 24x$

Factoring Perfect-Square Trinomials

Factor completely. Remember to look first for a common factor and to check by multiplying. If a polynomial is prime, state this.

19. $x^2 + 16x + 64$
20. $x^2 + 10x + 25$
21. $x^2 - 10x + 25$
22. $x^2 - 16x + 64$
23. $5p^2 + 20p + 20$
24. $3p^2 - 12p + 12$
25. $1 - 2t + t^2$
26. $1 + t^2 + 2t$
27. $18x^2 + 12x + 2$
28. $25x^2 + 10x + 1$
29. $49 - 56y + 16y^2$
30. $75 - 60m + 12m^2$
31. $-x^5 + 18x^4 - 81x^3$
32. $-2x^2 + 40x - 200$
33. $2n^3 + 40n^2 + 200n$
34. $x^3 + 24x^2 + 144x$
35. $20x^2 + 100x + 125$
36. $27m^2 - 36m + 12$
37. $49 - 42x + 9x^2$
38. $64 - 112x + 49x^2$
39. $16x^2 + 24x + 9$
40. $2a^2 + 28a + 98$
41. $2 + 20x + 50x^2$
42. $9x^2 + 30x + 25$

43. $9p^2 + 12px + 4x^2$

44. $x^2 - 3xy + 9y^2$

45. $a^2 - 12ab + 49b^2$

46. $25m^2 - 20mn + 4n^2$

47. $-64m^2 - 16mn - n^2$

48. $-81p^2 + 18pw - w^2$

49. $-32s^2 + 80st - 50t^2$

50. $-36a^2 - 96ab - 64b^2$

Recognizing Differences of Squares

Determine whether each of the following is a difference of squares.

51. $x^2 - 100$

52. $x^2 + 49$

53. $n^4 + 1$

54. $n^4 - 81$

55. $-1 + 64t^2$

56. $-12 + 25t^2$

Factoring Differences of Squares

Factor completely. Remember to look first for a common factor. If a polynomial is prime, state this.

57. $x^2 - 25$

58. $x^2 - 36$

59. $p^2 - 9$

60. $q^2 + 1$

61. $-49 + t^2$

62. $-64 + m^2$

63. $6a^2 - 24$

64. $x^2 - 8x + 16$

65. $49x^2 - 14x + 1$

66. $3t^2 - 3$

67. $200 - 2t^2$

68. $98 - 8w^2$

69. $-80a^2 + 45$

70. $25x^2 - 4$

71. $5t^2 - 80$

72. $-4t^2 + 64$

73. $8x^2 - 162$

74. $24x^2 - 54$

75. $36x - 49x^3$

76. $16x - 81x^3$

77. $49a^4 - 20$

78. $25a^4 - 9$

Factoring Completely

Factor completely.

79. $t^4 - 1$

80. $x^4 - 16$

81. $-3x^3 + 24x^2 - 48x$

82. $-2a^4 + 36a^3 - 162a^2$

83. $75t^3 - 27t$

84. $80s^4 - 45s^2$

85. $a^8 - 2a^7 + a^6$

86. $x^8 - 8x^7 + 16x^6$

87. $10a^2 - 10b^2$

88. $6p^2 - 6q^2$

89. $16x^4 - y^4$

90. $98x^2 - 32y^2$

91. $18t^2 - 8s^2$

92. $a^4 - 81b^4$

 93. Explain in your own words how to determine whether a polynomial is a perfect-square trinomial.

 94. Explain in your own words how to determine whether a polynomial is a difference of squares.

Skill Review

Perform the indicated operation.

95. $(2x^3 - x + 3) + (x^2 + x - 5)$ [4.4]

96. $(3t^2 - 2t - 5) - (t^2 - 8t + 6)$ [4.4]

97. $(2x^2 + y)(3x^2 - y)$ [4.7]

98. $-5x(-x^2 + 3x - 7)$ [4.5]

99. $(21x^3 - 3x^2 + 9x) \div (3x)$ [4.8]

100. $(x^2 - x - 10) \div (x - 5)$ [4.8]

Synthesis

101. Leon concludes that since $x^2 - 9 = (x - 3)(x + 3)$, it must follow that $x^2 + 9 = (x + 3)(x - 3)$. What mistake(s) is he making?

102. Write directions that would enable someone to construct a polynomial that contains a perfect-square trinomial, a difference of squares, and a common factor.

Factor completely. If a polynomial is prime, state this.

103. $x^8 - 2^8$

104. $3x^2 - \frac{1}{3}$

105. $18x^3 - \frac{8}{25}x$

106. $0.81t - t^3$

107. $(y - 5)^4 - z^8$

108. $x^2 - \left(\dfrac{1}{x}\right)^2$

109. $-x^4 + 8x^2 + 9$

110. $-16x^4 + 96x^2 - 144$

Aha! **111.** $(y + 3)^2 + 2(y + 3) + 1$

112. $49(x + 1)^2 - 42(x + 1) + 9$

113. $27p^3 - 45p^2 - 75p + 125$

114. $a^{2n} - 49b^{2n}$

115. $81 - b^{4k}$

116. $9b^{2n} + 12b^n + 4$

117. Subtract $(x^2 + 1)^2$ from $x^2(x + 1)^2$.

Factor by grouping. Look for a grouping of three terms that is a perfect-square trinomial.

118. $t^2 + 4t + 4 - 25$

119. $y^2 + 6y + 9 - x^2 - 8x - 16$

Find c such that each polynomial is the square of a binomial.

120. $cy^2 + 6y + 1$

121. $cy^2 - 24y + 9$

122. Find the only positive value of a for which $x^2 + a^2x + a^2$ factors into $(x + a)^2$.

123. Show that the difference of the squares of two consecutive integers is the sum of the integers. (*Hint*: Use x for the smaller number.)

 124. Use a geometric approach, similar to that shown on p. 312, to show that $x^2 + 6x + 9$ is a perfect square.

YOUR TURN ANSWERS: SECTION 5.4

1. Yes   **2.** $(x + 1)^2$ **3.** $(10a + b)^2$ **4.** $-n(2n - 3)^2$
5. Yes   **6.** $(a^2 + 3b)(a^2 - 3b)$
7. $(t^2 + 9)(t + 3)(t - 3)$

QUICK QUIZ: SECTIONS 5.1–5.4

Factor completely. If a polynomial is prime, state this.

1. $2x^3 + 6x^2 - x - 3$ [5.1]

2. $x^2 - 24x + 80$ [5.2]

3. $9a^3 - 6a^2 - 8a$ [5.3]

4. $y^2 + 16y + 64$ [5.4]

5. $3z^4 - 3$ [5.4]

PREPARE TO MOVE ON

Simplify.   [4.1]

1. $(2x^2y^4)^3$ 2. $(-5x^2y)^3$

Multiply.   [4.5]

3. $(x - 1)^3$ 4. $(p + t)^3$

Mid-Chapter Review

The following is a good strategy to follow when you encounter a mixed set of factoring problems.

1. Factor out any common factor.
2. If there are *four* terms, try factoring by grouping.
3. If there are *three* terms, determine whether it is a perfect-square trinomial. If so, factor using the pattern

   $A^2 + 2AB + B^2 = (A + B)^2$ or $A^2 - 2AB + B^2 = (A - B)^2$.

4. If there are *three* terms and it is not a perfect-square trinomial, try factoring using FOIL or by grouping.
5. If there are *two* terms, determine whether it is a difference of squares. If so, factor using the pattern

   $A^2 - B^2 = (A + B)(A - B)$.

GUIDED SOLUTIONS

Factor completely.

1. $12x^3y - 8xy^2 + 24x^2y = \boxed{} (3x^2 - 2y + 6x)$ [5.1]   Factoring out the largest common factor. No further factorization is possible.

2. $3a^3 - 3a^2 - 90a = 3a\left(\boxed{} - \boxed{} - \boxed{}\right)$ Factoring out the largest common factor

   $= 3a\left(a - \boxed{}\right)\left(a + \boxed{}\right)$ [5.2]   Factoring the trinomial

MIXED REVIEW

Factor completely. If a polynomial is prime, state this.

3. $6x^5 - 18x^2$ [5.1]

4. $x^2 + 10x + 16$ [5.2]

5. $2x^2 + 13x - 7$ [5.3]

6. $x^3 + 3x^2 + 2x + 6$ [5.1]

7. $64n^2 - 9$ [5.4]

8. $x^2 - 2x - 5$ [5.2]

9. $6p^2 - 6t^2$ [5.4]

10. $b^2 - 14b + 49$ [5.4]

11. $12x^2 - x - 1$ [5.3]

12. $a - 10a^2 + 25a^3$ [5.4]

13. $10x^4 - 10$ [5.4]

14. $t^2 + t - 10$ [5.2]

15. $15d^2 - 30d + 75$ [5.1]

16. $15p^2 + 16px + 4x^2$ [5.3]

17. $-2t^3 - 10t^2 - 12t$ [5.2]

18. $10c^2 + 20c + 10$ [5.4]

19. $5 + 3x - 2x^2$ [5.3]

20. $2m^3n - 10m^2n - 6mn + 30n$ [5.1]

5.5   Factoring Sums or Differences of Cubes

Factoring Sums or Differences of Cubes

Study Skills

A Good Night's Sleep
Plan to study only when you are alert. A good night's sleep or a 10-minute "power nap" can often make a problem suddenly seem much easier to solve.

Factoring Sums or Differences of Cubes

We have seen that a difference of two squares can be factored but a *sum* of two squares is usually prime. The situation is different with cubes: The difference *or* sum of two cubes can be factored. To see this, consider the following products:

$$(A + B)(A^2 - AB + B^2) = A(A^2 - AB + B^2) + B(A^2 - AB + B^2)$$
$$= A^3 - A^2B + AB^2 + A^2B - AB^2 + B^3$$
$$= A^3 + B^3 \quad \text{Combining like terms}$$

and

$$(A - B)(A^2 + AB + B^2) = A(A^2 + AB + B^2) - B(A^2 + AB + B^2)$$
$$= A^3 + A^2B + AB^2 - A^2B - AB^2 - B^3$$
$$= A^3 - B^3. \quad \text{Combining like terms}$$

These products allow us to factor a sum or a difference of two cubes. Note how the location of the + and − signs changes.

N	N^3
0.1	0.001
0.2	0.008
1	1
2	8
3	27
4	64
5	125
6	216

> **FACTORING A SUM OR A DIFFERENCE OF TWO CUBES**
>
> $$A^3 + B^3 = (A + B)(A^2 - AB + B^2);$$
> $$A^3 - B^3 = (A - B)(A^2 + AB + B^2)$$

Remembering the list of cubes shown at left may prove helpful when factoring. Since 2 cubed is 8 and 3 cubed is 27, we say that 2 is the *cube root* of 8, that 3 is the cube root of 27, and so on.

EXAMPLE 1   Write an equivalent expression by factoring: $x^3 + 27$.

SOLUTION   We first note that

$$x^3 + 27 = x^3 + 3^3. \quad \text{This is a sum of cubes.}$$

Next, in one set of parentheses, we write the first cube root, x, plus the second cube root, 3:

$$(x + 3)(\qquad).$$

To get the other factor, we think of $x + 3$ and do the following:

Square the first term: x^2.
Multiply the terms and then change the sign: $-3x$.
Square the second term: 3^2, or 9.

$$(x + 3)(x^2 - 3x + 9). \quad \text{This is factored completely.}$$

Check: $(x + 3)(x^2 - 3x + 9) = x^3 - 3x^2 + 9x + 3x^2 - 9x + 27$
$$= x^3 + 27. \quad \text{Combining like terms}$$

1. Write an equivalent expression by factoring: $t^3 + 125$.

Thus, $x^3 + 27 = (x + 3)(x^2 - 3x + 9)$.

 YOUR TURN

EXAMPLE 2   Factor.

a) $125x^3 - y^3$ **b)** $m^6 + 64$

c) $128y^7 - 250x^6y$ **d)** $r^6 - s^6$

SOLUTION

a) We have

$$125x^3 - y^3 = (5x)^3 - y^3. \qquad \text{Recognizing this as a difference of cubes}$$

In one set of parentheses, we write the cube root of the first term, $5x$, minus the cube root of the second term, y:

$$(5x - y)(\quad). \qquad \text{This can be regarded as } 5x \text{ plus the cube root of } (-y)^3, \text{ since } -y^3 = (-y)^3.$$

To get the other factor, we think of $5x + y$ and do the following:

Square the first term: $(5x)^2$, or $25x^2$.
Multiply the terms and then change the sign: $5xy$.
Square the second term: $(-y)^2 = y^2$.

$$(5x - y)(25x^2 + 5xy + y^2).$$

Check:

$$(5x - y)(25x^2 + 5xy + y^2) = 125x^3 + 25x^2y + 5xy^2 - 25x^2y - 5xy^2 - y^3$$
$$= 125x^3 - y^3. \qquad \text{Combining like terms}$$

Thus, $125x^3 - y^3 = (5x - y)(25x^2 + 5xy + y^2).$

b) We have

$$m^6 + 64 = (m^2)^3 + 4^3. \qquad \text{Rewriting as a sum of quantities cubed}$$

Next, we use the pattern for a sum of cubes:

$$A^3 \; + \; B^3 = (A \; + \; B)(\; A^2 \; - \; A \cdot B + B^2)$$
$$(m^2)^3 + 4^3 = (m^2 + 4)((m^2)^2 - m^2 \cdot 4 + 4^2) \qquad \begin{array}{l}\text{Regarding } m^2 \text{ as } A \\ \text{and 4 as } B\end{array}$$
$$= (m^2 + 4)(m^4 - 4m^2 + 16).$$

The check is left to the student. We have

$$m^6 + 64 = (m^2 + 4)(m^4 - 4m^2 + 16).$$

c) We have

$$128y^7 - 250x^6y = 2y(64y^6 - 125x^6) \qquad \begin{array}{l}\text{Remember: } \textit{Always} \text{ look for a} \\ \text{common factor.}\end{array}$$
$$= 2y[(4y^2)^3 - (5x^2)^3]. \qquad \begin{array}{l}\text{Rewriting as a difference of} \\ \text{quantities cubed}\end{array}$$

To factor $(4y^2)^3 - (5x^2)^3$, we use the pattern for a difference of cubes:

$$A^3 \; - \; B^3 \; = (A \; - \; B)(\; A^2 \; + \; A \cdot B + \; B^2)$$
$$(4y^2)^3 - (5x^2)^3 = (4y^2 - 5x^2)((4y^2)^2 + 4y^2 \cdot 5x^2 + (5x^2)^2)$$
$$= (4y^2 - 5x^2)(16y^4 + 20x^2y^2 + 25x^4).$$

The check is left to the student. We have

$$128y^7 - 250x^6y = 2y(4y^2 - 5x^2)(16y^4 + 20x^2y^2 + 25x^4).$$

Student Notes

If you think of $A^3 - B^3$ as $A^3 + (-B)^3$, you need remember only the pattern for factoring a sum of two cubes. Be sure to simplify your result if you do this.

d) We have

$$r^6 - s^6 = (r^3)^2 - (s^3)^2$$
$$= (r^3 + s^3)(r^3 - s^3) \qquad \text{Factoring a difference of two } squares$$
$$= (r + s)(r^2 - rs + s^2)(r - s)(r^2 + rs + s^2). \qquad \text{Factoring the sum and the difference of two cubes}$$

To check, read the steps in reverse order and inspect the multiplication.

2. Factor: $y^7 - y$.

YOUR TURN

In Example 2(d), suppose we first factored $r^6 - s^6$ as a difference of two cubes:

$$(r^2)^3 - (s^2)^3 = (r^2 - s^2)(r^4 + r^2s^2 + s^4)$$
$$= (r + s)(r - s)(r^4 + r^2s^2 + s^4).$$

In this case, we might have missed some factors; $r^4 + r^2s^2 + s^4$ can be factored as $(r^2 - rs + s^2)(r^2 + rs + s^2)$, but we probably would never have suspected that such a factorization exists. **Given a choice, it is generally better to factor as a difference of squares before factoring as a sum or a difference of cubes.**

USEFUL FACTORING FACTS

Sum of cubes: $A^3 + B^3 = (A + B)(A^2 - AB + B^2)$

Difference of cubes: $A^3 - B^3 = (A - B)(A^2 + AB + B^2)$

Difference of squares: $A^2 - B^2 = (A + B)(A - B)$

In general, a sum of two squares cannot be factored.

5.5 EXERCISE SET

FOR EXTRA HELP

MyMathLab® MathXL
PRACTICE   WATCH   READ   REVIEW

Vocabulary and Reading Check

Classify each binomial as either a sum of cubes, a difference of cubes, a difference of squares, or none of these.

1. $x^3 - 1$

2. $8 + t^3$

3. $9x^4 - 25$

4. $9x^2 + 25$

5. $1000t^3 + 1$

6. $x^3y^3 - 27z^3$

7. $25x^2 + 8x$

8. $100y^8 - 25x^4$

9. $s^{21} - t^{15}$

10. $14x^3 - 2x$

Factoring Sums or Differences of Cubes

Factor completely.

11. $x^3 - 64$

12. $t^3 - 27$

13. $z^3 + 1$

14. $x^3 + 8$

15. $t^3 - 1000$

16. $m^3 + 125$

17. $27x^3 + 1$

18. $8a^3 + 1$

19. $64 - 125x^3$

20. $27 - 8t^3$

21. $x^3 - y^3$

22. $y^3 - z^3$

23. $a^3 + \frac{1}{8}$

24. $x^3 + \frac{1}{27}$

25. $8t^3 - 8$

26. $2y^3 - 128$

27. $54x^3 + 2$

28. $8a^3 + 1000$

29. $rs^4 + 64rs$

30. $ab^5 + 1000ab^2$

31. $5x^3 - 40z^3$

32. $2y^3 - 54z^3$

33. $y^3 - \frac{1}{1000}$

34. $x^3 - \frac{1}{8}$

35. $x^3 + 0.001$

36. $y^3 + 0.125$

37. $64x^6 - 8t^6$

38. $125c^6 - 8d^6$

39. $54y^4 - 128y$

40. $3z^5 - 3z^2$

41. $z^6 - 1$

42. $t^6 + 1$

43. $t^6 + 64y^6$

44. $p^6 - q^6$

45. $x^{12} - y^3z^{12}$

46. $a^9 + b^{12}c^{15}$

47. How could you use factoring to convince someone that $x^3 + y^3 \neq (x + y)^3$?

48. Explain how to use the pattern for factoring $A^3 + B^3$ to factor $A^3 - B^3$.

Skill Review

Solve.

49. A serving of crackers contains 120 mg of sodium. According to nutrition information on the box, this is 5% of the daily recommended value of sodium. What is the daily recommended value of sodium? [2.4]

50. Blake stopped for gasoline twice on his drive home from college. He bought a total of 19.2 gal of gasoline. If he bought twice as much on his first stop as on his second stop, how many gallons of gasoline did he buy on his second stop? [2.5]

51. A tax-exempt charity received a bill of $551.20 for kitchen supplies. The bill incorrectly included sales tax of 6%. How much does the charity actually owe? [2.5]

52. Katie paid $34.50 for a jacket that was on sale at 25% off. What was the original price of the jacket? [2.5]

Synthesis

53. Explain how the geometric model below can be used to verify the formula for factoring $a^3 - b^3$.

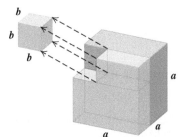

54. Explain how someone could construct a binomial that is both a difference of two cubes and a difference of two squares.

Factor.

55. $x^{6a} - y^{3b}$

56. $2x^{3a} + 16y^{3b}$

Aha! **57.** $(x + 5)^3 + (x - 5)^3$

58. $\frac{1}{16}x^{3a} + \frac{1}{2}y^{6a}z^{9b}$

59. $5x^3y^6 - \frac{5}{8}$

60. $x^3 - (x + y)^3$

61. $x^{6a} - (x^{2a} + 1)^3$

62. $(x^{2a} - 1)^3 - x^{6a}$

63. $t^4 - 8t^3 - t + 8$

🡒 **YOUR TURN ANSWERS: SECTION 5.5**

1. $(t + 5)(t^2 - 5t + 25)$

2. $y(y + 1)(y^2 - y + 1)(y - 1)(y^2 + y + 1)$

QUICK QUIZ: SECTIONS 5.1–5.5

Factor.

1. $6x^2p^3 + xp^2 - 3x^3p^4$ [5.1]

2. $x^2 - 11x - 12$ [5.2]

3. $4a^3 - 19a^2 - 5a$ [5.3]

4. $p^2 - w^2$ [5.4]

5. $p^3 - w^3$ [5.5]

PREPARE TO MOVE ON

Complete each statement.

1. When factoring, always check first for a(n) _____ factor. [5.3]

2. To factor a trinomial of the form $ax^2 + bx + c$, we can use FOIL or the _____ method. [5.4]

3. The formula for factoring a difference of squares is $A^2 - B^2 = $ _____ . [5.4]

4. A formula for factoring a perfect-square trinomial is $A^2 + 2AB + B^2 = $ _____ . [5.4]

5. The formula for factoring a sum of cubes is $A^3 + B^3 = $ _____ . [5.5]

5.6   Factoring: A General Strategy

Choosing the Right Method

Thus far, each section in this chapter has examined one or two different methods for factoring polynomials. In practice, when the need for factoring a polynomial arises, we must decide on our own which method to use. The following guidelines provide an approach for this.

TO FACTOR A POLYNOMIAL

A. Always look for a common factor. If there is one, factor out the largest common factor. Be sure to include it in your final answer.

B. Then look at the number of terms.

Two terms: If you have a difference of squares, factor accordingly:

$$A^2 - B^2 = (A + B)(A - B).$$

If you have a sum or a difference of cubes, factor accordingly:

$$A^3 + B^3 = (A + B)(A^2 - AB + B^2);$$
$$A^3 - B^3 = (A - B)(A^2 + AB + B^2).$$

Three terms: If the trinomial is a perfect-square trinomial, factor accordingly:

$$A^2 + 2AB + B^2 = (A + B)^2;$$
$$A^2 - 2AB + B^2 = (A - B)^2.$$

If it is not a perfect-square trinomial, try using FOIL or grouping.

Four terms: Try factoring by grouping.

C. Always *factor completely*. When a factor can itself be factored, be sure to factor it. Remember that some polynomials, like $x^2 + 9$, are prime.

D. Check.

We can always check a factorization by multiplying. Another way to check a factorization is to evaluate both the original polynomial and the factorization for one or more choices of the variable(s). Since the polynomial and its factorization are equivalent expressions, they have the same value for any replacements of the variable(s). This check becomes more certain if it is done for more than one replacement. In fact, for a polynomial in one variable of degree n, a check of $n + 1$ replacements is sufficient to show that the factorization is correct.

Student Notes

Quickly checking both the leading term and the constant term of a trinomial to see if they are squares can save you time. If they aren't both squares and there is no common factor, the trinomial can't possibly be a perfect-square trinomial.

Choosing the Right Method

EXAMPLE 1   Factor: $x^2 - 20x + 100$.

SOLUTION

A. We look first for a common factor. There is none.

B. This polynomial is a perfect-square trinomial. We factor it accordingly:

$$x^2 - 20x + 100 = x^2 - 2 \cdot x \cdot 10 + 10^2 \qquad \text{Try to do this step mentally.}$$
$$= (x - 10)^2.$$

C. Nothing can be factored further, so we have factored completely.

D. We check by multiplying: $(x - 10)(x - 10) = x^2 - 20x + 100$.

The factorization is $(x - 10)(x - 10)$, or $(x - 10)^2$.

1. Factor: $a^2 + 2a + 1$.

YOUR TURN

Study Skills

Keep Your Focus

When you are studying with someone else, it can be very tempting to talk about topics not related to what you need to study. If you see that this may happen, explain to your partner(s) that you enjoy the conversation, but would enjoy it more later—after the work has been completed.

EXAMPLE 2   Factor: $2x^3 + 10x^2 + x + 5$.

SOLUTION

A. We look for a common factor. There is none.

B. Because there are four terms, we try factoring by grouping:

$2x^3 + 10x^2 + x + 5$

$= (2x^3 + 10x^2) + (x + 5)$	Separating into two binomials
$= 2x^2(x + 5) + 1(x + 5)$	Factoring out the largest common factor from each binomial. The 1 serves as an aid.
$= (x + 5)(2x^2 + 1).$	Factoring out the common factor, $x + 5$

C. Nothing can be factored further, so we have factored completely.

D. As a partial check, we evaluate the original polynomial and the factorization for $x = 2$:

$2x^3 + 10x^2 + x + 5 = 2(2)^3 + 10(2)^2 + 2 + 5 = 2 \cdot 8 + 10 \cdot 4 + 2 + 5 = 63;$
$(x + 5)(2x^2 + 1) = (2 + 5)(2(2)^2 + 1) = 7 \cdot 9 = 63.$

The values are the same for $x = 2$. If we were to evaluate both expressions for three additional values of x, the check would be complete.

The factorization is $(x + 5)(2x^2 + 1)$.

2. Factor: $5x^3 + 15x - x^2 - 3$.

YOUR TURN

EXAMPLE 3   Factor: $-10n^5 - 80n^2$.

SOLUTION

A. We note that there is a common factor, $-10n^2$:

$-10n^5 - 80n^2 = -10n^2(n^3 + 8).$

B. The factor $n^3 + 8$ has two terms and is a sum of cubes. We factor:

$-10n^5 - 80n^2 = -10n^2(n^3 + 8)$
$= -10n^2(n + 2)(n^2 - 2n + 4).$

C. No factor can be factored further, so we have factored completely.

D. We check by multiplying:

$-10n^2(n + 2)(n^2 - 2n + 4) = -10n^2(n^3 + 8)$
$= -10n^5 - 80n^2.$

The factorization is $-10n^2(n + 2)(n^2 - 2n + 4)$.

3. Factor: $2000x^3 - 2$.

YOUR TURN

EXAMPLE 4 Factor: $6x^2y^4 - 21x^3y^5 + 3x^2y^6$.

SOLUTION

A. We first factor out the largest common factor, $3x^2y^4$:

$$6x^2y^4 - 21x^3y^5 + 3x^2y^6 = 3x^2y^4(2 - 7xy + y^2).$$

B. The constant term in $2 - 7xy + y^2$ is not a square, so we do not have a perfect-square trinomial. Note that x appears only in $-7xy$. The product of a form like $(1 - y)(2 - y)$ has no x in the middle term. Thus, $2 - 7xy + y^2$ cannot be factored.

C. Nothing can be factored further, so we have factored completely.

D. We check by multiplying:

$$3x^2y^4(2 - 7xy + y^2) = 6x^2y^4 - 21x^3y^5 + 3x^2y^6.$$

4. Factor:

$$12p^3w - 18p^2w^2 + 6p^2w.$$

The factorization is $3x^2y^4(2 - 7xy + y^2)$.

YOUR TURN

EXAMPLE 5 Factor: $98x^3 + 280x^2 + 200x$.

SOLUTION

A. We first factor out the largest common factor, $2x$:

$$98x^3 + 280x^2 + 200x = 2x(49x^2 + 140x + 100).$$

B. The trinomial in the parentheses is a perfect-square trinomial: $49x^2 = (7x)^2$, $100 = (10)^2$, and $140x = 2 \cdot 7x \cdot 10$. We factor it accordingly:

$$98x^3 + 280x^2 + 200x = 2x(49x^2 + 140x + 100)$$
$$= 2x(7x + 10)^2.$$

C. Nothing can be factored further, so we have factored completely.

D. As a partial check, we evaluate the original polynomial and the factorization for $x = 1$:

$$98x^3 + 280x^2 + 200x = 98(1)^3 + 280(1)^2 + 200(1) = 98 + 280 + 200 = 578;$$
$$2x(7x + 10)^2 = 2(1)[(7(1) + 10)^2] = 2(17)^2 = 2(289) = 578.$$

The values are the same for $x = 1$. If we were to evaluate both expressions for three additional values of x, the check would be complete.

5. Factor:

$$75a^4 + 30a^3 + 3a^2.$$

The factorization is $2x(7x + 10)^2$.

YOUR TURN

EXAMPLE 6 Factor: $-10m^2 - mn + 3n^2$.

SOLUTION

A. We first look for a common factor. Since the first term is negative, we factor out -1:

$$-1(10m^2 + mn - 3n^2).$$

B. There are three terms in the parentheses. Since none is a square, the trinomial is not a perfect square. We factor using FOIL. (We could also use grouping.) There are two possibilities for the first terms in the binomial factors:

$$(2m + \quad)(5m + \quad) \quad \text{or} \quad (m + \quad)(10m + \quad).$$

The possibilities for the second terms in the binomials are

$$n, -3n \qquad -3n, \quad n$$
$$\text{and}$$
$$-n, \quad 3n \qquad 3n, -n.$$

We check the possible combinations and find that the factorization of $10m^2 + mn - 3n^2$ is $(2m - n)(5m + 3n)$. Thus,

$$-10m^2 - mn + 3n^2 = -1(2m - n)(5m + 3n).$$

C. Nothing can be factored further, so we have factored completely.

D. We check by multiplying:

$$-1(2m - n)(5m + 3n) = -1(10m^2 + mn - 3n^2)$$
$$= -10m^2 - mn + 3n^2.$$

6. Factor: $-9x^2 - 37xy - 4y^2$.

The factorization is $-1(2m - n)(5m + 3n)$, or $-(2m - n)(5m + 3n)$.

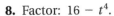 YOUR TURN

EXAMPLE 7   Factor: $x^2y^2 + 7xy + 12$.

SOLUTION

A. We first look for a common factor. There is none.

B. Since only one term is a square, we do not have a perfect-square trinomial. We use trial and error, treating the product xy as a single variable:

$$(xy + \quad)(xy + \quad).$$

We factor the last term, 12. All the signs are positive, so we consider only positive factors. Possibilities are 1, 12 and 2, 6 and 3, 4. The pair 3, 4 gives a sum of 7 for the coefficient of the middle term. Thus,

$$x^2y^2 + 7xy + 12 = (xy + 3)(xy + 4).$$

C. Nothing can be factored further, so we have factored completely.

D. *Check:* $(xy + 3)(xy + 4) = x^2y^2 + 7xy + 12$.

7. Factor: $c^2t^2 - 9ct + 20$.

The factorization is $(xy + 3)(xy + 4)$.

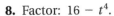 YOUR TURN

Compare the variables appearing in Example 6 with those in Example 7. Note that if the leading term contains one variable and a different variable is in the last term, as in Example 6, each factor contains two variable terms. When two variables appear in the leading term and no variables appear in the last term, as in Example 7, each factor contains just one variable term.

EXAMPLE 8   Factor: $a^4 - 16b^4$.

SOLUTION

A. We look first for a common factor. There is none.

B. There are two terms. Since $a^4 = (a^2)^2$ and $16b^4 = (4b^2)^2$, we see that we have a difference of squares. Thus,

$$a^4 - 16b^4 = (a^2 + 4b^2)(a^2 - 4b^2).$$

Chapter Resource:
Collaborative Activity (Matching Factorizations), p. 366

C. The factor $(a^2 - 4b^2)$ is itself a difference of squares. Thus,

$$a^4 - 16b^4 = (a^2 + 4b^2)(a + 2b)(a - 2b). \quad \text{Factoring } a^2 - 4b^2$$

D. *Check:* $(a^2 + 4b^2)(a + 2b)(a - 2b) = (a^2 + 4b^2)(a^2 - 4b^2)$
$$= a^4 - 16b^4.$$

8. Factor: $16 - t^4$.

The factorization is $(a^2 + 4b^2)(a + 2b)(a - 2b)$.

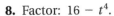 YOUR TURN

5.6 EXERCISE SET

FOR EXTRA HELP

 MyMathLab® Math XL

PRACTICE   WATCH   READ   REVIEW

Vocabulary and Reading Check

Choose the term from the following list that best completes each sentence. Not every term will be used.

common factor   multiplying
dividing   perfect-square trinomial
grouping   prime polynomial

1. As a first step when factoring polynomials, always check for a(n) _____.

2. When factoring a trinomial, if two terms are not squares, it cannot be a(n) _____.

3. If a polynomial has four terms and no common factor, it may be possible to factor by _____.

4. It is always possible to check a factorization by _____.

Factoring Polynomials

Factor completely. If a polynomial is prime, state this.

5. $5a^2 - 125$

6. $10c^2 - 810$

7. $y^2 + 49 - 14y$

8. $a^2 + 25 + 10a$

9. $3t^2 + 16t + 21$

10. $8t^2 + 31t - 4$

11. $x^3 + 18x^2 + 81x$

12. $x^3 - 24x^2 + 144x$

13. $x^3 - 5x^2 - 25x + 125$

14. $x^3 + 3x^2 - 4x - 12$

15. $27t^3 - 3t$

16. $98t^2 - 18$

17. $9x^3 + 12x^2 - 45x$

18. $20x^3 - 4x^2 - 72x$

19. $t^2 + 25$

20. $4x^2 + 20x - 144$

21. $6y^2 + 18y - 240$

22. $4n^2 + 81$

23. $-2a^6 + 8a^5 - 8a^4$

24. $-x^5 - 14x^4 - 49x^3$

25. $5x^5 - 80x$

26. $4x^4 - 64$

27. $t^4 - 9$

28. $9 + t^8$

29. $-x^6 + 2x^5 - 7x^4$

30. $-x^5 + 4x^4 - 3x^3$

31. $x^3 - y^3$

32. $8t^3 + 1$

33. $ax^2 + ay^2$

34. $12n^2 + 24n^3$

35. $2\pi rh + 2\pi r^2$

36. $4\pi r^2 + 2\pi r$

Aha! 37. $(a + b)5a + (a + b)3b$

38. $5c(a^3 + b) - (a^3 + b)$

39. $x^2 + x + xy + y$

40. $n^2 + 2n + np + 2p$

41. $160a^2m^4 - 10a^2$

42. $32t^4 - 162y^4$

43. $a^2 - 2a - ay + 2y$

44. $2x^2 - 4x + xz - 2z$

45. $3x^2 + 13xy - 10y^2$

46. $-x^2 - y^2 - 2xy$

47. $8m^3n - 32m^2n^2 + 24mn$

48. $a^2 - 7a - 6$

49. $\frac{9}{16} - y^2$

50. $\frac{1}{36}a^2 - m^2$

51. $4b^2 + a^2 - 4ab$

52. $7p^4 - 7q^4$

53. $16x^2 + 24xy + 9y^2$

54. $6a^2b^3 + 12a^3b^2 - 3a^4b^2$

55. $m^2 - 5m + 8$

56. $25z^2 + 10zy + y^2$

57. $10x^2 - 11x - 6$

58. $24x^2 - 47x - 21$

59. $a^4b^4 - 16$

60. $a^5 - 4a^4b - 5a^3b^2$

61. $80cd^2 - 36c^2d + 4c^3$

62. $2p^2 + pq + q^2$

63. $64t^6 - 1$

64. $m^6 - 1$

65. $-12 - x^2y^2 - 8xy$

66. $m^2n^2 - 4mn - 32$

67. $14t + 8t^2 - 15$

68. $8y - 15 + 12y^2$

69. $5p^2t^2 + 25pt - 30$

70. $a^4b^3 + 2a^3b^2 - 15a^2b$

71. $54a^4 + 16ab^3$

72. $54x^3y - 250y^4$

73. $x^6 + x^5y - 2x^4y^2$

74. $2s^6t^2 + 10s^3t^3 + 12t^4$

75. $36a^2 - 15a + \frac{25}{16}$

76. $a^2 + 2a^2bc + a^2b^2c^2$

77. $\frac{1}{81}x^2 - \frac{8}{27}x + \frac{16}{9}$

78. $\frac{1}{4}a^2 + \frac{1}{3}ab + \frac{1}{9}b^2$

79. $1 - 16x^{12}y^{12}$

80. $b^4a - 81a^5$

81. $4a^2b^2 + 12ab + 9$

82. $9c^2 + 6cd + d^2$

83. $z^4 + 6z^3 - 6z^2 - 36z$

84. $t^5 - 2t^4 + 5t^3 - 10t^2$

85. $x^3 + 5x^2 - x - 5$

86. $x^3 + 3x^2 - 16x - 48$

87. Kelly factored $16 - 8x + x^2$ as $(x - 4)^2$, while Tony factored it as $(4 - x)^2$. Are they both correct? Why or why not?

88. Describe in your own words or draw a diagram representing a strategy for factoring polynomials.

Skill Review

Solve.

89. In 2011, the 1.3 billion people of China owned 900 million mobile phones. Assuming that no one owned more than one mobile phone, what percent of the Chinese population owned a mobile phone? [2.4]

Sources: "China's mobile subscribers rise 1.1 pct to 916.53 mln in July," Reuters, 8/23/2011; *The World Factbook*

90. The number of billionaires in China increased from 120 at the end of 2009 to 189 at the end of 2010. What was the monthly average rate of increase? [3.4]

Source: sify.com

91. In 2011, U.S. shoppers spent $27.4 billion on gifts for Mother's Day and for Father's Day combined. They spent $5.2 billion more for Mother's Day than for Father's Day. How much did shoppers spend for each holiday? [2.5]

Source: National Retail Federation

92. Shelby plans to spend no more than $50 on roses for a Mother's Day gift. If the shipping for the flowers is $15 and each rose costs $6.50, how many roses can he purchase? [2.7]

Synthesis

93. There are third-degree polynomials in x that we are not yet able to factor, despite the fact that they are not prime. Explain how such a polynomial could be created.

94. Describe a method that could be used to find a binomial of degree 16 that can be expressed as the product of prime binomial factors.

Factor.

95. $36 - 12x + x^2 - a^2$

96. $100 + 20t + t^2 - 4y^2$

97. $-(x^5 + 7x^3 - 18x)$

98. $18 + a^3 - 9a - 2a^2$

99. $-x^4 + 7x^2 + 18$

100. $-3a^4 + 15a^2 - 12$

Aha! **101.** $y^2(y + 1) - 4y(y + 1) - 21(y + 1)$

102. $y^2(y - 1) - 2y(y - 1) + (y - 1)$

103. $(y + 4)^2 + 2x(y + 4) + x^2$

104. $6(x - 1)^2 + 7y(x - 1) - 3y^2$

105. $2(a + 3)^4 - (a + 3)^3(b - 2) - (a + 3)^2(b - 2)^2$

106. $5(t - 1)^5 - 6(t - 1)^4(s - 1) + (t - 1)^3(s - 1)^2$

107. $49x^4 + 14x^2 + 1 - 25x^6$

> **YOUR TURN ANSWERS: SECTION 5.6**
> **1.** $(a + 1)^2$ **2.** $(5x - 1)(x^2 + 3)$
> **3.** $2(10x - 1)(100x^2 + 10x + 1)$ **4.** $6p^2w(2p - 3w + 1)$
> **5.** $3a^2(5a + 1)^2$ **6.** $-1(9x + y)(x + 4y)$, or
> $-(9x + y)(x + 4y)$ **7.** $(ct - 5)(ct - 4)$
> **8.** $(4 + t^2)(2 + t)(2 - t)$

QUICK QUIZ: SECTIONS 5.1–5.6

Factor.

1. $10m^2 - 90$ [5.4]   **2.** $a + a^2 - 6$ [5.2]

3. $12x^3 - 6x^2 - 10x + 5$ [5.1]

4. $8m^2n^2 - 16mn + 8$ [5.4]

5. $6c^3 - 5c^2 - 6c$ [5.3]

PREPARE TO MOVE ON

Solve. [2.2]

1. $8x - 9 = 0$ **2.** $2x + 7 = 0$

3. $3 - x = 0$ **4.** $3x + 5 = 0$

5. $4x - 1 = 0$ **6.** $22 - 2x = 0$

5.7   Solving Quadratic Equations by Factoring

The Principle of Zero Products   •   Factoring to Solve Equations

When we factor a polynomial, we are forming an *equivalent expression*. We now use our factoring skills to *solve equations*. We already know how to solve linear equations like $x + 2 = 7$ and $2x = 9$. The equations we will learn to solve in this section contain a variable raised to a power greater than 1 and will usually have more than one solution.

Second-degree equations like $4t^2 - 7 = 2$ and $x^2 + 6x + 5 = 0$ are called **quadratic equations**.

> **QUADRATIC EQUATION**
>
> A *quadratic equation* is an equation equivalent to one of the form
>
> $$ax^2 + bx + c = 0,$$
>
> where a, b, and c are constants, with $a \neq 0$.

In order to solve quadratic equations, we need to develop a new principle.

The Principle of Zero Products

Suppose we are told that the product of two numbers is 6. From this alone, it is impossible to know the value of either number—the product could be $2 \cdot 3, 6 \cdot 1, 12 \cdot \frac{1}{2}$, and so on. However, if we are told that the product of two numbers is 0, we know that at least one of the two factors must itself be 0. For example, if $(x + 3)(x - 2) = 0$, we can conclude that either $x + 3$ is 0 or $x - 2$ is 0.

> **THE PRINCIPLE OF ZERO PRODUCTS**
>
> An equation $AB = 0$ is true if and only if $A = 0$ or $B = 0$, or both. (A product is 0 if and only if at least one factor is 0.)

EXAMPLE 1   Solve: $(x + 3)(x - 2) = 0$.

SOLUTION   We look for all values of x that make the equation true. The equation tells us that the product of $x + 3$ and $x - 2$ is 0. In order for any product to be 0, at least one factor must be 0. Thus we look for any value of x for which $x + 3 = 0$, as well as any value of x for which $x - 2 = 0$, that is, either

$$x + 3 = 0 \quad or \quad x - 2 = 0. \qquad \text{Using the principle of zero products. There are two equations to solve.}$$

We solve each equation:

$$x + 3 = 0 \quad or \quad x - 2 = 0$$
$$x = -3 \quad or \qquad x = 2.$$

Both -3 and 2 should be checked in the original equation.

Check: For -3:

$$\frac{(x + 3)(x - 2) = 0}{(-3 + 3)(-3 - 2) \mid 0}$$

The factor $x + 3$ is 0 when $x = -3$. $\longrightarrow 0(-5)$

$$0 \overset{?}{=} 0 \quad \text{TRUE}$$

For 2:

$$\frac{(x + 3)(x - 2) = 0}{(2 + 3)(2 - 2) \mid 0}$$

$5(0)$ $\longleftarrow$ The factor $x - 2$ is 0 when $x = 2$.

$$0 \overset{?}{=} 0 \quad \text{TRUE}$$

The solutions are -3 and 2.

YOUR TURN

When we are using the principle of zero products, the word "or" is meant to emphasize that any one of the factors could be the one that represents 0.

Study Skills

Identify the Highlights

If you haven't already tried one, consider using a highlighter as you read. By highlighting sentences or phrases that you find especially important, you will make it easier to review important material in the future.

1. Solve: $(x - 1)(x + 5) = 0$.

EXAMPLE 2   Solve: $3(5x + 1)(x - 7) = 0$.

SOLUTION   The factors in this equation are 3, $5x + 1$, and $x - 7$. Since the factor 3 is constant, the only way in which $3(5x + 1)(x - 7)$ can be 0 is for one of the other factors to be 0, that is,

$$5x + 1 = 0 \quad or \quad x - 7 = 0 \qquad \text{Using the principle of zero products}$$
$$5x = -1 \quad or \qquad x = 7 \qquad \text{Solving the two equations separately}$$
$$x = -\tfrac{1}{5} \quad or \qquad x = 7. \qquad 5x + 1 = 0 \text{ when } x = -\tfrac{1}{5}; x - 7 = 0$$
$$\text{when } x = 7.$$

Check: For $-\tfrac{1}{5}$:

$$\frac{3(5x + 1)(x - 7) = 0}{3\left(5\left(-\tfrac{1}{5}\right) + 1\right)\left(-\tfrac{1}{5} - 7\right)} \,\bigg|\, 0$$
$$3(-1 + 1)\left(-7\tfrac{1}{5}\right)$$
$$3(0)\left(-7\tfrac{1}{5}\right)$$
$$0 \stackrel{?}{=} 0 \quad \text{TRUE}$$

For 7:

$$\frac{3(5x + 1)(x - 7) = 0}{3(5(7) + 1)(7 - 7)} \,\bigg|\, 0$$
$$3(35 + 1)0$$
$$0 \stackrel{?}{=} 0 \quad \text{TRUE}$$

The solutions are $-\tfrac{1}{5}$ and 7.

2. Solve:

$$6(x + 2)(3x + 5) = 0.$$

YOUR TURN

The constant factor 3 in Example 2 is never 0 and is not a solution of the equation. However, a variable factor such as x or t *can* equal 0, and must be considered when using the principle of zero products.

EXAMPLE 3   Solve: $7t(t - 5) = 0$.

SOLUTION   We have

$$7 \cdot t(t - 5) = 0 \qquad \text{The factors are 7, } t, \text{ and } t - 5.$$
$$t = 0 \quad or \quad t - 5 = 0 \qquad \text{Using the principle of zero products}$$
$$t = 0 \quad or \qquad t = 5. \qquad \text{Solving. Note that the constant}$$
$$\text{factor, 7, is never 0.}$$

3. Solve: $10a(a + 9) = 0$.

The solutions are 0 and 5. The check is left to the student.

YOUR TURN

Factoring to Solve Equations

By factoring and using the principle of zero products, we can now solve a variety of quadratic equations.

EXAMPLE 4   Solve: $x^2 + 5x + 6 = 0$.

SOLUTION   We first factor the polynomial, and then use the principle of zero products:

$$x^2 + 5x + 6 = 0$$
$$(x + 2)(x + 3) = 0 \qquad \text{Factoring}$$
$$x + 2 = 0 \quad or \quad x + 3 = 0 \qquad \text{Using the principle of zero products}$$
$$x = -2 \quad or \qquad x = -3.$$

Check: For −2:

$$x^2 + 5x + 6 = 0$$

$$\begin{array}{c|c} (-2)^2 + 5(-2) + 6 & 0 \\ 4 - 10 + 6 & \\ -6 + 6 & \\ & 0 \overset{?}{=} 0 \quad \text{TRUE} \end{array}$$

For −3:

$$x^2 + 5x + 6 = 0$$

$$\begin{array}{c|c} (-3)^2 + 5(-3) + 6 & 0 \\ 9 - 15 + 6 & \\ -6 + 6 & \\ & 0 \overset{?}{=} 0 \quad \text{TRUE} \end{array}$$

4. Solve: $t^2 - 8t + 15 = 0$.

The solutions are −2 and −3.

 YOUR TURN

Student Notes

Checking for a common factor is an important step that is often overlooked. In Example 5, the equation must be factored. If we "divide both sides by x," we will not find the solution 0.

5. Solve: $n^2 - 8n = 0$.

EXAMPLE 5   Solve: $x^2 + 7x = 0$.

SOLUTION   Although there is no constant term, because of the x^2-term, the equation is still quadratic. We factor and use the principle of zero products:

$$x^2 + 7x = 0$$

$$x(x + 7) = 0 \qquad\qquad \text{Factoring out the largest common factor, } x$$

$$x = 0 \quad or \quad x + 7 = 0 \quad \text{Using the principle of zero products}$$

$$x = 0 \quad or \qquad\quad x = -7.$$

The solutions are 0 and −7. The check is left to the student.

 YOUR TURN

> **CAUTION!**   We *must* have 0 on one side of the equation before the principle of zero products can be used. Get all nonzero terms on one side and 0 on the other.

EXAMPLE 6   Solve: **(a)** $x^2 - 8x = -16$; **(b)** $4t^2 = 25$.

SOLUTION

a)   We first add 16 to get 0 on one side:

$$x^2 - 8x = -16$$

$$x^2 - 8x + 16 = 0 \qquad\qquad \text{Adding 16 to both sides to get 0 on one side}$$

$$(x - 4)(x - 4) = 0 \qquad\qquad \text{Factoring}$$

$$x - 4 = 0 \quad or \quad x - 4 = 0 \quad \text{Using the principle of zero products}$$

$$x = 4 \quad or \qquad x = 4.$$

There is only one solution, 4. The check is left to the student.

b)   We have

Get 0 on one side.

Factor.

Use the principle of zero products.

Solve each equation separately.

$$4t^2 = 25$$

$$4t^2 - 25 = 0 \qquad \text{Subtracting 25 from both sides to get 0 on one side}$$

$$(2t - 5)(2t + 5) = 0 \qquad \text{Factoring a difference of squares}$$

$$\left.\begin{array}{l} 2t - 5 = 0 \quad or \quad 2t + 5 = 0 \\ 2t = 5 \quad or \qquad 2t = -5 \\ t = \tfrac{5}{2} \quad or \qquad t = -\tfrac{5}{2}. \end{array}\right\} \begin{array}{l} \text{Solving the two equations} \\ \text{separately} \end{array}$$

6. Solve: $a^2 = -10a - 25$.

The solutions are $\tfrac{5}{2}$ and $-\tfrac{5}{2}$. The check is left to the student.

 YOUR TURN

EXAMPLE 7 Solve: $(x + 3)(2x - 1) = 9$.

SOLUTION Be careful with an equation like this! Since we need 0 on one side, we first multiply the product on the left and then subtract 9 from both sides.

$(x + 3)(2x - 1) = 9$	This is not a product equal to 0.
$2x^2 + 5x - 3 = 9$	Multiplying on the left
$2x^2 + 5x - 3 - 9 = 9 - 9$	Subtracting 9 from both sides to get 0 on one side
$2x^2 + 5x - 12 = 0$	Combining like terms
$(2x - 3)(x + 4) = 0$	Factoring. Now we have a product equal to 0.
$2x - 3 = 0 \quad or \quad x + 4 = 0$	Using the principle of zero products
$2x = 3 \quad or \qquad\quad x = -4$	
$x = \frac{3}{2} \quad or \qquad\quad x = -4$	

Check:

For $\frac{3}{2}$:

$$\frac{(x + 3)(2x - 1) = 9}{\left(\frac{3}{2} + 3\right)\left(2 \cdot \frac{3}{2} - 1\right) \;\Big|\; 9}$$
$$\left(\frac{9}{2}\right)(2) \;\Big|\;$$
$$9 \overset{?}{=} 9 \quad \text{TRUE}$$

For -4:

$$\frac{(x + 3)(2x - 1) = 9}{(-4 + 3)(2(-4) - 1) \;\Big|\; 9}$$
$$(-1)(-9) \;\Big|\;$$
$$9 \overset{?}{=} 9 \quad \text{TRUE}$$

The solutions are $\frac{3}{2}$ and -4.

7. Solve:

$(3x + 4)(x - 1) = -2$.

YOUR TURN

EXPLORING 🔍 THE CONCEPT

Since an x-intercept is on the x-axis, the y-coordinate of an x-intercept will be 0. In order to find any x-intercepts of the graph of an equation, we can replace y with 0 and solve for x.

Graphs of quadratic equations of the form $y = ax^2 + bx + c$ are shaped as shown below. Each x-intercept represents a solution of $ax^2 + bx + c = 0$. For example, since 3 is a solution of $x^2 - 2x - 3 = 0$, then $(3, 0)$ is an x-intercept of the graph of $y = x^2 - 2x - 3$.

$$\boxed{\begin{array}{c} y = ax^2 + bx + c \\ a \neq 0 \end{array}}$$

No x-intercept
No real solution of
$ax^2 + bx + c = 0$

Two x-intercepts
Two different real
solutions of
$ax^2 + bx + c = 0$

One x-intercept
One real solution of
$ax^2 + bx + c = 0$

1. The x-intercepts of the graph of $y = x^2 + x - 6$ are shown on the graph at right. What are the solutions of $x^2 + x - 6 = 0$?

2. The solutions of $x^2 + 4x - 5 = 0$ are -5 and 1. What are the x-intercepts of the graph of $y = x^2 + 4x - 5$?

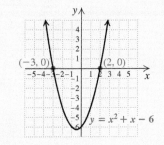

ANSWERS

1. $-3, 2$ 2. $(-5, 0), (1, 0)$

EXAMPLE 8   Find the x-intercepts of the graph of the equation shown. (The grid is intentionally not included.)

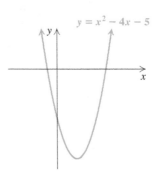

$$y = x^2 - 4x - 5$$

8. Find the x-intercepts of the graph of the equation shown.

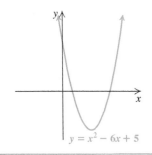

$$y = x^2 - 6x + 5$$

SOLUTION   To find the x-intercepts, we let $y = 0$ and solve for x:

$$0 = x^2 - 4x - 5 \qquad \text{Substituting 0 for } y$$
$$0 = (x - 5)(x + 1) \qquad \text{Factoring}$$
$$x - 5 = 0 \quad or \quad x + 1 = 0 \qquad \text{Using the principle of zero products}$$
$$x = 5 \quad or \qquad x = -1. \qquad \text{Solving for } x$$

The x-intercepts are $(5, 0)$ and $(-1, 0)$. The check is left to the student.

YOUR TURN

CONNECTING ⌘ THE CONCEPTS

Recall that an *equation* is a statement that two *expressions* are equal. When we simplify expressions, combine expressions, and form equivalent expressions, each result is an expression. When we are asked to solve an equation, the result is one or more numbers. Remember to read the directions to an exercise carefully so you do not attempt to "solve" an expression.

EXERCISES

For Exercises 1–4, tell whether each is an expression or an equation.

1. $x^2 - 25$

2. $x^2 - 25 = 0$

3. $x(x + 3) - 2(2x - 7) - (x - 5)$

4. $x = 10$

5. Add the expressions:
$$(2x^3 - 5x + 1) + (x^2 - 3x - 1).$$

6. Subtract the expressions:
$$(x^2 - x - 5) - (3x^2 - x + 6).$$

7. Solve the equation: $t^2 - 100 = 0$.

8. Multiply: $(3a - 2)(2a - 5)$.

9. Factor: $n^2 - 10n + 9$.

10. Solve: $x^2 + 16 = 10x$.

Technology Connection

A graphing calculator allows us to solve polynomial equations even when an equation cannot be solved by factoring. For example, to solve $x^2 - 3x - 5 = 0$, we can let $y_1 = x^2 - 3x - 5$ and $y_2 = 0$. Selecting a bold line type to the left of y_2 in the $\boxed{\text{Y=}}$ window makes the line easier to see. Using the INTERSECT option of the CALC menu, we select the two graphs in which we are interested, along with a guess. The graphing calculator displays the nearest point of intersection.

An alternative method uses only y_1 and the ZERO option of the CALC menu. This option requires you to enter an x-value to the left of each x-intercept as a LEFT BOUND. An x-value to the right of the x-intercept is then entered as a RIGHT BOUND. Finally, a GUESS value between the two bounds is entered and the x-intercept, or ZERO, is displayed.

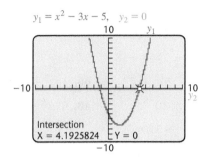

$y_1 = x^2 - 3x - 5, \quad y_2 = 0$

Intersection
X = 4.1925824   Y = 0

Use a graphing calculator to find the solutions, if they exist, accurate to two decimal places.

1. $x^2 + 4x - 3 = 0$
2. $x^2 - 5x - 2 = 0$
3. $x^2 + 13.54x + 40.95 = 0$
4. $x^2 - 4.43x + 6.32 = 0$
5. $1.235x^2 - 3.409x = 0$

5.7 EXERCISE SET

FOR EXTRA HELP

MyMathLab®   Math XP
PRACTICE   WATCH   READ   REVIEW

◆ Vocabulary and Reading Check

For each of Exercises 1–4, match the phrase with the most appropriate choice from the column on the right.

1. ____ The name of equations of the type $ax^2 + bx + c = 0$, with $a \neq 0$

2. ____ The maximum number of solutions of quadratic equations

3. ____ The idea that $A \cdot B = 0$ if and only if $A = 0$ or $B = 0$

4. ____ The number that a product must equal before the principle of zero products is used

    a) 2

    b) 0

    c) Quadratic

    d) The principle of zero products

The Principle of Zero Products

Solve using the principle of zero products.

5. $(x + 2)(x + 9) = 0$

6. $(x + 3)(x + 10) = 0$

7. $(x + 1)(x - 8) = 0$

8. $(x + 5)(x - 4) = 0$

9. $(2t - 3)(t + 6) = 0$

10. $(5t - 8)(t - 1) = 0$

11. $4(7x - 1)(10x - 3) = 0$

12. $6(4x - 3)(2x + 9) = 0$

13. $x(x - 7) = 0$

14. $x(x + 2) = 0$

15. $\left(\frac{2}{3}x - \frac{12}{11}\right)\left(\frac{7}{4}x - \frac{1}{12}\right) = 0$

16. $\left(\frac{1}{9} - 3x\right)\left(\frac{1}{5} + 2x\right) = 0$

17. $6n(3n + 8) = 0$

18. $10n(4n - 5) = 0$

19. $(20 - 0.4x)(7 - 0.1x) = 0$

20. $(1 - 0.05x)(1 - 0.3x) = 0$

Factoring to Solve Equations

Solve by factoring and using the principle of zero products.

21. $x^2 - 7x + 6 = 0$

22. $x^2 - 6x + 5 = 0$

23. $x^2 + 4x - 21 = 0$

24. $x^2 - 7x - 18 = 0$

25. $n^2 + 11n + 18 = 0$

26. $n^2 + 8n + 15 = 0$

27. $x^2 - 10x = 0$

28. $x^2 + 8x = 0$

29. $6t + t^2 = 0$

30. $3t - t^2 = 0$

31. $x^2 - 36 = 0$

32. $x^2 - 100 = 0$

33. $4t^2 = 49$

34. $9t^2 = 25$

35. $0 = 25 + x^2 + 10x$

36. $0 = 6x + x^2 + 9$

37. $64 + x^2 = 16x$

38. $x^2 + 1 = 2x$

39. $4t^2 = 8t$

40. $12t = 3t^2$

41. $4y^2 = 7y + 15$

42. $12y^2 - 5y = 2$

43. $(x - 7)(x + 1) = -16$

44. $(x + 2)(x - 7) = -18$

45. $15z^2 + 7 = 20z + 7$

46. $14z^2 - 3 = 21z - 3$

47. $36m^2 - 9 = 40$

48. $81x^2 - 5 = 20$

49. $(x + 3)(3x + 5) = 7$

50. $(x - 1)(5x + 4) = 2$

51. $3x^2 - 2x = 9 - 8x$

52. $x^2 - 2x = 18 + 5x$

53. $(6a + 1)(a + 1) = 21$

54. $(2t + 1)(4t - 1) = 14$

55. Use this graph to solve $x^2 - 3x - 4 = 0$.

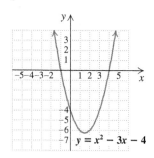

56. Use this graph to solve $x^2 + x - 6 = 0$.

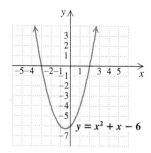

57. Use this graph to solve $-x^2 - x + 6 = 0$.

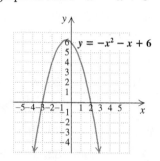

58. Use this graph to solve $-x^2 + 2x + 3 = 0$.

Find the x-intercepts for the graph of each equation. Grids are intentionally not included.

59. $y = x^2 - x - 6$

60. $y = x^2 + 3x - 4$

 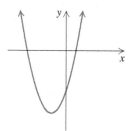

61. $y = x^2 + 2x - 8$

62. $y = x^2 - 2x - 15$

 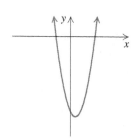

63. $y = 2x^2 + 3x - 9$

64. $y = 2x^2 + x - 10$

 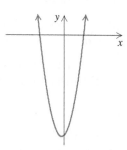

65. The equation $x^2 + 1 = 0$ has no real-number solutions. What implications does this have for the graph of $y = x^2 + 1$?

66. What is the difference between a quadratic polynomial and a quadratic equation?

Skill Review

67. Find the opposite of -65. [1.6]

68. Find the reciprocal of $\frac{3}{4}$. [1.7]

69. Find the absolute value of -1.65. [1.4]

70. Write 0.00068 in scientific notation. [4.2]

71. Write $-\frac{2}{3}$ in decimal notation. [1.4]

72. Write $\frac{5}{4}$ in percent notation. [2.4]

Synthesis

73. What is wrong with solving $x^2 = 3x$ by dividing both sides of the equation by x?

74. When the principle of zero products is used to solve a quadratic equation, will there always be two different solutions? Why or why not?

Solve.

75. $(2x - 11)(3x^2 + 29x + 56) = 0$

76. $(4x + 1)(15x^2 - 7x - 2) = 0$

77. Find an equation with integer coefficients that has the given numbers as solutions. For example, 3 and -2 are solutions of $x^2 - x - 6 = 0$.

    a) $-4, 5$ **b)** $-1, 7$ **c)** $\frac{1}{4}, 3$

    d) $\frac{1}{2}, \frac{1}{3}$ **e)** $\frac{2}{3}, \frac{3}{4}$ **f)** $-1, 2, 3$

Solve.

78. $16(x - 1) = x(x + 8)$

79. $a(9 + a) = 4(2a + 5)$

80. $(t - 5)^2 = 2(5 - t)$

81. $-x^2 + \frac{9}{25} = 0$

82. $a^2 = \frac{49}{100}$

Aha! **83.** $(t + 1)^2 = 9$

84. $\frac{27}{25}x^2 = \frac{1}{3}$

85. $x^3 - 2x^2 - x + 2 = 0$

86. $x^3 + 4x^2 - 9x - 36 = 0$

87. For each equation on the left, find an equivalent equation on the right.

    a) $x^2 + 10x - 2 = 0$ $4x^2 + 8x + 36 = 0$

    b) $(x - 6)(x + 3) = 0$ $(2x + 8)(2x - 5) = 0$

    c) $5x^2 - 5 = 0$ $9x^2 - 12x + 24 = 0$

    d) $(2x - 5)(x + 4) = 0$ $(x + 1)(5x - 5) = 0$

    e) $x^2 + 2x + 9 = 0$ $x^2 - 3x - 18 = 0$

    f) $3x^2 - 4x + 8 = 0$ $2x^2 + 20x - 4 = 0$

88. Explain how to construct an equation that has seven solutions.

89. Explain how the graph in Exercise 57 can be used to visualize the solutions of
$$-x^2 - x + 6 = 4.$$

Use a graphing calculator to find the solutions of each equation. Round solutions to the nearest hundredth.

90. $-x^2 + 0.63x + 0.22 = 0$

91. $x^2 - 9.10x + 15.77 = 0$

92. $6.4x^2 - 8.45x - 94.06 = 0$

93. $x^2 + 13.74x + 42.00 = 0$

94. $0.84x^2 - 2.30x = 0$

95. $1.23x^2 + 4.63x = 0$

96. $x^2 + 1.80x - 5.69 = 0$

97. The square of the sum of two consecutive integers is 225. What are the integers?

98. The sum of the squares of two consecutive integers is 313. What are the integers?

YOUR TURN ANSWERS: SECTION 5.7

1. $-5, 1$ **2.** $-2, -\frac{5}{3}$ **3.** $-9, 0$ **4.** $3, 5$ **5.** $0, 8$

6. -5 **7.** $-1, \frac{2}{3}$ **8.** $(1, 0)$ and $(5, 0)$

QUICK QUIZ: SECTIONS 5.1–5.7

1. Factor: $x^2 - 2x - 8$. [5.2]

2. Solve: $x^2 - 2x - 8 = 0$. [5.7]

3. Solve: $a^2 = 100$. [5.7]

4. Factor: $a^2 - 100$. [5.4]

5. Factor: $2a^2 + 40a + 200$. [5.4]

PREPARE TO MOVE ON

Translate to an algebraic expression. [1.1]

1. The square of the sum of two consecutive integers

2. The product of two consecutive integers

Solve. [2.5]

3. The first angle of a triangle is four times as large as the second. The measure of the third angle is 30° less than that of the second. How large are the angles?

4. A rectangular table top is twice as long as it is wide. The perimeter of the table is 192 in. What are the dimensions of the table?

5.8   Solving Applications

Applications   ■   The Pythagorean Theorem

Applications

We can use the five-step problem-solving process and our methods of solving quadratic equations to solve new types of problems.

EXAMPLE 1   *Race Numbers.*   Terry and Jody registered their boats in the Lakeport Race at the same time. The racing numbers assigned to their boats were consecutive numbers, the product of which was 156. Find the numbers.

Study Skills

Finishing a Chapter
Reaching the end of a chapter often signals the arrival of a quiz or a test. Almost always, it indicates the end of a particular area of study. Success in future work will depend on your mastery of previous topics studied. Use the chapter review and test to solidify your understanding of a chapter's material.

SOLUTION

1. **Familiarize.** Consecutive numbers are one apart, like 49 and 50. Let $x =$ the first boat number; then $x + 1 =$ the next boat number.

2. **Translate.** We reword the problem before translating:

    Rewording: The first boat number   times   the next boat number   is   156.

    Translating: x $\cdot$ $(x + 1)$ $=$ 156

3. **Carry out.** We solve the equation as follows:

$$x(x + 1) = 156$$
$$x^2 + x = 156 \qquad \text{Multiplying}$$
$$x^2 + x - 156 = 0 \qquad \text{Subtracting 156 to get 0 on one side}$$
$$(x - 12)(x + 13) = 0 \qquad \text{Factoring}$$
$$x - 12 = 0 \quad or \quad x + 13 = 0 \qquad \text{Using the principle of zero products}$$
$$x = 12 \quad or \qquad x = -13. \qquad \text{Solving each equation}$$

4. **Check.** The solutions of the equation are 12 and -13. Since race numbers are not negative, -13 must be rejected. On the other hand, if x is 12, then $x + 1$ is 13 and $12 \cdot 13 = 156$. Thus the solution 12 checks.

5. **State.** The boat numbers for Terry and Jody were 12 and 13.

YOUR TURN

1. Refer to Example 1. Suppose that the product of the racing numbers of the boats was 132. Find the numbers.

EXAMPLE 2   *Manufacturing.*   Wooden Work, Ltd., builds cutting boards that are twice as long as they are wide. The most popular board that Wooden Work makes has an area of 800 cm². What are the dimensions of the board?

SOLUTION

1. **Familiarize.** We first make a drawing. Recall that the area of any rectangle is Length · Width. We let $x =$ the width of the board, in centimeters. The length is then $2x$, since the board is twice as long as it is wide.

2. **Translate.** We reword and translate as follows:

Rewording: The area of the rectangle   is   800 cm².

Translating: $2x \cdot x$ $=$ 800

3. **Carry out.** We solve the equation as follows:

$$2x \cdot x = 800$$
$$2x^2 = 800$$
$$2x^2 - 800 = 0 \qquad \text{Subtracting 800 to get 0 on one side of the equation}$$
$$2(x^2 - 400) = 0 \qquad \text{Factoring out a common factor of 2}$$
$$2(x - 20)(x + 20) = 0 \qquad \text{Factoring a difference of squares}$$
$$x - 20 = 0 \quad or \quad x + 20 = 0 \qquad \text{Using the principle of zero products}$$
$$x = 20 \quad or \qquad x = -20. \qquad \text{Solving each equation}$$

2. Refer to Example 2. Wooden Work also builds a cutting board that has an area of 450 cm². This board is also twice as long as it is wide. What are the dimensions of this cutting board?

4. **Check.** The solutions of the equation are 20 and −20. Since the width must be positive, −20 cannot be a solution. To check 20 cm, we note that if the width is 20 cm, then the length is 2 · 20 cm = 40 cm and the area is 20 cm · 40 cm = 800 cm². Thus the solution 20 checks.

5. **State.** The cutting board is 20 cm wide and 40 cm long.

 YOUR TURN

EXAMPLE 3 *Dimensions of a Leaf.* Each leaf of one particular *Philodendron* species is approximately a triangle. A typical leaf has an area of 320 in². If the leaf is 12 in. longer than it is wide, find the length and the width of the leaf.

SOLUTION

1. **Familiarize.** The formula for the area of a triangle is Area = $\frac{1}{2} \cdot$ (base) · (height). We let $b =$ the width, in inches, of the triangle's base and $b + 12 =$ the height, in inches.

2. **Translate.** We reword and translate as follows:

Rewording: The area of the leaf   is   320 in².

Translating: $\frac{1}{2} \cdot b(b + 12)$ $=$ 320

3. Carry out. We solve the equation as follows:

$$\tfrac{1}{2} \cdot b \cdot (b + 12) = 320$$

$$\tfrac{1}{2}(b^2 + 12b) = 320 \qquad \text{Multiplying}$$

$$b^2 + 12b = 640 \qquad \text{Multiplying by 2 to clear fractions}$$

$$b^2 + 12b - 640 = 0 \qquad \text{Subtracting 640 to get 0 on one side}$$

$$(b + 32)(b - 20) = 0 \qquad \text{Factoring}$$

$$b + 32 = 0 \quad or \quad b - 20 = 0 \qquad \begin{array}{l}\text{Using the principle of} \\ \text{zero products}\end{array}$$

$$b = -32 \quad or \qquad b = 20.$$

3. Like the *Philodendron* in Example 3, each leaf of the *Triangular Leaf Senecio* approximates a triangle. One leaf of this plant is 6 in. longer than it is wide and has an area of 8 in². Find the length and the width of the leaf.

4. Check. The width must be positive, so -32 cannot be a solution. Suppose the base is 20 in. The height would be $20 + 12$, or 32 in., and the area $\tfrac{1}{2}(20)(32)$, or 320 in². These numbers check in the original problem.

5. State. The leaf is 32 in. long and 20 in. wide.

 YOUR TURN

Number of Minutes t After Injection	Number of Micrograms N of Epinephrine in the Bloodstream
2	160
5	250
8	160

EXAMPLE 4 *Medicine.* For certain people suffering an extreme allergic reaction, the drug epinephrine (adrenaline) is sometimes prescribed. The number of micrograms N of epinephrine in an adult's bloodstream t minutes after 250 micrograms have been injected is shown in the table at left for several values of t and can be approximated by

$$-10t^2 + 100t = N.$$

How long after an injection will there be about 210 micrograms of epinephrine in the bloodstream?

Source: Based on information in Chohan, Naina, Rita M. Doyle, and Patricia Nayle (eds.), *Nursing Handbook,* 21st ed. Springhouse, PA: Springhouse Corporation, 2001

SOLUTION

1. Familiarize. To familiarize ourselves with this problem, we could calculate N for different choices of t. We leave this to the student. Note that there may be two solutions, one on each side of the time at which the drug's effect peaks.

2. Translate. To find the length of time after injection when 210 micrograms are in the bloodstream, we replace N with 210 in the formula above:

$$-10t^2 + 100t = 210. \qquad \begin{array}{l}\text{Substituting 210 for } N. \text{ This is now an} \\ \text{equation in one variable.}\end{array}$$

3. Carry out. We solve the equation as follows:

$$-10t^2 + 100t = 210$$

$$-10t^2 + 100t - 210 = 0 \qquad \begin{array}{l}\text{Subtracting 210 from both sides} \\ \text{to get 0 on one side}\end{array}$$

$$-10(t^2 - 10t + 21) = 0 \qquad \begin{array}{l}\text{Factoring out the largest} \\ \text{common factor, } -10\end{array}$$

$$-10(t - 3)(t - 7) = 0 \qquad \text{Factoring}$$

$$t - 3 = 0 \quad or \quad t - 7 = 0 \qquad \begin{array}{l}\text{Using the principle of zero} \\ \text{products}\end{array}$$

$$t = 3 \quad or \qquad t = 7.$$

4. Refer to Example 4. How long after an injection will there be about 160 micrograms of epinephrine in the bloodstream?

4. Check. Since $-10 \cdot 3^2 + 100 \cdot 3 = -90 + 300 = 210$, the number 3 checks. Since $-10 \cdot 7^2 + 100 \cdot 7 = -490 + 700 = 210$, the number 7 also checks.

5. State. There will be 210 micrograms of epinephrine in the bloodstream approximately 3 minutes and 7 minutes after injection.

 YOUR TURN

Technology Connection

As a visual check for Example 4, we can either let $y_1 = -10x^2 + 100x$ and $y_2 = 210$, or let $y_1 = -10x^2 + 100x - 210$ and $y_2 = 0$. In either case, the points of intersection occur at $x = 3$ and $x = 7$, as shown.

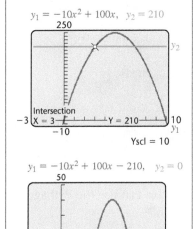

The Pythagorean Theorem

The following problems involve the Pythagorean theorem, which relates the lengths of the sides of a *right* triangle. A triangle is a **right triangle** if it has a 90°, or *right*, angle. The side opposite the 90° angle is called the **hypotenuse**. The other sides are called **legs**.

> ### THE PYTHAGOREAN THEOREM
>
> In any right triangle, if a and b are the lengths of the legs and c is the length of the hypotenuse, then
>
> $$a^2 + b^2 = c^2, \quad \text{or}$$
> $$(\text{Leg})^2 + (\text{Other leg})^2 = (\text{Hypotenuse})^2.$$
>
>
>
> The equation $a^2 + b^2 = c^2$ is called the **Pythagorean equation.**[*]

The Pythagorean theorem is named for the Greek mathematician Pythagoras (569?–500? B.C.). We can think of this relationship as adding areas.

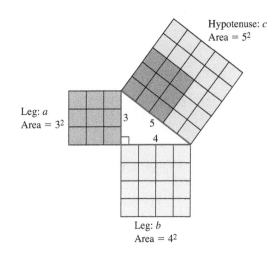

$$a^2 + b^2 = c^2$$
$$3^2 + 4^2 = 5^2$$
$$9 + 16 = 25$$

If we know the lengths of any two sides of a right triangle, we can use the Pythagorean equation to determine the length of the third side.

---

[*]The *converse* of the Pythagorean theorem is also true. That is, if $a^2 + b^2 = c^2$, then the triangle is a right triangle.

EXAMPLE 5   *Bridge Design.*   A 50-ft diagonal brace on a bridge connects a support under the road surface at the center of the bridge to a side support on the bridge. The horizontal distance that it spans is 10 ft longer than the height that it reaches at the center of the bridge. Find both distances.

SOLUTION

1. **Familiarize.** We first make a drawing. The diagonal brace and the missing distances form the hypotenuse and the legs of a right triangle. We let x = the length of the vertical leg. Then $x + 10$ = the length of the horizontal leg. The hypotenuse has length 50 ft.

2. **Translate.** Since the triangle is a right triangle, we can use the Pythagorean theorem:

$$a^2 + b^2 = c^2$$
$$x^2 + (x + 10)^2 = 50^2. \quad \text{Substituting}$$

3. **Carry out.** We solve the equation as follows:

$$x^2 + (x^2 + 20x + 100) = 2500 \qquad \text{Squaring}$$
$$2x^2 + 20x + 100 = 2500 \qquad \text{Combining like terms}$$
$$2x^2 + 20x - 2400 = 0 \qquad \text{Subtracting 2500 to get 0 on one side}$$
$$2(x^2 + 10x - 1200) = 0 \qquad \text{Factoring out a common factor}$$
$$2(x + 40)(x - 30) = 0 \qquad \text{Factoring. A calculator could be helpful here.}$$
$$x + 40 = 0 \quad or \quad x - 30 = 0 \qquad \text{Using the principle of zero products}$$
$$x = -40 \quad or \qquad x = 30.$$

4. **Check.** The integer -40 cannot be a length of a side because it is negative. If the length is 30 ft, then $x + 10 = 40$, and $30^2 + 40^2 = 900 + 1600 = 2500$, which is 50^2. So the solution 30 checks.

5. **State.** The height that the brace reaches at the center of the bridge is 30 ft, and the distance that it reaches to the middle of the bridge is 40 ft.

 YOUR TURN

Chapter Resource:
Translating for Success, p. 364

5. Refer to Example 5. Another brace on the bridge is also 50 ft long, but the horizontal distance that it spans is 34 ft longer than the height that it reaches at the center of the bridge. Find both distances.

5.8 EXERCISE SET

FOR EXTRA HELP

MyMathLab® Math XL

PRACTICE   WATCH   READ   REVIEW

Vocabulary and Reading Check

Complete each statement with the correct variable expression or number.

1. If x is an integer, then the next consecutive integer is _____.

2. If the length of a rectangle is twice its width and its width is w, then its length is _____.

3. A right triangle contains a(n) _____ angle.

4. If the legs of a right triangle have lengths a and b and the hypotenuse is length c, then _____.

Applications

Solve. Use the five-step problem-solving approach.

5. A number is 6 less than its square. Find all such numbers.

6. A number is 30 less than its square. Find all such numbers.

7. *Parking-Space Numbers.* The product of two consecutive parking space numbers is 132. Find the numbers.

8. *Page Numbers.* The product of the page numbers on two facing pages of a book is 420. Find the page numbers.

9. The product of two consecutive even integers is 168. Find the integers.

10. The product of two consecutive odd integers is 195. Find the integers.

11. *Construction.* The front porch on Trent's new home is five times as long as it is wide. If the area of the porch is 320 ft^2, find the dimensions.

12. *Furnishings.* The work surface of Anita's desk is a rectangle that is twice as long as it is wide. If the area of the desktop is 18 ft^2, find the length and the width of the desk.

13. A photo is 5 cm longer than it is wide. Find the length and the width if the area is 84 cm^2.

14. An envelope is 4 cm longer than it is wide. The area is 96 cm^2. Find the length and the width.

15. *Dimensions of a Sail.* The height of the jib sail on a Lightning sailboat is 5 ft greater than the length of its "foot." If the area of the sail is 42 ft^2, find the length of the foot and the height of the sail.

16. *Dimensions of a Sail.* The height of a triangular mainsail on a sailboat is 4 ft longer than the base of the sail. If the area of the sail is 38.5 ft^2, find the height and the base of the sail.

17. *Road Design.* A triangular traffic island has a base that is half as long as its height. Find the base and the height if the island has an area of 64 ft^2.

18. *Tent Design.* The triangular entrance to a tent is two-thirds as wide as it is tall. The area of the entrance is 12 ft^2. Find the height and the base.

Area = 12 ft^2 $\frac{2}{3}h$

19. *Cabin Design.* The front of an A-frame cabin in a national park is in the shape of a triangle, with an area of 60 ft^2. If the height is 1 ft less than twice the base, find the base and the height of the front of the cabin.

20. *Flower Garden Design.* The demonstration flower garden at a state fair is in the shape of a triangle. The base of the triangle is 6 m longer than twice the height. If the area is 28 m^2, find the base and the height of the flower garden.

Games in a League's Schedule. *In a sports league of x teams in which all teams play each other twice, the total number N of games played is given by*

$$x^2 - x = N.$$

Use this formula for Exercises 21 and 22.

21. The Colchester Youth Soccer League plays a total of 56 games, with all teams playing each other twice. How many teams are in the league?

22. The teams in a women's softball league play each other twice, for a total of 132 games. How many teams are in the league?

Number of Handshakes. *The number of possible handshakes H within a group of n people is given by H = $\frac{1}{2}(n^2 - n)$. Use this formula for Exercises 23–26.*

23. At a meeting, there are 12 people. How many handshakes are possible?

24. At a party, there are 25 people. How many handshakes are possible?

25. *High-Fives.* After winning the championship, all Dallas Maverick teammates exchanged hugs. Altogether there were 66 hugs. How many players were there?

26. *Toasting.* During a toast at a party, there were 105 "clicks" of glasses. How many people took part in the toast?

27. *Medicine.* For many people suffering from constricted bronchial muscles, the drug Albuterol is prescribed. The number of micrograms A of Albuterol in a person's bloodstream t minutes after 200 micrograms have been inhaled can be approximated by

$$A = -50t^2 + 200t.$$

How long after an inhalation will there be about 150 micrograms of Albuterol in the bloodstream?

Source: Based on information in Chohan, Naina, Rita M. Doyle, and Patricia Nayle (eds.), *Nursing Handbook*, 21st ed. Springhouse, PA: Springhouse Corporation, 2001

28. *Medicine.* For adults with certain heart conditions, the drug Primacor (milrinone lactate) is prescribed. The number of milligrams M of Primacor in the bloodstream of a 132-lb patient t hours after a 3-mg dose has been injected can be approximated by

$$M = -\tfrac{1}{2}t^2 + \tfrac{5}{2}t.$$

How long after an injection will there be about 2 mg in the bloodstream?

Source: Based on information in Chohan, Naina, Rita M. Doyle, and Patricia Nayle (eds.), *Nursing Handbook*, 21st ed. Springhouse, PA: Springhouse Corporation, 2001

29. *Wave Height.* The height of waves in a storm depends on the speed of the wind. Assuming the wind has no obstructions for a long distance, the maximum wave height H for a wind speed x can be approximated by

$$H = 0.03x^2 + 0.6x - 6,$$

where H is in feet and x is in knots (nautical miles per hour). For what wind speed would the maximum wave height be 3 ft?

Source: Based on information from Smith, Craig B., *Extreme Waves*, Joseph Henry Press, 2006

30. *Cabinet Making.* Dovetail Woodworking determines that the revenue R, in thousands of dollars, from the sale of x sets of cabinets is given by $R(x) = 2x^2 + x$. If the cost C, in thousands of dollars, of producing x sets of cabinets is given by $C(x) = x^2 - 2x + 10$, how many sets must be produced and sold in order for the company to break even?

The Pythagorean Theorem

31. *Construction.* The diagonal braces in a fire tower are 15 ft long and span a horizontal distance of 12 ft. How high does each brace reach vertically?

32. *Reach of a Ladder.* Twyla has a 26-ft ladder leaning against her house. If the bottom of the ladder is 10 ft from the base of the house, how high does the ladder reach?

33. *Zipline.* On one zipline in a canopy tour in Costa Rica, riders drop 58 ft while covering a distance of 840 ft along the ground. How long is the zipline?

34. *Roadway Design.* Elliott Street is 24 ft wide when it ends at Main Street in Brattleboro, Vermont. A 40-ft long diagonal crosswalk allows pedestrians to cross Main Street to or from either corner of Elliott Street (see the figure). Determine the width of Main Street.

35. *Archaeology.* Archaeologists have discovered that the 18th-century garden of the Charles Carroll House in Annapolis, Maryland, was a right triangle. One leg of the triangle was formed by a 400-ft long sea wall. The hypotenuse of the triangle was 200 ft longer than the other leg. What were the dimensions of the garden?

Source: www.bsos.umd.edu

36. *Guy Wire.* The height of a wind power assessment tower is 5 m shorter than the guy wire that supports it.

If the guy wire is anchored 15 m from the foot of the antenna, how tall is the antenna?

37. *Right Triangle.* The shortest side of a right triangle measures 7 m. The lengths of the other two sides are consecutive integers. Find the lengths of the other two sides.

38. *Right Triangle.* The shortest side of a right triangle measures 8 cm. The lengths of the other two sides are consecutive odd integers. Find the lengths of the other two sides.

39. *Right Triangle.* The longest side of a right triangle is 1 ft longer than three times the length of the shortest side. The other side of the triangle is 1 ft shorter than three times the length of the shortest side. Find the lengths of the sides of the triangle.

40. *Right Triangle.* The longest side of a right triangle is 5 yd shorter than six times the length of the shortest side. The other side of the triangle is 5 yd longer than five times the length of the shortest side. Find the lengths of the sides of the triangle.

Applications

41. *Architecture.* An architect has allocated a rectangular space of 264 ft^2 for a square dining room and a 10-ft wide kitchen, as shown in the figure. Find the dimensions of each room.

42. *Design.* A window panel for a sun porch consists of a 7-ft tall rectangular window stacked above a square window. The windows have the same width. If the total area of the window panel is 18 ft², find the dimensions of each window.

7 ft

Height of a Rocket. For Exercises 43–46, assume that a water rocket is launched upward with an initial velocity of 48 ft/sec. Its height h, in feet, after t seconds, is given by $h = 48t - 16t^2$.

43. Determine the height of the rocket $\frac{1}{2}$ sec after it has been launched.

44. Determine the height of the rocket 2.5 sec after it has been launched.

45. When will the rocket be exactly 32 ft above the ground?

46. When will the rocket crash into the ground?

47. Do we now have the ability to solve *any* problem that translates to a quadratic equation? Why or why not?

48. Write a problem for a classmate to solve such that only one of two solutions of a quadratic equation can be used as an answer.

Skill Review

Solve. Label any contradictions or identities.

49. $3(x - 2) = 5x + 2(3 - x)$ [2.2]

50. $9x - 2[4(x + 1)] = 4(x - 2 + x)$ [2.2]

51. $10x + 3 = 5(2x + 1) - 2$ [2.2]

Solve. Write the answers in both set-builder notation and interval notation.

52. $3 - y \geq 7$ [2.6]

53. $\frac{1}{3}x + \frac{1}{2} < \frac{1}{6}$ [2.6]

54. Solve $x + 2y = 7$ for y. [2.3]

Synthesis

The converse of the Pythagorean theorem is also true. That is, if $a^2 + b^2 = c^2$, then the triangle is a right triangle (where a and b are the lengths of the legs and c is the length of the hypotenuse). Use this result to answer Exercises 55 and 56.

55. An archaeologist has straight rods of 3 ft, 4 ft, and 5 ft. Explain how she could draw a 7-ft by 9-ft rectangle on a piece of land being excavated.

56. Explain how straight rods of 5 cm, 12 cm, and 13 cm can be used to draw a right triangle that has two 45° angles.

57. *Sailing.* The mainsail of a Lightning sailboat is a right triangle in which the hypotenuse is called the leech. If a 24-ft tall mainsail has a leech length of 26 ft and if Dacron® sailcloth costs $1.50 per square foot, find the cost of the fabric for a new mainsail.

26 ft

24 ft

58. *Roofing.* A *square* of shingles covers 100 ft² of surface area. How many squares will be needed to reshingle the house shown?

25 ft

16 ft

24 ft

32 ft

59. Solve for x.

60 cm

36 cm

x

63 cm

60. *Pool Sidewalk.* A cement walk of uniform width is built around a 20-ft by 40-ft rectangular pool. The total area of the pool and the walk is 1500 ft². Find the width of the walk.

61. *Folding Sheet Metal.* An open rectangular gutter is made by turning up the sides of a piece of metal 20 in. wide, as shown. The area of the cross section of the gutter is 48 in². Find the possible depths of the gutter.

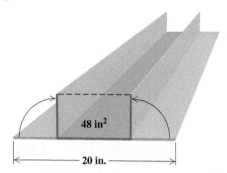

62. Find a polynomial for the shaded area surrounding the square in the figure below.

63. *Telephone Service.* Use the information in the figure below to determine the height of the telephone pole.

64. *Dimensions of a Closed Box.* The total surface area of a closed box is 350 m². The box is 9 m high and has a square base and lid. Find the length of a side of the base.

65. The maximum length of a postcard that can be mailed with one postcard stamp is $\frac{7}{4}$ in. longer than the maximum width. The maximum area is $\frac{51}{2}$ in². Find the maximum length and the maximum width of a postcard.

Source: USPS

 Medicine. For certain people with acid reflux, the drug Pepcid (famotidine) is used. The number of milligrams N of Pepcid in an adult's bloodstream t hours after a 20-mg tablet has been swallowed can be approximated by

$$N = -0.009t\,(t - 12)^3.$$

Use a graphing calculator with the window $[-1, 13, -1, 25]$ and the TRACE *feature to answer Exercises 66–68.*

Source: Based on information in Chohan, Naina, Rita M. Doyle, and Patricia Nayle (eds.), *Nursing Handbook*, 21st ed. Springhouse, PA: Springhouse Corporation, 2001

66. Approximately how long after a tablet has been swallowed will there be 18 mg in the bloodstream?

67. Approximately how long after a tablet has been swallowed will there be 10 mg in the bloodstream?

68. Approximately how long after a tablet has been swallowed will the peak dosage in the bloodstream occur?

69. *Research.* Find an online calculator that asks for the width, length, and height of a roof and calculates the roof area.

   a) The roof shown in Exercise 58 is a gable roof. Enter the dimensions of this roof in the online calculator and compare your answer with the one calculated for you.

   b) Develop a formula that could be used by the online calculator to find the roof area.

YOUR TURN ANSWERS: SECTION 5.8

1. 11 and 12   **2.** 15 cm wide and 30 cm long
3. 2 in. wide and 8 in. long   **4.** Approximately 2 min and 8 min after injection   **5.** Horizontal distance spanned: 48 ft; height at center of bridge: 14 ft

---

QUICK QUIZ: SECTIONS 5.1–5.8

1. Factor: $3x^3 - 15x^2 - 7x + 35$.   [5.1]

2. Solve: $20x^2 = 11x + 3$.   [5.7]

3. Factor: $10x^2 - 17x + 3$.   [5.3]

4. Factor: $6x^8 - 6$.   [5.4]

5. The hypotenuse of a right triangle is 1 ft longer than the length of the longer leg. The length of the shorter leg is 9 ft. Find the length of each side.   [5.8]

PREPARE TO MOVE ON

Simplify.   [1.3]

1. $\frac{24}{28}$ **2.** $\frac{90}{88}$ **3.** $\frac{124}{155}$

Divide, if possible.   [1.7]

4. $\frac{0}{7}$ **5.** $\frac{13}{0}$

1. *Angle Measures.* The degree measures of the angles of a triangle are three consecutive integers. Find the measures of the angles.

2. *Rectangle Dimensions.* The area of a rectangle is 3604 ft². The length is 15 ft longer than the width. Find the dimensions of the rectangle.

3. *Sales Tax.* Claire paid $3604 for a used pickup truck. This included 6% for sales tax. How much did the truck cost before tax?

4. *Wire Cutting.* A 180-m wire is cut into three pieces. The third piece is 2 m longer than the first. The second is two-thirds as long as the first. How long is each piece?

5. *Perimeter.* The perimeter of a rectangle is 240 ft. The length is 2 ft greater than the width. Find the length and the width.

Translating for Success

Use after Section 5.8.

Translate each word problem to an equation and select a correct translation from equations A–O.

A. $2x \cdot x = 288$

B. $x(x + 60) = 7021$

C. $59 = x \cdot 60$

D. $x^2 + (x + 15)^2 = 3604$

E. $x^2 + (x + 70)^2 = 130^2$

F. $0.06x = 3604$

G. $2(x + 2) + 2x = 240$

H. $\frac{1}{2}x(x - 1) = 1770$

I. $x + \frac{2}{3}x + (x + 2) = 180$

J. $0.59x = 60$

K. $x + 0.06x = 3604$

L. $2x^2 + x = 288$

M. $x(x + 15) \doteq 3604$

N. $x^2 + 60 = 7021$

O. $x + (x + 1) + (x + 2) = 180$

Answers on page A-26

An additional, animated version of this activity appears in MyMathLab. *To use MyMathLab, you need a course ID and a student access code. Contact your instructor for more information.*

6. *Cell-Phone Tower.* A guy wire on a cell-phone tower is 130 ft long and is attached to the top of the tower. The height of the tower is 70 ft longer than the distance from the point on the ground where the wire is attached to the bottom of the tower. Find the height of the tower.

7. *Sales Meeting Attendance.* PTQ Corporation holds a sales meeting in Tucson. Of the 60 employees, 59 of them attend the meeting. What percent attend the meeting?

8. *Dimensions of a Pool.* A rectangular swimming pool is twice as long as it is wide. The area of the surface is 288 ft². Find the dimensions of the pool.

9. *Dimensions of a Triangle.* The height of a triangle is 1 cm less than the length of the base. The area of the triangle is 1770 cm². Find the height and the length of the base.

10. *Width of a Rectangle.* The length of a rectangle is 60 ft longer than the width. Find the width if the area of the rectangle is 7021 ft².

Collaborative Activity   *Visualizing Factoring*

Focus: Visualizing factoring
Use after: Section 5.2
Time: 20–30 minutes
Group size: 3
Materials: Graph paper and scissors

Factoring a polynomial like $x^2 + 5x + 6$ can be thought of as determining the length and the width of a rectangle that has area $x^2 + 5x + 6$.

Activity

1. a) To factor $x^2 + 11x + 10$ geometrically, the group needs to cut out shapes like those below to represent x^2, $11x$, and 10. This can be done by either tracing the figures below or by selecting a value for x, say 4, and using the squares on the graph paper to cut out the following:

x^2:   Using the value selected for x, cut out a square that is x units on each side.

$11x$:   Using the value selected for x, cut out a rectangle that is 1 unit wide and x units long. Repeat this to form 11 such strips.

10:   Cut out two rectangles with whole-number dimensions and an area of 10. One should be 2 units by 5 units and the other 1 unit by 10 units.

b) The group, working together, should then attempt to use one of the two rectangles with area 10, along with all of the other shapes, to piece together one large rectangle. Only one of the rectangles with area 10 will work.

c) From the large rectangle formed in part (b), use the length and the width to determine the factorization of $x^2 + 11x + 10$. Where do the dimensions of the rectangle representing 10 appear in the factorization?

2. Repeat step (1) above, but this time use the other rectangle with area 10, and use only 7 of the 11 strips, along with the x^2-shape. Piece together the shapes to form one large rectangle. What factorization do the dimensions of this rectangle suggest?

3. Cut out rectangles with area 12 and use the above approach to factor $x^2 + 8x + 12$. What dimensions should be used for the rectangle with area 12?

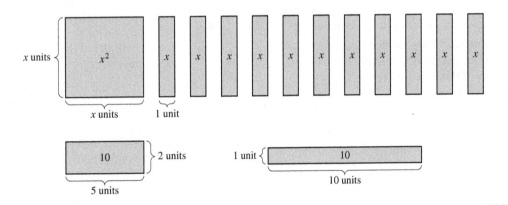

Collaborative Activity   *Matching Factorizations**

Focus: Factoring
Use after: Section 5.6
Time: 20 minutes
Group size: Begin with the entire class. If there is an odd number of students, the instructor should participate.
Materials: Prepared sheets of paper, pins or tape. On half of the sheets, the instructor writes a polynomial. On the remaining sheets, the instructor writes the factorization of those polynomials. The polynomials and factorizations are similar; for example,

$$x^2 - 2x - 8, \quad (x - 2)(x - 4),$$
$$x^2 - 6x + 8, \quad (x - 1)(x - 8),$$
$$x^2 - 9x + 8, \quad (x + 2)(x - 4)$$

Activity

1. As class members enter the room, the instructor pins or tapes either a polynomial or a factorization to the back of each student. Class members are told only whether their sheet of paper contains a polynomial or a factorization.

2. After all students are wearing a sheet of paper, they should mingle with one another, attempting to match up their factorization with the appropriate polynomial or vice versa. They may ask questions of one another that relate to factoring and polynomials. Answers to the questions should be yes or no. For example, a legitimate question might be "Is my last term negative?" or "Do my factors have opposite signs?"

3. The game is over when all factorization/polynomial pairs have "found" one another.

---

*Thanks to Jann MacInnes of Florida Community College at Jacksonville–Kent Campus for suggesting this activity.

Decision Making ℰ Connection

Designing a Tournament.   The number of games in a tournament varies widely depending on the type of tournament being played.

In a *single elimination* tournament, a player or team is eliminated after one loss.

In a *double elimination* tournament, a player or team is eliminated after losing twice.

In a *round-robin* tournament, each team plays every other team once, and a winner is chosen on the basis of the win–loss records.

In a *double round-robin* tournament, each team plays every other team twice.

Other types of tournaments include ladder and pyramid tournaments.

1. The number of games G required for a round-robin tournament with n teams is given by $G = \frac{1}{2}n^2 - \frac{1}{2}n$. If 15 basketball teams enter a round-robin tournament, how many games must be played?

2. The number of games G required for a double round-robin tournament with n teams is given by $G = n^2 - n$. If 15 basketball teams enter a double round-robin tournament, how many games must be played?

(Use after Section 5.1.)

3. Ideally, in a round-robin tournament, all the teams play at the same time. If there is an even number of teams, then there will be $n/2$ games occurring simultaneously during each round. If there is an odd number of teams, then $(n - 1)/2$ games will occur simultaneously, with one team resting for each round. Use this information and the formula given in Exercise 1 to find a formula for the number of rounds needed for an even number of teams and the number for an odd number of teams.

4. *Research.*   Find the number of games required in a single elimination tournament with n teams.

5. *Research.*   Find the number of games required in a double elimination tournament with n teams. Is there a minimum number or a maximum number?

6. If you were planning a chess tournament, what type of tournament would you choose? How many players would you invite to participate?

Study Summary

KEY TERMS AND CONCEPTS	EXAMPLES	PRACTICE EXERCISES

SECTION 5.1: *Introduction to Factoring*

KEY TERMS AND CONCEPTS	EXAMPLES	PRACTICE EXERCISES
To **factor** a polynomial means to write it as a product of polynomials. Always begin by factoring out the **largest common factor**.	$12x^4 - 30x^3 = 6x^3(2x - 5)$	**1.** Factor: $12x^4 - 18x^3 + 30x.$
Some polynomials with four terms can be **factored by grouping**.	$3x^3 - x^2 - 6x + 2 = x^2(3x - 1) - 2(3x - 1)$ $\qquad\qquad\qquad = (3x - 1)(x^2 - 2)$	**2.** Factor: $2x^3 - 6x^2 - x + 3.$

SECTION 5.2: *Factoring Trinomials of the Type $x^2 + bx + c$*

KEY TERMS AND CONCEPTS	EXAMPLES	PRACTICE EXERCISES
Some trinomials of the type $x^2 + bx + c$ can be factored by reversing the steps of FOIL.	Factor: $x^2 - 11x + 18.$ <table><tr><th>Pairs of Factors of 18</th><th>Sums of Factors</th></tr><tr><td>$-1, -18$</td><td>-19</td></tr><tr><td>$-2,\ -9$</td><td>-11</td></tr></table> The factorization is $(x - 2)(x - 9)$.	**3.** Factor: $x^2 - 7x - 18.$

SECTION 5.3: *Factoring Trinomials of the Type $ax^2 + bx + c$*

KEY TERMS AND CONCEPTS	EXAMPLES	PRACTICE EXERCISES
One method for factoring trinomials of the type $ax^2 + bx + c$ is a FOIL-based method.	Factor: $6x^2 - 5x - 6.$ The factors will be in the form $(3x + \ )(2x + \ )$ or $(6x + \ )(x + \ )$. We list all pairs of factors of -6, and check possible products by multiplying those possibilities that do not contain a common factor. $(3x - 2)(2x + 3) = 6x^2 + 5x - 6,$ $(3x + 2)(2x - 3) = 6x^2 - 5x - 6 \longleftarrow$ This is the correct product. The factorization is $(3x + 2)(2x - 3)$.	**4.** Factor: $6x^2 + x - 2.$

Another method for factoring trinomials of the type $ax^2 + bx + c$ involves factoring by grouping.

Factor: $6x^2 - 5x - 6$.

Multiply the leading coefficient and the constant term: $6(-6) = -36$. Look for factors of -36 that add to -5.

Pairs of Factors of −36	Sums of Factors
1, −36	−35
2, −18	−16
3, −12	−9
4, −9	−5

Rewrite $-5x$ as $4x - 9x$ and factor by grouping:
$$6x^2 - 5x - 6 = 6x^2 + 4x - 9x - 6$$
$$= 2x(3x + 2) - 3(3x + 2)$$
$$= (3x + 2)(2x - 3).$$

5. Factor:
$$8x^2 - 22x + 15.$$

SECTION 5.4: *Factoring Perfect-Square Trinomials and Differences of Squares*

Factoring a Perfect-Square Trinomial
$A^2 + 2AB + B^2 = (A + B)^2$;
$A^2 - 2AB + B^2 = (A - B)^2$

Factor: $y^2 + 100 - 20y$.

$$A^2 - 2AB + B^2 = (A - B)^2$$

$$y^2 + 100 - 20y = y^2 - 20y + 100 = (y - 10)^2$$

6. Factor:
$$100n^2 + 81 + 180n.$$

Factoring a Difference of Squares
$A^2 - B^2 = (A + B)(A - B)$

Factor: $9t^2 - 1$.

$$A^2 - B^2 = (A + B)(A - B)$$

$$9t^2 - 1 = (3t + 1)(3t - 1)$$

7. Factor:
$$144t^2 - 25.$$

SECTION 5.5: *Factoring Sums or Differences of Cubes*

Factoring a Sum or a Difference of Cubes
$A^3 + B^3$
$= (A + B)(A^2 - AB + B^2)$
$A^3 - B^3$
$= (A - B)(A^2 + AB + B^2)$

$x^3 + 1000 = (x + 10)(x^2 - 10x + 100)$

$z^6 - 8w^3 = (z^2 - 2w)(z^4 + 2wz^2 + 4w^2)$

8. Factor: $a^3 - 1$.

SECTION 5.6: *Factoring: A General Strategy*

A general strategy for factoring polynomials can be found in Section 5.6.

Factor: $5x^5 - 80x$.
$5x^5 - 80x = 5x(x^4 - 16)$ $5x$ is the largest common factor.

$= 5x(x^2 + 4)(x^2 - 4)$ $x^4 - 16$ is a difference of squares.

$= 5x(x^2 + 4)(x + 2)(x - 2)$ $x^2 - 4$ is also a difference of squares.

Check:
$$5x(x^2 + 4)(x + 2)(x - 2) = 5x(x^2 + 4)(x^2 - 4)$$
$$= 5x(x^4 - 16)$$
$$= 5x^5 - 80x.$$

9. Factor:
$$3x^3 - 36x^2 + 108x.$$

SECTION 5.7:   *Solving Quadratic Equations by Factoring*

The Principle of Zero Products An equation $AB = 0$ is true if and only if $A = 0$ or $B = 0$, or both A and B are 0.	Solve: $2x^2 = 8x$. $$2x^2 - 8x = 0 \quad \text{Getting 0 on one side}$$ $$2x(x - 4) = 0 \quad \text{Factoring}$$ $$2x = 0 \quad or \quad x - 4 = 0 \quad \text{Using the principle of zero products}$$ $$x = 0 \quad or \qquad x = 4$$ The solutions are 0 and 4.	**10.** Solve: $$x^2 + 7x = 30.$$

SECTION 5.8:   *Solving Applications*

The Pythagorean Theorem In any right triangle, if a and b are the lengths of the legs and c is the length of the hypotenuse, then $a^2 + b^2 = c^2$.	Find the lengths of the legs in this triangle. $$x^2 + (x + 1)^2 = 5^2$$ $$x^2 + x^2 + 2x + 1 = 25$$ $$2x^2 + 2x - 24 = 0$$ $$x^2 + x - 12 = 0$$ $$(x + 4)(x - 3) = 0$$ $$x + 4 = 0 \quad or \quad x - 3 = 0$$ $$x = -4 \quad or \qquad x = 3$$ Since lengths are not negative, -4 is not a solution. The lengths of the legs are 3 and 4.	**11.** Find the lengths of the sides in this triangle.

Review Exercises: Chapter 5

⮞ Concept Reinforcement

Classify each of the following statements as either true or false.

1. The largest common variable factor is the largest power of the variable in the polynomial.   [5.1]

2. A prime polynomial has no common factor other than 1 or -1.   [5.2]

3. Every perfect-square trinomial can be expressed as a binomial squared.   [5.4]

4. Every binomial can be regarded as a difference of squares.   [5.4]

5. Every quadratic equation has two different solutions.   [5.7]

6. The principle of zero products can be applied whenever a product equals 0.   [5.7]

7. In a right triangle, the hypotenuse is always longer than either leg.   [5.8]

8. The Pythagorean theorem can be applied to any triangle that has an angle measuring at least 90°.   [5.8]

Find three factorizations of each monomial.   [5.1]

9. $20x^3$

10. $-18x^5$

Factor completely. If a polynomial is prime, state this.

11. $12x^4 - 18x^3$ [5.1]

12. $100t^2 - 1$ [5.4]

13. $x^2 + x - 12$ [5.2]

14. $x^2 + 14x + 49$ [5.4]

15. $12x^3 + 12x^2 + 3x$ [5.4]

16. $6x^3 + 9x^2 + 2x + 3$ [5.1]

17. $6a^2 + a - 5$ [5.3]

18. $25t^2 + 9 - 30t$ [5.4]

19. $81a^4 - 1$ [5.4]

20. $9x^3 + 12x^2 - 45x$ [5.3]

21. $2x^3 - 250$ [5.5]

22. $x^4 + 4x^3 - 2x - 8$ [5.1]

23. $a^2b^4 - 64$ [5.4]

24. $-8x^6 + 32x^5 - 4x^4$ [5.1]

25. $75 + 12x^2 - 60x$ [5.4]

26. $y^2 + 9$ [5.4]

27. $-t^3 + t^2 + 42t$ [5.2]

28. $4x^2 - 25$ [5.4]

29. $n^2 - 60 - 4n$ [5.2]

30. $5z^2 - 30z + 10$ [5.1]

31. $8y^3 + 27x^6$ [5.5]

32. $2t^2 - 7t - 4$ [5.3]

33. $7x^3 + 35x^2 + 28x$ [5.2]

34. $-6x^3 + 150x$ [5.4]

35. $15 - 8x + x^2$ [5.2]

36. $3x + x^2 + 5$ [5.2]

37. $x^2y^2 + 6xy - 16$ [5.2]

38. $12a^2 + 84ab + 147b^2$ [5.4]

39. $m^2 + 5m + mt + 5t$ [5.1]

40. $6r^2 + rs - 15s^2$ [5.3]

Solve. [5.7]

41. $(x - 9)(x + 11) = 0$

42. $x^2 + 2x - 35 = 0$

43. $16x^2 = 9$

44. $3x^2 + 2 = 5x$

45. $(x + 1)(x - 2) = 4$

46. $9t - 15t^2 = 0$

47. $3x^2 + 3 = 6x$

48. The square of a number is 12 more than the number. Find all such numbers. [5.8]

49. A stone is tossed down from a cliff at an initial velocity of 4 ft/sec. The distance s that the stone falls after t seconds is given by $s = 4t + 16t^2$. If the cliff is 420 ft tall, in how many seconds will the stone reach the bottom of the cliff? [5.8]

50. Find the x-intercepts of the graph of $y = 2x^2 - 3x - 5$. [5.7]

51. The front of a house is a triangle that is as wide as it is tall. Its area is 98 ft². Find the height and the base. [5.8]

52. Josh needs to add a diagonal brace to his LEGO® robot. The brace must span a height of 8 holes and a width of 6 holes. How long should the brace be? [5.8]

Synthesis

53. On a quiz, Celia writes the factorization of $4x^2 - 100$ as $(2x - 10)(2x + 10)$. If this were a 10-point question, how many points would you give Celia? Why? [5.4]

54. How does solving quadratic equations differ from solving linear equations? [5.7]

Solve.

55. The pages of a book measure 15 cm by 20 cm. Margins of equal width surround the printing on each page and constitute one-half of the area of the page. Find the width of the margins. [5.8]

15 cm

20 cm

> When in the Course of human events, it becomes necessary for one people to dissolve the political bands which have connected them with another, and to assume among the powers of the earth, the separate and equal station to which the Laws of Nature and of

> Nature's God entitle them, a decent respect to the opinions of mankind requires that they should declare the causes which impel them to the separation.
> We hold these truths to be self-evident, that all men are created equal, that they are endowed by their Creator with certain unalienable

56. The cube of a number is the same as twice the square of the number. Find the number. [5.8]

57. The length of a rectangle is two times its width. When the length is increased by 20 cm and the width is decreased by 1 cm, the area is 160 cm². Find the original length and width. [5.8]

Solve. [5.7]

58. $(x - 2)2x^2 + x(x - 2) - (x - 2)15 = 0$

Aha! **59.** $x^2 + 25 = 0$

Test: Chapter 5

For step-by-step test solutions, access the Chapter Test Prep Videos in MyMathLab®, on YouTube® (search "Bittinger Combo AlgCA" and click on "Channels"), or by scanning the code.

Factor completely. If a polynomial is prime, state this.

1. $x^2 - 13x + 36$

2. $x^2 + 25 - 10x$

3. $6y^2 - 8y^3 + 4y^4$

4. $x^3 + x^2 + 2x + 2$

5. $t^7 - 3t^5$

6. $a^3 + 3a^2 - 4a$

7. $28x - 48 + 10x^2$

8. $4t^2 - 25$

9. $-6m^3 - 9m^2 - 3m$

10. $3r^3 - 3$

11. $45r^2 + 60r + 20$

12. $3x^4 - 48$

13. $49t^2 + 36 + 84t$

14. $x^4 + 2x^3 - 3x - 6$

15. $x^2 + 3x + 6$

16. $6t^3 + 9t^2 - 15t$

17. $3m^2 - 9mn - 30n^2$

Solve.

18. $x^2 - 6x + 5 = 0$

19. $2x^2 - 7x = 15$

20. $4t - 10t^2 = 0$

21. $25t^2 = 1$

22. $x(x - 1) = 20$

23. Find the x-intercepts of the graph of $y = 3x^2 - 5x - 8$.

24. The length of a rectangle is 6 m more than the width. The area of the rectangle is 40 m². Find the length and the width.

25. The number of possible handshakes H within a group of n people is given by $H = \frac{1}{2}(n^2 - n)$. At a meeting, everyone shook hands once with everyone else. If there were 45 handshakes, how many people were at the meeting?

26. A mason wants to be sure she has a right corner in a building's foundation. She marks a point 3 ft from the corner along one wall and another point 4 ft from the corner along the other wall. If the corner is a right angle, what should the distance be between the two marked points?

Synthesis

27. *Dimensions of an Open Box.*   A rectangular piece of cardboard is twice as long as it is wide. A 4-cm square is cut out of each corner, and the sides are turned up to make a box with an open top. The volume of the box is 616 cm³. Find the original dimensions of the cardboard.

28. Factor: $(a + 3)^2 - 2(a + 3) - 35$.

29. Solve: $20x(x + 2)(x - 1) = 5x^3 - 24x - 14x^2$.

Cumulative Review: Chapters 1–5

Simplify. Do not use negative exponents in the answer.

1. $\frac{3}{8} \div \frac{3}{4}$ [1.3]

2. $\frac{3}{8} + \frac{3}{4}$ [1.3]

3. $-2 + (20 \div 4)^2 - 6 \cdot (-1)^3$ [1.8]

4. $(3x^2y^3)^{-2}$ [4.2]

5. $(t^2)^3 \cdot t^4$ [4.1]

6. $(3x^4 - 2x^2 + x - 7) + (5x^3 + 2x^2 - 3)$ [4.4]

7. $\dfrac{3t^3s^{-1}}{12t^{-5}s}$ [4.2]

8. $\left(\dfrac{-2x^2y}{3z^4}\right)^3$ [4.1]

9. Evaluate $-x$ for $x = -8$. [1.6]

10. Determine the leading term of the polynomial
$4x^3 - 6x^2 - x^4 + 7$. [4.3]

11. Divide: $(8x^4 - 20x^3 + 2x^2 - 4x) \div (4x)$. [4.8]

Multiply.

12. $-4t^8(t^3 - 2t - 5)$ [4.5]

13. $(3x - 5)^2$ [4.6]

14. $(10x^5 + y)(10x^5 - y)$ [4.7]

Factor completely.

15. $c^2 - 1$ [5.4]

16. $5x + 5y + 10x^2 + 10xy$ [5.1]

17. $4r^2 - 4rt + t^2$ [5.4]

18. $10y^2 + 40$ [5.1]

19. $x^2y - 3xy + 2y$ [5.2]

20. $12x^2 - 5xy - 2y^2$ [5.3]

Solve.

21. $\frac{1}{3} + 2x = \frac{1}{2}$ [2.2]

22. $8y - 6(y - 2) = 3(2y + 7)$ [2.2]

23. $3x - 7 \geq 4 - 8x$ [2.6]

24. $x^2 + x = 12$ [5.7]

25. $3x^2 = 12$ [5.7]

26. $3x^2 = 12x$ [5.7]

27. Solve $a = bc + dc$ for c. [2.3]

28. Find the slope of the line containing the points $(6, 7)$ and $(-2, 7)$. [3.5]

29. Write the slope–intercept equation for the line with slope 5 that contains the point $\left(-\frac{1}{3}, 0\right)$. [3.7]

Graph.

30. $4(x + 1) = 8$ [3.3]

31. $x + y = 5$ [3.3]

32. $y = \frac{3}{2}x - 2$ [3.6]

33. $3x + 5y = 10$ [3.6]

Solve.

34. On average, men talk 97 min more per month on cell phones than do women. The sum of men's average minutes and women's average minutes is 647 min. What is the average number of minutes per month that men talk on cell phones? [2.5]

    Source: International Communications Research for Cingular Wireless

35. A 13-ft ladder is placed against a building in such a way that the distance from the top of the ladder to the ground is 7 ft more than the distance from the bottom of the ladder to the building. Find both distances. [5.8]

36. Donna's quiz grades are 8, 3, 5, and 10. What scores on the fifth quiz will make her average quiz grade at least 7? [2.7]

37. The average amount of sodium in a serving of Chef Boyardee foods dropped from 1100 mg in 2003 to 750 mg in 2011. [3.7]

    Source: The Indianapolis Star, 11/25/07; Chef Boyardee

    a) Graph the data and determine an equation for the related line. Let s represent the average amount of sodium per serving and t the number of years after 2000.

    b) Use the equation of part (a) to estimate the average amount of sodium in a serving of Chef Boyardee foods in 2007.

Synthesis

38. Solve $x = \dfrac{abx}{2 - b}$ for b. [2.3]

39. Solve: $6x^3 + 4x^2 = 2x$. [5.7]

Rational Expressions and Equations

BIRD OR AIRPLANE	WING SPAN	WING WIDTH
Grey heron	180 cm	24 cm
House sparrow	10 in.	1.8 in.
Albatross	9 ft	0.6 ft
Concorde (retired in 2003)	84 ft	47 ft
Boeing 747-400	64 m	8 m

Different Jobs Require Different Wings.

The shape of a wing determines whether a bird or an airplane excels at speed, hovering, or tight maneuvering. One description of a wing's shape is the *wing aspect ratio*: the ratio of the wing span to the wing width. Birds and planes that soar or glide have wings of high aspect ratio; wings of low aspect ratio allow more maneuverability and produce less drag at high speeds. Which of the birds in the table above do you think has a wing aspect ratio the same as that of a small single-engine airplane? (*See Exercises 53 and 54 in Exercise Set 6.7.*)

As a research wildlife biologist, I use math in many ways in every one of my projects.

Cheryl Dykstra, Ph.D., a wildlife biologist in West Chester, Ohio, has used math to calculate the surface area of the wings of nestling bald eagles in order to determine eaglets' heat exchange and energy needs. She also uses math, especially statistics, to understand and to explain her data to other researchers.

Rational expressions are similar to fractions in arithmetic. In this chapter, we learn how to simplify, add, subtract, multiply, and divide rational expressions. These skills are then used to solve equations that arise from real-life problems like the one on the preceding page.

6.1 Rational Expressions

Restricting Replacement Values ▪ Simplifying Rational Expressions ▪ Factors That Are Opposites

Just as a rational number is any number that can be written as a quotient of two integers, a **rational expression** is any expression that can be written as a quotient of two polynomials. The following are examples of rational expressions:

$$\frac{7}{3}, \quad \frac{5}{x+6}, \quad \frac{t^2 - 5t + 6}{4t^2 - 7}.$$

Rational expressions are examples of *algebraic fractions*. They are also examples of *fraction expressions*.

Study Skills

Try an Exercise Break
Often the best way to regain your energy or focus is to take a break from your studies in order to exercise. Jogging, biking, or walking briskly are just a few of the activities that can improve your concentration.

Restricting Replacement Values

Because rational expressions may contain variables in a denominator, and because division by 0 is undefined, we must avoid certain replacement values. For example, in the expression

$$\frac{x+5}{x-7},$$

when x is replaced with 7, the denominator is 0, and the expression is undefined:

$$\frac{x+5}{x-7} = \frac{7+5}{7-7} = \frac{12}{0}. \qquad \text{Division by 0 is undefined.}$$

When x is replaced with a number other than 7, such as 6, the expression *is* defined because the denominator is not 0:

$$\frac{x+5}{x-7} = \frac{6+5}{6-7} = \frac{11}{-1} = -11.$$

The expression is also defined when $x = -5$:

$$\frac{x+5}{x-7} = \frac{-5+5}{-5-7} = \frac{0}{-12} = 0. \qquad \text{0 divided by a nonzero number is 0.}$$

Any replacement for the variable that makes the *denominator* 0 will cause an expression to be undefined.

EXAMPLE 1 Find all numbers for which the rational expression

$$\frac{x+4}{x^2 - 3x - 10}$$

is undefined.

Technology Connection

To check Example 1 with a graphing calculator, let $y_1 = x^2 - 3x - 10$ and $y_2 = (x + 4)/y_1$ and use the TABLE feature. Since $x^2 - 3x - 10$ is 0 for $x = 5$, it is impossible to evaluate y_2 for $x = 5$.

TBLSTART = 0   ΔTBL = 1

X	Y₁	Y₂
0	−10	−.4
1	−12	−.4167
2	−12	−.5
3	−10	−.7
4	−6	−1.333
5	0	ERROR
6	8	1.25

X = 5

1. Find all numbers for which the rational expression $\dfrac{x^2 - x - 2}{x^2 - 25}$ is undefined.

SOLUTION   To determine which numbers make the rational expression undefined, we set the *denominator* equal to 0 and solve:

$$x^2 - 3x - 10 = 0 \qquad \text{We set the denominator equal to 0.}$$
$$(x - 5)(x + 2) = 0 \qquad \text{Factoring}$$
$$x - 5 = 0 \quad or \quad x + 2 = 0 \qquad \text{Using the principle of zero products}$$
$$x = 5 \quad or \qquad x = -2. \qquad \text{Solving each equation}$$

Check:

For $x = 5$:

$$\frac{x + 4}{x^2 - 3x - 10} = \frac{5 + 4}{5^2 - 3 \cdot 5 - 10}$$
$$= \frac{9}{25 - 15 - 10} = \frac{9}{0}. \qquad \text{This expression is undefined, as expected.}$$

For $x = -2$:

$$\frac{x + 4}{x^2 - 3x - 10} = \frac{-2 + 4}{(-2)^2 - 3(-2) - 10}$$
$$= \frac{2}{4 + 6 - 10} = \frac{2}{0}. \qquad \text{This expression is undefined, as expected.}$$

Thus, $\dfrac{x + 4}{x^2 - 3x - 10}$ is undefined for $x = 5$ and $x = -2$.

 YOUR TURN

Simplifying Rational Expressions

A rational expression is said to be *simplified* when the numerator and the denominator have no factors (other than 1) in common. To simplify a rational expression that contains variables, we use the same process we would use to simplify $\frac{15}{40}$:

$$\frac{15}{40} = \frac{3 \cdot 5}{8 \cdot 5} \qquad \text{Factoring the numerator and the denominator. Note the common factor, 5.}$$

$$= \frac{3}{8} \cdot \frac{5}{5} \qquad \text{Rewriting as a product of two fractions}$$

$$= \frac{3}{8} \cdot 1 \qquad \frac{5}{5} = 1$$

$$= \frac{3}{8}. \qquad \text{Using the identity property of 1 to remove the factor 1}$$

Student Notes

When using a graphing calculator or tutorial software, you may need to use parentheses around the numerator and around the denominator of rational expressions. For example,

$$5/3x \quad \text{means} \quad \frac{5}{3}x$$

and

$$5/(3x) \quad \text{means} \quad \frac{5}{3x}.$$

Similar steps are followed when simplifying rational expressions: We factor and remove a factor equal to 1, using the fact that

$$\frac{ab}{cb} = \frac{a}{c} \cdot \frac{b}{b} \quad \text{and} \quad \frac{a}{c} \cdot \frac{b}{b} = \frac{a}{c}.$$

EXAMPLE 2 Simplify: $\dfrac{8x^2}{24x}$.

SOLUTION

$$\dfrac{8x^2}{24x} = \dfrac{8 \cdot x \cdot x}{3 \cdot 8 \cdot x}$$
Factoring the numerator and the denominator. Note that the greatest common factor is $8 \cdot x$.

$$= \dfrac{x}{3} \cdot \dfrac{8x}{8x}$$
Rewriting as a product of two rational expressions

$$= \dfrac{x}{3} \cdot 1 \qquad \dfrac{8x}{8x} = 1$$

$$= \dfrac{x}{3}$$
Removing the factor 1

2. Simplify: $\dfrac{15ab^2}{20b}$.

 YOUR TURN

We say that $\dfrac{8x^2}{24x}$ *simplifies to* $\dfrac{x}{3}$. In more advanced courses, we would say that $8x^2/(24x)$ simplifies to $x/3$, *with the restriction that* $x \neq 0$. In the work that follows, we assume that all denominators are nonzero.

EXAMPLE 3 Simplify: $\dfrac{5a + 15}{10}$.

SOLUTION

$$\dfrac{5a + 15}{10} = \dfrac{5(a + 3)}{5 \cdot 2}$$
Factoring the numerator and the denominator. The greatest common factor is 5.

$$= \dfrac{5}{5} \cdot \dfrac{a + 3}{2}$$
Rewriting as a product of two rational expressions

$$= 1 \cdot \dfrac{a + 3}{2} \qquad \dfrac{5}{5} = 1$$

$$= \dfrac{a + 3}{2}$$
Removing the factor 1

3. Simplify: $\dfrac{16}{2x + 10}$.

 YOUR TURN

The result in Example 3 can be partially checked using a replacement for a—say, $a = 2$.

Original expression:

$$\dfrac{5a + 15}{10} = \dfrac{5 \cdot 2 + 15}{10}$$

$$= \dfrac{25}{10} = \dfrac{5}{2} \quad \text{The results are the same.}$$

Simplified expression:

$$\dfrac{a + 3}{2} = \dfrac{2 + 3}{2}$$

$$= \dfrac{5}{2}$$

Student Notes

Checking by evaluating is only a partial check. To see why this check is not foolproof, see Exercise 69.

If we do not get the same result when evaluating both expressions, we know that a mistake has been made. For example, if $(5a + 15)/10$ is *incorrectly* simplified as $(a + 15)/2$ and we evaluate using $a = 2$, we have the following.

Original expression:

$$\dfrac{5a + 15}{10} = \dfrac{5 \cdot 2 + 15}{10}$$

$$= \dfrac{5}{2} \quad \text{The results are different.}$$

Incorrectly simplified expression:

$$\dfrac{a + 15}{2} = \dfrac{2 + 15}{2}$$

$$= \dfrac{17}{2}$$

This demonstrates that a mistake has been made.

Sometimes the common factor has two or more terms.

EXAMPLE 4 Simplify.

a) $\dfrac{6x - 12}{7x - 14}$

b) $\dfrac{18t^2 + 6t}{6t^2 + 15t}$

c) $\dfrac{x^2 + 3x + 2}{x^2 - 1}$

SOLUTION

a) $\dfrac{6x - 12}{7x - 14} = \dfrac{6(x - 2)}{7(x - 2)}$ Factoring the numerator and the denominator. The greatest common factor is $x - 2$.

$= \dfrac{6}{7} \cdot \dfrac{x - 2}{x - 2}$ Rewriting as a product of two rational expressions

$= \dfrac{6}{7} \cdot 1 \qquad \dfrac{x - 2}{x - 2} = 1$

$= \dfrac{6}{7}$ Removing the factor 1

b) $\dfrac{18t^2 + 6t}{6t^2 + 15t} = \dfrac{3t \cdot 2(3t + 1)}{3t(2t + 5)}$ Factoring the numerator and the denominator. The greatest common factor is $3t$.

$= \dfrac{3t}{3t} \cdot \dfrac{2(3t + 1)}{2t + 5}$ Rewriting as a product of two rational expressions

$= 1 \cdot \dfrac{2(3t + 1)}{2t + 5} \qquad \dfrac{3t}{3t} = 1$

$= \dfrac{2(3t + 1)}{2t + 5}$ Removing the factor 1. The numerator and the denominator have no common factor so the simplification is complete.

c) $\dfrac{x^2 + 3x + 2}{x^2 - 1} = \dfrac{(x + 1)(x + 2)}{(x + 1)(x - 1)}$ Factoring; $x + 1$ is the greatest common factor.

$= \dfrac{x + 1}{x + 1} \cdot \dfrac{x + 2}{x - 1}$ Rewriting as a product of two rational expressions

$= 1 \cdot \dfrac{x + 2}{x - 1} \qquad \dfrac{x + 1}{x + 1} = 1$

$= \dfrac{x + 2}{x - 1}$ Removing the factor 1

YOUR TURN

Canceling is a shortcut that can be used—and easily *misused*—to simplify rational expressions. If done with care and understanding, canceling streamlines the process of removing a factor equal to 1. Example 4(c) could have been streamlined as follows:

$$\dfrac{x^2 + 3x + 2}{x^2 - 1} = \dfrac{\cancel{(x + 1)}(x + 2)}{\cancel{(x + 1)}(x - 1)}$$ When a factor equal to 1 is noted, it is "canceled": $\dfrac{x + 1}{x + 1} = 1$.

$$= \dfrac{x + 2}{x - 1}.$$ Simplifying

Technology Connection

To check Example 4(c) using a TABLE, we enter the original expression as y_1 and the simplified expression as y_2. We use the n/d mode or place parentheses around each numerator and around each denominator.

The values of y_1 and y_2 should match for all allowable replacements.

X	Y₁	Y₂
−4	.4	.4
−3	.25	.25
−2	0	0
−1	ERROR	−.5
0	−2	−2
1	ERROR	ERROR
2	4	4

X = −4

The ERROR messages indicate that −1 and 1 are not allowable replacements in y_1 and 1 is not an allowable replacement in y_2. For all other numbers, y_1 and y_2 are the same, so the simplification appears to be correct.

Use a TABLE to determine whether each of the following appears to be correct.

1. $\dfrac{5x + 15}{10} = \dfrac{x + 3}{2}$

2. $\dfrac{x^2 + 3x - 4}{x^2 - 16} = \dfrac{x - 1}{x + 4}$

4. Simplify: $\dfrac{x^2 - 5x}{x^2 - 3x - 10}$.

> **CAUTION!** Canceling is often used incorrectly:
>
> $$\frac{x + 7}{x + 3}; \qquad \frac{a^2 - 5}{5}; \qquad \frac{6x^2 + 5x + 1}{4x^2 - 3x}.$$
>
> Incorrect! Incorrect!   Incorrect!
>
> None of the above cancellations removes a factor equal to 1. Factors are parts of products. For example, in $x \cdot 7$, x and 7 are factors, but in $x + 7$, x and 7 are terms, *not* factors. *Only factors can be canceled.*

EXAMPLE 5   Simplify: $\dfrac{3x^2 - 2x - 1}{x^2 - 3x + 2}$.

SOLUTION   We factor the numerator and the denominator and look for common factors:

$$\frac{3x^2 - 2x - 1}{x^2 - 3x + 2} = \frac{(3x + 1)(x - 1)}{(x - 2)(x - 1)}$$

Try to visualize this as
$$\frac{3x + 1}{x - 2} \cdot \frac{x - 1}{x - 1}.$$

$$= \frac{3x + 1}{x - 2}.$$

Removing a factor equal to 1:
$$\frac{x - 1}{x - 1} = 1$$

5. Simplify: $\dfrac{n^2 - 16}{2n^2 + 7n - 4}$.

YOUR TURN

Factors That Are Opposites

Consider

$$\frac{x - 4}{8 - 2x}, \quad \text{or, equivalently,} \quad \frac{x - 4}{2(4 - x)}.$$

At first glance, the numerator and the denominator do not appear to have any common factors. But $x - 4$ and $4 - x$ are opposites, or additive inverses, of each other. Thus we can find a common factor by factoring out -1 in either expression.

EXAMPLE 6   Simplify $\dfrac{x - 4}{8 - 2x}$ and check by evaluating.

SOLUTION   We have

$$\frac{x - 4}{8 - 2x} = \frac{x - 4}{2(4 - x)}$$ Factoring

$$= \frac{x - 4}{2(-1)(x - 4)}$$ Note that $4 - x = -x + 4 = -1(x - 4)$.

$$= \frac{x - 4}{-2(x - 4)}$$ Had we originally factored out -2, we could have gone directly to this step.

$$= \frac{1}{-2} \cdot \frac{x - 4}{x - 4}$$ Rewriting as a product. It is important to write the 1 in the numerator.

$$= -\frac{1}{2}.$$ Removing a factor equal to 1: $(x - 4)/(x - 4) = 1$

As a partial check, note that for any choice of x other than 4, the value of the rational expression is $-\frac{1}{2}$. For example, if $x = 5$, then

$$\frac{x - 4}{8 - 2x} = \frac{5 - 4}{8 - 2 \cdot 5}$$

$$= \frac{1}{-2} = -\frac{1}{2}.$$

6. Simplify: $\dfrac{x - 2}{2 - x}$.

 YOUR TURN

6.1 EXERCISE SET   FOR EXTRA HELP

MyMathLab® Math XL
PRACTICE WATCH READ REVIEW

▸ Vocabulary and Reading Check

Choose the word written under the blank that best completes the statement.

1. A rational expression can be written as a _____ of two polynomials.
   difference/quotient

2. A rational expression is undefined when the _____ is zero.
   denominator/numerator

3. A rational expression is simplified when the numerator and the denominator have no _____
   factors/terms
   (other than 1) in common.

4. When we cancel, we remove _____.
   a factor equal to 1/a restricted value

▸ Concept Reinforcement

In each of Exercises 5–8, match the rational expression with the list of numbers in the column on the right for which the rational expression is undefined.

5. ___ $\dfrac{3t}{(t + 1)(t - 4)}$ a) $-1, 4$

6. ___ $\dfrac{2t + 7}{(2t - 1)(3t + 4)}$ b) $-3, 5$

                     c) $-\dfrac{4}{3}, \dfrac{1}{2}$

7. ___ $\dfrac{a + 7}{a^2 - a - 12}$ d) $-3, 4$

8. ___ $\dfrac{m - 3}{m^2 - 2m - 15}$

Restricting Replacement Values

List all numbers for which each rational expression is undefined.

9. $\dfrac{18}{-11x}$ 10. $\dfrac{13}{-5t}$

11. $\dfrac{y - 3}{y + 5}$ 12. $\dfrac{a + 6}{a - 10}$

13. $\dfrac{t - 5}{3t - 15}$ 14. $\dfrac{x^2 - 4}{5x + 10}$

15. $\dfrac{x^2 - 25}{x^2 - 3x - 28}$ 16. $\dfrac{p^2 - 9}{p^2 - 7p + 10}$

17. $\dfrac{t^2 + t - 20}{2t^2 + 11t - 6}$ 18. $\dfrac{x^2 + 2x + 1}{3x^2 - x - 14}$

Simplifying Rational Expressions

Simplify by removing a factor equal to 1. Show all steps.

19. $\dfrac{50a^2b}{40ab^3}$ 20. $\dfrac{-24x^4y^3}{6x^7y}$

21. $\dfrac{6t + 12}{6t - 18}$ 22. $\dfrac{5n - 30}{5n + 5}$

23. $\dfrac{21t - 7}{24t - 8}$ 24. $\dfrac{10n + 25}{8n + 20}$

25. $\dfrac{a^2 - 9}{a^2 + 4a + 3}$ 26. $\dfrac{a^2 + 5a + 6}{a^2 - 9}$

Simplify, if possible. Then check by evaluating, as in Example 6.

27. $\dfrac{-36x^8}{54x^5}$ 28. $\dfrac{45a^4}{30a^6}$

29. $\dfrac{-2y + 6}{-8y}$ 30. $\dfrac{4x - 12}{6x}$

31. $\dfrac{6a^2 + 3a}{7a^2 + 7a}$ 32. $\dfrac{-4m^2 + 4m}{-8m^2 + 12m}$

33. $\dfrac{t^2 - 16}{t^2 - t - 20}$ 34. $\dfrac{a^2 - 4}{a^2 + 5a + 6}$

35. $\dfrac{3a^2 + 9a - 12}{6a^2 - 30a + 24}$ 36. $\dfrac{2t^2 - 6t + 4}{4t^2 + 12t - 16}$

37. $\dfrac{x^2 - 8x + 16}{x^2 - 16}$ 38. $\dfrac{x^2 - 25}{x^2 + 10x + 25}$

39. $\dfrac{n - 2}{n^3 - 8}$ 40. $\dfrac{n^6 + 27}{n^2 + 3}$

41. $\dfrac{t^2 - 1}{t + 1}$

42. $\dfrac{a^2 - 1}{a - 1}$

43. $\dfrac{y^2 + 4}{y + 2}$

44. $\dfrac{m^2 + 9}{m + 3}$

45. $\dfrac{5x^2 + 20}{10x^2 + 40}$

46. $\dfrac{6x^2 + 54}{4x^2 + 36}$

47. $\dfrac{y^2 + 6y}{2y^2 + 13y + 6}$

48. $\dfrac{t^2 + 2t}{2t^2 + t - 6}$

49. $\dfrac{4x^2 - 12x + 9}{10x^2 - 11x - 6}$

50. $\dfrac{4x^2 - 4x + 1}{6x^2 + 5x - 4}$

Factors That Are Opposites

Simplify.

51. $\dfrac{10 - x}{x - 10}$

52. $\dfrac{x - 8}{8 - x}$

53. $\dfrac{7t - 14}{2 - t}$

54. $\dfrac{3 - n}{5n - 15}$

55. $\dfrac{a - b}{4b - 4a}$

56. $\dfrac{2p - 2q}{q - p}$

57. $\dfrac{3x^2 - 3y^2}{2y^2 - 2x^2}$

58. $\dfrac{7a^2 - 7b^2}{3b^2 - 3a^2}$

 59. $\dfrac{7s^2 - 28t^2}{28t^2 - 7s^2}$

60. $\dfrac{9m^2 - 4n^2}{4n^2 - 9m^2}$

61. Explain how simplifying is related to the identity property of 1.

62. If a rational expression is undefined for $x = 5$ and $x = -3$, what is the degree of the denominator? Why?

Skill Review

Factor.

63. $3x^3 + 15x^2 + x + 5$ [5.1]

64. $3x^2 + 16x + 5$ [5.3]

65. $18y^4 - 27y^3 + 3y^2$ [5.1]

66. $25a^2 - 16b^2$ [5.4]

67. $m^3 - 8m^2 + 16m$ [5.4]

68. $5x^2 - 35x + 60$ [5.2]

Synthesis

69. Luke *incorrectly* simplifies

$$\frac{x^2 + x - 2}{x^2 + 3x + 2} \quad \text{as} \quad \frac{x - 1}{x + 2}.$$

He then checks his simplification by evaluating both expressions for $x = 1$. Use this situation to explain why evaluating is not a foolproof check.

 70. How could you convince someone that $a - b$ and $b - a$ are opposites of each other?

Simplify.

71. $\dfrac{16y^4 - x^4}{(x^2 + 4y^2)(x - 2y)}$

72. $\dfrac{(x - 1)(x^4 - 1)(x^2 - 1)}{(x^2 + 1)(x - 1)^2(x^4 - 2x^2 + 1)}$

73. $\dfrac{x^5 - 2x^3 + 4x^2 - 8}{x^7 + 2x^4 - 4x^3 - 8}$

74. $\dfrac{10t^4 - 8t^3 + 15t - 12}{8 - 10t + 12t^2 - 15t^3}$

75. $\dfrac{(t^4 - 1)(t^2 - 9)(t - 9)^2}{(t^4 - 81)(t^2 + 1)(t + 1)^2}$

76. $\dfrac{(t + 2)^3(t^2 + 2t + 1)(t + 1)}{(t + 1)^3(t^2 + 4t + 4)(t + 2)}$

77. $\dfrac{x^3 + 6x^2 - 4x - 24}{x^2 + 4x - 12}$

78. $\dfrac{10x^2 - 10}{5x^3 - 30x^2 - 5x + 30}$

79. $\dfrac{(x^2 - y^2)(x^2 - 2xy + y^2)}{(x + y)^2(x^2 - 4xy - 5y^2)}$

80. $\dfrac{x^4 - y^4}{(y - x)^4}$

81. Select any number x, multiply by 2, add 5, multiply by 5, subtract 25, and divide by 10. What do you get? Explain how this procedure can be used for a number trick.

YOUR TURN ANSWERS: SECTION 6.1

1. $-5, 5$ **2.** $\dfrac{3ab}{4}$ **3.** $\dfrac{8}{x + 5}$ **4.** $\dfrac{x}{x + 2}$

5. $\dfrac{n - 4}{2n - 1}$ **6.** -1

PREPARE TO MOVE ON

Simplify.   [1.7]

1. $\dfrac{2}{15} \cdot \dfrac{10}{7}$

2. $\left(\dfrac{3}{4}\right)\left(\dfrac{-20}{9}\right)$

3. $\dfrac{5}{8} \div \dfrac{1}{6}$

4. $\dfrac{7}{10} \div \left(-\dfrac{8}{15}\right)$

6.2 Multiplication and Division

Multiplication ▪ Division

Multiplication and division of rational expressions are similar to multiplication and division with fractions. In this section, we again assume that all denominators are nonzero.

Multiplication

Recall that to multiply fractions, we multiply numerator times numerator and denominator times denominator. Rational expressions are multiplied in a similar way.

Study Skills

Strike While the Iron's Hot
Make an effort to do your homework as soon as possible after each class. Make this part of your routine, choosing a time and a place where you can focus with a minimum of interruptions.

> **THE PRODUCT OF TWO RATIONAL EXPRESSIONS**
>
> To multiply rational expressions, form the product of the numerators and the product of the denominators:
>
> $$\frac{A}{B} \cdot \frac{C}{D} = \frac{AC}{BD}.$$
>
> Then factor and, if possible, simplify the result.

For example,

$$\frac{3}{5} \cdot \frac{8}{11} = \frac{3 \cdot 8}{5 \cdot 11} \quad \text{and} \quad \frac{x}{3} \cdot \frac{x+2}{y} = \frac{x(x+2)}{3y}.$$

Fraction bars are grouping symbols, so parentheses are needed when writing some products.

EXAMPLE 1 Multiply. (Write the product as a single rational expression.) Then simplify, if possible, by removing a factor equal to 1.

a) $\dfrac{5a^3}{4} \cdot \dfrac{2}{5a}$

b) $(x^2 - 3x - 10) \cdot \dfrac{x+4}{x^2 - 10x + 25}$

c) $\dfrac{10x + 20}{2x^2 - 3x + 1} \cdot \dfrac{x^2 - 1}{5x + 10}$

SOLUTION

a) $\dfrac{5a^3}{4} \cdot \dfrac{2}{5a} = \dfrac{5a^3(2)}{4(5a)}$ Forming the product of the numerators and the product of the denominators

$\phantom{a) \dfrac{5a^3}{4} \cdot \dfrac{2}{5a}} = \dfrac{5 \cdot a \cdot a \cdot a \cdot 2}{2 \cdot 2 \cdot 5 \cdot a}$ Factoring the numerator and the denominator

$\phantom{a) \dfrac{5a^3}{4} \cdot \dfrac{2}{5a}} = \dfrac{\cancel{5} \cdot a \cdot \cancel{a} \cdot a \cdot \cancel{2}}{\cancel{2} \cdot 2 \cdot \cancel{5} \cdot \cancel{a}}$

$\phantom{a) \dfrac{5a^3}{4} \cdot \dfrac{2}{5a}} = \dfrac{a^2}{2}$ Removing a factor equal to 1: $\dfrac{2 \cdot 5 \cdot a}{2 \cdot 5 \cdot a} = 1$

b) $(x^2 - 3x - 10) \cdot \dfrac{x + 4}{x^2 - 10x + 25}$

$= \dfrac{x^2 - 3x - 10}{1} \cdot \dfrac{x + 4}{x^2 - 10x + 25}$ Writing $x^2 - 3x - 10$ as a rational expression

$= \dfrac{(x^2 - 3x - 10)(x + 4)}{1(x^2 - 10x + 25)}$ Multiplying the numerators and the denominators

$= \dfrac{(x - 5)(x + 2)(x + 4)}{(x - 5)(x - 5)}$ Factoring the numerator and the denominator

$= \dfrac{\cancel{(x - 5)}(x + 2)(x + 4)}{\cancel{(x - 5)}(x - 5)}$ Removing a factor equal to 1: $\dfrac{x - 5}{x - 5} = 1$

$= \dfrac{(x + 2)(x + 4)}{x - 5}$

c) $\dfrac{10x + 20}{2x^2 - 3x + 1} \cdot \dfrac{x^2 - 1}{5x + 10}$

$= \dfrac{(10x + 20)(x^2 - 1)}{(2x^2 - 3x + 1)(5x + 10)}$ Multiply.

$= \dfrac{5(2)(x + 2)(x + 1)(x - 1)}{(x - 1)(2x - 1)5(x + 2)}$ Factor. Try to go directly to this step.

$= \dfrac{\cancel{5}(2)(x + 2)(x + 1)\cancel{(x - 1)}}{\cancel{(x - 1)}(2x - 1)\cancel{5}\cancel{(x + 2)}}$ Simplify. $\dfrac{5(x + 2)(x - 1)}{5(x + 2)(x - 1)} = 1$

$= \dfrac{2(x + 1)}{2x - 1}$

➔ YOUR TURN

Because our results are often used in problems that require factored form, there is no need to routinely multiply out the numerator or the denominator.

Division

As with fractions, reciprocals of rational expressions are found by interchanging the numerator and the denominator. For example,

the reciprocal of $\dfrac{3x}{x + 5}$ is $\dfrac{x + 5}{3x}$ and   the reciprocal of $\dfrac{1}{y - 8}$ is $y - 8$.

THE QUOTIENT OF TWO RATIONAL EXPRESSIONS

To divide by a rational expression, multiply by its reciprocal:

$$\dfrac{A}{B} \div \dfrac{C}{D} = \dfrac{A}{B} \cdot \dfrac{D}{C} = \dfrac{AD}{BC}.$$

Then factor and, if possible, simplify.

Student Notes

Neatness is important for work with rational expressions. Consider using the lines on your notebook paper to indicate where the fraction bars should be drawn in each example. Write the equal sign at the same height as the fraction bars.

---

1. Multiply and, if possible, simplify:

$$\dfrac{t + 2}{2t} \cdot \dfrac{10t^2}{t^2 + t - 2}.$$

EXAMPLE 2   Divide: **(a)** $\dfrac{x}{5} \div \dfrac{7}{y}$; **(b)** $(x + 2) \div \dfrac{x - 1}{x + 3}$.

SOLUTION

a) $\dfrac{x}{5} \div \dfrac{7}{y} = \dfrac{x}{5} \cdot \dfrac{y}{7}$ Multiplying by the reciprocal of the divisor

$\qquad = \dfrac{xy}{35}$ Multiplying rational expressions

b) $(x + 2) \div \dfrac{x - 1}{x + 3} = \dfrac{x + 2}{1} \cdot \dfrac{x + 3}{x - 1}$ Multiplying by the reciprocal of the divisor. Writing $x + 2$ as $\dfrac{x + 2}{1}$ can be helpful.

$\qquad = \dfrac{(x + 2)(x + 3)}{x - 1}$

2. Divide:

$$\dfrac{x + 2}{x - 2} \div \dfrac{x - 3}{x + 1}.$$

 YOUR TURN

As usual, we should simplify when possible.

EXAMPLE 3   Divide and, if possible, simplify.

a) $\dfrac{x^2 - 2x - 3}{x^2 - 4} \div \dfrac{x + 1}{x + 5}$ **b)** $\dfrac{a^2 + 3a + 2}{a^2 + 4} \div (5a^2 + 10a)$

SOLUTION

a) $\dfrac{x^2 - 2x - 3}{x^2 - 4} \div \dfrac{x + 1}{x + 5}$

$\qquad = \dfrac{x^2 - 2x - 3}{x^2 - 4} \cdot \dfrac{x + 5}{x + 1}$ Multiply by the reciprocal.

$\qquad = \dfrac{(x - 3)(x + 1)(x + 5)}{(x - 2)(x + 2)(x + 1)}$ Multiply. Factor.

$\qquad = \dfrac{(x - 3)\cancel{(x + 1)}(x + 5)}{(x - 2)(x + 2)\cancel{(x + 1)}}$ Simplify.

$\qquad = \dfrac{(x - 3)(x + 5)}{(x - 2)(x + 2)}$ $\dfrac{x + 1}{x + 1} = 1$

b) $\dfrac{a^2 + 3a + 2}{a^2 + 4} \div (5a^2 + 10a)$

$\qquad = \dfrac{a^2 + 3a + 2}{a^2 + 4} \cdot \dfrac{1}{5a^2 + 10a}$ Multiplying by the reciprocal of the divisor

$\qquad = \dfrac{(a + 2)(a + 1)}{(a^2 + 4)5a(a + 2)}$ Multiplying rational expressions and factoring

$\qquad = \dfrac{\cancel{(a + 2)}(a + 1)}{(a^2 + 4)5a\cancel{(a + 2)}}$

$\qquad = \dfrac{a + 1}{(a^2 + 4)5a}$ Removing a factor equal to 1: $\dfrac{a + 2}{a + 2} = 1$

 YOUR TURN

Technology Connection

To perform a partial check of Example 3(a), we enter the original expression as y_1 and the simplified expression as y_2. If the n/d mode is not available, we enclose each numerator, each denominator, and each rational expression in parentheses.

Comparing values of y_1 and y_2, we see that the simplification is probably correct.

X	Y₁	Y₂
-5	ERROR	0
-4	-.5833	-.5833
-3	-2.4	-2.4
-2	ERROR	ERROR
-1	ERROR	5.3333
0	3.75	3.75
1	4	4

X = -5

1. Check Example 3(b).
2. Why are there 3 ERROR messages shown for y_1 on the screen above, and only 1 for y_2?

3. Divide and, if possible, simplify:

$$\dfrac{x + 1}{x^2 - 1} \div \dfrac{x + 1}{x^2 - 2x + 1}.$$

6.2　EXERCISE SET

Vocabulary and Reading Check

Choose from the following list the correct ending for each sentence.

a) interchange the numerator and the denominator.
b) multiply by its reciprocal.
c) multiply numerators and multiply denominators.
d) remove a factor equal to 1.

1. To simplify rational expressions, _____.

2. To multiply rational expressions, _____.

3. To find a reciprocal, _____.

4. To divide by a rational expression, _____.

Concept Reinforcement

In each of Exercises 5–10, match the product or quotient with an equivalent expression from the column on the right.

5. ____　$\dfrac{x}{2} \cdot \dfrac{5}{y}$　　　a) $\dfrac{5x}{y}$

6. ____　$\dfrac{x}{2} \div \dfrac{5}{y}$　　　b) $\dfrac{xy}{5}$

7. ____　$x \cdot \dfrac{5}{y}$　　　c) $\dfrac{xy}{10}$

8. ____　$\dfrac{x}{2} \div y$　　　d) $\dfrac{5x}{2y}$

9. ____　$x \div \dfrac{5}{y}$　　　e) $\dfrac{x}{2y}$

10. ____　$\dfrac{5}{y} \div \dfrac{x}{2}$　　　f) $\dfrac{10}{xy}$

Multiplication

Multiply. Leave each answer in factored form.

11. $\dfrac{3x}{8} \cdot \dfrac{x+2}{5x-1}$

12. $\dfrac{2x}{7} \cdot \dfrac{3x+5}{x-1}$

13. $\dfrac{a-4}{a+6} \cdot \dfrac{a+2}{a+6}$

14. $\dfrac{a+3}{a+6} \cdot \dfrac{a+3}{a-1}$

15. $\dfrac{n-4}{n^2+4} \cdot \dfrac{n+4}{n^2-4}$

16. $\dfrac{t+3}{t^2-2} \cdot \dfrac{t+3}{t^2-4}$

Multiply and, if possible, simplify.

17. $\dfrac{8t^3}{5t} \cdot \dfrac{3}{4t}$

18. $\dfrac{18}{a^5} \cdot \dfrac{2a^2}{3a}$

19. $\dfrac{3c}{d^2} \cdot \dfrac{8d}{6c^3}$

20. $\dfrac{3x^2y}{2} \cdot \dfrac{4}{xy^3}$

21. $\dfrac{y^2-16}{4y+12} \cdot \dfrac{y+3}{y-4}$

22. $\dfrac{m^2-n^2}{4m+4n} \cdot \dfrac{m+n}{m-n}$

23. $\dfrac{x^2-3x-10}{(x-2)^2} \cdot \dfrac{x-2}{x-5}$

24. $\dfrac{t+2}{t-2} \cdot \dfrac{t^2-5t+6}{(t+2)^2}$

25. $\dfrac{n^2-6n+5}{n+6} \cdot \dfrac{n-6}{n^2+36}$

26. $\dfrac{a+2}{a-2} \cdot \dfrac{a^2+4}{a^2+5a+4}$

27. $\dfrac{a^2-9}{a^2} \cdot \dfrac{7a}{a^2+a-12}$

28. $\dfrac{x^2+10x-11}{9x} \cdot \dfrac{x^3}{x+11}$

29. $\dfrac{y^2-y}{y^2+5y+4} \cdot (y+4)$

30. $(n-3) \cdot \dfrac{n^2+4n}{n^2-5n+6}$

31. $\dfrac{4v-8}{5v} \cdot \dfrac{15v^2}{4v^2-16v+16}$

32. $\dfrac{4a^2}{3a^2-12a+12} \cdot \dfrac{3a-6}{2a}$

33. $\dfrac{t^2+2t-3}{t^2+4t-5} \cdot \dfrac{t^2-3t-10}{t^2+5t+6}$

34. $\dfrac{x^2+5x+4}{x^2-6x+8} \cdot \dfrac{x^2+5x-14}{x^2+8x+7}$

35. $\dfrac{12y+12}{5y+25} \cdot \dfrac{3y^2-75}{8y^2-8}$

36. $\dfrac{9t^2-900}{5t^2-20} \cdot \dfrac{5t+10}{3t-30}$

Aha! 37. $\dfrac{x^2+4x+4}{(x-1)^2} \cdot \dfrac{x^2-2x+1}{(x+2)^2}$

38. $\dfrac{x^2+7x+12}{x^2+6x+8} \cdot \dfrac{4-x^2}{x^2+x-6}$

39. $\dfrac{t^2-4t+4}{2t^2-7t+6} \cdot \dfrac{2t^2+7t-15}{t^2-10t+25}$

40. $\dfrac{5y^2 - 4y - 1}{3y^2 + 5y - 12} \cdot \dfrac{y^2 + 6y + 9}{y^2 - 2y + 1}$

41. $(10x^2 - x - 2) \cdot \dfrac{4x^2 - 8x + 3}{10x^2 - 11x - 6}$

42. $\dfrac{2x^2 - 5x + 3}{6x^2 - 5x - 1} \cdot (6x^2 + 13x + 2)$

43. $\dfrac{49x^2 - 25}{4x - 14} \cdot \dfrac{6x^2 - 13x - 28}{28x - 20}$

44. $\dfrac{9t^2 - 4}{8t^2 - 10t + 3} \cdot \dfrac{10t - 5}{3t - 2}$

45. $\dfrac{8x^2 + 14xy - 15y^2}{3x^3 - x^2y} \cdot \dfrac{3x - y}{4xy - 3y^2}$

46. $\dfrac{2x^2 - xy}{6x^2 + 7xy + 2y^2} \cdot \dfrac{9x^2 - 6xy - 8y^2}{3xy - 4y^2}$

47. $\dfrac{c^3 + 8}{c^5 - 4c^3} \cdot \dfrac{c^6 - 4c^5 + 4c^4}{c^2 - 2c + 4}$

48. $\dfrac{t^3 - 27}{t^4 - 9t^2} \cdot \dfrac{t^5 - 6t^4 + 9t}{t^2 + 3t + 9}$

Division

Find the reciprocal of each expression.

49. $\dfrac{2x}{9}$

50. $\dfrac{3 - x}{x^2 + 4}$

51. $a^4 + 3a$

52. $\dfrac{1}{a^2 - b^2}$

Divide and, if possible, simplify.

53. $\dfrac{x}{4} \div \dfrac{5}{x}$

54. $\dfrac{5}{x} \div \dfrac{x}{12}$

55. $\dfrac{a^5}{b^4} \div \dfrac{a^2}{b}$

56. $\dfrac{x^5}{y^2} \div \dfrac{x^2}{y}$

57. $\dfrac{t - 3}{6} \div \dfrac{t + 1}{8}$

58. $\dfrac{10}{a + 3} \div \dfrac{15}{a}$

59. $\dfrac{4y - 8}{y + 2} \div \dfrac{y - 2}{y^2 - 4}$

60. $\dfrac{x^2 - 1}{x} \div \dfrac{x + 1}{2x - 2}$

61. $\dfrac{a}{a - b} \div \dfrac{b}{b - a}$

62. $\dfrac{x - y}{6} \div \dfrac{y - x}{3}$

63. $(n^2 + 5n + 6) \div \dfrac{n^2 - 4}{n + 3}$

64. $(v^2 - 1) \div \dfrac{(v + 1)(v - 3)}{v^2 + 9}$

65. $\dfrac{a + 2}{a - 1} \div \dfrac{3a + 6}{a - 5}$

66. $\dfrac{t - 3}{t + 2} \div \dfrac{4t - 12}{t + 1}$

67. $(2x - 1) \div \dfrac{2x^2 - 11x + 5}{4x^2 - 1}$

68. $(a + 7) \div \dfrac{3a^2 + 14a - 49}{a^2 + 8a + 7}$

69. $\dfrac{w^2 - 14w + 49}{2w^2 - 3w - 14} \div \dfrac{3w^2 - 20w - 7}{w^2 - 6w - 16}$

70. $\dfrac{2m^2 + 59m - 30}{m^2 - 10m + 25} \div \dfrac{2m^2 - 21m + 10}{m^2 + m - 30}$

71. $\dfrac{c^2 + 10c + 21}{c^2 - 2c - 15} \div (5c^2 + 32c - 21)$

72. $\dfrac{z^2 - 2z + 1}{z^2 - 1} \div (4z^2 - z - 3)$

73. $\dfrac{-3 + 3x}{16} \div \dfrac{x - 1}{5}$

74. $\dfrac{-4 + 2x}{15} \div \dfrac{x - 2}{3}$

75. $\dfrac{x - 1}{x + 2} \div \dfrac{1 - x}{4 + x^2}$

76. $\dfrac{-12 + 4x}{12} \div \dfrac{6 - 2x}{6}$

77. $\dfrac{x - y}{x^2 + 2xy + y^2} \div \dfrac{x^2 - y^2}{x^2 - 5xy + 4y^2}$

78. $\dfrac{a^2 - b^2}{a^2 - 4ab + 4b^2} \div \dfrac{a^2 - 3ab + 2b^2}{a - 2b}$

79. $\dfrac{x^3 - 64}{x^3 + 64} \div \dfrac{x^2 - 16}{x^2 - 4x + 16}$

80. $\dfrac{8y^3 - 27}{64y^3 - 1} \div \dfrac{4y^2 - 9}{16y^2 + 4y + 1}$

81. $\dfrac{8a^3 + b^3}{2a^2 + 3ab + b^2} \div \dfrac{8a^2 - 4ab + 2b^2}{4a^2 + 4ab + b^2}$

82. $\dfrac{x^3 + 8y^3}{2x^2 + 5xy + 2y^2} \div \dfrac{x^3 - 2x^2y + 4xy^2}{8x^2 - 2y^2}$

83. Why is it important to insert parentheses when multiplying rational expressions such as

$$\dfrac{x + 2}{5x - 7} \cdot \dfrac{3x - 1}{x + 4}?$$

84. As a first step in dividing $\dfrac{x}{3}$ by $\dfrac{7}{x}$, Jan canceled the x's.

Explain why this was incorrect, and show the correct division.

Skill Review

Graph.

85. $y = \frac{1}{2}x - 5$ [3.5]

86. $3x - 2y = 12$ [3.3]

87. $3(x - 1) = 4$ [3.6]

88. $y - 2 = -(x + 4)$ [3.7]

89. $3y = 5x$ [3.2]

90. $\frac{1}{2}y = 2$ [3.6]

Synthesis

91. Is the reciprocal of a product the product of the two reciprocals? Why or why not?

92. Explain why the quotient

$$\frac{x + 3}{x - 5} \div \frac{x - 7}{x + 1}$$

is undefined for $x = 5$, $x = -1$, and $x = 7$, but *is* defined for $x = -3$.

93. Find the reciprocal of $2\frac{1}{3}x$.

94. Find the reciprocal of $7.25x$.

Simplify.

95. $(x - 2a) \div \dfrac{a^2x^2 - 4a^4}{a^2x + 2a^3}$

96. $\dfrac{3x^2 - 2xy - y^2}{x^2 - y^2} \div (3x^2 + 4xy + y^2)^2$

97. $\dfrac{3a^2 - 5ab - 12b^2}{3ab + 4b^2} \div (3b^2 - ab)^2$

Aha! 98. $\dfrac{a^2 - 3b}{a^2 + 2b} \cdot \dfrac{a^2 - 2b}{a^2 + 3b} \cdot \dfrac{a^2 + 2b}{a^2 - 3b}$

99. $\dfrac{z^2 - 8z + 16}{z^2 + 8z + 16} \div \dfrac{(z - 4)^5}{(z + 4)^5} \div \dfrac{3z + 12}{z^2 - 16}$

100. $\dfrac{(t + 2)^3}{(t + 1)^3} \div \dfrac{t^2 + 4t + 4}{t^2 + 2t + 1} \cdot \dfrac{t + 1}{t + 2}$

101. $\dfrac{a^4 - 81b^4}{a^2c - 6abc + 9b^2c} \cdot \dfrac{a + 3b}{a^2 + 9b^2} \div \dfrac{a^2 + 6ab + 9b^2}{(a - 3b)^2}$

102. $\dfrac{3y^3 + 6y^2}{y^2 - y - 12} \div \dfrac{y^2 - y}{y^2 - 2y - 8} \cdot \dfrac{y^2 + 5y + 6}{y^2}$

103. $\dfrac{xy - 2x + y - 2}{xy + 4x - y - 4} \cdot \dfrac{xy + y + 4x + 4}{xy - y - 2x + 2}$

104. $\dfrac{ab^2 + 2b^2 + a + 2}{ab - a - 3b + 3} \cdot \dfrac{ab^2 - 3b^2 - a + 3}{ab + a + 2b + 2}$

105. $\dfrac{3x^2 - 12x + bx - 4b}{4x^2 - 16x - bx + 4b} \div \dfrac{3bx + b^2 + 6x + 2b}{4bx - b^2 + 8x - 2b}$

106. $\dfrac{2x^2y - xy^2 + 6x^2 - 3xy}{3y^2 - xy + 9y - 3x} \div \dfrac{2x^3 - x^2y + 8x^2 - 4xy}{3xy - x^2 + 6y - 2x}$

107. $\dfrac{8n^2 - 10n + 3}{4n^2 - 4n - 3} \cdot \dfrac{6n^2 - 5n - 6}{6n^2 + 7n - 5} \div \dfrac{12n^2 - 17n + 6}{6n^2 + 7n - 5}$

108. $\dfrac{2p^2 - p - 6}{16p^2 - 25} \cdot \dfrac{12p^2 + 13p - 35}{4p^2 + 12p + 9} \div \dfrac{12p^2 + 43p + 35}{2p^2 - p - 6}$

109. Use a graphing calculator to check that

$$\frac{x - 1}{x^2 + 2x + 1} \div \frac{x^2 - 1}{x^2 - 5x + 4}$$

is equivalent to

$$\frac{x^2 - 5x + 4}{(x + 1)^3}.$$

YOUR TURN ANSWERS: SECTION 6.2

1. $\dfrac{5t}{t - 1}$ **2.** $\dfrac{(x + 2)(x + 1)}{(x - 2)(x - 3)}$ **3.** $\dfrac{x - 1}{x + 1}$

QUICK QUIZ: SECTIONS 6.1–6.2

1. Simplify: $\dfrac{6x^2 - 54}{x^2 - 7x + 12}$. [6.1]

Perform the indicated operation and, if possible, simplify. [6.2]

2. $\dfrac{y + 1}{y + 2} \cdot \dfrac{y^2 - y - 6}{2y^2 + 3y + 1}$

3. $\dfrac{5x - 5}{2x + 2} \div \dfrac{10x}{x^2 - 1}$

4. $\dfrac{m - 2}{3m + 9} \cdot \dfrac{m^2 + 6m + 9}{2m^2 - 8}$

5. $\dfrac{x^2 - 16}{x^2 - 25} \div \dfrac{x^2 - 8x + 16}{x^2 - x - 20}$

PREPARE TO MOVE ON

Simplify.

1. $\dfrac{7}{8} + \dfrac{5}{6}$ [1.3]   **2.** $\dfrac{7}{15} - \dfrac{3}{10}$ [1.3]

3. $2x^2 - x + 1 - (x^2 - x - 2)$ [4.4]

4. $3x^2 + x - 7 - (5x^2 + 5x - 8)$ [4.4]

6.3   Addition, Subtraction, and Least Common Denominators

Addition When Denominators Are the Same ▪ Subtraction When Denominators Are the Same ▪
Least Common Multiples and Denominators

Addition When Denominators Are the Same

Recall that to add fractions having the same denominator, like $\frac{2}{7}$ and $\frac{3}{7}$, we add the numerators and keep the common denominator: $\frac{2}{7} + \frac{3}{7} = \frac{5}{7}$. The same procedure is used for all rational expressions that share a common denominator. In this section, we assume that all denominators are nonzero.

> **THE SUM OF TWO RATIONAL EXPRESSIONS**
>
> To add when the denominators are the same, add the numerators and keep the common denominator:
>
> $$\frac{A}{B} + \frac{C}{B} = \frac{A + C}{B}.$$

Study Skills

Visualize the Steps

If you have completed all assignments and are studying for a quiz or a test, don't feel that you need to redo every assigned problem. A more productive use of your time would be to work through one problem of each type. Then read through the other problems, visualizing the steps that lead to a solution. When you are unsure of how to solve a problem, work that problem in its entirety, seeking outside help as needed.

EXAMPLE 1   Add. Simplify the result, if possible.

a) $\dfrac{4}{a} + \dfrac{3 + a}{a}$

b) $\dfrac{2x^2 + 3x - 7}{2x + 1} + \dfrac{x^2 + x - 8}{2x + 1}$

c) $\dfrac{x - 5}{x^2 - 9} + \dfrac{2}{x^2 - 9}$

SOLUTION

a) $\dfrac{4}{a} + \dfrac{3 + a}{a} = \dfrac{7 + a}{a}$ When the denominators are alike, add the numerators and keep the common denominator.

b) $\dfrac{2x^2 + 3x - 7}{2x + 1} + \dfrac{x^2 + x - 8}{2x + 1} = \dfrac{(2x^2 + 3x - 7) + (x^2 + x - 8)}{2x + 1}$

$= \dfrac{3x^2 + 4x - 15}{2x + 1}$ Combining like terms

$= \dfrac{(3x - 5)(x + 3)}{2x + 1}$ Factoring. There are no common factors, so we cannot simplify further.

c) $\dfrac{x - 5}{x^2 - 9} + \dfrac{2}{x^2 - 9} = \dfrac{x - 3}{x^2 - 9}$ Combining like terms in the numerator: $x - 5 + 2 = x - 3$

$= \dfrac{x - 3}{(x - 3)(x + 3)}$ Factoring

$= \dfrac{1 \cdot (x - 3)}{(x - 3)(x + 3)}$ Removing a factor equal to 1: $\dfrac{x - 3}{x - 3} = 1$

$= \dfrac{1}{x + 3}$

1. Add. Simplify the result, if possible.

$$\dfrac{3x + 1}{x + 2} + \dfrac{x + 7}{x + 2}$$

↩ YOUR TURN

Subtraction When Denominators Are the Same

When two fractions have the same denominator, we subtract one numerator from the other and keep the common denominator, as in $\frac{5}{7} - \frac{2}{7} = \frac{3}{7}$. The same procedure is used with rational expressions.

THE DIFFERENCE OF TWO RATIONAL EXPRESSIONS

To subtract when the denominators are the same, subtract the second numerator from the first numerator and keep the common denominator:

$$\frac{A}{B} - \frac{C}{B} = \frac{A - C}{B}.$$

CAUTION!   The fraction bar under a numerator is a grouping symbol, just like parentheses. Thus, when a numerator is subtracted, it is important to subtract *every* term in that numerator.

EXAMPLE 2   Subtract and, if possible, simplify.

a) $\dfrac{3x}{x + 2} - \dfrac{x - 5}{x + 2}$

b) $\dfrac{x^2}{x - 4} - \dfrac{x + 12}{x - 4}$

SOLUTION

a) $\dfrac{3x}{x + 2} - \dfrac{x - 5}{x + 2} = \dfrac{3x - (x - 5)}{x + 2}$ The parentheses are needed to make sure that we subtract both terms.

$= \dfrac{3x - x + 5}{x + 2}$ Removing the parentheses and changing signs (using the distributive law)

$= \dfrac{2x + 5}{x + 2}$ Combining like terms

b) $\dfrac{x^2}{x - 4} - \dfrac{x + 12}{x - 4} = \dfrac{x^2 - (x + 12)}{x - 4}$ Remember the parentheses!

$= \dfrac{x^2 - x - 12}{x - 4}$ Removing parentheses (using the distributive law)

$= \dfrac{(x - 4)(x + 3)}{x - 4}$ Factoring, in hopes of simplifying

$= \dfrac{(x - 4)(x + 3)}{x - 4}$ Removing a factor equal to 1: $\dfrac{x - 4}{x - 4} = 1$

$= x + 3$

2. Subtract and, if possible, simplify:

$$\frac{3a}{2a - 1} - \frac{a - 1}{2a - 1}.$$

YOUR TURN

Least Common Multiples and Denominators

Thus far, every pair of rational expressions that we have added or subtracted shared a common denominator. To add or subtract rational expressions that have different denominators, we must first find equivalent rational expressions that *do* have a common denominator.

In algebra, we find a common denominator much as we do in arithmetic. Recall that to add $\frac{1}{12}$ and $\frac{7}{30}$, we first identify the smallest number that contains both 12 and 30 as factors. Such a number, the **least common multiple (LCM)** of the denominators, is then used as the **least common denominator (LCD)**.

Let's find the LCM of 12 and 30 using a method that can also be used with polynomials. We begin by writing the prime factorizations of 12 and 30:

$$12 = 2 \cdot 2 \cdot 3;$$
$$30 = 2 \cdot 3 \cdot 5.$$

The LCM must include the factors of each number, so it must include each prime factor the greatest number of times that it appears in either of the factorizations. To find the LCM for 12 and 30, we select one factorization, say

$$2 \cdot 2 \cdot 3,$$

and note that because it lacks a factor of 5, it does not contain the entire factorization of 30. If we multiply $2 \cdot 2 \cdot 3$ by 5, every prime factor occurs just often enough to contain both 12 and 30 as factors.

$$\text{LCM} = 2 \cdot 2 \cdot 3 \cdot 5$$

12 is a factor of the LCM.

30 is a factor of the LCM.

Note that each prime factor—2, 3, and 5—is used the greatest number of times that it appears in either of the individual factorizations. The factor 2 occurs twice and the factors 3 and 5 once each.

TO FIND THE LEAST COMMON DENOMINATOR (LCD)

1. Write the prime factorization of each denominator.
2. Select one of the factorizations and inspect it to see if it completely contains the other factorization.

   a) If it does, it represents the LCM of the denominators.
   b) If it does not, multiply that factorization by any factors of the other denominator that it lacks. The final product is the LCM of the denominators.

The LCD is the LCM of the denominators. It should contain each factor the greatest number of times that it occurs in any of the individual factorizations.

Student Notes

The terms *least common multiple* and *least common denominator* are similar enough that they may be confusing. We find the LCM of polynomials, and we find the LCD of rational expressions.

EXAMPLE 3 Find the LCD of $\dfrac{5}{36x^2}$ and $\dfrac{7}{24x}$.

SOLUTION

1. We begin by writing the prime factorizations of $36x^2$ and $24x$:

$$36x^2 = 2 \cdot 2 \cdot 3 \cdot 3 \cdot x \cdot x;$$
$$24x = 2 \cdot 2 \cdot 2 \cdot 3 \cdot x.$$

2. We select the factorization of $36x^2$. (We could have selected $24x$ instead.) Except for a third factor of 2, this factorization contains the entire factorization of $24x$. Thus we multiply $36x^2$ by a third factor of 2.

$$\text{LCM} = 2 \cdot 2 \cdot 3 \cdot 3 \cdot x \cdot x \cdot 2$$

$36x^2$ is a factor of the LCM.

Note that each factor appears the greatest number of times that it occurs in either of the above factorizations.

$24x$ is a factor of the LCM.

3. Find the LCD of

$$\frac{25}{12a^3} \quad \text{and} \quad \frac{8}{45a^2}.$$

The LCM of the denominators is thus $2^3 \cdot 3^2 \cdot x^2$, or $72x^2$. The LCD of the expressions is $72x^2$.

YOUR TURN

Let's now add $\dfrac{1}{12}$ and $\dfrac{7}{30}$:

$$\frac{1}{12} + \frac{7}{30} = \frac{1}{2 \cdot 2 \cdot 3} + \frac{7}{2 \cdot 3 \cdot 5}. \qquad \begin{array}{l}\text{The least common denominator} \\ \text{(LCD) is } 2 \cdot 2 \cdot 3 \cdot 5.\end{array}$$

We found above that the LCD is $2 \cdot 2 \cdot 3 \cdot 5$, or 60. To get the LCD, we see that the first denominator, 12, needs a factor of 5, and the second denominator, 30, needs another factor of 2. We multiply $\frac{1}{12}$ by 1, using $\frac{5}{5}$, and we multiply $\frac{7}{30}$ by 1, using $\frac{2}{2}$. Since $a \cdot 1 = a$, for any number a, the values of the fractions are not changed.

$$\frac{1}{12} + \frac{7}{30} = \frac{1}{2 \cdot 2 \cdot 3} \cdot \frac{5}{5} + \frac{7}{2 \cdot 3 \cdot 5} \cdot \frac{2}{2} \qquad \frac{5}{5} = 1 \text{ and } \frac{2}{2} = 1$$

$$= \frac{5}{60} + \frac{14}{60} \qquad \begin{array}{l}\text{Both denominators are now} \\ \text{the LCD.}\end{array}$$

$$= \frac{19}{60} \qquad \begin{array}{l}\text{Adding the numerators and} \\ \text{keeping the LCD}\end{array}$$

Expressions like $\dfrac{5}{36x^2}$ and $\dfrac{7}{24x}$ are added in much the same manner. In Example 3, we found that the LCD is $2 \cdot 2 \cdot 2 \cdot 3 \cdot 3 \cdot x \cdot x$, or $72x^2$. To obtain equivalent expressions with this LCD, we multiply each expression by 1, using the missing factors of the LCD to write 1:

$$\frac{5}{36x^2} + \frac{7}{24x} = \frac{5}{2 \cdot 2 \cdot 3 \cdot 3 \cdot x \cdot x} + \frac{7}{2 \cdot 2 \cdot 2 \cdot 3 \cdot x}$$

$$= \frac{5}{2 \cdot 2 \cdot 3 \cdot 3 \cdot x \cdot x} \cdot \frac{2}{2} + \frac{7}{2 \cdot 2 \cdot 2 \cdot 3 \cdot x} \cdot \frac{3 \cdot x}{3 \cdot x}$$

The LCD requires another factor of 2.

The LCD requires additional factors of 3 and x.

$$= \frac{10}{72x^2} + \frac{21x}{72x^2} \qquad \text{Both denominators are now the LCD.}$$

$$= \frac{21x + 10}{72x^2}.$$

You now have the "big picture" of why LCMs are needed when adding rational expressions. For the remainder of this section, we will practice finding LCMs and rewriting rational expressions so that they have the LCD as the denominator. In the next section, we will return to the addition and subtraction of rational expressions.

EXAMPLE 4   For each pair of polynomials, find the least common multiple.

a) $15a$ and $35b$

b) $21x^3y^6$ and $7x^5y^2$

c) $x^2 + 5x - 6$ and $x^2 - 1$

SOLUTION

a) We write the prime factorizations and then construct the LCM, starting with the factorization of $15a$.

$$15a = 3 \cdot 5 \cdot a$$
$$35b = 5 \cdot 7 \cdot b$$

$$\text{LCM} = 3 \cdot 5 \cdot a \cdot 7 \cdot b$$

15*a* is a factor of the LCM.

Each factor appears the greatest number of times that it occurs in either of the above factorizations.

35*b* is a factor of the LCM.

The LCM is $3 \cdot 5 \cdot a \cdot 7 \cdot b$, or $105ab$.

b) $21x^3y^6 = 3 \cdot 7 \cdot x \cdot x \cdot x \cdot y \cdot y \cdot y \cdot y \cdot y \cdot y$

$$7x^5y^2 = 7 \cdot x \cdot x \cdot x \cdot x \cdot x \cdot y \cdot y$$

Try to visualize the factors of *x* and *y* mentally.

$$\text{LCM} = 3 \cdot 7 \cdot x \cdot x \cdot x \cdot y \cdot y \cdot y \cdot y \cdot y \cdot y \cdot x \cdot x$$

We start with the prime factorization of $21x^3y^6$.
We multiply by the factors of $7x^5y^2$ that are lacking.

Note that we used the highest power of each factor in $21x^3y^6$ and $7x^5y^2$. The LCM is $21x^5y^6$.

c) $x^2 + 5x - 6 = (x - 1)(x + 6)$
      $x^2 - 1 = (x - 1)(x + 1)$

We start with the factorization of $x^2 + 5x - 6$.

$$\text{LCM} = (x - 1)(x + 6)(x + 1)$$

We multiply by the factor of $x^2 - 1$ that is missing.

The LCM is $(x - 1)(x + 6)(x + 1)$. There is no need to multiply this out.

4. Find the least common multiple of $2x^2 + 5x - 3$ and $x^2 + 6x + 9$.

YOUR TURN

The procedure above can be used to find the LCM of three or more polynomials as well. We factor each polynomial and then construct the LCM using each factor the greatest number of times that it appears in any one factorization.

EXAMPLE 5   For each group of polynomials, find the LCM.

a) $12x$, $16y$, and $8xyz$

b) $x^2 + 4$, $x + 1$, and 5

SOLUTION

a) $12x = 2 \cdot 2 \cdot 3 \cdot x$

$16y = 2 \cdot 2 \cdot 2 \cdot 2 \cdot y$

$8xyz = 2 \cdot 2 \cdot 2 \cdot x \cdot y \cdot z$

$$\text{LCM} = 2 \cdot 2 \cdot 3 \cdot x \cdot 2 \cdot 2 \cdot y \cdot z$$

We start with the factorization of $12x$. Any one of the three could be chosen.

We multiply by the factors of $16y$ that are missing.

We then multiply by the factor of $8xyz$ that is missing.

The LCM is $2^4 \cdot 3 \cdot xyz$, or $48xyz$.

b) Since $x^2 + 4$, $x + 1$, and 5 are not factorable, the LCM is their product: $5(x^2 + 4)(x + 1)$.

YOUR TURN

To add or subtract rational expressions with different denominators, we first write equivalent expressions that have the LCD. To do this, we multiply each rational expression by a carefully constructed form of 1.

EXAMPLE 6   Find equivalent expressions that have the LCD:

$$\frac{x + 3}{x^2 + 5x - 6}, \quad \frac{x + 7}{x^2 - 1}.$$

SOLUTION   From Example 4(c), we know that the LCD is

$$(x + 6)(x - 1)(x + 1).$$

The factor of the LCD that is missing from $x^2 + 5x - 6$ is $x + 1$. We multiply by 1 using $(x + 1)/(x + 1)$:

$$\frac{x + 3}{x^2 + 5x - 6} = \frac{x + 3}{(x + 6)(x - 1)} \cdot \frac{x + 1}{x + 1} = \frac{(x + 3)(x + 1)}{(x + 6)(x - 1)(x + 1)}.$$

The factor of the LCD that is missing from $x^2 - 1$ is $x + 6$. We multiply by 1 using $(x + 6)/(x + 6)$:

$$\frac{x + 7}{x^2 - 1} = \frac{x + 7}{(x + 1)(x - 1)} \cdot \frac{x + 6}{x + 6} = \frac{(x + 7)(x + 6)}{(x + 1)(x - 1)(x + 6)}.$$

Both rational expressions now have the same denominator. We leave the results in factored form.

YOUR TURN

Student Notes

If you prefer, the LCM for a group of three polynomials can be found by finding the LCM of two of them and then finding the LCM of that result and the remaining polynomial.

5. Find the LCM of $x^2 + 5x$, $x^2 - 25$, and $5x$.

6. Find equivalent expressions that have the LCD:

$$\frac{5}{x^2 + x}, \quad \frac{2}{3x}.$$

6.3 EXERCISE SET

FOR EXTRA HELP

MyMathLab® Math XL

PRACTICE   WATCH   READ   REVIEW

Vocabulary and Reading Check

Use one or more words to complete each of the following statements.

1. To add two rational expressions when the denominators are the same, add _____ and keep the common _____.

2. When a numerator is being subtracted, use parentheses to make sure that every _____ in that numerator is subtracted.

3. The least common multiple of two denominators is usually referred to as the _____ and is abbreviated _____.

4. The least common denominator of two rational expressions must contain every _____ that is in either denominator.

Addition and Subtraction When Denominators Are the Same

Perform the indicated operation. Simplify, if possible.

5. $\dfrac{3}{t} + \dfrac{5}{t}$

6. $\dfrac{8}{y^2} + \dfrac{2}{y^2}$

7. $\dfrac{x}{12} + \dfrac{2x + 5}{12}$

8. $\dfrac{a}{7} + \dfrac{3a - 4}{7}$

9. $\dfrac{4}{a + 3} + \dfrac{5}{a + 3}$

10. $\dfrac{5}{x + 2} + \dfrac{8}{x + 2}$

11. $\dfrac{11}{4x - 7} - \dfrac{3}{4x - 7}$

12. $\dfrac{9}{2x + 3} - \dfrac{5}{2x + 3}$

13. $\dfrac{3y + 8}{2y} - \dfrac{y + 1}{2y}$

14. $\dfrac{5 + 3t}{4t} - \dfrac{2t + 1}{4t}$

15. $\dfrac{5x + 7}{x + 3} + \dfrac{x + 11}{x + 3}$

16. $\dfrac{3x + 4}{x - 1} + \dfrac{2x - 9}{x - 1}$

17. $\dfrac{5x + 7}{x + 3} - \dfrac{x + 11}{x + 3}$

18. $\dfrac{3x + 4}{x - 1} - \dfrac{2x - 9}{x - 1}$

19. $\dfrac{a^2}{a - 4} + \dfrac{a - 20}{a - 4}$

20. $\dfrac{x^2}{x + 5} + \dfrac{7x + 10}{x + 5}$

21. $\dfrac{y^2}{y + 2} - \dfrac{5y + 14}{y + 2}$

22. $\dfrac{t^2}{t - 3} - \dfrac{8t - 15}{t - 3}$

Aha! 23. $\dfrac{t^2 - 5t}{t - 1} + \dfrac{5t - t^2}{t - 1}$

24. $\dfrac{y^2 + 6y}{y + 2} + \dfrac{2y + 12}{y + 2}$

25. $\dfrac{x - 6}{x^2 + 5x + 6} + \dfrac{9}{x^2 + 5x + 6}$

26. $\dfrac{x - 5}{x^2 - 4x + 3} + \dfrac{2}{x^2 - 4x + 3}$

27. $\dfrac{3a^2 + 14}{a^2 + 5a - 6} - \dfrac{13a}{a^2 + 5a - 6}$

28. $\dfrac{2a^2 + 15}{a^2 - 7a + 12} - \dfrac{11a}{a^2 - 7a + 12}$

29. $\dfrac{t^2 - 5t}{t^2 + 6t + 9} + \dfrac{4t - 12}{t^2 + 6t + 9}$

30. $\dfrac{y^2 - 7y}{y^2 + 8y + 16} + \dfrac{6y - 20}{y^2 + 8y + 16}$

31. $\dfrac{2y^2 + 3y}{y^2 - 7y + 12} - \dfrac{y^2 + 4y + 6}{y^2 - 7y + 12}$

32. $\dfrac{3a^2 + 7}{a^2 - 2a - 8} - \dfrac{7 + 3a^2}{a^2 - 2a - 8}$

33. $\dfrac{3 - 2x}{x^2 - 6x + 8} + \dfrac{7 - 3x}{x^2 - 6x + 8}$

34. $\dfrac{1 - 2t}{t^2 - 5t + 4} + \dfrac{4 - 3t}{t^2 - 5t + 4}$

35. $\dfrac{x - 9}{x^2 + 3x - 4} - \dfrac{2x - 5}{x^2 + 3x - 4}$

36. $\dfrac{5 - 3x}{x^2 - 2x + 1} - \dfrac{x + 1}{x^2 - 2x + 1}$

Least Common Multiples and Denominators

Find the LCM.

37. 15, 36

38. 18, 30

39. 8, 9

40. 12, 15

41. 6, 12, 15

42. 8, 32, 50

Find the LCM.

43. $18t^2$, $6t^5$

44. $8x^5$, $24x^2$

45. $15a^4b^7$, $10a^2b^8$

46. $6a^2b^7$, $9a^5b^2$

47. $2(y - 3)$, $6(y - 3)$

48. $4(x - 1)$, $8(x - 1)$

49. $x^2 - 2x - 15$, $x^2 - 9$

50. $t^2 - 4$, $t^2 + 7t + 10$

51. $t^3 + 4t^2 + 4t$, $t^2 - 4t$

52. $y^3 - y^2$, $y^4 - y^2$

53. $6xz^2$, $8x^2y$, $15y^3z$

54. $12s^3t$, $15sv^2$, $6t^4v$

55. $a + 1$, $(a - 1)^2$, $a^2 - 1$

56. $x - 2$, $(x + 2)^2$, $x^2 - 4$

57. $2n^2 + n - 1$, $2n^2 + 3n - 2$

58. $m^2 - 2m - 3$, $2m^2 + 3m + 1$

Aha! 59. $t - 3$, $t + 3$, $t^2 - 9$

60. $a - 5$, $a^2 - 10a + 25$

61. $6x^3 - 24x^2 + 18x, \ 4x^5 - 24x^4 + 20x^3$

62. $9x^3 - 9x^2 - 18x, \ 6x^5 - 24x^4 + 24x^3$

63. $2x^3 - 2, \ x^2 - 1$

64. $3a^3 + 24, \ a^2 - 4$

Find equivalent expressions that have the LCD.

65. $\dfrac{5}{6t^4}, \ \dfrac{s}{18t^2}$

66. $\dfrac{7}{10y^2}, \ \dfrac{x}{5y^6}$

67. $\dfrac{7}{3x^4y^2}, \ \dfrac{4}{9xy^3}$

68. $\dfrac{3}{2a^2b}, \ \dfrac{7}{8ab^2}$

69. $\dfrac{2x}{x^2 - 4}, \ \dfrac{4x}{x^2 + 5x + 6}$

70. $\dfrac{5x}{x^2 - 9}, \ \dfrac{2x}{x^2 + 11x + 24}$

71. Explain why the product of two numbers is not always their least common multiple.

72. If the LCM of two numbers is their product, what can you conclude about the two numbers?

Skill Review

Solve.

73. $2x - 7 = 5x + 3$ [2.2]

74. $\frac{1}{3}x < \frac{2}{5}x - 1$ [2.6]

75. $x^2 - 8x = 20$ [5.7]

76. $-x \geq 16 + x$ [2.6]

77. $2x^2 + 4x + 2 = 0$ [5.7]

78. $2 - 3(x - 7) = 15$ [2.2]

Synthesis

79. If the LCM of two third-degree polynomials is a sixth-degree polynomial, what can be concluded about the two polynomials?

80. If the LCM of a binomial and a trinomial is the trinomial, what relationship exists between the two expressions?

Perform the indicated operations. Simplify, if possible.

81. $\dfrac{6x - 1}{x - 1} + \dfrac{3(2x + 5)}{x - 1} + \dfrac{3(2x - 3)}{x - 1}$

82. $\dfrac{2x + 11}{x - 3} \cdot \dfrac{3}{x + 4} + \dfrac{-1}{4 + x} \cdot \dfrac{6x + 3}{x - 3}$

83. $\dfrac{x^2}{3x^2 - 5x - 2} - \dfrac{2x}{3x + 1} \cdot \dfrac{1}{x - 2}$

84. $\dfrac{x + y}{x^2 - y^2} + \dfrac{x - y}{x^2 - y^2} - \dfrac{2x}{x^2 - y^2}$

African Artistry. In Southeast Mozambique, the design of every woven handbag, or *gipatsi* *(plural, sipatsi)* is created by repeating two or more geometric patterns.

Each pattern encircles the bag, sharing the strands of fabric with any pattern above or below. The length, or period, of each pattern is the number of strands required to construct the pattern. For a gipatsi to be considered beautiful, each individual pattern must fit a whole number of times around the bag.

Source: Gerdes, Paulus, *Women, Art and Geometry in Southern Africa.* Asmara, Eritrea: Africa World Press, Inc., p. 5

85. A weaver is using two patterns to create a gipatsi. Pattern A is 10 strands long, and pattern B is 3 strands long. What is the smallest number of strands that can be used to complete the gipatsi?

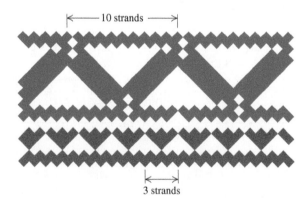

86. A weaver is using a four-strand pattern, a six-strand pattern, and an eight-strand pattern. What is the smallest number of strands that can be used to complete the gipatsi?

87. For technical reasons, the number of strands is generally a multiple of 4. Answer Exercise 83 with this additional requirement in mind.

Find the LCM.

88. 80, 96, 108

89. $4x^2 - 25, \ 6x^2 - 7x - 20, \ (9x^2 + 24x + 16)^2$

90. $9n^2 - 9$, $(5n^2 - 10n + 5)^2$, $15n - 15$

91. *Copiers.* The Lanier 365C copier can print 60 color pages per minute. The Copystar CS3550ci copier can print 35 color pages per minute. If both machines begin printing at the same instant, how long will it be until they again begin printing a page at exactly the same time?

92. *Running.* Joni and Trey leave the starting point of a jogging loop at the same time. Joni jogs a lap in 6 min and Trey jogs one in 8 min. Assuming they continue to run at the same pace, when will they next meet at the starting place?

93. *Bus Schedules.* Beginning at 5:00 A.M., a hotel shuttle bus leaves Salton Airport every 15 min, and the downtown shuttle bus leaves the airport every 25 min. What time will it be when both shuttles again leave at the same time?

94. *Appliances.* Smoke detectors last an average of 10 years, water heaters an average of 12 years, and refrigerators an average of 15 years. If an apartment house is equipped with new smoke detectors, water heaters, and refrigerators in 2014, in what year will all three appliances need to be replaced at once?

Source: Demesne.info

95. Explain how evaluating can be used to perform a partial check on the result of Example 1(c):

$$\frac{x - 5}{x^2 - 9} + \frac{2}{x^2 - 9} = \frac{1}{x + 3}.$$

96. On p. 389, the second step in finding an LCD is to select one of the factorizations of the denominators. Does it matter which one is selected? Why or why not?

97. *Research.* Determine the average life of three or more appliances in your apartment or house. If all these appliances were new when your home was built, when can you expect them all to fail in the same year?

☞ YOUR TURN ANSWERS: SECTION 6.3

1. 4　**2.** $\dfrac{2a + 1}{2a - 1}$　**3.** $180a^3$

4. $(2x - 1)(x + 3)^2$　**5.** $5x(x + 5)(x - 5)$

6. $\dfrac{15}{3x(x + 1)}, \dfrac{2(x + 1)}{3x(x + 1)}$

QUICK QUIZ: SECTIONS 6.1–6.3

1. Simplify: $\dfrac{x + 3}{x^2 + 10x + 21}$.　[6.1]

2. Find the LCM: $x^2 - 6x, x^2 - 7x + 6$.　[6.3]

Perform the indicated operation and, if possible, simplify.

3. $\dfrac{x + 1}{x^2 + 10x + 21} \cdot \dfrac{x + 7}{x^2 - 1}$　[6.2]

4. $\dfrac{2t - 10}{9t^2} \div \dfrac{t^3 - 7t^2 + 10t}{6t}$　[6.2]

5. $\dfrac{x + 3}{x - 2} - \dfrac{x - 5}{x - 2}$　[6.3]

PREPARE TO MOVE ON

Using the identity $-\dfrac{a}{b} = \dfrac{-a}{b} = \dfrac{a}{-b}$, *write each number in two equivalent forms.*　[1.7]

1. $-\dfrac{5}{8}$　　　　**2.** $\dfrac{4}{-11}$

Write an equivalent expression without parentheses.　[1.8]

3. $-(x - y)$　　　　**4.** $-(3 - a)$

Multiply and simplify.　[1.8]

5. $-1(2x - 7)$　　　**6.** $-1(a - b)$

6.4 Addition and Subtraction with Unlike Denominators

Adding and Subtracting with LCDs ■ When Factors Are Opposites

Adding and Subtracting with LCDs

We now know how to rewrite two rational expressions in equivalent forms that use the LCD. Once rational expressions share a common denominator, they can be added or subtracted. We assume all denominators are nonzero.

TO ADD OR SUBTRACT RATIONAL EXPRESSIONS HAVING DIFFERENT DENOMINATORS

1. Find the LCD.
2. Multiply each rational expression by a form of 1 made up of the factors of the LCD missing from that expression's denominator.
3. Add or subtract the numerators, as indicated. Write the sum or the difference over the LCD.
4. Simplify, if possible.

EXAMPLE 1 Add: $\dfrac{5x^2}{8} + \dfrac{7x}{12}$.

SOLUTION

1. First, we find the LCD:

$$\left.\begin{array}{l} 8 = 2 \cdot 2 \cdot 2 \\ 12 = 2 \cdot 2 \cdot 3 \end{array}\right\} \quad \text{LCD} = 2 \cdot 2 \cdot 2 \cdot 3, \text{ or } 24.$$

2. The denominator 8 must be multiplied by 3 in order to obtain the LCD. The denominator 12 must be multiplied by 2 in order to obtain the LCD. Thus we multiply the first expression by $\frac{3}{3}$ and the second expression by $\frac{2}{2}$ to get the LCD:

$$\dfrac{5x^2}{8} + \dfrac{7x}{12} = \dfrac{5x^2}{2 \cdot 2 \cdot 2} + \dfrac{7x}{2 \cdot 2 \cdot 3}$$

$$= \dfrac{5x^2}{2 \cdot 2 \cdot 2} \cdot \dfrac{3}{3} + \dfrac{7x}{2 \cdot 2 \cdot 3} \cdot \dfrac{2}{2} \qquad \text{Multiplying by a form of 1 to get the LCD}$$

$$= \dfrac{15x^2}{24} + \dfrac{14x}{24}.$$

3. Next, we add the numerators: $\dfrac{15x^2}{24} + \dfrac{14x}{24} = \dfrac{15x^2 + 14x}{24}$.

4. We factor in hope of simplifying: $\dfrac{x(15x + 14)}{24}$.

The expression cannot be simplified.

YOUR TURN

EXAMPLE 2 Subtract: $\dfrac{7}{8x} - \dfrac{5}{12x^2}$.

SOLUTION We follow the four steps shown above. First, we find the LCD:

$$\left.\begin{array}{l} 8x = 2 \cdot 2 \cdot 2 \cdot x \\ 12x^2 = 2 \cdot 2 \cdot 3 \cdot x \cdot x \end{array}\right\} \quad \text{LCD} = 2 \cdot 2 \cdot 3 \cdot x \cdot x \cdot 2, \text{ or } 24x^2.$$

The denominator $8x$ must be multiplied by $3x$ in order to obtain the LCD. The denominator $12x^2$ must be multiplied by 2 in order to obtain the LCD. Thus we multiply by $\dfrac{3x}{3x}$ and $\dfrac{2}{2}$ to get the LCD. Then we subtract and, if possible, simplify.

$$\dfrac{7}{8x} - \dfrac{5}{12x^2} = \dfrac{7}{8x} \cdot \dfrac{3x}{3x} - \dfrac{5}{12x^2} \cdot \dfrac{2}{2}$$

$$= \dfrac{21x}{24x^2} - \dfrac{10}{24x^2}$$

$$= \dfrac{21x - 10}{24x^2} \qquad \text{This cannot be simplified, so we are done.}$$

> **CAUTION!** Do not simplify *these* rational expressions or you will lose the LCD.

YOUR TURN

Study Skills

If a Question Stumps You

Don't be surprised if a quiz or a test includes a question that you feel unsure about. Should this happen, do not get rattled—simply skip the question and continue with the quiz or test, returning to the trouble spot after you have answered the other questions.

1. Add: $\dfrac{2x}{9} + \dfrac{5}{12}$.

2. Subtract: $\dfrac{3}{10x^2} - \dfrac{5}{4x}$.

EXAMPLE 3 Add: $\dfrac{2a}{a^2 - 1} + \dfrac{1}{a^2 + a}$.

SOLUTION First, we find the LCD:

Find the LCD.

$\left.\begin{array}{l} a^2 - 1 = (a - 1)(a + 1) \\ a^2 + a = a(a + 1). \end{array}\right\}$ $\quad$ LCD $= (a - 1)(a + 1)a$

We multiply by a form of 1 to get the LCD in each expression:

Write each expression with the LCD.

$\dfrac{2a}{a^2 - 1} + \dfrac{1}{a^2 + a} = \dfrac{2a}{(a - 1)(a + 1)} \cdot \dfrac{a}{a} + \dfrac{1}{a(a + 1)} \cdot \dfrac{a - 1}{a - 1}$ $\quad$ Multiplying by $\dfrac{a}{a}$ and $\dfrac{a - 1}{a - 1}$ to get the LCD

$\qquad\qquad\qquad = \dfrac{2a^2}{(a - 1)(a + 1)a} + \dfrac{a - 1}{a(a + 1)(a - 1)}$

Add numerators. $\qquad = \dfrac{2a^2 + a - 1}{a(a - 1)(a + 1)}$ $\quad$ Adding numerators

Simplify. $\qquad\qquad = \dfrac{(2a - 1)\cancel{(a + 1)}}{a(a - 1)\cancel{(a + 1)}}$ $\quad\left.\right\}$ Simplifying by factoring and removing a factor equal to 1: $\dfrac{a + 1}{a + 1} = 1$

$\qquad\qquad\qquad = \dfrac{2a - 1}{a(a - 1)}.$

3. Add: $\dfrac{4x}{x^2 - 25} + \dfrac{x}{x + 5}$.

↩ YOUR TURN

EXAMPLE 4 Subtract.

a) $\dfrac{x + 4}{x - 2} - \dfrac{x - 7}{x + 5}$

b) $\dfrac{x}{x^2 + 5x + 6} - \dfrac{2}{x^2 + 3x + 2}$

SOLUTION

a) First, we find the LCD. It is just the product of the denominators:

$\qquad$ LCD $= (x - 2)(x + 5).$

We multiply by a form of 1 to get the LCD in each expression. Then we subtract and try to simplify.

$\dfrac{x + 4}{x - 2} - \dfrac{x - 7}{x + 5} = \dfrac{x + 4}{x - 2} \cdot \dfrac{x + 5}{x + 5} - \dfrac{x - 7}{x + 5} \cdot \dfrac{x - 2}{x - 2}$

$\qquad\qquad = \dfrac{x^2 + 9x + 20}{(x - 2)(x + 5)} - \dfrac{x^2 - 9x + 14}{(x - 2)(x + 5)}$ $\quad$ Multiplying out numerators (but not denominators)

$\qquad\qquad = \dfrac{x^2 + 9x + 20 - (x^2 - 9x + 14)}{(x - 2)(x + 5)}$ $\quad$ Parentheses are important.

$\qquad\qquad = \dfrac{x^2 + 9x + 20 - x^2 + 9x - 14}{(x - 2)(x + 5)}$ $\quad$ Removing parentheses and subtracting every term

$\qquad\qquad = \dfrac{18x + 6}{(x - 2)(x + 5)}$

$\qquad\qquad = \dfrac{6(3x + 1)}{(x - 2)(x + 5)}$ $\quad$ We cannot simplify.

Student Notes

As you can see, adding or subtracting rational expressions can involve many steps. Therefore, it is wise to double-check each step of your work as you work through each problem. Waiting to inspect your work at the end of each problem is usually a less efficient use of your time.

b) $\dfrac{x}{x^2 + 5x + 6} - \dfrac{2}{x^2 + 3x + 2}$

Find the LCD.

$= \dfrac{x}{(x+2)(x+3)} - \dfrac{2}{(x+2)(x+1)}$ Factoring denominators. The LCD is $(x+2)(x+3)(x+1)$.

Write each expression with the LCD.

$= \dfrac{x}{(x+2)(x+3)} \cdot \dfrac{x+1}{x+1} - \dfrac{2}{(x+2)(x+1)} \cdot \dfrac{x+3}{x+3}$

$= \dfrac{x^2 + x}{(x+2)(x+3)(x+1)} - \dfrac{2x + 6}{(x+2)(x+3)(x+1)}$

Subtract numerators.

$= \dfrac{x^2 + x - (2x + 6)}{(x+2)(x+3)(x+1)}$ Don't forget the parentheses!

$= \dfrac{x^2 + x - 2x - 6}{(x+2)(x+3)(x+1)}$ Remember to subtract each term in $2x + 6$.

$= \dfrac{x^2 - x - 6}{(x+2)(x+3)(x+1)}$ Combining like terms in the numerator

Simplify.

$= \dfrac{\cancel{(x+2)}(x-3)}{\cancel{(x+2)}(x+3)(x+1)}$

$= \dfrac{x-3}{(x+3)(x+1)}$ Factoring and simplifying; $\dfrac{x+2}{x+2} = 1$

4. Subtract:

$$\dfrac{x}{x^2 + 3x + 2} - \dfrac{3}{x^2 - x - 2}.$$

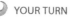 YOUR TURN

When Factors Are Opposites

A special case arises when one denominator is the opposite of the other. When this occurs, we can multiply either expression by 1 using $\dfrac{-1}{-1}$.

EXAMPLE 5   Add: $\dfrac{3}{8a} + \dfrac{1}{-8a}$.

SOLUTION

$\dfrac{3}{8a} + \dfrac{1}{-8a} = \dfrac{3}{8a} + \dfrac{-1}{-1} \cdot \dfrac{1}{-8a}$

$= \dfrac{3}{8a} + \dfrac{-1}{8a} = \dfrac{2}{8a}$

$= \dfrac{2 \cdot 1}{2 \cdot 4a} = \dfrac{1}{4a}$ Simplifying by removing a factor equal to 1: $\frac{2}{2} = 1$

> When denominators are opposites, we multiply one rational expression by $-1/-1$ to get the LCD.

5. Add: $\dfrac{t}{2} + \dfrac{3}{-2}$.

 YOUR TURN

Expressions of the form $a - b$ and $b - a$ are opposites of each other. When either of these binomials is multiplied by -1, the result is the other binomial:

$$-1(a - b) = -a + b = b + (-a) = b - a;$$
$$-1(b - a) = -b + a = a + (-b) = a - b.$$

   Multiplication by -1 reverses the order in which subtraction occurs.

EXAMPLE 6 Subtract: $\dfrac{5x}{x-7} - \dfrac{3x}{7-x}$.

SOLUTION

$$\dfrac{5x}{x-7} - \dfrac{3x}{7-x} = \dfrac{5x}{x-7} - \dfrac{-1}{-1} \cdot \dfrac{3x}{7-x}$$ Note that $x-7$ and $7-x$ are opposites.

$$= \dfrac{5x}{x-7} - \dfrac{-3x}{x-7}$$ Performing the multiplication. *Note:* $-1(7-x) = -7 + x$
$= x - 7$.

$$= \dfrac{5x-(-3x)}{x-7} \left.\vphantom{\dfrac{1}{1}}\right\}$$

$$= \dfrac{5x+3x}{x-7} \left.\vphantom{\dfrac{1}{1}}\right\}$$ Subtracting. The parentheses are important.

$$= \dfrac{8x}{x-7}$$ Simplifying

6. Subtract:

$$\dfrac{x}{x-5} - \dfrac{7}{5-x}.$$

YOUR TURN

Sometimes, after factoring to find the LCD, we find a factor in one denominator that is the opposite of a factor in the other denominator. When this happens, multiplication by $-1/-1$ can again be helpful.

EXAMPLE 7 Perform the indicated operations and simplify.

a) $\dfrac{x}{x^2-25} + \dfrac{3}{5-x}$

b) $\dfrac{x+9}{x^2-4} + \dfrac{6-x}{4-x^2} - \dfrac{1+x}{x^2-4}$

Student Notes

Your answer may differ slightly from the answer found at the back of the book and still be correct. For example, an equivalent answer to Example 7(a) is $-\dfrac{2x+15}{(x-5)(x+5)}$:

$$\dfrac{-2x-15}{(x-5)(x+5)} = \dfrac{-(2x+15)}{(x-5)(x+5)}$$

$$= -\dfrac{2x+15}{(x-5)(x+5)}.$$

Before reworking an exercise, be sure that your answer is indeed incorrect.

SOLUTION

a) $\dfrac{x}{x^2-25} + \dfrac{3}{5-x} = \dfrac{x}{(x-5)(x+5)} + \dfrac{3}{5-x}$ Factoring

$$= \dfrac{x}{(x-5)(x+5)} + \dfrac{3}{5-x} \cdot \dfrac{-1}{-1}$$ Multiplication by $-1/-1$ changes $5-x$ to $x-5$.

$$= \dfrac{x}{(x-5)(x+5)} + \dfrac{-3}{x-5}$$ $(5-x)(-1) = x - 5$

$$= \dfrac{x}{(x-5)(x+5)} + \dfrac{-3}{(x-5)} \cdot \dfrac{x+5}{x+5}$$ The LCD is $(x-5)(x+5)$.

$$= \dfrac{x}{(x-5)(x+5)} + \dfrac{-3x-15}{(x-5)(x+5)}$$

$$= \dfrac{-2x-15}{(x-5)(x+5)}$$

Technology Connection

The TABLE feature can be used to check addition or subtraction of rational expressions. Below we check Example 7(a), using

$$y_1 = \dfrac{x}{x^2-25} + \dfrac{3}{5-x}$$

and

$$y_2 = \dfrac{-2x-15}{(x-5)(x+5)}.$$

ΔTBL = 1

X	Y₁	Y₂
1	.70833	.70833
2	.90476	.90476
3	1.3125	1.3125
4	2.5556	2.5556
5	ERROR	ERROR
6	−2.455	−2.455
7	−1.208	−1.208
X = 1		

Because the values for y_1 and y_2 match, we have a check.

b) Since $4 - x^2$ is the opposite of $x^2 - 4$, multiplying the second rational expression by $-1/-1$ will lead to a common denominator:

$$\frac{x + 9}{x^2 - 4} + \frac{6 - x}{4 - x^2} - \frac{1 + x}{x^2 - 4} = \frac{x + 9}{x^2 - 4} + \frac{6 - x}{4 - x^2} \cdot \frac{-1}{-1} - \frac{1 + x}{x^2 - 4}$$

$$= \frac{x + 9}{x^2 - 4} + \frac{x - 6}{x^2 - 4} - \frac{1 + x}{x^2 - 4}$$

$$= \frac{x + 9 + x - 6 - 1 - x}{x^2 - 4} \quad \text{Adding and subtracting numerators}$$

$$= \frac{x + 2}{x^2 - 4}$$

$$\left. \begin{array}{l} = \dfrac{(x + 2) \cdot 1}{(x + 2)(x - 2)} \\[2mm] = \dfrac{1}{x - 2}. \end{array} \right\} \quad \text{Simplifying}$$

7. Perform the indicated operations and simplify:

$$\frac{x + 4}{x + 1} - \frac{x}{3 - x} - \frac{4x}{x^2 - 2x - 3}.$$

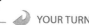 YOUR TURN

6.4 EXERCISE SET

FOR EXTRA HELP

MyMathLab® Math XL

PRACTICE   WATCH   READ   REVIEW

Vocabulary and Reading Check

In Exercises 1–4, the four steps for adding rational expressions with different denominators are listed. Fill in the missing word or words for each step.

1. To add or subtract when the denominators are different, first find the _____.

2. Multiply each rational expression by a form of 1 made up of the factors of the LCD that are _____ from that expression's _____.

3. Add or subtract the _____, as indicated. Write the sum or the difference over the _____.

4. _____, if possible.

Adding and Subtracting with LCDs

Perform the indicated operation. Simplify, if possible.

5. $\dfrac{3}{x^2} + \dfrac{5}{x}$

6. $\dfrac{6}{x} + \dfrac{7}{x^2}$

7. $\dfrac{1}{6r} - \dfrac{3}{8r}$

8. $\dfrac{4}{9t} - \dfrac{7}{6t}$

9. $\dfrac{3}{uv^2} + \dfrac{4}{u^3v}$

10. $\dfrac{8}{cd^2} + \dfrac{1}{c^2d}$

11. $\dfrac{-2}{3xy^2} - \dfrac{6}{x^2y^3}$

12. $\dfrac{8}{9t^3} - \dfrac{5}{6t^2}$

13. $\dfrac{x + 3}{8} + \dfrac{x - 2}{6}$

14. $\dfrac{x - 4}{9} + \dfrac{x + 5}{12}$

15. $\dfrac{x - 2}{6} - \dfrac{x + 1}{3}$

16. $\dfrac{a + 2}{2} - \dfrac{a - 4}{4}$

17. $\dfrac{a + 3}{15a} + \dfrac{2a - 1}{3a^2}$

18. $\dfrac{5a + 1}{2a^2} + \dfrac{a + 2}{6a}$

19. $\dfrac{4z - 9}{3z} - \dfrac{3z - 8}{4z}$

20. $\dfrac{x - 1}{4x} - \dfrac{2x + 3}{x}$

21. $\dfrac{3c + d}{cd^2} + \dfrac{c - d}{c^2d}$

22. $\dfrac{u + v}{u^2v} + \dfrac{2u + v}{uv^2}$

23. $\dfrac{4x + 2t}{3xt^2} - \dfrac{5x - 3t}{x^2t}$

24. $\dfrac{5x + 3y}{2x^2y} - \dfrac{3x + 4y}{xy^2}$

25. $\dfrac{3}{x - 2} + \dfrac{3}{x + 2}$

26. $\dfrac{5}{x - 1} + \dfrac{5}{x + 1}$

27. $\dfrac{t}{t + 3} - \dfrac{1}{t - 1}$

28. $\dfrac{y}{y - 3} + \dfrac{12}{y + 4}$

29. $\dfrac{3}{x + 1} + \dfrac{2}{3x}$

30. $\dfrac{2}{x + 5} + \dfrac{3}{4x}$

31. $\dfrac{3}{2t^2 - 2t} - \dfrac{5}{2t - 2}$

32. $\dfrac{8}{3t^2 - 15t} - \dfrac{3}{2t - 10}$

33. $\dfrac{3a}{a^2 - 9} + \dfrac{a}{a + 3}$

34. $\dfrac{5p}{p^2 - 16} + \dfrac{p}{p - 4}$

35. $\dfrac{6}{z + 4} - \dfrac{2}{3z + 12}$

36. $\dfrac{t}{t - 3} - \dfrac{5}{4t - 12}$

37. $\dfrac{5}{q - 1} + \dfrac{2}{(q - 1)^2}$

38. $\dfrac{3}{w + 2} + \dfrac{7}{(w + 2)^2}$

39. $\dfrac{3a}{4a - 20} + \dfrac{9a}{6a - 30}$

40. $\dfrac{4a}{5a - 10} + \dfrac{3a}{10a - 20}$

41. $\dfrac{y}{y - 1} - \dfrac{y - 1}{y}$

42. $\dfrac{x + 4}{x} + \dfrac{x}{x + 4}$

43. $\dfrac{6}{a^2 + a - 2} + \dfrac{4}{a^2 - 4a + 3}$

44. $\dfrac{x}{x^2 + 2x + 1} + \dfrac{1}{x^2 + 5x + 4}$

45. $\dfrac{x}{x^2 + 9x + 20} - \dfrac{4}{x^2 + 7x + 12}$

46. $\dfrac{x}{x^2 + 5x + 6} - \dfrac{2}{x^2 + 3x + 2}$

47. $\dfrac{3z}{z^2 - 4z + 4} + \dfrac{10}{z^2 + z - 6}$

48. $\dfrac{3}{x^2 - 9} + \dfrac{2}{x^2 - x - 6}$

Aha! **49.** $\dfrac{-7}{x^2 + 25x + 24} - \dfrac{0}{x^2 + 11x + 10}$

50. $\dfrac{x}{x^2 + 17x + 72} - \dfrac{1}{x^2 + 15x + 56}$

51. $3 + \dfrac{4}{2x + 1}$

52. $2 + \dfrac{1}{5 - x}$

53. $3 - \dfrac{2}{4 - x}$

54. $4 - \dfrac{3}{3x + 2}$

When Factors Are Opposites

Perform the indicated operation. Simplify, if possible.

55. $\dfrac{5x}{4} - \dfrac{x - 2}{-4}$

56. $\dfrac{x}{6} - \dfrac{2x - 3}{-6}$

Aha! **57.** $\dfrac{x}{x - 5} + \dfrac{x}{5 - x}$

58. $\dfrac{y}{y - 2} - \dfrac{y}{2 - y}$

59. $\dfrac{y^2}{y - 3} + \dfrac{9}{3 - y}$

60. $\dfrac{t^2}{t - 2} + \dfrac{4}{2 - t}$

61. $\dfrac{c - 5}{c^2 - 64} - \dfrac{5 - c}{64 - c^2}$

62. $\dfrac{b - 4}{b^2 - 49} + \dfrac{b - 4}{49 - b^2}$

63. $\dfrac{t - 3}{t^3 - 1} - \dfrac{2}{1 - t^3}$

64. $\dfrac{1 - 6m}{1 - m^3} - \dfrac{5}{m^3 - 1}$

65. $\dfrac{4 - p}{25 - p^2} + \dfrac{p + 1}{p - 5}$

66. $\dfrac{y + 2}{y - 7} + \dfrac{3 - y}{49 - y^2}$

67. $\dfrac{x}{x - 4} - \dfrac{3}{16 - x^2}$

68. $\dfrac{x}{3 - x} - \dfrac{2}{x^2 - 9}$

69. $\dfrac{a}{a^2 - 1} + \dfrac{2a}{a - a^2}$

70. $\dfrac{3x + 2}{3x + 6} + \dfrac{x}{4 - x^2}$

71. $\dfrac{4x}{x^2 - y^2} - \dfrac{6}{y - x}$

72. $\dfrac{4 - a^2}{a^2 - 9} - \dfrac{a - 2}{3 - a}$

Adding and Subtracting

Perform the indicated operations. Simplify, if possible.

73. $\dfrac{x - 3}{2 - x} - \dfrac{x + 3}{x + 2} + \dfrac{x + 6}{4 - x^2}$

74. $\dfrac{t - 5}{1 - t} - \dfrac{t + 4}{t + 1} + \dfrac{t + 2}{t^2 - 1}$

75. $\dfrac{2x + 5}{x + 1} + \dfrac{x + 7}{x + 5} - \dfrac{5x + 17}{(x + 1)(x + 5)}$

76. $\dfrac{x + 5}{x + 3} + \dfrac{x + 7}{x + 2} - \dfrac{7x + 19}{(x + 3)(x + 2)}$

77. $\dfrac{1}{x + y} + \dfrac{1}{x - y} - \dfrac{2x}{x^2 - y^2}$

78. $\dfrac{2r}{r^2 - s^2} + \dfrac{1}{r + s} - \dfrac{1}{r - s}$

79. $\dfrac{1}{x^2 + 7x + 12} - \dfrac{2}{x^2 + 4x + 3} + \dfrac{3}{x^2 + 5x + 4}$

80. $\dfrac{4}{x^2 + x - 2} + \dfrac{2}{x^2 - 4x + 3} - \dfrac{5}{x^2 - x - 6}$

81. What is the advantage of using the *least* common denominator—rather than just *any* common denominator—when adding or subtracting rational expressions?

82. Describe a procedure that can be used to add any two rational expressions.

Skill Review

Simplify.

83. $3 - 12 \div (-4)$ [1.8]

84. $|-6 - 1|$ [1.8]

85. $(1.2 \times 10^8)(2.5 \times 10^6)$ [4.2]

86. $(2a^3b^{-5})(-3ab^4)$ [4.2]

87. $(3a^{-1}b)^{-2}$ [4.2]

88. $-(-12)$ [1.6]

Synthesis

 89. How could you convince someone that

$$\frac{1}{3-x} \quad \text{and} \quad \frac{1}{x-3}$$

are opposites of each other?

 90. Are parentheses as important for adding rational expressions as they are for subtracting rational expressions? Why or why not?

Write expressions for the perimeter and the area of each rectangle.

91.

92.

Perform the indicated operations. Simplify, if possible.

93. $\dfrac{x^2}{3x^2 - 5x - 2} - \dfrac{2x}{3x + 1} \cdot \dfrac{1}{x - 2}$

94. $\dfrac{2x + 11}{x - 3} \cdot \dfrac{3}{x + 4} + \dfrac{2x + 1}{4 + x} \cdot \dfrac{3}{3 - x}$

95. $\dfrac{2x - 16}{x^2 - x - 2} - \dfrac{x + 2}{x^2 - 5x + 6} - \dfrac{x + 6}{x^2 - 2x - 3}$

96. $\dfrac{2x + 8}{x^2 + 3x + 2} - \dfrac{x - 2}{x^2 + 5x + 6} - \dfrac{x + 2}{x^2 + 4x + 3}$

Aha! **97.** $\left(\dfrac{x}{x + 7} - \dfrac{3}{x + 2}\right)\left(\dfrac{x}{x + 7} + \dfrac{3}{x + 2}\right)$

98. $\dfrac{1}{ay - 3a + 2xy - 6x} - \dfrac{xy + ay}{a^2 - 4x^2}\left(\dfrac{1}{y - 3}\right)^2$

99. $\left(\dfrac{a}{a - b} + \dfrac{b}{a + b}\right)\left(\dfrac{1}{3a + b} + \dfrac{2a + 6b}{9a^2 - b^2}\right)$

100. $\dfrac{2x^2 + 5x - 3}{2x^2 - 9x + 9} + \dfrac{x + 1}{3 - 2x} + \dfrac{4x^2 + 8x + 3}{x - 3} \cdot \dfrac{x + 3}{9 - 4x^2}$

101. Express

$$\frac{a - 3b}{a - b}$$

as a sum of two rational expressions with denominators that are opposites of each other. Answers may vary.

 102. Use a graphing calculator to check the answer to Exercise 29.

 103. Why does the word ERROR appear in the table displayed in the Technology Connection on p. 399?

YOUR TURN ANSWERS: SECTION 6.4

1. $\dfrac{8x + 15}{36}$　**2.** $\dfrac{-25x + 6}{20x^2}$　**3.** $\dfrac{x(x - 1)}{(x - 5)(x + 5)}$

4. $\dfrac{x - 6}{(x - 2)(x + 2)}$　**5.** $\dfrac{t - 3}{2}$　**6.** $\dfrac{x + 7}{x - 5}$

7. $\dfrac{2(x + 2)}{x + 1}$

QUICK QUIZ: SECTIONS 6.1–6.4

Perform the indicated operation and, if possible, simplify.

1. $\dfrac{x^2 - 64}{10x^2} \cdot \dfrac{5x}{2x + 16}$ 　[6.2]

2. $\dfrac{2x - 3}{x - 4} - \dfrac{x}{x + 2}$ 　[6.4]

3. $\dfrac{x^2 - 6}{x - 3} - \dfrac{x}{x - 3}$ 　[6.3]

4. $\dfrac{2t}{2t + 1} + \dfrac{t}{t - 1}$ 　[6.4]

5. $\dfrac{2x^2 - x - 1}{x^2 - 4x + 4} \div \dfrac{x - 2}{x - 1}$ 　[6.2]

PREPARE TO MOVE ON

Divide and, if possible, simplify.

1. $\dfrac{\frac{3}{4}}{\frac{5}{6}}$ 　[1.3]　　**2.** $\dfrac{\frac{8}{15}}{\frac{9}{10}}$ 　[1.3]

3. $\dfrac{2x + 6}{x - 1} \div \dfrac{3x + 9}{x - 1}$ 　[6.2]

4. $\dfrac{x^2 - 9}{x^2 - 4} \div \dfrac{x^2 + 6x + 9}{x^2 + 4x + 4}$ 　[6.2]

Mid-Chapter Review

The process of adding and subtracting rational expressions is significantly different from multiplying and dividing. The first thing to note when combining rational expressions is the operation sign.

Operation	Need Common Denominator?	Procedure	Tips and Cautions
Addition	Yes	Write equivalent expressions with a common denominator. Add numerators. Keep denominator.	Do not simplify after writing with the LCD. Instead, simplify after adding the numerators.
Subtraction	Yes	Write equivalent expressions with a common denominator. Subtract numerators. Keep denominator.	Use parentheses around the numerator being subtracted. Simplify after subtracting the numerators.
Multiplication	No	Multiply numerators. Multiply denominators.	Do not perform the polynomial multiplication. Instead, factor and try to simplify.
Division	No	Multiply by the reciprocal of the divisor.	Begin by rewriting as a multiplication using the reciprocal of the divisor.

GUIDED SOLUTIONS

1. Divide: $\dfrac{a^2}{a-10} \div \dfrac{a^2+5a}{a^2-100}$. Simplify, if possible. [6.2]

Solution

$$\dfrac{a^2}{a-10} \div \dfrac{a^2+5a}{a^2-100}$$

$$= \dfrac{a^2}{a-10} \cdot \dfrac{\boxed{}}{\boxed{}} \qquad \text{Multiplying by the reciprocal of the divisor}$$

$$= \dfrac{a \cdot a \cdot (a+10) \cdot \boxed{}}{(a-10) \cdot a \cdot \boxed{}} \qquad \text{Multiplying and factoring}$$

$$= \dfrac{\boxed{}}{\boxed{}} \cdot \dfrac{a(a+10)}{a+5} \qquad \text{Factoring out a factor equal to 1}$$

$$= \dfrac{a(a+10)}{a+5} \qquad \text{Simplifying}$$

2. Add: $\dfrac{2}{x} + \dfrac{1}{x^2+x}$. Simplify, if possible. [6.4]

Solution

$$\dfrac{2}{x} + \dfrac{1}{x^2+x}$$

$$= \dfrac{2}{x} + \dfrac{1}{x\boxed{}} \qquad \begin{array}{l}\text{Factoring denominators.} \\ \text{The LCD is } x(x+1).\end{array}$$

$$= \dfrac{2}{x} \cdot \dfrac{\boxed{}}{\boxed{}} + \dfrac{1}{x(x+1)} \qquad \begin{array}{l}\text{Multiplying by 1} \\ \text{to get the LCD in} \\ \text{the first denominator}\end{array}$$

$$= \dfrac{\boxed{}}{x(x+1)} + \dfrac{1}{x(x+1)} \qquad \text{Multiplying}$$

$$= \dfrac{\boxed{}}{x(x+1)} \qquad \begin{array}{l}\text{Adding numerators.} \\ \text{We cannot simplify.}\end{array}$$

MIXED REVIEW

Perform the indicated operation and, if possible, simplify.

3. $\dfrac{3}{5x} + \dfrac{2}{x^2}$ [6.4]

4. $\dfrac{3}{5x} \cdot \dfrac{2}{x^2}$ [6.2]

5. $\dfrac{3}{5x} \div \dfrac{2}{x^2}$ [6.2]

6. $\dfrac{3}{5x} - \dfrac{2}{x^2}$ [6.4]

7. $\dfrac{2x - 6}{5x + 10} \cdot \dfrac{x + 2}{6x - 12}$ [6.2]

8. $\dfrac{2}{x - 5} \div \dfrac{6}{x - 5}$ [6.2]

9. $\dfrac{x}{x + 2} - \dfrac{1}{x - 1}$ [6.4]

10. $\dfrac{2}{x + 3} + \dfrac{3}{x + 4}$ [6.4]

11. $\dfrac{5}{2x - 1} + \dfrac{10x}{1 - 2x}$ [6.4]

12. $\dfrac{3}{x - 4} - \dfrac{2}{4 - x}$ [6.4]

13. $\dfrac{(x - 2)(2x + 3)}{(x + 1)(x - 5)} \div \dfrac{(x - 2)(x + 1)}{(x - 5)(x + 3)}$ [6.2]

14. $\dfrac{a}{6a - 9b} - \dfrac{b}{4a - 6b}$ [6.4]

15. $\dfrac{x^2 - 16}{x^2 - x} \cdot \dfrac{x^2}{x^2 - 5x + 4}$ [6.2]

16. $\dfrac{x + 1}{x^2 - 7x + 10} + \dfrac{3}{x^2 - x - 2}$ [6.4]

17. $\dfrac{3u^2 - 3}{4} \div \dfrac{4u + 4}{3}$ [6.2]

18. $(t^2 + t - 20) \cdot \dfrac{t + 5}{t - 4}$ [6.2]

19. $\dfrac{a^2 - 2a + 1}{a^2 - 4} \div (a^2 - 3a + 2)$ [6.2]

20. $\dfrac{2x - 7}{x} - \dfrac{3x - 5}{2}$ [6.4]

6.5 Complex Rational Expressions

Using Division to Simplify • Multiplying by the LCD

Study Skills

Multiple Methods

When more than one method is presented, as is the case for simplifying complex rational expressions, it can be helpful to learn both methods. If two different approaches yield the same result, you can be confident that your answer is correct.

A **complex rational expression** is a rational expression that has one or more rational expressions within its numerator or denominator. Here are some examples:

$$\dfrac{1 + \dfrac{2}{x}}{3}, \quad \dfrac{\dfrac{x + y}{7}}{\dfrac{2x}{x + 1}}, \quad \dfrac{\dfrac{4}{3} + \dfrac{1}{5}}{\dfrac{2}{x} - \dfrac{x}{y}}.$$

These are rational expressions within the complex rational expression.

To simplify a complex rational expression is to write an equivalent expression that is no longer complex. We will consider two methods for simplifying complex rational expressions. We assume all denominators are nonzero.

Using Division to Simplify (Method 1)

Our first method for simplifying complex rational expressions involves rewriting the expression as a quotient of two rational expressions.

TO SIMPLIFY A COMPLEX RATIONAL EXPRESSION BY DIVIDING

1. Add or subtract, as needed, to get a single rational expression in the numerator.
2. Add or subtract, as needed, to get a single rational expression in the denominator.
3. Divide the numerator by the denominator (invert the divisor and multiply).
4. If possible, simplify by removing a factor equal to 1.

The key here is to express a complex rational expression as one rational expression divided by another.

EXAMPLE 1 Simplify: $\dfrac{\dfrac{x}{x-3}}{\dfrac{4}{5x-15}}$.

SOLUTION Here the numerator and the denominator are already single rational expressions. This allows us to start by dividing (step 3):

$$\frac{\dfrac{x}{x-3}}{\dfrac{4}{5x-15}} = \frac{x}{x-3} \div \frac{4}{5x-15} \qquad \text{Rewriting with a division symbol}$$

$$= \frac{x}{x-3} \cdot \frac{5x-15}{4} \qquad \begin{array}{l}\text{Multiplying by the reciprocal of the}\\ \text{divisor (inverting and multiplying)}\end{array}$$

$$= \frac{x}{x-3} \cdot \frac{5(x-3)}{4} \qquad \begin{array}{l}\text{Factoring and removing a factor}\\ \text{equal to 1: } \dfrac{x-3}{x-3} = 1\end{array}$$

$$= \frac{5x}{4}.$$

1. Simplify: $\dfrac{\dfrac{1}{x^2+x}}{\dfrac{2}{5x+5}}$.

YOUR TURN

EXAMPLE 2 Simplify.

a) $\dfrac{\dfrac{5}{2a} + \dfrac{1}{a}}{\dfrac{1}{4a} - \dfrac{5}{6}}$

b) $\dfrac{\dfrac{x^2}{y} - \dfrac{5}{x}}{xz}$

SOLUTION

a)

$$\frac{\dfrac{5}{2a} + \dfrac{1}{a}}{\dfrac{1}{4a} - \dfrac{5}{6}} = \frac{\left.\dfrac{5}{2a} + \dfrac{1}{a}\cdot\dfrac{2}{2}\right\}}{\left.\dfrac{1}{4a}\cdot\dfrac{3}{3} - \dfrac{5}{6}\cdot\dfrac{2a}{2a}\right\}} \begin{array}{l}\leftarrow \begin{array}{l}\text{Multiplying by 1 to get the LCD, } 2a, \text{ for}\\ \text{the numerator of the complex rational}\\ \text{expression}\end{array}\\[1em] \leftarrow \begin{array}{l}\text{Multiplying by 1 to get the LCD, } 12a, \text{ for}\\ \text{the denominator of the complex rational}\\ \text{expression}\end{array}\end{array}$$

1. Form a single rational expression in the numerator.

2. Form a single rational expression in the denominator.

3. Divide the numerator by the denominator.

$$= \frac{\dfrac{5}{2a} + \dfrac{2}{2a}}{\dfrac{3}{12a} - \dfrac{10a}{12a}} = \frac{\dfrac{7}{2a}}{\dfrac{3-10a}{12a}} \begin{array}{l}\leftarrow \text{Adding}\\[1.5em] \leftarrow \text{Subtracting}\end{array}$$

$$= \frac{7}{2a} \div \frac{3-10a}{12a} \qquad \begin{array}{l}\text{Rewriting with a division symbol. This is often}\\ \text{done mentally.}\end{array}$$

$$= \frac{7}{2a} \cdot \frac{12a}{3-10a} \qquad \begin{array}{l}\text{Multiplying by the reciprocal of the divisor}\\ \text{(inverting and multiplying)}\end{array}$$

4. Simplify.

$$= \frac{7}{2a} \cdot \frac{2a \cdot 6}{3-10a} \qquad \text{Removing a factor equal to 1: } \frac{2a}{2a} = 1$$

$$= \frac{42}{3-10a}$$

b)
$$\frac{\dfrac{x^2}{y} - \dfrac{5}{x}}{xz} = \frac{\dfrac{x^2}{y} \cdot \dfrac{x}{x} - \dfrac{5}{x} \cdot \dfrac{y}{y}}{xz} \leftarrow \text{Multiplying by 1 to get the LCD, } xy, \text{ for the numerator of the complex rational expression}$$

$$= \frac{\dfrac{x^3}{xy} - \dfrac{5y}{xy}}{xz}$$

$$= \frac{\dfrac{x^3 - 5y}{xy}}{xz} \quad \leftarrow \text{———— Subtracting}$$

$$\quad\quad\quad\quad \leftarrow \text{———— If you prefer, write } xz \text{ as } \dfrac{xz}{1}.$$

$$= \frac{x^3 - 5y}{xy} \div (xz) \quad \text{Rewriting with a division symbol}$$

$$= \frac{x^3 - 5y}{xy} \cdot \frac{1}{xz} \quad \begin{array}{l}\text{Multiplying by the reciprocal of the divisor} \\ \text{(inverting and multiplying)}\end{array}$$

$$= \frac{x^3 - 5y}{x^2 yz}$$

2. Simplify: $\dfrac{\dfrac{1}{t} - \dfrac{1}{5}}{\dfrac{t-5}{t}}$.

↪ YOUR TURN

Multiplying by the LCD (Method 2)

A second method for simplifying complex rational expressions relies on multiplying by a carefully chosen expression that is equal to 1. This multiplication by 1 will result in an expression that is no longer complex.

> **TO SIMPLIFY A COMPLEX RATIONAL EXPRESSION BY MULTIPLYING BY THE LCD**
>
> 1. Find the LCD of *all* rational expressions within the complex rational expression.
> 2. Multiply the complex rational expression by an expression equal to 1. Write 1 as the LCD over itself: LCD/LCD.
> 3. Simplify. No fraction expressions should remain within the complex rational expression.
> 4. Factor and, if possible, simplify the remaining expression.

EXAMPLE 3   Simplify: $\dfrac{\dfrac{1}{2} + \dfrac{3}{4}}{\dfrac{5}{6} - \dfrac{3}{8}}$.

Student Notes

Pay careful attention to the different ways in which Method 1 and Method 2 use an LCD. In Method 1, one LCD is found in the numerator and one in the denominator. In Method 2, *all* rational expressions are considered in order to find one LCD.

SOLUTION

1. The LCD of $\frac{1}{2}, \frac{3}{4}, \frac{5}{6}$, and $\frac{3}{8}$ is 24.

2. We multiply by an expression equal to 1:

$$\frac{\dfrac{1}{2} + \dfrac{3}{4}}{\dfrac{5}{6} - \dfrac{3}{8}} = \frac{\dfrac{1}{2} + \dfrac{3}{4}}{\dfrac{5}{6} - \dfrac{3}{8}} \cdot \frac{24}{24} \quad \begin{array}{l}\text{Multiplying by an expression equal to 1,} \\ \text{using the LCD: } \dfrac{24}{24} = 1\end{array}$$

3. Using the distributive law, we perform the multiplication:

$$\frac{\dfrac{1}{2}+\dfrac{3}{4}}{\dfrac{5}{6}-\dfrac{3}{8}}\cdot\frac{24}{24}=\frac{\left(\dfrac{1}{2}+\dfrac{3}{4}\right)24}{\left(\dfrac{5}{6}-\dfrac{3}{8}\right)24}$$ ← Multiplying the numerator by 24
Don't forget the parentheses!
← Multiplying the denominator by 24

$$=\frac{\dfrac{1}{2}(24)+\dfrac{3}{4}(24)}{\dfrac{5}{6}(24)-\dfrac{3}{8}(24)}$$ Using the distributive law

$$=\frac{\dfrac{24}{2}+\dfrac{3(24)}{4}}{\dfrac{5(24)}{6}-\dfrac{3(24)}{8}}$$

3. Simplify: $\dfrac{\dfrac{5}{2}-\dfrac{4}{3}}{\dfrac{2}{3}+\dfrac{3}{4}}.$

$$=\frac{12+18}{20-9},\ \text{ or }\ \frac{30}{11}.\quad\text{Simplifying}$$

4. The result, $\frac{30}{11}$, cannot be factored or simplified, so we are done.

YOUR TURN

Multiplying like this effectively clears fractions in both the top and the bottom of the complex rational expression.

EXAMPLE 4 Simplify.

a) $\dfrac{\dfrac{5}{2a}+\dfrac{1}{a}}{\dfrac{1}{4a}-\dfrac{5}{6}}$

b) $\dfrac{1-\dfrac{1}{x}}{1-\dfrac{1}{x^2}}$

SOLUTION

1. Find the LCD.

a) The denominators within the complex expression are $2a$, a, $4a$, and 6, so the LCD is $12a$. We multiply by 1 using $(12a)/(12a)$:

2. Multiply by LCD/LCD.

$$\frac{\dfrac{5}{2a}+\dfrac{1}{a}}{\dfrac{1}{4a}-\dfrac{5}{6}}=\frac{\dfrac{5}{2a}+\dfrac{1}{a}}{\dfrac{1}{4a}-\dfrac{5}{6}}\cdot\frac{12a}{12a}=\frac{\dfrac{5}{2a}(12a)+\dfrac{1}{a}(12a)}{\dfrac{1}{4a}(12a)-\dfrac{5}{6}(12a)}$$ Using the distributive law

3., 4. Simplify.

$$=\frac{\dfrac{5(12a)}{2a}+\dfrac{12a}{a}}{\dfrac{12a}{4a}-\dfrac{5(12a)}{6}}$$

$$=\frac{\dfrac{5\cdot2\cdot6\cdot a}{2\cdot a}+\dfrac{12\cdot a}{a}}{\dfrac{4\cdot3\cdot a}{4\cdot a}-\dfrac{5\cdot2\cdot6\cdot a}{6}}$$ All fractions have been cleared.

$$=\frac{30+12}{3-10a}=\frac{42}{3-10a}.$$

b) $\dfrac{1 - \dfrac{1}{x}}{1 - \dfrac{1}{x^2}} = \dfrac{1 - \dfrac{1}{x}}{1 - \dfrac{1}{x^2}} \cdot \dfrac{x^2}{x^2}$ The LCD is x^2 so we multiply by 1 using x^2/x^2.

$= \dfrac{1 \cdot x^2 - \dfrac{1}{x} \cdot x^2}{1 \cdot x^2 - \dfrac{1}{x^2} \cdot x^2}$ Using the distributive law

$= \dfrac{x^2 - x}{x^2 - 1}$ All fractions have been cleared within the complex rational expression.

$= \dfrac{x(x-1)}{(x+1)(x-1)}$ Factoring and simplifying: $\dfrac{x-1}{x-1} = 1$

$= \dfrac{x}{x+1}$

4. Simplify: $\dfrac{1 - \dfrac{2}{3x}}{x - \dfrac{4}{9x}}$.

YOUR TURN

It is important to understand both of the methods studied in this section. Sometimes, as in Example 1, the complex rational expression is either given as—or easily written as—a quotient of two rational expressions. In these cases, Method 1 (using division) is probably the easier method to use. Other times, as in Example 4, it is not difficult to find the LCD of all denominators in the complex rational expression. When this occurs, it is usually easier to use Method 2 (multiplying by the LCD). The more practice you get using both methods, the better you will be at selecting the easier method for any given problem.

6.5 EXERCISE SET

FOR EXTRA HELP

MyMathLab® MathXL
PRACTICE   WATCH   READ   REVIEW

Vocabulary and Reading Check

Consider the expression

$$\dfrac{\dfrac{2}{3} + \dfrac{1}{x}}{\dfrac{5}{x}}.$$

Choose the word from the following list that best completes each statement, with reference to the above expression. Not all words in the list will be used.

complex
denominator
least common denominator
numerator
opposite
reciprocal

1. The expression given above is a(n) _____ rational expression.

2. The expression $\dfrac{5}{x}$ is the _____ of the above expression.

3. The _____ of the rational expressions within the expression above is $3x$.

4. To simplify, we can multiply the numerator by the _____ of $\dfrac{5}{x}$.

Concept Reinforcement

*Each of Exercises 5–8 shows a complex rational expression and the first step taken to simplify that expression. Indicate for each which method is being used: **(a)** using division to simplify (Method 1), or **(b)** multiplying by the LCD (Method 2).*

5. _____ $\dfrac{\dfrac{1}{x} + \dfrac{1}{2}}{\dfrac{1}{3} - \dfrac{1}{x}} = \dfrac{\dfrac{1}{x} + \dfrac{1}{2}}{\dfrac{1}{3} - \dfrac{1}{x}} \cdot \dfrac{6x}{6x}$

6. _____ $\dfrac{\dfrac{1}{x} + \dfrac{1}{2}}{\dfrac{1}{3} - \dfrac{1}{x}} = \dfrac{\dfrac{1}{x} \cdot \dfrac{2}{2} + \dfrac{1}{2} \cdot \dfrac{x}{x}}{\dfrac{1}{3} \cdot \dfrac{x}{x} - \dfrac{1}{x} \cdot \dfrac{3}{3}}$

7. ___ $\dfrac{\dfrac{x-1}{x}}{\dfrac{x^2}{x^2-1}} = \dfrac{x-1}{x} \div \dfrac{x^2}{x^2-1}$

8. ___ $\dfrac{\dfrac{x-1}{x}}{\dfrac{x^2}{x^2-1}} = \dfrac{\dfrac{x-1}{x}}{\dfrac{x^2}{x^2-1}} \cdot \dfrac{x(x+1)(x-1)}{x(x+1)(x-1)}$

Complex Rational Expressions

Simplify. Use either method or the method specified by your instructor.

9. $\dfrac{\dfrac{1}{2}+\dfrac{1}{3}}{\dfrac{1}{4}-\dfrac{1}{6}}$

10. $\dfrac{\dfrac{2}{5}-\dfrac{1}{10}}{\dfrac{7}{20}-\dfrac{4}{15}}$

11. $\dfrac{1+\dfrac{1}{4}}{2+\dfrac{3}{4}}$

12. $\dfrac{3+\dfrac{1}{4}}{1+\dfrac{1}{2}}$

13. $\dfrac{\dfrac{x}{4}+x}{\dfrac{4}{x}+x}$

14. $\dfrac{\dfrac{1}{c}+2}{\dfrac{1}{c}-5}$

15. $\dfrac{\dfrac{x+2}{x-1}}{\dfrac{x+4}{x-3}}$

16. $\dfrac{\dfrac{x-1}{x+3}}{\dfrac{x-6}{x+2}}$

17. $\dfrac{\dfrac{10}{t}}{\dfrac{2}{t^2}-\dfrac{5}{t}}$

18. $\dfrac{\dfrac{5}{x}-\dfrac{2}{x^2}}{\dfrac{2}{x^2}}$

19. $\dfrac{\dfrac{2a-5}{3a}}{\dfrac{a-7}{6a}}$

20. $\dfrac{\dfrac{a+5}{a^2}}{\dfrac{a-2}{3a}}$

21. $\dfrac{\dfrac{x}{6}-\dfrac{3}{x}}{\dfrac{1}{3}+\dfrac{1}{x}}$

22. $\dfrac{\dfrac{2}{x}+\dfrac{x}{4}}{\dfrac{3}{4}-\dfrac{2}{x}}$

23. $\dfrac{\dfrac{1}{s}-\dfrac{1}{5}}{\dfrac{s-5}{s}}$

24. $\dfrac{\dfrac{1}{9}-\dfrac{1}{n}}{\dfrac{n+9}{9}}$

25. $\dfrac{\dfrac{1}{t^2}+1}{\dfrac{1}{t}-1}$

26. $\dfrac{2+\dfrac{1}{x}}{2-\dfrac{1}{x^2}}$

27. $\dfrac{\dfrac{x^2}{x^2-y^2}}{\dfrac{x}{x+y}}$

28. $\dfrac{\dfrac{a^2-b^2}{ab}}{\dfrac{a-b}{b}}$

29. $\dfrac{\dfrac{7}{c^2}+\dfrac{4}{c}}{\dfrac{6}{c}-\dfrac{3}{c^3}}$

30. $\dfrac{\dfrac{4}{t^3}-\dfrac{1}{t^2}}{\dfrac{3}{t}+\dfrac{5}{t^2}}$

31. $\dfrac{\dfrac{2}{7a^4}-\dfrac{1}{14a}}{\dfrac{3}{5a^2}+\dfrac{2}{15a}}$

32. $\dfrac{\dfrac{5}{4x^3}-\dfrac{3}{8x}}{\dfrac{3}{2x}+\dfrac{3}{4x^3}}$

Aha! 33. $\dfrac{\dfrac{x}{5y^3}+\dfrac{3}{10y}}{\dfrac{3}{10y}+\dfrac{x}{5y^3}}$

34. $\dfrac{\dfrac{a}{6b^3}+\dfrac{4}{9b^2}}{\dfrac{5}{6b}-\dfrac{1}{9b^3}}$

35. $\dfrac{\dfrac{3}{ab^4}+\dfrac{4}{a^3b}}{\dfrac{5}{a^3b}-\dfrac{3}{ab}}$

36. $\dfrac{\dfrac{2}{x^2y}+\dfrac{3}{xy^2}}{\dfrac{3}{xy^2}+\dfrac{2}{x^2y}}$

37. $\dfrac{t-\dfrac{9}{t}}{t+\dfrac{4}{t}}$

38. $\dfrac{s+\dfrac{2}{s}}{s-\dfrac{3}{s}}$

39. $\dfrac{y+y^{-1}}{y-y^{-1}}$

$\left(\text{Hint: } y^{-1}=\dfrac{1}{y}.\right)$

40. $\dfrac{x-x^{-1}}{x+x^{-1}}$

41. $\dfrac{\dfrac{1}{a-h}-\dfrac{1}{a}}{h}$

42. $\dfrac{\dfrac{1}{x+h}-\dfrac{1}{x}}{h}$

43. $\dfrac{\dfrac{x^{-1}+y^{-1}}{x^2-y^2}}{xy}$

44. $\dfrac{\dfrac{a^{-1}+b^{-1}}{a^2-b^2}}{ab}$

45. $\dfrac{\dfrac{1}{a}+\dfrac{1}{b}}{\dfrac{1}{a^3}+\dfrac{1}{b^3}}$

46. $\dfrac{x-y}{\dfrac{1}{x^3}-\dfrac{1}{y^3}}$

47. $\dfrac{t+5+\dfrac{3}{t}}{t+2+\dfrac{1}{t}}$

48. $\dfrac{a+3+\dfrac{2}{a}}{a+2+\dfrac{5}{a}}$

49. $\dfrac{x-2-\dfrac{1}{x}}{x-5-\dfrac{4}{x}}$

50. $\dfrac{x-3-\dfrac{2}{x}}{x-4-\dfrac{3}{x}}$

51. $\dfrac{\dfrac{a^2-4}{a^2+3a+2}}{\dfrac{a^2-5a-6}{a^2-6a-7}}$

52. $\dfrac{\dfrac{x^2-x-12}{x^2-2x-15}}{\dfrac{x^2+8x+12}{x^2-5x-14}}$

53. $\dfrac{\dfrac{x}{x^2+3x-4}-\dfrac{1}{x^2+3x-4}}{\dfrac{x}{x^2+6x+8}+\dfrac{3}{x^2+6x+8}}$

54. $\dfrac{\dfrac{x}{x^2+5x-6}+\dfrac{6}{x^2+5x-6}}{\dfrac{x}{x^2-5x+4}-\dfrac{2}{x^2-5x+4}}$

55. Is it possible to simplify complex rational expressions without knowing how to divide rational expressions? Why or why not?

56. Why is the distributive law important when simplifying complex rational expressions?

Skill Review

Factor.

57. $6x^3 - 9x^2 - 4x + 6$ [5.1]

58. $12a^2b + 4ab^2 - 8ab$ [5.1]

59. $30n^3 - 3n^2 - 9n$ [5.3]

60. $25a^2 - 40ab + 16b^2$ [5.4]

61. $n^4 - 1$ [5.4]

62. $p^2w^2 - 2pw - 120$ [5.2]

Synthesis

63. Which of the two methods presented would you use to simplify Exercise 36? Why?

64. Which of the two methods presented would you use to simplify Exercise 19? Why?

In each of Exercises 65–68, find all x-values for which the given expression is undefined.

65. $\dfrac{\dfrac{x-5}{x-6}}{\dfrac{x-7}{x-8}}$

66. $\dfrac{\dfrac{x+1}{x+2}}{\dfrac{x+3}{x+4}}$

67. $\dfrac{\dfrac{2x+3}{5x+4}}{\dfrac{3}{7} - \dfrac{x^2}{21}}$

68. $\dfrac{\dfrac{3x-5}{2x-7}}{\dfrac{4x}{5} - \dfrac{8}{15}}$

69. Use multiplication by the LCD (Method 2) to show that

$$\frac{A}{B} \div \frac{C}{D} = \frac{A}{B} \cdot \frac{D}{C}.$$

(*Hint*: Begin by forming a complex rational expression.)

70. The formula

$$\frac{P\left(1 + \dfrac{i}{12}\right)^2}{\dfrac{\left(1 + \dfrac{i}{12}\right)^2 - 1}{\dfrac{i}{12}}},$$

where P is a loan amount and i is an interest rate, arises in certain business situations. Simplify this expression. (*Hint*: Expand the binomials.)

Simplify.

71. $\dfrac{\dfrac{x}{x+5} + \dfrac{3}{x+2}}{\dfrac{2}{x+2} - \dfrac{x}{x+5}}$

72. $\dfrac{\dfrac{z}{1 - \dfrac{z}{2+2z}} - 2z}{\dfrac{2z}{5z-2} - 3}$

Aha! **73.** $\left[\dfrac{\dfrac{x-1}{x-1} - 1}{\dfrac{x+1}{x-1} + 1}\right]^5$

74. $1 + \dfrac{1}{1 + \dfrac{1}{1 + \dfrac{1}{x}}}$

75. $\dfrac{1 - \dfrac{25}{x^2}}{1 + \dfrac{2}{x} - \dfrac{15}{x^2}}$

76. $\dfrac{1 - \dfrac{1}{y} + \dfrac{1}{y^2} - \dfrac{1}{y^3}}{1 - \dfrac{1}{y^4}}$

77. Find the simplified form for the reciprocal of

$$\frac{2}{x-1} - \frac{1}{3x-2}.$$

78. Under what circumstance(s) will there be no restrictions on the variable appearing in a complex rational expression?

↪ **YOUR TURN ANSWERS: SECTION 6.5**

1. $\dfrac{5}{2x}$ **2.** $-\dfrac{1}{5}$ **3.** $\dfrac{14}{17}$ **4.** $\dfrac{3}{3x+2}$

QUICK QUIZ: SECTIONS 6.1–6.5

Simplify.

1. $\dfrac{8x^2 - 20x - 12}{4x^2 - 14x + 6}$ [6.1] **2.** $\dfrac{\dfrac{2}{x} + \dfrac{2}{3}}{\dfrac{1}{x^2}}$ [6.5]

Perform the indicated operation and, if possible, simplify.

3. $\dfrac{a+2}{a+1} \cdot \dfrac{a+3}{a+2}$ [6.2]

4. $\dfrac{4}{x-3} - \dfrac{5x-2}{x+1}$ [6.4]

5. $\dfrac{x+2}{2x} + \dfrac{x+1}{3x}$ [6.4]

PREPARE TO MOVE ON

Solve.

1. $(x-1)7 - (x+1)9 = 4(x+2)$ [2.2]

2. $\dfrac{5}{9} - \dfrac{2x}{3} = \dfrac{5x}{6} + \dfrac{4}{3}$ [2.2] **3.** $x^2 - 7x + 12 = 0$ [5.7]

4. $x^2 + 13x - 30 = 0$ [5.7]

6.6 Rational Equations

Solving Rational Equations

Our study of rational expressions allows us to solve a type of equation that we could not have solved prior to this chapter.

Solving Rational Equations

A **rational equation** is an equation containing one or more rational expressions, often with the variable in a denominator. Here are some examples:

$$\frac{2}{3} + \frac{5}{6} = \frac{x}{9}, \qquad t + \frac{7}{t} = -5, \qquad \frac{x^2}{x-1} = \frac{1}{x-1}.$$

TO SOLVE A RATIONAL EQUATION

1. List any restrictions that exist. Numbers that make a denominator equal 0 can never be solutions.
2. Clear the equation of fractions by multiplying both sides by the LCM of the denominators.
3. Solve the resulting equation using the addition principle, the multiplication principle, and the principle of zero products, as needed.
4. Check the possible solution(s) in the original equation.

When clearing an equation of fractions, we use the terminology LCM instead of LCD because the LCM is not used as a denominator in this setting.

EXAMPLE 1   Solve: $\dfrac{x}{6} - \dfrac{x}{8} = \dfrac{1}{12}$.

Study Skills

Does More Than One Solution Exist?

Keep in mind that many problems—in math and elsewhere—have more than one solution. When asked to solve an equation, we are expected to find any and all solutions of the equation.

SOLUTION   Because no variable appears in a denominator, no restrictions exist. The LCM of 6, 8, and 12 is 24, so we multiply both sides by 24:

$$24\left(\frac{x}{6} - \frac{x}{8}\right) = 24 \cdot \frac{1}{12}$$

Using the multiplication principle to multiply both sides by the LCM. Parentheses are important!

$$24 \cdot \frac{x}{6} - 24 \cdot \frac{x}{8} = 24 \cdot \frac{1}{12}$$

Using the distributive law

Be sure to multiply *each* term by the LCM.

$$\left. \begin{array}{c} \dfrac{24x}{6} - \dfrac{24x}{8} = \dfrac{24}{12} \\[2mm] 4x - 3x = 2 \end{array} \right\}$$

Simplifying. Note that all fractions have been cleared. If fractions remain, we have either made a mistake or have not used the LCM of the denominators.

$$x = 2.$$

Check:
$$\frac{x}{6} - \frac{x}{8} = \frac{1}{12}$$

$$\frac{\frac{2}{6} - \frac{2}{8}}{\begin{array}{c}\frac{1}{3} - \frac{1}{4}\\[4pt]\frac{4}{12} - \frac{3}{12}\\[4pt]\frac{1}{12}\end{array}} \;\Big|\; \frac{1}{12}$$

$$\frac{1}{12} \overset{?}{=} \frac{1}{12} \quad \text{TRUE}$$

This checks, so the solution is 2.

1. Solve: $\dfrac{t}{3} + \dfrac{t}{5} = 1.$

↩ YOUR TURN

Recall that the multiplication principle states that $a = b$ is equivalent to $a \cdot c = b \cdot c$, *provided c is not 0.* To clear fractions in rational equations, we often must multiply by a variable expression. For example, to clear the fraction in $1/x = 5$, we multiply both sides of the equation by x. Since x *could* represent 0, the new equation may not be equivalent to the original equation. For this reason, **checking in the original equation is essential.**

EXAMPLE 2 Solve.

a) $\dfrac{2}{3x} + \dfrac{1}{x} = 10$

b) $x + \dfrac{6}{x} = -5$

SOLUTION

List restrictions.

a) Note that in $\dfrac{2}{3x} + \dfrac{1}{x} = 10$, if $x = 0$, both denominators are 0. We list this restriction:

$$x \neq 0.$$

We now clear the equation of fractions and solve, using the LCM of the denominators, $3x$.

Clear fractions.

$$3x\left(\frac{2}{3x} + \frac{1}{x}\right) = 3x \cdot 10 \qquad \begin{array}{l}\text{Using the multiplication principle to}\\\text{multiply both sides by the LCM.}\\\textit{Don't forget the parentheses!}\end{array}$$

$$3x \cdot \frac{2}{3x} + 3x \cdot \frac{1}{x} = 3x \cdot 10 \qquad \text{Using the distributive law}$$

$$2 + 3 = 30x \qquad \begin{array}{l}\text{Removing factors equal to 1:}\\(3x)/(3x) = 1 \text{ and } x/x = 1. \text{ This clears}\\\text{all fractions.}\end{array}$$

Solve.

$$5 = 30x$$

$$\frac{5}{30} = x, \quad \text{so } x = \frac{1}{6}. \qquad \begin{array}{l}\text{Dividing both sides by 30, or}\\\text{multiplying both sides by } 1/30\end{array}$$

Since $\frac{1}{6} \neq 0$, and 0 is the only restricted value, $\frac{1}{6}$ *should* check.

Check.

Check:
$$\frac{2}{3x} + \frac{1}{x} = 10$$

$$\frac{\dfrac{2}{3 \cdot \frac{1}{6}} + \dfrac{1}{\frac{1}{6}}}{\begin{array}{c}\frac{2}{\frac{1}{2}} + \frac{1}{\frac{1}{6}}\\[4pt]2 \cdot \frac{2}{1} + 1 \cdot \frac{6}{1}\\[4pt]4 + 6\end{array}} \;\Big|\; 10$$

$$10 \overset{?}{=} 10 \quad \text{TRUE}$$

The solution is $\frac{1}{6}$.

b) To solve $x + \dfrac{6}{x} = -5$, note that if $x = 0$, the expression $\dfrac{6}{x}$ is undefined. We list the restriction:

$$x \neq 0.$$

We now clear the equation of fractions and solve:

$$x\left(x + \frac{6}{x}\right) = x(-5) \qquad \text{Multiplying both sides by the LCM, } x.$$
Don't forget the parentheses!

$$x \cdot x + \cancel{x} \cdot \frac{6}{\cancel{x}} = -5x \qquad \text{Using the distributive law}$$

$$x^2 + 6 = -5x \qquad \text{Removing a factor equal to 1: } x/x = 1. \text{ We are left with a quadratic equation.}$$

$$x^2 + 5x + 6 = 0 \qquad \text{Using the addition principle to add } 5x \text{ to both sides}$$

$$(x + 3)(x + 2) = 0 \qquad \text{Factoring}$$

$$x + 3 = 0 \quad or \quad x + 2 = 0 \qquad \text{Using the principle of zero products}$$

$$x = -3 \quad or \quad x = -2. \qquad \text{The only restricted value is 0, so both answers should check.}$$

Student Notes

Not all checking is for finding errors in computation. For these equations, the solution process itself can introduce numbers that do not check.

Check: For -3:

$$x + \frac{6}{x} = -5$$

$$\begin{array}{c|c} -3 + \dfrac{6}{-3} & -5 \\ \hline -3 - 2 & \\ -5 \overset{?}{=} -5 & \text{TRUE} \end{array}$$

For -2:

$$x + \frac{6}{x} = -5$$

$$\begin{array}{c|c} -2 + \dfrac{6}{-2} & -5 \\ \hline -2 - 3 & \\ -5 \overset{?}{=} -5 & \text{TRUE} \end{array}$$

Both of these check, so there are two solutions, -3 and -2.

2. Solve: $\dfrac{2}{3} - \dfrac{1}{n} = \dfrac{7}{3n}$.

YOUR TURN

EXAMPLE 3   Solve.

a) $1 + \dfrac{3x}{x + 2} = \dfrac{-6}{x + 2}$

b) $\dfrac{3}{x - 5} + \dfrac{1}{x + 5} = \dfrac{2}{x^2 - 25}$

c) $\dfrac{x^2}{x - 1} = \dfrac{1}{x - 1}$

SOLUTION

a) The only denominator in $1 + \dfrac{3x}{x + 2} = \dfrac{-6}{x + 2}$ is $x + 2$. To find restrictions, we set this equal to 0 and solve:

$$x + 2 = 0$$

$$x = -2.$$

If $x = -2$, the rational expressions are undefined. We list the restriction:

$$x \neq -2.$$

Technology Connection

We can use a table to check possible solutions of rational equations. Consider the equation in Example 3(c) and the possible solutions that were found, 1 and −1. To check these solutions, we enter

$$y_1 = \frac{x^2}{x - 1} \text{ and } y_2 = \frac{1}{x - 1}.$$

After setting Indpnt to Ask and Depend to Auto in the TBLSET menu, we display the table and enter $x = 1$. The ERROR messages indicate that 1 is not a solution because it is not an allowable replacement for x in the equation. Next, we enter $x = -1$. Since y_1 and y_2 have the same value, we know that the equation is true when $x = -1$, and thus −1 is a solution.

X	Y1	Y2
1	ERROR	ERROR
−1	−.5	−.5

X =

Use a graphing calculator to check the possible solutions of Examples 3(a) and 3(b).

We clear fractions using the LCM $x + 2$ and solve.

$$(x + 2)\left(1 + \frac{3x}{x + 2}\right) = (x + 2)\frac{-6}{x + 2}$$

Multiplying both sides by the LCM. *Don't forget the parentheses!*

$$(x + 2) \cdot 1 + (x + 2)\frac{3x}{x + 2} = (x + 2)\frac{-6}{x + 2}$$

Using the distributive law; removing a factor equal to 1: $(x + 2)/(x + 2) = 1$

$$x + 2 + 3x = -6$$
$$4x + 2 = -6$$
$$4x = -8$$
$$x = -2.$$

Above, we stated that $x \neq -2$.

Because of the above restriction, −2 must be rejected as a solution. The check below simply confirms this.

Check:
$$1 + \frac{3x}{x + 2} = \frac{-6}{x + 2}$$

$$\frac{1 + \frac{3(-2)}{-2 + 2}}{} \quad \bigg| \quad \frac{-6}{-2 + 2}$$

$$1 + \frac{-6}{0} \overset{?}{=} \frac{-6}{0} \qquad \text{FALSE}$$

The equation has no solution.

b) The denominators in $\dfrac{3}{x - 5} + \dfrac{1}{x + 5} = \dfrac{2}{x^2 - 25}$ are $x - 5$, $x + 5$, and $x^2 - 25$. Setting them equal to 0 and solving, we find that the rational expressions are undefined when $x = 5$ or $x = -5$. We list the restrictions:

$$x \neq 5, \qquad x \neq -5.$$

We clear fractions using the LCM, $(x - 5)(x + 5)$, and solve.

$$(x - 5)(x + 5)\left(\frac{3}{x - 5} + \frac{1}{x + 5}\right) = (x - 5)(x + 5)\frac{2}{(x - 5)(x + 5)}$$

$$\frac{(x - 5)(x + 5)3}{x - 5} + \frac{(x - 5)(x + 5)}{x + 5} = \frac{2(x - 5)(x + 5)}{(x - 5)(x + 5)}$$

Using the distributive law

$$(x + 5)3 + (x - 5) = 2$$

Removing factors equal to 1: $(x - 5)/(x - 5) = 1$, $(x + 5)/(x + 5) = 1$, and $\dfrac{(x - 5)(x + 5)}{(x - 5)(x + 5)} = 1$

$$3x + 15 + x - 5 = 2$$

Using the distributive law

$$4x + 10 = 2$$
$$4x = -8$$
$$x = -2.$$

−2 is not restricted, so it *should* check.

The student can check to confirm that −2 is the solution.

Student Notes

When solving an equation like $\dfrac{x^2}{x-1} = \dfrac{1}{x-1}$ in Example 3(c), we can simply equate numerators since the denominators are equal. We must still note restrictions first.

3. Solve:

$$\frac{6}{x^2-4} = \frac{x+1}{x^2-2x}.$$

c) To solve $\dfrac{x^2}{x-1} = \dfrac{1}{x-1}$, note that if $x = 1$, the denominators are 0. We list the restriction:

$$x \neq 1.$$

We clear fractions using the LCM, $x-1$, and solve.

$$\cancel{(x-1)} \cdot \frac{x^2}{\cancel{x-1}} = \cancel{(x-1)} \cdot \frac{1}{\cancel{x-1}} \qquad \text{Multiplying both sides by } x-1, \text{ the LCM}$$

$$x^2 = 1 \qquad \text{Removing a factor equal to 1: } (x-1)/(x-1) = 1$$

$$x^2 - 1 = 0 \qquad \text{Subtracting 1 from both sides}$$

$$(x-1)(x+1) = 0 \qquad \text{Factoring}$$

$$x - 1 = 0 \ \ or \ \ x + 1 = 0 \qquad \text{Using the principle of zero products}$$

$$x = 1 \ \ or \ \ \ \ \ \ x = -1 \qquad \text{Above, we stated that } x \neq 1.$$

Because of the above restriction, 1 must be rejected as a solution. The student should check in the original equation that -1 *does* check. The solution is -1.

YOUR TURN

CONNECTING 🔗 THE CONCEPTS

An equation contains an equal sign; an expression does not. Be careful not to confuse simplifying an expression with solving an equation. When expressions are simplified, the result is an equivalent expression. When equations are solved, the result is a solution. Compare the following.

Simplify: $\dfrac{x-1}{6x} + \dfrac{4}{9}$.

SOLUTION

$$\frac{x-1}{6x} + \frac{4}{9} = \frac{x-1}{6x} \cdot \frac{3}{3} + \frac{4}{9} \cdot \frac{2x}{2x}$$

> The equal signs indicate that all the expressions are equivalent.

$$= \frac{3x-3}{18x} + \frac{8x}{18x} \qquad \text{Writing with the LCD, } 18x$$

$$= \frac{11x-3}{18x} \qquad \text{The result is an expression.}$$

The expressions

$$\frac{11x-3}{18x} \quad \text{and} \quad \frac{x-1}{6x} + \frac{4}{9}$$

are equivalent.

Solve: $\dfrac{x-1}{6x} = \dfrac{4}{9}$.

SOLUTION

$$\frac{x-1}{6x} = \frac{4}{9} \qquad \boxed{\text{Each line is an equivalent equation.}}$$

$$18x \cdot \frac{x-1}{6x} = 18x \cdot \frac{4}{9} \qquad \text{Multiplying by the LCM, } 18x$$

$$3 \cdot \cancel{6x} \cdot \frac{x-1}{\cancel{6x}} = 2 \cdot \cancel{9} \cdot x \cdot \frac{4}{\cancel{9}}$$

$$3(x-1) = 2x \cdot 4$$

$$3x - 3 = 8x$$

$$-3 = 5x$$

$$-\frac{3}{5} = x \qquad \text{The result is a solution.}$$

The solution is $-\dfrac{3}{5}$.

(continued)

EXERCISES

Tell whether each exercise contains an expression or an equation. Then simplify the expression or solve the equation, as indicated.

1. Add and, if possible, simplify: $\dfrac{2}{5n} + \dfrac{3}{2n-1}$.

2. Solve: $\dfrac{3}{y} - \dfrac{1}{4} = \dfrac{1}{y}$.

3. Solve: $\dfrac{5}{x+3} = \dfrac{3}{x+2}$.

4. Multiply and, if possible, simplify:
$$\dfrac{8t+8}{2t^2+t-1} \cdot \dfrac{t^2-1}{t^2-2t+1}.$$

5. Subtract and, if possible, simplify:
$$\dfrac{2a}{a+1} - \dfrac{4a}{1-a^2}.$$

6. Solve: $\dfrac{20}{x} = \dfrac{x}{5}$.

6.6 EXERCISE SET

FOR EXTRA HELP

MyMathLab® Math XL
PRACTICE   WATCH   READ   REVIEW

Vocabulary and Reading Check

Classify each of the following statements as either true or false.

1. Every rational equation has at least one solution.

2. It is possible for a rational equation to have more than one solution.

3. When both sides of an equation are multiplied by a variable expression, the result is not always an equivalent equation.

4. All the equation-solving principles studied thus far may be needed when solving a rational equation.

Solving Rational Equations

Solve. If no solution exists, state this.

5. $\dfrac{3}{5} - \dfrac{2}{3} = \dfrac{x}{6}$

6. $\dfrac{5}{8} - \dfrac{3}{5} = \dfrac{x}{10}$

7. $\dfrac{1}{8} + \dfrac{1}{12} = \dfrac{1}{t}$

8. $\dfrac{1}{6} + \dfrac{1}{10} = \dfrac{1}{t}$

9. $\dfrac{x}{6} - \dfrac{6}{x} = 0$

10. $\dfrac{x}{7} - \dfrac{7}{x} = 0$

11. $\dfrac{2}{x} = \dfrac{5}{x} - \dfrac{1}{4}$

12. $\dfrac{3}{t} = \dfrac{4}{t} - \dfrac{1}{5}$

13. $\dfrac{5}{3t} + \dfrac{3}{t} = 1$

14. $\dfrac{3}{4x} + \dfrac{5}{x} = 1$

15. $\dfrac{12}{x} = \dfrac{x}{3}$

16. $\dfrac{x}{2} = \dfrac{18}{x}$

17. $y + \dfrac{4}{y} = -5$

18. $n + \dfrac{3}{n} = -4$

19. $\dfrac{n+2}{n-6} = \dfrac{1}{2}$

20. $\dfrac{a-4}{a+6} = \dfrac{1}{3}$

21. $x + \dfrac{12}{x} = -7$

22. $x + \dfrac{8}{x} = -9$

23. $\dfrac{3}{x-4} = \dfrac{5}{x+1}$

24. $\dfrac{1}{x+3} = \dfrac{4}{x-1}$

25. $\dfrac{a}{6} - \dfrac{a}{10} = \dfrac{1}{6}$

26. $\dfrac{t}{8} - \dfrac{t}{12} = \dfrac{1}{8}$

27. $\dfrac{x+1}{3} - 1 = \dfrac{x-1}{2}$

28. $\dfrac{x+2}{5} - 1 = \dfrac{x-2}{4}$

29. $\dfrac{y+3}{y-3} = \dfrac{6}{y-3}$

30. $\dfrac{3}{a+7} = \dfrac{a+10}{a+7}$

31. $\dfrac{3}{x+4} = \dfrac{5}{x}$

32. $\dfrac{2}{x+3} = \dfrac{7}{x}$

33. $\dfrac{n+1}{n+2} = \dfrac{n-3}{n+1}$

34. $\dfrac{n+2}{n-3} = \dfrac{n+1}{n-2}$

35. $\dfrac{5}{t-2} + \dfrac{3t}{t-2} = \dfrac{4}{t^2-4t+4}$

36. $\dfrac{4}{t-3} + \dfrac{2t}{t-3} = \dfrac{12}{t^2-6t+9}$

37. $\dfrac{x}{x+5} - \dfrac{5}{x-5} = \dfrac{14}{x^2-25}$

38. $\dfrac{5}{x+1} + \dfrac{2x}{x^2-1} = \dfrac{1}{x+1}$

39. $\dfrac{3}{x-3} + \dfrac{5}{x+2} = \dfrac{5x}{x^2-x-6}$

40. $\dfrac{2}{x-2} + \dfrac{1}{x+4} = \dfrac{x}{x^2+2x-8}$

41. $\dfrac{5}{t-3} - \dfrac{30}{t^2-9} = 1$

42. $\dfrac{1}{y + 3} + \dfrac{1}{y - 3} = \dfrac{1}{y^2 - 9}$

43. $\dfrac{7}{6 - a} = \dfrac{a + 1}{a - 6}$

44. $\dfrac{t - 12}{t - 10} = \dfrac{1}{10 - t}$

Aha! **45.** $\dfrac{-2}{x + 2} = \dfrac{x}{x + 2}$

46. $\dfrac{3}{2x - 6} = \dfrac{x}{2x - 6}$

47. $\dfrac{5}{3x + 3} + \dfrac{1}{2x - 2} = \dfrac{1}{x^2 - 1}$

48. $\dfrac{4}{x^2 - 4} + \dfrac{1}{x + 2} + \dfrac{2}{3x - 6} = 0$

49. When solving rational equations, why do we multiply each side by the LCM of the denominators?

50. Explain the difference between adding rational expressions and solving rational equations.

Skill Review

51. Find the x-intercept and the y-intercept of the line given by $6x - y = 18$. [3.3]

52. Find the slope of the line containing the points $(6, 0)$ and $(-3, -1)$. [3.5]

53. Find the slope and the y-intercept of the line given by $2x + y = 5$. [3.6]

54. Determine whether the graphs of the following equations are parallel:

$$y = 2 - x,$$
$$3x + 3y = 7. \quad [3.6]$$

55. Write the slope–intercept equation of the line with slope $\frac{1}{3}$ and y-intercept $(0, -2)$. [3.6]

56. Write a point–slope equation for the line with slope -4 that contains the point $(1, -5)$. [3.7]

Synthesis

57. Describe a method that can be used to create rational equations that have no solution.

58. How can a graph be used to determine how many solutions an equation has?

Solve.

59. $1 + \dfrac{x - 1}{x - 3} = \dfrac{2}{x - 3} - x$

60. $\dfrac{4}{y - 2} + \dfrac{3}{y^2 - 4} = \dfrac{5}{y + 2} + \dfrac{2y}{y^2 - 4}$

61. $\dfrac{12 - 6x}{x^2 - 4} = \dfrac{3x}{x + 2} - \dfrac{3 - 2x}{2 - x}$

62. $\dfrac{x}{x^2 + 3x - 4} + \dfrac{x + 1}{x^2 + 6x + 8} = \dfrac{2x}{x^2 + x - 2}$

63. $7 - \dfrac{a - 2}{a + 3} = \dfrac{a^2 - 4}{a + 3} + 5$

64. $\dfrac{x^2}{x^2 - 4} = \dfrac{x}{x + 2} - \dfrac{2x}{2 - x}$

65. $\dfrac{1}{x - 1} + x - 5 = \dfrac{5x - 4}{x - 1} - 6$

66. $\dfrac{5 - 3a}{a^2 + 4a + 3} - \dfrac{2a + 2}{a + 3} = \dfrac{3 - a}{a + 1}$

67.

68.

69. Use a graphing calculator to check your answers to Exercises 13, 21, 31, and 59.

70. The reciprocal of a number is the number itself. What is the number?

YOUR TURN ANSWERS: SECTION 6.6

1. $\frac{15}{8}$ **2.** 5   **3.** 1

QUICK QUIZ: SECTIONS 6.1–6.6

1. Multiply and, if possible, simplify:

$$\dfrac{x^2 - 12x + 11}{x + 7} \cdot \dfrac{7}{x - 1}. \quad [6.2]$$

2. Find the LCM: $x^3 - 4x, x^2 - x - 2$. [6.3]

3. Subtract and, if possible, simplify: $\dfrac{3}{2n} - \dfrac{n - 1}{n + 2}$. [6.4]

4. Simplify: [6.5]

5. Solve: $\dfrac{1}{x} - \dfrac{2}{x - 4} = \dfrac{3}{x^2 - 4x}$. [6.6]

PREPARE TO MOVE ON

Solve.

1. The sum of two consecutive odd numbers is 276. Find the numbers. [2.5]

2. The product of two consecutive even integers is 48. Find the numbers. [5.8]

3. The height of a triangle is 3 cm longer than its base. If the area of the triangle is 54 cm², find the measurements of the base and the height. [5.8]

4. Between June 9 and June 24, Seth's beard grew 0.9 cm. Find the rate at which Seth's beard grows. [3.4]

6.7 Applications Using Rational Equations and Proportions

Problems Involving Work ▪ Problems Involving Motion ▪ Problems Involving Proportions

In many areas of study, applications involving rates, proportions, or reciprocals translate to rational equations.

Problems Involving Work

EXAMPLE 1 Brian and Reba volunteer in a community garden. Brian can mulch the garden alone in 8 hr and Reba can mulch the garden alone in 10 hr. How long will it take the two of them, working together, to mulch the garden?

SOLUTION

1. **Familiarize.** This *work problem* is a type of problem we have not yet encountered. Work problems are often *incorrectly* translated to mathematical language in several ways.

   a) Add the times together: $8\,\text{hr} + 10\,\text{hr} = 18\,\text{hr}$. ←Incorrect

   This cannot be the correct approach since it should not take Brian and Reba longer to do the job together than it takes either of them working alone.

   b) Average the times: $(8\,\text{hr} + 10\,\text{hr})/2 = 9\,\text{hr}$. ←Incorrect

   Again, this is longer than it would take Brian to do the job alone.

   c) Assume that each person does half the job. ← Incorrect

   If each person does half the job, Brian would be finished with his half in 4 hr, and Reba with her half in 5 hr. Since they are working together, Brian would continue to help Reba after completing his half. This does tell us that the job will take between 4 hr and 5 hr when they work together.

   Each incorrect approach began with the time it takes each worker to do the job. The correct approach instead focuses on the *rate* of work, or the amount of the job that each person completes in 1 hr.

   Since it takes Brian 8 hr to mulch the entire garden, in 1 hr he mulches $\frac{1}{8}$ of the garden. Since it takes Reba 10 hr to mulch the entire garden, in 1 hr she mulches $\frac{1}{10}$ of the garden. Together, they mulch $\frac{1}{8} + \frac{1}{10} = \frac{5}{40} + \frac{4}{40} = \frac{9}{40}$ of the garden per hour. The rates are thus

   Brian: $\frac{1}{8}$ of the garden per hour,

   Reba: $\frac{1}{10}$ of the garden per hour,

   Together: $\frac{9}{40}$ of the garden per hour.

   We are looking for the time required to mulch 1 entire garden.

Study Skills

Take Advantage of Free Checking

Always check an answer if it is possible to do so. When an applied problem is being solved, do check an answer in the equation from which it came. However, it is even more important to check the answer with the words of the original problem.

	Fraction of the Garden Mulched		
Time	**By Brian**	**By Reba**	**Together**
1 hr	$\frac{1}{8}$	$\frac{1}{10}$	$\frac{1}{8} + \frac{1}{10}$, or $\frac{9}{40}$
2 hr	$\frac{1}{8} \cdot 2$	$\frac{1}{10} \cdot 2$	$\left(\frac{1}{8} + \frac{1}{10}\right)2$, or $\frac{9}{40} \cdot 2$, or $\frac{9}{20}$
3 hr	$\frac{1}{8} \cdot 3$	$\frac{1}{10} \cdot 3$	$\left(\frac{1}{8} + \frac{1}{10}\right)3$, or $\frac{9}{40} \cdot 3$, or $\frac{27}{40}$
t hr	$\frac{1}{8} \cdot t$	$\frac{1}{10} \cdot t$	$\left(\frac{1}{8} + \frac{1}{10}\right)t$, or $\frac{9}{40} \cdot t$

2. Translate. From the table, we see that t must be some number for which

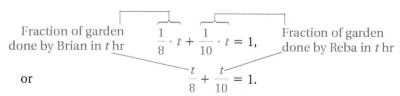

Fraction of garden done by Brian in t hr $\dfrac{1}{8} \cdot t + \dfrac{1}{10} \cdot t = 1,$ Fraction of garden done by Reba in t hr

or $\dfrac{t}{8} + \dfrac{t}{10} = 1.$

3. Carry out. We solve the equation:

$$\frac{t}{8} + \frac{t}{10} = 1 \qquad \text{The LCD is 40.}$$

$$40\left(\frac{t}{8} + \frac{t}{10}\right) = 40 \cdot 1 \qquad \text{Multiplying to clear fractions}$$

$$\frac{40t}{8} + \frac{40t}{10} = 40$$

$$5t + 4t = 40 \qquad \text{Simplifying}$$

$$9t = 40$$

$$t = \frac{40}{9}, \text{ or } 4\frac{4}{9}.$$

4. Check. In $\frac{40}{9}$ hr, Brian mulches $\frac{1}{8} \cdot \frac{40}{9}$, or $\frac{5}{9}$, of the garden and Reba mulches $\frac{1}{10} \cdot \frac{40}{9}$, or $\frac{4}{9}$, of the garden. Together, they mulch $\frac{5}{9} + \frac{4}{9}$, or 1 garden. The fact that our solution is between 4 hr and 5 hr (see step 1 above) is also a check.

5. State. It will take $4\frac{4}{9}$ hr for Brian and Reba, working together, to mulch the garden.

YOUR TURN

1. Refer to Example 1. Suppose that Brian can pick the produce alone in 60 min and Reba can pick the produce alone in 45 min. How long will it take the two of them, working together, to pick the produce?

THE WORK PRINCIPLE

If

a = the time needed for A to complete the work alone,

b = the time needed for B to complete the work alone, and

t = the time needed for A and B to complete the work together,

then

$$\frac{t}{a} + \frac{t}{b} = 1.$$

The following are equivalent equations that can also be used:

$$\left(\frac{1}{a} + \frac{1}{b}\right)t = 1, \qquad \frac{1}{a} \cdot t + \frac{1}{b} \cdot t = 1, \quad \text{and} \quad \frac{1}{a} + \frac{1}{b} = \frac{1}{t}.$$

EXAMPLE 2 It takes Manuel 9 hr longer than it does Zoe to rebuild an engine. Working together, they can do the job in 20 hr. How long would it take each, working alone, to rebuild an engine?

SOLUTION

1. **Familiarize.** Unlike Example 1, this problem does not provide us with the times required by the individuals to do the job alone. We let $z =$ the number of hours it would take Zoe working alone and $z + 9 =$ the number of hours it would take Manuel working alone.

2. **Translate.** Using the same reasoning as in Example 1, we see that Zoe completes $\frac{1}{z}$ of the job in 1 hr and Manuel completes $\frac{1}{z + 9}$ of the job in 1 hr. Thus, in 20 hr, Zoe completes $\frac{1}{z} \cdot 20$ of the job and Manuel completes $\frac{1}{z + 9} \cdot 20$ of the job. Together, Zoe and Manuel can complete the entire job in 20 hr. This gives the following:

Fraction of job done by Zoe in 20 hr $\quad \frac{1}{z} \cdot 20 + \frac{1}{z + 9} \cdot 20 = 1,$ Fraction of job done by Manuel in 20 hr

or $\qquad \frac{20}{z} + \frac{20}{z + 9} = 1.$

3. **Carry out.** We solve the equation:

$$\frac{20}{z} + \frac{20}{z + 9} = 1 \qquad \text{The LCM is } z(z + 9).$$

$$z(z + 9)\left(\frac{20}{z} + \frac{20}{z + 9}\right) = z(z + 9)1 \qquad \text{Multiplying to clear fractions}$$

$$(z + 9)20 + z \cdot 20 = z(z + 9) \qquad \text{Distributing and simplifying}$$

$$40z + 180 = z^2 + 9z$$

$$0 = z^2 - 31z - 180 \qquad \text{Getting 0 on one side}$$

$$0 = (z - 36)(z + 5) \qquad \text{Factoring}$$

$$z - 36 = 0 \quad or \quad z + 5 = 0 \qquad \text{Principle of zero products}$$

$$z = 36 \quad or \qquad z = -5.$$

4. **Check.** Since negative time has no meaning in the problem, -5 is not a solution to the original problem. The number 36 checks since, if Zoe takes 36 hr alone and Manuel takes $36 + 9 = 45$ hr alone, in 20 hr they would have finished

$\frac{20}{36} + \frac{20}{45} = \frac{5}{9} + \frac{4}{9} = 1$ complete rebuild.

5. **State.** It would take Zoe 36 hr to rebuild an engine alone, and Manuel 45 hr.

YOUR TURN

2. Oliver can paint the trim on the Polinskis' Queen Anne house in 12 fewer days than it takes Tammy to do the same job. Working together, they can do the job in 8 days. How long would it take each, working alone, to paint the house?

Problems Involving Motion

Problems dealing with distance, rate (or speed), and time are called **motion problems**. To translate them, we use either the basic motion formula, $d = rt$, or the formulas $r = d/t$ or $t = d/r$, which can be derived from $d = rt$.

EXAMPLE 3   On her road bike, Olivia bikes 5 km/h faster than Jason does on his mountain bike. In the time it takes Olivia to travel 50 km, Jason travels 40 km. Find the speed of each bicyclist.

r km/h
40 km

(r + 5) km/h
50 km

SOLUTION

1. **Familiarize.** Let's make a guess and check it.

   Guess: Jason's speed: 10 km/h

   Olivia's speed: 10 + 5, or 15 km/h

   Jason's time: 40/10 = 4 hr   ⎱ The times are
   Olivia's time: 50/15 = $3\frac{1}{3}$ hr ⎰ not the same.

   Our guess is wrong, but we can make some observations. If Jason's speed = r, in kilometers/hour, then Olivia's speed = $r + 5$. Jason's travel time is the same as Olivia's travel time.
   We can also make a sketch and label it to help us visualize the situation.

2. **Translate.** We organize the information in a table. By looking at how we checked our guess, we see that we can fill in the **Time** column of the table using the formula *Time = Distance/Rate.*

	Distance	Speed	Time
Jason's Mountain Bike	40	r	$40/r$
Olivia's Road Bike	50	$r + 5$	$50/(r + 5)$

Since we know that the times are the same, we can write an equation:

$$\frac{40}{r} = \frac{50}{r + 5}.$$

3. **Carry out.** We solve the equation:

   $$\frac{40}{r} = \frac{50}{r + 5} \qquad \text{The LCM is } r(r + 5).$$

   $$r(r + 5)\frac{40}{r} = r(r + 5)\frac{50}{r + 5} \qquad \text{Multiplying to clear fractions}$$

   $$40r + 200 = 50r \qquad \text{Simplifying}$$

   $$200 = 10r$$

   $$20 = r.$$

4. **Check.** If our answer checks, Jason's mountain bike is going 20 km/h and Olivia's road bike is going 20 + 5 = 25 km/h.
   Traveling 50 km at 25 km/h, Olivia is riding for $\frac{50}{25}$ = 2 hr. Traveling 40 km at 20 km/h, Jason is riding for $\frac{40}{20}$ = 2 hr. Our answer checks since the two times are the same.

5. **State.** Olivia's speed is 25 km/h, and Jason's speed is 20 km/h.

   YOUR TURN

Student Notes

You need remember only the motion formula $d = rt$. Then you can divide both sides by t to get $r = d/t$, or you can divide both sides by r to get $t = d/r$.

3. Peter can drive 25 mph faster on the highway than he can on county roads. In the time it would take Peter to drive 70 mi on county roads, he could drive 120 mi on the highway. How fast can he drive on each type of road?

EXAMPLE 4   A Hudson River tugboat goes 10 mph in still water. It travels 24 mi upstream and 24 mi back in a total time of 5 hr. What is the speed of the current?

Sources: Based on information from the Department of the Interior, U.S. Geological Survey, and *The Tugboat Captain*, Montgomery County Community College

SOLUTION

1. **Familiarize.** Let's make a guess and check it.

   Guess: Speed of current: 4 mph

            Tugboat's speed upstream: $10 - 4 = 6$ mph

            Tugboat's speed downstream: $10 + 4 = 14$ mph

            Travel time upstream: $24/6 = 4$ hr   ⎫   The total time

            Travel time downstream: $24/14 = 1\frac{5}{7}$ hr ⎬   is not 5 hr.

Our guess is wrong, but we can make some observations. If $c =$ the current's rate, in miles per hour, we have the following.

   The tugboat's speed upstream is $(10 - c)$ mph.

   The tugboat's speed downstream is $(10 + c)$ mph.

   The total travel time is 5 hr.

We make a sketch and label it, using the information we know.

$(10 - c)$ mph upstream

24 mi

$(10 + c)$ mph downstream

24 mi

2. **Translate.** We organize the information in a table. From examining our guess, we see that the time traveled can be represented using the formula *Time = Distance/Rate.*

	Distance	Speed	Time
Upstream	24	$10 - c$	$24/(10 - c)$
Downstream	24	$10 + c$	$24/(10 + c)$

Since the total time upstream and back is 5 hr, we use the last column of the table to form an equation:

$$\frac{24}{10 - c} + \frac{24}{10 + c} = 5.$$

3. **Carry out.** We solve the equation:

$$\frac{24}{10 - c} + \frac{24}{10 + c} = 5 \qquad \text{The LCM is } (10 - c)(10 + c).$$

$$(10 - c)(10 + c)\left[\frac{24}{10 - c} + \frac{24}{10 + c}\right] = (10 - c)(10 + c)5 \qquad \text{Multiplying to clear fractions}$$

$$24(10 + c) + 24(10 - c) = (100 - c^2)5$$

$$480 = 500 - 5c^2 \qquad \text{Simplifying}$$

$$5c^2 - 20 = 0$$

$$5(c^2 - 4) = 0$$

$$5(c - 2)(c + 2) = 0$$

$$c = 2 \quad or \quad c = -2.$$

4. **Check.** Since speed cannot be negative in this problem, -2 cannot be a solution. You should confirm that 2 checks in the original problem.

5. **State.** The speed of the current is 2 mph.

4. At a length of 4 km, the Comal River in Texas is the shortest navigable river in the United States. Tristan paddled his canoe up and back down the river in $1\frac{1}{3}$ hr. If he paddles 8 km/h in still water, what was the speed of the current?

YOUR TURN

EXPLORING THE CONCEPT

Motion problems are often much simpler to solve if the information is organized in a table. For each motion problem, fill in the missing entries in the table using the list of options given below.

1. Tara runs 1 km/h faster than Cassie. Tara can run 20 km in the same time that it takes Cassie to run 18 km. Find the speed of each runner.

	Distance	Speed	Time
Tara	20	**(a)**_____	**(b)**_____
Cassie	**(c)**_____	r	**(d)**_____

Options: 18 $r + 1$ $\dfrac{20}{r+1}$ $\dfrac{18}{r}$

2. Damon rode 50 mi to a state park at a certain speed. Had he been able to ride 3 mph faster, the trip would have been $\frac{1}{4}$ hr shorter. How fast did he ride?

	Distance	Speed	Time
Actual Trip	**(a)**_____	r	**(b)**_____
Faster Trip	50	**(c)**_____	**(d)**_____

Options: 50 $r + 3$ $\dfrac{50}{r+3}$ $\dfrac{50}{r}$

3. The speed of the Green River current is 4 mph. In the same time that it takes Blair to motor 48 mi downstream, he can travel only 32 mi upstream. What is the speed of the boat in still water?

	Distance	Speed	Time
Downstream	48	**(a)**_____	$\dfrac{48}{x+4}$
Upstream	**(b)**_____	**(c)**_____	**(d)**_____

Options: 32 $\dfrac{32}{x-4}$ $x + 4$ $x - 4$

ANSWERS

1. (a) $r + 1$; (b) $\dfrac{20}{r+1}$; (c) 18; (d) $\dfrac{18}{r}$

2. (a) 50; (b) $\dfrac{50}{r}$; (c) $r + 3$; (d) $\dfrac{50}{r+3}$

3. (a) $x + 4$; (b) 32; (c) $x - 4$; (d) $\dfrac{32}{x-4}$

Problems Involving Proportions

A **ratio** of two quantities is their quotient. For example, 37% is the ratio of 37 to 100, or $\frac{37}{100}$. A **proportion** is an equation stating that two ratios are equal.

> **PROPORTION**
>
> An equality of ratios,
>
> $$\frac{A}{B} = \frac{C}{D},$$
>
> is called a *proportion*. The fractions within a proportion are said to be *proportional* to each other.

In geometry, if two triangles are **similar**, then their corresponding angles have the same measure and their corresponding sides are *proportional*. To illustrate, if triangle *ABC* is similar to triangle *RST*, then angles *A* and *R* have the same measure, angles *B* and *S* have the same measure, angles *C* and *T* have the same measure, and

$$\frac{a}{r} = \frac{b}{s} = \frac{c}{t}.$$

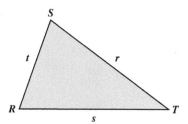

EXAMPLE 5 *Similar Triangles.* Triangles *ABC* and *XYZ* are similar. Solve for *z* if *x* = 10, *a* = 8, and *c* = 5.

SOLUTION We make a drawing, write a proportion, and then solve. Note that side *a* is always opposite angle *A*, side *x* is always opposite angle *X*, and so on.

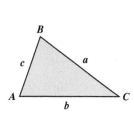

We have

$$\frac{z}{5} = \frac{10}{8} \qquad \text{The proportions } \frac{5}{z} = \frac{8}{10}, \ \frac{5}{8} = \frac{z}{10}, \text{ or}$$

$$\frac{8}{5} = \frac{10}{z} \text{ could also be used.}$$

$$40 \cdot \frac{z}{5} = 40 \cdot \frac{10}{8} \qquad \text{Multiplying both sides by the LCM, 40}$$

$$8z = 50 \qquad \text{Simplifying}$$

$$z = \frac{50}{8}, \text{ or } 6.25.$$

5. Triangles *QRS* and *MNP* are similar. Solve for *r* if *m* = 5, *n* = 8, and *q* = 4.

YOUR TURN

EXAMPLE 6 *Architecture.* A *blueprint* is a scale drawing of a building representing an architect's plans. Ellia is adding 12 ft to the length of an apartment and needs to indicate the addition on an existing blueprint. If a 10-ft long bedroom is represented by $2\frac{1}{2}$ in. on the blueprint, how much longer should Ellia make the drawing in order to represent the addition?

SOLUTION We let w represent the width, in inches, of the addition that Ellia is drawing. Because the drawing must have the correct proportions, we have

$$\text{Inches on drawing} \rightarrow \frac{w}{12} = \frac{2.5}{10} \leftarrow \text{Inches on drawing}$$
$$\text{Feet in real life} \rightarrow \qquad\quad\; \leftarrow \text{Feet in real life}$$

To solve for w, we multiply both sides by the LCM of the denominators, 60:

$$60 \cdot \frac{w}{12} = 60 \cdot \frac{2.5}{10}$$
$$5w = 6 \cdot 2.5 \qquad \text{Simplifying}$$
$$w = \tfrac{15}{5}, \text{or } 3.$$

Ellia should make the blueprint 3 in. longer.

6. Refer to Example 6. Suppose that the width of the apartment is represented on the blueprint by 4 in. How wide is the apartment?

YOUR TURN

EXAMPLE 7 *Text Messaging.* Brent sent or received 384 messages in 8 days. At this rate, how many text messages would he send or receive in 30 days?

SOLUTION We let $x =$ the number of text messages Brent would send or receive in 30 days. We form a proportion in which the ratio of the number of text messages to the number of days is expressed in two ways:

$$\text{Number of text messages} \rightarrow \frac{384}{8} = \frac{x}{30} \leftarrow \text{Number of text messages}$$
$$\text{Number of days} \rightarrow \qquad\quad\; \leftarrow \text{Number of days}$$

To solve for x, we multiply both sides by the LCM of the denominators, 120:

$$120 \cdot \frac{384}{8} = 120 \cdot \frac{x}{30}$$
$$15 \cdot 8 \cdot \frac{384}{8} = 4 \cdot 30 \cdot \frac{x}{30}$$
$$15 \cdot 384 = 4x$$
$$5760 = 4x$$
$$1440 = x.$$

7. Refer to Example 7. Suppose that Brent sent or received 534 messages in 6 days. At this rate, how many text messages would he send or receive in 30 days?

At this rate, Brent will send or receive 1440 text messages in 30 days.

YOUR TURN

EXAMPLE 8 *Wildlife Population.* To determine the number of brook trout in River Denys, Cape Breton, Nova Scotia, a team of volunteers and professionals caught and marked 1190 brook trout. Later, they captured 915 brook trout, of which 24 were marked. Estimate the number of brook trout in River Denys.

Source: www.gov.ns.ca

Chapter Resources:
Translating for Success, p. 432;
Collaborative Activity, p. 433;
Decision Making: Connection,
p. 433

SOLUTION We let T = the brook trout population in River Denys. If we assume that the percentage of marked trout in the second group of trout captured is the same as the percentage of marked trout in the entire river, we can form a proportion in which this percentage is expressed in two ways:

$$\text{Trout originally marked} \rightarrow \dfrac{1190}{T} = \dfrac{24}{915} \leftarrow \text{Marked trout in second group}$$
$$\text{Entire population} \rightarrow \phantom{\dfrac{1190}{T}} \phantom{\dfrac{24}{915}} \leftarrow \text{Total trout in second group}$$

To solve for T, we multiply by the LCM, $915T$:

$$915T \cdot \dfrac{1190}{T} = 915T \cdot \dfrac{24}{915} \qquad \text{Multiplying both sides by } 915T$$

$$915 \cdot 1190 = 24T \qquad \begin{array}{l}\text{Removing factors equal to 1:}\\ T/T = 1 \text{ and } 915/915 = 1\end{array}$$

$$\dfrac{915 \cdot 1190}{24} = T \text{ or } T \approx 45{,}369. \qquad \text{Dividing both sides by 24}$$

There are about 45,369 brook trout in the river.

 YOUR TURN

8. Refer to Example 8. Suppose that a second team of volunteers in another section of the river captured 875 brook trout, of which 35 were marked. On the basis of these data, estimate the number of brook trout in the River Denys.

6.7 EXERCISE SET

FOR EXTRA HELP MyMathLab® Math
PRACTICE   WATCH   READ   REVIEW

Vocabulary and Reading Check

Classify each of the following statements as either true or false.

1. In order to find the time that it would take two people to complete a job working together, we average the time that it takes each of them to complete the job working separately.

2. To find the rate at which two people work together, we add the rates at which they work separately.

3. Distance equals rate times time.

4. Rate equals distance divided by time.

5. Time equals distance divided by rate.

6. If two triangles are similar, their corresponding sides are of equal length.

Concept Reinforcement

Find each rate.

7. If Sandy can decorate a cake in 2 hr, what is her hourly rate?

8. If Eric can decorate a cake in 3 hr, what is his hourly rate?

9. If Sandy can decorate a cake in 2 hr and Eric can decorate the same cake in 3 hr, what is their hourly rate, working together?

10. If Lisa and Mark can mow a lawn together in 1 hr, what is their hourly rate?

11. If Lisa can mow a lawn by herself in 3 hr, what is her hourly rate?

12. If Lisa and Mark can mow a lawn together in 1 hr, and Lisa can mow the same lawn by herself in 3 hr, what is Mark's hourly rate, working alone?

Problems Involving Work

13. *Volunteerism.* It takes Kelby 10 hr per week to prepare food for delivery to senior citizens. Natalie can do the same job in 15 hr. How long would it take Kelby and Natalie to prepare the food working together?

14. *Pumping Water.* An ABS Robusta 300 TS sump pump can remove water from Martha's flooded basement in 70 min. The Little Giant 1-A sump pump can complete the same job in 30 min. How

long would it take the two pumps together to pump out the basement?

Source: Based on data from www.shoppumps.com

15. *Home Restoration.* Bryan can refinish the floor of an apartment in 8 hr. Armando can refinish the floor in 6 hr. How long will it take them, working together, to refinish the floor?

16. *Custom Embroidery.* Chandra can embroider logos on a team's sweatshirts in 6 hr. Traci, a new employee, needs 9 hr to complete the same job. Working together, how long will it take them to do the job?

17. *Filling a Pool.* The San Paulo community swimming pool can be filled in 12 hr if water enters through a pipe alone or in 30 hr if water enters through a hose alone. If water is entering through both the pipe and the hose, how long will it take to fill the pool?

18. *Filling a Tank.* A community water tank can be filled in 18 hr by the town office well alone and in 22 hr by the high school well alone. How long will it take to fill the tank if both wells are working?

19. *Scanners.* The Epson WorkForce G7-1500 takes twice the time required by the Epson WorkForce Pro GT-S50 to scan the manuscript for a book. If, working together, the two machines can complete the job in 5 min, how long would it take each machine, working alone, to scan the manuscript?

Source: epson.com

20. *Cutting Firewood.* Kent can cut and split a cord of wood twice as fast as Brent can. When they work together, it takes them 4 hr. How long would it take each of them to do the job alone?

21. *Mulching.* Anita can mulch the college gardens in 3 fewer days than it takes Tori to mulch the same areas. When they work together, it takes them 2 days. How long would it take each of them to do the job alone?

22. *Photo Printing.* It takes the Canon PIXMA MP495 15 min longer to print a set of photo proofs than it takes the Canon PIXMA MG8220. Together it would take them 10 min to print the photos. How long would it take each machine, working alone, to print the photos?

Source: www.usa.canon.com

23. *Software Development.* Tristan, an experienced programmer, can write video-game software three times as fast as Sara, who is just learning to program. Working together on one project, it took them 1 month to complete the job. How long would it take each of them to complete the project alone?

24. *Forest Fires.* The Erickson Air-Crane helicopter can scoop water and douse a certain forest fire four times as fast as an S-58T helicopter. Working together, the two helicopters can douse the fire in 8 hr. How long would it take each helicopter, working alone, to douse the fire?

Sources: Based on information from www.emergency.com and www.arishelicopters.com

25. *Sorting Recyclables.* Together, it takes Kim and Chris 2 hr 55 min to sort recyclables. Alone, Chris would require 2 fewer hours than Kim. How long would it take Chris to do the job alone? (*Hint:* Convert minutes to hours or hours to minutes.)

26. *Paving.* Together, Steve and Bill require 4 hr 48 min to pave a driveway. Alone, Steve would require 4 hr more than Bill. How long would it take Bill to do the job alone? (*Hint:* Convert minutes to hours.)

Problems Involving Motion

27. *Train Speeds.* A CSX freight train is traveling 14 km/h slower than an AMTRAK passenger train. The CSX train travels 330 km in the same time that it takes the AMTRAK train to travel 400 km. Find their speeds. Complete the following table as part of the familiarization.

Distance =	Rate	·	Time
	Distance (in km)	Speed (in km/h)	Time (in hours)
CSX	330		
AMTRAK	400	r	$\dfrac{400}{r}$

28. *Speed of Travel.* A loaded Roadway truck is moving 40 mph faster than a New York Railways freight train. In the time that it takes the train to travel 150 mi, the truck travels 350 mi. Find their speeds. Complete the following table as part of the familiarization.

Distance =	Rate	·	Time
	Distance (in miles)	Speed (in miles per hour)	Time (in hours)
Truck	350	r	$\dfrac{350}{r}$
Train	150		

29. *Driving Speed.* Sean's Camaro travels 15 mph faster than Rita's Harley. In the same time that Sean travels 156 mi, Rita travels 120 mi. Find their speeds.

30. *Bicycle Speed.* Ada bicycles 5 km/h slower than Elin. In the same time that it takes Ada to ride 48 km, Elin can ride 63 km. How fast does each bicyclist travel?

31. *Kayaking.* The speed of the current in Catamount Creek is 3 mph. Sean can kayak 4 mi upstream in the same time that it takes him to kayak 10 mi downstream. What is the speed of Sean's kayak in still water?

32. *Boating.* The current in the Lazy River moves at a rate of 4 mph. Mickie's dinghy motors 6 mi upstream in the same time that it takes to motor 12 mi downstream. What is the speed of the dinghy in still water?

33. *Moving Sidewalks.* The moving sidewalk at O'Hare Airport in Chicago moves 1.8 ft/sec. Walking on the moving sidewalk, Roslyn travels 105 ft forward in the time that it takes to travel 51 ft in the opposite direction. How fast does Roslyn walk on a nonmoving sidewalk?

34. *Moving Sidewalks.* Newark Airport's moving sidewalk moves at a speed of 1.7 ft/sec. Walking on the moving sidewalk, Drew can travel 120 ft forward in the same time that it takes to travel 52 ft in the opposite direction. What is Drew's walking speed on a nonmoving sidewalk?

Aha! **35.** *Tractor Speed.* Manley's tractor is just as fast as Caledonia's. It takes Manley 1 hr more than it takes Caledonia to drive to town. If Manley is 20 mi from town and Caledonia is 15 mi from town, how long does it take Caledonia to drive to town?

36. *Boat Speed.* Tory and Emilio's motorboats travel at the same speed. Tory pilots her boat 40 km before

docking. Emilio continues for another 2 hr, traveling a total of 100 km before docking. How long did it take Tory to navigate the 40 km?

37. *Aviation.* A Citation CV jet travels 460 mph in still air and flies 525 mi into the wind and 525 mi with the wind in a total of 2.3 hr. Find the wind speed.

Source: Blue Star Jets, Inc.

38. *Canoeing.* Chad paddles 55 m/min in still water. He paddles 150 m upstream and 150 m downstream in a total time of 5.5 min. What is the speed of the current?

39. *Train Travel.* A freight train covered 120 mi at a certain speed. Had the train been able to travel 10 mph faster, the trip would have been 2 hr shorter. How fast did the train go?

40. *Moped Speed.* Dexter rode 60 mi on his moped at a certain speed. Had he been able to travel 5 mph faster, the trip would have taken 1 hr less time. How fast did Dexter go?

Problems Involving Proportions

Geometry. For each pair of similar triangles, find the value of the indicated letter.

41. *b*

42. *a*

43. *f*

44. *r*
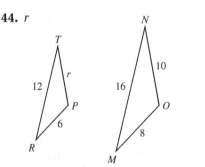

Graphing. Find the indicated length.

45. *r*

46. *s*

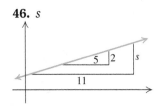

Architecture. Use the blueprint below to find the indicated length.

47. *p*, in inches on blueprint

48. *s*, in inches on blueprint

49. *r*, in feet on actual building

50. *n*, in feet on actual building

Find the indicated length.

51. *l*

52. *h*

Flight Mechanics. The wing aspect ratio for a bird or an airplane is the ratio of the wing span to the wing width. Generally, higher-aspect ratios are more efficient during low-speed flying. Use the table below for Exercises 53 and 54.

Bird or Airplane	Wing Span	Wing Width
Grey heron	180 cm	24 cm
House sparrow	10 in.	1.8 in.
Albatross	9 ft	0.6 ft
Concorde (retired in 2003)	84 ft	47 ft
Boeing 747-400	64 m	8 m

53. Herons and storks, both waders, have the same wing aspect ratios. A white stork has a wing span of 200 cm. What is the wing width of a white stork?

54. The Piper PA-28 Cherokee airplane, with a wing span of 35 ft, has the same wing aspect ratio as a house sparrow. What is the width of a wing of the Piper airplane?

55. *Spending Habits.* In the first 8 days of September, Felicia spent $17.40 on coffee. At this rate, how much will she spend in September? (September has 30 days.)

56. *Burning Calories.* The average 140-lb adult burns about 380 calories bicycling 10 mi at a moderate rate. How far should the average 140-lb adult ride in order to burn 100 calories?

Source: www.livestrong.com

Aha! **57.** *Photography.* Aziza snapped 234 photos over a period of 14 days. At this rate, how many would she take in 42 days?

58. *Mileage.* The Toyota Prius is a hybrid car that travels approximately 204 mi on 4 gal of gas. Find the amount of gas required for a 714-mi trip.

Source: www.toyota.com

59. *Light Bulbs.* A sample of 220 compact fluorescent light bulbs contained 8 defective bulbs. How many defective bulbs would you expect in a batch of 1430 bulbs?

60. *Flash Drives.* A sample of 150 flash drives contained 7 defective drives. How many defective flash drives would you expect in a batch of 2700 flash drives?

61. *Veterinary Science.* The amount of water needed by a small dog depends on its weight. A moderately active 8-lb Shih Tzu needs approximately 12 oz of water per day. How much water does a moderately active 5-lb Bolognese require each day?

Source: www.smalldogsparadise.com

62. *Miles Driven.* Emmanuel is allowed to drive his leased car for 45,000 mi in 4 years without penalty. In the first $1\frac{1}{2}$ years, Emmanuel has driven 16,000 mi. At this rate, will he exceed the mileage allowed for 4 years?

63. *Environmental Science.* To determine the number of humpback whales in a pod, a marine biologist, using tail markings, identifies 27 members of the pod. Several weeks later, 40 whales from the pod are randomly sighted. Of the 40 sighted, 12 are from the 27 originally identified. Estimate the number of whales in the pod.

64. *Fox Population.* To determine the number of foxes in King County, a naturalist catches, tags, and then releases 25 foxes. Later, 36 foxes are caught; 4 of them have tags. Estimate the fox population of the county.

65. Is it correct to assume that two workers will complete a task twice as quickly as one person working alone? Why or why not?

66. If two triangles are exactly the same shape and size, are they similar? Why or why not?

Skill Review

Perform the indicated operation and simplify.

67. $(x^3 - 3x - 7) - (x^2 - 4x + 8)$ [4.4]

68. $(2x^3 - 7)(x + 3)$ [4.5]

69. $(3y^2z - 2yz^2 + y^2) + (4yz^2 + 5y^2 - 6yz)$ [4.7]

70. $(6a^2b^3 + 12ab^2 - 3a^2b) \div (3ab)$ [4.8]

71. $(8n^3 + 3)(8n^3 - 3)$ [4.6]

72. $(x^3 - x + 7) \div (x - 1)$ [4.8]

Synthesis

73. Two steamrollers are paving a parking lot. Working together, will the two steamrollers take less than half as long as the slower steamroller would working alone? Why or why not?

74. Two fuel lines are filling a freighter with oil. Will the faster fuel line take more or less than twice as long to fill the freighter by itself? Why?

75. *Filling a Bog.* The Norwich cranberry bog can be filled in 9 hr and drained in 11 hr. How long will it take to fill the bog if the drainage gate is left open?

76. *Filling a Tub.* Gretchen's hot tub can be filled in 10 min and drained in 8 min. How long will it take to empty a full tub if the water is left on?

77. *Car Cleaning.* Together, Michelle, Sal, and Kristen can clean and wax a car in 1 hr 20 min. To complete the job alone, Michelle needs twice the time that Sal needs and 2 hr more than Kristen. How long would it take each to clean and wax the car working alone?

78. *Grading.* Alma can grade a batch of placement exams in 3 hr. Kevin can grade a batch in 4 hr. If they work together to grade a batch of exams, what percentage of the exams will have been graded by Alma?

79. Refer to Exercise 31. How long will it take Sean to kayak 5 mi downstream?

80. Refer to Exercise 32. How long will it take Mickie to motor 3 mi downstream?

81. *Escalators.* Together, a 100-cm wide escalator and a 60-cm wide escalator can empty a 1575-person auditorium in 14 min. The wider escalator moves twice as many people as the narrower one. How many people per hour does the 60-cm wide escalator move?

Source: McGraw-Hill Encyclopedia of Science and Technology

82. *Aviation.* A Coast Guard plane has enough fuel to fly for 6 hr, and its speed in still air is 240 mph. The plane departs with a 40-mph tailwind and returns to the same airport flying into the same wind. How far can the plane travel under these conditions?

83. *Boating.* Shoreline Travel operates a 3-hr paddleboat cruise on the Missouri River. If the speed of the boat in still water is 12 mph, how far upriver can the pilot travel against a 5-mph current before it is time to turn around?

84. *Travel by Car.* Angenita drives to work at 50 mph and arrives 1 min late. She drives to work at 60 mph and arrives 5 min early. How far does Angenita live from work?

85. According to the U.S. Census Bureau, Population Division, in July 2012, there was one birth every 8 sec, one death every 14 sec, and one new international migrant every 44 sec. How many seconds does it take for a net gain of one person?

86. *Home Maintenance.* Fuel used in many chain saws is made by pouring a 3.2-oz bottle of 2-cycle oil into 160 oz of gasoline. Gus accidentally poured 5.6 oz of 2-cycle oil into 200 oz of gasoline. How much more oil or gasoline should he add in order for the fuel to have the proper ratio of oil to gasoline?

87. At what time after 4:00 will the minute hand and the hour hand of a clock first be in the same position?

88. At what time after 10:30 will the hands of a clock first be perpendicular?

Average speed is defined as total distance divided by total time.

89. Ferdaws drove 200 km. For the first 100 km of the trip, she drove at a speed of 40 km/h. For the second half of the trip, she traveled at a speed of 60 km/h. What was the average speed of the entire trip? (It was *not* 50 km/h.)

90. For the first 50 mi of a 100-mi trip, Garry drove 40 mph. What speed would he have to travel for the last half of the trip so that the average speed for the entire trip would be 45 mph?

91. *Commuting.* To reach an appointment 50 mi away, Dr. Wright allowed 1 hr. After driving 30 mi, she realized that her speed would have to be increased 15 mph for the remainder of the trip. What was her speed for the first 30 mi?

92. Given that

$$\frac{A}{B} = \frac{C}{D},$$

write three other proportions using A, B, C, and D.

93. Show that the four equations in the box labeled "The Work Principle" in this section are equivalent.

94. If two triangles are similar, are their areas and perimeters proportional? Why or why not?

95. Are the equations

$$\frac{A + B}{B} = \frac{C + D}{D} \quad \text{and} \quad \frac{A}{B} = \frac{C}{D}$$

equivalent? Why or why not?

YOUR TURN ANSWERS: SECTION 6.7

1. $25\frac{5}{7}$ min **2.** Oliver: 12 days; Tammy: 24 days
3. Country roads: 35 mph; highway: 60 mph
4. 4 km/h **5.** $\frac{32}{5}$, or 6.4 **6.** 16 ft
7. 2670 text messages **8.** 29,750 brook trout

QUICK QUIZ: SECTIONS 6.1–6.7

1. Simplify: $\dfrac{x^2y^2 - 5x^2y + 6x^2}{7x^3y - 7x^3}.$ [6.1]

2. Divide and, if possible, simplify:

$$\frac{7x + 21}{x - 4} \div \frac{x + 3}{5x - 20}. \quad [6.2]$$

3. Add and, if possible, simplify:

$$\frac{1}{x^2 + 3x + 2} + \frac{1}{x^2 - x - 2}. \quad [6.4]$$

4. Solve: $\dfrac{7}{x} = \dfrac{3}{x + 4}.$ [6.6]

5. Scot can prepare a tray of appetizers in 75 min. Steve can prepare the same tray in 60 min. How long would it take them, working together, to prepare the tray of appetizers? [6.7]

PREPARE TO MOVE ON

Graph each pair of equations on the same set of axes.

1. $y = 2x - 1$,
 $y = x + 3$ [3.6]

2. $x + y = 3$,
 $x - y = 2$ [3.3]

3. $y = \frac{1}{2}x + 2$,
 $y = \frac{1}{2}x - 1$ [3.6]

4. $x + y = 2$,
 $2x + 2y = 4$ [3.3]

1. *Internet Search-Engine Ads.* In 2010, North American advertisers spent $16.6 billion in marketing through Internet search engines such as Google®. This was a 14% increase over the amount spent in 2009. How much was spent in 2009?

Source: Search Engine Marketing Professional Organization

2. *Bicycling.* The speed of one bicyclist is 2 km/h faster than the speed of another bicyclist. The first bicyclist travels 60 km in the same amount of time that it takes the second to travel 50 km. Find the speed of each bicyclist.

3. *Filling Time.* A swimming pool can be filled in 5 hr by hose A alone and in 6 hr by hose B alone. How long would it take to fill the tank if both hoses were working?

4. *Payroll.* In 2010, the total payroll for Kraftside Productions was $16.6 million. Of this amount, 14% was paid to employees working on an assembly line. How much money was paid to assembly-line workers?

Translating for Success

Use after Section 6.7.

Translate each word problem to an equation and select a correct translation from equations A–O.

A. $2x + 2(x + 1) = 613$

B. $x^2 + (x + 1)^2 = 613$

C. $\dfrac{60}{x + 2} = \dfrac{50}{x}$

D. $x = 14\% \cdot 16.6$

E. $\dfrac{197}{7} = \dfrac{x}{30}$

F. $x + (x + 1) = 613$

G. $\dfrac{7}{197} = \dfrac{x}{30}$

H. $x^2 + (x + 2)^2 = 612$

I. $x^2 + (x + 1)^2 = 612$

J. $\dfrac{50}{x + 2} = \dfrac{60}{x}$

K. $x + 14\% \cdot x = 16.6$

L. $\dfrac{5 + 6}{2} = t$

M. $x^2 + (x + 1)^2 = 452$

N. $\dfrac{1}{5} + \dfrac{1}{6} = \dfrac{1}{t}$

O. $x^2 + (x + 2)^2 = 452$

Answers on page A-31

An additional, animated version of this activity appears in MyMathLab. *To use MyMathLab, you need a course ID and a student access code. Contact your instructor for more information.*

5. *Cycling Distance.* A bicyclist traveled 197 mi in 7 days. At this rate, how many miles could the cyclist travel in 30 days?

6. *Sides of a Square.* If the sides of a square are increased by 2 ft, the area of the original square plus the area of the enlarged square is 452 ft². Find the length of a side of the original square.

7. *Consecutive Integers.* The sum of two consecutive integers is 613. Find the integers.

8. *Sums of Squares.* The sum of the squares of two consecutive odd integers is 612. Find the integers.

9. *Sums of Squares.* The sum of the squares of two consecutive integers is 613. Find the integers.

10. *Rectangle Dimensions.* The length of a rectangle is 1 ft longer than its width. Find the dimensions of the rectangle if the perimeter is 613 ft.

Collaborative Activity   *Sharing the Workload*

Focus: Modeling, estimation, and work problems
Use after: Section 6.7
Time: 10–15 minutes
Group size: 3
Materials: Paper, pencils, textbooks, and a watch

Many tasks can be done by two people working together. If both people work at the same rate, each does half the task, and the project is completed in half the time. However, when the work rates differ, the faster worker performs more than half of the task.

Activity

1. The project is to write the numbers from 1 to 100 on a sheet of paper. Two of the members in each group should write the numbers, one working slowly and one working quickly. The third group member should record the time required for each to write the numbers.

2. Using the times from step (1), calculate how long it will take the two workers, working together, to complete the task.

3. Next, have the same workers as in step (1)—working at the same speeds as in step (1)—perform the task together. To do this, one person should begin writing with 1, while the other worker, using a separate sheet of paper, begins with 100 and writes the numbers counting backward. The third member is again the timekeeper and should note when the two workers have written all the numbers.

4. Compare the actual experimental time from part (3) with the time predicted by the model in part (2). List reasons that might account for any discrepancy.

5. Let t_1, t_2, and t_3 represent the times required for the first worker, the second worker, and the two workers together, respectively, to complete a task. Then develop a model that can be used to find t_3 when t_1 and t_2 are known.

Decision Making & Connection   (*Use after Section 6.7.*)

Phone Costs.   Unless you use your cell phone strictly for voice calls, your monthly cell bill will include charges for texting and/or data use. In order to save money, many users choose plans that limit the amount of texting or data each month. In order to realize those savings, it is important not to exceed the specified amounts of text messages and data usage.

1. One popular text-messaging plan allows up to 500 text messages (received or sent) each 30-day month. At the end of the 8th day of one month, Xavier checked his account and found that he had sent or received 160 text messages. At that rate, will he exceed the 500-message limit by the end of the month?

2. One popular data package allows up to 250 MB (megabytes) of data (received or sent) each 30-day month. Xavier checked his account at the end of the 16th day of the month and found that he had sent or received 130 MB of data. At that rate, will he exceed the 250-MB limit by the end of the month?

3. Suppose that Xavier continues to use text messaging and data at the rates described in Exercises 1 and 2. His plan charges $0.20 for every text message sent or received over the limit and $10 for an additional GB (gigabyte; 1 GB = 1000 MB) of data. If his monthly cell bill is $64.99 before text and data charges are added, what will his bill be for the month described?

4. Xavier can change his text messaging to 1000 text messages per month for an additional $5 per month. If the month described in Exercise 1 is a typical month for him, should he change his text messaging plan?

5. *Research.*   Find what phone plans are available in your area. If you already have a phone plan, compare your plan and monthly usage with other plans available. If you do not have a phone plan, estimate your monthly text and data usage and compare the plans using those estimates. Which is the best plan for you?

Study Summary

KEY TERMS AND CONCEPTS	EXAMPLES	PRACTICE EXERCISES

SECTION 6.1: *Rational Expressions*

A **rational expression** can be written as a quotient of two polynomials and is undefined when the denominator is 0. We simplify rational expressions by removing a factor equal to 1.	$$\frac{x^2 - 3x - 4}{x^2 - 1} = \frac{(x+1)(x-4)}{(x+1)(x-1)}$$ $$= \frac{x-4}{x-1} \quad \frac{x+1}{x+1} = 1$$	**1.** Simplify: $$\frac{3x^2 - 6x + 3}{x^2 - 4x + 3}.$$

SECTION 6.2: *Multiplication and Division*

The Product of Two Rational Expressions $$\frac{A}{B} \cdot \frac{C}{D} = \frac{AC}{BD}$$	$$\frac{5v + 5}{v - 2} \cdot \frac{2v^2 - 8v + 8}{v^2 - 1}$$ $$= \frac{5(v+1) \cdot 2(v-2)(v-2)}{(v-2)(v+1)(v-1)}$$ $$= \frac{10(v-2)}{v-1} \quad \frac{(v+1)(v-2)}{(v+1)(v-2)} = 1$$	**2.** Multiply and, if possible, simplify: $$\frac{10a + 20}{a^2 - 4} \cdot \frac{a^2 - a - 2}{4a}.$$
The Quotient of Two Rational Expressions $$\frac{A}{B} \div \frac{C}{D} = \frac{A}{B} \cdot \frac{D}{C} = \frac{AD}{BC}$$	$$(x^2 - 5x - 6) \div \frac{x^2 - 1}{x + 6}$$ $$= \frac{x^2 - 5x - 6}{1} \cdot \frac{x + 6}{x^2 - 1}$$ $$= \frac{(x-6)(x+1)(x+6)}{(x+1)(x-1)}$$ $$= \frac{(x-6)(x+6)}{x-1} \quad \frac{x+1}{x+1} = 1$$	**3.** Divide and, if possible, simplify: $$\frac{t^2 - 100}{t^2 - 2t} \div \frac{t^2 + 8t - 20}{t^3}.$$

SECTION 6.3: *Addition, Subtraction, and Least Common Denominators*

The Sum of Two Rational Expressions $$\frac{A}{B} + \frac{C}{B} = \frac{A + C}{B}$$	$$\frac{7x + 8}{x + 1} + \frac{4x + 3}{x + 1} = \frac{7x + 8 + 4x + 3}{x + 1}$$ $$= \frac{11x + 11}{x + 1}$$ $$= \frac{11(x + 1)}{x + 1}$$ $$= 11 \quad \frac{x+1}{x+1} = 1$$	**4.** Add and, if possible, simplify: $$\frac{2x + 4}{x + 5} + \frac{x - 5}{x + 5}.$$
The Difference of Two Rational Expressions $$\frac{A}{B} - \frac{C}{B} = \frac{A - C}{B}$$	$$\frac{7x + 8}{x + 1} - \frac{4x + 3}{x + 1} = \frac{7x + 8 - (4x + 3)}{x + 1}$$ $$= \frac{7x + 8 - 4x - 3}{x + 1}$$ $$= \frac{3x + 5}{x + 1}$$	**5.** Subtract and, if possible, simplify: $$\frac{4x + 1}{3x - 7} - \frac{x + 8}{3x - 7}.$$

| To find the **least common multiple, LCM,** of a set of polynomials, write the prime factorizations of the polynomials. The LCM contains each factor the greatest number of times that it occurs in any of the individual factorizations. | Find the LCM of $m^2 - 5m + 6$ and $m^2 - 4m + 4$.

$\left.\begin{array}{l} m^2 - 5m + 6 = (m - 2)(m - 3) \\ m^2 - 4m + 4 = (m - 2)(m - 2) \end{array}\right\}$ Factoring each expression

LCM $= (m - 2)(m - 2)(m - 3)$ | **6.** Find the LCM of $a^2 - 25$ and $a^2 - 6a + 5$. |

SECTION 6.4: *Addition and Subtraction with Unlike Denominators*

| To add or subtract rational expressions with different denominators, first rewrite the expressions as equivalent expressions with a common denominator. The **least common denominator, LCD,** is the LCM of the denominators. | $\dfrac{2x}{x^2 - 16} + \dfrac{x}{x - 4}$

$= \dfrac{2x}{(x + 4)(x - 4)} + \dfrac{x}{x - 4}$ The LCD is $(x + 4)(x - 4)$.

$= \dfrac{2x}{(x + 4)(x - 4)} + \dfrac{x}{x - 4} \cdot \dfrac{x + 4}{x + 4}$

$= \dfrac{2x}{(x + 4)(x - 4)} + \dfrac{x^2 + 4x}{(x + 4)(x - 4)}$

$= \dfrac{x^2 + 6x}{(x + 4)(x - 4)} = \dfrac{x(x + 6)}{(x + 4)(x - 4)}$ | **7.** Subtract and, if possible, simplify:

$\dfrac{3x - 1}{x - 1} - \dfrac{x + 1}{x - 2}.$ |

SECTION 6.5: *Complex Rational Expressions*

| **Complex rational expressions** contain one or more rational expressions within the numerator and/or the denominator. They can be simplified either by using division or by multiplying by a form of 1 to clear the fractions. | **Using division to simplify:**

$\dfrac{\dfrac{1}{6} - \dfrac{1}{x}}{\dfrac{6 - x}{6}} = \dfrac{\dfrac{1}{6} \cdot \dfrac{x}{x} - \dfrac{1}{x} \cdot \dfrac{6}{6}}{\dfrac{6 - x}{6}} = \dfrac{\dfrac{x - 6}{6x}}{\dfrac{6 - x}{6}}$ Forming a single rational expression in the numerator

$= \dfrac{x - 6}{6x} \div \dfrac{6 - x}{6} = \dfrac{x - 6}{6x} \cdot \dfrac{6}{6 - x}$

$= \dfrac{6(x - 6)}{6x(-1)(x - 6)} = \dfrac{1}{-x} = -\dfrac{1}{x}$ $\dfrac{6(x - 6)}{6(x - 6)} = 1$

Multiplying by 1 to simplify:

$\dfrac{\dfrac{4}{x}}{\dfrac{3}{x} + \dfrac{2}{x^2}} = \dfrac{\dfrac{4}{x}}{\dfrac{3}{x} + \dfrac{2}{x^2}} \cdot \dfrac{x^2}{x^2}$ The LCD of all the denominators is x^2; multiplying by $\dfrac{x^2}{x^2}$

$= \dfrac{\dfrac{4}{x} \cdot \dfrac{x^2}{1}}{\left(\dfrac{3}{x} + \dfrac{2}{x^2}\right) \cdot \dfrac{x^2}{1}}$

$= \dfrac{\dfrac{4 \cdot x \cdot x}{x}}{\dfrac{3 \cdot x \cdot x}{x} + \dfrac{2 \cdot x^2}{x^2}} = \dfrac{4x}{3x + 2}$ | **8.** Simplify:

$\dfrac{1 - \dfrac{2}{3x}}{x - \dfrac{4}{9x}}.$ |

SECTION 6.6:   *Rational Equations*

To Solve a Rational Equation

1. List any restrictions.
2. Clear the equation of fractions.
3. Solve the resulting equation.
4. Check the possible solution(s) in the original equation.

Solve: $\dfrac{2}{x+1} = \dfrac{1}{x-2}$.   The restrictions are $x \neq -1$ and $x \neq 2$.

$$\frac{2}{x+1} = \frac{1}{x-2}$$

$$(x+1)(x-2) \cdot \frac{2}{x+1} = (x+1)(x-2) \cdot \frac{1}{x-2}$$

$$2(x-2) = x+1$$

$$2x-4 = x+1$$

$$x = 5$$

Check: Since $\dfrac{2}{5+1} = \dfrac{1}{5-2}$, the solution is 5.

9. Solve: $\dfrac{1}{3} + \dfrac{1}{6} = \dfrac{1}{t}$.

SECTION 6.7:   *Applications Using Rational Equations and Proportions*

The Work Principle

If $a =$ the time needed for A to complete the work alone,

$b =$ the time needed for B to complete the work alone,

and

$t =$ the time needed for A and B to complete the work together, then:

$$\frac{t}{a} + \frac{t}{b} = 1;$$

$$\left(\frac{1}{a} + \frac{1}{b}\right)t = 1;$$

$$\frac{1}{a} \cdot t + \frac{1}{b} \cdot t = 1;$$

$$\frac{1}{a} + \frac{1}{b} = \frac{1}{t}.$$

Brian and Reba volunteer in a community garden. Brian can mulch the garden alone in 8 hr and Reba can mulch the garden alone in 10 hr. How long would it take them, working together, to mulch the garden?

If $t =$ the time, in hours, that it takes Brian and Reba to do the job working together, then

$$\cdot \ \frac{1}{8} \cdot t + \frac{1}{10} \cdot t = 1 \qquad \text{Using the work principle}$$

$$t = 4\tfrac{4}{9}\text{hr.} \qquad \text{Solving the equation}$$

See Example 1 in Section 6.7 for a complete solution of this problem.

10. It takes Kenesha 3 hr to stain a large bookshelf. It takes Fletcher 2 hr to stain the same size bookshelf. How long would it take them, working together, to stain the bookshelf?

The Motion Formula

$d = r \cdot t,$

$r = \dfrac{d}{t},$

or

$t = \dfrac{d}{r}$

On her road bike, Olivia bikes 5 km/h faster than Jason does on his mountain bike. In the time it takes Olivia to travel 50 km, Jason travels 40 km. Find the speed of each bicyclist.

If $r =$ Jason's speed, in kilometers/hour, then $r + 5 =$ Olivia's speed. Using $t = d/r$ and the fact that the times are equal, we have

$$\frac{40}{r} = \frac{50}{r+5}$$

$$r = 20. \qquad \text{Solving the equation}$$

Olivia's speed is 25 km/h, and Jason's speed is 20 km/h.

See Example 3 in Section 6.7 for a complete solution of this problem.

11. Jerry jogs 5 mph faster than he walks. In the time it would take Jerry to walk 8 mi, he could jog 18 mi. Find how fast Jerry jogs and how fast he walks.

In geometry, proportions arise in the study of **similar triangles**. 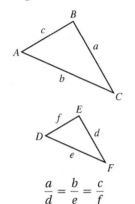 $$\frac{a}{d} = \frac{b}{e} = \frac{c}{f}$$	Triangles *DEF* and *UVW* are similar. Solve for *u*. 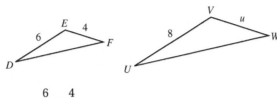 $$\frac{6}{8} = \frac{4}{u}$$ $$u = \frac{32}{6} = \frac{16}{3}$$	**12.** Triangles *ABC* and *QRS* are similar. Solve for *r*. 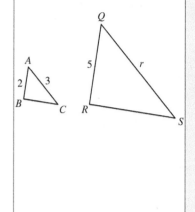

Review Exercises: Chapter 6

Concept Reinforcement

Classify each of the following statements as either true or false.

1. Every rational expression can be simplified.   [6.1]

2. The expression $(t - 3)/(t^2 - 4)$ is undefined for $t = 2$.   [6.1]

3. The expression $(t - 3)/(t^2 - 4)$ is undefined for $t = 3$.   [6.1]

4. To multiply rational expressions, a common denominator is never required.   [6.2]

5. To divide rational expressions, a common denominator is never required.   [6.2]

6. To add rational expressions, a common denominator is never required.   [6.3]

7. To subtract rational expressions, a common denominator is never required.   [6.3]

8. The number 0 can never be a solution of a rational equation.   [6.6]

List all numbers for which each expression is undefined.   [6.1]

9. $\dfrac{17}{-x^2}$

10. $\dfrac{x - 5}{x^2 - 36}$

11. $\dfrac{x^2 + 3x + 2}{x^2 + x - 30}$

12. $\dfrac{-6}{(t + 2)^2}$

Simplify.   [6.1]

13. $\dfrac{3x^2 - 9x}{3x^2 + 15x}$

14. $\dfrac{14x^2 - x - 3}{2x^2 - 7x + 3}$

15. $\dfrac{6y^2 - 36y + 54}{4y^2 - 36}$

16. $\dfrac{5x^2 - 20y^2}{2y - x}$

Multiply or divide and, if possible, simplify.   [6.2]

17. $\dfrac{a^2 - 36}{10a} \cdot \dfrac{2a}{a + 6}$

18. $\dfrac{6y - 12}{2y^2 + 3y - 2} \cdot \dfrac{y^2 - 4}{8y - 8}$

19. $\dfrac{16 - 8t}{3} \div \dfrac{t - 2}{12t}$

20. $\dfrac{4x^4}{x^2 - 1} \div \dfrac{2x^3}{x^2 - 2x + 1}$

21. $\dfrac{x^2 + 1}{x - 2} \cdot \dfrac{2x + 1}{x + 1}$

22. $(t^2 + 3t - 4) \div \dfrac{t^2 - 1}{t + 4}$

Find the LCM.   [6.3]

23. $10a^3b^8,\ 12a^5b$

24. $x^2 - x,\ x^5 - x^3,\ x^4$

25. $y^2 - y - 2,\ y^2 - 4$

Add or subtract and, if possible, simplify.

26. $\dfrac{x+6}{x+3} + \dfrac{9-4x}{x+3}$ [6.3]

27. $\dfrac{6x-3}{x^2-x-12} - \dfrac{2x-15}{x^2-x-12}$ [6.3]

28. $\dfrac{3x-1}{2x} - \dfrac{x-3}{x}$ [6.4]

29. $\dfrac{2a+4b}{5ab^2} - \dfrac{5a-3b}{a^2b}$ [6.4]

30. $\dfrac{y^2}{y-2} + \dfrac{6y-8}{2-y}$ [6.4]

31. $\dfrac{t}{t+1} + \dfrac{t}{1-t^2}$ [6.4]

32. $\dfrac{d^2}{d-2} + \dfrac{4}{2-d}$ [6.4]

33. $\dfrac{1}{x^2-25} - \dfrac{x-5}{x^2-4x-5}$ [6.4]

34. $\dfrac{3x}{x+2} - \dfrac{x}{x-2} + \dfrac{8}{x^2-4}$ [6.4]

35. $\dfrac{3}{4t} + \dfrac{3}{3t+2}$ [6.4]

Simplify.   [6.5]

36. $\dfrac{\dfrac{1}{z}+1}{\dfrac{1}{z^2}-1}$

37. $\dfrac{\dfrac{5}{2x^2}}{\dfrac{3}{4x}+\dfrac{4}{x^3}}$

38. $\dfrac{\dfrac{c}{d}-\dfrac{d}{c}}{\dfrac{1}{c}+\dfrac{1}{d}}$

Solve.   [6.6]

39. $\dfrac{3}{x} - \dfrac{1}{4} = \dfrac{1}{2}$

40. $\dfrac{3}{x+4} = \dfrac{1}{x-1}$

41. $x + \dfrac{6}{x} = -7$

42. $1 = \dfrac{2}{x-1} + \dfrac{2}{x+2}$

Solve.   [6.7]

43. Jackson can sand the oak floors and stairs in a two-story home in 12 hr. Charis can do the same job in 9 hr. How long would it take if they worked together? (Assume that two sanders are available.)

44. Ben and Jon are working for the summer building trails in a state park. Ben can build one section of the trail in 15 hr less time than Jon. Working together, they can build the section of the trail in 18 hr. How long does it take each to build the section?

45. The Black River's current is 6 mph. A boat travels 50 mi downstream in the same time that it takes to travel 30 mi upstream. What is the speed of the boat in still water?

46. Jennifer's home is 105 mi from her college dorm, and Elizabeth's home is 93 mi away. One Friday afternoon, they left school at the same time and arrived at their homes at the same time. If Jennifer drove 8 mph faster than Elizabeth, how fast did each drive?

47. To estimate the harbor seal population in Bristol Bay, scientists radio-tagged 33 seals. Several days later, they collected a sample of 40 seals, and 24 of them were tagged. Estimate the seal population of the bay.

48. Triangles *ABC* and *XYZ* are similar. Find the value of *x*.

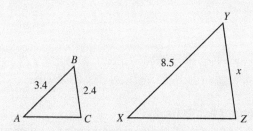

49. A sample of 30 weather-alert radios contained 4 defective ones. How many defective radios would you expect to find in a batch of 540?

Synthesis

50. For what procedures in this chapter is the LCM of denominators used to clear fractions?   [6.5], [6.6]

51. A student always uses the common denominator found by multiplying the denominators of the expressions being added. How could this approach be improved?   [6.3]

Simplify.

52. $\dfrac{2a^2+5a-3}{a^2} \cdot \dfrac{5a^3+30a^2}{2a^2+7a-4} \div \dfrac{a^2+6a}{a^2+7a+12}$ [6.2]

53. $\dfrac{12a}{(a-b)(b-c)} - \dfrac{2a}{(b-a)(c-b)}$ [6.4]

Aha! **54.** $\dfrac{5(x-y)}{(x-y)(x+2y)} - \dfrac{5(x-3y)}{(x+2y)(x-3y)}$ [6.3]

55. The last major-league baseball player to average at least 4 hits in every 10 at bats was Ted Williams in 1941. Suppose that Miguel Cabrera currently has 153 hits after 395 at bats. If he is assured 125 more at bats, what percentage of those must be hits if he is to average 4 hits for every 10 at bats?   [6.7]

Test: Chapter 6

For step-by-step test solutions, access the Chapter Test Prep Videos in MyMathLab®, on YouTube (search "Bittinger Combo Alg CA" and click on "Channels"), or by scanning the code.

List all numbers for which each expression is undefined.

1. $\dfrac{2 - x}{5x}$

2. $\dfrac{x^2 + x - 30}{x^2 - 3x + 2}$

3. Simplify: $\dfrac{6x^2 + 17x + 7}{2x^2 + 7x + 3}$.

Multiply or divide and, if possible, simplify.

4. $\dfrac{t^2 - 9}{12t} \cdot \dfrac{8t^2}{t^2 - 4t + 3}$

5. $\dfrac{25y^2 - 1}{9y^2 - 6y} \div \dfrac{5y^2 + 9y - 2}{3y^2 + y - 2}$

6. $\dfrac{4a^2 + 1}{4a^2 - 1} \div \dfrac{4a^2}{4a^2 + 4a + 1}$

7. $(x^2 + 6x + 9) \cdot \dfrac{(x - 3)^2}{x^2 - 9}$

8. Find the LCM:
$$y^2 - 9, \qquad y^2 + 10y + 21, \qquad y^2 + 4y - 21.$$

Add or subtract, and, if possible, simplify.

9. $\dfrac{2 + x}{x^3} + \dfrac{7 - 4x}{x^3}$

10. $\dfrac{5 - t}{t^2 + 1} - \dfrac{t - 3}{t^2 + 1}$

11. $\dfrac{2x - 4}{x - 3} + \dfrac{x - 1}{3 - x}$

12. $\dfrac{2x - 4}{x - 3} - \dfrac{x - 1}{3 - x}$

13. $\dfrac{7}{t - 2} + \dfrac{4}{t}$

14. $\dfrac{y}{y^2 + 6y + 9} + \dfrac{1}{y^2 + 2y - 3}$

15. $\dfrac{1}{x - 1} + \dfrac{4}{x^2 - 1} - \dfrac{2}{x^2 - 2x + 1}$

Simplify.

16. $\dfrac{9 - \dfrac{1}{y^2}}{3 - \dfrac{1}{y}}$

17. $\dfrac{\dfrac{x}{8} - \dfrac{8}{x}}{\dfrac{1}{8} + \dfrac{1}{x}}$

Solve.

18. $\dfrac{1}{t} + \dfrac{1}{3t} = \dfrac{1}{2}$

19. $\dfrac{15}{x} - \dfrac{15}{x - 2} = -2$

20. Kopy Kwik has 2 copiers. One can produce a year-end report in 20 min. The other can produce the same document in 30 min. How long would it take both machines, working together, to produce the report?

21. Katie and Tyler work together to prepare a meal at a soup kitchen in $2\frac{6}{7}$ hr. Working alone, it would take Katie 6 hr more than it would take Tyler. How long would it take each of them to complete the meal, working alone?

22. The average 140-lb adult burns about 320 calories walking 4 mi at a moderate speed. How far should the average 140-lb adult walk in order to burn 100 calories?

Source: www.walking.about.com

23. Ryan drives 20 km/h faster than Alicia. In the same time that Alicia drives 225 km, Ryan drives 325 km. Find the speed of each car.

Synthesis

24. Simplify: $1 - \dfrac{1}{1 - \dfrac{1}{1 - \dfrac{1}{a}}}$.

25. The square of a number is the opposite of the number's reciprocal. Find the number.

Cumulative Review: Chapters 1–6

1. Use the commutative law of multiplication to write an expression equivalent to $a + bc$.   [1.2]

2. Evaluate $-x^2$ for $x = 5$.   [1.8]

3. Evaluate $(-x)^2$ for $x = 5$.   [1.8]

4. Simplify: $-3[2(x - 3) - (x + 5)]$.   [1.8]

Solve.

5. $4(y - 5) = -2(y - 2)$ [2.2]

6. $x^2 + 11x + 10 = 0$ [5.7]

7. $49 = x^2$ [5.7]   8. $\frac{4}{9}t + \frac{2}{3} = \frac{1}{3}t - \frac{2}{9}$ [2.2]

9. $\frac{4}{x} + x = 5$ [6.6]   10. $\frac{2}{x - 3} = \frac{5}{3x + 1}$ [6.6]

11. $2x^2 + 7x = 4$ [5.7]   12. $4(x + 7) < 5(x - 3)$ [2.6]

13. $\frac{2}{x^2 - 9} + \frac{5}{x - 3} = \frac{3}{x + 3}$ [6.6]

14. Solve $3a - b + 9 = c$ for b.   [2.3]

Graph.   [3.2], [3.3], [3.6]

15. $y = \frac{3}{4}x + 5$ 16. $x = -3$

17. $4x + 5y = 20$ 18. $y = 6$

19. Find the slope of the line containing the points $(1, 5)$ and $(2, 3)$.   [3.5]

20. Find the slope and the y-intercept of the line given by $2x - 4y = 1$.   [3.6]

21. Write the slope–intercept equation of the line with slope $-\frac{5}{8}$ and y-intercept $(0, -4)$.   [3.6]

Simplify.

22. $\frac{x^{-5}}{x^{-3}}$ [4.2]   23. $-(2a^2b^7)^2$ [4.1]

24. Subtract:
   $(-8y^2 - y + 2) - (y^3 - 6y^2 + y - 5)$.   [4.4]

Multiply.

25. $(2x^2 - 1)(x^3 + x - 3)$ [4.5]

26. $(6x - 5y)^2$ [4.6]

27. $(3n + 2)(n - 5)$ [4.6]

28. $(2x^3 + 1)(2x^3 - 1)$ [4.6]

Factor.

29. $6x - 2x^2 - 24x^4$ [5.1]   30. $16x^2 - 81$ [5.4]

31. $t^2 - 10t + 24$ [5.2]   32. $10t^3 + 10$ [5.5]

33. $6x^2 - 28x + 16$ [5.3]

34. $25t^2 + 40t + 16$ [5.4]

35. $x^2y^2 - xy - 20$ [5.2]

36. $x^4 + 2x^3 - 3x - 6$ [5.1]

Simplify.

37. $\frac{4t - 20}{t^2 - 16} \cdot \frac{t - 4}{t - 5}$ [6.2]

38. $\frac{x^2 - 1}{x^2 - x - 2} \div \frac{x - 1}{x - 2}$ [6.2]

39. $\frac{5ab}{a^2 - b^2} + \frac{a + b}{a - b}$ [6.4]

40. $\frac{x + 2}{4 - x} - \frac{x + 3}{x - 4}$ [6.4]   41. $\dfrac{1 + \dfrac{2}{x}}{1 - \dfrac{4}{x^2}}$ [6.5]

42. Divide:
   $(15x^4 - 12x^3 + 6x^2 + 2x + 18) \div (x + 3)$.   [4.8]

Solve.

43. For each order, alibris.com charges a shipping fee of $1.80 plus $2.19 per book. The shipping cost for Dae's book order was $34.65. How many books did she order?   [2.5]

   Source: alibris.com

44. Nikki is laying out two square flower gardens in a client's lawn. Each side of one garden is 2 ft longer than each side of the smaller garden. Together, the area of the gardens is 340 ft². Find the length of a side of the smaller garden.   [5.8]

45. It takes Wes 25 min to file a week's worth of receipts. Corey, a new employee, takes 75 min to do the same job. How long would it take if they worked together?   [6.7]

46. Rachel burned 450 calories in a workout. She burned twice as many in her aerobics session as she did doing calisthenics. How many calories did she burn doing calisthenics?   [2.5]

Synthesis

47. Solve: $\frac{1}{3}|n| + 8 = 56$.   [1.4], [2.2]

48. Solve: $x(x^2 + 3x - 28) - 12(x^2 + 3x - 28) = 0$.   [5.7]

49. Solve: $\dfrac{2}{x - 3} \cdot \dfrac{3}{x + 3} - \dfrac{4}{x^2 - 7x + 12} = 0$.   [6.6]

Systems of Linear Equations and Problem Solving

SERVING SIZE	CALORIES	PROTEIN (in grams)	VITAMIN C (in milligrams)
Roast beef, 3 oz	300	20	0
Baked potato, 1	100	5	20
Broccoli, 156 g	50	5	100
Asparagus, 180 g	50	5	44

What's Good for You Ought to Be Good to You.

Dieticians and nutritionists face the daily challenge of making nutritious meals both attractive and appetizing. Using nutrition information such as that in the table above, they design meal plans that meet individual needs and tastes.

In this chapter, we design two simple meals with equivalent requirements using the foods listed here. You may find that you would prefer eating one of these meals over the other. (*See Exercises 23 and 24 in Section 8.5.*)

In the field of nutrition and dietetics, the use of math is absolutely essential.

Anju Agarwal, a nutritionist in Huntersville, North Carolina, uses math to interpret food labels, to analyze the nutrition composition of foods, and to calculate body mass index (BMI), energy needs, energy expenditure, and nutritional intake.

In fields ranging from business to zoology, problems arise that are most easily solved using a *system of equations*. In this chapter, we solve systems and applications using graphing, substitution, elimination, and matrices.

8.1   Systems of Equations in Two Variables

Translating ▪ Identifying Solutions ▪ Solving Systems Graphically

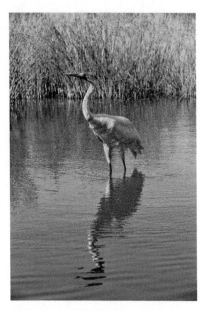

The whooping crane was one of the first animals on the U.S. endangered list. Conservation efforts have increased the number of whooping cranes from 16 in 1941 to over 500 in 2012.

1. Refer to Example 1. In 2012, there were 25 species of amphibians in the United States that were considered threatened or endangered. The number of species considered endangered was 1.5 times the number considered threatened. Write a system of equations that models the number of amphibian species considered endangered or threatened in 2012.

Source: U.S. Fish and Wildlife Service

Translating

Problems involving two unknown quantities are often translated most easily using two equations in two unknowns. Together, these equations form a **system of equations**. We look for a solution to the problem by attempting to find a pair of numbers for which *both* equations are true.

EXAMPLE 1   *Endangered Species.*   In 2012, there were 92 species of birds in the United States that were considered threatened (likely to become endangered) or endangered (in danger of becoming extinct). The number of species considered threatened was 3 less than one-fourth of the number considered endangered. Write a system of equations that models the number of U.S. bird species considered endangered or threatened in 2012.

Source: U.S. Fish and Wildlife Service

SOLUTION

1. **Familiarize.** We let t represent the number of threatened bird species and d the number of endangered bird species in 2012.

2. **Translate.** There are two statements to translate. First, we look at the total number of endangered or threatened species of birds:

Rewording:	The number of threatened species	plus	the number of endangered species	was	92.
Translating:	t	$+$	d	$=$	92

The second statement compares the two amounts, d and t:

Rewording:	The number of threatened species	was	3 less than one-fourth of the number of endangered species.
Translating:	t	$=$	$\frac{1}{4}d - 3$

We have now translated the problem to a pair, or **system, of equations**:

$$t + d = 92,$$
$$t = \tfrac{1}{4}d - 3.$$

 YOUR TURN

Study Skills

Speak Up

Don't hesitate to ask questions at appropriate times. Most instructors welcome questions and encourage students to ask them. Other students in your class may have the same questions that you do.

> ## SYSTEM OF EQUATIONS
>
> A *system of equations* is a set of two or more equations, in two or more variables, for which a common solution is sought.

Problems like Example 1 *can* be solved using one variable; however, as problems become complicated, you will find that using more than one variable (and more than one equation) is often the preferable approach.

EXAMPLE 2 *Jewelry Design.* Star Bright Jewelry Design purchased 80 beads for a total of $39 (excluding tax) to make a necklace. Some of the beads were sterling silver beads costing 40¢ each and the rest were gemstone beads costing 65¢ each. How many of each type were bought? Translate to a system of equations.

SOLUTION

1. **Familiarize.** To familiarize ourselves with this problem, let's guess that the designer bought 20 beads at 40¢ each and 60 beads at 65¢ each. The total cost would then be

$$20 \cdot 40¢ + 60 \cdot 65¢ = 800¢ + 3900¢, \quad \text{or} \quad 4700¢.$$

Since 4700¢ = $47 and $47 ≠ $39, our guess is incorrect. Rather than guess again, let's see how algebra can be used to translate the problem.

2. **Translate.** We let s = the number of silver beads and g = the number of gemstone beads. Since the cost of each bead is given in cents and the total cost is in dollars, we must choose one of the units to use throughout the problem. We choose to work in cents, so the total cost is 3900¢. The information can be organized in a table, which will help with the translating.

Type of Bead	Silver	Gemstone	Total	
Number Bought	s	g	80	→ $s + g = 80$
Price	40¢	65¢		
Amount	$40s$¢	$65g$¢	3900¢	→ $40s + 65g = 3900$

The first row of the table and the first sentence of the problem indicate that a total of 80 beads were bought:

$$s + g = 80.$$

Since each silver bead cost 40¢ and s of them were bought, $40s$ cents was paid for the silver beads. Similarly, $65g$ cents was paid for the gemstone beads. This leads to a second equation:

$$40s + 65g = 3900.$$

We now have the following system of equations as the translation:

$$s + g = 80,$$
$$40s + 65g = 3900.$$

2. Refer to Example 2. For another necklace, Star Bright Jewelry Design purchased 60 sterling silver beads and gemstone beads for a total of $30. How many of each type did the designer buy? Translate to a system of equations.

 YOUR TURN

Student Notes

We complete the solutions of Examples 1 and 2 in Section 8.3.

Identifying Solutions

A *solution* of a system of two equations in two variables is an ordered pair of numbers that makes *both* equations true.

EXAMPLE 3 Determine whether $(-4, 7)$ is a solution of the system

$$x + y = 3,$$
$$5x - y = -27.$$

SOLUTION Unless stated otherwise, we use alphabetical order of the variables. Thus we replace x with -4 and y with 7:

> **CAUTION!** Be sure to check the ordered pair in *both* equations.

$$\frac{x + y = 3}{-4 + 7 \ | \ 3}$$
$$3 \overset{?}{=} 3 \quad \text{TRUE}$$

$$\frac{5x - y = -27}{5(-4) - 7 \ | \ -27}$$
$$-20 - 7 \ |$$
$$-27 \overset{?}{=} -27 \quad \text{TRUE}$$

3. Determine whether $(6, -1)$ is a solution of the system

$$x + \ y = 5,$$
$$x - 3y = 3.$$

The pair $(-4, 7)$ makes both equations true, so it is a solution of the system. We can also describe the solution by writing $x = -4$ and $y = 7$. Set notation can also be used to list the solution set $\{(-4, 7)\}$.

⮌ YOUR TURN

Solving Systems Graphically

Recall that the graph of an equation is a drawing that represents its solution set. If we graph the equations in Example 3, we find that $(-4, 7)$ is the only point common to both lines. Thus one way to solve a system of two equations is to graph both equations and identify any points of intersection. **The coordinates of each point of intersection represent a solution of that system.**

$$x + y = 3,$$
$$5x - y = -27$$

The point of intersection of the graphs is $(-4, 7)$.

The solution of the system is $(-4, 7)$.

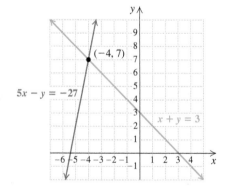

Most pairs of lines have exactly one point in common. We will soon see, however, that this is not always the case.

EXAMPLE 4 Solve each system graphically.

a) $y - x = 1,$
$\quad y + x = 3$

b) $y = -3x + 5,$
$\quad y = -3x - 2$

c) $\quad 3y - 2x = 6,$
$\quad -12y + 8x = -24$

SOLUTION

a) We begin by graphing the equations. All ordered pairs from line L_1 are solutions of the first equation. All ordered pairs from line L_2 are solutions of the second equation. The point of intersection has coordinates that make *both* equations true. Apparently, $(1, 2)$ is the solution. Graphs are not always accurate, so solving by graphing may yield approximate answers. Our check below shows that $(1, 2)$ is indeed the solution.

Graph both
equations.

Look for any points
in common.

$$y - x = 1,$$
$$y + x = 3$$

The solution of the
system is $(1, 2)$.

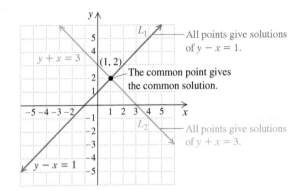

Check.

Check:

$$\frac{y - x = 1}{2 - 1 \,\vert\, 1}$$
$$1 \overset{?}{=} 1 \quad \text{TRUE}$$

$$\frac{y + x = 3}{2 + 1 \,\vert\, 3}$$
$$3 \overset{?}{=} 3 \quad \text{TRUE}$$

b) We graph the equations. The lines have the same slope, -3, and different y-intercepts, so they are parallel. There is no point at which they cross, so the system has no solution.

$$y = -3x + 5,$$
$$y = -3x - 2$$

The system has no solution.

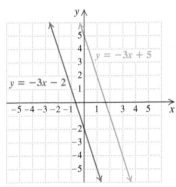

c) We graph the equations and find that the same line is drawn twice. Thus any solution of one equation is a solution of the other. Each point on the line is a solution of both equations, so the system itself has an infinite number of solutions. We check one solution, $(0, 2)$, which is the y-intercept of each equation.

$$3y - 2x = 6,$$
$$-12y + 8x = -24$$

The solution of the system is
$\{(x, y) \,|\, 3y - 2x = 6\}$.

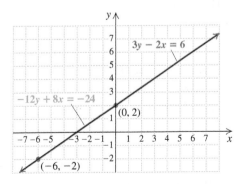

Check:

$$\frac{3y - 2x = 6}{3(2) - 2(0) \,\vert\, 6}$$
$$6 - 0$$
$$6 \overset{?}{=} 6 \quad \text{TRUE}$$

$$\frac{-12y + 8x = -24}{-12(2) + 8(0) \,\vert\, -24}$$
$$-24 + 0$$
$$-24 \overset{?}{=} -24 \quad \text{TRUE}$$

Technology Connection

On most graphing calculators, an INTERSECT option allows us to find the coordinates of the intersection directly.

To illustrate, consider the following system:

$$3.45x + 4.21y = 8.39,$$
$$7.12x - 5.43y = 6.18.$$

After solving for y in each equation, we obtain the graph below. Using INTERSECT, we see that, to the nearest hundredth, the coordinates of the intersection are $(1.47, 0.79)$.

$y_1 = (8.39 - 3.45x)/4.21,$
$y_2 = (6.18 - 7.12x)/(-5.43)$

Use a graphing calculator to solve each of the following systems. Round all x- and y-coordinates to the nearest hundredth.

1. $y = -5.43x + 10.89,$
   $y = 6.29x - 7.04$
2. $-9.25x - 12.94y = -3.88,$
   $21.83x + 16.33y = 13.69$

4. Solve graphically:

$$x = y,$$
$$y = 2x - 4.$$

You can check that $(-6, -2)$ is another solution of both equations. In fact, any pair that is a solution of one equation is a solution of the other equation as well. Thus the solution set is $\{(x, y) \mid 3y - 2x = 6\}$ or, in words, "the set of all pairs (x, y) for which $3y - 2x = 6$." Since the two equations are equivalent, we could have written instead $\{(x, y) \mid -12y + 8x = -24\}$.

 YOUR TURN

When we graph a system of two linear equations in two variables, one of the following three outcomes will occur.

Student Notes

Although the system in Example 4(c) is true for an infinite number of ordered pairs, those pairs must be of a certain form. Only pairs that are solutions of $3y - 2x = 6$ or $-12y + 8x = -24$ are solutions of the system. It is incorrect to think that *all* ordered pairs are solutions.

1. The lines have one point in common, and that point is the only solution of the system (see Example 4a). Any system that has *at least one solution* is said to be **consistent**.

2. The lines are parallel, with no point in common, and the system has *no solution* (see Example 4b). This type of system is called **inconsistent**.

3. The lines coincide, sharing the same graph. Because every solution of one equation is a solution of the other, the system has an infinite number of solutions (see Example 4c). Since it has at least one solution, this type of system is also **consistent**.

When one equation in a system can be obtained by multiplying both sides of another equation by a constant, the two equations are said to be **dependent**. Thus the equations in Example 4(c) are dependent, but those in Examples 4(a) and 4(b) are **independent**. For systems of three or more equations, the definitions of dependent and independent will be slightly modified.

Algebraic 🔗 Graphical Connection

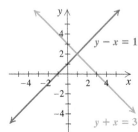

Graphs intersect at one point.

The system

$$y - x = 1,$$
$$y + x = 3$$

is *consistent* and has one solution.

Since neither equation is a multiple of the other, the equations are *independent*.

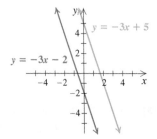

Graphs are parallel.

The system

$$y = -3x - 2,$$
$$y = -3x + 5$$

is *inconsistent* because there is no solution.

Since neither equation is a multiple of the other, the equations are *independent*.

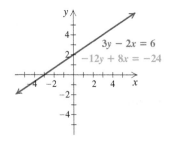

Equations have the same graph.

The system

$$3y - 2x = 6,$$
$$-12y + 8x = -24$$

is *consistent* and has an infinite number of solutions.

Since one equation is a multiple of the other, the equations are *dependent*.

 Chapter Resource:
Visualizing for Success, p. 565

Graphing is helpful when solving systems because it allows us to "see" the solution. It can also be used on systems of nonlinear equations, and in many applications, it provides a satisfactory answer. However, graphing often lacks precision, especially when fraction solutions or decimal solutions are involved.

Vocabulary and Reading Check

Classify each of the following statements as either true or false.

1. Every system of equations has at least one solution.

2. It is possible for a system of equations to have an infinite number of solutions.

3. Every point of intersection of the graphs of the equations in a system corresponds to a solution of the system.

4. The graphs of the equations in a system of two equations may coincide.

5. The graphs of the equations in a system of two equations could be parallel lines.

6. Any system of equations that has at most one solution is said to be consistent.

7. Any system of equations that has more than one solution is said to be inconsistent.

8. The equations $x + y = 5$ and $2(x + y) = 2(5)$ are dependent.

Identifying Solutions

Determine whether the ordered pair is a solution of the given system of equations. Remember to use alphabetical order of variables.

9. $(2, 3)$; $2x - y = 1$,
   $5x - 3y = 1$

10. $(4, 0)$; $2x + 7y = 8$,
    $x - 9y = 4$

11. $(-5, 1)$; $x + 5y = 0$,
    $y = 2x + 9$

12. $(-1, -2)$; $x + 3y = -7$,
    $3x - 2y = 12$

13. $(0, -5)$; $x - y = 5$,
    $y = 3x - 5$

14. $(5, 2)$; $a + b = 7$,
    $2a - 8 = b$

Aha! 15. $(3, -1)$; $3x - 4y = 13$,
    $6x - 8y = 26$

16. $(4, -2)$; $-3x - 2y = -8$,
    $8 = 3x + 2y$

Solving Systems Graphically

Solve each system graphically. Be sure to check your solution. If a system has an infinite number of solutions, use set-builder notation to write the solution set. If a system has no solution, state this.

17. $x - y = 1$,
    $x + y = 5$

18. $x + y = 6$,
    $x - y = 4$

19. $3x + y = 5$,
    $x - 2y = 4$

20. $2x - y = 4$,
    $5x - y = 13$

21. $2y = 3x + 5$,
    $x = y - 3$

22. $4x - y = 9$,
    $x - 3y = 16$

23. $x = y - 1$,
    $2x = 3y$

24. $a = 1 + b$,
    $b = 5 - 2a$

25. $y = -1$,
    $x = 3$

26. $y = 2$,
    $x = -4$

27. $t + 2s = -1$,
    $s = t + 10$

28. $b + 2a = 2$,
    $a = -3 - b$

29. $2b + a = 11$,
    $a - b = 5$

30. $y = -\frac{1}{3}x - 1$,
    $4x - 3y = 18$

31. $y = -\frac{1}{4}x + 1$,
    $2y = x - 4$

32. $6x - 2y = 2$,
    $9x - 3y = 1$

33. $y - x = 5$,
    $2x - 2y = 10$

34. $y = x + 2$,
    $3y - 2x = 4$

35. $y = 3 - x$,
    $2x + 2y = 6$

36. $2x - 3y = 6$,
    $3y - 2x = -6$

37. For the systems in the odd-numbered exercises 17–35, which are consistent?

38. For the systems in the even-numbered exercises 18–36, which are consistent?

39. For the systems in the odd-numbered exercises 17–35, which contain dependent equations?

40. For the systems in the even-numbered exercises 18–36, which contain dependent equations?

Translating

Translate each problem situation to a system of equations. Do not attempt to solve, but save for later use.

41. The sum of two numbers is 10. The first number is $\frac{2}{3}$ of the second number. What are the numbers?

42. The sum of two numbers is 30. The first number is twice the second number. What are the numbers?

43. *e-Mail Usage.* In 2012, the average e-mail user sent or received 115 e-mails each day. The number of e-mails received was 1 more than twice the number sent. How many were sent and how many were received each day?

Source: The Radicati Group, Inc.

44. *Nontoxic Furniture Polish.* A nontoxic wood furniture polish can be made by mixing mineral (or olive) oil with vinegar. To make a 16-oz batch for a squirt bottle, Jazmun uses an amount of mineral oil that is 4 oz more than twice the amount of vinegar. How much of each ingredient is required?

Sources: Based on information from Chittenden Solid Waste District and *Clean House, Clean Planet* by Karen Logan

45. *Geometry.* Two angles are supplementary.* One angle is 3° less than twice the other. Find the measures of the angles.

Supplementary angles

46. *Geometry.* Two angles are complementary.† The sum of the measures of the first angle and half the second angle is 64°. Find the measures of the angles.

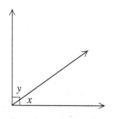

Complementary angles

47. *Basketball Scoring.* Wilt Chamberlain once scored 100 points, setting a record for points scored in an NBA game. Chamberlain took only two-point shots and (one-point) foul shots and made a total of 64 shots. How many shots of each type did he make?

48. *Basketball Scoring.* The Fenton College Cougars made 40 field goals in a recent basketball game, some 2-pointers and the rest 3-pointers. Altogether, the 40 baskets counted for 89 points. How many of each type of field goal was made?

---

*The sum of the measures of two supplementary angles is 180°.
†The sum of the measures of two complementary angles is 90°.

49. *Retail Sales.* Simply Souvenirs sold 45 hats and tee shirts. The hats sold for $14.50 each and the tee shirts for $19.50 each. In all, $697.50 was taken in for the souvenirs. How many of each type of souvenir were sold?

50. *Retail Sales.* Cool Treats sold 60 ice cream cones. Single-dip cones sold for $2.50 each and double-dip cones for $4.15 each. In all, $179.70 was taken in for the cones. How many of each size cone were sold?

51. *Fitness Equipment.* In 2012, the Mio® Classic Heart Rate watch cost $39.99 and the Mio® Drive Plus Heart Rate Watch cost $59.99. A nonprofit community health organization purchased 35 heart-rate watches for use at a wellness center. If the organization spent $1639.65 for the watches, how many of each type did they purchase?

52. *Fundraising.* The Buck Creek Fire Department served 250 dinners. A child's plate cost $5.50 and an adult's plate cost $9.00. A total of $1935 was collected. How many of each type of plate were served?

53. *Lacrosse.* The perimeter of an NCAA men's lacrosse field is 340 yd. The length is 50 yd longer than the width. Find the dimensions.

$P = 340$ yd

54. *Tennis.* The perimeter of a standard tennis court used for doubles is 228 ft. The width is 42 ft less than the length. Find the dimensions.

55. Write a problem for a classmate to solve that requires writing a system of two equations. Devise the problem so that the solution is "The Bucks made 6 three-point baskets and 31 two-point baskets."

56. Write a problem for a classmate to solve that can be translated into a system of two equations. Devise the problem so that the solution is "In 2012, Diana took five 3-credit classes and two 4-credit classes."

Skill Review

Simplify. Do not use negative exponents in the answer.

57. $-\frac{1}{2} - \frac{3}{10}$ [1.6]

58. $(0.05)(-1.2)$ [1.7]

59. $(-3)^2 - 2 - 4 \cdot 6 \div 2 \cdot 3$ [1.8]

60. $(-3x^2y^{-4})(-2x^{-7}y^{12})$ [4.2]

61. -10^{-2} [4.2]

62. $(5a^2b^6)^0$ [4.1]

Synthesis

Advertising Media.   For Exercises 63 and 64, consider the following graph showing the U.S. market share for various advertising media.

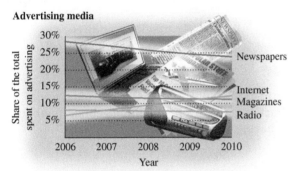

Advertising media

Source: ZenithOptimedia

63. In what year did the Internet and radio have the same advertising market share? Explain.

64. Will Internet advertising ever exceed that of newspapers? If so, when? Explain your answers.

65. For each of the following conditions, write a system of equations. Answers may vary.

   a) $(5, 1)$ is a solution.
   b) There is no solution.
   c) There is an infinite number of solutions.

66. A system of linear equations has $(1, -1)$ and $(-2, 3)$ as solutions. Determine:

   a) a third point that is a solution (answers may vary), and
   b) how many solutions there are.

67. The solution of the following system is $(4, -5)$. Find A and B.

$$Ax - 6y = 13,$$
$$x - By = -8.$$

Translate to a system of equations. Do not solve.

68. *Ages.*   Tyler is twice as old as his son. Ten years ago, Tyler was three times as old as his son. How old are they now?

69. *Work Experience.*   Dell and Juanita are mathematics professors at a state university. Together, they have 46 years of service. Two years ago, Dell had taught 2.5 times as many years as Juanita. How long has each taught at the university?

70. *Design.*   A piece of posterboard has a perimeter of 156 in. If you cut 6 in. off the width, the length becomes four times the width. What are the dimensions of the original piece of posterboard?

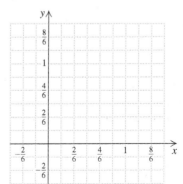

$P = 156$ in.

71. *Nontoxic Scouring Powder.*   A nontoxic scouring powder is made up of 4 parts baking soda and 1 part vinegar. How much of each ingredient is needed for a 16-oz mixture?

72. Solve Exercise 41 graphically.

73. Solve Exercise 44 graphically.

Solve graphically.

74. $y = |x|,$
$\quad 3y - x = 8$

75. $x - y = 0,$
$\quad y = x^2$

In Exercises 76–79, use a graphing calculator to solve each system of linear equations for x and y. Round all coordinates to the nearest hundredth.

76. $y = 8.23x + 2.11,$
$\quad y = -9.11x - 4.66$

77. $y = -3.44x - 7.72,$
$\quad y = 4.19x - 8.22$

78. $14.12x + 7.32y = 2.98,$
$\quad 21.88x - 6.45y = -7.22$

79. $5.22x - 8.21y = -10.21,$
$\quad -12.67x + 10.34y = 12.84$

80. Solve graphically using the grid below:

$$2x - 3y = 0,$$
$$-4x + 3y = -1.$$

81. *Research.* Refer to Exercise 63. Find advertising market share for a recent year and extend the graph before Exercise 63 to include the new data. Do the 2006–2010 trends continue? If any new trends emerge, try to find reasons for the change.

YOUR TURN ANSWERS: SECTION 8.1

1. Let t represent the number of threatened amphibian species and d the number of endangered amphibian species; $t + d = 25, d = 1.5t$
2. $s + g = 60, 40s + 65g = 3000$ **3.** No   **4.** $(4, 4)$

PREPARE TO MOVE ON

Solve.   [2.2]

1. $3x + 2(5x - 1) = 6$

2. $4(3y + 2) - 7y = 3$

3. $2x - (x - 7) = 18$

Solve.   [2.3]

4. $3x - y = 4$, for y

5. $5y - 2x = 7$, for x

8.2   Solving by Substitution or Elimination

The Substitution Method   ▪   The Elimination Method

Study Skills

Learn from Your Mistakes
Immediately after each quiz or test, write out a step-by-step solution to any questions you missed. Visit your professor during office hours or consult a tutor for help with problems that still give you trouble. Misconceptions tend to persist if not corrected as soon as possible.

The Substitution Method

Algebraic (nongraphical) methods for solving systems are often superior to graphing, especially when fractions are involved. One algebraic method, the *substitution method*, relies on having a variable isolated.

EXAMPLE 1   Solve the system

$$x + y = 4, \quad (1)$$
$$x = y + 1. \quad (2)$$

For easy reference, we have numbered the equations.

SOLUTION   Equation (2) says that x and $y + 1$ name the same number. Thus we can substitute $y + 1$ for x in equation (1):

$$x + y = 4 \quad \text{Equation (1)}$$
$$(y + 1) + y = 4. \quad \text{Substituting } y + 1 \text{ for } x$$

We solve this last equation, using methods learned earlier:

$$(y + 1) + y = 4$$
$$2y + 1 = 4 \quad \text{Removing parentheses and combining like terms}$$
$$2y = 3 \quad \text{Subtracting 1 from both sides}$$
$$y = \tfrac{3}{2}. \quad \text{Dividing both sides by 2}$$

We now return to the original pair of equations and substitute $\tfrac{3}{2}$ for y in either equation so that we can solve for x. For this problem, calculations are slightly easier if we use equation (2):

$$x = y + 1 \quad \text{Equation (2)}$$
$$= \tfrac{3}{2} + 1 \quad \text{Substituting } \tfrac{3}{2} \text{ for } y$$
$$= \tfrac{3}{2} + \tfrac{2}{2} = \tfrac{5}{2}.$$

We obtain the ordered pair $\left(\tfrac{5}{2}, \tfrac{3}{2}\right)$. A check ensures that it is a solution.

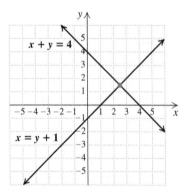

A visualization of Example 1. Note that the coordinates of the intersection are not obvious.

1. Solve the system

$$x - y = 3,$$
$$x = 2 - y.$$

Check:

$$\begin{array}{c|c} x + y = 4 \\ \hline \frac{5}{2} + \frac{3}{2} & 4 \\ \frac{8}{2} & \\ 4 \overset{?}{=} 4 & \text{TRUE} \end{array} \qquad \begin{array}{c|c} x = y + 1 \\ \hline \frac{5}{2} & \frac{3}{2} + 1 \\ & \frac{3}{2} + \frac{2}{2} \\ \frac{5}{2} \overset{?}{=} \frac{5}{2} & \text{TRUE} \end{array}$$

Since $\left(\frac{5}{2}, \frac{3}{2}\right)$ checks, it is the solution.

YOUR TURN

The exact solution to Example 1 is difficult to find graphically because it involves fractions. The graph shown serves as a partial check and provides a visualization of the problem.

If neither equation in a system has a variable alone on one side, we first isolate a variable in one equation and then substitute.

EXAMPLE 2   Solve the system

$$2x + \ y = 6, \qquad (1)$$
$$3x + 4y = 4. \qquad (2)$$

SOLUTION   First, we select an equation and solve for one variable. We can isolate y by subtracting $2x$ from both sides of equation (1):

$$2x + y = 6 \qquad (1)$$
$$y = 6 - 2x. \qquad (3) \qquad \text{Subtracting } 2x \text{ from both sides}$$

Next, we proceed as in Example 1, by substituting:

$$3x + 4(6 - 2x) = 4 \qquad \text{Substituting } 6 - 2x \text{ for } y \text{ in equation (2).}$$
$$\text{Use parentheses!}$$
$$3x + 24 - 8x = 4 \qquad \text{Distributing to remove parentheses}$$
$$3x - 8x = 4 - 24 \qquad \text{Subtracting 24 from both sides}$$
$$-5x = -20$$
$$x = 4. \qquad \text{Dividing both sides by } -5$$

Next, we substitute 4 for x in equation (1), (2), or (3). It is easiest to use equation (3) because it has already been solved for y:

$$y = 6 - 2x$$
$$= 6 - 2(4)$$
$$= 6 - 8 = -2.$$

A visualization of Example 2

The pair $(4, -2)$ appears to be the solution. We check in equations (1) and (2).

Check:

$$\begin{array}{c|c} 2x + y = 6 \\ \hline 2(4) + (-2) & 6 \\ 8 - 2 & \\ 6 \overset{?}{=} 6 & \text{TRUE} \end{array} \qquad \begin{array}{c|c} 3x + 4y = 4 \\ \hline 3(4) + 4(-2) & 4 \\ 12 - 8 & \\ 4 \overset{?}{=} 4 & \text{TRUE} \end{array}$$

Since $(4, -2)$ checks, it is the solution.

YOUR TURN

2. Solve the system

$$x + 2y = 4,$$
$$2x + 3y = 1.$$

For a system with no solution, the graphs of the equations do not intersect. How do we recognize such systems when solving by an algebraic method?

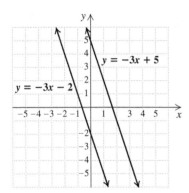

A visualization of Example 3

3. Solve the system

$$x + y = 1,$$
$$x + y = 2.$$

EXAMPLE 3   Solve the system

$$y = -3x + 5 \quad (1)$$
$$y = -3x - 2. \quad (2)$$

SOLUTION   If we solve this system graphically, we see that the lines are parallel and the system has no solution. Let's now try to solve the system by substitution. Proceeding as in Example 1, we substitute $-3x - 2$ for y in the first equation:

$$-3x - 2 = -3x + 5 \qquad \text{Substituting } -3x - 2 \text{ for } y \text{ in equation (1)}$$
$$-2 = 5. \qquad \text{Adding } 3x \text{ to both sides; } -2 = 5 \text{ is a contradiction. The equation is always false.}$$

Since there is no solution of $-2 = 5$, there is no solution of the system. We state that there is no solution.

 YOUR TURN

When solving a system algebraically yields a contradiction, the system has no solution. As we will see in Example 7, when solving a system of two equations algebraically yields an equation that is always true, the system has an infinite number of solutions.

The Elimination Method

The *elimination method* for solving systems of equations makes use of the *addition principle*: If $a = b$, then $a + c = b + c$.

EXAMPLE 4   Solve the system

$$2x - 3y = 0, \quad (1)$$
$$-4x + 3y = -1. \quad (2)$$

SOLUTION   According to equation (2), $-4x + 3y$ and -1 are the same number. Thus we can use the addition principle and add $-4x + 3y$ to the left side of equation (1) and -1 to the right side:

$$2x - 3y = 0 \qquad (1)$$
$$\underline{-4x + 3y = -1} \qquad (2)$$
$$-2x + 0y = -1. \qquad \text{Adding. Note that } y \text{ has been "eliminated."}$$

The resulting equation has just one variable, x, for which we solve:

$$-2x = -1$$
$$x = \tfrac{1}{2}.$$

Next, we substitute $\tfrac{1}{2}$ for x in equation (1) and solve for y:

$$2 \cdot \tfrac{1}{2} - 3y = 0 \qquad \text{Substituting. We also could have used equation (2).}$$
$$1 - 3y = 0$$
$$-3y = -1, \text{ so } y = \tfrac{1}{3}.$$

Check:

$$\begin{array}{c|c}
2x - 3y = 0 \\
\hline
2(\tfrac{1}{2}) - 3(\tfrac{1}{3}) & 0 \\
1 - 1 & \\
0 \overset{?}{=} 0 & \text{TRUE}
\end{array} \qquad
\begin{array}{c|c}
-4x + 3y = -1 \\
\hline
-4(\tfrac{1}{2}) + 3(\tfrac{1}{3}) & -1 \\
-2 + 1 & \\
-1 \overset{?}{=} -1 & \text{TRUE}
\end{array}$$

Since $(\tfrac{1}{2}, \tfrac{1}{3})$ checks, it is the solution. See also the graph at left.

 YOUR TURN

A visualization of Example 4

4. Solve the system

$$-2x - 7y = 3,$$
$$6x + 7y = -2.$$

Adding in Example 4 eliminated the variable y because two terms, $-3y$ in equation (1) and $3y$ in equation (2), are opposites. For some systems, we must multiply before adding.

Student Notes

It is wise to double-check each step of your work as you go, rather than checking all steps at the end of a problem. One common error is to forget to multiply *both* sides of an equation when using the multiplication principle.

EXAMPLE 5   Solve the system

$$5x + 4y = 22, \quad (1)$$
$$-3x + 8y = 18. \quad (2)$$

SOLUTION   If we add the left sides of the two equations, we will not eliminate a variable. However, if the $4y$ in equation (1) were changed to $-8y$, we would. To accomplish this change, we multiply both sides of equation (1) by -2:

$$
\begin{array}{ll}
-10x - 8y = -44 & \text{Multiplying both sides of equation (1) by } -2 \\
\underline{-3x + 8y = 18} & \\
-13x + 0 = -26 & \text{Adding} \\
x = 2. & \text{Solving for } x
\end{array}
$$

$$
\begin{array}{ll}
\text{Then} \quad -3 \cdot 2 + 8y = 18 & \text{Substituting 2 for } x \text{ in equation (2)} \\
 -6 + 8y = 18 & \\
\left. \begin{array}{l} 8y = 24 \\ y = 3. \end{array} \right\} & \text{Solving for } y
\end{array}
$$

We obtain $(2, 3)$, or $x = 2, y = 3$. We leave it to the student to confirm that this checks and is the solution.

5. Solve the system

$$2x - 3y = 8,$$
$$6x + 5y = 4.$$

YOUR TURN

Sometimes we must multiply twice in order to make two terms become opposites.

EXAMPLE 6   Solve the system

$$2x + 3y = 17, \quad (1)$$
$$5x + 7y = 29. \quad (2)$$

SOLUTION   We multiply so that the x-terms will be eliminated when we add.

Multiply to get terms that are opposites.

Solve for one variable.

$$
\begin{array}{l}
2x + 3y = 17, \xrightarrow{\text{Multiplying both}} 10x + 15y = 85 \\
 \text{sides by 5} \\
5x + 7y = 29 \xrightarrow{\text{Multiplying both}} \underline{-10x - 14y = -58} \\
 \text{sides by } -2 0 + y = 27 \quad \text{Adding} \\
 y = 27
\end{array}
$$

Next, we substitute to find x:

Substitute.

Solve for the other variable.

Check in both equations.

State the solution as an ordered pair.

$$
\begin{array}{ll}
2x + 3 \cdot 27 = 17 & \text{Substituting 27 for } y \text{ in equation (1)} \\
2x + 81 = 17 & \\
\left. \begin{array}{l} 2x = -64 \\ x = -32. \end{array} \right\} & \text{Solving for } x
\end{array}
$$

Check:

$$
\begin{array}{c|c}
\multicolumn{1}{c}{2x + 3y = 17} \\
\hline
2(-32) + 3(27) & 17 \\
-64 + 81 & \\
17 \stackrel{?}{=} 17 & \text{TRUE}
\end{array}
\qquad
\begin{array}{c|c}
\multicolumn{1}{c}{5x + 7y = 29} \\
\hline
5(-32) + 7(27) & 29 \\
-160 + 189 & \\
29 \stackrel{?}{=} 29 & \text{TRUE}
\end{array}
$$

6. Solve the system

$$4x + 3y = 11,$$
$$3x + 2y = 7.$$

We obtain $(-32, 27)$, or $x = -32, y = 27$, as the solution.

YOUR TURN

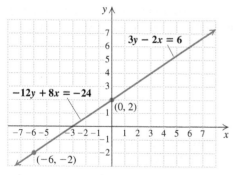

A visualization of Example 7

7. Solve the system

$$x - 3y = 2,$$
$$-5x + 15y = -10.$$

EXAMPLE 7   Solve the system

$$3y - 2x = 6, \qquad (1)$$
$$-12y + 8x = -24. \qquad (2)$$

SOLUTION   If we solve this system graphically, as shown at left, we find that the lines coincide and the system has an infinite number of solutions. Suppose we were to solve this system using the elimination method:

$$12y - 8x = 24 \qquad \text{Multiplying both sides of equation (1) by 4}$$
$$\underline{-12y + 8x = -24}$$
$$0 = 0. \qquad \text{We obtain an identity; } 0 = 0 \text{ is always true.}$$

Note that both variables have been eliminated and what remains is an identity—that is, an equation that is always true. Any pair that is a solution of equation (1) is also a solution of equation (2). The equations are dependent and the solution set is infinite:

$$\{(x, y) \mid 3y - 2x = 6\}, \text{ or equivalently, } \{(x, y) \mid -12y + 8x = -24\}.$$

YOUR TURN

Example 3 and Example 7 illustrate how to tell algebraically whether a system of two equations is inconsistent or whether the equations are dependent.

RULES FOR SPECIAL CASES

When solving a system of two linear equations in two variables:

1. If we obtain an identity such as $0 = 0$, then the system has an infinite number of solutions. The equations are dependent and, since a solution exists, the system is consistent.*
2. If we obtain a contradiction such as $0 = 7$, then the system has no solution. The system is inconsistent.

When decimals or fractions appear, it often helps to *clear* before solving.

EXAMPLE 8   Solve the system

$$0.2x + 0.3y = 1.7,$$
$$\tfrac{1}{7}x + \tfrac{1}{5}y = \tfrac{29}{35}.$$

SOLUTION   We have

$$0.2x + 0.3y = 1.7, \; \rightarrow \text{ Multiplying both sides by 10} \; \rightarrow \; 2x + 3y = 17$$
$$\tfrac{1}{7}x + \tfrac{1}{5}y = \tfrac{29}{35} \; \rightarrow \text{ Multiplying both sides by 35} \; \rightarrow \; 5x + 7y = 29.$$

8. Solve the system

$$\tfrac{1}{2}x - \tfrac{1}{3}y = \tfrac{1}{6},$$
$$0.3x + 0.4y = 1.2.$$

We multiplied both sides of the first equation by 10 to clear the decimals. Multiplication by 35, the least common denominator, clears the fractions in the second equation. The problem now happens to be identical to Example 6. The solution is $(-32, 27)$, or $x = -32, y = 27$.

YOUR TURN

---

*Consistent systems and dependent equations are discussed in greater detail in Section 8.4.

The steps in each algebraic method for solving systems of two equations are given below. Note that in both methods, we find the value of one variable and then substitute to find the corresponding value of the other variable.

TO SOLVE A SYSTEM USING SUBSTITUTION

1. Isolate a variable in one of the equations (unless one is already isolated).
2. Substitute for that variable in the other equation, using parentheses.
3. Solve the equation in which the substitution was made.
4. Substitute the solution from step (3) in any of the equations, and solve for the other variable.
5. Form an ordered pair and check in the original equations.

Chapter Resource:
Collaborative Activity, p. 566

TO SOLVE A SYSTEM USING ELIMINATION

1. Write both equations in standard form.
2. Multiply both sides of one or both equations by a constant, if necessary, so that the coefficients of one of the variables are opposites.
3. Add the left sides and the right sides of the resulting equations. One variable should be eliminated in the sum.
4. Solve for the remaining variable.
5. Substitute the value of the second variable in any of the equations, and solve for the other variable.
6. Form an ordered pair and check in the original equations.

CONNECTING THE CONCEPTS

We now have three different methods for solving systems of two linear equations. Each method has certain strengths and weaknesses, as outlined below.

Method	Strengths	Weaknesses
Graphical	Solutions are displayed graphically. Can be used with any system that can be graphed.	For some systems, only approximate solutions can be found graphically. The graph drawn may not be large enough to show the solution.
Substitution	Yields exact solutions. Easy to use when a variable has a coefficient of 1.	Introduces extensive computations with fractions when solving more complicated systems. Solutions are not displayed graphically.
Elimination	Yields exact solutions. Easy to use when fractions or decimals appear in the system.	Solutions are not displayed graphically.

(continued)

EXERCISES

Solve using an appropriate method.

1. $x = y$,
   $x + y = 2$

2. $x + y = 10$,
   $x - y = 8$

3. $y = \frac{1}{2}x + 1$,
   $y = 2x - 5$

4. $y = 2x - 3$,
   $x + y = 12$

5. $12x - 19y = 13$,
   $8x + 19y = 7$

6. $2x - 5y = 1$,
   $3x + 2y = 11$

7. $y = \frac{5}{3}x + 7$,
   $y = \frac{5}{3}x - 8$

8. $x = 2 - y$,
   $3x + 3y = 6$

8.2 EXERCISE SET

FOR EXTRA HELP

MyMathLab® Math XL
PRACTICE   WATCH   READ   REVIEW

Vocabulary and Reading Check

Choose the word from the following list that best completes each statement. Not all words will be used.

consistent   opposite
elimination   substitution
inconsistent

1. To use the _____ method, a variable must be isolated.

2. The _____ method makes use of the addition principle.

3. To eliminate a variable by adding, two terms must be _____.

4. A(n) _____ system has no solution.

Concept Reinforcement

In each of Exercises 5–10, match the system listed with the choice from the column on the right that would be a subsequent step in solving the system.

5. ____ $3x - 4y = 6$,
        $5x + 4y = 1$

6. ____ $2x - y = 8$,
        $y = 5x + 3$

7. ____ $x - 2y = 3$,
        $5x + 3y = 4$

8. ____ $8x + 6y = -15$,
        $5x - 3y = 8$

9. ____ $y = 4x - 7$,
        $6x + 3y = 19$

10. ____ $y = 4x - 1$,
        $y = -\frac{2}{3}x - 1$

a) $-5x + 10y = -15$,
   $5x + 3y = 4$

b) The lines intersect at $(0, -1)$.

c) $6x + 3(4x - 7) = 19$

d) $8x = 7$

e) $2x - (5x + 3) = 8$

f) $8x + 6y = -15$,
   $10x - 6y = 16$

For Exercises 11–58, if a system has an infinite number of solutions, use set-builder notation to write the solution set. If a system has no solution, state this.

The Substitution Method

Solve using the substitution method.

11. $y = 3 - 2x$,
     $3x + y = 5$

12. $3y + x = 4$,
     $x = 2y - 1$

13. $3x + 5y = 3$,
     $x = 8 - 4y$

14. $9x - 2y = 3$,
     $3x - 6 = y$

15. $3s - 4t = 14$,
     $5s + t = 8$

16. $m - 2n = 16$,
     $4m + n = 1$

17. $4x - 2y = 6$,
     $2x - 3 = y$

18. $t = 4 - 2s$,
     $t + 2s = 6$

19. $-5s + t = 11$,
     $4s + 12t = 4$

20. $5x + 6y = 14$,
     $-3y + x = 7$

21. $2x + 2y = 2$,
     $3x - y = 1$

22. $4p - 2q = 16$,
     $5p + 7q = 1$

23. $2a + 6b = 4$,
     $3a - b = 6$

24. $3x - 4y = 5$,
     $2x - y = 1$

25. $2x - 3 = y$,
     $y - 2x = 1$

26. $a - 2b = 3$,
     $3a = 6b + 9$

The Elimination Method

Solve using the elimination method.

27. $x + 3y = 7$,
     $-x + 4y = 7$

28. $2x + y = 6$,
     $x - y = 3$

29. $x - 2y = 11$,
     $3x + 2y = 17$

30. $5x - 3y = 8$,
     $-5x + y = 4$

31. $9x + 3y = -3$,
     $2x - 3y = -8$

32. $6x - 3y = 18$,
     $6x + 3y = -12$

33. $5x + 3y = 19,$
$x - 6y = 11$

34. $3x + 2y = 3,$
$9x - 8y = -2$

35. $5r - 3s = 24,$
$3r + 5s = 28$

36. $5x - 7y = -16,$
$2x + 8y = 26$

37. $6s + 9t = 12,$
$4s + 6t = 5$

38. $10a + 6b = 8,$
$5a + 3b = 2$

39. $\frac{1}{2}x - \frac{1}{6}y = 10,$
$\frac{2}{5}x + \frac{1}{2}y = 8$

40. $\frac{1}{3}x + \frac{1}{5}y = 7,$
$\frac{1}{6}x - \frac{2}{5}y = -4$

41. $\frac{x}{2} + \frac{y}{3} = \frac{7}{6},$
$\frac{2x}{3} + \frac{3y}{4} = \frac{5}{4}$

42. $\frac{2x}{3} + \frac{3y}{4} = \frac{11}{12},$
$\frac{x}{3} + \frac{7y}{18} = \frac{1}{2}$

Aha! **43.** $12x - 6y = -15,$
$-4x + 2y = 5$

44. $8s + 12t = 16,$
$6s + 9t = 12$

45. $0.3x + 0.2y = 0.3,$
$0.5x + 0.4y = 0.4$

46. $0.3x + 0.2y = 5,$
$0.5x + 0.4y = 11$

The Substitution and Elimination Methods

Solve using any algebraic method.

47. $a - 2b = 16,$
$b + 3 = 3a$

48. $5x - 9y = 7,$
$7y - 3x = -5$

49. $10x + y = 306,$
$10y + x = 90$

50. $3(a - b) = 15,$
$4a = b + 1$

51. $6x - 3y = 3,$
$4x - 2y = 2$

52. $x + 2y = 8,$
$x = 4 - 2y$

53. $3s - 7t = 5,$
$7t - 3s = 8$

54. $2s - 13t = 120,$
$-14s + 91t = -840$

55. $0.05x + 0.25y = 22,$
$0.15x + 0.05y = 24$

56. $2.1x - 0.9y = 15,$
$-1.4x + 0.6y = 10$

57. $13a - 7b = 9,$
$2a - 8b = 6$

58. $3a - 12b = 9,$
$4a - 5b = 3$

59. Describe a procedure that can be used to write an inconsistent system of equations.

60. Describe a procedure that can be used to write a system that has an infinite number of solutions.

Skill Review

61. Use an associative law to write an equation equivalent to $(4 + m) + n$. [1.2]

62. Combine like terms: $a^2 - 4a - 3a^2 + 4a + 7$. [1.8]

63. Simplify: $8x - 3[5x + 2(6 - 9x)]$. [1.8]

64. Evaluate $-p^2$ for $p = -1$. [1.8]

65. Convert 30,050,000 to scientific notation. [4.2]

66. Convert 6.1×10^{-4} to decimal notation. [4.2]

Synthesis

67. Some systems are more easily solved by substitution and some are more easily solved by elimination. What guidelines could be used to help someone determine which method to use?

68. Explain how it is possible to solve Exercise 43 mentally.

69. If $(1, 2)$ and $(-3, 4)$ are two solutions of $f(x) = mx + b$, find m and b.

70. If $(0, -3)$ and $\left(-\frac{3}{2}, 6\right)$ are two solutions of $px - qy = -1$, find p and q.

71. Determine a and b for which $(-4, -3)$ is a solution of the system
$ax + by = -26,$
$bx - ay = 7.$

72. Solve for x and y in terms of a and b:
$5x + 2y = a,$
$x - y = b.$

Solve.

73. $\frac{x + y}{2} - \frac{x - y}{5} = 1,$
$\frac{x - y}{2} + \frac{x + y}{6} = -2$

74. $3.5x - 2.1y = 106.2,$
$4.1x + 16.7y = -106.28$

Each of the following is a system of nonlinear equations. However, each is reducible to linear, since an appropriate substitution (say, u for $1/x$ and v for $1/y$) yields a linear system. Make such a substitution, solve for the new variables, and then solve for the original variables.

75. $\frac{2}{x} + \frac{1}{y} = 0,$
$\frac{5}{x} + \frac{2}{y} = -5$

76. $\frac{1}{x} - \frac{3}{y} = 2,$
$\frac{6}{x} + \frac{5}{y} = -34$

Solve using a system of equations.

77. *Energy Consumption.* With average use, a toaster oven and a convection oven together consume 15 kilowatt hours (kWh) of electricity each month. A convection oven uses four times as much electricity as a toaster oven. How much does each use per month?

Source: Lee County Electric Cooperative

78. *Communication.* Terri has two monthly bills: one for her cell phone and one for the data package for her tablet. The total of the two bills is $69.98 per month. Her cell-phone bill is $40 more per month than the bill for her tablet's data package. How much is each bill?

79. To solve the system

$$17x + 19y = 102,$$
$$136x + 152y = 826$$

Preston graphs both equations on a graphing calculator and gets the following screen. He then (incorrectly) concludes that the equations are dependent and the solution set is infinite. How can algebra be used to convince Preston that a mistake has been made?

 YOUR TURN ANSWERS: SECTION 8.2
1. $\left(\frac{5}{2}, -\frac{1}{2}\right)$ **2.** $(-10, 7)$ **3.** No solution **4.** $\left(\frac{1}{4}, -\frac{1}{2}\right)$
5. $\left(\frac{13}{7}, -\frac{10}{7}\right)$ **6.** $(-1, 5)$ **7.** $\{(x, y) \mid x - 3y = 2\}$
8. $\left(\frac{14}{9}, \frac{11}{6}\right)$

QUICK QUIZ: SECTIONS 8.1–8.2

1. Determine whether $(4, -1)$ is a solution of

$$x + y = 3,$$
$$x - y = 5. \quad [8.1]$$

2. Solve graphically:

$$x + y = 4,$$
$$y = 2x - 5. \quad [8.1]$$

3. Solve using substitution:

$$3x - y = 1,$$
$$y = 2x - 4. \quad [8.2]$$

4. Solve using elimination:

$$x - y = 2,$$
$$2x + 3y = 1. \quad [8.2]$$

5. Solve using any appropriate method:

$$2x = 1 - 3y,$$
$$y - 3x = 0. \quad [8.1], [8.2]$$

PREPARE TO MOVE ON

Solve. [2.5]

1. After her condominium had been on the market for 6 months, Gilena reduced the price to $94,500. This was $\frac{9}{10}$ of the original asking price. How much did Gilena originally ask for her condominium?

2. Ellia needs to average 80 on her tests in order to earn a B in her math class. Her average after four tests is 77.5. What score is needed on the fifth test in order to raise the average to 80?

3. North American Truck and Trailer rents vans for $53 per day plus 5¢ per mile. Anazi rented a van for 2 days. The bill was $120.50. How far did Anazi drive the van?

Source: www.northamericantrucktrailer.com

8.3 Solving Applications: Systems of Two Equations

Total-Value Problems and Mixture Problems ▪ Motion Problems

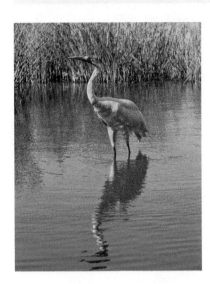

You are in a much better position to solve problems now that you know how systems of equations can be used. Using systems often makes the translating step easier.

EXAMPLE 1 *Endangered Species.* In 2012, there were 92 species of birds in the United States that were considered threatened or endangered. The number considered threatened was 3 less than one-fourth of the number considered endangered. How many U.S. bird species were considered endangered or threatened in 2012?

Source: U.S. Fish and Wildlife Service

SOLUTION The *Familiarize* and *Translate* steps were completed in Example 1 of Section 8.1. The resulting system of equations is

$$t + d = 92,$$
$$t = \tfrac{1}{4}d - 3,$$

where d is the number of endangered bird species and t is the number of threatened bird species in the United States in 2012.

3. **Carry out.** We solve the system of equations. Since one equation already has a variable isolated, let's use the substitution method:

$t + d = 92$	
$\tfrac{1}{4}d - 3 + d = 92$	Substituting $\tfrac{1}{4}d - 3$ for t
$\tfrac{5}{4}d - 3 = 92$	Combining like terms
$\tfrac{5}{4}d = 95$	Adding 3 to both sides
$d = \tfrac{4}{5} \cdot 95$	Multiplying both sides by $\tfrac{4}{5}$: $\tfrac{4}{5} \cdot \tfrac{5}{4} = 1$
$d = 76.$	Simplifying

Next, using either of the original equations, we substitute and solve for t:

$$t = \tfrac{1}{4} \cdot 76 - 3 = 19 - 3 = 16.$$

4. **Check.** The sum of 76 and 16 is 92, so the total number of species is correct. Since 3 less than one-fourth of 76 is $19 - 3$, or 16, the numbers check.

5. **State.** In 2012, there were 76 bird species considered endangered and 16 considered threatened.

1. Refer to Example 1. In 2012, there were 25 species of amphibians in the United States that were considered threatened or endangered. The number of species considered endangered was 1.5 times the number considered threatened. How many U.S. amphibian species were considered endangered and how many were considered threatened in 2012?

Source: U.S. Fish and Wildlife Service

 YOUR TURN

Total-Value Problems and Mixture Problems

EXAMPLE 2 *Jewelry Design.* In order to make a necklace, Star Bright Jewelry Design purchased 80 beads for a total of $39 (excluding tax). Some of the beads were sterling silver beads costing 40¢ each and the rest were gemstone beads costing 65¢ each. How many of each type were bought?

Student Notes

It is very important that you clearly label precisely what each variable represents. Not only will this help with writing equations, but it will help you identify and state solutions.

2. Refer to Example 2. For another necklace, the jewelry designer purchased 60 sterling silver beads and gemstone beads for a total of $30. How many of each type did the designer buy?

SOLUTION The *Familiarize* and *Translate* steps were completed in Example 2 of Section 8.1.

3. Carry out. We are to solve the system of equations

$$s + g = 80, \qquad (1)$$
$$40s + 65g = 3900, \qquad (2) \qquad \text{Working in cents rather than dollars}$$

where s is the number of sterling silver beads bought and g is the number of gemstone beads bought. Because both equations are in the form $Ax + By = C$, let's use the elimination method to solve the system. We can eliminate s by multiplying both sides of equation (1) by -40 and adding them to the corresponding sides of equation (2):

$$
\begin{array}{rl}
-40s - 40g = -3200 & \text{Multiplying both sides of equation (1) by } -40 \\
\underline{40s + 65g = 3900} & \\
25g = 700 & \text{Adding} \\
g = 28. & \text{Solving for } g
\end{array}
$$

To find s, we substitute 28 for g in equation (1) and solve for s:

$$
\begin{array}{rl}
s + g = 80 & \text{Equation (1)} \\
s + 28 = 80 & \text{Substituting 28 for } g \\
s = 52. & \text{Solving for } s
\end{array}
$$

We obtain $(28, 52)$, or $g = 28$ and $s = 52$.

4. Check. We check in the original problem. Recall that g is the number of gemstone beads and s is the number of silver beads.

Number of beads:	$g + s = 28 + 52 = 80$
Cost of gemstone beads:	$65g = 65 \times 28 = 1820\text{¢}$
Cost of silver beads:	$\underline{40s = 40 \times 52 = 2080\text{¢}}$
	Total $= 3900\text{¢}$

The numbers check.

5. State. The designer bought 28 gemstone beads and 52 sterling silver beads.

YOUR TURN

Example 2 involved two types of items (sterling silver beads and gemstone beads), the quantity of each type bought, and the total value of the items. We refer to this type of problem as a *total-value problem*.

EXAMPLE 3 *Blending Teas.* TeaPots n Treasures sells loose Oolong tea for $2.15 per ounce. Donna mixed Oolong tea with shaved almonds that sell for $0.95 per ounce to create the Market Street Oolong blend that sells for $1.85 per ounce. One week, she made 300 oz of Market Street Oolong. How much tea and how much shaved almonds did Donna use?

SOLUTION

1. **Familiarize.** Since we know the price per ounce of the blend, we can find the total value of the blend by multiplying 300 ounces times $1.85 per ounce. We let $l =$ the number of ounces of Oolong tea and $a =$ the number of ounces of shaved almonds.

2. **Translate.** Since a 300-oz batch was made, we must have

$$l + a = 300.$$

To find a second equation, note that the total value of the 300-oz blend must match the combined value of the separate ingredients:

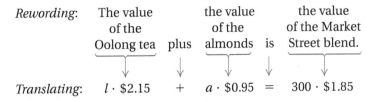

Rewording: The value of the Oolong tea plus the value of the almonds is the value of the Market Street blend.

Translating: $l \cdot \$2.15$ + $a \cdot \$0.95$ = $300 \cdot \$1.85$

These equations can also be obtained from a table.

	Oolong Tea	Almonds	Market Street Blend	
Number of Ounces	l	a	300	$\rightarrow l + a = 300$
Price per Ounce	$2.15	$0.95	$1.85	
Value of Tea	$2.15l	$0.95a	300 · $1.85, or $555	$\rightarrow 2.15l + 0.95a = 555$

Study Skills

Expect to be Challenged

Do not be surprised if your success rate drops some as you work on real-world problems. *This is normal.* Your success rate will increase as you gain experience with these types of problems and use some of the study skills already listed.

3. Refer to Example 3. TeaPots n Treasures also sells loose rooibos tea for $1.50 per ounce. Donna mixed rooibos tea with shaved almonds to create the State Street Rooibos blend that sells for $1.39 per ounce. One week, she made 200 oz of State Street Rooibos. How much tea and how much shaved almonds did Donna use?

Clearing decimals in the second equation, we have $215l + 95a = 55{,}500$. We have translated to a system of equations:

$$l + a = 300, \qquad (1)$$
$$215l + 95a = 55{,}500. \qquad (2)$$

3. **Carry out.** We can solve using substitution. When equation (1) is solved for l, we have $l = 300 - a$. Substituting $300 - a$ for l in equation (2), we find a:

$215(300 - a) + 95a = 55{,}500$	Substituting
$64{,}500 - 215a + 95a = 55{,}500$	Using the distributive law
$-120a = -9000$	Combining like terms; subtracting 64,500 from both sides
$a = 75.$	Dividing both sides by -120

We have $a = 75$ and, from equation (1) above, $l + a = 300$. Thus, $l = 225$.

4. **Check.** Combining 225 oz of Oolong tea and 75 oz of almonds will give a 300-oz blend. The value of 225 oz of Oolong tea is 225($2.15), or $483.75. The value of 75 oz of almonds is 75($0.95), or $71.25. Thus the combined value of the blend is $483.75 + $71.25, or $555. A 300-oz blend priced at $1.85 per ounce would also be worth $555, so our answer checks.

5. **State.** The Market Street blend was made by combining 225 oz of Oolong tea and 75 oz of almonds.

YOUR TURN

EXAMPLE 4 *Student Loans.* Rani's student loans totaled $9600. Part was a PLUS loan made at 7.9% interest, and the rest was a Stafford loan made at 6.8% interest. After one year, Rani's loans accumulated $702.30 in interest. What was the original amount of each loan?

SOLUTION

1. **Familiarize.** We begin with a guess. If $3000 was borrowed at 7.9% and $6600 was borrowed at 6.8%, the two loans would total $9600. The interest would then be 0.079($3000), or $237, and 0.068($6600), or $448.80, for a total of only $685.80 in interest. Our guess was wrong, but checking the guess familiarized us with the problem. More than $3000 was borrowed at the higher rate.

2. Translate. We let $p =$ the amount of the PLUS loan and $s =$ the amount of the Stafford loan. Next, we organize a table in which the entries in each column come from the formula for simple interest:

$$Principal \cdot Rate \cdot Time = Interest.$$

	PLUS Loan	Stafford Loan	Total	
Principal	p	s	$9600	$\longrightarrow p + s = 9600$
Rate of Interest	7.9%	6.8%		
Time	1 year	1 year		
Interest	$0.079p$	$0.068s$	$702.30	$\longrightarrow 0.079p + 0.068s = 702.30$

The total amount borrowed is found in the first row of the table:

$$p + s = 9600.$$

A second equation, representing accumulated interest, is found in the last row:

$$0.079p + 0.068s = 702.30, \quad \text{or} \quad 79p + 68s = 702{,}300. \qquad \text{Clearing decimals}$$

3. Carry out. The system can be solved by elimination:

$$
\begin{aligned}
p + s &= 9600, \quad \longrightarrow \text{Multiplying both} \longrightarrow &-79p - 79s &= -758{,}400 \\
79p + 68s &= 702{,}300 \quad \text{sides by } -79 & \underline{79p + 68s} &= \underline{702{,}300} \\
& & -11s &= -56{,}100 \\
& p + s = 9600 \longleftarrow & s &= 5100 \\
& p + 5100 = 9600 & & \\
& p = 4500. & &
\end{aligned}
$$

We find that $p = 4500$ and $s = 5100$.

4. Refer to Example 4. Chin-Sun's student loans totaled $8400. Part was a PLUS loan at 7.9% interest, and the rest was a Stafford loan at 6.8% interest. After one year, Chin-Sun's loans accumulated $620.70 in interest. What was the original amount of each loan?

4. Check. The total amount borrowed is $4500 + $5100, or $9600. The interest on $4500 at 7.9% for 1 year is $0.079(\$4500)$, or $355.50. The interest on $5100 at 6.8% for 1 year is $0.068(\$5100)$, or $346.80. The total amount of interest is $355.50 + $346.80, or $702.30, so the numbers check.

5. State. The PLUS loan was for $4500, and the Stafford loan was for $5100.

YOUR TURN

Before proceeding to Example 5, briefly scan Examples 2–4 for similarities. Note that in each case, one of the equations in the system is a simple sum while the other equation represents a sum of products. Example 5 continues this pattern with what is commonly called a *mixture problem*.

PROBLEM-SOLVING TIP

When solving a problem, see if it is patterned or modeled after a problem that you have already solved.

EXAMPLE 5 *Mixing Fertilizers.* Nature's Green Gardening, Inc., carries two brands of fertilizer containing nitrogen and water. "Gentle Grow" is 3% nitrogen and "Sun Saver" is 8% nitrogen. Nature's Green needs to combine the two types of solution into a 90-L mixture that is 6% nitrogen. How much of each brand should be used?

SOLUTION

1. **Familiarize.** We must consider not only the size of the mixture, but also its strength.

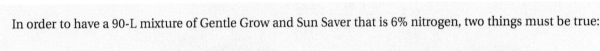
EXPLORING THE CONCEPT

In order to have a 90-L mixture of Gentle Grow and Sun Saver that is 6% nitrogen, two things must be true:

The total amount of the mixture must be 90 L.

The total amount of the nitrogen must be 6% of 90 L, or 5.4 L.

For each mixture illustrated below, find **(a)** the total amount of the mixture and **(b)** the total amount of the nitrogen.

1.

30 L Gentle Grow   60 L Sun Saver   Mixture

2.

10 L Gentle Grow   80 L Sun Saver   Mixture

3.

45 L Gentle Grow   45 L Sun Saver   Mixture

4. Are any of the mixtures illustrated 6% nitrogen?

ANSWERS
1. (a) 90 L; (b) 5.7 L **2.** (a) 90 L; (b) 6.7 L **3.** (a) 90 L; (b) 4.95 L **4.** No

2. **Translate.** We let g = the number of liters of Gentle Grow and s = the number of liters of Sun Saver. The information can be organized in a table.

	Gentle Grow	Sun Saver	Mixture	
Number of Liters	g	s	90	$\longrightarrow g + s = 90$
Percent of Nitrogen	3%	8%	6%	
Amount of Nitrogen	$0.03g$	$0.08s$	0.06×90, or 5.4 liters	$\longrightarrow 0.03g + 0.08s = 5.4$

If we add g and s in the first row, we get one equation. It represents the total amount of mixture: $g + s = 90$.

If we add the amounts of nitrogen listed in the third row, we get a second equation. This equation represents the amount of nitrogen in the mixture: $0.03g + 0.08s = 5.4$.

After clearing decimals, we have translated the problem to the system

$$g + s = 90, \qquad (1)$$
$$3g + 8s = 540. \qquad (2)$$

3. **Carry out.** We use the elimination method to solve the system:

$$
\begin{array}{ll}
-3g - 3s = -270 & \text{Multiplying both sides of equation (1) by } -3 \\
\underline{3g + 8s = 540} & \\
5s = 270 & \text{Adding} \\
s = 54; & \text{Solving for } s \\
g + 54 = 90 & \text{Substituting into equation (1)} \\
g = 36. & \text{Solving for } g
\end{array}
$$

4. **Check.** Remember, g is the number of liters of Gentle Grow and s is the number of liters of Sun Saver.

Total amount of mixture:		$g + s = 36 + 54 = 90$
Total amount of nitrogen:	3% of 36 + 8% of 54	$= 1.08 + 4.32 = 5.4$
Percentage of nitrogen in mixture:	$\dfrac{\text{Total amount of nitrogen}}{\text{Total amount of mixture}}$	$= \dfrac{5.4}{90} = 6\%$

The numbers check in the original problem.

5. **State.** The mixture should contain 36 L of Gentle Grow and 54 L of Sun Saver.

YOUR TURN

5. Refer to Example 5. Nature's Green also carries "Friendly Feed" fertilizer that is 9% nitrogen. How much Friendly Feed and how much Gentle Grow, containing 3% nitrogen, should be combined in order to form a 60-L mixture that is 4% nitrogen?

Motion Problems

When a problem deals with distance, speed (rate), and time, recall the following.

Student Notes

Be sure to remember one of the equations shown in the box at right. You can multiply or divide on both sides, as needed, to obtain the others.

DISTANCE, RATE, AND TIME EQUATIONS

If r represents rate, t represents time, and d represents distance, then:

$$d = rt, \quad r = \frac{d}{t}, \quad \text{and} \quad t = \frac{d}{r}.$$

EXAMPLE 6 *Train Travel.* A Vermont Railways freight train, loaded with logs, leaves Boston, heading to Washington D.C., at a speed of 60 km/h. Two hours later, an Amtrak® Metroliner leaves Boston, bound for Washington D.C., on a parallel track at 90 km/h. At what point will the Metroliner catch up to the freight train?

SOLUTION

1. **Familiarize.** Let's make a guess and check to see if it is correct. Suppose the trains meet after traveling 180 km. We can calculate the time for each train.

	Distance	Rate	Time
Freight Train	180 km	60 km/h	$\frac{180}{60} = 3$ hr
Metroliner	180 km	90 km/h	$\frac{180}{90} = 2$ hr

We see that the distance cannot be 180 km, since the difference in travel times for the trains is *not* 2 hr. Although our guess is wrong, we can use a similar chart to organize the information in this problem.

The distance at which the trains meet is unknown, but we do know that the trains will have traveled the same distance when they meet. We let d = this distance.

The time that the trains are running is also unknown, but we do know that the freight train has a 2-hr head start. Thus if we let t = the number of hours that the freight train is running before they meet, then $t - 2$ is the number of hours that the Metroliner runs before catching up to the freight train.

60 km/h
d kilometers
t hours

90 km/h
d kilometers
t − 2 hours

Trains meet here

2. **Translate.** We can organize the information in a chart. The formula *Distance = Rate · Time* guides our choice of rows and columns.

	Distance	Rate	Time
Freight Train	d	60	t	→ $d = 60t$
Metroliner	d	90	$t - 2$	→ $d = 90(t - 2)$

Student Notes

Always be careful to answer the question asked in the problem. In Example 6, the problem asks for distance, not time. Answering "6 hr" would be incorrect.

6. An Amtrak® Metroliner traveling 90 mph leaves Washington, D.C., 3 hr after a freight train traveling 60 mph. If they travel on parallel tracks, at what point will the Metroliner catch up to the freight train?

Using *Distance = Rate · Time* twice, we get two equations:

$$d = 60t, \qquad (1)$$
$$d = 90(t - 2). \qquad (2)$$

3. **Carry out.** We solve the system using substitution:

$$60t = 90(t - 2) \qquad \text{Substituting } 60t \text{ for } d \text{ in equation (2)}$$
$$60t = 90t - 180$$
$$-30t = -180$$
$$t = 6.$$

The time for the freight train is 6 hr, which means that the time for the Metroliner is $6 - 2$, or 4 hr. Remember that it is distance, not time, that the problem asked for. Thus for $t = 6$, we have $d = 60 \cdot 6 = 360$ km.

4. **Check.** At 60 km/h, the freight train travels $60 \cdot 6$, or 360 km, in 6 hr. At 90 km/h, the Metroliner travels $90 \cdot (6 - 2) = 360$ km in 4 hr. The numbers check.

5. **State.** The Metroliner catches up to the freight train 360 km from Boston.

YOUR TURN

EXAMPLE 7 *Jet Travel.* A Boeing 747-400 jet flies 4 hr west with a 60-mph tailwind. Returning *against* the wind takes 5 hr. Find the speed of the jet with no wind.

SOLUTION

1. **Familiarize.** We imagine the situation and make a drawing. Note that the wind *speeds up* the outbound flight but *slows down* the return flight.

Let's make a guess of 400 mph for the jet's speed if there were no wind. Note that the distances traveled each way must be the same.

Speed with no wind:	400 mph
Speed with the wind:	400 + 60 = 460 mph
Speed against the wind:	400 − 60 = 340 mph
Distance with the wind:	460 · 4 = 1840 mi ⎤
Distance against the wind:	340 · 5 = 1700 mi ⎦ These must match.

Since the distances are not the same, our guess of 400 mph is incorrect.

We let r = the speed, in miles per hour, of the jet in still air. Then $r + 60$ = the jet's speed with the wind and $r − 60$ = the jet's speed against the wind. We also let d = the distance traveled, in miles.

2. **Translate.** The information can be organized in a chart. The distances traveled are the same, so we use *Distance* = *Rate* (or *Speed*) · *Time*. Each row of the chart gives an equation.

	Distance	Rate	Time	
With Wind	d	$r + 60$	4	→ $d = (r + 60)4$
Against Wind	d	$r − 60$	5	→ $d = (r − 60)5$

We now have a system of equations:

$$d = (r + 60)4, \quad (1)$$
$$d = (r − 60)5. \quad (2)$$

3. **Carry out.** We solve the system using substitution:

$(r − 60)5 = (r + 60)4$	Substituting $(r − 60)5$ for d in equation (1)
$5r − 300 = 4r + 240$	Using the distributive law
$r = 540.$	Solving for r

7. A motorboat travels 30 min upstream against a 4-mph current. Returning with the current takes 18 min. Find the speed of the motorboat in still water.

4. Check. When $r = 540$, the speed with the wind is $540 + 60 = 600$ mph, and the speed against the wind is $540 - 60 = 480$ mph. The distance with the wind, $600 \cdot 4 = 2400$ mi, matches the distance into the wind, $480 \cdot 5 = 2400$ mi, so we have a check.

5. State. The speed of the jet with no wind is 540 mph.

YOUR TURN

TIPS FOR SOLVING MOTION PROBLEMS

1. Draw a diagram using an arrow or arrows to represent distance and the direction of each object in motion.
2. Organize the information in a chart.
3. Look for times, distances, or rates that are the same. These often can lead to an equation.
4. Translating to a system of equations allows for the use of two variables. Label the variables carefully.
5. Always make sure that you have answered the question asked.

8.3 EXERCISE SET

FOR EXTRA HELP

MyMathLab® Math XL
PRACTICE   WATCH   READ   REVIEW

Vocabulary and Reading Check

Choose the word from the following list that best completes each statement. Not every word will be used.

difference   distance   mixture
principal   sum   total value

1. If 10 coffee mugs are sold for $8 each, the _____ of the mugs is $80.

2. To find simple interest, multiply the _____ by the rate and the time.

3. To solve a motion problem, we often use the fact that _____ divided by rate equals time.

4. When a boat travels downstream, its speed is the _____ of the speed of the current and the speed of the boat in still water.

Applications

5.–18. *For Exercises 5–18, solve Exercises 41–54, respectively, from Section 8.1.*

19. *Renewable Energy.* In 2010, solar and wind energy generation totaled 1033 trillion Btu's. Wind generated 52 trillion Btu's more than eight times that generated by solar energy. How much was generated by each source?

Source: U.S. Energy Information Administration

20. *Snowmen.* The tallest snowman ever recorded—really a snow *woman* named Olympia—was built by residents of Bethel, Maine, and surrounding towns. Her body and head together made up her total record height of 122 ft. The body was 2 ft longer than 14 times the height of the head. What were the separate heights of Olympia's head and body?

Source: Based on information from *Guinness World Records*

Total-Value Problems and Mixture Problems

21. *College Credits.* Each course at Mt. Regis College is worth either 3 or 4 credits. The members of the men's swim team are taking a total of 48 courses that are worth a total of 155 credits. How many 3-credit courses and how many 4-credit courses are being taken?

22. *College Credits.* Each course at Pease County Community College is worth either 3 or 4 credits. The members of the women's golf team are taking a total of 27 courses that are worth a total of 89 credits. How many 3-credit courses and how many 4-credit courses are being taken?

23. *Recycled Paper.* Staples® recently charged $38.39 per case of regular paper and $44.79 per case of paper made of recycled fibers. Last semester, Valley College Copy Center spent $1106.93 for 27 cases of paper. How many of each type were purchased?

24. *Photocopying.* Quick Copy recently charged 49¢ per page for color copies and 9¢ per page for black-and-white copies. If Shirlee's bill for 90 copies was $12.90, how many copies of each type were made?

25. *Lighting.* The Home Depot® recently sold 23-watt CFL bulbs for $2.50 each and 42-watt CFL bulbs for $8.25 each. If River Memorial Hospital purchased 200 such bulbs for a total of $1305, how many of each type did they purchase?

26. *Office Supplies.* Hancock County Social Services is preparing materials for a seminar. They purchase a combination of 80 large binders and small binders. The large binders cost $8.49 each and the small ones cost $5.99 each. If the total cost of the binders was $544.20, how many of each size were purchased?

27. *Museum Admission.* The Indianapolis Children's Museum charges $12.50 for a one-day youth admission and $17.50 for a one-day adult admission. One Friday, the museum collected $1535 from a total of 110 youths and adults. How many admissions of each type were sold?

28. *Amusement Park Admission.* Cedar Point Amusement Park charges $51.99 for an adult admission and $26.99 for a junior admission. One Thursday, the park collected $15,591.40 from a total of 360 adults and juniors. How many admissions of each type were sold?

Aha! **29.** *Blending Coffees.* The Roasted Bean charges $17.00 per pound for Fair Trade Organic Mexican coffee and $15.00 per pound for Fair Trade Organic Peruvian coffee. How much of each type should be used to make a 28-lb blend that sells for $16.00 per pound?

30. *Mixed Nuts.* Oh Nuts! sells pistachio kernels for $10.00 per pound and almonds for $8.00 per pound. How much of each type should be used to make a 50-lb mixture that sells for $8.80 per pound?

31. *Event Planning.* As part of the refreshments for Yvette's 25th birthday party, Kim plans to provide a bowl of M&M candies. She wants to mix custom-printed M&Ms costing 60¢ per ounce with bulk M&Ms costing 25¢ per ounce to create 20 lb of a mixture costing 32¢ per ounce. How much of each type of M&M should she use?

Source: www.mymms.com

32. *Blending Spices.* Spice of Life sells ground sumac for $1.35 per ounce and ground thyme for $1.85 per ounce. Aman wants to make a 20-oz Zahtar seasoning blend using the two spices that sells for $1.65 per ounce. How much of each spice should Aman use?

33. *Catering.* Cati's Catering is planning an office reception. The office administrator has requested a candy mixture that is 25% chocolate. Cati has available mixtures that are either 50% chocolate or 10% chocolate. How much of each type should be mixed to get a 20-lb mixture that is 25% chocolate?

34. *Ink Remover.* Etch Clean Graphics uses one cleanser that is 25% acid and a second that is 50% acid. How many liters of each should be mixed to get 30 L of a solution that is 40% acid?

35. *Blending Granola.* Deep Thought Granola is 25% nuts and dried fruit. Oat Dream Granola is 10% nuts and dried fruit. How much of Deep Thought and how much of Oat Dream should be mixed to form a 20-lb batch of granola that is 19% nuts and dried fruit?

36. *Livestock Feed.* Soybean meal is 16% protein and corn meal is 9% protein. How many pounds of each should be mixed to get a 350-lb mixture that is 12% protein?

37. *Student Loans.* Stacey's two student loans totaled $12,000. One of her loans was at 6.5% simple interest and the other at 7.2%. After one year, Stacey owed $811.50 in interest. What was the amount of each loan?

38. *Investments.* A self-employed contractor nearing retirement made two investments totaling $15,000. In one year, these investments yielded $573 in simple interest. Part of the money was invested at 3% and the rest at 4.5%. How much was invested at each rate?

39. *Automotive Maintenance.* "Steady State" antifreeze is 18% alcohol and "Even Flow" is 10% alcohol. How many liters of each should be mixed to get 20 L of a mixture that is 15% alcohol?

40. *Chemistry.* E-Chem Testing has a solution that is 80% base and another that is 30% base. A technician needs 150 L of a solution that is 62% base. The 150 L will be prepared by mixing the two solutions on hand. How much of each should be used?

41. *Octane Ratings.* The octane rating of a gasoline is a measure of the amount of isooctane in a gallon of gas. Manufacturers recommend using 93-octane gasoline on retuned motors. How much 87-octane gas and how much 95-octane gas should Yousef mix in order to make 10 gal of 93-octane gas for his retuned Ford F-150?

Source: Champlain Electric and Petroleum Equipment

42. *Octane Ratings.* The octane rating of a gasoline is a measure of the amount of isooctane in a gallon of gas. Subaru recommends 91-octane gasoline for the 2008 Legacy 3.0 R. How much 87-octane gas and how much 93-octane gas should Kelsey mix in order to make 12 gal of 91-octane gas for her Legacy?

Sources: Champlain Electric and Petroleum Equipment; Dean Team Ballwin

43. *Food Science.* The following bar graph shows the milk fat percentages in three dairy products.

How many pounds each of whole milk and cream should be mixed to form 200 lb of milk for cream cheese?

Milk fat

44. *Food Science.* How much lowfat milk (1% fat) and how much whole milk (4% fat) should be mixed to make 5 gal of reduced fat milk (2% fat)?

Motion Problems

45. *Train Travel.* A train leaves Danville Union and travels north at 75 km/h. Two hours later, an express train leaves on a parallel track and travels north at 125 km/h. How far from the station will they meet?

46. *Car Travel.* Two cars leave Salt Lake City, traveling in opposite directions. One car travels at a speed of 80 km/h and the other at 96 km/h. In how many hours will they be 528 km apart?

47. *Canoeing.* Kahla paddled for 4 hr with a 6-km/h current to reach a campsite. The return trip against the same current took 10 hr. Find the speed of Kahla's canoe in still water.

48. *Boating.* Chen's motorboat took 3 hr to make a trip downstream with a 6-mph current. The return trip against the same current took 5 hr. Find the speed of the boat in still water.

49. *Point of No Return.* A plane flying the 3458-mi trip from New York City to London has a 50-mph tailwind. The flight's *point of no return* is the point at which the flight time required to return to New York is the same as the time required to continue to London. If the speed of the plane in still air is 360 mph, how far is New York from the point of no return?

50. *Point of No Return.* A plane is flying the 2553-mi trip from Los Angeles to Honolulu into a 60-mph headwind. If the speed of the plane in still air is 310 mph, how far from Los Angeles is the plane's point of no return? (See Exercise 49.)

Applications

51. *Architecture.* The rectangular ground floor of the John Hancock building has a perimeter of 860 ft. The length is 100 ft more than the width. Find the length and the width.

$x + 100$

x

52. *Real Estate.* The perimeter of a rectangular ocean-front lot is 190 m. The width is one-fourth of the length. Find the dimensions.

53. By February 2012, Nintendo had sold one and one-half as many Wii game machines worldwide as Sony had sold PlayStation 3 consoles. Together, they had sold 154 million game machines. How many of each were sold?

Source: vgchartz.com

54. *Hockey Rankings.* Hockey teams receive 2 points for a win and 1 point for a tie. The Wildcats once won a championship with 60 points. They won 9 more games than they tied. How many wins and how many ties did the Wildcats have?

55. At one time, Netflix offered members an unlimited number of movies and television episodes streamed to their TVs and computers for $7.99 per month. For $7.99 more per month, Netflix offered an unlimited one DVD-at-a-time by mail rental plan in addition to the unlimited streaming. During one week, 280 new subscribers paid a total of $2956.30 for their plans. How many $7.99 plans and how many $15.98 plans were purchased?

56. *Radio Airplay.* Akio must play 12 commercials during his 1-hr radio show. Each commercial is either 30 sec or 60 sec long. If the total commercial time during that hour is 10 min, how many commercials of each type does Akio play?

57. *Making Change.* Monica buys a $9.25 book using a $20 bill. The store has no bills and gives change in quarters and fifty-cent pieces. There are 30 coins in all. How many of each kind are there?

58. *Teller Work.* Sabina goes to a bank and changes a $50 bill for $5 bills and $1 bills. There are 22 bills in all. How many of each kind are there?

59. In what ways are Examples 3 and 4 similar? In what sense are their systems of equations similar?

60. Write at least three study tips of your own for someone beginning this exercise set.

Skill Review

Let $h(x) = x - 7$ and $f(x) = x^2 + 2$. Find the following.

61. $h(0)$ [7.1]

62. $f(-10)$ [7.1]

63. $(h \cdot f)(7)$ [7.4]

64. $(h + f)(x)$ [7.4]

65. The domain of $h + f$ [7.4]

66. The domain of f/h [7.4]

Synthesis

67. Suppose that in Example 3 you are asked only for the amount of almonds needed for the Market Street blend. Would the method of solving the problem change? Why or why not?

68. Write a problem similar to Example 2 for a classmate to solve. Design the problem so that the solution is "The bakery sold 24 loaves of bread and 18 packages of sandwich rolls."

69. *Recycled Paper.* Unable to purchase 60 reams of paper that contains 20% post-consumer fiber, the Naylor School bought paper that was either 0% post-consumer fiber or 30% post-consumer fiber. How many reams of each should be purchased in order to use the same amount of post-consumer fiber as if the 20% post-consumer fiber paper were available?

70. *Automotive Maintenance.* The radiator in Natalie's car contains 6.3 L of antifreeze and water. This mixture is 30% antifreeze. How much of this mixture should she drain and replace with pure antifreeze so that there will be a mixture of 50% antifreeze?

71. *Metal Alloys.* For a metal to be labeled "sterling silver," the silver alloy must contain at least 92.5% pure silver. Nicole has 32 oz of coin silver, which is 90% pure silver. How much pure silver must she add to the coin silver in order to have a sterling-silver alloy?

Source: *The Jewelry Repair Manual*, R. Allen Hardy, Courier Dover Publications, 1996, p. 271.

72. *Exercise.* Huan jogs and walks to school each day. She averages 4 km/h walking and 8 km/h jogging. From home to school is 6 km and Huan makes the trip in 1 hr. How far does she jog in a trip?

73. *Bakery.* Gigi's Cupcakes offers a gift box with six cupcakes for $15.99. Gigi's also sells cupcakes individually for $3 each. Gigi's sold a total of 256 cupcakes one Saturday for a total of $701.67 in sales (excluding tax). How many six-cupcake gift boxes were included in that day's sales total?

74. The tens digit of a two-digit positive integer is 2 more than three times the units digit. If the digits are interchanged, the new number is 13 less than half the given number. Find the given integer. (*Hint:* Let x = the tens-place digit and y = the units-place digit; then $10x + y$ is the number.)

75. *Wood Stains.* Williams' Custom Flooring has 0.5 gal of stain that is 20% brown and 80% neutral. A customer orders 1.5 gal of a stain that is 60% brown and 40% neutral. How much pure brown stain and how much neutral stain should be added to the original 0.5 gal in order to make up the order?*

76. *Train Travel.* A train leaves Union Station for Central Station, 216 km away, at 9 A.M. One hour later, a train leaves Central Station for Union Station. They meet at noon. If the second train had started at 9 A.M. and the first train at 10:30 A.M., they would still have met at noon. Find the speed of each train.

77. *Fuel Economy.* Grady's station wagon gets 18 miles per gallon (mpg) in city driving and 24 mpg in highway driving. The car is driven 465 mi on 23 gal of gasoline. How many miles were driven in the city and how many were driven on the highway?

78. *Biochemistry.* Industrial biochemists routinely use a machine to mix a buffer of 10% acetone by adding 100% acetone to water. One day, instead of adding 5 L of acetone to a vat of water to create the buffer, a machine added 10 L. How much additional water was needed to bring the concentration down to 10%?

 79. See Exercise 75 above. Let x = the amount of pure brown stain added to the original 0.5 gal. Find a function $P(x)$ that can be used to determine the percentage of brown stain in the 1.5-gal mixture. On a graphing calculator, draw the graph of P and use INTERSECT to confirm the answer to Exercise 75.

80. *Siblings.* Fred and Phyllis are twins. Phyllis has twice as many brothers as she has sisters. Fred has the same number of brothers as sisters. How many girls and how many boys are in the family?

YOUR TURN ANSWERS: SECTION 8.3

1. Endangered species: 15; threatened species: 10
2. Silver beads: 36; gemstone beads: 24   **3.** Rooibos: 160 oz; almonds: 40 oz   **4.** PLUS loan: $4500; Stafford loan: $3900   **5.** Friendly Feed: 10 L; Gentle Grow: 50 L
6. 540 mi from Washington D.C.   **7.** 16 mph

QUICK QUIZ: SECTIONS 8.1–8.3

Solve. If a system has an infinite number of solutions, use set-builder notation to write the solution set. If a system has no solution, state this. [8.1], [8.2]

1. $x - 2y = 7,$
$\quad x = 2y - 5$

2. $3x - 4y = 11,$
$\quad x + 4y = 12$

3. $y = 2x - 4,$
$\quad y = \frac{1}{2}x + 2$

4. $\quad x + 3y = 3,$
$\quad 2x + 5y = 6$

5. In order to raise funds for a concert tour, Arie's choir sold rolls of trash bags. Large trash bags sold for $17 per roll and small trash bags sold for $12 per roll. If Arie sold 28 rolls and collected $441, how many rolls of each type of trash bag did he sell? [8.3]

PREPARE TO MOVE ON

Evaluate. [4.7]

1. $2x - 3y - z$, for $x = 5$, $y = 2$, and $z = 3$

2. $4x + y - 6z$, for $x = \frac{1}{2}$, $y = \frac{1}{2}$, and $z = \frac{1}{3}$

3. $3a - b + 2c$, for $a = 1$, $b = -6$, and $c = 4$

4. $a - 2b - 3c$, for $a = -2$, $b = 3$, and $c = -5$

---

*This problem was suggested by Professor Chris Burditt of Yountville, California, and is based on a real-world situation.

Elementary Algebra Review

This chapter is a review of the first six chapters of this text. Each section corresponds to a chapter of the text. For further explanation of the topics in this chapter, refer to the section or pages referenced in the index at the end of each section.

R.1 Introduction to Algebraic Expressions

The Real Numbers • Operations on Real Numbers • Algebraic Expressions

The Real Numbers

SETS OF NUMBERS

Natural numbers: $\{1, 2, 3, \ldots\}$

Whole numbers: $\{0, 1, 2, 3, \ldots\}$

Integers: $\{\ldots, -3, -2, -1, 0, 1, 2, 3, \ldots\}$

Rational numbers: $\left\{\dfrac{a}{b} \middle| a \text{ and } b \text{ are integers and } b \neq 0\right\}$

Rational numbers can always be written as **terminating** decimals or **repeating** decimals. **Irrational numbers**, like $\sqrt{2}$ or π, can be thought of as nonterminating, nonrepeating decimals. The set of **real numbers** consists of all rational numbers and irrational numbers, taken together.

Real numbers can be represented by points on the number line.

We can compare, or **order**, real numbers by their graphs on the number line. For any two numbers, the number to the left is less than the number to the right. To compare numbers, we use the symbols $>$ (is greater than), $<$ (is less than), $\geq$ (is greater than or equal to), or $\leq$ (is less than or equal to).

EXAMPLE 1 Use either $<$ or $>$ for ▮ to write a true sentence.

a) -12 ▮ 5 **b)** -3 ▮ -7

SOLUTION

1. Use either $<$ or $>$ for ▮ to write a true sentence:

-0.1 ▮ 0.

a) Since -12 is to the left of 5 on the number line, we know that -12 is less than 5, so $-12 < 5$.

b) Since -3 is to the right of -7 on the number line, we have $-3 > -7$.

YOUR TURN

The distance of a number from 0 is called the **absolute value** of the number. The notation $|-4|$ represents the absolute value of -4. The absolute value of a number is never negative.

EXAMPLE 2 Find the absolute value: **(a)** $|-4|$; **(b)** $\left|\frac{11}{3}\right|$; **(c)** $|0|$.

SOLUTION

2. Find the absolute value:

$|287|$.

a) $|-4| = 4$ since -4 is 4 units from 0.

b) $\left|\frac{11}{3}\right| = \frac{11}{3}$ since $\frac{11}{3}$ is $\frac{11}{3}$ units from 0.

c) $|0| = 0$ since 0 is 0 units from itself.

YOUR TURN

Operations on Real Numbers

> **RULES FOR ADDITION OF REAL NUMBERS**
>
> 1. *Positive numbers*: Add as usual. The answer is positive.
> 2. *Negative numbers*: Add absolute values and make the answer negative.
> 3. *A positive number and a negative number*: Subtract the smaller absolute value from the greater absolute value. Then:
>   **a)** If the positive number has the greater absolute value, the answer is positive.
>   **b)** If the negative number has the greater absolute value, the answer is negative.
>   **c)** If the numbers have the same absolute value, the answer is 0.
> 4. *One number is zero*: The sum is the other number.

Every real number has an **opposite**. The opposite of -6 is 6, the opposite of 3.7 is -3.7, and the opposite of 0 is itself. When opposites are added, the result is 0. Finding the opposite of a number is often called "changing its sign."

Subtraction of real numbers is defined in terms of addition and opposites.

> **SUBTRACTION OF REAL NUMBERS**
>
> To subtract, add the opposite of the number being subtracted.

The rules for multiplication and division of real numbers can be stated together.

RULES FOR MULTIPLICATION AND DIVISION

To multiply or divide two nonzero real numbers:

1. Using the absolute values, multiply or divide, as indicated.
2. If the signs are the same, the answer is positive.
3. If the signs are different, the answer is negative.

EXAMPLE 3   Perform the indicated operations.

a) $-13 + (-9)$ **b)** $-\frac{4}{5} + \frac{1}{10}$ **c)** $-6 - (-7.3)$

d) $3(-1.5)$ **e)** $\left(-\frac{4}{9}\right) \div \left(-\frac{2}{5}\right)$

SOLUTION

a) $-13 + (-9) = -22$ Adding two negatives. *Think*: Add the absolute values, 13 and 9, to get 22. Make the answer *negative*, -22.

b) $-\frac{4}{5} + \frac{1}{10} = -\frac{8}{10} + \frac{1}{10} = -\frac{7}{10}$ Adding a negative and a positive. *Think*: The difference of absolute values is $\frac{8}{10} - \frac{1}{10}$, or $\frac{7}{10}$. The negative number has the larger absolute value, so the answer is *negative*, $-\frac{7}{10}$.

c) $-6 - (-7.3) = -6 + 7.3 = 1.3$ Subtracting. *Think*: Change the subtraction to addition. Add the opposite of -7.3.

d) $3(-1.5) = -4.5$ Multiplying. *Think*: $3(1.5) = 4.5$. The signs are different, so the answer is negative.

e) $\left(-\frac{4}{9}\right) \div \left(-\frac{2}{5}\right) = \left(-\frac{4}{9}\right) \cdot \left(-\frac{5}{2}\right)$ Dividing. *Think*: Multiply by the reciprocal of $-\frac{2}{5}$. The answer is positive.

$\quad\quad\quad\quad = \frac{20}{18} = \frac{10}{9} \cdot \frac{2}{2} = \frac{10}{9}$

3. Perform the indicated operation: $-10 - 15$.

YOUR TURN

Addition, subtraction, and multiplication are defined for all real numbers, but we cannot **divide by 0**. For example, $\frac{0}{3} = 0 \div 3 = 0$, but $\frac{3}{0} = 3 \div 0$ is **undefined**.

A product like $2 \cdot 2 \cdot 2 \cdot 2$, in which the **factors** are the same, is called a **power**. Powers are often written using **exponential notation**:

$\quad\quad 2 \cdot 2 \cdot 2 \cdot 2 = 2^4.$ ← There are 4 factors; 4 is the *exponent*.

$\quad\quad\quad\quad\quad\quad$ 2 is the *base*.

A number raised to an exponent of 1 is the number itself; for example, $3^1 = 3$.

An expression containing a series of operations is not necessarily evaluated from left to right. Instead, we perform the operations according to the following rules.

RULES FOR ORDER OF OPERATIONS

1. Calculate within the innermost grouping symbols, ( ), [ ], { }, | |, and above or below fraction bars.
2. Simplify all exponential expressions.
3. Perform all multiplications and divisions, working from left to right.
4. Perform all additions and subtractions, working from left to right.

EXAMPLE 4   Simplify: $3 - [(4 \times 5) + 12 \div 2^3 \times 6] + 5$.

SOLUTION

$$3 - [(4 \times 5) + 12 \div 2^3 \times 6] + 5$$

$$= 3 - [20 + 12 \div 2^3 \times 6] + 5 \qquad \text{Doing the calculations in the innermost parentheses first}$$

$$= 3 - [20 + 12 \div 8 \times 6] + 5 \qquad \text{Working inside the brackets; evaluating } 2^3$$

$$= 3 - [20 + 1.5 \times 6] + 5 \qquad 12 \div 8 \text{ is the first multiplication or division working from left to right.}$$

$$= 3 - [20 + 9] + 5 \qquad \text{Multiplying}$$

$$= 3 - 29 + 5 \qquad \text{Completing the calculations within the brackets}$$

$$= -26 + 5 \Big\} \qquad \text{Adding and subtracting from left to right}$$

$$= -21$$

4. Simplify:

$2 - 4[5 - (1 + 10 \div 5 \cdot 2)] + 4^2$.

YOUR TURN

Algebraic Expressions

In an **algebraic expression** like $2xt^3$, the number 2 is a **constant** and x and t are **variables**. Algebraic expressions containing variables can be **evaluated** by **substituting** a number for each variable in the expression and following the rules for order of operations.

EXAMPLE 5   The perimeter P of a rectangle of length l and width w is given by the formula $P = 2l + 2w$. Find the perimeter when l is 16 in. and w is 7.5 in.

SOLUTION   We evaluate, substituting 16 in. for l and 7.5 in. for w and carrying out the operations:

Substitute.

Carry out the operations.

$$P = 2l + 2w$$
$$= 2 \cdot 16 + 2 \cdot 7.5$$
$$= 32 + 15$$
$$= 47 \text{ in.}$$

YOUR TURN

5. Use the formula in Example 5 to find the perimeter of a rectangle when l is 5 m and w is 2 m.

Expressions that represent the same number are said to be **equivalent**. The laws that follow provide methods for writing equivalent expressions.

LAWS AND PROPERTIES OF REAL NUMBERS	
Commutative laws:	$a + b = b + a$; $ab = ba$
Associative laws:	$a + (b + c) = (a + b) + c$; $a(bc) = (ab)c$
Distributive law:	$a(b + c) = ab + ac$
Identity property of 1:	$1 \cdot a = a \cdot 1 = a$
Identity property of 0:	$a + 0 = 0 + a = a$
Law of opposites:	$a + (-a) = 0$
Multiplicative property of 0:	$0 \cdot a = a \cdot 0 = 0$
Property of -1:	$-1 \cdot a = -a$
Opposite of a sum:	$-(a + b) = -a + (-b)$
Opposites in fractions:	$\dfrac{-a}{b} = \dfrac{a}{-b} = -\dfrac{a}{b}$; $\dfrac{-a}{-b} = \dfrac{a}{b}$

The distributive law can be used to multiply and to **factor** expressions. We factor an expression when we write an equivalent expression that is a product.

EXAMPLE 6   Write an equivalent expression as indicated.

a) Multiply: $-2(5x - 3)$.   **b)** Factor: $5x + 10y + 5$.

SOLUTION

a) $-2(5x - 3) = -2(5x + (-3))$ Adding the opposite

$\qquad\qquad\qquad = -2 \cdot 5x + (-2) \cdot (-3)$ Using the distributive law

$\qquad\qquad\qquad = (-2 \cdot 5)x + 6$ Using the associative law for multiplication

$\qquad\qquad\qquad = -10x + 6$

b) $5x + 10y + 5 = 5 \cdot x + 5 \cdot 2y + 5 \cdot 1$ The common factor is 5.

$\qquad\qquad\qquad\quad = 5(x + 2y + 1)$ Using the distributive law

Factoring can be checked by multiplying:

$$5(x + 2y + 1) = 5 \cdot x + 5 \cdot 2y + 5 \cdot 1 = 5x + 10y + 5.$$

6. Factor: $7 + 14m + 70x$.

YOUR TURN

The **terms** of an algebraic expression are separated by plus signs. When two terms have variable factors that are exactly the same, the terms are called **like**, or **similar**, **terms**. The distributive law enables us to **combine**, or **collect**, **like terms**.

EXAMPLE 7   Combine like terms: $-5m + 3n - 4n + 10m$.

SOLUTION

$-5m + 3n - 4n + 10m$

$\quad = -5m + 3n + (-4n) + 10m$ Rewriting as addition

$\quad = -5m + 10m + 3n + (-4n)$ Using the commutative law of addition

$\quad = (-5 + 10)m + (3 + (-4))n$ Using the distributive law

$\quad = 5m + (-n)$

$\quad = 5m - n$ Rewriting as subtraction

7. Combine like terms:

$2 - x - 6x - 9$.

YOUR TURN

We can also use the distributive law to help simplify algebraic expressions containing parentheses.

EXAMPLE 8   Simplify: **(a)** $4x - (y - 2x)$; **(b)** $3(t + 2) - 6(t - 1)$.

SOLUTION

a) $4x - (y - 2x) = 4x - y + 2x$ Removing parentheses and changing the sign of every term

$\qquad\qquad\qquad = 6x - y$ Combining like terms

b) $3(t + 2) - 6(t - 1) = 3t + 6 - 6t + 6$ Multiplying each term of $t + 2$ by 3 and each term of $t - 1$ by -6

$\qquad\qquad\qquad\qquad\quad = -3t + 12$ Combining like terms

8. Simplify:

$5x - 2(4x - 7) + 10$.

YOUR TURN

Certain word phrases can be translated to algebraic expressions. These in turn can often be used to translate problems to equations.

EXAMPLE 9 *Energy Use.* Translate the following problem to an equation. Do not solve.

The average energy use of food-service buildings is 51 Btu per square foot. This is three times the energy use of buildings providing lodging. What is the energy use per square foot of buildings providing lodging?

Source: Energy Information Administration

SOLUTION   We let c represent the energy use per square foot of a building providing lodging. We then reword the problem to make the translation more direct.

Rewording: 3   times   lodging energy use   is   51.

Translating: 3   · c =   51

9. Translate the following problem to an equation. Do not solve. Charron paid $285 for season passes to all the home college games. This was five times what she paid for her parking pass. How much did she pay for her parking pass?

YOUR TURN

R.1   EXERCISE SET

FOR EXTRA HELP

MyMathLab® Math XL
PRACTICE   WATCH   READ   REVIEW

The Real Numbers

Use either < or > for ▇ to write a true sentence.

1. 8 ▇ −16

2. −7 ▇ 1

3. −6.1 ▇ −1.3

4. −4.2 ▇ −10.7

5. 0 ▇ −15

6. −98 ▇ 0

Find each absolute value.

7. $|22|$

8. $\left|\frac{11}{4}\right|$

9. $|-1.3|$

10. $|-105|$

Operations on Real Numbers

Simplify.

11. $(-14) + (-11)$

12. $3 - (-2)$

13. $-\frac{1}{3} - \frac{2}{5}$

14. $\frac{3}{8} \div \frac{3}{5}$

15. $4.2 - 10.7$

16. $(-1.3)(2.8)$

17. $-9 + 0$

18. $\left(-\frac{1}{2}\right) + \frac{1}{8}$

19. $0 \div (-10)$

20. $0 - 32$

21. $\left(-\frac{3}{10}\right) + \left(-\frac{1}{5}\right)$

22. $\left(-\frac{4}{7}\right)\left(\frac{7}{4}\right)$

23. $-3.8 + 9.6$

24. $-0.01 + 1$

25. $(-12) \div 4$

26. $(-87)(0)$

27. $32 - (-7)$

28. $-100 + 35$

29. $(-10)(-17.5)$

30. $-10 - 2.68$

31. $(-68) + 36$

32. $175 \div (-25)$

33. $2 + (-3) + 7 + 10$

34. $-5 + (-15) + 13 + (-1)$

35. $3 \cdot (-2) \cdot (-1) \cdot (-1)$

36. $(-6) \cdot (-5) \cdot (-4) \cdot (-3) \cdot (-2) \cdot (-1)$

37. $(-1)^4 + 2^3$

38. $(-1)^5 + 2^4$

39. $2 \times 6 - 3 \times 5$

40. $12 \div 4 + 15 \div 3$

41. $3 - (11 + 2 \cdot 4)$

42. $3 - 11 + 2 \cdot 4$

43. $4 \cdot 5^2$

44. $7 \cdot 2^3$

45. $25 - 8 \times 3 + 1$

46. $12 - 16 \times 5 + 4$

47. $2 - (3^3 + 16 \div (-2)^3)$

48. $-7 - (8 + 10 \cdot 2^2)$

49. $|6(-3)| + |(-2)(-9)|$

50. $3 - |2 - 7 + 4|$

51. $\dfrac{7000 + (-10)^3}{10^2 \times (2 + 4)}$

52. $\dfrac{3 - 2 \times 6 - 5}{2(3 + 7)^2}$

53. $2 + 8 \div 2 \times 2$

54. $2 + 8 \div (2 \times 2)$

Algebraic Expressions

Evaluate.

55. $y - x$, for $x = 10$ and $y = 3$

56. $n - 2m$, for $m = 6$ and $n = 11$

57. $-3 - x^2 + 12x$, for $x = 5$

58. $14 + (y - 5)^2 - 12 \div y$, for $y = -2$

59. The area of a parallelogram with base b and height h is bh. Find the area of the parallelogram when the height is 3.5 cm and the base is 8 cm.

60. The area of a triangle with base b and height h is $\frac{1}{2}bh$. Find the area of the triangle when the height is 2 in. and the base is 6.2 in.

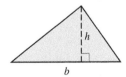

Multiply.

61. $4(2x + 7)$

62. $3(5y + 1)$

63. $-2(15 - 3x)$

64. $-7(3x - 5)$

65. $2(4a + 6b - 3c)$

66. $5(8p + q - 5r)$

67. $-3(2x - y + z)$

68. $-10(-6 - y - z)$

Factor.

69. $8x + 6y$

70. $7p + 14q$

71. $3 + 3w$

72. $4x + 4y$

73. $10x + 50y + 100$

74. $81p + 27q + 9$

Combine like terms.

75. $3p - 2p$

76. $4x + 3x$

77. $4m + 10 - 5m + 12$

78. $3a - 4b - b - 6a$

79. $-6x + 7 + x$

80. $16r + (-7r) + 3s$

Remove parentheses and simplify.

81. $2p - (7 - 4p)$

82. $4r - (3r + 5)$

83. $6x + 5y - 7(x - y)$

84. $14m - 6(2n - 3m) + n$

85. $6[2a + 4(a - 2b)]$

86. $2[2a + 1 - (3a - 6)]$

87. $3 - 2[5(x - 10y) - (3 + 2y)]$

88. $7 - 4[2(3 - 2x) - 5(4x - 3)]$

Translate each problem to an equation. Do not solve.

89. Three times what number is 348?

90. What number added to 256 is 113?

91. *Coca-Cola® Consumption.* The average U.S. citizen consumes 412 servings of Coca-Cola beverages each year. This is 5.15 times the international average. What is the international per capita consumption of Coca-Cola beverages?

Source: thecoca-colacompany.com

92. *Vegetable Production.* It takes 42 gal of water to produce 1 lb of broccoli. This is twice the amount of water used to produce 1 lb of lettuce. How many gallons of water does it take to produce 1 lb of lettuce?

93. *Breakfast Calories.* International House of Pancakes strawberry banana French toast contains 1060 calories. This is 20 more calories than 2 orders of McDonald's hotcakes and sausage provide. How many calories are in an order of McDonald's hotcakes and sausage?

Source: www.calorieking.com

94. *University Revenue.* In 2009, public university revenue was approximately $36,000 per student. This was $4000 more than four times the tuition revenue per student. What was the tuition revenue per student?

Source: www.freeby50.com

YOUR TURN ANSWERS: SECTION R.1

1. $<$ **2.** 287 **3.** -25 **4.** 18 **5.** 14 m
6. $7(1 + 2m + 10x)$ **7.** $-7x - 7$ **8.** $-3x + 24$
9. Let p represent what Charron paid for her parking pass; $285 = 5p$

REFERENCES

Absolute value, p. 34
Addition, Section 1.5
Algebraic expression, p. 2
Combine like terms, p. 41
Constant, p. 2
Division, Section 1.7
Division by 0, p. 56
Equivalent expressions, p. 12
Evaluate, p. 2
Exponential notation, p. 60
Factor, pp. 14, 16
Irrational numbers, p. 31
Multiplication, Section 1.7
Opposite, p. 44
Order, p. 33
Order of operations, p. 61
Real numbers, p. 32
Repeating decimals, p. 30
Sets of real numbers, Section 1.4
Substitute, p. 2
Subtraction, Section 1.6
Terminating decimals, p. 30
Terms, p. 16
Translating to algebraic expressions, p. 3
Translating to equations, p. 5
Variable, p. 2

R.2   Equations, Inequalities, and Problem Solving

Solving Equations and Formulas   ▪   Solving Inequalities   ▪   Problem Solving

Solving Equations and Formulas

Any replacement for the variable in an equation that makes the equation true is called a *solution* of the equation. To **solve** an equation means to find all of its solutions.

We use the following principles to write equations with the same solutions, called **equivalent equations**.

THE ADDITION AND MULTIPLICATION PRINCIPLES FOR EQUATIONS

The Addition Principle

For any real numbers a, b, and c,

$$a = b \quad \text{is equivalent to} \quad a + c = b + c.$$

The Multiplication Principle

For any real numbers a, b, and c, with $c \neq 0$,

$$a = b \quad \text{is equivalent to} \quad a \cdot c = b \cdot c.$$

To solve $x + a = b$ for x, we add $-a$ to (or subtract a from) both sides. To solve $ax = b$ for x, we multiply both sides by $\dfrac{1}{a}$ (or divide both sides by a).

To solve an equation like $-3x - 10 = 14$, we first isolate the variable term, $-3x$, using the addition principle. Then we use the multiplication principle to get the variable by itself.

EXAMPLE 1   Solve: $-3x - 10 = 14$.

SOLUTION

$$-3x - 10 = 14$$

$$-3x - 10 + 10 = 14 + 10 \qquad \text{Using the addition principle:}$$
$$\text{Adding 10 to both sides}$$

Isolate the x-term. $-3x = 24$ Simplifying

$$\frac{-3x}{-3} = \frac{24}{-3} \qquad \text{Dividing both sides by } -3$$

Isolate x. $x = -8$ Simplifying

Check:
$$\begin{array}{c|c} -3x - 10 = 14 \\ \hline -3(-8) - 10 & 14 \\ 24 - 10 & \\ 14 \stackrel{?}{=} 14 & \text{TRUE} \end{array}$$

The solution is -8.

1. Solve: $5 + 2x = 4$.

↩ YOUR TURN

Equations are generally easier to solve when they do not contain fractions. In general, the easiest way to clear an equation of fractions is to multiply *every term on both sides* of the equation by the least common denominator.

EXAMPLE 2 Solve: $\frac{5}{2} - \frac{1}{6}t = \frac{2}{3}$.

SOLUTION The number 6 is the least common denominator, so we multiply both sides by 6.

$$\frac{5}{2} - \frac{1}{6}t = \frac{2}{3}$$

$$6\left(\frac{5}{2} - \frac{1}{6}t\right) = 6 \cdot \frac{2}{3} \qquad \text{Multiplying both sides by 6}$$

$$6 \cdot \frac{5}{2} - 6 \cdot \frac{1}{6}t = 6 \cdot \frac{2}{3} \qquad \text{Using the distributive law. Be sure to multiply every term by 6.}$$

$$15 - t = 4 \qquad \text{The fractions are cleared.}$$

$$15 - t - 15 = 4 - 15 \qquad \text{Subtracting 15 from both sides}$$

$$-t = -11 \qquad \begin{aligned}15 - t - 15 &= 15 + (-t) + (-15) \\ &= -t + 15 + (-15) = -t\end{aligned}$$

$$(-1)(-t) = (-1)(-11) \qquad \text{Multiplying both sides by } -1 \text{ to change the sign}$$

$$t = 11$$

Check:
$$\frac{5}{2} - \frac{1}{6}t = \frac{2}{3}$$

$$\begin{array}{c|c} \frac{5}{2} - \frac{1}{6}(11) & \frac{2}{3} \\ \frac{5}{2} - \frac{11}{6} & \\ \frac{15}{6} - \frac{11}{6} & \\ \frac{2}{3} \overset{?}{=} \frac{2}{3} & \text{TRUE} \end{array}$$

The solution is 11.

2. Solve: $\dfrac{x}{4} - 2 = \dfrac{1}{5}$.

YOUR TURN

To solve equations that contain parentheses, we can use the distributive law to first remove the parentheses. If like terms appear in an equation, we combine them and then solve.

EXAMPLE 3 Solve: $1 - 3(4 - x) = 2(x + 5) - 3x$.

SOLUTION

$$1 - 3(4 - x) = 2(x + 5) - 3x$$

$$1 - 12 + 3x = 2x + 10 - 3x \qquad \text{Using the distributive law}$$

$$-11 + 3x = -x + 10 \qquad \begin{aligned}&\text{Combining like terms;} \\ &1 - 12 = -11 \text{ and } 2x - 3x = -x\end{aligned}$$

$$-11 + 3x + x = 10 \qquad \begin{aligned}&\text{Adding } x \text{ to both sides to get all} \\ &x\text{-terms on one side}\end{aligned}$$

$$-11 + 4x = 10 \qquad \text{Combining like terms}$$

$$4x = 10 + 11 \qquad \begin{aligned}&\text{Adding 11 to both sides to isolate} \\ &\text{the } x\text{-term}\end{aligned}$$

$$4x = 21 \qquad \text{Simplifying}$$

$$x = \tfrac{21}{4} \qquad \text{Dividing both sides by 4}$$

Check:

$$1 - 3(4 - x) = 2(x + 5) - 3x$$

$1 - 3(4 - \frac{21}{4})$	$2(\frac{21}{4} + 5) - 3(\frac{21}{4})$
$1 - 3(-\frac{5}{4})$	$2(\frac{41}{4}) - \frac{63}{4}$
$1 + \frac{15}{4}$	$\frac{82}{4} - \frac{63}{4}$
$\frac{19}{4}$	$\overset{?}{=}$	$\frac{19}{4}$

TRUE

3. Solve:

$3(n - 2) - 5n = 2 - (n - 7)$.

The solution is $\frac{21}{4}$.

YOUR TURN

The equations in Examples 1–3 are **conditional**—that is, they are true for some values of x and false for other values of x. An **identity** is an equation like $x + 1 = x + 1$ that is true for all values of x. A **contradiction** is an equation like $x + 1 = x + 2$ that is never true.

A **formula** is an equation using two or more letters that represents a relationship between two or more quantities. A formula can be solved for a specified letter using the principles for solving equations.

EXAMPLE 4 The formula

$$A = \frac{a + b + c + d}{4}$$

gives the average A of four test scores a, b, c, and d. Solve for d.

SOLUTION We have

$$A = \frac{a + b + c + d}{4} \qquad \text{We want the letter } d \text{ alone.}$$

$$4A = a + b + c + d \qquad \text{Multiplying by 4 to clear the fraction}$$

$$4A - a - b - c = d. \qquad \text{Subtracting } a + b + c \text{ from (or adding } -a - b - c \text{ to) both sides. The letter } d \text{ is now isolated.}$$

4. Solve $Q = \dfrac{p - q}{2}$ for p.

We can also write this as $d = 4A - a - b - c$. This formula can be used to determine the test score needed to obtain a specified average if three tests have already been taken.

YOUR TURN

Solving Inequalities

A **solution of an inequality** is a replacement of the variable that makes the inequality true. The solutions of an inequality in one variable can be **graphed**, or represented by a drawing, on the number line. All points that are solutions are shaded. A parenthesis indicates an endpoint that is not a solution and a bracket indicates an endpoint that is a solution.

Since it is impossible to list all the solutions of most inequalities, we use **set-builder notation** or **interval notation** to write such sets. To use set-builder notation for the set of all solutions of $m \leq 2$, we write

$$\{m \mid m \leq 2\},$$

read

"the set of all m such that m is less than or equal to 2."

Interval notation uses parentheses, ( ), and brackets, [ ], to describe a set of real numbers.

Interval Notation	Set-Builder Notation	Graph
(a, b) open interval	$\{x \mid a < x < b\}$	
$[a, b]$ closed interval	$\{x \mid a \le x \le b\}$	
$(a, b]$ half-open interval	$\{x \mid a < x \le b\}$	
$[a, b)$ half-open interval	$\{x \mid a \le x < b\}$	
(a, ∞)	$\{x \mid x > a\}$	
$[a, \infty)$	$\{x \mid x \ge a\}$	
$(-\infty, a)$	$\{x \mid x < a\}$	
$(-\infty, a]$	$\{x \mid x \le a\}$	

As with equations, our goal when solving inequalities is to isolate the variable on one side. We use principles that enable us to write **equivalent inequalities**—that is, inequalities having the same solution set. The addition principle for inequalities is similar to the addition principle for equations; the multiplication principle for inequalities contains an important difference.

THE ADDITION AND MULTIPLICATION PRINCIPLES FOR INEQUALITIES

The Addition Principle

For any real numbers a, b, and c,

$$a < b \quad \text{is equivalent to} \quad a + c < b + c, \quad \text{and}$$
$$a > b \quad \text{is equivalent to} \quad a + c > b + c.$$

The Multiplication Principle

For any real numbers a and b, and for any *positive* number c,

$$a < b \quad \text{is equivalent to} \quad ac < bc, \quad \text{and}$$
$$a > b \quad \text{is equivalent to} \quad ac > bc.$$

For any real numbers a and b, and for any *negative* number c,

$$a < b \quad \text{is equivalent to} \quad ac > bc, \quad \text{and}$$
$$a > b \quad \text{is equivalent to} \quad ac < bc.$$

Similar statements hold for $\le$ and $\ge$.

Note that when we multiply both sides of an inequality by a negative number, we must reverse the direction of the inequality symbol in order to have an equivalent inequality.

EXAMPLE 5 Solve $-2x \geq 5$ and then graph the solution.

SOLUTION We have

$$-2x \geq 5$$

$$\frac{-2x}{-2} \leq \frac{5}{-2} \qquad \text{Multiplying by } -\frac{1}{2} \text{ or dividing by } -2$$

The symbol must be reversed!

$$x \leq -\frac{5}{2}.$$

Any number less than or equal to $-\frac{5}{2}$ is a solution. The graph is as follows:

5. Solve $12 > -3x$ and graph the solution.

The solution set is $\left\{x \mid x \leq -\frac{5}{2}\right\}$, or $\left(-\infty, -\frac{5}{2}\right]$.

YOUR TURN

We can use the addition and multiplication principles together to solve inequalities. We can also combine like terms, multiply to remove parentheses, and clear fractions and decimals.

EXAMPLE 6 Solve: $2 - 3(x + 5) > 4 - 6(x - 1)$.

SOLUTION We have

$$2 - 3(x + 5) > 4 - 6(x - 1)$$

$$2 - 3x - 15 > 4 - 6x + 6 \qquad \text{Using the distributive law to remove parentheses}$$

$$-3x - 13 > -6x + 10 \qquad \text{Simplifying}$$

$$-3x + 6x > 10 + 13 \qquad \text{Adding } 6x \text{ and also 13, to get all } x\text{-terms on one side and all constant terms on the other side}$$

$$3x > 23 \qquad \text{Combining like terms}$$

$$x > \frac{23}{3}. \qquad \text{Multiplying by } \frac{1}{3}. \text{ The inequality symbol stays the same because } \frac{1}{3} \text{ is positive.}$$

6. Solve:

$$10(x - 2) - 3x \leq 5 - (2 - x).$$

The solution set is $\left\{x \mid x > \frac{23}{3}\right\}$, or $\left(\frac{23}{3}, \infty\right)$.

YOUR TURN

Problem Solving

One of the most important uses of algebra is as a tool for problem solving. The following five steps can be used to help solve problems of many types.

> **FIVE STEPS FOR PROBLEM SOLVING IN ALGEBRA**
> 1. *Familiarize* yourself with the problem.
> 2. *Translate* to mathematical language. (This often means writing an equation.)
> 3. *Carry out* some mathematical manipulation. (This often means *solving* an equation.)
> 4. *Check* your possible answer in the original problem.
> 5. *State* the answer clearly, using a complete English sentence.

EXAMPLE 7 *Kitchen Cabinets.* Cherry kitchen cabinets cost 10% more than oak cabinets. Shelby Custom Cabinets designs a kitchen using $7480 worth of cherry cabinets. How much would the same kitchen cost using oak cabinets?

SOLUTION

1. **Familiarize.** The *Familiarize* step is often the most important of the five steps, and may require a significant amount of time. Sometimes it helps to make a drawing or a table, make a guess and check it, or look up further information. For this problem, we could review percent notation, and note that 10% of the price of the oak cabinets must be added to the price of the oak cabinets in order to get the price of the cherry cabinets. We let c = the cost of the oak cabinets.

2. **Translate.** We rewrite and translate:

Cost of oak cabinets	plus	10% of cost of oak cabinets	is	cost of cherry cabinets.
c	$+$	$0.10c$	$=$	7480

3. **Carry out.** We solve the equation:

$$c + 0.10c = 7480$$
$$1c + 0.10c = 7480 \quad \text{Writing } c \text{ as } 1c \text{ before combining terms}$$
$$1.10c = 7480 \quad \text{Combining like terms}$$
$$c = \frac{7480}{1.10} \quad \text{Dividing by } 1.10$$
$$c = 6800.$$

4. **Check.** We check in the wording of the stated problem: Cherry cabinets cost 10% more, so the additional cost is

$$10\% \text{ of } \$6800 = 0.10(\$6800) = \$680.$$

The total cost of the cherry cabinets is then

$$\$6800 + \$680 = \$7480,$$

which is the amount stated in the problem.

5. **State.** The oak cabinets would cost $6800.

7. Refer to Example 7. The cherry cabinets cost 5% more than hickory cabinets. How much would the same kitchen cost using hickory cabinets?

 YOUR TURN

Sometimes the translation of a problem is an inequality.

EXAMPLE 8 *Fitness Club.* Elyse pays $30 per month to be a member of Perfect Fitness. An hour-long class costs an additional $2.50. How many classes can she take per month and not exceed a cost of $50 per month?

SOLUTION

1. **Familiarize.** Suppose that Elyse takes 10 classes in one month. Her cost would then be the monthly membership fee plus the fee for classes, or $30 + \$2.50(10) = \$55$. This exceeds $50, so we know that the number of classes must be less than 10. We let $c =$ the number of classes taken in one month.

2. **Translate.** The *Familiarize* step helps us reword and translate.

Rewording:	The monthly fee	plus	the cost of classes	cannot exceed	$50.
Translating:	30	+	2.5c	≤	50

3. **Carry out.** We solve the inequality:

$$30 + 2.5c \leq 50$$
$$2.5c \leq 20 \qquad \text{Subtracting 30 from both sides}$$
$$m \leq 8. \qquad \text{Dividing by 2.5. The inequality symbol stays the same.}$$

4. **Check.** As a partial check, note that the monthly cost including the cost for 8 classes is

$$\$30 + \$2.50(8) = \$50.$$

Since fewer classes will cost even less, our answer checks. We also note that 8 is less than 10 classes, as noted in the *Familiarize* step.

5. **State.** Elyse will not exceed a cost of $50 if she takes no more than 8 classes.

8. Refer to Example 8. Elyse can work out in the Super Athlete room for $2 per hour. For how many hours can she work out in that room and not exceed a cost of $50 for the month?

 YOUR TURN

R.2 EXERCISE SET   FOR EXTRA HELP   MyMathLab® Math XL
PRACTICE   WATCH   READ   REVIEW

Solving Equations and Formulas

Solve.

1. $-6 + x = 10$

2. $y + 7 = -3$

3. $t + \frac{1}{3} = \frac{1}{4}$

4. $-\frac{2}{3} + p = \frac{1}{6}$

5. $-1.9 = x - 1.1$

6. $x + 4.6 = 1.7$

7. $-x = \frac{5}{3}$

8. $-y = -\frac{2}{5}$

9. $-\frac{2}{7}x = -12$

10. $-\frac{1}{4}x = 3$

11. $\frac{-t}{5} = 1$

12. $\frac{2}{3} = -\frac{z}{8}$

13. $3y + 10 = 15$

14. $12 = 5y + 18$

15. $4x + 7 = 3 - 5x$

16. $2x = 5 + 7x$

17. $2x - 7 = 5x + 1 - x$

18. $a + 7 - 2a = 14 + 7a - 10$

19. $\frac{2}{5} + \frac{1}{3}t = 5$

20. $-\frac{5}{6} + t = \frac{1}{2}$

21. $x + 0.45 = 2.6x$

22. $1.8x + 0.16 = 4.2 - 0.05x$

23. $8(3 - m) + 7 = 47$

24. $2(5 - m) = 5(6 + m)$

25. $4 - (6 + x) = 13$

26. $18 = 9 - (3 - x)$

27. $2 + 3(4 + c) = 1 - 5(6 - c)$

28. $b + (b + 5) - 2(b - 5) = 18 + b$

29. $0.1(a - 0.2) = 1.2 + 2.4a$

30. $\frac{2}{3}\left(\frac{1}{2} - x\right) + \frac{5}{6} = \frac{3}{2}\left(\frac{2}{3}x + 1\right)$

31. $A = lw$, for l **32.** $A = lw$, for w

33. $I = \dfrac{P}{V}$, for P **34.** $b = \dfrac{A}{h}$, for A

35. $q = \dfrac{p + r}{2}$, for p **36.** $q = \dfrac{p - r}{2}$, for r

37. $A = \pi r^2 + \pi r^2 h$, for π **38.** $ax + by = c$, for a

Solving Inequalities

Solve and graph. Write each answer in set-builder notation and in interval notation.

39. $x + 3 \le 15$ **40.** $y + 7 < -10$

41. $m - 17 > -5$ **42.** $x + 9 \ge -8$

43. $2x \ge -3$ **44.** $-\frac{1}{2}n \le 4$

45. $-5t > 15$ **46.** $3x > 10$

Solve. Write each answer in set-builder notation and in interval notation.

47. $2y - 7 > 13$ **48.** $2 - 6y \le 18$

49. $6 - 5a \le a$ **50.** $4b + 7 > 2 - b$

51. $2(3 + 5x) \ge 7(10 - x)$

52. $2(x + 5) < 8 - 3x$

53. $\frac{2}{3}(6 - x) < \frac{1}{4}(x + 3)$

54. $\frac{2}{3}t + \frac{8}{9} \ge \frac{4}{6} - \frac{1}{4}t$

55. $0.7(2 + x) \ge 1.1x + 5.75$

56. $0.4x + 5.7 \le 2.6 - 3(1.2x - 7)$

Problem Solving

Solve. Use the five-step problem-solving process.

57. Three less than the sum of 2 and some number is 6. What is the number?

58. Five times some number is 10 less than the number. What is the number?

59. The sum of two consecutive even integers is 34. Find the numbers.

60. The sum of three consecutive integers is 195. Find the numbers.

61. *Reading.*   Leisa is reading a 500-page book. She has twice as many pages to read as she has already finished. How many pages has she already read?

62. *Mowing.*   It takes Caleb 50 min to mow his lawn. As he takes a break to answer his phone, he calculates that it will take him three times as many minutes to finish as he has already spent mowing. How long has he already spent mowing?

63. *Perimeter of a Rectangle.*   The perimeter of a rectangle is 28 cm. The width is 5 cm less than the length. Find the width and the length.

64. *Triangles.*   The second angle of a triangle is one-third as large as the first. The third angle is 5° more than the first. Find the measure of the second angle.

65. *Water Usage.*   Rural Water Company charges a monthly service fee of $9.70 plus a volume charge of $2.60 for every hundred cubic feet of water used. How much water was used if the monthly bill is $33.10?

66. *Telephone Bills.*   Brandon pays $2.95 per month for a long-distance telephone service that offers a flat rate of 5¢ per minute. One month his total long-distance telephone bill was $7.05. How many minutes of long-distance telephone calls were made that month?

67. *Sale Price.*   A can of tomatoes is on sale at 20% off for 88¢. What is the normal selling price of the tomatoes?

68. *Plywood.*   The price of a piece of plywood rose 5% to $42. What was the original price of the plywood?

69. *Practice.*   Dierdre's basketball coach requires each team member to average at least 15 min per day shooting baskets. One week Dierdre spent 10 min, 20 min, 5 min, 0 min, 25 min, and 15 min shooting baskets. How long must she practice shooting baskets on the seventh day if she is to meet the requirement?

70. *Perimeter of a Garden.*   The perimeter of Garry's rectangular garden cannot exceed the 100 ft of fencing that he purchased. He wants the length to be twice the width. What widths of the garden will meet these conditions?

71. *Meeting Costs.* Great Space charges a $75 cleaning fee plus $45 per hour for the use of its meeting room. Complete Consultants has budgeted $200 to rent a room for a seminar. For how many hours can they rent the meeting room at Great Space?

72. *Meeting Costs.* Spring Haven charges a $15 setup fee, a $30 cleanup fee, and $50 per hour for the use of its meeting room. For what lengths of time will Spring Haven's room be less expensive than the room at Great Space (see Exercise 71)?

 YOUR TURN ANSWERS: SECTION R.2

1. $-\frac{1}{2}$ **2.** $\frac{44}{5}$ **3.** -15 **4.** $p = 2Q + q$

5. $\{x \mid x > -4\}$, or $(-4, \infty)$; ←———→
                                                    -4 0

6. $\left\{x \mid x \le \frac{23}{6}\right\}$, or $\left(-\infty, \frac{23}{6}\right]$ **7.** $7123.81

8. No more than 10 hr

REFERENCES

The addition principle, p. 81
The addition principle for inequalities, p. 130
Clearing fractions, p. 91
Conditional equation, p. 93
Contradiction, p. 93
Equivalent equations, p. 81
Equivalent inequalities, p. 130
Familiarization step, p. 113
Formulas, Section 2.3
Graphs of inequalities, p. 128
Identity, p. 93
Interval notation, p. 129
The multiplication principle, p. 83
The multiplication principle for inequalities, p. 132
Percent, Section 2.4
Problem solving, Section 2.5
Set-builder notation, p. 129
Solutions of inequalities, p. 128
Solving applications with inequalities, Section 2.7

R.3 Introduction to Graphing

Points and Ordered Pairs ▪ Graphs and Slope ▪ Linear Equations

Points and Ordered Pairs

We can represent, or graph, pairs of numbers such as $(2, -5)$ on a plane. To do so, we use two perpendicular number lines called **axes**. The axes cross at a point called the **origin**. Arrows on the axes show the positive directions.

The order of the **coordinates**, or numbers in a pair, is important. The **first coordinate** indicates horizontal position and the **second coordinate** indicates vertical position. Such pairs of numbers are called **ordered pairs**. Thus the ordered pairs $(1, -2)$ and $(-2, 1)$ correspond to different points, as shown in the accompanying figure.

The axes divide the plane into four regions, or **quadrants**, as indicated by Roman numerals in the figure below. Points on the axes are not considered to be in any quadrant. The horizontal axis is often labeled the x-axis, and the vertical axis the y-axis.

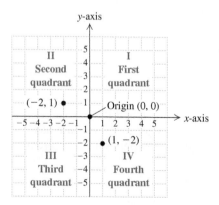

Graphs and Slope

When an equation contains two variables, solutions must be ordered pairs. Unless stated otherwise, the first number in each pair replaces the variable that occurs first alphabetically.

EXAMPLE 1   Determine whether $(1, 4)$ is a solution of $y - x = 3$.

SOLUTION   We substitute 1 for x and 4 for y since x occurs first alphabetically:

$$\frac{y - x = 3}{4 - 1 \mid 3}$$
$$3 \overset{?}{=} 3 \quad \text{TRUE}$$

Since $3 = 3$ is true, the pair $(1, 4)$ *is* a solution.

1. Determine whether $(-2, 5)$ is a solution of $y - x = 3$.

 YOUR TURN

The **graph** of an equation represents all of its solutions.

EXAMPLE 2   Graph: $y = -2x + 1$.

SOLUTION   We select a value for x, calculate the corresponding value of y, and form an ordered pair.

If $x = 0$, then $y = -2 \cdot 0 + 1 = 1$, and $(0, 1)$ is a solution. Repeating this step, we find other ordered pairs and list the results in a table. We then plot the points corresponding to the pairs. They appear to form a straight line, so we draw a line through the points.

$y = -2x + 1$

x	y	(x, y)
0	1	$(0, 1)$
-1	3	$(-1, 3)$
3	-5	$(3, -5)$
1	-1	$(1, -1)$

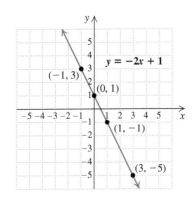

2. Graph: $y = 2x - 1$.

 YOUR TURN

The graph in Example 2 is a straight line. An equation whose graph is a straight line is a **linear equation**. The *rate of change* of y with respect to x is called the **slope** of a graph. A linear graph has constant slope. It can be found using any two points on a line.

SLOPE

The *slope* of the line containing points (x_1, y_1) and (x_2, y_2) is given by

$$m = \frac{\text{change in } y}{\text{change in } x} = \frac{\text{rise}}{\text{run}} = \frac{y_2 - y_1}{x_2 - x_1}.$$

EXAMPLE 3 Find the slope of the line containing the points $(-2, 1)$ and $(3, -4)$.

SOLUTION From $(-2, 1)$ to $(3, -4)$, the change in y, or the rise, is $-4 - 1$, or -5. The change in x, or the run, is $3 - (-2)$, or 5. Thus

$$\text{Slope} = \frac{\text{change in } y}{\text{change in } x} = \frac{\text{rise}}{\text{run}} = \frac{-4 - 1}{3 - (-2)} = \frac{-5}{5} = -1.$$

3. Find the slope of the line containing the points $(0, -9)$ and $(4, 3)$.

YOUR TURN

The slope of a line indicates the direction and the steepness of its slant. The larger the absolute value of the slope, the steeper the line. The direction of the slant is indicated by the sign of the slope, as shown in the figures below.

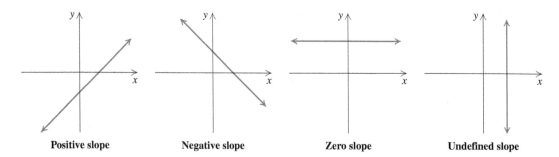

Positive slope   Negative slope   Zero slope   Undefined slope

The **x-intercept** of a line, if it exists, is the point at which the graph crosses the x-axis. To find an x-intercept, we replace y with 0 and solve for x.

The **y-intercept** of a line, if it exists, is the point at which the graph crosses the y-axis. To find a y-intercept, we replace x with 0 and solve for y.

Linear Equations

Any equation that can be written in the **standard form** $Ax + By = C$ is linear. Linear equations can also be written in other forms.

FORMS OF LINEAR EQUATIONS

Standard form: $Ax + By = C$

Slope–intercept form: $y = mx + b$

Point–slope form: $y - y_1 = m(x - x_1)$

The slope and the y-intercept of a line can be read from the slope–intercept form of the line's equation.

SLOPE AND y-INTERCEPT

For the graph of any equation $y = mx + b$,

• the slope is m, and

• the y-intercept is $(0, b)$.

EXAMPLE 4 Find the slope and the *y*-intercept of the line given by the equation $4x - 3y = 9$.

SOLUTION We write the equation in slope–intercept form $y = mx + b$:

$$4x - 3y = 9 \qquad \text{We must solve for } y.$$
$$-3y = -4x + 9 \qquad \text{Adding } -4x \text{ to both sides}$$
$$y = \tfrac{4}{3}x - 3. \qquad \text{Dividing both sides by } -3$$

The slope is $\tfrac{4}{3}$ and the *y*-intercept is $(0, -3)$.

4. Find the slope and the *y*-intercept of the line given by the equation $y - x = 10$.

 YOUR TURN

If we know that an equation is a straight line, we can plot two points on the line and draw the line through those points. The intercepts are often convenient points to use. A third point can be used as a check.

EXAMPLE 5 Graph $2x - 5y = 10$ using intercepts.

SOLUTION To find the *x*-intercept, we let $y = 0$ and solve for *x*:

$$2x - 5 \cdot 0 = 10 \qquad \text{Replacing } y \text{ with } 0$$
$$2x = 10$$
$$x = 5.$$

To find the *y*-intercept, we let $x = 0$ and solve for *y*:

$$2 \cdot 0 - 5y = 10 \qquad \text{Replacing } x \text{ with } 0$$
$$-5y = 10$$
$$y = -2.$$

Thus the *x*-intercept is $(5, 0)$ and the *y*-intercept is $(0, -2)$. The graph is a line, since $2x - 5y = 10$ is in the form $Ax + By = C$. It passes through these two points. We leave it to the student to calculate a third point as a check.

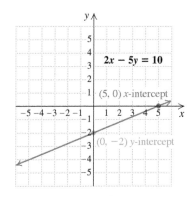

5. Graph $x + 3y = 3$ using intercepts.

 YOUR TURN

Alternatively, if we know a point on the line and its slope, we can plot the point and "count off" its slope to locate another point on the line.

EXAMPLE 6 Graph: $y = -\tfrac{1}{2}x + 3$.

SOLUTION The equation is in slope–intercept form, so we can read the slope and the *y*-intercept directly from the equation.

Slope: $-\tfrac{1}{2}$

y-intercept: $(0, 3)$

We plot the *y*-intercept and use the slope to find another point.

Another way to write the slope is $\dfrac{-1}{2}$. This means that for a run of 2 units, there is a negative rise, or a drop, of 1 unit. Starting at $(0, 3)$, we move 2 units in the positive horizontal direction and then 1 unit down, to locate the point $(2, 2)$. Then we draw the graph. A third point can be calculated and plotted as a check.

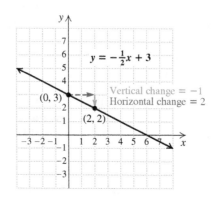

6. Graph: $y = \frac{2}{3}x - 5$.

YOUR TURN

Horizontal lines and vertical lines intersect only one axis.

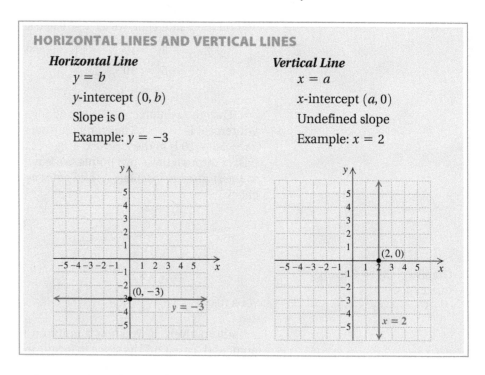

HORIZONTAL LINES AND VERTICAL LINES

Horizontal Line
$y = b$
y-intercept $(0, b)$
Slope is 0
Example: $y = -3$

Vertical Line
$x = a$
x-intercept $(a, 0)$
Undefined slope
Example: $x = 2$

If we know the slope of a line and the coordinates of a point on the line, we can find an equation of the line, using either the slope–intercept equation, $y = mx + b$, or the point–slope equation, $y - y_1 = m(x - x_1)$.

EXAMPLE 7   Find the slope–intercept equation of a line given the following:

a) The slope is 2, and the y-intercept is $(0, -5)$.

b) The graph contains the points $(-2, 1)$ and $(3, -4)$.

SOLUTION

a) Since the slope and the y-intercept are given, we use the slope–intercept equation:

$$y = mx + b$$
$$y = 2x - 5. \qquad \text{Substituting 2 for } m \text{ and } -5 \text{ for } b$$

b) To use the point–slope equation, we need to know a point on the line and the line's slope. The slope can be found from the points given:

Find the slope.
$$m = \frac{1 - (-4)}{-2 - 3} = \frac{5}{-5} = -1.$$

Either point can be used as (x_1, y_1). Using $(-2, 1)$, we have

Find a point–slope equation for the line.

$$y - y_1 = m(x - x_1)$$
$$y - 1 = -1(x - (-2)) \qquad \text{Substituting } -2 \text{ for } x_1, 1 \text{ for } y_1, \text{ and } -1 \text{ for } m$$
$$y - 1 = -(x + 2)$$

Find the slope–intercept equation for the line.

$$y - 1 = -x - 2$$
$$y = -x - 1. \qquad \text{This is in slope–intercept form.}$$

 YOUR TURN

7. Find the slope–intercept equation of the line containing the points $(1, 2)$ and $(5, -3)$.

We can tell from the slopes of two lines whether they are parallel or perpendicular.

> **PARALLEL LINES AND PERPENDICULAR LINES**
> Two lines are parallel if they have the same slope.
> Two lines are perpendicular if the product of the slopes is -1.

EXAMPLE 8   Determine whether the graphs of $4x - y = 8$ and $3x + 12y = 24$ are parallel, perpendicular, or neither.

SOLUTION   We solve both equations for y in order to determine the slopes of the lines:

$$4x - y = 8$$
$$-y = -4x + 8$$
$$y = 4x - 8.$$

The slope of $4x - y = 8$ is 4.
  For the second line, we have

$$3x + 12y = 24$$
$$12y = -3x + 24$$
$$y = -\tfrac{1}{4}x + 2.$$

8. Determine whether the graphs of the lines are parallel, perpendicular, or neither:

$$2x + 5y = 7,$$
$$2x = 5y + 1.$$

The slope of $3x + 12y = 24$ is $-\tfrac{1}{4}$. Since $4 \cdot \left(-\tfrac{1}{4}\right) = -1$, the lines are perpendicular.

 YOUR TURN

R.3 EXERCISE SET

FOR EXTRA HELP

MyMathLab® Math XL
PRACTICE　WATCH　READ　REVIEW

Points and Ordered Pairs

1. Plot the following points.

$(2, -3), (5, 1), (0, 2), (-1, 0),$
$(0, 0), (-2, -5), (-1, 1), (1, -1)$

2. Plot the following points.

$(0, -4), (-4, 0), (5, -2), (2, 5),$
$(3, 3), (-3, -1), (-1, 4), (0, 1)$

In which quadrant or on what axis is each point located?

3. $(-2, 5)$ **4.** $(15, 27)$

5. $(-6, 0)$ **6.** $(-1.7, -5.9)$

7. $(18, -7)$ **8.** $(0, 3)$

Graphs and Slope

Determine whether each equation has the given ordered pair as a solution.

9. $y = 2x - 5$; $(1, 3)$ **10.** $4x + 3y = 8$; $(-1, 4)$

11. $a - 5b = -3$; $(2, 1)$ **12.** $c = d + 1$; $(1, 2)$

Graph.

13. $y = \frac{1}{3}x + 3$ **14.** $y = -x - 2$

15. $y = -4x$ **16.** $y = \frac{3}{4}x + 1$

Find the slope of the line containing each given pair of points. If the slope is undefined, state this.

17. $(3, 6)$ and $(2, 7)$

18. $(-1, 7)$ and $(-5, 1)$

19. $(-2, -\frac{1}{2})$ and $(5, -\frac{1}{2})$

20. $(6.8, 7.5)$ and $(6.8, -3.2)$

Linear Equations

Find the slope and the y-intercept of each equation.

21. $y = 2x - 5$ **22.** $y = 4 - x$

23. $2x + 7y = 1$ **24.** $x - 2y = 3$

Find the intercepts. Then graph.

25. $3 - y = 2x$ **26.** $2x + 5y = 10$

27. $y = 3x + 5$ **28.** $y = -x + 7$

29. $3x - 2y = 6$ **30.** $2y + 1 = x$

Determine the coordinates of the y-intercept of each equation. Then graph the equation.

31. $y = 2x - 5$ **32.** $y = -\frac{5}{4}x - 3$

33. $2y + 4x = 6$ **34.** $3y + x = 4$

Find the slope of each line. Then graph.

35. $y = 4$ **36.** $x = -5$

37. $x = 3$ **38.** $y = -1$

Find the slope–intercept equation of a line with the given conditions.

39. The slope is 5 and the y-intercept is $(0, 9)$.

40. The slope is $\frac{2}{3}$ and the y-intercept is $(0, -5)$.

41. The graph contains the points $(0, 3)$ and $(-1, 4)$.

42. The graph contains the points $(5, 1)$ and $(8, 0)$.

Determine whether each pair of lines is parallel, perpendicular, or neither.

43. $x + y = 5,$ **44.** $2x + y = 3,$
     $x - y = 1$ $y = 4 - 2x$

45. $2x + 3y = 1,$ **46.** $y = \frac{1}{3}x - 7,$
     $2x - 3y = 5$ $y + 3x = 1$

YOUR TURN ANSWERS: SECTION R.3

1. No   **2.**   **3.** 3

4. Slope: 1; y-intercept: $(0, 10)$

5.   **6.**

7. $y = -\frac{5}{4}x + \frac{13}{4}$ **8.** Neither

REFERENCES

Coordinates, p. 156
Graphing ordered pairs, p. 156
Horizontal line, p. 178
Parallel lines, p. 207
Perpendicular lines, p. 208
Quadrants, p. 157
Slope, p. 190
Solutions of equations, p. 163
Vertical line, p. 178
x-intercept, p. 173
y-intercept, p. 173

R.4 Polynomials

Exponents ▪ Polynomials ▪ Addition and Subtraction of Polynomials ▪ Multiplication of Polynomials ▪ Division of Polynomials

Exponents

The following properties hold for any integers m and n and any real numbers a and b, provided no denominators are 0 and 0^0 is not considered.

> **PROPERTIES OF EXPONENTS**
>
> The Zero Exponent: $\qquad a^0 = 1$
>
> Negative Exponents: $\qquad a^{-n} = \dfrac{1}{a^n}$
>
> The Product Rule: $\qquad a^m \cdot a^n = a^{m+n}$
>
> The Quotient Rule: $\qquad \dfrac{a^m}{a^n} = a^{m-n}$
>
> The Power Rule: $\qquad (a^m)^n = a^{mn}$
>
> Raising a product to a power: $\quad (ab)^n = a^n b^n$
>
> Raising a quotient to a power: $\quad \left(\dfrac{a}{b}\right)^n = \dfrac{a^n}{b^n}$

EXAMPLE 1 Simplify. Do not use negative exponents in your answer.

a) $(97)^0$ 　　　　　**b)** $7y^{-1}$ 　　　　　**c)** $\dfrac{1}{x^{-2}}$

SOLUTION

a) $(97)^0 = 1$ 　　Any number (other than 0 itself) raised to the 0 power is 1.

b) $7y^{-1} = 7\left(\dfrac{1}{y^1}\right) = \dfrac{7}{y}$ 　　y^{-1} is the reciprocal of y^1.

c) $\dfrac{1}{x^{-2}} = x^{-(-2)} = x^2$ 　　The reciprocal of x^{-2} is $x^{-(-2)}$, or x^2.

 1. Simplify $(2x)^0$ for $x = -10$.

 YOUR TURN

EXAMPLE 2 Simplify. If negative exponents appear in the answer, write an equivalent answer using only positive exponents.

a) $(x^2y^{-1})(xy^{-3})$ 　　　**b)** $\dfrac{(3p)^3}{(3p)^{-2}}$ 　　　**c)** $\left(\dfrac{ab^2}{3c^3}\right)^{-4}$

SOLUTION

a) $(x^2y^{-1})(xy^{-3}) = x^2y^{-1}xy^{-3}$ 　　Using an associative law

$\qquad\qquad\qquad\quad = x^2x^1y^{-1}y^{-3}$ 　　Using a commutative law; $x = x^1$

$\qquad\qquad\qquad\quad = x^{2+1}y^{-1+(-3)}$ 　　Using the product rule: Adding exponents

$\qquad\qquad\qquad\quad = x^3y^{-4}$, or $\dfrac{x^3}{y^4}$

b) $\dfrac{(3p)^3}{(3p)^{-2}} = (3p)^{3-(-2)}$ Using the quotient rule: Subtracting exponents

$= (3p)^5$

$= 3^5 p^5$ Raising each factor to the fifth power

$= 243p^5$

2. Simplify. If negative exponents appear in the answer, write an equivalent answer using only positive exponents.

$(2x^{-3}y^5)^{-2}$

c) $\left(\dfrac{ab^2}{3c^3}\right)^{-4} = \dfrac{(ab^2)^{-4}}{(3c^3)^{-4}}$ Raising the numerator and the denominator to the -4 power

$= \dfrac{a^{-4}(b^2)^{-4}}{3^{-4}(c^3)^{-4}}$ Raising each factor to the -4 power

$= \dfrac{a^{-4}b^{-8}}{3^{-4}c^{-12}}$ Multiplying exponents

$= \dfrac{3^4 c^{12}}{a^4 b^8}, \text{ or } \dfrac{81c^{12}}{a^4 b^8}$ Rewriting without negative exponents

↩ YOUR TURN

Polynomials

The algebraic expression $4y^2 - 8y^5 + y^3 - 6y + 7$ is an example of a **polynomial**. A polynomial has *terms, coefficients,* and a *degree*.

Definition	Example, for the polynomial $4y^2 - 8y^5 + y^3 - 6y + 7$
The **terms** of a polynomial are separated by addition signs.	Terms: $4y^2, -8y^5, y^3, -6y, 7$
The part of a term that is a constant factor is the **coefficient** of the term.	Coefficients: $4, -8, 1, -6, 7$
The **degree of a term** is the number of variable factors in that term.	Degree of each term: $2, 5, 3, 1, 0$
The **leading term** of a polynomial is the term of highest degree.	Leading term: $-8y^5$
The **degree of a polynomial** is the degree of the leading term.	Degree of polynomial: 5
The coefficient of the leading term is the **leading coefficient** of the polynomial.	Leading coefficient: -8

A polynomial is written in *descending order* when the leading term appears first, followed by the term of next highest degree, and so on.

Polynomials are classified by the number of terms and by degree.

A **monomial** has one term.   *Example*: $-2x^3 y$

A **binomial** has two terms.   *Example*: $1.4x^2 - 10$

A **trinomial** has three terms.   *Example*: $x^2 - 3x - 6$

A **constant** polynomial has degree 0.   *Example*: 7

A **linear** polynomial has degree 1.   *Example*: $3x + 5$

A **quadratic** polynomial has degree 2.   *Example*: $5x^2 - x$

A **cubic** polynomial has degree 3.   *Example*: $x^3 + 2x^2 - \frac{1}{3}$

A **quartic** polynomial has degree 4.   *Example*: $-6x^4 - 2x^2 + 19$

Like, or *similar*, *terms* are either constant terms or terms containing the same variable(s) raised to the same power(s). Polynomials containing like terms can be simplified by *combining* those terms.

EXAMPLE 3   Combine like terms: $4x^2 + 2x - x^2 + x^3$. Write the answer in descending order.

SOLUTION   The like terms are $4x^2$ and $-x^2$. Thus we have

$$4x^2 + 2x - x^2 + x^3 = 4x^2 - x^2 + 2x + x^3$$
$$= 3x^2 + 2x + x^3 \qquad \text{Combining like terms}$$
$$= x^3 + 3x^2 + 2x. \qquad \text{Writing in descending order}$$

3. Combine like terms:

$-4 + 6x^3 - x^2 + 1 + x^2.$

Write the answer in descending order.
_____

YOUR TURN

A polynomial is evaluated by replacing the variable or variables with a number or numbers.

EXAMPLE 4   Evaluate $-a^2 + 2ab + 5b^2$ for $a = -1$ and $b = 3$.

SOLUTION   We replace a with -1 and b with 3 and calculate the value using the rules for order of operations:

$$-a^2 + 2ab + 5b^2 = -(-1)^2 + 2 \cdot (-1) \cdot 3 + 5 \cdot 3^2$$
$$= -1 - 6 + 45 = 38.$$

4. Evaluate $2x^3 - x^2 - 3x + 1$ for $x = -1$.
_____

YOUR TURN

Polynomials can be added, subtracted, multiplied, and divided.

Addition and Subtraction of Polynomials

To add polynomials, we write a plus sign between them and combine like terms.

EXAMPLE 5   Add: $(4x^3 + 3x^2 + 2x - 7) + (-5x^2 + x - 10)$.

SOLUTION

$$(4x^3 + 3x^2 + 2x - 7) + (-5x^2 + x - 10)$$
$$= 4x^3 + (3 - 5)x^2 + (2 + 1)x + (-7 - 10)$$
$$= 4x^3 - 2x^2 + 3x - 17$$

5. Add:

$(3x^2 + x - 12) + (x - 6).$
_____

YOUR TURN

To find the **opposite of a polynomial**, we replace each term with its opposite. This process is called *changing the sign* of each term. Thus the opposite of

$$3y^4 - 7y^2 - \tfrac{1}{3}y + 17$$

is

$$-\left(3y^4 - 7y^2 - \tfrac{1}{3}y + 17\right) = -3y^4 + 7y^2 + \tfrac{1}{3}y - 17.$$

To subtract polynomials, we add the opposite of the polynomial being subtracted.

EXAMPLE 6   Subtract: $(3a^4 - 2a + 7) - (-a^3 + 5a - 1)$.

SOLUTION

6. Subtract:

$(5y^3 - 6y - 8) - (y^3 - y^2 + 7)$.

$$(3a^4 - 2a + 7) - (-a^3 + 5a - 1)$$
$$= 3a^4 - 2a + 7 + a^3 - 5a + 1 \qquad \text{Adding the opposite}$$
$$= 3a^4 + a^3 - 7a + 8 \qquad \text{Combining like terms}$$

YOUR TURN

Multiplication of Polynomials

To multiply two monomials, we multiply coefficients and then multiply variables using the product rule for exponents. To multiply a monomial and a polynomial, we multiply each term of the polynomial by the monomial, using the distributive law.

EXAMPLE 7   Multiply: $4x^3(3x^4 - 2x^3 + 7x - 5)$.

SOLUTION

7. Multiply:

$2xy(3x^2 - 4y^2 + 5)$.

$$\textit{Think:}\quad \overbrace{4x^3 \cdot 3x^4} - \overbrace{4x^3 \cdot 2x^3} + \overbrace{4x^3 \cdot 7x} - \overbrace{4x^3 \cdot 5}$$
$$4x^3(3x^4 - 2x^3 + 7x - 5) = 12x^7 \quad - \quad 8x^6 \quad + \quad 28x^4 \quad - \quad 20x^3$$

YOUR TURN

To multiply any two polynomials P and Q, we select one of the polynomials—say, P. We then multiply each term of P by every term of Q and combine like terms.

EXAMPLE 8   Multiply: $(2a^3 + 3a - 1)(a^2 - 4a)$.

SOLUTION   It is often helpful to use columns for a long multiplication. We multiply each term at the top by every term at the bottom, write like terms in columns, and add the results.

$$
\begin{array}{r}
2a^3 + 3a - 1 \\
a^2 - 4a \\
\hline
-8a^4 \qquad\quad - 12a^2 + 4a \\
2a^5 \qquad\;\; + 3a^3 - a^2 \\
\hline
2a^5 - 8a^4 + 3a^3 - 13a^2 + 4a
\end{array}
$$

Multiplying the top row by $-4a$
Multiplying the top row by a^2
Combining like terms. Be sure that like terms are lined up in columns.

8. Multiply:

$(t + 2)(2t^2 - 3t + 4)$.

YOUR TURN

Two binomials can be multiplied efficiently using the FOIL method.

THE FOIL METHOD

To multiply two binomials, $A + B$ and $C + D$, multiply the First terms AC, the Outer terms AD, the Inner terms BC, and then the Last terms BD. Then combine like terms, if possible.

$$(A + B)(C + D) = AC + AD + BC + BD$$

  1. Multiply First terms: AC.
  2. Multiply Outer terms: AD.
  3. Multiply Inner terms: BC.
  4. Multiply Last terms: BD.

FOIL

EXAMPLE 9   Multiply: $(3x + 4)(x - 2)$.

SOLUTION

$$(3x + 4)(x - 2) = 3x^2 - 6x + 4x - 8$$

$$F \quad O \quad I \quad L$$

$$= 3x^2 - 2x - 8 \quad \text{Combining like terms}$$

9. Multiply: $(3a^2 + 1)(a - 5)$.

YOUR TURN

Special products occur so often that specific formulas or methods for computing them have been developed.

SPECIAL PRODUCTS

The product of a sum and a difference of the same two terms:

$$(A + B)(A - B) = \underbrace{A^2 - B^2}$$

This is called a *difference of squares*.

The square of a binomial:

$$(A + B)^2 = A^2 + 2AB + B^2$$
$$(A - B)^2 = A^2 - 2AB + B^2$$

EXAMPLE 10   Multiply: **(a)** $(x + 3y)(x - 3y)$; **(b)** $(x^3 + 2)^2$.

SOLUTION

$$(A + B)(A - B) = A^2 - B^2$$

a) $(x + 3y)(x - 3y) = x^2 - (3y)^2 \qquad A = x \text{ and } B = 3y$

$$= x^2 - 9y^2$$

$$(A + B)^2 = A^2 + 2 \cdot A \cdot B + B^2$$

b) $(x^3 + 2)^2 = (x^3)^2 + 2 \cdot x^3 \cdot 2 + 2^2 \qquad A = x^3 \text{ and } B = 2$

$$= x^6 + 4x^3 + 4$$

10. Multiply: $(y + 1)(y - 1)$.

YOUR TURN

Division of Polynomials

To divide a polynomial by a monomial, we divide each term by the monomial.

EXAMPLE 11   Divide: $(3x^5 + 8x^3 - 12x) \div (4x)$.

SOLUTION   This division can be written

$$\frac{3x^5 + 8x^3 - 12x}{4x} = \frac{3x^5}{4x} + \frac{8x^3}{4x} - \frac{12x}{4x} \qquad \text{Dividing each term by } 4x$$

$$= \frac{3}{4}x^{5-1} + \frac{8}{4}x^{3-1} - \frac{12}{4}x^{1-1} \qquad \text{Dividing coefficients and subtracting exponents}$$

$$= \frac{3}{4}x^4 + 2x^2 - 3.$$

11. Divide:

$(15w^4 - 35w^2 + 5w) \div (5w)$.

To check, we multiply the quotient by $4x$:

$$\left(\tfrac{3}{4}x^4 + 2x^2 - 3\right)4x = 3x^5 + 8x^3 - 12x.$$ The answer checks.

YOUR TURN

To use long division, we write polynomials in descending order, including terms with 0 coefficients for missing terms. As shown below in Example 12, the procedure ends when the degree of the remainder is less than the degree of the divisor.

EXAMPLE 12   Divide: $(4x^3 - 7x + 1) \div (2x + 1)$.

SOLUTION   The polynomials are already written in descending order, but there is no x^2-term in the dividend. We fill in $0x^2$ for that term.

$$
\begin{array}{r}
2x^2 \\
2x + 1\overline{)4x^3 + 0x^2 - 7x + 1} \\
\underline{4x^3 + 2x^2} \\
-2x^2
\end{array}
$$

Divide the first term of the dividend, $4x^3$, by the first term in the divisor, $2x$: $4x^3/(2x) = 2x^2$.

Multiply $2x^2$ by the divisor, $2x + 1$.

Subtract: $(4x^3 + 0x^2) - (4x^3 + 2x^2) = -2x^2$.

Then we bring down the next term of the dividend, $-7x$.

$$
\begin{array}{r}
2x^2 - x \\
2x + 1\overline{)4x^3 + 0x^2 - 7x + 1} \\
\underline{4x^3 + 2x^2} \\
-2x^2 - 7x \\
\underline{-2x^2 - x} \\
-6x
\end{array}
$$

Divide the first term of $-2x^2 - 7x$ by the first term in the divisor: $-2x^2/(2x) = -x$.

The $-7x$ has been "brought down."

Multiply $-x$ by the divisor, $2x + 1$.

Subtract: $(-2x^2 - 7x) - (-2x^2 - x) = -6x$.

Since the degree of the remainder, $-6x$, is *not* less than the degree of the divisor, we must continue dividing.

$$
\begin{array}{r}
2x^2 - x - 3 \\
2x + 1\overline{)4x^3 + 0x^2 - 7x + 1} \\
\underline{4x^3 + 2x^2} \\
-2x^2 - 7x \\
\underline{-2x^2 - x} \\
-6x + 1 \\
\underline{-6x - 3} \\
4
\end{array}
$$

Divide the first term of $-6x + 1$ by the first term in the divisor: $-6x/(2x) = -3$.

The 1 has been "brought down."

Multiply -3 by $2x + 1$.

Subtract.

The answer is $2x^2 - x - 3$ with R4, or

Quotient $\longrightarrow$ $2x^2 - x - 3 + \dfrac{4}{2x + 1}$. $\longleftarrow$ Remainder $\longleftarrow$ Divisor

Check: To check, we can multiply by the divisor and add the remainder:

$$(2x + 1)(2x^2 - x - 3) + 4 = 4x^3 - 7x - 3 + 4$$
$$= 4x^3 - 7x + 1.$$

12. Divide:

$(6x^3 - 15x^2 + 2x - 5) \div (2x - 5)$.

YOUR TURN

R.4 EXERCISE SET

Exponents

Simplify.

1. a^0, for $a = -25$

2. y^0, for $y = 6.97$

3. $4^0 - 4^1$

4. $8^1 - 8^0$

Write an equivalent expression using positive exponents. Then, if possible, simplify.

5. 8^{-2}

6. $(-2)^{-3}$

7. $10x^{-5}$

8. $-16y^{-3}$

9. $(ab)^{-2}$

10. ab^{-2}

11. $\dfrac{1}{y^{-10}}$

12. $\dfrac{1}{x^{-t}}$

Simplify.

13. $x^5 \cdot x^{10}$

14. $a^4 \cdot a^{-2}$

15. $\dfrac{a}{a^{-5}}$

16. $\dfrac{p^{-3}}{p^{-8}}$

17. $\dfrac{(4x)^{11}}{(4x)^2}$

18. $\dfrac{a^2 b^9}{a^9 b^2}$

19. $(7^8)^5$

20. $(x^3)^{-7}$

21. $(x^{-2}y^{-3})^{-4}$

22. $(-2a^2)^3$

23. $\left(\dfrac{y^2}{4}\right)^3$

24. $\left(\dfrac{ab^2}{c^3}\right)^4$

25. $\left(\dfrac{2p^3}{3q^4}\right)^{-2}$

26. $\left(\dfrac{2}{x}\right)^{-5}$

Polynomials

Identify the terms of each polynomial.

27. $8x^3 - 6x^2 + x - 7$

28. $-a^2b + 4a^2 - 8b + 17$

Determine the coefficient and the degree of each term in each polynomial. Then find the degree of each polynomial.

29. $18x^3 + 36x^9 - 7x + 3$

30. $-8y^7 + y + 19$

31. $-x^2y + 4y^3 - 2xy$

32. $8 - x^2y^4 + y^7$

Determine the leading term and the leading coefficient of each polynomial.

33. $-p^2 + 5 + 8p^4 - 7p$

34. $13 + 20t - 30t^2 - t^3$

Combine like terms. Write each answer in descending order.

35. $3x^3 - x^2 + x^4 + x^2$

36. $5t - 8t^2 + 4t^2$

37. $3 - 2t^2 + 8t - 3t - 5t^2 + 7$

38. $8x^5 - \frac{1}{3} + \frac{4}{5}x + 1 - \frac{1}{2}x$

Evaluate each polynomial for the given replacements of the variables.

39. $3x^2 - 7x + 10$, for $x = -2$

40. $-y + 3y^2 + 2y^3$, for $y = 3$

41. $a^2b^3 + 2b^2 - 6a$, for $a = 2$ and $b = -1$

42. $2pq^3 - 5q^2 + 8p$, for $p = -4$ and $q = -2$

Memorizing Words. Participants in a psychology experiment were able to memorize an average of M words in t minutes, where $M = -0.001t^3 + 0.1t^2$.

43. Find the average number of words memorized in 10 min.

44. Find the average number of words memorized in 14 min.

Addition and Subtraction of Polynomials

Add or subtract, as indicated.

45. $(3x^3 + 2x^2 + 8x) + (x^3 - 5x^2 + 7)$

46. $(-6x^4 + 3x^2 - 16) + (4x^2 + 4x - 7)$

47. $(8y^2 - 2y - 3) - (9y^2 - 7y - 1)$

48. $(4t^2 + 6t - 7) - (t + 5)$

49. $(-x^2y + 2y^2 + y) - (3y^2 + 2x^2y - 7y)$

50. $(ab + x^2y^2) + (2ab - x^2y^2)$

Multiplication of Polynomials

Multiply.

51. $4x^2(3x^3 - 7x + 7)$

52. $a^2b(a^3 + b^2 - ab - 2b)$

53. $(2a + y)(4a + b)$

54. $(x + 7y)(y - 3x)$

55. $(x + 7)(x^2 - 3x + 1)$

56. $(2x - 3)(x^2 - x - 1)$

57. $(x + 7)(x - 7)$

58. $(2x + 1)^2$

59. $(x + y)^2$

60. $(xy + 1)(xy - 1)$

61. $(2x^2 + 7)(3x^2 - 2)$

62. $(1.1x^2 + 5)(0.1x^2 - 2)$

63. $(6a - 5y)(7a + 3y)$

64. $(3p^2 - q^3)^2$

Division of Polynomials

Divide and check.

65. $(3t^5 + 9t^3 - 6t^2 + 15t) \div (-3t)$

66. $(4x^5 + 10x^4 - 16x^2) \div (4x^2)$

67. $(15x^2 - 16x - 15) \div (3x - 5)$

68. $(x^3 - 2x^2 - 14x + 1) \div (x - 5)$

69. $(2x^3 - x^2 + 1) \div (x + 1)$

70. $(2x^3 + 3x^2 - 50) \div (2x - 5)$

71. $(5x^3 + 3x^2 - 5x) \div (x^2 - 1)$

72. $(2x^3 + 3x^2 + 6x + 10) \div (x^2 + 3)$

⮌ **YOUR TURN ANSWERS: SECTION R.4**

1. 1   **2.** $\dfrac{x^6}{4y^{10}}$ **3.** $6x^3 - 3$ **4.** 1   **5.** $3x^2 + 2x - 18$

6. $4y^3 + y^2 - 6y - 15$ **7.** $6x^3y - 8xy^3 + 10xy$

8. $2t^3 + t^2 - 2t + 8$ **9.** $3a^3 - 15a^2 + a - 5$

10. $y^2 - 1$ **11.** $3w^3 - 7w + 1$ **12.** $3x^2 + 1$

REFERENCES

Addition of polynomials, Section 4.4
Coefficient, p. 247
Degree of a polynomial, p. 248
Degree of a term, p. 247
Division of polynomials, Section 4.6
Evaluating a polynomial, p. 249
The exponent zero, p. 232
FOIL, p. 271
Leading coefficient, p. 248
Leading term, p. 248
Multiplication of polynomials, Section 4.5
Multiplying sums and differences of
    two terms, p. 272
Negative exponents, p. 238
Opposite of a polynomial, p. 256
Polynomials, Section 4.3
The power rule, p. 233
The product rule, p. 230
The quotient rule, p. 231
Raising a product to a power, p. 234
Raising a quotient to a power, p. 234
Squaring binomials, p. 273
Subtraction of polynomials, Section 4.4
Term, p. 246

R.5 | Polynomials and Factoring

Common Factors and Factoring by Grouping • Factoring Trinomials • Factoring Special Forms •
Solving Polynomial Equations by Factoring

Common Factors and Factoring by Grouping

To *factor* a polynomial is to find an equivalent expression that is a product. For example, three factorizations of $50x^6$ are $5 \cdot 10x^6$, $5x^3 \cdot 10x^3$, and $2x \cdot 25x^5$.

If all terms in a polynomial share a common factor, that factor can be "factored out." When factoring a polynomial with two or more terms, we use the largest common factor of the terms, if one exists.

EXAMPLE 1   Factor: $3x^6 + 15x^4 - 9x^3$.

SOLUTION   The largest factor common to 3, 15, and −9 is 3. The largest power of x common to x^6, x^4, and x^3 is x^3. Thus the largest common factor of the terms of the polynomial is $3x^3$. We factor as follows:

$$3x^6 + 15x^4 - 9x^3 = 3x^3 \cdot x^3 + 3x^3 \cdot 5x - 3x^3 \cdot 3 \qquad \text{Factoring each term}$$

$$= 3x^3(x^3 + 5x - 3). \qquad \text{Factoring out } 3x^3$$

Factorizations can always be checked by multiplying:

$$3x^3(x^3 + 5x - 3) = 3x^6 + 15x^4 - 9x^3.$$

1. Factor:

$$2a^4d^3 - 15ad^2 - 8a^2d^4.$$

YOUR TURN

A polynomial with two or more terms can itself be a common factor. For example, $3x^2(x - 2) + 5(x - 2) = (x - 2)(3x^2 + 5)$.

If a polynomial with four terms can be split into two groups of terms, and both groups share a common binomial factor, the polynomial can be factored. This method is known as **factoring by grouping**.

EXAMPLE 2   Factor by grouping: $2x^3 + 6x^2 - x - 3$.

SOLUTION   First, we consider the polynomial as two groups of terms, $2x^3 + 6x^2$ and $-x - 3$. Then we factor each group separately:

$$2x^3 + 6x^2 - x - 3 = 2x^2(x + 3) - 1(x + 3) \qquad \begin{array}{l}\text{Factoring out } 2x^2 \text{ and} \\ -1 \text{ to find the common} \\ \text{binomial factor, } x + 3\end{array}$$

$$= (x + 3)(2x^2 - 1).$$

2. Factor by grouping:

$$3x^3 + 12x^2 - x - 4.$$

The check is left to the student.

YOUR TURN

Not every polynomial with four terms is factorable by grouping. Any polynomial that is not factorable is said to be **prime**.

Student Notes

When factoring $x^2 + bx + c$, we look for a pair of factors that have c as their product and b as their sum. The signs of b and c help us determine the signs of the factors.

Sign of c	Sign of b	Signs of factors
+	+	+, +
+	−	−, −
−	+	+, −
−	−	+, −

Factoring Trinomials

Many trinomials that have no common factor can be written as the product of two binomials. We look first at trinomials of the form $x^2 + bx + c$, for which the leading coefficient is 1.

Factoring trinomials involves a trial-and-error process. In order for the product of two binomials to be $x^2 + bx + c$, the binomials must look like

$$(x + p)(x + q),$$

where p and q are constants that must be determined. We look for two numbers whose product is c and whose sum is b.

EXAMPLE 3   Factor.

a) $x^2 - 2x - 24$

b) $3t^2 - 33st + 84s^2$

SOLUTION

a) The factorization is of the form

$$(x + \quad)(x + \quad).$$

To find the constant terms, we need a pair of factors whose product is −24 and whose sum is −2. Since −24 is negative, one factor of −24 will be negative and one will be positive. Since b is also negative, the negative factor must have the larger absolute value.

Pairs of Factors of -24	Sums of Factors
1, -24	-23
2, -12	-10
3, -8	-5
4, -6	-2 ← The numbers we need are 4 and -6.

The factorization is $(x + 4)(x - 6)$.

Check: $(x + 4)(x - 6) = x^2 - 6x + 4x - 24 = x^2 - 2x - 24.$

b) Always look first for a common factor. There is a common factor, 3, which we factor out first:

$$3t^2 - 33st + 84s^2 = 3(t^2 - 11st + 28s^2).$$

Now we consider $t^2 - 11st + 28s^2$. Think of $28s^2$ as the "constant" term c and $-11s$ as the "coefficient" b of the middle term. We try to express $28s^2$ as the product of two factors whose sum is $-11s$. These factors are $-4s$ and $-7s$. Thus the factorization of $t^2 - 11st + 28s^2$ is

$(t - 4s)(t - 7s).$ This is not the entire factorization of $3t^2 - 33st + 84s^2$.

Finally, we include the common factor, 3, and write

$$3t^2 - 33st + 84s^2 = 3(t - 4s)(t - 7s).$$ This is the factorization.

Check: $3(t - 4s)(t - 7s) = 3(t^2 - 11st + 28s^2) = 3t^2 - 33st + 84s^2.$

3. Factor: $n^2 + 2n - 24$.

⟳ YOUR TURN

When the leading coefficient of a trinomial is not 1, the number of trials needed to find a factorization can increase dramatically. We will consider two methods for factoring trinomials of the type $ax^2 + bx + c$: factoring with FOIL and the grouping method.

TO FACTOR $ax^2 + bx + c$ USING FOIL

1. Make certain that all common factors have been removed. If any remain, factor out the largest common factor.

2. Find two First terms whose product is ax^2:

$(\ x + \ )(\ x + \ ) = ax^2 + bx + c.$
$\underline{\qquad}\text{FOIL}$

3. Find two Last terms whose product is c:

$(\ x + \ )(\ x + \ ) = ax^2 + bx + c.$
$\underline{\qquad}\text{FOIL}$

4. Check by multiplying to see if the sum of the Outer and Inner products is bx. If necessary, repeat steps (2) and (3) until the correct combination is found.

$(\ x + \ )(\ x + \ ) = ax^2 + bx + c.$
$\underline{\text{I}}$
$\underline{\text{O}}\qquad\text{FOIL}$

If no correct combination exists, state that the polynomial is prime.

EXAMPLE 4 Factor: $20x^3 - 22x^2 - 12x$.

SOLUTION

1. First, we factor out the largest common factor, $2x$:
$$20x^3 - 22x^2 - 12x = 2x(10x^2 - 11x - 6).$$

2. Next, in order to factor the trinomial $10x^2 - 11x - 6$, we search for two terms whose product is $10x^2$. The possibilities are
$$(x +)(10x +) \quad \text{or} \quad (2x +)(5x +).$$

3. There are four pairs of factors of -6. The first terms of the binomials differ, so the order of the factors is important. There are eight possibilities for the last terms:

$$
\begin{array}{cc}
1, -6 & -6, \ 1 \\
-1, \ 6 & 6, -1 \\
2, -3 \quad \text{and} & -3, \ 2 \\
-2, \ 3 & 3, -2.
\end{array}
$$

4. Since each of the eight possibilities from step (3) could be used in either of the two possibilities from step (2), there are $2 \cdot 8$, or 16, possible factorizations. We check the possibilities systematically until we find one that gives the correct factorization. Let's first try factors with $(2x +)(5x +)$.

Pair of Factors	Corresponding Trial	Product	
1, −6	$(2x + 1)(5x - 6)$	$10x^2 - 7x - 6$	← Wrong middle term
−1, 6	$(2x - 1)(5x + 6)$	$10x^2 + 7x - 6$	← Wrong middle term. Changing the signs in the binomials changed only the sign of the middle term in the product.
2, −3	$(2x + 2)(5x - 3)$	$10x^2 + 4x - 6$	← Wrong middle term
−6, 1	$(2x - 6)(5x + 1)$	$10x^2 - 28x - 6$	← Wrong middle term
−3, 2	$(2x - 3)(5x + 2)$	$10x^2 - 11x - 6$	← Correct middle term

We can stop when we find a correct factorization. Including the common factor $2x$, we now have
$$20x^3 - 22x^2 - 12x = 2x(2x - 3)(5x + 2).$$

This can be checked by multiplying.

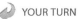 YOUR TURN

With practice, some of the trials can be skipped or performed mentally.

The second method of factoring trinomials of the type $ax^2 + bx + c$ involves factoring by grouping.

Student Notes

Both the third and the fourth trial factorizations in Example 4 contain a binomial with a common factor: $2x + 2 = 2(x + 1)$ and $2x - 6 = 2(x - 3)$. If all common factors are factored out as a first step, you can immediately eliminate any trial factorization containing a binomial with a common factor.

---

4. Factor: $10x^2 + 19x + 6$.

TO FACTOR $ax^2 + bx + c$ USING THE GROUPING METHOD

1. Factor out the largest common factor, if one exists.
2. Multiply the leading coefficient a and the constant c.
3. Find a pair of factors of ac whose sum is b.
4. Rewrite the middle term, bx, as a sum or a difference using the factors found in step (3).
5. Factor by grouping.
6. Include any common factor from step (1) and check by multiplying.

EXAMPLE 5 Factor: $7x^2 + 31x + 12$.

SOLUTION

1. There is no common factor (other than 1 or -1).
2. We multiply the leading coefficient, 7, and the constant, 12: $7 \cdot 12 = 84$.
3. We look for a pair of factors of 84 whose sum is 31. Since both 84 and 31 are positive, we need consider only positive factors.

Pairs of Factors of 84	Sums of Factors
1, 84	85
2, 42	44
3, 28	31 ← ———— $3 + 28 = 31$

4. Next, we rewrite $31x$ using the factors 3 and 28: $31x = 3x + 28x$.
5. We now factor by grouping:

$$7x^2 + 31x + 12 = 7x^2 + 3x + 28x + 12 \qquad \text{Substituting } 3x + 28x \text{ for } 31x$$

$$= x(7x + 3) + 4(7x + 3)$$

$$= (7x + 3)(x + 4). \qquad \text{Factoring out the common factor, } 7x + 3$$

5. Factor:

$8n^3 - 34n^2 + 15n.$

6. *Check:* $(7x + 3)(x + 4) = 7x^2 + 31x + 12.$

↩ YOUR TURN

Factoring Special Forms

We can factor certain types of polynomials directly, without using trial and error.

FACTORING FORMULAS

Perfect-square trinomial:	$A^2 + 2AB + B^2 = (A + B)^2,$
	$A^2 - 2AB + B^2 = (A - B)^2$
Difference of squares:	$A^2 - B^2 = (A + B)(A - B)$
Sum of cubes:	$A^3 + B^3 = (A + B)(A^2 - AB + B^2)$
Difference of cubes:	$A^3 - B^3 = (A - B)(A^2 + AB + B^2)$

Before using the factoring formulas, it is important to check carefully that the expression being factored is indeed in one of the forms listed. Note that there is no factoring formula for the sum of two squares.

EXAMPLE 6 Factor.

a) $2x^2 - 2$

b) $x^2y^2 + 20xy + 100$

c) $p^3 - 64$

d) $3y^2 + 27$

SOLUTION

a) We first factor out a common factor, 2:

$$2x^2 - 2 = 2(x^2 - 1).$$

Looking at $x^2 - 1$, we see that it is a difference of squares, $A^2 - B^2$, with $A = x$ and $B = 1$. The factorization is thus

$$2x^2 - 2 = 2(x^2 - 1) = 2(x + 1)(x - 1).$$
$$\underbrace{}_{A^2 - B^2}\quad\underbrace{}_{(A + B)(A - B)}$$

b) First, we check for a common factor; there is none. The polynomial is a perfect-square trinomial, $A^2 + 2AB + B^2$, with $A = xy$ and $B = 10$. The factorization is thus

$$x^2y^2 + 20xy + 100 = (xy)^2 + 2 \cdot xy \cdot 10 + 10^2 = (xy + 10)^2.$$
$$\underbrace{}_{A^2} + \underbrace{}_{2 \cdot A \cdot B} + \underbrace{}_{B^2} = \underbrace{}_{(A + B)^2}$$

c) This is a difference of cubes, $A^3 - B^3$, with $A = p$ and $B = 4$:

$$p^3 - 64 = (p)^3 - (4)^3$$
$$= (p - 4)(p^2 + 4p + 16).$$

d) We factor out the common factor, 3:

$$3y^2 + 27 = 3(y^2 + 9).$$

Since $y^2 + 9$ is a sum of squares, no further factorization is possible.

6. Factor: $4y^2 - 20y + 25$.

 YOUR TURN

A polynomial is *factored completely* when no factor can be factored further.

EXAMPLE 7 Factor completely: $x^4 - 1$.

SOLUTION

$$x^4 - 1 = (x^2 + 1)(x^2 - 1) \qquad \text{Factoring a difference of squares}$$
$$= (x^2 + 1)(x + 1)(x - 1) \qquad \text{The factor } x^2 - 1 \text{ is itself a difference of squares.}$$

7. Factor completely:

$$x^3 + 2x^2 - x - 2.$$

YOUR TURN

Solving Polynomial Equations by Factoring

A **polynomial equation** is formed by setting two polynomials equal to each other. A **quadratic equation** is a polynomial equation equivalent to one of the form $ax^2 + bx + c = 0$, where $a \neq 0$. Polynomial equations that can be factored can be solved using the principle of zero products.

> **THE PRINCIPLE OF ZERO PRODUCTS**
>
> An equation $ab = 0$ is true if and only if $a = 0$ or $b = 0$, or both. (A product is 0 if and only if at least one factor is 0.)

EXAMPLE 8   Solve: **(a)** $x^2 - 11x = 12$; **(b)** $5x^2 + 10x + 5 = 0$.

SOLUTION

a) We must have 0 on one side of the equation before using the principle of zero products:

Get 0 on one side.

Factor.

Use the principle of zero products.

Solve.

$$x^2 - 11x = 12$$
$$x^2 - 11x - 12 = 0 \qquad \text{Subtracting 12 from both sides}$$
$$(x - 12)(x + 1) = 0 \qquad \text{Factoring}$$
$$x - 12 = 0 \quad or \quad x + 1 = 0 \qquad \text{Using the principle of zero products}$$
$$x = 12 \quad or \qquad x = -1.$$

The solutions are 12 and -1. To check, we substitute 12 and then -1 for x in the original equation and confirm that each makes the equation true.

b) We have

$$5x^2 + 10x + 5 = 0$$
$$5(x^2 + 2x + 1) = 0 \qquad \text{Factoring out a common factor}$$
$$5(x + 1)(x + 1) = 0 \qquad \text{Factoring completely}$$
$$x + 1 = 0 \quad or \quad x + 1 = 0 \qquad \text{Using the principle of zero products}$$
$$x = -1 \quad or \qquad x = -1.$$

There is only one solution, -1. The check is left to the student.

YOUR TURN

Student Notes

In the factorization

$$5(x + 1)(x + 1),$$

5 is a factor, but it does not contain a variable and thus does not yield a solution of $5(x + 1)(x + 1) = 0$.

8. Solve: $9x^2 = 1$.

Quadratic equations can be used to solve problems. One important result that uses squared quantities is the Pythagorean theorem.

> **THE PYTHAGOREAN THEOREM**
>
> The sum of the squares of the legs of a right triangle is equal to the square of the hypotenuse:
>
> $$a^2 + b^2 = c^2.$$

EXAMPLE 9 *Hiking.* Cheri hiked 500 ft up a steep incline. Her global positioning unit (GPS) indicated that her horizontal position had changed by 100 ft more than her vertical position had changed. What was the change in altitude?

SOLUTION

1. **Familiarize.** We first make a drawing and let x = the change in altitude, in feet. We know then that the horizontal change is $x + 100$, since Cheri's horizontal position has changed by 100 ft more than her vertical position. The hypotenuse has length 500 ft.

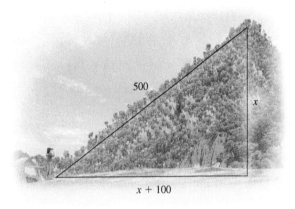

500

x

$x + 100$

2. **Translate.** Applying the Pythagorean theorem gives us

$$a^2 + b^2 = c^2$$
$$x^2 + (x + 100)^2 = 500^2.$$

3. **Carry out.** We solve the equation:

$$x^2 + (x + 100)^2 = 500^2$$

$$x^2 + x^2 + 200x + 10{,}000 = 250{,}000 \qquad \text{Squaring } x + 100; \\ \text{squaring } 500$$

$$2x^2 + 200x + 10{,}000 = 250{,}000 \qquad \text{Combining like terms}$$

$$2x^2 + 200x - 240{,}000 = 0 \qquad \text{Getting 0 on one side}$$

$$2(x^2 + 100x - 120{,}000) = 0 \qquad \text{Factoring out a common factor}$$

$$2(x + 400)(x - 300) = 0 \qquad \text{Factoring a trinomial}$$

$$x + 400 = 0 \quad or \quad x - 300 = 0 \qquad \text{Using the principle of zero products}$$

$$x = -400 \quad or \qquad x = 300.$$

9. The length of a hypotenuse of a right triangle is 13 ft. One leg of the triangle is 7 ft longer than the other leg. Find the lengths of the legs.

4. **Check.** We know that the change in altitude is positive, so -400 cannot be a solution. When $x = 300$, the horizontal change is 400. Since $300^2 + 400^2 = 500^2$, the solution checks.

5. **State.** Cheri's change in altitude was 300 ft.

YOUR TURN

R.5 EXERCISE SET

FOR EXTRA HELP

MyMathLab® *Math* XL
PRACTICE   WATCH   READ   REVIEW

Factoring Polynomials

Factor completely. If a polynomial is prime, state this.

1. $18t^5 - 12t^4 + 6t^3$
2. $x^2y^4 - 2xy^5 + 3x^3y^6$
3. $y^2 - 6y + 9$
4. $4z^2 - 25$
5. $2p^3(p + 2) + (p + 2)$
6. $6y^2 + y - 1$
7. $x^2 + 100$
8. $y^3 - 1$
9. $8t^3 + 27$
10. $a^2b^2 + 24ab + 144$
11. $m^2 + 13m + 42$
12. $2x^3 - 6x^2 + x - 3$
13. $x^4 - 81$
14. $x^2 + x + 3$
15. $8x^2 + 22x + 15$
16. $4x^2 - 40x + 100$
17. $x^3 + 2x^2 - x - 2$
18. $(x + 2y)(x - 1) + (x + 2y)(x - 2)$
19. $0.001t^6 - 0.008$
20. $x^2 - 20 - x$
21. $-\frac{1}{16} + x^4$
22. $5x^8 - 5z^{16}$
23. $mn - 2m + 3n - 6$
24. $t^6 - p^6$
25. $5mn + m^2 - 150n^2$
26. $\frac{1}{27} + x^3$
27. $24x^2y - 6y - 10xy$
28. $-3y^2 - 12y - 12$
29. $y^2 + 121 - 22y$
30. $t^3 - 2t^2 - 5t + 10$

Solving Polynomial Equations by Factoring

Solve.

31. $(x - 1)(x + 3) = 0$
32. $(3x - 5)(7 - 4x) = 0$
33. $8x(11 - x) = 0$
34. $(x - 3)(x + 1)(2x - 9) = 0$
35. $x^2 = 9$
36. $8x^2 = 2x$
37. $4x^2 - 18x = 70$
38. $x^2 + 6x + 9 = 0$
39. $2x^2 - 10x = 0$
40. $100x^2 = 9$
41. $(a + 1)(a - 5) = 7$
42. $d(d - 3) = 40$
43. $x^2 + 6x - 55 = 0$
44. $x^2 + 7x - 60 = 0$
45. $\frac{1}{2}x^2 + 5x + \frac{25}{2} = 0$
46. $3 + 10x^2 = 11x$

47. *Design.*   The base of a triangular window is 3 ft longer than its height. The area of the window is 20 ft². What are the dimensions of the window?

48. *Page Numbers.*   The product of the page numbers on two facing pages of a book is 156. Find the page numbers.

49. *Swing Sets.*   The length of a slide on a swing set is 10 ft. The distance from the base of the ladder to the base of the slide is 2 ft more than the height of the ladder. Find the height of the ladder.

50. *Right Triangles.*   The hypotenuse of a right triangle is 17 ft. One leg is 1 ft shorter than twice the length of the other leg. Find the lengths of the legs.

↘ YOUR TURN ANSWERS: SECTION R.5

1. $ad^2(2a^3d - 15 - 8ad^2)$ 2. $(x + 4)(3x^2 - 1)$
3. $(n + 6)(n - 4)$ 4. $(5x + 2)(2x + 3)$
5. $n(2n - 1)(4n - 15)$ 6. $(2y - 5)^2$
7. $(x + 2)(x + 1)(x - 1)$ 8. $-\frac{1}{3}, \frac{1}{3}$ 9. 5 ft, 12 ft

---

REFERENCES

Common factor, p. 304
Difference of squares, p. 330
Factor by grouping, p. 307
Factoring completely, p. 316
Factoring trinomials of the type
  $ax^2 + bx + c$, Section 5.3
Factoring trinomials of the type
  $x^2 + bx + c$, Section 5.2
Factoring with FOIL, p. 319
The grouping method, p. 324
Perfect-square trinomials, p. 328
Prime polynomial, p. 316
The principle of zero products, p. 346
The Pythagorean theorem, p. 357
Quadratic equation, p. 345
Sum or difference of cubes, Section 5.5

R.6 Rational Expressions and Equations

Rational Expressions • Multiplication and Division of Rational Expressions • Addition and Subtraction of Rational Expressions • Complex Rational Expressions • Solving Rational Equations

Rational Expressions

A **rational expression** is a quotient of two polynomials. Because division by 0 is undefined, a rational expression is undefined for any number that will make its denominator 0.

EXAMPLE 1   Find all numbers for which the rational expression

$$\frac{2x + 5}{x^2 - 9x - 10}$$

is undefined.

SOLUTION   We set the denominator equal to 0 and solve:

$$x^2 - 9x - 10 = 0$$
$$(x - 10)(x + 1) = 0 \qquad \text{Factoring}$$
$$x - 10 = 0 \quad or \quad x + 1 = 0 \qquad \text{Using the principle of zero products}$$
$$x = 10 \quad or \qquad x = -1.$$

If x is replaced with 10 or with -1, the denominator is 0. Thus,

$$\frac{2x + 5}{x^2 - 9x - 10} \quad \text{is undefined for } x = 10 \text{ and } x = -1.$$

1. Find all numbers for which the rational expression

$$\frac{x - 7}{2x^2 + 4x}$$

is undefined.

YOUR TURN

Multiplication and Division of Rational Expressions

Multiplication and division of rational expressions is similar to multiplication and division with fractions.

> ### THE PRODUCT AND THE QUOTIENT OF TWO RATIONAL EXPRESSIONS
>
> To multiply two rational expressions, multiply numerators and multiply denominators:
>
> $$\frac{A}{B} \cdot \frac{C}{D} = \frac{AC}{BD}.$$
>
> To divide by a rational expression, multiply by its reciprocal:
>
> $$\frac{A}{B} \div \frac{C}{D} = \frac{A}{B} \cdot \frac{D}{C} = \frac{AD}{BC}.$$

We simplify rational expressions by removing a factor equal to 1.

EXAMPLE 2   Simplify: $\dfrac{9x^2 + 12x}{6x^2 - 3x}$.

SOLUTION

$$\dfrac{9x^2 + 12x}{6x^2 - 3x} = \dfrac{3x(3x + 4)}{3x(2x - 1)} \qquad \text{Factoring the numerator and the denominator}$$

$$\dfrac{3x(3x + 4)}{3x(2x - 1)} = \dfrac{3x}{3x} \cdot \dfrac{3x + 4}{2x - 1} \qquad \text{Rewriting as a product of two rational expressions}$$

$$= 1 \cdot \dfrac{3x + 4}{2x - 1} \qquad \dfrac{3x}{3x} = 1$$

$$= \dfrac{3x + 4}{2x - 1} \qquad \text{Removing a factor equal to 1}$$

2. Simplify: $\dfrac{x^2 - x - 6}{2x^2 - 3x - 9}$.

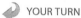 YOUR TURN

After multiplying or dividing rational expressions, we simplify, if possible.

EXAMPLE 3   Perform each indicated operation and, if possible, simplify.

a) $\dfrac{x^2 - x - 6}{3x} \cdot \dfrac{12x^3}{x + 2}$

b) $\dfrac{x^2 - 1}{x + 5} \div \dfrac{x^2 + 2x + 1}{2x + 10}$

SOLUTION

a) $\dfrac{x^2 - x - 6}{3x} \cdot \dfrac{12x^3}{x + 2} = \dfrac{(x^2 - x - 6)(12x^3)}{3x(x + 2)}$ Multiplying the numerators and the denominators

$$= \dfrac{(x - 3)(x + 2)(3x)(4x^2)}{3x(x + 2)} \qquad \begin{array}{l}\text{Factoring the numerator.}\\ \text{Try to go directly to this}\\ \text{step.}\end{array}$$

$$= \dfrac{(x - 3)(\cancel{x + 2})(\cancel{3x})(4x^2)}{(\cancel{3x})(\cancel{x + 2})} \qquad \begin{array}{l}\text{Removing a factor equal}\\ \text{to 1: } \dfrac{(x + 2)(3x)}{(x + 2)(3x)} = 1\end{array}$$

$$= 4x^2(x - 3)$$

b) $\dfrac{x^2 - 1}{x + 5} \div \dfrac{x^2 + 2x + 1}{2x + 10} = \dfrac{x^2 - 1}{x + 5} \cdot \dfrac{2x + 10}{x^2 + 2x + 1}$ Multiplying by the reciprocal of the divisor

$$= \dfrac{(x + 1)(x - 1)(2)(x + 5)}{(x + 5)(x + 1)(x + 1)} \qquad \begin{array}{l}\text{Multiplying rational}\\ \text{expressions and}\\ \text{factoring}\end{array}$$

$$= \dfrac{(\cancel{x + 1})(x - 1)(2)(\cancel{x + 5})}{(\cancel{x + 5})(\cancel{x + 1})(x + 1)} \qquad \begin{array}{l}\text{Removing a factor}\\ \text{equal to 1:}\\ \dfrac{(x + 1)(x + 5)}{(x + 1)(x + 5)} = 1\end{array}$$

$$= \dfrac{2(x - 1)}{x + 1} \qquad \begin{array}{l}\text{We leave the}\\ \text{numerator in}\\ \text{factored form.}\end{array}$$

3. Divide and, if possible, simplify:

$$\dfrac{a - b}{b^2} \div \dfrac{a^2 - b^2}{b^2 - b}.$$

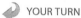 YOUR TURN

Addition and Subtraction of Rational Expressions

Like multiplication and division, addition and subtraction of rational expressions is similar to addition and subtraction of fractions.

THE SUM AND THE DIFFERENCE OF TWO RATIONAL EXPRESSIONS

To add when denominators are the same, add the numerators and keep the same denominator:

$$\frac{A}{B} + \frac{C}{B} = \frac{A + C}{B}.$$

To subtract when denominators are the same, subtract the second numerator from the first and keep the same denominator:

$$\frac{A}{B} - \frac{C}{B} = \frac{A - C}{B}.$$

EXAMPLE 4 Add and, if possible, simplify:

$$\frac{x - 6}{x^2 - 6x + 5} + \frac{5}{x^2 - 6x + 5}.$$

SOLUTION

$$\frac{x - 6}{x^2 - 6x + 5} + \frac{5}{x^2 - 6x + 5} = \frac{x - 6 + 5}{x^2 - 6x + 5} \qquad \text{Adding numerators}$$

$$= \frac{x - 1}{(x - 5)(x - 1)} \qquad \text{Factoring the denominator}$$

$$= \frac{1(x - 1)}{(x - 5)(x - 1)} \qquad \text{Removing a factor equal to 1: } \frac{x - 1}{x - 1} = 1$$

$$= \frac{1}{x - 5}$$

4. Subtract and, if possible, simplify:

$$\frac{t + 5}{t^2 - 9} - \frac{t}{t^2 - 9}.$$

 YOUR TURN

When two rational expressions have different denominators, we must rewrite them in an equivalent form with a common denominator. We generally rewrite them using their **least common denominator (LCD)**, which is the **least common multiple (LCM)** of the denominators.

TO FIND THE LEAST COMMON DENOMINATOR (LCD)

1. Write the prime factorization of each denominator.
2. Select one factorization and inspect it to see if it completely contains the other.

    a) If it does, it represents the LCM of the denominators.
    b) If it does not, multiply that factorization by any factors of the other denominator that it lacks. The final product is the LCM of the denominators.

EXAMPLE 5 Subtract: $\dfrac{x+2}{x^2-1} - \dfrac{x}{x^2+4x+3}$.

SOLUTION To find the LCD, we factor each denominator and use these factorizations to construct the LCM:

$$x^2 - 1 = (x+1)(x-1);$$
$$x^2 + 4x + 3 = (x+1)(x+3).$$

We select the factorization of $x^2 - 1$. Since it does not contain the factor $(x+3)$, we multiply $(x+1)(x-1)$ by $(x+3)$:

Find the LCD.

$$\text{LCM} = (x+1)(x-1)(x+3).$$

We multiply each rational expression by a form of 1 that is made up of the factors of the LCM that it is missing:

Rewrite each expression with the LCD.

$$\dfrac{x+2}{x^2-1} - \dfrac{x}{x^2+4x+3} = \dfrac{x+2}{(x+1)(x-1)} \cdot \dfrac{x+3}{x+3} - \dfrac{x}{(x+1)(x+3)} \cdot \dfrac{x-1}{x-1}$$

$$= \dfrac{x^2+5x+6}{(x+1)(x-1)(x+3)} - \dfrac{x^2-x}{(x+1)(x-1)(x+3)}$$

Subtract numerators. Keep the denominator.

$$= \dfrac{x^2+5x+6-(x^2-x)}{(x+1)(x-1)(x+3)} \qquad \text{Parentheses are important.}$$

$$= \dfrac{x^2+5x+6-x^2+x}{(x+1)(x-1)(x+3)} \qquad \text{Removing parentheses by subtracting each term}$$

$$= \dfrac{6x+6}{(x+1)(x-1)(x+3)}$$

Simplify if possible.

$$= \dfrac{6\cancel{(x+1)}}{\cancel{(x+1)}(x-1)(x+3)} \qquad \begin{array}{l}\text{Factoring and removing}\\ \text{a factor equal to 1:}\\ (x+1)/(x+1)=1\end{array}$$

5. Add and, if possible, simplify:

$$\dfrac{n+7}{n^2-n-2} + \dfrac{1}{n^2+n-6}.$$

$$= \dfrac{6}{(x-1)(x+3)}.$$

↪ YOUR TURN

When denominators are opposites, we can find a common denominator by multiplying either rational expression by $-1/-1$.

EXAMPLE 6 Add: $\dfrac{a}{a-b} + \dfrac{5}{b-a}$.

SOLUTION

$$\dfrac{a}{a-b} + \dfrac{5}{b-a} = \dfrac{a}{a-b} + \dfrac{5}{b-a} \cdot \dfrac{-1}{-1} \qquad \begin{array}{l}\text{Writing 1 as } -1/-1 \text{ and}\\ \text{multiplying to obtain a}\\ \text{common denominator}\end{array}$$

$$= \dfrac{a}{a-b} + \dfrac{-5}{a-b} \qquad \begin{array}{l}(b-a)(-1) = -b+a\\ \qquad\qquad = a-b\end{array}$$

6. Add and, if possible, simplify:

$$\dfrac{2x+3}{x-1} + \dfrac{x+4}{1-x}.$$

$$= \dfrac{a-5}{a-b}$$

↪ YOUR TURN

Complex Rational Expressions

A **complex rational expression** is a rational expression that has one or more rational expressions within its numerator or denominator. We examine two methods for simplifying complex rational expressions. The first involves writing the expression as a quotient of two rational expressions.

> **TO SIMPLIFY A COMPLEX RATIONAL EXPRESSION BY DIVIDING**
> 1. Add or subtract, as needed, to get a single rational expression in the numerator.
> 2. Add or subtract, as needed, to get a single rational expression in the denominator.
> 3. Divide the numerator by the denominator.
> 4. If possible, simplify by removing a factor equal to 1.

EXAMPLE 7 Simplify by dividing: $\dfrac{\dfrac{2}{x+1}}{\dfrac{1}{x+2}+\dfrac{1}{x}}$.

SOLUTION

1. There is already a single rational expression in the numerator.

2. We add to get a single rational expression in the denominator:

$$\frac{\dfrac{2}{x+1}}{\dfrac{1}{x+2}+\dfrac{1}{x}} = \frac{\dfrac{2}{x+1}}{\dfrac{1}{x+2}\cdot\dfrac{x}{x}+\dfrac{1}{x}\cdot\dfrac{x+2}{x+2}}$$

Multiplying by 1 to get the LCD, $x(x+2)$, for the denominator

$$= \frac{\dfrac{2}{x+1}}{\dfrac{x}{x(x+2)}+\dfrac{x+2}{x(x+2)}} = \frac{\dfrac{2}{x+1}}{\dfrac{2x+2}{x(x+2)}}.$$

Adding in the denominator

3. Next, we divide the numerator by the denominator:

$$\frac{\dfrac{2}{x+1}}{\dfrac{2x+2}{x(x+2)}} = \frac{2}{x+1}\div\frac{2x+2}{x(x+2)} = \frac{2}{x+1}\cdot\frac{x(x+2)}{2x+2}.$$

4. Simplifying, we have

$$\frac{2}{(x+1)}\cdot\frac{x(x+2)}{2x+2} = \frac{2\cdot x(x+2)}{2(x+1)(x+1)}$$

Factoring in the denominator and removing a factor equal to 1: $\frac{2}{2}=1$

$$= \frac{x(x+2)}{(x+1)^2}.$$

7. Simplify by dividing: $\dfrac{\dfrac{2x}{x-1}}{\dfrac{1}{x}-3}$.

 YOUR TURN

A second method involves multiplying by the LCD.

> **TO SIMPLIFY A COMPLEX RATIONAL EXPRESSION BY MULTIPLYING BY THE LCD**
> 1. Find the LCD of *all* rational expressions within the complex rational expression.
> 2. Multiply the complex rational expression by a factor equal to 1. Write 1 as the LCD over itself (LCD/LCD).
> 3. Simplify. No rational expressions should remain within the complex rational expression.
> 4. Factor and, if possible, simplify.

EXAMPLE 8 Simplify by multiplying by the LCD: $\dfrac{1 + \dfrac{2}{t}}{\dfrac{4}{t^2} - 1}$.

SOLUTION

1. The denominators *within* the complex rational expression are t and t^2, so the LCD is t^2.

2. We multiply by a form of 1 using t^2/t^2:

$$\frac{1 + \dfrac{2}{t}}{\dfrac{4}{t^2} - 1} = \frac{1 + \dfrac{2}{t}}{\dfrac{4}{t^2} - 1} \cdot \frac{t^2}{t^2}.$$

3. We distribute and simplify:

$$\frac{1 + \dfrac{2}{t}}{\dfrac{4}{t^2} - 1} \cdot \frac{t^2}{t^2} = \frac{1 \cdot t^2 + \dfrac{2}{t} \cdot t^2}{\dfrac{4}{t^2} \cdot t^2 - 1 \cdot t^2}$$

$$= \frac{t^2 + 2t}{4 - t^2}. \qquad \text{No rational expression remains within the numerator or the denominator.}$$

8. Simplify by multiplying by the LCD:

$$\frac{\dfrac{1}{a} + \dfrac{1}{b}}{\dfrac{a}{b}}.$$

4. Finally, we simplify:

$$\frac{t^2 + 2t}{4 - t^2} = \frac{t\cancel{(t + 2)}}{\cancel{(2 + t)}(2 - t)} \qquad \text{Factoring and simplifying; } \frac{t + 2}{t + 2} = 1$$

$$= \frac{t}{2 - t}.$$

 YOUR TURN

Solving Rational Equations

A **rational equation** is an equation containing one or more rational expressions, often with the variable in a denominator.

TO SOLVE A RATIONAL EQUATION

1. List any restrictions that exist. Numbers that make a denominator equal 0 can never be solutions.
2. Clear the equation of fractions by multiplying both sides by the LCM of the denominators.
3. Solve the resulting equation using the addition principle, the multiplication principle, and the principle of zero products, as needed.
4. Check the possible solution(s) in the original equation.

Because a possible solution in step (3) may make a denominator 0, checking is essential when solving rational equations.

EXAMPLE 9   Solve: $x + \dfrac{10}{x} = 7$.

SOLUTION   First, we note that x cannot be 0. The LCD is x, so we multiply both sides by x:

List restrictions.

$$x + \frac{10}{x} = 7 \qquad \textit{Note: } x \neq 0.$$

Clear fractions.

$$x\left(x + \frac{10}{x}\right) = 7x \qquad \text{Don't forget the parentheses!}$$

$$x \cdot x + x \cdot \frac{10}{x} = 7x \qquad \text{Using the distributive law}$$

$$x^2 + 10 = 7x \qquad \text{We have a quadratic equation.}$$

$$x^2 - 7x + 10 = 0 \qquad \text{Getting 0 on one side}$$

$$(x - 2)(x - 5) = 0 \qquad \text{Factoring}$$

Solve the equation.

$$x - 2 = 0 \quad or \quad x - 5 = 0 \qquad \text{Using the principle of zero products}$$

$$x = 2 \quad or \qquad x = 5.$$

Check.

Check: For 2:

$$x + \frac{10}{x} = 7$$

$$\begin{array}{c|c} 2 + \dfrac{10}{2} & 7 \\ \hline 2 + 5 & \\ 7 \overset{?}{=} 7 & \text{TRUE} \end{array}$$

For 5:

$$x + \frac{10}{x} = 7$$

$$\begin{array}{c|c} 5 + \dfrac{10}{5} & 7 \\ \hline 5 + 2 & \\ 7 \overset{?}{=} 7 & \text{TRUE} \end{array}$$

9. Solve: $\dfrac{1}{x} + \dfrac{1}{x+2} = \dfrac{7}{24}$.

Both numbers check, so there are two solutions, 2 and 5.

YOUR TURN

Many problems translate to rational equations. **Work problems**, which involve the time that it takes to complete a task, can often be solved using the work principle.

THE WORK PRINCIPLE

If

$a =$ the time needed for A to complete the work alone,

$b =$ the time needed for B to complete the work alone, and

$t =$ the time needed for A and B to complete the work together,

then $\dfrac{t}{a} + \dfrac{t}{b} = 1$.

EXAMPLE 10   *Painting.*   It takes Kerry 30 hr to repaint a mural. It takes Jesse 45 hr to repaint the same mural. How long would it take Kerry and Jesse, working together, to repaint the mural?

SOLUTION

1. **Familiarize.** We reason that if Kerry and Jesse each repaint half the mural, it would take Kerry 15 hr and Jesse $22\frac{1}{2}$ hr. So the time it takes them working together should be between 15 hr and $22\frac{1}{2}$ hr. We let $t =$ the time that it takes them to repaint the mural, working together.

2. Translate. We use the work principle to translate the problem:

$$\frac{t}{a} + \frac{t}{b} = 1 \qquad \begin{array}{l} a \text{ is the time that it takes Kerry to repaint the mural;} \\ b \text{ is the time that it takes Jesse to repaint the mural.} \end{array}$$

$$\frac{t}{30} + \frac{t}{45} = 1.$$

3. Carry out. We solve the equation:

$$\frac{t}{30} + \frac{t}{45} = 1$$

$$90\left(\frac{t}{30} + \frac{t}{45}\right) = 90 \cdot 1 \qquad \text{The LCD is } 2 \cdot 3 \cdot 3 \cdot 5, \text{ or } 90.$$

$$90 \cdot \frac{t}{30} + 90 \cdot \frac{t}{45} = 90$$

$$3t + 2t = 90$$

$$5t = 90$$

$$t = 18.$$

10. Refer to Example 10. Suppose that it takes Kerry 10 hr to paint a garage, and it takes Jesse 8 hr to paint the same garage. How long would it take them, working together, to paint the garage?

4. Check. We note that, as predicted in the *Familiarize* step, the answer is between 15 hr and $22\frac{1}{2}$ hr. Also, if each works 18 hr, Kerry will do $\frac{18}{30}$ of the job and Jesse will do $\frac{18}{45}$ of the job, and

$$\frac{18}{30} + \frac{18}{45} = \frac{3}{5} + \frac{2}{5} = 1. \qquad \text{The entire job will be completed.}$$

5. State. Together it will take them 18 hr to repaint the mural.

YOUR TURN

Motion problems deal with distance, speed (or rate), and time, and are often translated using the distance formula $d = rt$.

EXAMPLE 11 *Driving Time.* Karen and Eva are each driving to a sales meeting. Because of road conditions, Karen is able to drive 15 mph faster than Eva. In the same time that it takes Karen to travel 120 mi, Eva travels only 90 mi. Find their speeds.

SOLUTION

1. Familiarize. We let $t =$ the time, in hours, that is spent traveling and $r =$ Karen's speed, in miles per hour. Then Eva's speed $= r - 15$. From the distance formula, we have $t = d/r$, so we can organize the information as follows.

	Distance	Speed	Time
Karen	120	r	$120/r$
Eva	90	$r - 15$	$90/(r - 15)$

2. Translate. Since the times are the same, we have the equation

$$\frac{120}{r} = \frac{90}{r - 15}.$$

3. **Carry out.** We solve the equation:

$$\frac{120}{r} = \frac{90}{r-15}$$

$$r(r-15)\frac{120}{r} = r(r-15)\frac{90}{r-15} \qquad \text{The LCD is } r(r-15).$$

$$120(r-15) = 90r \qquad \text{Simplifying}$$

$$120r - 1800 = 90r \qquad \text{Removing parentheses}$$

$$-1800 = -30r \qquad \text{Subtracting } 120r \text{ from both sides}$$

$$60 = r. \qquad \text{Dividing both sides by } -30$$

11. Refer to Example 11. Suppose that Karen is able to drive 25 mph faster than Eva. In the same time that it takes Karen to travel 240 mi, Eva travels only 140 mi. Find their speeds.

4. **Check.** If $r = 60$, then $r - 15 = 45$. If Karen travels 120 mi at 60 mph, she will have traveled for 2 hr. If Eva travels 90 mi at 45 mph, she will also have traveled for 2 hr. Since the times are the same, the speeds check.

5. **State.** Karen is traveling at 60 mph, while Eva is traveling at 45 mph.

YOUR TURN

Another type of problem that translates to a rational equation involves proportions. A **ratio** of two quantities is their quotient. A **proportion** is an equation stating that two ratios are equal.

EXAMPLE 12 *Baking.* Rob discovers there is $2\frac{1}{2}$ cups of pancake mix left in the box. The directions on the mix indicate that $1\frac{1}{3}$ cups of milk should be added to 2 cups of mix. How much milk should Rob add to the $2\frac{1}{2}$ cups of mix?

SOLUTION Since the problem translates directly to a proportion, we will not follow all five steps of the problem-solving process. We write the ratio of mix to milk in two ways:

$$\begin{array}{c}\text{Mix} \longrightarrow \\ \text{Milk} \longrightarrow\end{array} \frac{2}{1\frac{1}{3}} = \frac{2\frac{1}{2}}{x} \begin{array}{c}\longleftarrow \text{Mix} \\ \longleftarrow \text{Milk}\end{array}$$

The LCD is $x\left(1\frac{1}{3}\right)$. We solve for x:

$$x\left(1\tfrac{1}{3}\right)\frac{2}{1\frac{1}{3}} = x\left(1\tfrac{1}{3}\right)\frac{2\frac{1}{2}}{x} \qquad \text{Multiplying by the LCD}$$

$$2x = \left(1\tfrac{1}{3}\right)\left(2\tfrac{1}{2}\right) \qquad \text{Simplifying}$$

$$2x = \tfrac{10}{3} \qquad \text{Converting to fraction notation and multiplying}$$

$$x = \tfrac{5}{3}. \qquad \text{Multiplying both sides by } \tfrac{1}{2} \text{ and simplifying}$$

12. It takes Keri $3\frac{1}{2}$ hr to grade 50 journal entries. At that rate, how long would it take her to grade 40 entries?

Rob needs to add $\frac{5}{3}$, or $1\frac{2}{3}$, cups of milk.

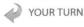 YOUR TURN

R.6 EXERCISE SET

Rational Expressions

List all numbers for which each rational expression is undefined.

1. $\dfrac{x - 7}{3x + 1}$

2. $\dfrac{10 - y}{-5y}$

3. $\dfrac{p^2 - 1}{p^2 - 4}$

4. $\dfrac{10x}{x^2 + 9x + 8}$

Simplify by removing a factor equal to 1.

5. $\dfrac{16x^2y}{18xy^2}$

6. $\dfrac{2x + 10}{6x + 30}$

7. $\dfrac{t^2 - 2t - 8}{t^2 - 16}$

8. $\dfrac{a^3 + 2a^2 + a}{a^2 + 4a + 3}$

9. $\dfrac{2 - x}{x^2 - 4}$

10. $\dfrac{n - 3}{3 - n}$

Addition, Subtraction, Multiplication, and Division of Rational Expressions

Perform each indicated operation. Then, if possible, simplify.

11. $\dfrac{3x}{x + y} \cdot \dfrac{2x + 2y}{x^2}$

12. $\dfrac{5}{x + 7} \cdot \dfrac{x + 7}{10}$

13. $\dfrac{a^2 + 2a + 1}{a} \div \dfrac{a^2}{a^2 - 1}$

14. $\dfrac{x}{x + 3} + \dfrac{3 - x}{x + 3}$

15. $\dfrac{2x}{x - 7} - \dfrac{x + 7}{x - 7}$

16. $\dfrac{x}{x + y} \div \dfrac{y}{x + y}$

17. $\dfrac{5}{x} + \dfrac{4}{x^2}$

18. $\dfrac{x^2 + 4x + 3}{x^2 + x - 2} \cdot \dfrac{x^2 + 3x + 2}{x^2 + 2x - 3}$

19. $\dfrac{2a + b}{a - b} - \dfrac{4}{3a - 3b}$

20. $(x^2 - 16) \div \dfrac{4x + 16}{3x^2}$

21. $\dfrac{2 - x}{5x^2} \div \dfrac{x^2 - 4}{3x}$

22. $\dfrac{2x}{x - 5} + \dfrac{3}{x + 4}$

23. $\dfrac{x^3 + 2x^2 + x}{x^2 - 4} \cdot \dfrac{x^2 - x - 2}{x^4 + x^3}$

24. $\dfrac{-1}{x^2 + 7x + 10} - \dfrac{3}{x^2 + 8x + 15}$

25. $\dfrac{2}{(x + 1)^2} + \dfrac{1}{x + 1}$

26. $\dfrac{2x}{x^2 - 3x} \div (x - 3)$

27. $\dfrac{x}{x - 2} + \dfrac{2}{2 - x}$

28. $\dfrac{3}{y - 1} - \dfrac{y}{1 - y}$

29. $\dfrac{t}{t^2 - 1} - \dfrac{1}{1 - t}$

30. $\dfrac{1}{5 - x} + \dfrac{x}{2x - 10}$

31. $\dfrac{x - y}{2x} \cdot \dfrac{3x^2}{y - x}$

32. $\dfrac{1}{x + y} + \dfrac{2}{x^2 + y^2}$

33. $\dfrac{x - 2}{x + 5} - \dfrac{x + 3}{x - 4}$

34. $\dfrac{z^2 + 2z + 1}{8z} \div \dfrac{z^2 - z - 2}{4z^2 - 4}$

Complex Rational Expressions

Simplify.

35. $\dfrac{\dfrac{2}{x} - \dfrac{1}{x^2}}{\dfrac{x}{4}}$

36. $\dfrac{\dfrac{x}{3} - \dfrac{3}{x}}{\dfrac{1}{x} + \dfrac{1}{3}}$

37. $\dfrac{\dfrac{3}{x - 7}}{\dfrac{4x + 3}{x + 1}}$

38. $\dfrac{\dfrac{a}{a - b}}{\dfrac{a^2}{a^2 - b^2}}$

39. $\dfrac{x - \dfrac{3}{x - 2}}{x - \dfrac{12}{x + 1}}$

40. $\dfrac{t + \dfrac{1}{t}}{t - \dfrac{2}{t}}$

41. $\dfrac{\dfrac{1}{2} - \dfrac{1}{x}}{\dfrac{2 - x}{2}}$

42. $\dfrac{\dfrac{x}{2y^2} + \dfrac{y}{3x^2}}{\dfrac{1}{6xy} + \dfrac{2}{x^2y}}$

Solving Rational Equations

Solve.

43. $\dfrac{1}{2} + \dfrac{1}{3} = \dfrac{1}{t}$

44. $\dfrac{1}{4} + \dfrac{1}{t} = \dfrac{1}{3}$

45. $x + \dfrac{1}{x} = 2$

46. $\dfrac{x - 7}{x + 1} = \dfrac{2}{3}$

47. $\dfrac{3}{y + 7} = \dfrac{1}{y - 8}$

48. $\dfrac{x + 1}{x - 2} = \dfrac{3}{x - 2}$

49. $\dfrac{1}{x - 3} - \dfrac{x - 4}{x^2 - 9} = 1$

50. $\dfrac{3}{a + 4} = \dfrac{a - 1}{4 - a}$

51. *Painting.* Quentin can paint the turret on a Queen Anne house in 40 hr. It takes Austin 50 hr to paint the same turret. How long would it take them, working together, to paint the turret?

52. *Building Fences.* Lindsay can build a fence in 6 hr. Laura can do the same job in 5 hr. How long will it take them, working together, to build the fence?

53. *Snowmobiling.* Jessica can ride her snowmobile through the fields 20 km/h faster than Josh can ride his through the woods. In the time that it takes Jessica to ride 18 km, Josh travels 10 km. Find the speed of each snowmobile.

54. *Bicycling.* Ani bicycles 8 mi and Lia bicycles 12 mi to meet at a park for lunch. Because Ani's trip is mostly uphill, she rides 5 mph slower than Lia. Ani and Lia leave their homes at the same time and arrive at the park at the same time. Find the speed of each bicyclist.

55. *Elk Population.* To determine the size of a park's elk population, rangers tag 15 elk and set them free. Months later, 40 elk are caught, of which 12 have tags. Estimate the size of the elk population.

56. *Manufacturing Pegs.* A sample of 136 wooden pegs contained 17 defective pegs. How many defective pegs would you expect in a sample of 840 pegs?

 YOUR TURN ANSWERS: SECTION R.6

1. $-2, 0$ **2.** $\dfrac{x + 2}{2x + 3}$ **3.** $\dfrac{b - 1}{b(a + b)}$ **4.** $\dfrac{5}{t^2 - 9}$

5. $\dfrac{n^2 + 11n + 22}{(n - 2)(n + 1)(n + 3)}$ **6.** 1 **7.** $\dfrac{-2x^2}{(x - 1)(3x - 1)}$

8. $\dfrac{a + b}{a^2}$ **9.** $-\dfrac{8}{7}, 6$ **10.** $\dfrac{40}{9}$ hr, or $4\dfrac{4}{9}$ hr   **11.** Karen: 60 mph; Eva: 35 mph   **12.** 2.8 hr

---

REFERENCES

Addition and subtraction of
   rational expressions, Sections 6.3–6.4
Complex rational expressions, Section 6.5
Factors that are opposites, p. 378
Least common denominator, p. 389
Least common multiple, p. 389
Motion problems, p. 420
Multiplication and division of
   rational expressions, Section 6.2
Proportion, p. 424
Ratio, p. 424
Rational expressions, p. 374
Solving rational equations, Section 6.6
Work problems, p. 418

APPENDIXES

A | Mean, Median, and Mode

Mean ■ Median ■ Mode

One way to analyze data is to look for a single representative number, called a **center point** or **measure of central tendency**. Those most often used are the **mean** (or **average**), the **median**, and the **mode**.

Mean

The *mean* of a set of numbers is often called an *average*.

> **MEAN, OR AVERAGE**
>
> The *mean*, or *average*, of a set of numbers is the sum of the numbers divided by the number of addends.

EXAMPLE 1 Find the mean of the following set of prices for a milkshake:

$2.20, $2.60, $3.30, $4.10, $5.30.

What is the mean price?

SOLUTION We add the numbers and divide by the number of addends, 5:

$$\frac{(2.20 + 2.60 + 3.30 + 4.10 + 5.30)}{5} = \frac{17.50}{5} = 3.50.$$

The mean, or average, price is $3.50.

1. Find the mean:

13, 19, 6, 11, 28, 37.

YOUR TURN

Median

The *median* is useful when we wish to de-emphasize extreme scores. For example, suppose five workers in a technology company manufactured the following number of computers during one day's work:

Sarah: 88

Matt: 92

Pat: 66

Jen: 94

Mark: 91

Let's first list the scores in order from smallest to largest:

66 88 91 92 94.

Middle number

The middle number—in this case, 91—is the **median**.

> **MEDIAN**
>
> Once a set of data has been arranged from smallest to largest, the *median* of the set of data is the middle number if there is an odd number of data numbers. If there is an even number of data numbers, then there are two middle numbers and the median is the *average* of the two middle numbers.

EXAMPLE 2 Find the median of the following set of household incomes:

$76,000, $58,000, $87,000, $32,500, $64,800, $62,500.

SOLUTION We first rearrange the numbers in order from smallest to largest.

$32,500, $58,000, $62,500, $64,800, $76,000, $87,000

Median

There is an even number of numbers. We look for the middle two, which are $62,500 and $64,800. The median is the average of $62,500 and $64,800:

2. Find the median:

4, 6, 12, 8, 3.

$$\frac{\$62,500 + \$64,800}{2} = \$63,650.$$

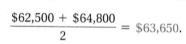 YOUR TURN

Mode

The last center point we consider is called the *mode*. A number that occurs most often in a set of data is sometimes considered a representative number, or center point.

> **MODE**
>
> The *mode* of a set of data is the number or numbers that occur most often. If each number occurs the same number of times, then there is *no* mode.

EXAMPLE 3 Find the mode of the following data:

3. Find the mode:

1.6, 8.5, 1.6, 3.7, 1.6.

23,   24,   27,   18,   19,   27.

SOLUTION The number that occurs most often is 27. Thus the mode is 27.

YOUR TURN

It is easier to find the mode of a set of data if the data are ordered.

EXAMPLE 4 Find the mode of the following data:

83, 84, 84, 84, 85, 86, 87, 87, 87, 88, 89, 90.

4. Find the mode:

3, 8, 4, 3, 2, 2, 2, 3.

SOLUTION There are two numbers that occur most often, 84 and 87. Thus the modes are 84 and 87.

YOUR TURN

EXAMPLE 5 Find the mode of the following data:

115, 117, 211, 213, 219.

5. Find the mode:

1, 2, 3, 4, 5, 6.

SOLUTION Each number occurs the same number of times. The set of data has *no* mode.

YOUR TURN

A EXERCISE SET

FOR EXTRA HELP

MyMathLab®
PRACTICE   WATCH   READ   REVIEW

Mean, Median, and Mode

For each set of numbers, find the mean (average), the median, and any modes that exist.

1. 13, 21, 18, 13, 20

2. 5, 2, 8, 10, 7, 1, 9

3. 3, 8, 20, 3, 20, 10

4. 19, 19, 8, 16, 8, 7

5. 4.7, 2.3, 4.6, 4.9, 3.8

6. 13.4, 13.4, 12.6, 42.9

7. 234, 228, 234, 228, 234, 278

8. $29.95, $28.79, $30.95, $29.95

9. *Hurricanes.* The following bar graph shows the number of hurricanes that struck the United States by month from 1851 to 2010. What is the average number for the 8 months given? the median? the mode?

Atlantic Storms and Hurricanes

Source: Atlantic Oceanographic and Meteorological Laboratory

10. *Camera Prices.* A price comparison showed the following online prices for a Canon S95 camera:

$399.99, $329.95, $379.95, $399.99, $288.00.

What was the average price? the median price? the mode?

11. *PBA Scores.* Kelly Kulick rolled scores of 254, 202, 184, 269, 151, 223, 258, 222, and 202 in a recent tour trial for the Professional Bowlers Association. What was her average? her median? her mode?

Source: Professional Bowlers Association

12. *Salmon Prices.* The following prices per pound of Atlantic salmon were found at six fish markets:

$17.99, $15.99, $17.99, $16.99, $17.49, $19.99.

What was the average price per pound? the median price? the mode?

Synthesis

13. *Hank Aaron.* Hank Aaron averaged $34\frac{7}{22}$ home runs per year over a 22-year career. After 21 years, Aaron had averaged $35\frac{10}{21}$ home runs per year. How many home runs did Aaron hit in his final year?

14. *Length of Pregnancy.* Marta was pregnant 270 days, 259 days, and 272 days for her first three pregnancies. In order for Marta's average length of pregnancy to equal the worldwide average of 266 days, how long must her fourth pregnancy last?

Source: David Crystal (ed.), *The Cambridge Factfinder.* Cambridge CB2 1RP: Cambridge University Press, 1993, p. 84.

15. The ordered set of data 18, 21, 24, a, 36, 37, b has a median of 30 and an average of 32. Find a and b.

16. *Male Height.* Jason's brothers are 174 cm, 180 cm, 179 cm, and 172 cm tall. The average male is 176.5 cm tall. How tall is Jason if he and his brothers have an average height of 176.5 cm?

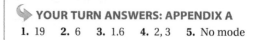

YOUR TURN ANSWERS: APPENDIX A

1. 19   **2.** 6   **3.** 1.6   **4.** 2, 3   **5.** No mode

B   Sets

Naming Sets • Membership • Subsets • Intersections • Unions

Naming Sets

A **set** is a collection of objects. In mathematics the objects, or **elements**, of a set are generally numbers.

To name the set of whole numbers less than 6, we can use *roster notation*, as follows:

$$\{0, 1, 2, 3, 4, 5\}.$$

The set of real numbers x for which x is less than 6 cannot be named by listing all its members because there is an infinite number of them. We name such a set using *set-builder notation*, as follows:

$$\{x \mid x < 6\}.$$

This is read

"The set of all x such that x is less than 6."

The **empty set** contains no elements and is written $\varnothing$. It can also be written { }. Note that $\{0\}$ contains 0 and is thus *not* empty.

Membership

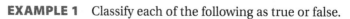

The symbol $\in$ means *is a member of* or *belongs to*, or *is an element of*. Thus, $x \in A$ means

    x is a member of A,   or x belongs to A,   or x is an element of A.

EXAMPLE 1   Classify each of the following as true or false.

a) $1 \in \{1, 2, 3\}$ **b)** $1 \in \{2, 3\}$

c) $4 \in \{x \mid x \text{ is an even whole number}\}$

SOLUTION

a) Since 1 is listed as a member of the set, $1 \in \{1, 2, 3\}$ is true.

b) Since 1 is *not* a member of $\{2, 3\}$, the statement $1 \in \{2, 3\}$ is false.

c) Since 4 is an even whole number, $4 \in \{x \mid x \text{ is an even whole number}\}$ is true.

YOUR TURN

1. Classify as true or false.

    $5 \in \{x \mid x \text{ is an even whole number}\}$.

Subsets

If every element of A is also an element of B, then A is a *subset* of B. This is denoted $A \subseteq B$.

For example, the set of whole numbers is a subset of the set of integers, and the set of rational numbers is a subset of the set of real numbers.

EXAMPLE 2 Classify each of the following as true or false.

a) $\{1, 2\} \subseteq \{1, 2, 3, 4\}$ **b)** $\{p, q, r, w\} \subseteq \{a, p, r, z\}$

c) $\{x \mid x < 6\} \subseteq \{x \mid x \leq 11\}$

SOLUTION

a) Since every element of $\{1, 2\}$ is in the set $\{1, 2, 3, 4\}$, it follows that $\{1, 2\} \subseteq \{1, 2, 3, 4\}$ is true.

b) Since $q \in \{p, q, r, w\}$, but $q \notin \{a, p, r, z\}$, it follows that $\{p, q, r, w\} \subseteq \{a, p, r, z\}$ is false.

2. Classify as true or false:

$\{8, 9, 10\} \subseteq \{8, 9\}$.

c) Since every number that is less than 6 is also less than 11, the statement $\{x \mid x < 6\} \subseteq \{x \mid x \leq 11\}$ is true.

YOUR TURN

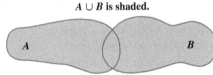
$A \cap B$

Intersections

The *intersection* of sets A and B, denoted $A \cap B$, is the set of members common to both sets.

EXAMPLE 3 Find each intersection.

a) $\{0, 1, 3, 5, 25\} \cap \{2, 3, 4, 5, 6, 7, 9\}$

b) $\{a, p, q, w\} \cap \{m, n, x, y\}$

SOLUTION

a) $\{0, 1, 3, 5, 25\} \cap \{2, 3, 4, 5, 6, 7, 9\} = \{3, 5\}$

3. Find the intersection:

$\{3, 4, 5\} \cap \{3, 4, 5, 6\}$.

b) $\{a, p, q, w\} \cap \{m, n, x, y\} = \varnothing$ These sets have no members in common. Their intersection is the empty set.

YOUR TURN

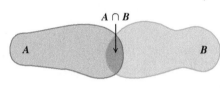
$A \cup B$ is shaded.

Unions

Two sets A and B can be combined to form a set that contains the members of both A and B. The new set is called the *union* of A and B, denoted $A \cup B$.

EXAMPLE 4 Find each union.

a) $\{0, 5, 7, 13, 27\} \cup \{0, 2, 3, 4, 5\}$ **b)** $\{a, c, e, g\} \cup \{b, d, f\}$

SOLUTION

a) $\{0, 5, 7, 13, 27\} \cup \{0, 2, 3, 4, 5\} = \{0, 2, 3, 4, 5, 7, 13, 27\}$

Note that the 0 and the 5 are *not* listed twice in the union.

4. Find the union:

$\{1, 3, 5, 7\} \cup \{2, 3, 5, 8\}$.

b) $\{a, c, e, g\} \cup \{b, d, f\} = \{a, b, c, d, e, f, g\}$

YOUR TURN

B **EXERCISE SET**   FOR EXTRA HELP   MyMathLab®
PRACTICE   WATCH   READ   REVIEW

Naming Sets

Name each set using the roster method.

1. The set of whole numbers 8 through 11

2. The set of whole numbers 83 through 89

3. The set of odd numbers between 40 and 50

4. The set of multiples of 5 between 10 and 40

5. $\{x \mid$ the square of x is $9\}$

6. $\{x \mid x$ is the cube of $\frac{1}{2}\}$

Membership and Subsets

Classify each statement as either true or false.

7. $5 \in \{x \mid x$ is an odd number$\}$

8. $8 \in \{x \mid x$ is an odd number$\}$

9. Skiing ∈ The set of all sports

10. Pharmacist ∈ The set of all professions requiring a college degree

11. 3 ∈ {−4, −3, 0, 1}

12. 0 ∈ {−4, −3, 0, 1}

13. $\frac{2}{3}$ ∈ {x | x is a rational number}

14. $\frac{2}{3}$ ∈ {x | x is a real number}

15. {−1, 0, 1} ⊆ {−3, −2, −1, 1, 2, 3}

16. The set of vowels ⊆ The set of consonants

17. The set of integers ⊆ The set of rational numbers

18. {2, 4, 6} ⊆ {1, 2, 3, 4, 5, 6, 7}

Intersections

Find each intersection.

19. {a, b, c, d, e} ∩ {c, d, e, f, g}

20. {a, e, i, o, u} ∩ {q, u, i, c, k}

21. {1, 2, 3, 4, 6, 12} ∩ {1, 2, 3, 6, 9, 18}

22. {1, 2, 3, 4, 6, 12} ∩ {1, 5, 7, 35}

23. {2, 4, 6, 8} ∩ {1, 3, 5, 7}

24. {a, e, i, o, u} ∩ {m, n, f, g, h}

Unions

Find each union.

25. {a, e, i, o, u} ∪ {q, u, i, c, k}

26. {a, b, c, d, e} ∪ {c, d, e, f, g}

27. {1, 2, 3, 4, 6, 12} ∪ {1, 2, 3, 6, 9, 18}

28. {1, 2, 3, 4, 6, 12} ∪ {1, 5, 7, 35}

29. {2, 4, 6, 8} ∪ {1, 3, 5, 7}

30. {a, e, i, o, u} ∪ {m, n, f, g, h}

31. What advantage(s) does set-builder notation have over roster notation?

32. What advantage(s) does roster notation have over set-builder notation?

Synthesis

33. Find the union of the set of integers and the set of whole numbers.

34. Find the intersection of the set of odd integers and the set of even integers.

35. Find the union of the set of rational numbers and the set of irrational numbers.

36. Find the intersection of the set of even integers and the set of positive rational numbers.

37. Find the intersection of the set of rational numbers and the set of irrational numbers.

38. Find the union of the set of negative integers, the set of positive integers, and the set containing 0.

39. For a set A, find each of the following.
    a) $A \cup \varnothing$
    b) $A \cup A$
    c) $A \cap A$
    d) $A \cap \varnothing$

Classify each statement as either true or false.

40. The empty set can be written ∅, { }, or {0}.

41. For any set A, ∅ ⊆ A.

42. For any set A, A ⊆ A.

43. For any sets A and B, A ∩ B ⊆ A.

44. A set is *closed* under an operation if, when the operation is performed on its members, the result is in the set. For example, the set of real numbers is closed under the operation of addition since the sum of any two real numbers is a real number.
    a) Is the set of even numbers closed under addition?
    b) Is the set of odd numbers closed under addition?
    c) Is the set {0, 1} closed under addition?
    d) Is the set {0, 1} closed under multiplication?
    e) Is the set of real numbers closed under multiplication?
    f) Is the set of integers closed under division?

45. Experiment with sets of various types and determine whether the following distributive law for sets is true:

$$A \cap (B \cup C) = (A \cap B) \cup (A \cap C).$$

 YOUR TURN ANSWERS: APPENDIX B

1. False   2. False   3. {3, 4, 5}   4. {1, 2, 3, 5, 7, 8}

C   Synthetic Division and the Remainder Theorem

Synthetic Division   ■   The Remainder Theorem

Synthetic Division

To divide a polynomial by a binomial of the type $x - a$, we can streamline the usual procedure to develop a process called *synthetic division*.

Compare the following. In each stage, we attempt to write less than in the previous stage, while retaining enough essentials to solve the problem.

When a polynomial is written in descending order, the coefficients provide the essential information.

Long Division

$$
\begin{array}{r}
4x^2 + 5x + 11 \\
x - 2 \overline{)4x^3 - 3x^2 + x + 7} \\
\underline{4x^3 - 8x^2} \\
5x^2 + x \\
\underline{5x^2 - 10x} \\
11x + 7 \\
\underline{11x - 22} \\
29
\end{array}
$$

Stage 1

$$
\begin{array}{r}
4 + 5 + 11 \\
1 - 2 \overline{)4 - 3 + 1 + 7} \\
\underline{4 - 8} \\
5 + 1 \\
\underline{5 - 10} \\
11 + 7 \\
\underline{11 - 22} \\
29
\end{array}
$$

Because the leading coefficient in $x - 2$ is 1, each time we multiply it by a term in the answer, the leading coefficient of that product is the same as the coefficient in the answer. In stage 2, rather than duplicate these numbers, we focus on where -2 is used. We also drop the 1 from the divisor. To simplify further, in stage 3, we reverse the sign of the -2 in the divisor and, in exchange, *add* at each step in the long division.

Stage 2

$$
\begin{array}{r}
4 + 5 + 11 \\
-2 \overline{)4 - 3 + 1 + 7} \\
- 8 \\
5 + 1 \\
- 10 \\
11 + 7 \\
- 22 \\
29
\end{array}
$$

Multiply: $-2 \cdot 4 = -8.$
Subtract: $-3 - (-8) = 5.$
Multiply: $-2 \cdot 5 = -10.$
Subtract: $1 - (-10) = 11.$
Multiply: $-2 \cdot 11 = -22.$
Subtract: $7 - (-22) = 29.$

Stage 3

$$
\begin{array}{r}
4 + 5 + 11 \\
2 \overline{)4 - 3 + 1 + 7} \\
8 \\
5 + 1 \\
10 \\
11 + 7 \\
22 \\
29
\end{array}
$$

Replace the -2 with 2.

Multiply: $2 \cdot 4 = 8.$
Add: $-3 + 8 = 5.$
Multiply: $2 \cdot 5 = 10.$
Add: $1 + 10 = 11.$
Multiply: $2 \cdot 11 = 22.$
Add: $7 + 22 = 29.$

The blue numbers can be eliminated if we look at the red numbers instead, as shown in stage 4 below. Note that the 5 and the 11 preceding the remainder 29 coincide with the 5 and the 11 following the 4 on the top line. By writing a 4 to the left of 5 on the bottom line, we can eliminate the top line in stage 4 and read our answer from the bottom line. This final stage is commonly called **synthetic division**.

Student Notes

You will not need to write out all five stages when performing synthetic division on your own. We show the steps to help you understand the reasoning behind the method.

Stage 4

$$
\begin{array}{r}
4 \quad 5 \quad 11 \\
2\overline{)4 \quad -3 \quad 1 \quad 7} \\
8 \quad 10 \quad 22 \\
\hline
5 \quad 11 \quad 29
\end{array}
$$

Stage 5

$$
\begin{array}{r}
2\,\lfloor 4 \quad -3 \quad 1 \quad 7 \\
8 \quad 10 \quad 22 \\
\hline
4 \quad 5\,\lfloor 11 \quad 29
\end{array}
$$

← This is the remainder.

── This is the zero-degree coefficient.

── This is the first-degree coefficient.

── This is the second-degree coefficient.

The quotient is $4x^2 + 5x + 11$ with a remainder of 29.

> Remember that in order for this method to work, the divisor must be of the form $x - a$, that is, a variable minus a constant. Note that the coefficient of the variable is 1.

Before using synthetic division in Example 1, let's review how stage 5, above, is formed.

This is the constant being subtracted in the divisor. → $2\,\lfloor 4 \quad -3 \quad 1 \quad 7$ ← These are the coefficients in the dividend.

This line is formed by adding in each column. → $\dfrac{8 \quad 10 \quad 22}{4 \quad 5 \quad 11\,\lfloor 29}$ ← These are found by multiplying 2 by the number below and to the left.

This is found first by bringing down the 4.

EXAMPLE 1 Use synthetic division to divide: $(x^3 + 6x^2 - x - 30) \div (x - 2)$.

SOLUTION

$2\,\lfloor 1 \quad 6 \quad -1 \quad -30$ Write the 2 of $x - 2$ and the coefficients of the dividend.

$\underline{}$

1 Bring down the first coefficient.

$2\,\lfloor 1 \quad 6 \quad -1 \quad -30$
  2 Multiply 1 by 2 to get 2.
$\overline{1 \quad 8}$ Add 6 and 2.

$2\,\lfloor 1 \quad 6 \quad -1 \quad -30$
  $2 \quad 16$ Multiply 8 by 2.
$\overline{1 \quad 8 \quad 15}$ Add −1 and 16.

$2\,\lfloor 1 \quad 6 \quad -1 \quad -30$
  $2 \quad 16 \quad 30$ Multiply 15 by 2 and add.
$\overline{1 \quad 8 \quad 15 \quad 0}$

The answer is $x^2 + 8x + 15$ with R 0, or just $x^2 + 8x + 15$.

YOUR TURN

1. Use synthetic division to divide:

$(x^3 + 2x^2 - 17x + 6) \div (x - 3)$.

EXAMPLE 2   Use synthetic division to divide.

a) $(2x^3 + 7x^2 - 5) \div (x + 3)$

b) $(10x^2 - 13x + 3x^3 - 20) \div (4 + x)$

SOLUTION

a) $(2x^3 + 7x^2 - 5) \div (x + 3)$

The dividend has no x-term, so we need to write 0 as the coefficient of x. Note that $x + 3 = x - (-3)$, so we write -3 inside the ⌐.

$$
\begin{array}{r|rrrr}
-3 & 2 & 7 & 0 & -5 \\
   &   & -6 & -3 & 9 \\
\hline
   & 2 & 1 & -3 & 4
\end{array}
$$

The answer is $2x^2 + x - 3$, with R 4, or $2x^2 + x - 3 + \dfrac{4}{x + 3}$.

b) We first rewrite $(10x^2 - 13x + 3x^3 - 20) \div (4 + x)$ in descending order:

$$(3x^3 + 10x^2 - 13x - 20) \div (x + 4).$$

Next, we use synthetic division. Note that $x + 4 = x - (-4)$.

$$
\begin{array}{r|rrrr}
-4 & 3 & 10 & -13 & -20 \\
   &   & -12 & 8 & 20 \\
\hline
   & 3 & -2 & -5 & 0
\end{array}
$$

The answer is $3x^2 - 2x - 5$.

2. Use synthetic division to divide:

$$(3x - 9 + 2x^3) \div (x + 2).$$

YOUR TURN

The Remainder Theorem

When a polynomial function $f(x)$ is divided by $x - a$, the remainder is related to the function value $f(a)$. Compare the following from Examples 1 and 2.

Polynomial Function	Divisor	Remainder	Function Value
Example 1: $f(x) = x^3 + 6x^2 - x - 30$	$x - 2$	0	$f(2) = 0$
Example 2(a): $g(x) = 2x^3 + 7x^2 - 5$	$x + 3$, or $x - (-3)$	4	$g(-3) = 4$
Example 2(b): $p(x) = 10x^2 - 13x + 3x^3 - 20$	$4 + x$, or $x - (-4)$	0	$p(-4) = 0$

When the remainder is 0, the divisor $x - a$ is a factor of the polynomial being divided. We can write $f(x) = x^3 + 6x^2 - x - 30$ in Example 1 as

$$f(x) = (x - 2)(x^2 + 8x + 15).$$

Then

$$
\left.
\begin{aligned}
f(2) &= (2 - 2)(2^2 + 8 \cdot 2 + 15) \\
     &= 0(2^2 + 8 \cdot 2 + 15) = 0.
\end{aligned}
\right\}
$$

Since $x - 2$ is a factor, $f(2) = 0$.

Technology Connection

In Example 1, the division by $x - 2$ gave a remainder of 0. The remainder theorem tells us that this means that when $x = 2$, the value of $x^3 + 6x^2 - x - 30$ is 0. Check this both graphically and algebraically (by substitution). Then perform a similar check for Example 2(b).

Thus, when the remainder is 0 after division by $x - a$, the function value $f(a)$ is also 0. Remarkably, this pattern extends to nonzero remainders as well. The fact that the remainder and the function value coincide is predicted by the remainder theorem.

> **THE REMAINDER THEOREM**
>
> The remainder obtained by dividing $P(x)$ by $x - r$ is $P(r)$.

A proof of this result is outlined in Exercise 37.

EXAMPLE 3   Let $f(x) = 8x^5 - 6x^3 + x - 8$. Use synthetic division to find $f(2)$.

SOLUTION   The remainder theorem tells us that $f(2)$ is the remainder when $f(x)$ is divided by $x - 2$. We use synthetic division to find that remainder:

$$
\begin{array}{r|rrrrrr}
2 & 8 & 0 & -6 & 0 & 1 & -8 \\
  &   & 16 & 32 & 52 & 104 & 210 \\
\hline
  & 8 & 16 & 26 & 52 & 105 & 202
\end{array}
$$

Although the bottom line can be used to find the quotient for the division $(8x^5 - 6x^3 + x - 8) \div (x - 2)$, what we are really interested in is the remainder. It tells us that $f(2) = 202$. The calculations are easier than the more typical calculation of $f(2)$.

3. Let
$$f(x) = 5x^4 + 3x^2 + 2x - 7.$$
Use synthetic division to find $f(-2)$.

YOUR TURN

The remainder theorem is often used to check division. Thus Example 2(a) can be checked by computing $g(-3) = 2(-3)^3 + 7(-3)^2 - 5$. Since $g(-3) = 4$ and the remainder in Example 2(a) is also 4, our division was probably correct.

C EXERCISE SET

FOR EXTRA HELP

MyMathLab® Math XL

PRACTICE   WATCH   READ   REVIEW

Vocabulary and Reading Check

Classify each of the following statements as either true or false.

1. If $P(-5) = 39$ and $P(x) = x^3 + 7x^2 + 3x + 4$, then

$$
\begin{array}{r|rrrr}
-5 & 1 & 7 & 3 & 4 \\
   &   & -5 & -10 & 35 \\
\hline
   & 1 & 2 & -7 & 39
\end{array}
$$

2. In order to use synthetic division, we must be sure that the divisor is of the form $x - a$.

3. Synthetic division can be used in problems in which long division could not be used.

4. In order for $f(x)/g(x)$ to exist, $g(x)$ must be 0.

5. If $x - 2$ is a factor of some polynomial $P(x)$, then $P(2) = 0$.

6. If $p(3) = 0$ for some polynomial $p(x)$, then $x - 3$ is a factor of $p(x)$.

Synthetic Division

Use synthetic division to divide.

7. $(x^3 - 4x^2 - 2x + 5) \div (x - 1)$

8. $(x^3 - 4x^2 + 5x - 6) \div (x - 3)$

9. $(a^2 + 8a + 11) \div (a + 3)$

10. $(a^2 + 8a + 11) \div (a + 5)$

11. $(2x^3 - x^2 - 7x + 14) \div (x + 2)$

12. $(3x^3 - 10x^2 - 9x + 15) \div (x - 4)$

13. $(a^3 - 10a + 12) \div (a - 2)$

14. $(a^3 - 14a + 15) \div (a - 3)$

15. $(3y^3 - 7y^2 - 20) \div (y - 3)$

16. $(2x^3 - 3x^2 + 8) \div (x + 2)$

17. $(x^5 - 32) \div (x - 2)$

18. $(y^5 - 1) \div (y - 1)$

19. $(3x^3 + 1 - x + 7x^2) \div \left(x + \frac{1}{3}\right)$

20. $(8x^3 - 1 + 7x - 6x^2) \div \left(x - \frac{1}{2}\right)$

The Remainder Theorem

Use synthetic division to find the indicated function value.

21. $f(x) = 5x^4 + 12x^3 + 28x + 9; f(-3)$

22. $g(x) = 3x^4 - 25x^2 - 18; g(3)$

23. $P(x) = 2x^4 - x^3 - 7x^2 + x + 2; P(-3)$

24. $F(x) = 3x^4 + 8x^3 + 2x^2 - 7x - 4; F(-2)$

25. $f(x) = x^4 - 6x^3 + 11x^2 - 17x + 20; f(4)$

26. $p(x) = x^4 + 7x^3 + 11x^2 - 7x - 12; p(2)$

27. Why is it that we *add* when performing synthetic division, but *subtract* when performing long division?

28. Explain how synthetic division could be useful when attempting to factor a polynomial.

Synthesis

29. Let $Q(x)$ be a polynomial function with $p(x)$ a factor of $Q(x)$. If $p(3) = 0$, does it follow that $Q(3) = 0$? Why or why not? If $Q(3) = 0$, does it follow that $p(3) = 0$? Why or why not?

30. What adjustments must be made if synthetic division is to be used to divide a polynomial by a binomial of the form $ax + b$, with $a > 1$?

31. To prove the remainder theorem, note that any polynomial $P(x)$ can be rewritten as $(x - r) \cdot Q(x) + R$, where $Q(x)$ is the quotient polynomial that arises when $P(x)$ is divided by $x - r$, and R is some constant (the remainder).

a) How do we know that R must be a constant?

b) Show that $P(r) = R$ (this says that $P(r)$ is the remainder when $P(x)$ is divided by $x - r$).

32. Let $f(x) = 6x^3 - 13x^2 - 79x + 140$. Find $f(4)$ and then solve the equation $f(x) = 0$.

33. Let $f(x) = 4x^3 + 16x^2 - 3x - 45$. Find $f(-3)$ and then solve the equation $f(x) = 0$.

34. Use the TRACE feature on a graphing calculator to check your answer to Exercise 32.

35. Use the TRACE feature on a graphing calculator to check your answer to Exercise 33.

Nested Evaluation.   *One way to evaluate a polynomial function like $P(x) = 3x^4 - 5x^3 + 4x^2 - 1$ is to successively factor out x as shown:*

$$P(x) = x(x(x(3x - 5) + 4) + 0) - 1.$$

Computations are then performed using this "nested" form of $P(x)$.

36. Use nested evaluation to find $f(4)$ in Exercise 32. Note the similarities to the calculations performed with synthetic division.

37. Use nested evaluation to find $f(-3)$ in Exercise 33. Note the similarities to the calculations performed with synthetic division.

 YOUR TURN ANSWERS: APPENDIX C

1. $x^2 + 5x - 2$ **2.** $2x^2 - 4x + 11 + \dfrac{-31}{x + 2}$ **3.** 81

TABLES

TABLE 1   Fraction and Decimal Equivalents

Fraction Notation	$\frac{1}{10}$	$\frac{1}{8}$	$\frac{1}{6}$	$\frac{1}{5}$	$\frac{1}{4}$	$\frac{3}{10}$	$\frac{1}{3}$	$\frac{3}{8}$	$\frac{2}{5}$	$\frac{1}{2}$
Decimal Notation	0.1	0.125	$0.16\overline{6}$	0.2	0.25	0.3	$0.333\overline{3}$	0.375	0.4	0.5
Percent Notation	10%	12.5%, or $12\frac{1}{2}\%$	$16.6\overline{6}\%$, or $16\frac{2}{3}\%$	20%	25%	30%	$33.3\overline{3}\%$, or $33\frac{1}{3}\%$	37.5%, or $37\frac{1}{2}\%$	40%	50%
Fraction Notation	$\frac{3}{5}$	$\frac{5}{8}$	$\frac{2}{3}$	$\frac{7}{10}$	$\frac{3}{4}$	$\frac{4}{5}$	$\frac{5}{6}$	$\frac{7}{8}$	$\frac{9}{10}$	$\frac{1}{1}$
Decimal Notation	0.6	0.625	$0.666\overline{6}$	0.7	0.75	0.8	$0.83\overline{3}$	0.875	0.9	1
Percent Notation	60%	62.5%, or $62\frac{1}{2}\%$	$66.6\overline{6}\%$, or $66\frac{2}{3}\%$	70%	75%	80%	$83.3\overline{3}\%$, or $83\frac{1}{3}\%$	87.5%, or $87\frac{1}{2}\%$	90%	100%

TABLE 2   Squares and Square Roots with Approximations to Three Decimal Places

N	$\sqrt{N}$	N^2	N	$\sqrt{N}$	N^2	N	$\sqrt{N}$	N^2	N	$\sqrt{N}$	N^2
1	1	1	26	5.099	676	51	7.141	2601	76	8.718	5776
2	1.414	4	27	5.196	729	52	7.211	2704	77	8.775	5929
3	1.732	9	28	5.292	784	53	7.280	2809	78	8.832	6084
4	2	16	29	5.385	841	54	7.348	2916	79	8.888	6241
5	2.236	25	30	5.477	900	55	7.416	3025	80	8.944	6400
6	2.449	36	31	5.568	961	56	7.483	3136	81	9	6561
7	2.646	49	32	5.657	1024	57	7.550	3249	82	9.055	6724
8	2.828	64	33	5.745	1089	58	7.616	3364	83	9.110	6889
9	3	81	34	5.831	1156	59	7.681	3481	84	9.165	7056
10	3.162	100	35	5.916	1225	60	7.746	3600	85	9.220	7225
11	3.317	121	36	6	1296	61	7.810	3721	86	9.274	7396
12	3.464	144	37	6.083	1369	62	7.874	3844	87	9.327	7569
13	3.606	169	38	6.164	1444	63	7.937	3969	88	9.381	7744
14	3.742	196	39	6.245	1521	64	8	4096	89	9.434	7921
15	3.873	225	40	6.325	1600	65	8.062	4225	90	9.487	8100
16	4	256	41	6.403	1681	66	8.124	4356	91	9.539	8281
17	4.123	289	42	6.481	1764	67	8.185	4489	92	9.592	8464
18	4.243	324	43	6.557	1849	68	8.246	4624	93	9.644	8649
19	4.359	361	44	6.633	1936	69	8.307	4761	94	9.695	8836
20	4.472	400	45	6.708	2025	70	8.367	4900	95	9.747	9025
21	4.583	441	46	6.782	2116	71	8.426	5041	96	9.798	9216
22	4.690	484	47	6.856	2209	72	8.485	5184	97	9.849	9409
23	4.796	529	48	6.928	2304	73	8.544	5329	98	9.899	9604
24	4.899	576	49	7	2401	74	8.602	5476	99	9.950	9801
25	5	625	50	7.071	2500	75	8.660	5625	100	10	10,000

PHOTO CREDITS

1 (top), Spaxiax/Shutterstock   1 (bottom), Ben Sarle   6 (top), Mexico's Presidency/ZUMA Press/Newscom   6 (bottom), Spaxiax/Shutterstock   8, Philip Lange/Shutterstock   9, *Spring Arcs* (2004), Edward Tufte, Solid stainless steel, 12' × 67'. 18, Blend RM/Glow Images   29, Ralf Broskvar/Shutterstock   43, Photo Resource Hawaii/Nature Picture Library   48, Michal Ninger/Shutterstock   51, Barbara Johnson   59, Stanley Fellerman/Corbis, Glow Images   78, Eric Gevaert/Shutterstock 79 (top), Ingo Schulz/AGE Fotostock   79 (bottom), Courtesy of Carlton Riffel   99, Rostislav Glinsky/Shutterstock 104, Melissa Dockstader/Shutterstock   110, William K. Daby/Newscom   114, Amy Griffiths/Courtesy of Ken Looi 115, Ingo Schulz/AGE Fotostock   121, Jim West/Alamy   124, ICHPL Imaginechina/AP Images   137, Papa Roux, Inc. 138, Rob Marmion/Shutterstock   141, Steve Heap/Shutterstock   153 (top), Kutay Tanir/Getty Images   153 (bottom), Courtesy of A. V. Krishnan   183, Heritage Imagestate/Glow Images   186, Leo and Mandy Dickinson/Nature Picture Library   189, Natalia Bratslavsky/Shutterstock   200, Nancy Wright/AbbiOrca Photography   215, Kutay Tanir/Getty Images 229 (top), Stephanie Roeser/SuperStock   229 (bottom), Uda Walawe Elephant Research Project   246, Ocean Image Photography/Shutterstock   249, Barbara Johnson   252, Norman Kent Productions   283, Stephanie Roeser/SuperStock 284, Natalia Barsukova/Shutterstock   299, Lisa S/Shutterstock   303 (top), Jill Chen/Vetta/Getty Images   303 (bottom), Courtesy of Neil Kao   327, Peter Chadwick/LRPS/Getty Images   355, Ron Kaufmann/University of San Diego   356, Jill Chen/Vetta/Getty Images   360, Andrej Pol/Shutterstock   370, Kushnirov Avraham/Fotolia   373 (top), Hans Reinhard/ zefa/Glow Images   373 (bottom), Jeff Hays   394, Paulus Gerdes   418, Barbara Johnson   420, Sheltered Images/SuperStock 428, Thomas Barrat/Shutterstock   429, Hans Reinhard/zefa/Glow Images   430, Stephen Meese/Fotolia   441 (top), Masterzphotofo/Fotolia   441 (bottom), Courtesy of Chen-Hui Li Spicer/Gensler   464, Bloomberg/Getty Images 480, NASA   482, Ulichka7/Fotolia   487, Daniel E. Johnson   489, Masterzphotofo/Fotolia   496, Matt Dunham/AP Images 497, John Wang/Getty Images   501 (top), Martin Mistretta/Getty Images   501 (bottom), Courtesy of Anju Agarwal 502, Gino Santa Maria/Fotolia   503, Steve Heap/Shutterstock   519, Gino Santa Maria/Fotolia   520 (top), Steve Heap/ Shutterstock   520 (bottom), TeaPots N Treasures   528, Ali Kabas/Alamy   545 (left), R. Legosyn/Shutterstock   545 (right), Richard Wareham Fotografie (Nieuws)/Alamy   546 (left), Erica Guilane-Nachez/Fotolia   546 (right), Martin Mistretta/ Getty Images   559, Andres Rodriguez/Fotolia   563, Fido Products   575 (top), Katrina Brown/Shutterstock   575 (bottom), Courtesy of Gonzalo Calderone/Woody Armstrong   578, Katrina Brown/Shutterstock   592, TEA/Shutterstock   612, Pavel Svoboda/Shutterstock   613, Christina Richards/Shutterstock   627 (top), Shutterstock   627 (bottom), Courtesy of Beth Lopez   643, Shutterstock   648, Barbara Johnson   654, Marco Cannizzaro/Shutterstock   669, Eric Gay/Ontario Science Center/Newscom   676, Pat Benic/UPI/Newscom   678, Skyscan Photolibrary/Alamy   697 (top), Adam Radosavljevic/ Shutterstock   697 (bottom), Shane Kimberlin and Alex Van Wyhe of Tea Mug Collective   705, Forcdan/Fotolia   707, Eric Kieboom/Rex USA   720 (top), Tatiana Popova/Shutterstock   720 (bottom), Sam Greenwood/Getty Images Sport/Getty Images   725, AFP/Getty Images   751, Adam Radosavljevic/Shutterstock   767, Pedro Vieira/Shutterstock   773, Barbara Johnson   777 (top), Robert Kyllo/Shutterstock   777 (bottom), Courtesy of Tim Morgan   778, Alex Van Wyhe and Shane Kimberlin of Tea Mug Collective   796, Doug Lindstrand/Alaska Stock/Superstock   827, AP Images   832, Tasha Treadwell/ The Baltimore Sun   833, Robert Kyllo/Shutterstock   836, Anthony Devlin/AP Images   837, Bill Tiernan/AP Images 844, Pablo77/Shutterstock   847 (top), Merkushev Vasiliy/Shutterstock   847 (bottom), Courtesy of Howard Wu 856, Merkushev Vasiliy/Shutterstock   862, Patrick Wright/Photographic Services/Clemson University   883, Kmiragaya/ Fotolia   889 (top), Gyuszkofoto/Shutterstock   889 (bottom), Courtesy of Wayne Benbow   895, Michal Lowalski/ Shutterstock   913, Gyuszkofoto/Shutterstock

CHAPTER 1

Technology Connection, p. 7

1. 3438   **2.** 47,531

Exercise Set 1.1, pp. 8–11

1. Constant   **2.** Evaluate   **3.** Model   **4.** Equation
5. Expression   **6.** Equation   **7.** Equation
8. Expression   **9.** Equation   **10.** Expression
11. Equation   **12.** Expression   **13.** 45   **15.** 8   **17.** 5
19. 4   **21.** 5   **23.** 3   **25.** 24 ft^2 **27.** 15 cm^2
29. 804 ft^2 **31.** Let r represent Ron's age; $r + 5$, or $5 + r$
33. $6b$, or $b \cdot 6$ **35.** $c - 9$ **37.** $6 + q$, or $q + 6$
39. $p - t$ **41.** $y - x$ **43.** $x \div w$, or $\dfrac{x}{w}$
45. Let l represent the length of the box and h the height; $l + h$, or $h + l$ **47.** $9 \cdot 2m$, or $2m \cdot 9$
49. Let y represent "some number"; $\dfrac{1}{4}y - 13$, or $\dfrac{y}{4} - 13$
51. Let a and b represent the two numbers; $5(a - b)$
53. Let w represent the number of women attending; 64% of w, or $0.64w$ **55.** Let x represent the unknown number; $73 + x = 201$ **57.** Let x represent the unknown number; $42x = 2352$ **59.** Let s represent the number of unoccupied squares; $s + 19 = 64$ **61.** Let w represent the amount of solid waste generated, in millions of tons; 34% of $w = 82$, or $0.34w = 82$ **63.** $f = a + 5$ **65.** $n = m + 2.21$
67. $v = 10{,}000d$ **69.** (f)   **71.** (d)   **73.** (g)
75. (e)   **77.** ☑   **79.** ☑   **81.** $450   **83.** 2
85. 6   **87.** $w + 4$ **89.** $l + w + l + w$, or $2l + 2w$
91. $t + 8$ **93.** ☑

Exercise Set 1.2, pp. 16–18

1. Equivalent   **2.** Commutative   **3.** Sum   **4.** Factors
5. Commutative   **6.** Associative   **7.** Distributive
8. Commutative   **9.** Commutative   **10.** Distributive
11. $t + 11$ **13.** $8x + 4$ **15.** $3y + 9x$ **17.** $5(1 + a)$
19. $x \cdot 7$ **21.** ts **23.** $5 + ba$ **25.** $(a + 1)5$
27. $x + (8 + y)$ **29.** $(u + v) + 7$ **31.** $ab + (c + d)$
33. $10(xy)$ **35.** $(2a)b$ **37.** $(3 \cdot 2)(a + b)$
39. $(s + t) + 6$; $(t + 6) + s$ **41.** $17(ab)$; $b(17a)$
43. $(1 + x) + 2 = (x + 1) + 2$ Commutative law
$ = x + (1 + 2)$ Associative law
$ = x + 3$ Simplifying
45. $(m \cdot 3)7 = m(3 \cdot 7)$ Associative law
$ = m \cdot 21$ Simplifying
$ = 21m$ Commutative law
47. $x, xyz, 1$ **49.** $2a, \dfrac{a}{3b}, 5b$ **51.** $4x, 4y$ **53.** $5, n$
55. $3, (x + y)$ **57.** $7, a, b$ **59.** $(a - b), (x - y)$

61. $2x + 30$ **63.** $4 + 4a$ **65.** $90x + 60$
67. $5r + 10 + 15t$ **69.** $2a + 2b$ **71.** $5x + 5y + 10$
73. $2(a + b)$ **75.** $7(1 + y)$ **77.** $2(16x + 1)$
79. $5(x + 2 + 3y)$ **81.** $7(a + 5b)$ **83.** $11(4x + y + 2z)$
85. Commutative law of addition; distributive law
87. Distributive law; associative law of multiplication
89. ☑   **91.** ☑   **93.** Distributive law; associative law of addition; commutative law of addition; associative law of addition; distributive law   **95.** Yes; distributive law
97. No; for example, let $m = 1$. Then $7 \div 3 \cdot 1 = \dfrac{7}{3}$ and $1 \cdot 3 \div 7 = \dfrac{3}{7}$.   **99.** No; for example, let $x = 1$ and $y = 2$. Then $30 \cdot 2 + 1 \cdot 15 = 60 + 15 = 75$ and $5[2(1 + 3 \cdot 2)] = 5[2(7)] = 5 \cdot 14 = 70$.   **101.** ☑
103. Answers may vary. **(a)** Aidan: $10(1.5x + 40)$; Beth: $10 \cdot 40 + 10(1.5)x$; Cody: $15x + 400$; **(b)** all expressions are equivalent to $15x + 400$.

Quick Quiz: Sections 1.1–1.2, p. 18

1. 9   **2.** $2(m + 3)$ **3.** Let n represent the number; $\dfrac{1}{3} \cdot n = 18$ **4.** $3x + 15y + 21$ **5.** $7(2a + t + 1)$

Exercise Set 1.3, pp. 26–28

1. Numerator   **2.** Prime   **3.** Reciprocal   **4.** Add
5. (b)   **6.** (c)   **7.** (d)   **8.** (a)   **9.** Composite
11. Prime   **13.** Composite   **15.** Prime   **17.** Neither
19. 1, 2, 5, 10, 25, 50   **21.** 1, 2, 3, 6, 7, 14, 21, 42
23. $3 \cdot 13$ **25.** $2 \cdot 3 \cdot 5$ **27.** $3 \cdot 3 \cdot 3$ **29.** $2 \cdot 3 \cdot 5 \cdot 5$
31. Prime   **33.** $2 \cdot 3 \cdot 5 \cdot 7$ **35.** $5 \cdot 23$ **37.** $\dfrac{3}{5}$
39. $\dfrac{2}{7}$ **41.** $\dfrac{1}{4}$ **43.** 4   **45.** $\dfrac{1}{4}$ **47.** 6   **49.** $\dfrac{21}{25}$
51. $\dfrac{60}{41}$ **53.** $\dfrac{15}{7}$ **55.** $\dfrac{3}{10}$ **57.** 6   **59.** $\dfrac{1}{2}$ **61.** $\dfrac{7}{6}$
63. $\dfrac{3b}{7a}$ **65.** $\dfrac{10}{n}$ **67.** $\dfrac{5}{6}$ **69.** 1   **71.** $\dfrac{5}{18}$ **73.** 0
75. $\dfrac{35}{18}$ **77.** 27   **79.** 1   **81.** $\dfrac{6}{35}$ **83.** 18   **85.** ☑
87. ☑   **89.** Row 1: 7, 2, 36, 14, 8, 8; row 2: 9, 18, 2, 10, 12, 21
91. $\dfrac{2}{5}$ **93.** $\dfrac{5q}{t}$ **95.** $\dfrac{6}{25}$ **97.** $\dfrac{5ap}{2cm}$ **99.** $\dfrac{23r}{18t}$
101. $\dfrac{28}{45}$ m^2 **103.** $14\frac{2}{9}$ m   **105.** $27\frac{3}{5}$ cm

Quick Quiz: Sections 1.1–1.3, p. 28

1. Let w represent the width of the box; $w - 4$
2. $5(3 + x)$, or $(x + 3)5$ **3.** $2 \cdot 2 \cdot 2 \cdot 5$ **4.** $\dfrac{9}{11}$ **5.** $\dfrac{11}{x}$

Technology Connection, p. 32

1. 2.236067977   **2.** 2.645751311   **3.** 3.605551275
4. 5.196152423

Exercise Set 1.4, pp. 34–36

1. Terminating   **2.** Integer   **3.** Whole number
4. Irrational number   **5.** Opposite   **6.** Absolute value
7. $-n$ **8.** $|x|$ **9.** $-10 < x$ **10.** $6 \geq y$
11. $-9500; 5000$ **13.** $100; -80$ **15.** $-777.68; 936.42$
17. $10,000; -4500$ **19.** $8; -5$
21.
23.
25.
27. 0.875 **29.** -0.75 **31.** $-1.1\overline{6}$ **33.** $0.\overline{6}$
35. -0.5 **37.** 0.13 **39.**
41. $-\sqrt{22}$
   43. $>$ **45.** $<$
47. $<$ **49.** $>$ **51.** $<$ **53.** $<$ **55.** $x < -2$
57. $y \geq 10$ **59.** $-83, -4.7, 0, \frac{5}{9}, 2.\overline{16}, 62$ **61.** $-83, 0, 62$
63. $-83, -4.7, 0, \frac{5}{9}, 2.\overline{16}, \pi, \sqrt{17}, 62$ **65.** 58 **67.** 12.2
69. $\sqrt{2}$ **71.** $\frac{9}{7}$ **73.** 0 **75.** 8 **77.** 🗒
79. 🗒   **81.** 🗒   **83.** $-23, -17, 0, 4$
85. $-\frac{4}{3}, \frac{4}{9}, \frac{4}{8}, \frac{4}{6}, \frac{4}{5}, \frac{4}{3}, \frac{4}{2}$ **87.** $<$ **89.** $=$ **91.** $-2, -1, 0, 1, 2$
93. $\frac{1}{9}$ **95.** $\frac{50}{9}$ **97.** $a < 0$ **99.** $|x| \leq 10$ **101.** 🗒

Quick Quiz: Sections 1.1–1.4, p 36

1. 1 **2.** $5(x + y + 3)$ **3.** $\frac{1}{6}$ **4.** 2 **5.** $0 > -0.5$

Mid-Chapter Review: Chapter 1, p. 37

1. $\dfrac{x - y}{3} = \dfrac{22 - 10}{3} = \dfrac{12}{3} = 4$
2. $14x + 7 = 7 \cdot 2x + 7 \cdot 1 = 7(2x + 1)$
3. 15 **4.** 4 **5.** $d - 10$ **6.** Let h represent the
number of hours worked; $8h$ **7.** Let s represent the
number of students originally enrolled; $s - 5 = 27$
8. No   **9.** $10x + 7$ **10.** $(3a)b$ **11.** $8x + 32$
12. $6m + 15n + 30$ **13.** $3(6x + 5)$ **14.** $3(3c + 4d + 1)$
15. $2 \cdot 2 \cdot 3 \cdot 7$ **16.** $\frac{3}{7}$ **17.** $\frac{13}{24}$ **18.** $\frac{44}{45}$
19.
   20. -0.15 **21.** $>$
22. $<$ **23.** $9 \leq x$ **24.** 5.6 **25.** 0

Exercise Set 1.5, pp. 41–43

1. Add; negative   **2.** Subtract; positive   **3.** Subtract;
negative   **4.** Identity   **5.** Identity   **6.** Like
7. (f)   **8.** (d)   **9.** (e)   **10.** (a)   **11.** (b)   **12.** (c)
13. -3 **15.** 4 **17.** -7 **19.** -8 **21.** -11
23. -5 **25.** 0 **27.** -41 **29.** 0 **31.** 9 **33.** -36
35. 11 **37.** -43 **39.** 0 **41.** 18 **43.** -16
45. -0.8 **47.** -9.1 **49.** $\frac{3}{5}$ **51.** $\frac{-6}{7}$ **53.** $-\frac{1}{15}$
55. $\frac{2}{9}$ **57.** -3 **59.** 0 **61.** The price dropped 1¢.
63. Her new balance was \$95.   **65.** The total gain was 20 yd.
67. The lake dropped $\frac{7}{10}$ ft.   **69.** The elevation of the
peak is 13,796 ft.   **71.** $17a$ **73.** $9x$ **75.** $-2m$

77. $-10y$ **79.** $1 - 2x$ **81.** $-4m$ **83.** $-5x - 3.9$
85. $12x + 17$ **87.** $7r + 8t + 16$ **89.** $18n + 16$
91. 🗒   **93.** 🗒   **95.** \$451.70   **97.** $-5y$
99. $-7m$ **101.** $-7t, -23$ **103.** 1 under par

Quick Quiz: Sections 1.1–1.5, p. 43

1. $18a + 12c + 3$ **2.** $\frac{7}{5}$ **3.** $\frac{1}{12}$ **4.** 505 **5.** $-2 - 7x$

Exercise Set 1.6, pp. 48–51

1. Opposites   **2.** Sign   **3.** Opposite   **4.** Difference
5. (d)   **6.** (g)   **7.** (f)   **8.** (h)   **9.** (a)   **10.** (c)
11. (b)   **12.** (e)   **13.** Six minus ten   **15.** Two
minus negative twelve   **17.** The opposite of x minus y
19. Negative three minus the opposite of n **21.** -51
23. $\frac{11}{3}$ **25.** 3.14 **27.** 45 **29.** $\frac{14}{9}$ **31.** -0.101
33. 37 **35.** $-\frac{2}{5}$ **37.** 1 **39.** -15 **41.** -3
43. -6 **45.** -7 **47.** -6 **49.** 0 **51.** -5
53. -10 **55.** 0 **57.** 0 **59.** 8 **61.** -11 **63.** 16
65. -19 **67.** -1 **69.** 17 **71.** 3 **73.** -3
75. -21 **77.** -11 **79.** -8 **81.** -60 **83.** -23
85. -7.3 **87.** 1.1 **89.** -5.5 **91.** -0.928 **93.** $-\frac{7}{11}$
95. $-\frac{4}{5}$ **97.** $\frac{5}{17}$ **99.** 32 **101.** -62 **103.** -139
105. 0 **107.** $-3y, -8x$ **109.** $9, -5t, -3st$ **111.** $-3x$
113. $-5a + 4$ **115.** $-n - 9$ **117.** $-3x - 6$
119. $-8t - 7$ **121.** $-12x + 3y + 9$ **123.** $8x + 66$
125. -40 **127.** 43 **129.** $3.8 - (-5.2); 9$
131. $114 - (-79); 193$ **133.** 950 m   **135.** $213.8°$F
137. 8.9 points   **139.** 🗒   **141.** 🗒
143. 11:00 P.M., on August 14   **145.** False. For example,
let $m = -3$ and $n = -5$. Then $-3 > -5$, but
$-3 + (-5) = -8 \not> 0$.   **147.** True. For example,
for $m = 4$ and $n = -4$, $4 = -(-4)$ and $4 + (-4) = 0$;
for $m = -3$ and $n = 3$, $-3 = -3$ and $-3 + 3 = 0$.
149. (−) 9 − (−) 7 ENTER

Quick Quiz: Sections 1.1–1.6, p. 51

1. Let p represent the total PC sales; $0.11p = 9.25$
2. $1, 2, 4, 13, 26, 52$ **3.** $2 \cdot 2 \cdot 13$ **4.** -29 **5.** 5

Connecting the Concepts, p. 57

1. -10 **2.** 16 **3.** 4 **4.** -6 **5.** -1 **6.** 1
7. -3.77 **8.** -7 **9.** 0 **10.** -92

Exercise Set 1.7, pp. 57–59

1. Positive   **2.** Odd   **3.** Undefined   **4.** Reciprocal
5. Opposite   **6.** Reciprocal   **7.** 1 **8.** 0 **9.** 0
10. 1 **11.** 0 **12.** 1 **13.** 1 **14.** 0 **15.** 1
16. 0 **17.** -40 **19.** -56 **21.** -40 **23.** 72
25. 190 **27.** -132 **29.** -126 **31.** 11.5 **33.** 0
35. $-\frac{2}{7}$ **37.** $\frac{1}{12}$ **39.** -11.13 **41.** $-\frac{5}{12}$ **43.** 252
45. 0 **47.** $\frac{1}{28}$ **49.** 150 **51.** 0 **53.** -720
55. $-30,240$ **57.** -9 **59.** -4 **61.** -7 **63.** 4
65. -9 **67.** 5.1 **69.** $\frac{100}{11}$ **71.** -8 **73.** Undefined
75. -4 **77.** 0 **79.** 0 **81.** $-\frac{8}{3}; \frac{8}{-3}$ **83.** $-\frac{29}{35}, \frac{-29}{35}$

85. $\frac{-7}{3}; \frac{7}{-3}$ **87.** $-\frac{x}{2}; \frac{x}{-2}$ **89.** $-\frac{5}{4}$ **91.** $-\frac{10}{51}$ **93.** $-\frac{1}{10}$

95. $\frac{1}{4.3}$, or $\frac{10}{43}$ **97.** -4 **99.** Does not exist   **101.** $\frac{21}{20}$

103. -1 **105.** 1 **107.** $\frac{3}{11}$ **109.** $-\frac{7}{4}$ **111.** -12

113. -3 **115.** 1 **117.** $\frac{1}{10}$ **119.** $-\frac{7}{6}$

121. Undefined   **123.** $-\frac{14}{15}$ **125.** 🖉   **127.** 🖉

129. $\dfrac{1}{a+b}$ **131.** $-(a+b)$ **133.** $x = -x$

135. For 2 and 3, the reciprocal of the sum is $1/(2+3)$, or $1/5$. But $1/5 \neq 1/2 + 1/3$.   **137.** 5°F   **139.** Positive
141. Positive   **143.** Positive   **145.** Distributive law; law of opposites; multiplicative property of zero   **147.** 🖥

Quick Quiz: Sections 1.1–1.7, p. 59

1. $11(2x + 1 + 3y)$ **2.**
$$\xleftarrow{\;\;} \overset{\overset{-3.5}{\bullet}}{\underset{-5\,-4\,-3\,-2\,-1\;\;0\;\;1\;\;2\;\;3\;\;4\;\;5}{\;|\;|\;|\;|\;|\;|\;|\;|\;|\;|\;}} \xrightarrow{\;\;}$$

3. -6.1 **4.** $-x - 8m$ **5.** -2

Exercise Set 1.8, pp. 66–68

1. (c)   **2.** (b)   **3.** (a)   **4.** (f)   **5.** (e)   **6.** (d)
7. Division   **8.** Subtraction   **9.** Addition
10. Multiplication   **11.** Subtraction   **12.** Multiplication
13. x^6 **15.** $(-5)^3$ **17.** $(3t)^5$ **19.** $2n^4$ **21.** 16
23. 9   **25.** -9 **27.** 64   **29.** 625   **31.** 7   **33.** -32
35. $81t^4$ **37.** $-343x^3$ **39.** 26   **41.** 51   **43.** -15
45. 1   **47.** 298   **49.** 11   **51.** -36 **53.** 1291
55. 152   **57.** 24   **59.** 1   **61.** -44 **63.** 41
65. -10 **67.** -5 **69.** -19 **71.** -3 **73.** -75
75. 9   **77.** 30   **79.** 6   **81.** -17 **83.** $13x + 33$
85. $17x^2 - 17x$ **87.** $21t - r$ **89.** $-t^3 + 4t$
91. $-9x - 1$ **93.** $7n - 8$ **95.** $-4a + 3b - 7c$
97. $-3x^2 - 5x + 1$ **99.** $2x - 7$ **101.** $-9x + 6$
103. $9y - 25z$ **105.** $x^2 + 6$ **107.** $37a^2 - 23ab + 35b^2$
109. $-22t^3 - t^2 + 9t$ **111.** $2x - 25$ **113.** 🖉
115. 🖉   **117.** $-6r - 5t + 21$ **119.** $-2x - f$
121. 🖉   **123.** True   **125.** False   **127.** 0   **129.** 17
131. 39,000   **133.** $44x^3$

Quick Quiz: Sections 1.1–1.8, p. 68

1. Let m and n represent the numbers; $\frac{1}{2}(m + n)$
2. $-10 < x$ **3.** $-1.\overline{2}$ **4.** -2.94 **5.** $8x - 9y$

Translating for Success, p. 69

1. H   **2.** E   **3.** K   **4.** B   **5.** O   **6.** L   **7.** M
8. C   **9.** D   **10.** F

Decision Making: Connection, p. 71

1. -100; 500; -100; weight-loss diet: Monday, Wednesday; weight-gain diet: Tuesday   **2.** 2649 calories

Study Summary: Chapter 1, pp. 72–75

1. 8   **2.** 4 ft^2 **3.** Let n represent some number; $78 = n - 92$ **4.** $10n + 6$ **5.** $(3a)b$
6. $50m + 90n + 10$ **7.** $13(2x + 1)$ **8.** Composite

9. $2 \cdot 2 \cdot 3 \cdot 7$ **10.** 1   **11.** $\frac{9}{10}$ **12.** $\frac{3}{2}$ **13.** $\frac{9}{20}$
14. $\frac{25}{6}$ **15.** 25   **16.** $0, -15, \frac{30}{3}$ **17.** $-1.\overline{1}$ **18.** $>$
19. 1.5   **20.** -5 **21.** -2.9 **22.** -12 **23.** 15
24. $-7c + 9d - 2$ **25.** 21   **26.** -4 **27.** -100
28. -21 **29.** $a - 2b + 3c$ **30.** $5m + 7n - 15$

Review Exercises: Chapter 1, pp. 75–77

1. True   **2.** True   **3.** False   **4.** True   **5.** False
6. False   **7.** True   **8.** False   **9.** False   **10.** True
11. 24   **12.** -16 **13.** -15 **14.** $y - 7$
15. $xz + 10$, or $10 + xz$ **16.** Let b represent Brandt's speed and w the wind speed; $15(b - w)$ **17.** Let b represent the number of calories per hour that Katie burns while backpacking; $b = 2 \cdot 237$ **18.** $c = 200t$ **19.** $t \cdot 3 + 5$
20. $2x + (y + z)$ **21.** $(4x)y, 4(yx), (4y)x$; answers may vary
22. $18x + 30y$ **23.** $40x + 24y + 16$ **24.** $3(7x + 5y)$
25. $11(2a + 9b + 1)$ **26.** $2 \cdot 2 \cdot 2 \cdot 7$ **27.** $\frac{5}{12}$ **28.** $\frac{9}{4}$
29. $\frac{19}{24}$ **30.** $\frac{3}{16}$ **31.** $\frac{3}{5}$ **32.** $\frac{27}{25}$ **33.** -3600; 1350
34.
$$\xleftarrow{\;\;} \overset{\overset{\frac{-1}{3}}{\bullet}}{\underset{-5\,-4\,-3\,-2\,-1\;\;0\;\;1\;\;2\;\;3\;\;4\;\;5}{\;|\;|\;|\;|\;|\;|\;|\;|\;|\;|\;}} \xrightarrow{\;\;}$$
35. $x > -3$ **36.** $<$
37. $-0.\overline{4}$ **38.** 1   **39.** -12 **40.** -10 **41.** $-\frac{7}{12}$
42. -5 **43.** 8   **44.** $-\frac{7}{5}$ **45.** -9.18 **46.** $-\frac{2}{7}$
47. -140 **48.** -7 **49.** -3 **50.** $\frac{9}{4}$ **51.** 48
52. 168   **53.** $\frac{21}{8}$ **54.** 18   **55.** 53   **56.** $\frac{103}{17}$
57. $7a - b$ **58.** $-4x + 5y$ **59.** 7   **60.** $-\frac{1}{7}$
61. $(2x)^4$ **62.** $-125x^3$ **63.** $-3a + 9$ **64.** $3x^4 + 10x$
65. $17n^2 + m^2 + 20mn$ **66.** $5x + 28$
67. 🖉 The value of a constant never varies. A variable can represent a variety of numbers.   **68.** 🖉 A term is one of the parts of an expression that is separated from the other parts by plus signs. A factor is part of a product.   **69.** 🖉 The distributive law is used in factoring algebraic expressions, multiplying algebraic expressions, combining like terms, finding the opposite of a sum, and subtracting algebraic expressions.   **70.** 🖉 A negative number raised to an even power is positive; a negative number raised to an odd power is negative.   **71.** 25,281   **72.** (a) $\frac{3}{11}$; (b) $\frac{10}{11}$
73. $-\frac{5}{8}$ **74.** -2.1 **75.** (i)   **76.** (j)   **77.** (a)
78. (h)   **79.** (k)   **80.** (b)   **81.** (c)   **82.** (e)
83. (d)   **84.** (f)   **85.** (g)

Test: Chapter 1, p. 78

1. [1.1] 4   **2.** [1.1] Let x and y represent the numbers; $xy - 9$ **3.** [1.1] 240 ft^2 **4.** [1.2] $q + 3p$
5. [1.2] $(x \cdot 4) \cdot y$ **6.** [1.1] Let t represent the number of golden lion tamarins living in zoos; $1500 = t + 1050$
7. [1.2] $35 + 7x$ **8.** [1.7] $-5y + 10$ **9.** [1.2] $11(1 + 4x)$
10. [1.2] $7(x + 1 + 7y)$ **11.** [1.3] $2 \cdot 2 \cdot 3 \cdot 5 \cdot 5$
12. [1.3] $\frac{3}{7}$ **13.** [1.4] $<$ **14.** [1.4] $>$ **15.** [1.4] $\frac{9}{4}$
16. [1.4] 3.8   **17.** [1.6] $\frac{2}{3}$ **18.** [1.7] $-\frac{7}{4}$ **19.** [1.6] 10
20. [1.4] $-5 \geq x$ **21.** [1.6] 7.8   **22.** [1.5] -8
23. [1.6] $-\frac{7}{8}$ **24.** [1.7] -48 **25.** [1.7] $\frac{2}{9}$ **26.** [1.7] $\frac{3}{4}$
27. [1.7] -9.728 **28.** [1.8] 20   **29.** [1.6] 15
30. [1.8] -64 **31.** [1.8] 448   **32.** [1.6] $21a + 22y$
33. [1.8] $16x^4$ **34.** [1.8] $x + 7$ **35.** [1.8] $9a - 12b - 7$
36. [1.8] $-y - 16$ **37.** [1.1] 5
38. [1.8] $9 - (3 - 4) + 5 = 15$ **39.** [1.4] $n \geq 0$
40. [1.8] $4a$ **41.** [1.8] False

CHAPTER 2

Exercise Set 2.1, pp. 86–87

1. (c) **2.** (b) **3.** (f) **4.** (a) **5.** (d) **6.** (e)
7. (d) **8.** (b) **9.** (c) **10.** (a) **11.** No **13.** Yes
15. Yes **17.** Yes **19.** 11 **21.** -25 **23.** -31
25. 41 **27.** 19 **29.** -6 **31.** $\frac{7}{3}$ **33.** $-\frac{1}{10}$
35. $\frac{41}{24}$ **37.** $-\frac{1}{20}$ **39.** 9.1 **41.** -5 **43.** 7
45. 12 **47.** -38 **49.** 8 **51.** -7 **53.** 8
55. 88 **57.** 20 **59.** -54 **61.** $-\frac{5}{9}$ **63.** 1
65. $\frac{9}{2}$ **67.** -7.6 **69.** -2.5 **71.** -15 **73.** -5
75. $-\frac{7}{6}$ **77.** -128 **79.** $-\frac{1}{2}$ **81.** -15 **83.** 9
85. 310.756 **87.** **89.** $\frac{1}{3}y - 7$ **90.** $12x + 66$

91. $5(7a + 11c + 1)$ **92.**
93. ☑ **95.** 11.6 **97.** 2 **99.** $-23, 23$
101. 9000 **103.** $2500

Prepare to Move On, p. 87

1. -6 **2.** 2 **3.** $-x + 10$ **4.** $-5x + 28$

Technology Connection, p. 90

1.

X	Y₁
0	5
1	4
2	3
3	2
4	1
5	0
6	-1

X = 0

2.

X	Y₁	Y₂
0	5	17
1	4	13
2	3	9
3	2	5
4	1	1
5	0	-3
6	-1	-7

X = 0

3. 4; not reliable because, depending on the choice of ΔTbl, it is easy to scroll past a solution without realizing it.

Exercise Set 2.2, pp. 94–95

1. Addition principle **2.** Multiplication principle
3. Multiplication principle **4.** Distributive law
5. Addition principle **6.** Distributive law
7. (c) **8.** (e) **9.** (a) **10.** (f) **11.** (b) **12.** (d)
13. 8 **15.** 5 **17.** $\frac{10}{3}$ **19.** -7 **21.** -5 **23.** -4
25. 19 **27.** -2.8 **29.** 3 **31.** 15 **33.** -6
35. $-\frac{25}{2}$ **37.** $\frac{9}{8}$ **39.** -3 **41.** -6 **43.** 0
45. 10 **47.** 4 **49.** $\frac{16}{3}$ **51.** $\frac{2}{5}$ **53.** 1 **55.** -4
57. $1.\overline{6}$ **59.** $-\frac{60}{37}$ **61.** 11 **63.** 2 **65.** 0 **67.** 6
69. All real numbers; identity **71.** $-\frac{1}{2}$ **73.** 0
75. No solution; contradiction **77.** $\frac{5}{2}$ **79.** $\frac{1}{6}$ **81.** 2
83. No solution; contradiction **85.** 8 **87.** $\frac{16}{15}$
89. $-\frac{1}{31}$ **91.** All real numbers; identity **93.** 2
95. ☑ **97.** $\frac{7}{8}$ **98.** 1 **99.** $-0.\overline{1}$ **100.** 16
101. ☑ **103.** $\frac{1136}{909}$, or $1.\overline{2497}$ **105.** No solution;
contradiction **107.** All real numbers are solutions;
identity **109.** $\frac{2}{3}$ **111.** 0 **113.** 500 mi

Quick Quiz: Sections 2.1–2.2, p. 95

1. Yes **2.** -5.4 **3.** 25 **4.** -4 **5.** $\frac{1}{2}$

Prepare to Move On, p. 95

1. -7 **2.** 15 **3.** -15 **4.** -28

Technology Connection, p. 96

1. 14.4

Exercise Set 2.3, pp. 99–102

1. False **2.** True **3.** Circumference **4.** Formula
5. 309.6 m **7.** 1423 students **9.** 8.4734
11. 255 mg **13.** $b = \dfrac{A}{h}$ **15.** $P = \dfrac{I}{rt}$
17. $m = 65 - H$ **19.** $l = \dfrac{P - 2w}{2}$, or $l = \dfrac{P}{2} - w$
21. $\pi = \dfrac{A}{r^2}$ **23.** $h = \dfrac{2A}{b}$ **25.** $c^2 = \dfrac{E}{m}$
27. $d = 2Q - c$ **29.** $q = p + r - 2$ **31.** $r = wf$
33. $T = \dfrac{550H}{V}$ **35.** $C = \frac{5}{9}(F - 32)$ **37.** $y = 2x - 1$
39. $y = -\frac{2}{5}x + 2$ **41.** $y = \frac{4}{3}x - 2$ **43.** $y = -\frac{9}{8}x + \frac{1}{2}$
45. $y = \frac{3}{5}x - \frac{8}{5}$ **47.** $x = \dfrac{z - 13}{2} - y$, or $x = \dfrac{z - 13 - 2y}{2}$
49. $l = 4(t - 27) + w$ **51.** $t = \dfrac{A}{a + b}$ **53.** $h = \dfrac{2A}{a + b}$
55. $L = W - \dfrac{N(R - r)}{400}$, or $L = \dfrac{400W - NR + Nr}{400}$
57. ☑ **59.** -10 **60.** -196 **61.** 0
62. -32 **63.** -13 **64.** 65 **65.** ☑
67. 40 years old **69.** 27 in³ **71.** $a = \dfrac{w}{c} \cdot d$
73. $c = \dfrac{d}{a - b}$ **75.** $a = \dfrac{c}{3 + b + d}$
77. $K = 9.632w + 19.685h - 10.54a + 102.3$

Quick Quiz: Sections 2.1–2.3, p. 102

1. 7 **2.** $\frac{64}{3}$ **3.** -0.025 **4.** -21 **5.** $y = -3x + \frac{1}{2}$

Prepare to Move On, p. 102

1. 0.25 **2.** 1.125 **3.** $0.\overline{6}$ **4.** $0.8\overline{3}$

Mid-Chapter Review: Chapter 2, p. 103

1. $2x + 3 - 3 = 10 - 3$
$2x = 7$
$\frac{1}{2} \cdot 2x = \frac{1}{2} \cdot 7$
$x = \frac{7}{2}$
2. $6 \cdot \frac{1}{2}(x - 3) = 6 \cdot \frac{1}{3}(x - 4)$
$3(x - 3) = 2(x - 4)$
$3x - 9 = 2x - 8$
$3x - 9 + 9 = 2x - 8 + 9$
$3x = 2x + 1$
$3x - 2x = 2x + 1 - 2x$
$x = 1$
3. 1 **4.** 3 **5.** $\frac{5}{3}$ **6.** -8 **7.** 48 **8.** 0.5
9. -5 **10.** $\frac{8}{3}$ **11.** 6 **12.** 0 **13.** $\frac{49}{9}$
14. $-\frac{4}{11}$ **15.** $\frac{23}{7}$ **16.** $A = \dfrac{E}{w}$ **17.** $y = \dfrac{C - Ax}{B}$
18. $a = \dfrac{m}{t + p}$ **19.** $a = \dfrac{F}{m}$ **20.** $b = vt + f$

Exercise Set 2.4, pp. 108–112

1. Left   **2.** Hundred   **3.** Percent   **4.** Base
5. Sale   **6.** Approximately   **7.** (d)   **8.** (c)   **9.** (e)
10. (b)   **11.** (c)   **12.** (d)   **13.** (f)   **14.** (a)
15. (b)   **16.** (e)   **17.** 0.67   **19.** 0.05   **21.** 0.032
23. 0.1   **25.** 0.0625   **27.** 0.002   **29.** 1.75
31. 21%   **33.** 7.9%   **35.** 70%   **37.** 0.09%
39. 106%   **41.** 60%   **43.** 32%   **45.** 25%
47. $46\frac{2}{3}$, or $\frac{140}{3}$ **49.** 2.5   **51.** 10,000   **53.** 125%
55. 0.8   **57.** 50%   **59.** $33.\overline{3}\%$, or $33\frac{1}{3}\%$
61. 2.48 quadrillion Btu's   **63.** 0.88 quadrillion Btu's
65. 75 credits   **67.** 573 at-bats   **69. (a)** 16%;
(b) \$29   **71.** $33.\overline{3}\%$, or $33\frac{1}{3}\%$; $66.\overline{6}\%$, or $66\frac{2}{3}\%$
73. \$163.20   **75.** 285 women   **77.** \$19.20 per hour
79. About 462%   **81.** About 31.5 lb   **83.** About 90%
85. 50 calories   **87.** ☑   **89.** $\frac{1}{3}$ **90.** −3   **91.** −12
92. $9x^2$ **93.** ☑   **95.** 18,500 people
97. About 6 ft 7 in.   **99.** About 27%   **101.** ☑

Quick Quiz: Sections 2.1–2.4, p. 112

1. 0   **2.** $\frac{62}{3}$ **3.** $p = \dfrac{T}{4 + m}$ **4.** 0.012   **5.** 25

Prepare to Move On, p. 112

1. Let l represent the length and w represent the width; $2l + 2w$ **2.** $0.05 \cdot 180$ **3.** $10\left(\frac{1}{2}a\right)$
4. Let n represent the number; $3n + 10$
5. Let l represent the board's length and w represent the width; $w = l - 2$ **6.** Let x represent the first number and y represent the second number; $x = 4y$

Exercise Set 2.5, pp. 121–127

1. (1) Familiarize. **(2)** Translate. **(3)** Carry out.
(4) Check. **(5)** State.   **2.** Carry out.   **3.** State.
4. Familiarize.   **5.** Translate.   **6.** Familiarize.
7. Familiarize.   **8.** Check.   **9.** 11   **11.** $\frac{11}{2}$
13. 16.4 mi   **15.** 290 mi   **17.** 1204 and 1205
19. 285 and 287   **21.** 32, 33, 34   **23.** Man: 104 years;
woman: 102 years   **25.** Spam: 264.6 billion messages;
nonspam: 29.4 billion messages   **27.** 140 and 141
29. Width: 21 m; length: 25 m   **31.** $1\frac{1}{2}$ in. by $3\frac{1}{2}$ in.
33. 30°, 90°, 60°   **35.** 70°   **37.** Bottom: 144 ft; middle:
72 ft; top: 24 ft   **39.** 12 mph   **41.** 1 hr   **43.** 12.5%
45. 50%   **47.** \$1225   **49.** \$280.80   **51.** \$320
53. \$36,000   **55.** \$100   **57.** 256,850 vehicles
59. \$125,000   **61.** $7\frac{1}{4}$ mi   **63.** $128\frac{1}{3}$ mi   **65.** 65°, 25°
67. 140°, 40°   **69.** Length: 27.9 cm; width: 21.6 cm
71. \$6600   **73.** 830 points   **75.** 2015
77. 160 chirps per minute   **79.** ☑   **81.** $8n + 32t + 4$
82. $3(4 + 6x + 7y)$ **83.** $7x - 18$ **84.** 0   **85.** ☑
87. \$37   **89.** 20   **91.** Half-dollars: 5; quarters: 10;
dimes: 20; nickels: 60   **93.** \$95.99   **95.** 5 DVDs
97. 6 mi   **99.** ☑   **101.** Width: 23.31 cm;
length: 27.56 cm

Quick Quiz: Sections 2.1–2.5, p. 127

1. $\frac{25}{6}$ **2.** −3   **3.** $v = \dfrac{3}{B}$ **4.** \$10.50   **5.** $52\frac{1}{2}$ min

Prepare to Move On, p. 127

1. <   **2.** >   **3.** $-4 \le x$ **4.** $y < 5$

Connecting the Concepts, p. 134

1. 21   **2.** $\{x \mid x \le 21\}$, or $(-\infty, 21]$ **3.** −6
4. $\{x \mid x > -6\}$, or $(-6, \infty)$ **5.** $\left\{x \mid x \le -\frac{1}{3}\right\}$, or $\left(-\infty, -\frac{1}{3}\right]$
6. $-\frac{1}{3}$ **7.** 66   **8.** $\{n \mid n < 66\}$, or $(-\infty, 66)$
9. $\{a \mid a \ge 0\}$, or $[0, \infty)$ **10.** 0

Exercise Set 2.6, pp. 134–136

1. Solution   **2.** Set-builder   **3.** Closed   **4.** Bracket
5. ≥   **6.** ≤   **7.** <   **8.** >   **9.** Equivalent
10. Equivalent   **11.** Equivalent   **12.** Not equivalent
13. (a) Yes; **(b)** no; **(c)** no   **15. (a)** Yes; **(b)** no; **(c)** yes
17. (a) Yes; **(b)** yes; **(c)** yes

19. $y < 2$
21. $x \ge -1$
23. $0 \le t$
25. $-5 \le x < 2$
27. $-4 < x < 0$
29. $\{y \mid y < 6\}$, $(-\infty, 6)$
31. $\{x \mid x \ge -4\}$, $[-4, \infty)$
33. $\{t \mid t > -3\}$, $(-3, \infty)$
35. $\{x \mid x \le -7\}$, $(-\infty, -7]$
37. $\{x \mid x > -4\}$, $(-4, \infty)$ **39.** $\{x \mid x \le 2\}$, $(-\infty, 2]$
41. $\{x \mid x < -1\}$, $(-\infty, -1)$ **43.** $\{x \mid x \ge 0\}$, $[0, \infty)$
45. $\{y \mid y > 3\}$, $(3, \infty)$
47. $\{n \mid n < 17\}$, $(-\infty, 17)$,
49. $\{x \mid x \le -9\}$, $(-\infty, -9]$,
51. $\{t \mid t \le -3\}$, $(-\infty, -3]$,
53. $\left\{t \mid t > \frac{5}{8}\right\}$, $\left(\frac{5}{8}, \infty\right)$,
55. $\{x \mid x < 0\}$, $(-\infty, 0)$,
57. $\{t \mid t < 23\}$, $(-\infty, 23)$,
59. $\{x \mid x < 7\}$, $(-\infty, 7)$,
61. $\{t \mid t < -3\}$, $(-\infty, -3)$,
63. $\{n \mid n \ge -1.5\}$, $[-1.5, \infty)$,
65. $\left\{y \mid y \ge -\frac{1}{10}\right\}$, $\left[-\frac{1}{10}, \infty\right)$,
67. $\left\{x \mid x < -\frac{4}{5}\right\}$, $\left(-\infty, -\frac{4}{5}\right)$,
69. $\{x \mid x < 6\}$, or $(-\infty, 6)$ **71.** $\{t \mid t \le 7\}$, or $(-\infty, 7]$
73. $\{x \mid x > -4\}$, or $(-4, \infty)$ **75.** $\left\{y \mid y < -\frac{10}{3}\right\}$, or $\left(-\infty, -\frac{10}{3}\right)$
77. $\{x \mid x > -10\}$, or $(-10, \infty)$ **79.** $\{y \mid y < 0\}$, or $(-\infty, 0)$
81. $\{x \mid x > -4\}$, or $(-4, \infty)$ **83.** $\{t \mid t > 1\}$, or $(1, \infty)$
85. $\{x \mid x \le -9\}$, or $(-\infty, -9]$ **87.** $\{t \mid t < 14\}$, or $(-\infty, 14)$
89. $\{y \mid y \le -4\}$, or $(-\infty, -4]$ **91.** $\left\{t \mid t < -\frac{5}{3}\right\}$, or $\left(-\infty, -\frac{5}{3}\right)$
93. $\{r \mid r > -3\}$, or $(-3, \infty)$ **95.** $\{x \mid x \le 7\}$, or $(-\infty, 7]$

97. $\left\{x\,|\,x > -\frac{5}{32}\right\}$, or $\left(-\frac{5}{32}, \infty\right)$ **99.** 🖥   **101.** $17x - 6$
102. $2m - 16n$ **103.** $7x - 8y - 46$ **104.** $-21x + 32$
105. 🖥   **107.** $\{x\,|\,x \text{ is a real number}\}$, or $(-\infty, \infty)$
109. $\left\{x\,|\,x \le \frac{5}{6}\right\}$, or $\left(-\infty, \frac{5}{6}\right]$ **111.** $\{x\,|\,x \le -4a\}$, or
$(-\infty, -4a]$ **113.** $\left\{x\,\middle|\,x > \dfrac{y-b}{a}\right\}$, or $\left(\dfrac{y-b}{a}, \infty\right)$
115. $\{x\,|\,x \text{ is a real number}\}$, or $(-\infty, \infty)$ **117. (a)** No;
(b) There is more than 6 g of fat per serving.

Quick Quiz: Sections 2.1–2.6, p. 136

1. $-\frac{28}{3}$ **2.** $\left\{x\,|\,x < -\frac{10}{3}\right\}$, or $\left(-\infty, -\frac{10}{3}\right)$ **3.** $\$15.00$
4. $\$19.34$ **5.** $c = \dfrac{X - 12 + 5d}{5}$

Prepare to Move On, p. 136

1. Let h represent the height of the triangle; $\frac{1}{2} \cdot 3 \cdot h = 5$
2. Let s represent the shortest side of the triangle;
$s + (s + 1) + \left(s + \frac{1}{2}\right) = 12$

Exercise Set 2.7, pp. 139–143

1. Is at least   **2.** Cannot exceed   **3.** No less than
4. Minimum   **5.** $b \le a$ **6.** $b < a$ **7.** $a \le b$
8. $a < b$ **9.** $b \le a$ **10.** $a \le b$ **11.** $b < a$
12. $a < b$ **13.** Let n represent the number; $n < 10$
15. Let t represent the temperature; $t \le -3$
17. Let d represent the number of years of driving
experience; $d \ge 5$ **19.** Let a represent the age of the
altar; $a > 1200$ **21.** Let h represent Bianca's hourly
wage, in dollars; $h \ge 12$ **23.** Let s represent the number
of hours of sunshine; $1100 < s < 1600$ **25.** More than
2.375 hr   **27.** At least 2.25   **29.** Scores greater than or
equal to 97   **31.** 8 credits or more   **33.** At least 3 plate
appearances   **35.** Lengths greater than 6 cm
37. Depths less than 437.5 ft   **39.** Blue-book value is
greater than or equal to $\$10,625$ **41.** Lengths less than
55 in.   **43.** Temperatures greater than 37°C   **45.** No
more than 3 ft tall   **47.** A serving contains at least $6\frac{2}{3}$ g of
fat.   **49.** Dates after September 16   **51.** No more than
134 text messages   **53.** Years after 2012
55. Distances less than or equal to 139 mi   **57.** 🖥
59. $7 + xy$ **60.** $3 \cdot 3 \cdot 5 \cdot 5$ **61.** -18 **62.** -5
63. 🖥   **65.** Temperatures between -15°C and $-9\frac{4}{9}$°C
67. Lengths less than or equal to 8 cm
69. At least $\$42$ **71.** 🖥   **73.** 🖥

Quick Quiz: Sections 2.1–2.7, p. 143

1. $\{x\,|\,x \le 4\}$, or $(-\infty, 4]$ **2.** $\frac{1210}{3}$ **3.** 20%   **4.** 48 km
5. 72 or higher

Prepare to Move On, p. 143

1.   **2.**
3. 79.5   **4.** 8.5

Translating for Success, p. 144

1. F   **2.** I   **3.** C   **4.** E   **5.** D   **6.** J   **7.** O
8. M   **9.** B   **10.** L

Decision Making: Connection, p. 145

1. Barry should remain a crew manager.   **2.** $A = 1.2x$
3. 🖥

Study Summary: Chapter 2, pp. 146–148

1. 5   **2.** 4.8   **3.** -1 **4.** $-\frac{1}{10}$ **5.** $c = \dfrac{d}{a - b}$
6. 80   **7.** $47\frac{1}{2}$ mi; $72\frac{1}{2}$ mi   **8.** $(-\infty, 0]$
9. $\{x\,|\,x > 7\}$, or $(7, \infty)$ **10.** $\left\{x\,|\,x \ge -\frac{1}{4}\right\}$, or $\left[-\frac{1}{4}, \infty\right)$
11. Let d represent the distance Luke runs, in miles; $d \ge 3$

Review Exercises: Chapter 2, pp. 149–150

1. True   **2.** False   **3.** True   **4.** True
5. True   **6.** False   **7.** True   **8.** True   **9.** -25
10. 7   **11.** -65 **12.** 1.11   **13.** $\frac{1}{2}$ **14.** $-\frac{3}{2}$
15. -8 **16.** -4 **17.** $-\frac{1}{3}$ **18.** 4   **19.** No
solution; contradiction   **20.** 4   **21.** 16   **22.** 1
23. $-\frac{7}{5}$ **24.** 0   **25.** All real numbers; identity
26. $d = \dfrac{C}{\pi}$ **27.** $B = \dfrac{3V}{h}$ **28.** $y = \frac{5}{2}x - 5$
29. $x = \dfrac{b}{t - a}$ **30.** 0.012   **31.** 44%   **32.** 70%
33. 140   **34.** No   **35.** Yes   **36.** No
37.
$5x - 6 < 2x + 3$
38.
$-2 < x \le 5$
39.
$t > 0$
40. $\left\{t\,|\,t \ge -\frac{1}{2}\right\}$, or $\left[-\frac{1}{2}, \infty\right)$ **41.** $\{y\,|\,y > 3\}$, or $(3, \infty)$
42. $\{y\,|\,y \le -4\}$, or $(-\infty, -4]$ **43.** $\{y\,|\,y > -7\}$, or $(-7, \infty)$
44. $\{x\,|\,x > -6\}$, or $(-6, \infty)$ **45.** $\left\{x\,|\,x > -\frac{9}{11}\right\}$, or $\left(-\frac{9}{11}, \infty\right)$
46. $\{t\,|\,t \le -12\}$, or $(-\infty, -12]$ **47.** $\{x\,|\,x \le -8\}$,
or $(-\infty, -8]$ **48.** 68.75%   **49.** 8 ft, 10 ft
50. Indian students: 104,000; Chinese students: 158,000
51. About 157,000 students   **52.** 57, 59
53. Width: 11 cm; length: 17 cm   **54.** $\$160$
55. 35°, 85°, 60°   **56.** $\$105$ or less   **57.** 14 or fewer
copies   **58.** 🖥 Multiplying both sides of an equation
by *any* nonzero number results in an equivalent equation.
When multiplying on both sides of an inequality, the sign of
the number being multiplied by must be considered. If the
number is positive, the direction of the inequality symbol
remains unchanged; if the number is negative, the direction of the inequality symbol must be reversed to produce
an equivalent inequality.   **59.** 🖥 The solutions of an
equation can usually each be checked. The solutions of an
inequality are normally too numerous to check. Checking
a few numbers from the solution set found cannot guarantee that the answer is correct, although if any number
does not check, the answer found is incorrect.

60. About 1 hr 36 min   **61.** Nile: 4160 mi; Amazon: 4225 mi   **62.** $-23, 23$ **63.** $-20, 20$
64. $a = \dfrac{y-3}{2-b}$ **65.** $F = \dfrac{0.3(12w)}{9}$, or $F = 0.4w$

Test: Chapter 2, p. 151

1. [2.1] 9   **2.** [2.1] -3 **3.** [2.1] 49   **4.** [2.1] -12
5. [2.2] 2   **6.** [2.1] -8 **7.** [2.2] $-\frac{23}{67}$ **8.** [2.2] 7
9. [2.2] $\frac{23}{3}$ **10.** All real numbers; identity
11. [2.6] $\{x \,|\, x > -5\}$, or $(-5, \infty)$ **12.** [2.6] $\{x \,|\, x > -13\}$, or $(-13, \infty)$ **13.** [2.6] $\{y \,|\, y \le -13\}$, or $(-\infty, -13]$
14. [2.6] $\{n \,|\, n < -5\}$, or $(-\infty, -5)$ **15.** [2.6] $\{x \,|\, x < -7\}$, or $(-\infty, -7)$ **16.** [2.6] $\{t \,|\, t \ge -1\}$, or $[-1, \infty)$
17. [2.6] $\{x \,|\, x \le -1\}$, or $(-\infty, -1]$ **18.** [2.3] $r = \dfrac{A}{2\pi h}$
19. [2.3] $l = 2w - P$ **20.** [2.4] 2.3   **21.** [2.4] 0.3%
22. [2.4] 14.8   **23.** [2.4] 44%

24. [2.6] $y < 4$
$-10\,{-}8\,{-}6\,{-}4\,{-}2\ 0\ 2\ 4\ 6\ 8\ 10$
$-2 \le x \le 2$

25. [2.6]
$-5\,{-}4\,{-}3\,{-}2\,{-}1\ 0\ 1\ 2\ 3\ 4\ 5$

26. [2.5] Width: 7 cm; length: 11 cm
27. [2.5] 123.75 mi from Buffalo River and 41.25 mi from Lake Ft. Smith State Park   **28.** [2.5] 81 mm, 83 mm, 85 mm
29. [2.4] $65   **30.** [2.7] More than 35 one-way trips per month   **31.** [2.3] $d = \dfrac{a}{3}$ **32.** [1.4], [2.2] $-15, 15$
33. [2.7] Let $h =$ the number of hours of sun each day; $4 \le h \le 6$ **34.** [2.5] 60 tickets

Cumulative Review: Chapters 1–2, p. 152

1. -12 **2.** $\frac{3}{4}$ **3.** -4.2 **4.** 10   **5.** 134
6. $\frac{1}{2}$ **7.** $2x + 1$ **8.** $-21n + 36$
9. $-\frac{5}{2}$
$-5\,{-}4\,{-}3\,{-}2\,{-}1\ 0\ 1\ 2\ 3\ 4\ 5$ **10.** $2(3x + 2y + 4z)$
11. 16   **12.** 9   **13.** $\frac{13}{18}$ **14.** 1   **15.** $-\frac{7}{2}$
16. $z = \dfrac{x}{4y}$ **17.** $y = \frac{4}{9}x - \frac{1}{9}$ **18.** $n = \dfrac{p}{a+r}$
19. 1.83   **20.** 37.5%   **21.** $t > -\frac{5}{2}$
$-5\,{-}4\,{-}3\,{-}2\,{-}1\ 0\ 1\ 2\ 3\ 4\ 5$
22. $\{t \,|\, t \le -2\}$, or $(-\infty, -2]$ **23.** $\{t \,|\, t < 3\}$, or $(-\infty, 3)$
24. $\{x \,|\, x < 30\}$, or $(-\infty, 30)$ **25.** $\{n \,|\, n \ge 2\}$, or $[2, \infty)$
26. 48 million   **27.** $14\frac{1}{3}$ m   **28.** 9 ft, 15 ft
29. No more than $52   **30.** About 54%   **31.** $105°$
32. For widths greater than 27 cm   **33.** $4t$ **34.** $-5, 5$
35. $1025

CHAPTER 3

Exercise Set 3.1, pp. 159–163

1. E **2.** C **3.** G **4.** B **5.** H **6.** I
7. (a)   **8.** (c)   **9.** (b)   **10.** (d)   **11.** 2 drinks
13. The person weighs more than 140 lb.
15. $17 billion   **17.** 2000   **19.** 2006

21.
23.

25.

27. $A(-4, 5)$; $B(-3, -3)$; $C(0, 4)$; $D(3, 4)$; $E(3, -4)$
29. $A(4, 1)$; $B(0, -5)$; $C(-4, 0)$; $D(-3, -2)$; $E(3, 0)$
31. IV   **33.** III   **35.** y-axis   **37.** II   **39.** x-axis
41. I   **43.** I and IV   **45.** I and III

47.
49.

51.
53.

55.

57. 📝   **59.** $-\frac{1}{6}$ **60.** -11.7 **61.** -120 **62.** 5
63. 24   **64.** 3   **65.** 📝   **67.** II or IV   **69.** $(-1, -5)$

71.

73. $\frac{65}{2}$ sq units   **75.** About 1.2 lb   **77.** About 0.4 lb
79. Latitude 27° North; longitude 81° West   **81.** 🖱️

Prepare to Move On, p. 163

1. $y = \frac{2}{5}x$ **2.** $y = -\frac{3}{2}x$ **3.** $y = x - 8$
4. $y = -\frac{2}{5}x + 2$ **5.** $y = \frac{5}{8}x - \frac{1}{8}$

Technology Connection, p. 169

1. $y = -5x + 6.5$ **2.** $y = 3x + 4.5$

3. $7y - 4x = 22$, or   **4.** $5y + 11x = -20$, or
$y = \frac{4}{7}x + \frac{22}{7}$ $y = -\frac{11}{5}x - 4$

5. $2y - x^2 = 0$, or   **6.** $y + x^2 = 8$, or
$y = 0.5x^2$ $y = -x^2 + 8$

Exercise Set 3.2, pp. 170–173

1. False   **2.** True   **3.** True   **4.** True   **5.** True
6. False   **7.** Yes   **9.** No   **11.** No
13. $y = x + 3$ $y = x + 3$
$\begin{array}{c|c} 2 & -1 + 3 \\ 2 \overset{?}{=} 2 & \text{True} \end{array}$ $\begin{array}{c|c} 7 & 4 + 3 \\ 7 \overset{?}{=} 7 & \text{True} \end{array}$
$(2, 5)$; answers may vary

15. $y = \frac{1}{2}x + 3$ $y = \frac{1}{2}x + 3$
$\begin{array}{c|c} 5 & \frac{1}{2} \cdot 4 + 3 \\ & 2 + 3 \\ 5 \overset{?}{=} 5 & \text{True} \end{array}$ $\begin{array}{c|c} 2 & \frac{1}{2}(-2) + 3 \\ & -1 + 3 \\ 2 \overset{?}{=} 2 & \text{True} \end{array}$
$(0, 3)$; answers may vary

17. $\begin{array}{c|c} y + 3x = 7 \\ \hline 1 + 3 \cdot 2 & 7 \\ 1 + 6 \\ 7 \overset{?}{=} 7 & \text{True} \end{array}$ $\begin{array}{c|c} y + 3x = 7 \\ \hline -5 + 3 \cdot 4 & 7 \\ -5 + 12 \\ 7 \overset{?}{=} 7 & \text{True} \end{array}$
$(1, 4)$; answers may vary

19. $\begin{array}{c|c} 4x - 2y = 10 \\ \hline 4 \cdot 0 - 2(-5) & 10 \\ 0 + 10 \\ 10 \overset{?}{=} 10 & \text{True} \end{array}$ $\begin{array}{c|c} 4x - 2y = 10 \\ \hline 4 \cdot 4 - 2 \cdot 3 & 10 \\ 16 - 6 \\ 10 \overset{?}{=} 10 & \text{True} \end{array}$
$(2, -1)$; answers may vary

21.   **23.**

25.   **27.**

29.   **31.**

33.   **35.**

37.   **39.**

41.

$4x = 3y$

43.

$5x - y = 0$

45.

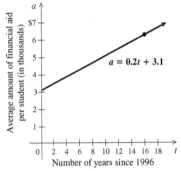

$6x - 3y = 9$

47.

$6y + 2x = 8$

49. About $6300

$a = 0.2t + 3.1$

51. About 6.5 mpg

$t = -0.1s + 13.1$

53. About $34

$p = 0.7n + 16$

55. About 85,000 apps

$a = 0.23d - 7$

57. About $1700

$T = \frac{5}{4}c + 2$

59.   **61.** 3   **62.** $-\frac{21}{5}$

63. $Q = 2A - T$

64. $p = \dfrac{w}{q + 1}$

65. $y = \dfrac{C - Ax}{B}$

66. $y = m(x - h) + k$

67.

69.

$s + n = 24$

71. $x + y = 5$, or
  $y = -x + 5$

73. $y = x + 2$

75.

$25d + 5l = 225$

Answers may vary.
1 dinner, 40 lunches;
5 dinners, 20 lunches;
8 dinners, 5 lunches

77.

$y = -|x|$

79.

$y = x^2$

81. $y = -2.8x + 3.5$

83. $y = 2.8x - 3.5$
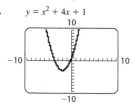

3. $5x + 6y = 84$, or $y = -\frac{5}{6}x + 14$

Xscl = 5, Yscl = 5

4. $2x - 7y = 150$, or $y = \frac{2}{7}x - \frac{150}{7}$

Xscl = 10, Yscl = 5

85. $y = x^2 + 4x + 1$

87.

5. $19x - 17y = 200$, or $y = \frac{19}{17}x - \frac{200}{17}$

6. $6x + 5y = 159$, or $y = -\frac{6}{5}x + \frac{159}{5}$

Xscl = 5, Yscl = 5

Quick Quiz: Sections 3.1–3.2, p. 173

1.

2. IV   **3.** No

4.

5.

Prepare to Move On, p. 173

1. $\frac{12}{5}$ **2.** $-\frac{3}{4}$ **3.** $-\frac{7}{8}$ **4.** $\frac{7}{6}$

Technology Connection, p. 176

1. $y = -0.72x - 15$

Xscl = 5, Yscl = 5

2. $y - 2.13x = 27$, or $y = 2.13x + 27$

Xscl = 5, Yscl = 5

Exercise Set 3.3, pp. 178–181

1. y-intercept   **2.** x-intercept   **3.** y-intercept
4. x-intercept   **5.** x-intercept   **6.** y-intercept
7. (f)   **8.** (e)   **9.** (d)   **10.** (c)   **11.** (b)
12. (a)   **13. (a)** $(0, 5)$; **(b)** $(2, 0)$ **15. (a)** $(0, -4)$;
(b) $(3, 0)$ **17. (a)** $(0, -2)$; **(b)** $(-3, 0)$, $(3, 0)$
19. (a) $(0, 0)$; **(b)** $(-2, 0)$, $(0, 0)$, $(5, 0)$ **21. (a)** $(0, 3)$;
(b) $(5, 0)$ **23. (a)** $(0, -18)$; **(b)** $(4, 0)$ **25. (a)** $(0, 16)$;
(b) $(-20, 0)$ **27. (a)** None; **(b)** $(12, 0)$
29. (a) $(0, -9)$; **(b)** none

31.

33.

35.

37.

39.

41.

43.

45.

67.

69.

47.

49.

71.

73.

51.

53.

75.

77. $y = -1$ **79.** $x = 4$
81. $x = 0$ **83.**
85. $d - 7$ **86.** $w + 5$,
or $5 + w$ **87.** Let n
represent the number;
$7 + 4n$ **88.** Let n
represent the number; $3n$

55.

57.

89. Let x and y represent the numbers; $2(x + y)$
90. Let a and b represent the numbers; $\frac{1}{2}(a + b)$
91. [ ]   **93.** $y = 0$ **95.** $x = -2$
97. $(-3, 4)$ **99.** $-5x + 3y = 15$, or $y = \frac{5}{3}x + 5$
101. -24 **103.** $\left(\dfrac{C - D}{A}, 0\right)$ **105.** $\left(0, -\dfrac{80}{7}\right)$, or
$(0, -11.\overline{428571})$; $(40, 0)$ **107.** $(0, -9)$; $(45, 0)$
109. $\left(0, \frac{1}{25}\right)$, or $(0, 0.04)$; $\left(\frac{1}{50}, 0\right)$, or $(0.02, 0)$

Quick Quiz: Sections 3.1–3.3, p. 181

59.

61.

1.

2.

63.

65.

3.

4.

5.

Prepare to Move On, p. 181

1. 40   **2.** 518   **3.** $\frac{1720}{103}$ **4.** 0.6108

Exercise Set 3.4, pp. 185–190

1. True   **2.** True   **3.** False   **4.** True

5. Miles per hour, or $\frac{\text{miles}}{\text{hour}}$

6. Hours per chapter, or $\frac{\text{hours}}{\text{chapter}}$

7. Dollars per mile, or $\frac{\text{dollars}}{\text{mile}}$

8. Cups of flour per cake, or $\frac{\text{cups of flour}}{\text{cake}}$

9. **(a)** 30 mpg; **(b)** \$39.33/day; **(c)** 130 mi/day;
(d) 30¢/mi   **11.** **(a)** 7 mph; **(b)** \$7.50/hr;
(c) \$1.07/mi   **13.** **(a)** \$22/hr; **(b)** 20.6 pages/hr;
(c) \$1.07/page   **15.** \$1285.8 billion/year
17. **(a)** 14.5 floors/min; **(b)** 4.14 sec/floor
19. **(a)** 23.12 ft/min; **(b)** 0.04 min/ft
21.

23.

25.

27.

29.

31. 20 calls/hr   **33.** 75 mi/hr   **35.** 12¢/min
37. −10,000 people/year   **39.** Approximately 0.02 gal/mi
41. (e)   **43.** (d)   **45.** (b)   **47.** ⬜

49. $2 \cdot 3 \cdot 5 \cdot 5$ **50.** ⟵+++•++++++++⟶
                                            −5 −4 −3 −2 −1 0 1 2 3 4 5
                                                        −3.5

51. −1.375   **52.** $\frac{1}{3}$ **53.** $-\frac{3}{2}$ **54.** $\frac{2}{3}$ **55.** ⬜
57.   **59.**

61. 0.45 min/mi   **63.** About 41.6 min   **65.** 3.6 bu/hr

Quick Quiz: Sections 3.1–3.4, p. 190

1. y-axis   **2.** No
3.   **4.**

5. 730 pilots per year

Prepare to Move On, p. 190

1. 5   **2.** −6   **3.** −1   **4.** $-\frac{4}{3}$ **5.** $-\frac{4}{3}$ **6.** 1
7. 0   **8.** Undefined

Exercise Set 3.5, pp. 196–201

1. y, x **2.** $\dfrac{\text{change in } y}{\text{change in } x}$ **3.** $\dfrac{\text{rise}}{\text{run}}$ **4.** $\dfrac{y_2 - y_1}{x_2 - x_1}$
5. Positive, negative   **6.** Zero, undefined   **7.** Positive

8. Negative   **9.** Negative   **10.** Positive
11. Zero   **12.** Positive   **13.** Negative   **14.** Zero
15. $25/post   **17.** −$200/year   **19.** $\frac{1}{2}$ point/$1000 income
21. About −2.1°/min   **23.** $\frac{4}{3}$ **25.** $\frac{1}{3}$ **27.** −1
29. 0   **31.** −2   **33.** Undefined   **35.** −$\frac{1}{3}$
37. 5   **39.** $\frac{5}{4}$ **41.** −$\frac{4}{5}$ **43.** $\frac{2}{3}$ **45.** −1
47. −$\frac{1}{2}$ **49.** 0   **51.** 1   **53.** Undefined   **55.** 0
57. Undefined   **59.** Undefined   **61.** 0
63. 14.375%, or 14$\frac{3}{8}$%   **65.** 35%   **67.** $\frac{29}{98}$, or about 30%
69. About 5.1%; yes   **71.** 📋   **73.** 12 + 3a
74. 7(2 + 5x)   **75.** 15   **76.** 3 ≤ x   **77.** $(5t)^3$
78. $16y^4$ **79.** 📋   **81.** 0.364, or 36.4%
83. $\{m \mid m \geq \frac{5}{2}\}$ **85.** $\frac{1}{2}$

Quick Quiz: Sections 3.1–3.5, p. 201

1.

2.

3.

4. −1   **5.** 0

Prepare to Move On, p. 201

1. $y = -\frac{2}{3}x + \frac{7}{3}$ **2.** $y = \frac{3}{4}x - 2$ **3.** $y = \dfrac{c - ax}{b}$

4. $y = \dfrac{ax - c}{b}$

Mid-Chapter Review: Chapter 3, p. 202

1. *y-intercept*: $y - 3 \cdot 0 = 6$
$\qquad\qquad\qquad\quad y = 6$
The *y*-intercept is (0, 6).
x-intercept: $0 - 3x = 6$
$\qquad\qquad\quad -3x = 6$
$\qquad\qquad\qquad\; x = -2$
The *x*-intercept is (−2, 0).

2. $m = \dfrac{y_2 - y_1}{x_2 - x_1} = \dfrac{-1 - 5}{3 - 1}$
$\qquad\qquad\qquad\quad = \dfrac{-6}{2}$
$\qquad\qquad\qquad\quad = -3$

3.

4. IV   **5.** No

6.

7.

8.

9.

10.

11.
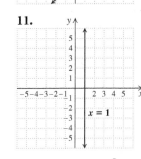

12. 14 homes/month   **13.** About 29%   **14.** $\frac{5}{3}$
15. −3   **16.** Undefined   **17.** 0   **18.** 0
19. Undefined   **20.** (−4, 0), (0, 6)

Exercise Set 3.6, pp. 209–211

1. Slope   **2.** *y*-intercept   **3.** *y*-intercept   **4.** Slope
5. *y*-intercept   **6.** Slope   **7.** (f)   **8.** (b)
9. (d)   **10.** (c)   **11.** (e)   **12.** (a)
13.

15.

17.

19.

21.

23.

25. $-\frac{2}{7}$; $(0, 5)$ **27.** $\frac{1}{3}$; $(0, 7)$ **29.** $\frac{9}{5}$; $(0, -4)$

31. 3; $(0, 7)$ **33.** -2; $(0, 4)$ **35.** 0; $(0, 3)$

37. $\frac{2}{5}$; $\left(0, \frac{8}{5}\right)$ **39.** $\frac{9}{8}$; $(0, 0)$ **41.** $y = 5x + 7$

43. $y = \frac{7}{8}x - 1$ **45.** $y = -\frac{5}{3}x - 8$ **47.** $y = \frac{1}{3}$

49. $y = \frac{2}{3}x + 44$, where y is the number of federal credit union members, in millions, and x is the number of years since 2000   **51.** $y = \frac{3}{5}x + 16$, where y is the number of jobs, in thousands, and x is the number of years since 2008

53.

55.

57.

59.

61.

63.

65.

67.

69. Yes   **71.** Yes   **73.** No   **75.** Yes   **77.** No

79. 🗒️   **81.** 12%   **82.** 250 words   **83.** $2400

84. Width: 20 ft; length: 50 ft   **85.** 🗒️

87. When $x = 0, y = b$, so $(0, b)$ is on the line. When $x = 1, y = m + b$, so $(1, m + b)$ is on the line. Then

$$\text{slope} = \frac{(m + b) - b}{1 - 0} = m.$$

89. $y = \frac{1}{2}x$ **91.** $y = -\frac{4}{5}x + 4$ **93.** $y = -\frac{5}{3}x + 3$

95. $y = \frac{5}{2}x + 1$

Quick Quiz: Sections 3.1–3.6, p. 211

1.

2.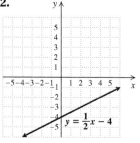

3. III   **4.** x-intercept: $(-7, 0)$; y-intercept: $(0, 7)$ **5.** 1

Prepare to Move On, p. 211

1. $y = m(x - h) + k$ **2.** $y = -2(x + 4) + 9$

3. -7 **4.** 13   **5.** -9

Connecting the Concepts, p. 217

1. Slope–intercept form   **2.** Standard form

3. None of these   **4.** Standard form   **5.** Point–slope form   **6.** None of these   **7.** $2x - 5y = 10$

8. $-2x + y = 7$, or $2x - y = -7$ **9.** $y = \frac{2}{7}x - \frac{8}{7}$

10. $y = -x - 8$

Exercise Set 3.7, pp. 218–220

1. False   **2.** True   **3.** False   **4.** True

5. True   **6.** True   **7.** $\frac{1}{4}$; $(5, 3)$ **9.** -7; $(2, -1)$

11. $-\frac{10}{3}$; $(-4, 6)$ **13.** 5; $(0, 0)$

15.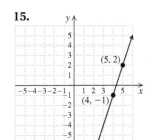

$y - 2 = 3(x - 5)$

17.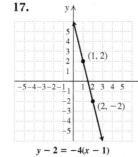

$y - 2 = -4(x - 1)$

19.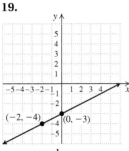

$y - (-4) = \frac{1}{2}(x - (-2))$, or

$y + 4 = \frac{1}{2}(x + 2)$

21.

$y - 0 = -1(x - 8)$, or
$y = -(x - 8)$

23. $y = 3x + 4$ **25.** $y = \frac{4}{3}x - 12$

27. $y = \frac{2}{3}x + \frac{1}{2}$ **29.** $y = x - 32$

31. $y - 1 = 6(x - 7)$ **33.** $y - 4 = -5(x - 3)$

35. $y - (-5) = \frac{1}{2}(x - (-2))$ **37.** $y - 0 = -1(x - 9)$

39. $y = 2x - 6$ **41.** $y = -\frac{3}{5}x + \frac{28}{5}$

43. $y = -0.6x - 5.8$ **45.** $y = \frac{2}{7}x - 6$

47. $y = \frac{3}{5}x + \frac{42}{5}$ **49.** $y = \frac{1}{2}x + 4$ **51.** $y = -x - 1$

53. $y = -\frac{2}{3}x - \frac{13}{3}$ **55.** $x = 5$ **57.** $y = -\frac{3}{2}x + \frac{11}{2}$

59. $y = x + 6$ **61.** $y = -\frac{1}{3}x - \frac{8}{3}$ **63.** $y = -\frac{5}{3}x - \frac{41}{3}$

65. $x = -3$ **67.** $y = 4x - 5$ **69.** $y = 4.5x - 9.4$

71. $y = -2x - 1$ **73.** $y = \frac{5}{3}x$ **75.** $y = -6$

77. $x = -10$ **79. (a)** $y = \frac{11}{14}x + \frac{131}{25}$; **(b)** 10.0 million volunteers; 14.7 million volunteers   **81. (a)** $y = 0.075x + 1.425$; **(b)** 1.95 million graduates; 2.55 million graduates   **83. (a)** Let x represent the number of years after 2000 and y the percent of the U.S. population living in metropolitan areas; $y = -\frac{5}{18}x + 79$;

(b) 77.6%; 75.7%   **85.** ✏️   **87.** -64 **88.** 9

89. 18   **90.** $\frac{11}{2}$ **91.** $\left\{x \mid x < -\frac{17}{3}\right\}$, or $\left(-\infty, -\frac{17}{3}\right)$

92. $\{x \mid x \geq -2\}$, or $[-2, \infty)$ **93.** ✏️

95.

$y - 3 = 0(x - 52)$

97. $y = 2x - 9$

99. $y = \frac{1}{5}x - 2$

101. $y = \frac{1}{2}x + 1$

103. 7

105. $(10, 0), (0, -3)$

107. $y = 1.876712329x + 11.28767123$

1.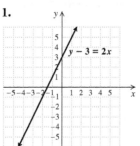

$y - 3 = 2x$

2.

$x + 7 = 8$

3.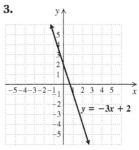

$y = -3x + 2$

4.

$3x - 6y = 6$

5.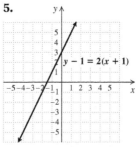

$y - 1 = 2(x + 1)$

Prepare to Move On, p. 220

1. -125 **2.** 64   **3.** -64 **4.** 8   **5.** -4

Visualizing for Success, p. 221

1. C   **2.** G   **3.** F   **4.** B   **5.** D   **6.** A

7. I   **8.** H   **9.** J   **10.** E

Decision Making: Connection, p. 222

1.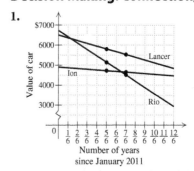

2. Ion: \$18.75/month, or \$225/year; Lancer: \$68.75/month, or \$825/year; Rio: \$156.25/month, or \$1875/year. The slopes of the lines illustrate the depreciation rates.
3. Ion: $y = -225x + 4912.50$; Lancer:
$y = -825x + 6487.50$; Rio: $y = -1875x + 6687.50$
4. Ion: \$4462.50; Lancer: \$4837.50; Rio: \$2937.50
5.   **6.**

Study Summary: Chapter 3, pp. 223–224

1.   **2.** III

3. 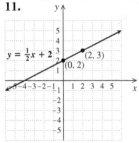   **4.** x-intercept: $(1, 0)$; y-intercept: $(0, -10)$

5.   **6.**

7. $\frac{4}{9}$ meal/min   **8.** $\frac{1}{10}$ **9.** 0
10. Slope: -4; y-intercept: $\left(0, \frac{2}{5}\right)$
11.   **12.** No

13. $y - 6 = \frac{1}{4}(x - (-1))$

Review Exercises: Chapter 3, pp. 225–226

1. True   **2.** True   **3.** False   **4.** False   **5.** True
6. True   **7.** True   **8.** False   **9.** True   **10.** True

11. 4 million people   **12.** About 80,000 people
13.–15.
16. III   **17.** IV
18. II   **19.** $(-5, -1)$
20. $(-2, 5)$
21. $(3, 0)$

22.   **23.** (a) No; (b) yes

24.

$$\frac{2x - y = 3}{2 \cdot 0 - (-3) \mid 3}$$
$$0 + 3 \mid$$
$$3 \overset{?}{=} 3 \quad \text{True}$$

$$\frac{2x - y = 3}{2 \cdot 2 - 1 \mid 3}$$
$$4 - 1 \mid$$
$$3 \overset{?}{=} 3 \quad \text{True}$$

$(-1, -5)$; answers may vary

25.   **26.**

27.   **28.**

29.   **30.**

31.

32.

33.

34.

35. About 11.2 years

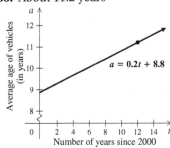

36. (a) $\frac{2}{15}$ mi/min; (b) 7.5 min/mi   **37.** $\frac{1}{20}$ gal/mi
38. 0   **39.** $\frac{7}{3}$ **40.** $-\frac{3}{7}$ **41.** $-\frac{6}{5}$ **42.** 0
43. Undefined   **44.** 2   **45.** $(16, 0), (0, -10)$
46. $-\frac{3}{5}$; $(0, 9)$ **47.** $8.\overline{3}\%$ **48.** Perpendicular
49. Parallel   **50.** $y = \frac{3}{8}x + 7$
51. $y - 9 = -\frac{1}{3}(x - (-2))$ **52.** $y = x + 7$
53. $y = -\frac{5}{3}x - \frac{5}{3}$ **54.** (a) Let x represent the number of years after 2000 and y the average in-state tuition at a public two-year college; $y = 144.\overline{3}x + 1125.\overline{3}$; Answers may vary. (b) \$2568.67; \$3001.67   **55.** ✏ Two perpendicular lines share the same y-intercept if their point of intersection is on the y-axis.   **56.** ✏ The graph of a vertical line has only an x-intercept. The graph of a horizontal line has only a y-intercept. The graph of a nonvertical, nonhorizontal line will have only one intercept if it passes through the origin: $(0, 0)$ is both the x-intercept and the y-intercept.   **57.** -1
58. Area: 45 sq units; perimeter: 28 units
59. $(0, 4), (1, 3), (-1, 3)$; answers may vary

Test: Chapter 3, p. 227

1. [3.1] \$4000   **2.** [3.1] 2000 and 2007   **3.** [3.1] III
4. [3.1] II   **5.** [3.1] $(3, 4)$ **6.** [3.1] $(0, -4)$
7. [3.1] $(-5, 2)$

8. [3.2]

9. [3.3]

10. [3.3]

11. [3.2]

12. [3.2]

13. [3.3]

14. [3.7]

15. [3.5] 5   **16.** [3.5] $-\frac{9}{4}$ **17.** [3.5] Undefined
18. [3.4] $\frac{1}{3}$ km/min   **19.** [3.5] 31.5%
20. [3.3] $(6, 0), (0, -30)$ **21.** [3.6] 8; $(0, 10)$
22. [3.6] $y = -\frac{1}{3}x - 11$
23. [3.6] Parallel   **24.** [3.6] Perpendicular
25. [3.7] $y = -\frac{5}{2}x - \frac{11}{2}$
26. [3.7] (a)   (b) 138 beats per minute

27. [3.6] $y = \frac{2}{5}x + 9$ **28.** [3.1] Area: 25 sq units; perimeter: 20 units   **29.** [3.2], [3.7] $(0, 12)$, $(-3, 15)$, $(5, 7)$

Cumulative Review: Chapters 1–3, p. 228

1. 7   **2.** $12a - 6b + 18$ **3.** $2(4x - 2y + 1)$
4. $2 \cdot 3^3$ **5.** -0.15 **6.** 0.367 **7.** $\frac{11}{60}$
8. 2.6   **9.** 7.28   **10.** $-\frac{5}{12}$ **11.** -3
12. $5x + 11$ **13.** -27 **14.** 16   **15.** -6
16. 2   **17.** $\frac{7}{9}$ **18.** -17 **19.** $\{x \mid x < 16\}$, or
$(-\infty, 16)$ **20.** $h = \dfrac{A - \pi r^2}{2\pi r}$ **21.** IV

22. $-1 < x \le 2$

23.

24.

25.

26.

27.

28.

29. 3; $(0, -2)$
30. $-\frac{1}{3}$ **31.** $y = \frac{2}{7}x - 4$
32. $y - 4 = -\frac{3}{8}(x - (-6))$

33. (a)

(b) About 353 calories per hour

34. \$57,413   **35.** 4 hr   **36.** \$25,000   **37.** $-4, 4$
38. 3   **39.** No solution

CHAPTER 4

Exercise Set 4.1, pp. 235–237

1. (e)   **2.** (f)   **3.** (b)   **4.** (h)   **5.** (g)   **6.** (a)
7. (c)   **8.** (d)   **9.** Base: $2x$; exponent: 5
10. Base: $x + 1$; exponent: 0   **11.** Base: x; exponent: 3
12. Base: y; exponent: 6   **13.** Base: $\dfrac{4}{y}$; exponent: 7
14. Base: $-5x$; exponent: 4   **15.** d^{13} **17.** a^7 **19.** 6^{15}
21. $(3y)^{12}$ **23.** $5p$ **25.** $(x + 3)^{13}$ **27.** a^5b^9 **29.** r^{10}
31. m^4n^9 **33.** 7^3, or 343   **35.** t^7 **37.** $5a$ **39.** 1
41. $(r + s)^8$ **43.** $\frac{4}{5}d^7$ **45.** $4a^7b^6$ **47.** $x^{12}y^7$ **49.** 1
51. 5   **53.** 2   **55.** -4 **57.** x^{33} **59.** 5^{32} **61.** t^{80}
63. $100x^2$ **65.** $-8a^3$ **67.** $25n^{14}$ **69.** $a^{14}b^7$
71. $r^{17}t^{11}$ **73.** $24x^{19}$ **75.** $\dfrac{x^3}{125}$ **77.** $\dfrac{49}{36n^2}$
79. $\dfrac{a^{18}}{b^{48}}$ **81.** $\dfrac{x^8y^4}{z^{12}}$ **83.** $\dfrac{a^{12}}{16b^{20}}$ **85.** $-\dfrac{125x^{21}y^3}{8z^{12}}$
87. 1   **89.** 📋   **91.** -21 **92.** $\left\{x \mid x \le \frac{7}{4}\right\}$, or $\left(-\infty, \frac{7}{4}\right]$
93. -1 **94.** 0   **95.** $\left\{n \mid n < \frac{16}{3}\right\}$, or $\left(-\infty, \frac{16}{3}\right)$
96. 1   **97.** 📋   **99.** 📋   **101.** Let $x = 1$;
then $3x^2 = 3$, but $(3x)^2 = 9$.   **103.** Let $t = -1$;
then $\dfrac{t^6}{t^2} = 1$, but $t^3 = -1$.   **105.** y^{6x} **107.** x^t
109. 13   **111.** $<$ **113.** $<$ **115.** $>$
117. 4,000,000; 4,194,304; 194,304   **119.** 2,000,000,000;
2,147,483,648; 147,483,648   **121.** 1,536,000 bytes,
or approximately 1,500,000 bytes

Prepare to Move On, p. 237

1. -24 **2.** -15 **3.** -11 **4.** 16   **5.** -14 **6.** 4

Technology Connection, p. 242

1. 1.71×10^{17} **2.** $5.\overline{370} \times 10^{-15}$ **3.** 3.68×10^{16}

Connecting the Concepts, p. 243

1. x^{14} **2.** $\dfrac{1}{x^{14}}$ **3.** $\dfrac{1}{x^{14}}$ **4.** x^{14} **5.** x^{40} **6.** x^{40}

7. c^8 **8.** $\dfrac{1}{c^8}$ **9.** $\dfrac{a^{15}}{b^{20}}$ **10.** $\dfrac{b^{20}}{a^{15}}$

Exercise Set 4.2, pp. 243–246

1. True   **2.** False   **3.** True   **4.** False   **5.** (c)
6. (d)   **7.** (a)   **8.** (b)   **9.** Positive power of 10
10. Negative power of 10   **11.** Negative power of 10
12. Positive power of 10   **13.** Positive power of 10

14. Negative power of 10   **15.** $\dfrac{1}{x^3} = \dfrac{1}{8}$

17. $\dfrac{1}{(-2)^6} = \dfrac{1}{64}$ **19.** $\dfrac{1}{t^9}$ **21.** $\dfrac{8}{x^3}$ **23.** a^8

25. $\frac{1}{7}$ **27.** $\dfrac{3a^8}{b^6}$ **29.** $\left(\dfrac{2}{x}\right)^5 = \dfrac{32}{x^5}$ **31.** $\dfrac{1}{3x^5z^4}$

33. 9^{-2} **35.** y^{-3} **37.** t^{-1} **39.** 2^3, or 8

41. $\dfrac{1}{x^{12}}$ **43.** $\dfrac{1}{t^2}$ **45.** $\dfrac{10}{a^6b^2}$ **47.** $\dfrac{1}{n^{15}}$ **49.** t^{18}

51. $\dfrac{1}{m^7n^7}$ **53.** $\dfrac{9}{x^5}$ **55.** $\dfrac{25t^6}{r^8}$ **57.** t^{14}

59. $\dfrac{1}{y^4}$ **61.** $5y^3$ **63.** $2x^5$ **65.** $\dfrac{-3b^9}{2a^7}$ **67.** 1

69. $3s^2t^4u^4$ **71.** $\dfrac{1}{x^{12}y^{15}}$ **73.** $\dfrac{m^{10}n^6}{9}$ **75.** $\dfrac{b^5c^4}{a^8}$

77. $\dfrac{9}{a^8}$ **79.** $\dfrac{n^{12}}{m^3}$ **81.** $\dfrac{27b^{12}}{8a^6}$ **83.** 1   **85.** $\dfrac{2b^3}{a^4}$

87. $\dfrac{5y^4z^{10}}{4x^{11}}$ **89.** 4920   **91.** 0.00892

93. 904,000,000   **95.** 0.000003497   **97.** 3.6×10^7
99. 5.83×10^{-3} **101.** 7.8×10^{10} **103.** 1.032×10^{-6}
105. 6×10^{13} **107.** 2.47×10^8 **109.** 3.915×10^{-16}
111. 2.5×10^{13} **113.** 5.0×10^{-6} **115.** 3×10^{-21}
117.   **119.** $-\frac{1}{6}$ **120.** 7   **121.** $-32a^5$
122. 1   **123.** 5   **124.** -15 **125.** 🖋   **127.** 🖋
129. 2^{-12} **131.** 5   **133.** 5^6 **135.** $\frac{1}{3} + \frac{1}{4} = \frac{7}{12}$
137. 3×10^8 mi   **139.** 2.31×10^8
141. 2×10^4 strands

Quick Quiz: Sections 4.1–4.2, p. 246

1. $200n^8m^{11}$ **2.** $\dfrac{1}{6^{11}}$ **3.** $\dfrac{y^3}{8x^6}$ **4.** 1   **5.** 3.007×10^7

Prepare to Move On, p. 246

1. $8x$ **2.** $-3a - 6b$ **3.** $-2x - 7$ **4.** $-4t - r - 5$
5. 1004   **6.** 9

Technology Connection, p. 250

1. 1141.0023

Exercise Set 4.3, pp. 251–254

1. (b)   **2.** (f)   **3.** (h)   **4.** (d)   **5.** (g)   **6.** (e)
7. (a)   **8.** (c)   **9.** Yes   **10.** Yes   **11.** No   **12.** Yes
13. Yes   **14.** No   **15.** $8x^3, -11x^2, 6x, 1$ **17.** $-t^6, -3t^3,$
$9t, -4$ **19.** Trinomial   **21.** Polynomial with no
special name   **23.** Binomial   **25.** Monomial
27.

Term	Coefficient	Degree of the Term	Degree of the Polynomial
$8x^5$	8	5	
$-\frac{1}{2}x^4$	$-\frac{1}{2}$	4	
$-4x^3$	-4	3	5
$7x^2$	7	2	
6	6	0	

29. Coefficients: 8, 2; degrees: 4, 1
31. Coefficients: 9, -3, 4; degrees: 2, 1, 0
33. Coefficients: 1, -1, 4, -3; degrees: 4, 3, 1, 0
35. (a) 1, 3, 4; (b) $8t^4$, 8; (c) 4
37. (a) 2, 0, 4; (b) $2a^4$, 2; (c) 4
39. (a) 0, 2, 1, 5; (b) $-x^5$, -1; (c) 5
41. $11n^2 + n$ **43.** $4a^4$ **45.** $11b^3 + b^2 - b$
47. $-x^4 - x^3$ **49.** $\frac{1}{15}x^4 + 10$ **51.** $-1.1a^2 + 5.3a - 7.5$
53. -3; 21   **55.** 16; 34   **57.** -38; 148   **59.** 159; 165
61. 1112 ft   **63.** 62.8 cm   **65.** 153.86 m²
67. About 135 ft   **69.** 14; 55 oranges
71. About 2.3 mcg/mL   **73.** 🖋
75.   **76.**
77.   **78.**

79.

80.

81.   **83.** $2x^5 + 4x^4 + 6x^3 + 8$; answers may vary
85. \$2510   **87.** $3x^6$ **89.** After about 3.4 hr and 8.5 hr
91. 85.0   **93.**

95.

t	$-t^2 + 10t - 18$
3	3
4	6
5	7
6	6
7	3

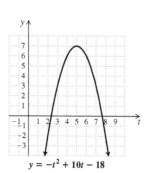

$y = -t^2 + 10t - 18$

Quick Quiz: Sections 4.1–4.3, p. 254

1. $9x^{10}y^8$ **2.** $-16a^4$ **3.** $1, -6, \frac{1}{2}$ **4.** -1290
5. 1

Prepare to Move On, p. 254

1. $x - 3$ **2.** $-2x - 6$ **3.** $6a - 3$ **4.** $-t - 1$
5. $-t^4 + 17t$ **6.** $0.4a^2 - a + 11$

Technology Connection, p. 259

1. In each case, let $y_1 =$ the expression before the addition or subtraction has been performed, $y_2 =$ the simplified sum or difference, and $y_3 = y_2 - y_1$; and note that the graph of y_3 coincides with the x-axis. That is, $y_3 = 0$.

Exercise Set 4.4, pp. 259–262

1. Opposite   **2.** Ascending   **3.** Opposite; sign
4. Like; missing   **5.** x^2 **6.** -6 **7.** $-$ **8.** $+$
9. $4x + 9$ **11.** $-6t + 8$ **13.** $-3x^2 + 6x - 2$
15. $9t^2 + t + 3$ **17.** $8m^3 - 3m - 7$
19. $7 + 13a - a^2 + 7a^3$ **21.** $2x^6 + 9x^4 + 2x^3 - 4x^2 + 5x$
23. $x^4 + \frac{1}{4}x^3 - \frac{3}{4}x^2 - \frac{5}{6}x + 3$
25. $4.2t^3 + 3.5t^2 - 6.4t - 1.8$ **27.** $-4x^3 + 4x^2 + 6x$
29. $1.3x^4 + 0.35x^3 + 9.53x^2 + 2x + 0.96$
31. $-(-3t^3 + 4t^2 - 7)$; $3t^3 - 4t^2 + 7$
33. $-(x^4 - 8x^3 + 6x)$; $-x^4 + 8x^3 - 6x$
35. $-3a^4 + 5a^2 - 1.2$ **37.** $4x^4 - 6x^2 - \frac{3}{4}x + 8$
39. $-2x - 7$ **41.** $-t^2 - 12t + 13$
43. $8a^3 + 8a^2 + a - 10$ **45.** 0
47. $1 + a + 12a^2 - 3a^3$ **49.** $\frac{9}{8}x^3 - \frac{1}{2}x$
51. $0.05t^3 - 0.07t^2 + 0.01t + 1$
53. $2x^2 + 6$ **55.** $-3x^4 - 8x^3 - 7x^2$
57. **(a)** $5x^2 + 4x$; **(b)** 145; 273   **59.** $16y + 26$

61. $(r + 11)(r + 9)$; $9r + 99 + 11r + r^2$
63. $(x + 3)^2$; $x^2 + 3x + 9 + 3x$ **65.** $m^2 - 40$
67. $\pi r^2 - 49$ **69.** $(x^2 - 12)\ \text{ft}^2$ **71.** $(z^2 - 36\pi)\ \text{ft}^2$
73. $\left(144 - \dfrac{d^2}{4}\pi\right)\text{m}^2$ **75.** 🖳   **77.** $y = \frac{1}{3}x + 2$
78. $y = 4x + 24$ **79.** $y = 10$ **80.** $y = -3x + 8$
81. $y = -\frac{4}{7}x - 4$ **82.** $y = -\frac{4}{3}x - \frac{8}{3}$
83. 🖳   **85.** $9t^2 - 20t + 11$ **87.** $-6x + 14$
89. $250.591x^3 + 2.812x$ **91.** $20w + 42$ **93.** $2x^2 + 20x$
95. **(a)** $P = -x^2 + 175x - 5000$; **(b)** \$2500; **(c)** \$1600

Quick Quiz: Sections 4.1–4.4, p. 262

1. $\dfrac{9y^{10}}{4x^6}$ **2.** $(y + 3)^{12}$ **3.** 4   **4.** $-y^3 - 6y^2 + 2y$
5. $5y^2 + 10$

Prepare to Move On, p. 262

1. $2x^2 - 2x + 6$ **2.** $-15x^2 + 10x + 35$ **3.** x^8
4. y^7 **5.** $2n^3$ **6.** $-6n^{12}$

Mid-Chapter Review, p. 263

1. $\dfrac{x^{-3}y}{x^{-4}y^7} = x^{-3-(-4)}y^{1-7} = x^1 y^{-6} = \dfrac{x}{y^6}$

2. $(x^2 + 7x - 12) - (3x^2 - 6x - 1) =$
$x^2 + 7x - 12 - 3x^2 + 6x + 1 = -2x^2 + 13x - 11$

3. $x^{16}y^{40}$ **4.** 1   **5.** $\frac{1}{4}a^{10}$ **6.** $-\frac{8}{3}b$ **7.** $\dfrac{5}{x^2}$

8. $\dfrac{a^2}{bc^3}$ **9.** $\dfrac{27}{8a^6}$ **10.** $\dfrac{2}{3m^6n^4}$ **11.** 0.00000189
12. 2.7×10^{10} **13.** 3   **14.** $2a^2 - 5a - 3$
15. $3x^2 + 3x + 3$ **16.** $7x + 7$
17. $-6x^2 + 2x - 12$ **18.** $t^9 + 5t^7$
19. $3a^4 - 13a^3 - 13a^2 - 4$ **20.** $-x^5 + 2x^4 - 2x^2$

Technology Connection, p. 268

1. Let $y_1 = (5x^4 - 2x^2 + 3x)(x^2 + 2x)$ and
$y_2 = 5x^6 + 10x^5 - 2x^4 - x^3 + 6x^2$. With the table set in AUTO mode, note that the value in the Y_1- and Y_2-columns match, regardless of how far we scroll up or down.
2. Use TRACE, a table, or a boldly drawn graph to confirm that y_3 is always 0.

Exercise Set 4.5, pp. 268–270

1. (c)   **2.** (d)   **3.** (b)   **4.** (a)   **5.** (c)
6. (d)   **7.** (d)   **8.** (a)   **9.** (c)   **10.** (b)
11. $21x^5$ **13.** $-x^7$ **15.** x^8 **17.** $36t^4$
19. $-0.12x^9$ **21.** $-\frac{1}{20}x^{12}$ **23.** $5n^3$ **25.** $72y^{10}$
27. $20x^2 + 5x$ **29.** $3a^2 - 27a$ **31.** $x^5 + x^2$
33. $-6n^3 + 24n^2 - 3n$ **35.** $-15t^3 - 30t^2$
37. $4a^9 - 8a^7 - \frac{5}{12}a^4$ **39.** $x^2 + 7x + 12$
41. $t^2 + 4t - 21$ **43.** $a^2 - 1.3a + 0.42$ **45.** $x^2 - 9$
47. $28 - 15x + 2x^2$ **49.** $t^2 + \frac{17}{6}t + 2$
51. $\frac{3}{16}a^2 + \frac{5}{4}a - 2$

53.

55.

57.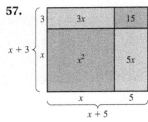

73. $q^{10} - 1$ **75.** $15t^5 - 3t^4 + 3t^3$
77. $36x^8 - 36x^5 + 9x^2$ **79.** $18a^4 + 0.8a^3 + 4.5a + 0.2$
81. $\frac{1}{25} - 36x^8$ **83.** $a^3 + 1$ **85.** $x^2 + 6x + 9$
87. $t^2 + 7t + 12$ **89.** $x^2 + 10x + 21$
91. $25t^2 + 20t + 4$

93.   **95.**

97.   **99.**

101. Refrigerator: 360 kWh/year; freezer: 720 kWh/year; washing machine: 120 kWh/year
102. For heat pumps costing $6666.67 or less
103. $a = \dfrac{c}{3b}$ **104.** $x = \dfrac{by + c}{a}$
105. 🖰   **107.** $16x^4 - 81$ **109.** $81t^4 - 72t^2 + 16$
111. $t^{24} - 4t^{18} + 6t^{12} - 4t^6 + 1$ **113.** 396   **115.** -7
117. $17F + 7(F - 17)$, $F^2 - (F - 17)(F - 7)$; other equivalent expressions are possible.
119. $(y + 1)(y - 1)$, $y(y + 1) - y - 1$; other equivalent expressions are possible.   **121.** $y^2 - 4y + 4$ **123.** 🖼

59. $x^3 + 2x + 3$ **61.** $2a^3 - a^2 - 11a + 10$
63. $3y^6 - 21y^4 + y^3 + 2y^2 - 7y - 14$
65. $33x^2 + 25x + 2$ **67.** $x^4 + 4x^3 - 3x^2 + 16x - 3$
69. $10t^4 + 3t^3 - 20t^2 + \frac{9}{2}t - 2$
71. $x^4 + 8x^3 + 12x^2 + 9x + 4$
73. 🖰   **75.** $c = 2A - b$ **76.** 80%
77. ← [———— → $-3 \quad 0$ **78.** x-axis
79. $-\frac{4}{3}$ **80.** Slope: $\frac{1}{3}$; y-intercept: $\left(0, -\frac{5}{3}\right)$
81. 🖰   **83.** $75y^2 - 45y$ **85.** 5
87. $V = (4x^3 - 48x^2 + 144x)$ in³; $S = (-4x^2 + 144)$ in²
89. $(x^3 - 5x^2 + 8x - 4)$ cm³
91. (a) $\left(8 - \frac{4}{3}\pi\right)x^3$; (b) 11.6 in³
93. $2x^2 + 18x + 36$ **95.** $16x + 16$
97. $x^3 - 9x^2 + 27x - 27$ **99.** 🖼

Quick Quiz: Sections 4.1–4.5, p. 270

1. $-6x^9 + 16x^5 - 24x^4$ **2.** $10x^4 - 15x + 1$
3. $7a^2 - 10a - 2$ **4.** $125x^5y^4$ **5.** Trinomial

Prepare to Move On, p. 270

1. 0.49   **2.** $49x^6$ **3.** $\frac{9}{4}$ **4.** $\frac{3}{2}x$ **5.** $2a$ **6.** $\frac{1}{9}t^8$

Exercise Set 4.6, pp. 276–278

1. True   **2.** False   **3.** False   **4.** True
5. $x^3 + 3x^2 + 2x + 6$ **7.** $t^5 + 7t^4 - 2t - 14$
9. $y^2 - y - 6$ **11.** $9x^2 + 21x + 10$
13. $5x^2 + 17x - 12$ **15.** $15 - 13t + 2t^2$
17. $x^4 - 4x^2 - 21$ **19.** $p^2 - \frac{1}{16}$
21. $x^2 - 0.09$ **23.** $100x^4 - 9$ **25.** $1 - 25t^6$
27. $t^2 - 4t + 4$ **29.** $x^2 + 20x + 100$
31. $9x^2 + 12x + 4$ **33.** $1 - 20a + 100a^2$
35. $x^6 + 24x^3 + 144$ **37.** $x^5 + 3x^3 - x^2 - 3$
39. $x^2 - 64$ **41.** $-3n^2 - 19n + 14$
43. $x^2 + 6x + 9$ **45.** $49x^6 - 14x^3 + 1$
47. $81a^6 - 1$ **49.** $x^8 - 0.01$ **51.** $t^2 - \frac{9}{16}$
53. $1 - 3t + 5t^2 - 15t^3$ **55.** $a^2 - \frac{4}{5}a + \frac{4}{25}$
57. $t^8 + 6t^4 + 9$ **59.** $45x^2 - 56x - 45$
61. $14n^5 - 7n^3$ **63.** $a^3 - a^2 - 10a + 12$
65. $49 - 42x^4 + 9x^8$ **67.** $4 - 12x^4 + 9x^8$
69. $25t^2 + 60t^3 + 36t^4$ **71.** $5x^3 + 30x^2 - 10x$

Quick Quiz: Sections 4.1–4.6, p. 278

1. $-20a^4b^{12}$ **2.** n^{14} **3.** $4x^3 - 13x^2 + 5x - 6$
4. $100x^{10} - 1$ **5.** $9a^2 + 24a + 16$

Prepare to Move On, p. 278

1. 4   **2.** 19   **3.** $12a - 7c$ **4.** $13y - w$

Technology Connection, p. 282

1. 36.22   **2.** 22,312

Exercise Set 4.7, pp. 283–286

1. (b)   **2.** (d)   **3.** (a)   **4.** (c)   **5.** (a)   **6.** (b)
7. (b)   **8.** (a)   **9.** (c)   **10.** (c)   **11.** -13
13. -68 **15.** About 735 kg   **17.** 73.005 in²
19. 66.4 m   **21.** 3, 2, 2, 0; 3   **23.** 0, 3, 3, 3; 3
25. $2r - 6s$ **27.** $5xy^2 - 2x^2y + x + 3x^2$
29. $9u^2v - 11uv^2 + 11u^2$ **31.** $6a^2c - 7ab^2 + a^2b$
33. $11x^2 - 10xy - y^2$ **35.** $-6a^4 - 8ab + 7ab^2$
37. $-6r^2 - 5rt - t^2$ **39.** $3x^3 - x^2y + xy^2 - 3y^3$
41. $-2y^4x^3 - 3y^3x$ **43.** $-8x + 8y$
45. $12c^2 + 5cd - 2d^2$ **47.** $x^2y^2 + 4xy - 5$
49. $4a^2 - b^2$ **51.** $20r^2t^2 - 23rt + 6$
53. $m^6n^2 + 2m^3n - 48$ **55.** $30x^2 - 28xy + 6y^2$

57. $0.01 - p^2q^2$　　**59.** $x^2 + 2xh + h^2$
61. $16a^2 - 40ab + 25b^2$　　**63.** $a^2b^2 - c^2d^4$
65. $x^3y^2 + x^2y^3 + 2x^2y^2 + 2xy^3 + 3xy + 3y^2$
67. $a^2 + 2ab + b^2 - c^2$　　**69.** $a^2 - b^2 - 2bc - c^2$
71. $x^2 + 2xy + y^2$　　**73.** $\frac{1}{2}a^2b^2 - 2$
75. $a^2 + c^2 + ab + 2ac + ad + bc + bd + cd$
77. $m^2 - n^2$
79. We draw a rectangle with　　**81.**
dimensions $r + s$ by $u + v$.

83. 　　**85.** 6　　**86.** 7　　**87.** 6　　**88.** -21
89. $17a + 3x - 21$　　**90.** $5y + 21$　　**91.**
93. $4xy - 4y^2$　　**95.** $2\pi ab - \pi b^2$
97. $x^3 + 2y^3 + x^2y + xy^2$　　**99.** $2x^2 - 2\pi r^2 + 4xh + 2\pi rh$
101. 　　**103.** 40　　**105.** $P + 2Pr + Pr^2$
107. \$12,960.29

Quick Quiz: Sections 4.1–4.7, p. 286

1. 31　　**2.** $4.1x^2 - 2.9x + 6.1$
3. $5x^4 + 15x^3 - x^2 + x + 12$　　**4.** $a^4 - 100$　　**5.** -21

Prepare to Move On, p. 286

1. $x^2 - 8x - 4$　　**2.** $2x^3 - x^2 - x + 4$
3. $-2x + 5$　　**4.** $5x^2 + x$

Exercise Set 4.8, pp. 290–292

1. Divisor　　**2.** Quotient　　**3.** Dividend
4. Remainder　　**5.** $8x^6 - 5x^3$　　**7.** $1 - 2u + u^6$
9. $6t^2 - 8t + 2$　　**11.** $7x^3 - 6x + \frac{3}{2}$　　**13.** $-4t^2 - 2t + 1$
15. $4x - 5 + \dfrac{1}{2x}$　　**17.** $x + 2x^3y + 3$
19. $-3rs - r + 2s$　　**21.** $x - 6$　　**23.** $t - 5 + \dfrac{-45}{t - 5}$
25. $2x - 1 + \dfrac{1}{x + 6}$　　**27.** $t^2 - 3t + 9$
29. $a + 5 + \dfrac{4}{a - 5}$　　**31.** $x - 3 - \dfrac{3}{5x - 1}$
33. $3a + 1 + \dfrac{3}{2a + 5}$　　**35.** $t^2 - 3t + 1$　　**37.** $x^2 + 1$
39. $t^2 - 1 + \dfrac{3t - 1}{t^2 + 5}$　　**41.** $2x^2 + 1 + \dfrac{-x}{2x^2 - 3}$
43.
45.

$y = -\frac{2}{3}x + 4$

46.

$8x = 4y$

47. Slope: 4; y-intercept: $\left(0, \frac{7}{2}\right)$　　**48.** $y = \frac{5}{4}x - \frac{9}{2}$
49. 　　**51.** $5x^{6k} - 16x^{3k} + 14$　　**53.** $3t^{2h} + 2t^h - 5$
55. $a + 3 + \dfrac{5}{5a^2 - 7a - 2}$　　**57.** $2x^2 + x - 3$　　**59.** 3
61. -1　　**63.** **(a)** $(a + 1)$ cm; **(b)** $(a^2 + 2a + 1)$ cm²

Quick Quiz: Sections 4.1–4.8, p. 292

1. $-t^5$　　**2.** $-15x^6 - 18x^5 + 3x^4$　　**3.** $\frac{1}{9}a^4 + 4a^2 + 36$
4. $8ab^2 - 10ab$　　**5.** $4n^3 - 2n^2 + 1$

Prepare to Move On, p. 292

1. $3, x + 7$　　**2.** $x - 3, x + 10$　　**3.** $x, x + 1, 2x - 5$
4. $3(3x + 5y)$　　**5.** $7(2a + c + 1)$

Visualizing for Success, p. 293

1. E, F　　**2.** B, O　　**3.** S, K　　**4.** R, G　　**5.** D, M
6. J, P　　**7.** C, L　　**8.** N, Q　　**9.** A, H　　**10.** I, T

Decision Making: Connection, p. 294

1. 80 movies　　**2.** 32 GB or 64 GB　　**3.** 　　**4.**

Study Summary: Chapter 4, pp. 295–297

1. 6　　**2.** 1　　**3.** x^{16}　　**4.** 8^7　　**5.** y^{15}　　**6.** $x^{30}y^{10}$
7. $\dfrac{x^{10}}{7^5}$　　**8.** $\frac{1}{10}$　　**9.** $\dfrac{y^3}{x}$　　**10.** 9.04×10^{-4}
11. 690,000　　**12.** $x^2, -10, 5x, -8x^6$　　**13.** 1　　**14.** 1
15. $-8x^6$　　**16.** -8　　**17.** 6　　**18.** Trinomial
19. $3x^2 - 4x$　　**20.** 4　　**21.** $8x^2 + x$　　**22.** $10x^2 - 7x$
23. $x^3 - 2x^2 - x + 2$　　**24.** $2x^2 + 11x + 12$
25. $25 - 9x^2$　　**26.** $x^2 + 18x + 81$　　**27.** $64x^2 - 16x + 1$
28. -7　　**29.** 6　　**30.** $3cd^2 + 4cd - 7c$　　**31.** $-2p^2w$
32. $49x^2y^2 - 14x^3y + x^4$　　**33.** $y^3 - 2y + 4$
34. $x - 2 + \dfrac{6}{x + 1}$

Review Exercises: Chapter 4, pp. 298–299

1. True　　**2.** True　　**3.** True　　**4.** False
5. False　　**6.** False　　**7.** True　　**8.** True　　**9.** n^{12}
10. $(7x)^{10}$　　**11.** t^6　　**12.** 4^3, or 64　　**13.** 1
14. $-9c^4d^2$　　**15.** $-8x^3y^6$　　**16.** $18x^5$　　**17.** a^7b^6
18. $\dfrac{4t^{10}}{9s^8}$　　**19.** $\dfrac{1}{8^6}$　　**20.** a^{-9}　　**21.** $\dfrac{1}{4^2}$, or $\dfrac{1}{16}$　　**22.** $\dfrac{2b^9}{a^{13}}$
23. $\dfrac{1}{w^{15}}$　　**24.** $\dfrac{x^6}{4y^2}$　　**25.** $\dfrac{y^3}{8x^3}$　　**26.** 470,000,000
27. 1.09×10^{-5}　　**28.** 2.09×10^4　　**29.** 5.12×10^{-5}
30. $-4y^5, 7y^2, -3y, -2$　　**31.** $7, -\frac{5}{6}, -4, 10$
32. **(a)** 2, 0, 5; **(b)** $15t^5, 15$; **(c)** 5　　**33.** **(a)** 5, 0, 2, 1;
(b) $-2x^5, -2$; **(c)** 5　　**34.** Trinomial
35. Polynomial with no special name　　**36.** Monomial
37. $t - 1$　　**38.** $14a^5 - 2a^2 - a - \frac{2}{3}$　　**39.** -24

40. 16   **41.** $x^5 + 8x^4 + 6x^3 - 2x - 9$
42. $6a^5 - a^3 - 12a^2$ **43.** $x^5 - 3x^3 - 2x^2 + 8$
44. $\frac{3}{4}x^4 + \frac{1}{4}x^3 - \frac{1}{3}x^2 - \frac{7}{4}x + \frac{3}{8}$
45. $-x^5 + x^4 - 5x^3 - 2x^2 + 2x$
46. (a) $4w + 6$; (b) $w^2 + 3w$ **47.** $-30x^5$
48. $49x^2 + 14x + 1$ **49.** $a^2 - 3a - 28$ **50.** $d^2 - 64$
51. $12x^3 - 23x^2 + 13x - 2$ **52.** $15t^5 - 6t^4 + 12t^3$
53. $4a^2 - 81$ **54.** $x^2 - 1.3x + 0.4$
55. $x^7 + x^5 - 3x^4 + 3x^3 - 2x^2 + 5x - 3$
56. $16y^6 - 40y^3 + 25$ **57.** $2t^4 - 11t^2 - 21$
58. $a^2 + \frac{1}{6}a - \frac{1}{3}$ **59.** $-49 + 4n^2$ **60.** 49
61. Coefficients: 1, −7, 9, −8; degrees: 6, 2, 2, 0; 6
62. Coefficients: 1, −1, 1; degrees: 13, 22, 15; 22
63. $-4u + 4v - 7$ **64.** $6m^3 + 4m^2n - mn^2$
65. $2a^2 - 16ab$ **66.** $11x^3y^2 - 8x^2y - 6x^2 - 6x + 6$
67. $2x^2 - xy - 15y^2$ **68.** $25a^2b^2 - 10abcd^2 + c^2d^4$
69. $\frac{1}{2}x^2 - \frac{1}{2}y^2$ **70.** $y^4 - \frac{1}{3}y + 4$
71. $3x^2 - 7x + 4 + \dfrac{1}{2x + 3}$ **72.** $t^3 + 2t - 3$

73. 📝 In the expression $5x^3$, the exponent refers only to the x. In the expression $(5x)^3$, the entire expression $5x$ is the base.
74. 📝 It is possible to determine two possibilities for the binomial that was squared by using the equation $(A - B)^2 = A^2 - 2AB + B^2$ in reverse. Since, in $x^2 - 6x + 9$, $A^2 = x^2$ and $B^2 = 9$, or 3^2, the binomial that was squared was $A - B$, or $x - 3$. If the polynomial is written $9 - 6x + x^2$, then $A^2 = 9$ and $B^2 = x^2$, so the binomial that was squared was $3 - x$. We cannot determine without further information whether the binomial squared was $x - 3$ or $3 - x$.   **75.** (a) 9; (b) 28   **76.** $64x^{16}$
77. $8x^4 + 4x^3 + 5x - 2$ **78.** $-16x^6 + x^2 - 10x + 25$
79. $\frac{94}{13}$ **80.** 2.28×10^{11} platelets

Test: Chapter 4, p. 300

1. [4.1] x^{13} **2.** [4.1] 3   **3.** [4.1] 1   **4.** [4.1] t^{45}
5. [4.1] $-27y^6$ **6.** [4.1] $-40x^{19}y^4$ **7.** [4.1] $\frac{6}{5}a^5b^3$
8. [4.1] $\dfrac{16p^2}{25q^6}$ **9.** [4.2] $\dfrac{1}{y^7}$ **10.** [4.2] 5^{-6}
11. [4.2] $\dfrac{1}{t^9}$ **12.** [4.2] $\dfrac{3y^5}{x^5}$ **13.** [4.2] $\dfrac{b^4}{16a^{12}}$
14. [4.2] $\dfrac{c^3}{a^3b^3}$ **15.** [4.2] 3.06×10^9
16. [4.2] 0.00000005   **17.** [4.2] 1.75×10^{17}
18. [4.2] 1.296×10^{22} **19.** [4.3] Binomial
20. [4.3] 3, −1, $\frac{1}{9}$ **21.** [4.3] Degrees of terms: 3, 1, 5, 0; leading term: $7t^5$; leading coefficient: 7; degree of polynomial: 5   **22.** [4.3] −7   **23.** [4.3] $\frac{7}{4}y^2 - 4y$
24. [4.3] $4x^3 + 4x^2 + 3$
25. [4.4] $4x^5 + x^4 + 5x^3 - 8x^2 + 2x - 7$
26. [4.4] $5x^4 + 5x^2 + x + 5$
27. [4.4] $-2a^4 + 3a^3 - a - 7$
28. [4.4] $-t^4 + 2.5t^3 - 0.6t^2 - 9$
29. [4.5] $-6x^4 + 6x^3 + 10x^2$ **30.** [4.6] $x^2 - \frac{2}{3}x + \frac{1}{9}$
31. [4.6] $25t^2 - 49$ **32.** [4.6] $6b^2 + 7b - 5$
33. [4.6] $x^{14} - 4x^8 + 4x^6 - 16$ **34.** [4.6] $48 + 34y - 5y^2$
35. [4.5] $6x^3 - 7x^2 - 11x - 3$
36. [4.6] $64a^6 + 48a^3 + 9$ **37.** [4.7] 24
38. [4.7] $-4x^3y - x^2y^2 + xy^3 - y^3 + 19$
39. [4.7] $8a^2b^2 + 6ab + 6ab^2 + ab^3 - 4b^3$

40. [4.7] $9x^{10} - y^2$ **41.** [4.8] $4x^2 + 3x - 5$
42. [4.8] $6x^2 - 20x + 26 + \dfrac{-39}{x + 2}$
43. [4.5], [4.6] $V = l(l - 2)(l - 1) = l^3 - 3l^2 + 2l$
44. [4.2] $\frac{1}{2} - \frac{1}{4} = \frac{1}{4}$ **45.** [4.6] About 2.9×10^8 hr

Cumulative Review: Chapters 1–4, p. 301

1. 6   **2.** −8   **3.** $-\frac{7}{45}$ **4.** 6   **5.** $y + 10$ **6.** t^{12}
7. $-4x^5y^3$ **8.** $50a^4b^7$ **9.** $2(5a - 3b + 6)$ **10.** 6
11. II
12.
13.
14.
15.
16. Slope: $\frac{1}{10}$; y-intercept: $\left(0, \frac{3}{8}\right)$ **17.** $-\frac{5}{8}$
18. $y = -\frac{2}{3}x - 10$ **19.** −4   **20.** $\frac{8}{3}$ **21.** −7
22. $\{t \mid t \geq -8\}$, or $[-8, \infty)$ **23.** $\left\{x \mid x < \frac{1}{2}\right\}$, or $\left(-\infty, \frac{1}{2}\right)$
24. $t = \dfrac{5pq}{2c}$ **25.** $7u^2v - 2uv^2 + uv + 3u^2$
26. $x^5 - 2x$ **27.** $-16x^5 - 48x^4 + 56x^3$
28. $x^3 - x^2 - 7x + 10$ **29.** $16t^4 + 24t^2 + 9$
30. $\frac{1}{4}x^2 - 1$ **31.** $6r^4 - 5r^2s - 4s^2$ **32.** $x + \dfrac{3}{x - 1}$
33. $\dfrac{1}{7^{10}}$ **34.** $\dfrac{x^7y^2}{3}$ **35.** 53 thousand megawatts
36. 4 trillion kWh   **37.** No more than 4 hr
38. $0.1 billion per year   **39.** 0   **40.** No solution
41. $\frac{1}{7} + 1 = \frac{8}{7}$ **42.** $15x^{12}$

CHAPTER 5

Technology Connection, p. 309

1. Correct   **2.** Correct   **3.** Not correct
4. Not correct   **5.** Not correct   **6.** Correct
7. Not correct   **8.** Correct

Exercise Set 5.1, pp. 310–311

1. False   **2.** True   **3.** True   **4.** False   **5.** (h)
6. (f)   **7.** (b)   **8.** (e)   **9.** (c)   **10.** (g)   **11.** (d)
12. (a)   **13.** Answers may vary.
$(14x)(x^2), (7x^2)(2x), (-2)(-7x^3)$ **15.** Answers may vary.
$(-15)(a^4), (-5a)(3a^3), (-3a^2)(5a^2)$ **17.** Answers may vary. $(5t^2)(5t^3), (25t)(t^4), (-5t)(-5t^4)$ **19.** $8(x + 3)$

21. $2(x^2 + x - 4)$ **23.** $t(3t + 1)$ **25.** $-5y(y + 2)$
27. $x^2(x + 6)$ **29.** $8a^2(2a^2 - 3)$ **31.** $-t^2(6t^4 - 9t^2 + 4)$
33. $6x^2(x^6 + 2x^4 - 4x^2 + 5)$ **35.** $x^2y^2(x^3y^3 + x^2y + xy - 1)$
37. $-5a^2b^2(7ab^2 - 2b + 3a)$ **39.** $(n - 6)(n + 3)$
41. $(x + 3)(x^2 - 7)$ **43.** $(2y - 9)(y^2 + 1)$
45. $(x + 2)(x^2 + 5)$ **47.** $(3n - 2)(3n^2 + 1)$
49. $(t - 5)(4t^2 + 3)$ **51.** $(7x + 5)(x^2 - 3)$
53. $(6a + 7)(a^2 + 1)$ **55.** $(x - 6)(2x^2 - 1)$
57. Not factorable by grouping   **59.** $(y + 8)(y^2 - 2)$
61. $(x - 4)(2x^2 - 9)$ **63.**   **65.** $\frac{3}{25}$ **66.** 24
67. $\dfrac{y^4}{2x}$ **68.** $a^7b^7c^3$ **69.** $4x^2 + 5x - 13$
70. $-w^2y + yz + wz$ **71.** 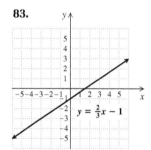   **73.** $(2x^3 + 3)(2x^2 + 3)$
75. $2x(x + 1)(x^2 - 2)$ **77.** $(x - 1)(5x^4 + x^2 + 3)$
79. Answers may vary. $8x^4y^3 - 24x^2y^4 + 16x^3y^4$

Prepare to Move On, p. 311

1. $x^2 + 9x + 14$ **2.** $x^2 - 9x + 14$ **3.** $x^2 - 5x - 14$
4. $x^2 + 5x - 14$ **5.** 1, 2, 3, 4, 5, 6, 10, 12, 15, 20, 30, 60
6. 1, 2, 3, 6, 9, 18

Exercise Set 5.2, pp. 317–318

1. False   **2.** True   **3.** True   **4.** True
5. Positive; positive   **6.** Negative; negative
7. Negative; positive   **8.** Positive; positive   **9.** Positive
10. Negative   **11.** $(x + 4)(x + 4)$ **13.** $(x + 1)(x + 10)$
15. $(t - 2)(t - 7)$ **17.** $(b - 4)(b - 1)$
19. $(d - 2)(d - 5)$ **21.** $(x - 5)(x + 3)$
23. $(x + 5)(x - 3)$ **25.** $2(x + 2)(x - 9)$
27. $-x(x + 2)(x - 8)$ **29.** $(y - 5)(y + 9)$
31. $(x - 6)(x + 12)$ **33.** $-5(b - 3)(b + 10)$
35. $x^3(x - 2)(x + 1)$ **37.** Prime   **39.** $(t + 4)(t + 8)$
41. $(x + 9)(x + 11)$ **43.** $3x(x - 25)(x + 4)$
45. $-4(x + 5)(x + 5)$ **47.** $(y - 12)(y - 8)$
49. $-a^4(a - 6)(a + 15)$ **51.** $\left(t + \frac{1}{3}\right)\left(t + \frac{1}{3}\right)$
53. Prime   **55.** $(p - 5q)(p - 2q)$ **57.** Prime
59. $(s - 6t)(s + 2t)$ **61.** $6a^8(a - 2)(a + 7)$
63.   **65.** -10 **66.** 1.13   **67.** $\frac{5}{3}$ **68.** $\frac{5}{2}$
69. -11 **70.** 2   **71.** 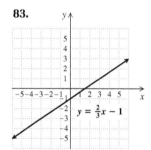   **73.** $-5, 5, -23, 23, -49, 49$
75. $(y + 0.2)(y - 0.4)$ **77.** $-\frac{1}{3}a(a - 3)(a + 2)$
79. $(x^m + 4)(x^m + 7)$ **81.** $(a + 1)(x + 2)(x + 1)$
83. $(x + 3)^3$, or $(x^3 + 9x^2 + 27x + 27)$ cubic meters
85. $x^2\left(\frac{3}{4}\pi + 2\right)$, or $\frac{1}{4}x^2(3\pi + 8)$
87. $x^2\left(9 - \frac{1}{2}\pi\right)$ **89.** $(x + 4)(x + 5)$

Quick Quiz: Sections 5.1–5.2, p. 318

1. $6x^2(2x^2 - 5x + 1)$ **2.** $(x - 4)(3x^2 + 5)$
3. $(x - 2)(x - 1)$ **4.** $(a + 4b)(a - 2b)$
5. $3(x + 2)(x + 3)$

Prepare to Move On, p. 318

1. $6x^2 + 17x + 12$ **2.** $6x^2 + x - 12$ **3.** $6x^2 - x - 12$
4. $6x^2 - 17x + 12$ **5.** $5x^2 - 36x + 7$
6. $3x^2 + 13x - 30$

Exercise Set 5.3, pp. 326–327

1. (d)   **2.** (a)   **3.** (b)   **4.** (c)   **5.** $(2x - 1)(x + 4)$

7. $(3x + 1)(x - 6)$ **9.** $(2t + 1)(2t + 5)$
11. $(5a - 3)(3a - 1)$ **13.** $(3x + 4)(2x + 3)$
15. $2(3x + 1)(x - 2)$ **17.** $t(7t + 1)(t + 2)$
19. $(4x - 5)(3x - 2)$ **21.** $-1(7x + 4)(5x + 2)$, or
$-(7x + 4)(5x + 2)$ **23.** Prime   **25.** $(5x + 4)^2$
27. $(20y - 1)(y + 3)$ **29.** $(7x + 5)(2x + 9)$
31. $-1(x - 3)(2x + 5)$, or $-(x - 3)(2x + 5)$
33. $-3(2x + 1)(x + 5)$ **35.** $2(a + 1)(5a - 9)$
37. $4(3x - 1)(x + 6)$ **39.** $(3x + 1)(x + 1)$
41. $(x + 3)(x - 2)$ **43.** $(4t - 3)(2t - 7)$
45. $(3x + 2)(2x + 5)$ **47.** $(y + 4)(2y - 1)$
49. $(3a - 4)(2a - 1)$ **51.** $(16t + 7)(t + 1)$
53. $-1(3x + 1)(3x + 5)$, or $-(3x + 1)(3x + 5)$
55. $10(x^2 + 3x - 7)$ **57.** $3x(3x - 1)(2x + 3)$
59. $(x + 1)(25x + 64)$ **61.** $3x(7x + 1)(8x + 1)$
63. $-t^2(2t - 3)(7t + 1)$ **65.** $2(2y + 9)(8y - 3)$
67. $(2a - b)(a - 2b)$ **69.** $2(s + t)(4s + 7t)$
71. $3(3x - 4y)^2$ **73.** $-2(3a - 2b)(4a - 3b)$
75. $x^2(2x + 3)(7x - 1)$ **77.** $a^6(3a + 4)(3a + 2)$
79.

81.
$2x - 5y = 10$

82.
$-5x = 10$

83.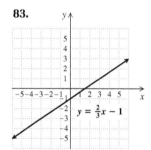
$y = \frac{2}{3}x - 1$

84.
$y - 2 = -2(x + 4)$

85.
$\frac{1}{2}y = 1$

86.
$x = -y$

87.   **89.** $(3xy + 2)(6xy - 5)$ **91.** Prime
93. $(4t^5 - 1)^2$ **95.** $-1(5x^m - 2)(3x^m - 4)$, or
$-(5x^m - 2)(3x^m - 4)$ **97.** $(3a^{3n} + 1)(a^{3n} - 1)$
99. $[7(t - 3)^n - 2][(t - 3)^n + 1]$ **101.** 7 ft

Quick Quiz: Sections 5.1–5.3, p. 327

1. $3ab^3(2a - 3b + 5a^2b^2)$ **2.** $x(x - 3)(x - 4)$
3. Prime   **4.** $(2a + 3)(2a + 5)$ **5.** $(6x + 5)(x - 1)$

Prepare to Move On, p. 327

1. $x^2 - 4x + 4$ **2.** $x^2 + 4x + 4$ **3.** $x^2 - 4$
4. $25t^2 - 30t + 9$ **5.** $16a^2 + 8a + 1$ **6.** $4n^2 - 49$

Exercise Set 5.4, pp. 332–334

1. Prime polynomial   **2.** Difference of squares
3. Difference of squares   **4.** None of these
5. Perfect-square trinomial   **6.** Perfect-square trinomial
7. None of these   **8.** Prime polynomial   **9.** Difference
of squares   **10.** Perfect-square trinomial   **11.** Yes
13. No   **15.** No   **17.** Yes   **19.** $(x + 8)^2$
21. $(x - 5)^2$ **23.** $5(p + 2)^2$ **25.** $(1 - t)^2$, or $(t - 1)^2$
27. $2(3x + 1)^2$ **29.** $(7 - 4y)^2$, or $(4y - 7)^2$
31. $-x^3(x - 9)^2$ **33.** $2n(n + 10)^2$ **35.** $5(2x + 5)^2$
37. $(7 - 3x)^2$, or $(3x - 7)^2$ **39.** $(4x + 3)^2$
41. $2(1 + 5x)^2$, or $2(5x + 1)^2$ **43.** $(3p + 2x)^2$
45. Prime   **47.** $-1(8m + n)^2$, or $-(8m + n)^2$
49. $-2(4s - 5t)^2$ **51.** Yes   **53.** No   **55.** Yes
57. $(x + 5)(x - 5)$ **59.** $(p + 3)(p - 3)$
61. $(7 + t)(-7 + t)$, or $(t + 7)(t - 7)$
63. $6(a + 2)(a - 2)$ **65.** $(7x - 1)^2$
67. $2(10 + t)(10 - t)$ **69.** $-5(4a + 3)(4a - 3)$
71. $5(t + 4)(t - 4)$ **73.** $2(2x + 9)(2x - 9)$
75. $x(6 + 7x)(6 - 7x)$ **77.** Prime
79. $(t^2 + 1)(t + 1)(t - 1)$ **81.** $-3x(x - 4)^2$
83. $3t(5t + 3)(5t - 3)$ **85.** $a^6(a - 1)^2$
87. $10(a + b)(a - b)$ **89.** $(4x^2 + y^2)(2x + y)(2x - y)$
91. $2(3t + 2s)(3t - 2s)$ **93.** ☐   **95.** $2x^3 + x^2 - 2$
96. $2t^2 + 6t - 11$ **97.** $6x^4 + x^2y - y^2$
98. $5x^3 - 15x^2 + 35x$ **99.** $7x^2 - x + 3$
100. $x + 4 + \dfrac{10}{x - 5}$ **101.** ☐
103. $(x^4 + 2^4)(x^2 + 2^2)(x + 2)(x - 2)$, or
$(x^4 + 16)(x^2 + 4)(x + 2)(x - 2)$
105. $2x\left(3x - \frac{2}{5}\right)\left(3x + \frac{2}{5}\right)$
107. $[(y - 5)^2 + z^4][(y - 5) + z^2][(y - 5) - z^2]$, or
$(y^2 - 10y + 25 + z^4)(y - 5 + z^2)(y - 5 - z^2)$
109. $-1(x^2 + 1)(x + 3)(x - 3)$, or
$-(x^2 + 1)(x + 3)(x - 3)$ **111.** $(y + 4)^2$
113. $(3p + 5)(3p - 5)^2$ **115.** $(9 + b^{2k})(3 + b^k)(3 - b^k)$
117. $2x^3 - x^2 - 1$ **119.** $(y + x + 7)(y - x - 1)$
121. 16   **123.** $(x + 1)^2 - x^2 = [(x + 1) + x][(x + 1) - x] =$
$2x + 1 = (x + 1) + x$

Quick Quiz: Sections 5.1–5.4, p. 334

1. $(x + 3)(2x^2 - 1)$ **2.** $(x - 20)(x - 4)$
3. $a(3a - 4)(3a + 2)$ **4.** $(y + 8)^2$
5. $3(z^2 + 1)(z + 1)(z - 1)$

Prepare to Move On, p. 334

1. $8x^6y^{12}$ **2.** $-125x^6y^3$ **3.** $x^3 - 3x^2 + 3x - 1$
4. $p^3 + 3p^2t + 3pt^2 + t^3$

Mid-Chapter Review: Chapter 5, p. 335

1. $12x^3y - 8xy^2 + 24x^2y = 4xy(3x^2 - 2y + 6x)$
2. $3a^3 - 3a^2 - 90a = 3a(a^2 - a - 30) =$
$3a(a - 6)(a + 5)$ **3.** $6x^2(x^3 - 3)$ **4.** $(x + 2)(x + 8)$

5. $(x + 7)(2x - 1)$ **6.** $(x + 3)(x^2 + 2)$
7. $(8n + 3)(8n - 3)$ **8.** Prime   **9.** $6(p + t)(p - t)$
10. $(b - 7)^2$ **11.** $(3x - 1)(4x + 1)$ **12.** $a(1 - 5a)^2$
13. $10(x^2 + 1)(x + 1)(x - 1)$ **14.** Prime
15. $15(d^2 - 2d + 5)$ **16.** $(3p + 2x)(5p + 2x)$
17. $-2t(t + 2)(t + 3)$ **18.** $10(c + 1)^2$
19. $-1(2x - 5)(x + 1)$ **20.** $2n(m - 5)(m^2 - 3)$

Exercise Set 5.5, pp. 338–339

1. Difference of cubes   **2.** Sum of cubes   **3.** Difference
of squares   **4.** None of these   **5.** Sum of cubes
6. Difference of cubes   **7.** None of these
8. Difference of squares   **9.** Difference of cubes
10. None of these   **11.** $(x - 4)(x^2 + 4x + 16)$
13. $(z + 1)(z^2 - z + 1)$ **15.** $(t - 10)(t^2 + 10t + 100)$
17. $(3x + 1)(9x^2 - 3x + 1)$
19. $(4 - 5x)(16 + 20x + 25x^2)$
21. $(x - y)(x^2 + xy + y^2)$ **23.** $\left(a + \frac{1}{2}\right)\left(a^2 - \frac{1}{2}a + \frac{1}{4}\right)$
25. $8(t - 1)(t^2 + t + 1)$
27. $2(3x + 1)(9x^2 - 3x + 1)$
29. $rs(s + 4)(s^2 - 4s + 16)$
31. $5(x - 2z)(x^2 + 2xz + 4z^2)$
33. $\left(y - \frac{1}{10}\right)\left(y^2 + \frac{1}{10}y + \frac{1}{100}\right)$
35. $(x + 0.1)(x^2 - 0.1x + 0.01)$
37. $8(2x^2 - t^2)(4x^4 + 2x^2t^2 + t^4)$
39. $2y(3y - 4)(9y^2 + 12y + 16)$
41. $(z + 1)(z^2 - z + 1)(z - 1)(z^2 + z + 1)$
43. $(t^2 + 4y^2)(t^4 - 4t^2y^2 + 16y^4)$
45. $(x^4 - yz^4)(x^8 + x^4yz^4 + y^2z^8)$ **47.** ☐
49. 2400 mg   **50.** 6.4 gal   **51.** $520   **52.** $46
53. ☐   **55.** $(x^{2a} - y^b)(x^{4a} + x^{2a}y^b + y^{2b})$
57. $2x(x^2 + 75)$ **59.** $5\left(xy^2 - \frac{1}{2}\right)\left(x^2y^4 + \frac{1}{2}xy^2 + \frac{1}{4}\right)$
61. $-(3x^{4a} + 3x^{2a} + 1)$ **63.** $(t - 8)(t - 1)(t^2 + t + 1)$

Quick Quiz: Sections 5.1–5.5, p. 339

1. $xp^2(6xp + 1 - 3x^2p)$ **2.** $(x - 12)(x + 1)$
3. $a(4a + 1)(a - 5)$ **4.** $(p + w)(p - w)$
5. $(p - w)(p^2 + pw + w^2)$

Prepare to Move On, p. 339

1. Common   **2.** Grouping or ac **3.** $(A + B)(A - B)$
4. $(A + B)^2$ **5.** $(A + B)(A^2 - AB + B^2)$

Exercise Set 5.6, pp. 344–345

1. Common factor   **2.** Perfect-square trinomial
3. Grouping   **4.** Multiplying   **5.** $5(a + 5)(a - 5)$
7. $(y - 7)^2$ **9.** $(3t + 7)(t + 3)$ **11.** $x(x + 9)^2$
13. $(x - 5)^2(x + 5)$ **15.** $3t(3t + 1)(3t - 1)$
17. $3x(3x - 5)(x + 3)$ **19.** Prime   **21.** $6(y - 5)(y + 8)$
23. $-2a^4(a - 2)^2$ **25.** $5x(x^2 + 4)(x + 2)(x - 2)$
27. $(t^2 + 3)(t^2 - 3)$ **29.** $-x^4(x^2 - 2x + 7)$
31. $(x - y)(x^2 + xy + y^2)$ **33.** $a(x^2 + y^2)$
35. $2\pi r(h + r)$ **37.** $(a + b)(5a + 3b)$
39. $(x + 1)(x + y)$ **41.** $10a^2(4m^2 + 1)(2m + 1)(2m - 1)$
43. $(a - 2)(a - y)$ **45.** $(3x - 2y)(x + 5y)$
47. $8mn(m^2 - 4mn + 3)$ **49.** $\left(\frac{3}{4} + y\right)\left(\frac{3}{4} - y\right)$
51. $(a - 2b)^2$ **53.** $(4x + 3y)^2$ **55.** Prime

57. $(2x - 3)(5x + 2)$ **59.** $(a^2b^2 + 4)(ab + 2)(ab - 2)$
61. $4c(4d - c)(5d - c)$
63. $(2t + 1)(4t^2 - 2t + 1)(2t - 1)(4t^2 + 2t + 1)$
65. $-1(xy + 2)(xy + 6)$, or $-(xy + 2)(xy + 6)$
67. $(2t + 5)(4t - 3)$ **69.** $5(pt + 6)(pt - 1)$
71. $2a(3a + 2b)(9a^2 - 6ab + 4b^2)$
73. $x^4(x + 2y)(x - y)$ **75.** $\left(6a - \frac{5}{4}\right)^2$ **77.** $\left(\frac{1}{9}x - \frac{4}{3}\right)^2$
79. $(1 + 4x^6y^6)(1 + 2x^3y^3)(1 - 2x^3y^3)$ **81.** $(2ab + 3)^2$
83. $z(z + 6)(z^2 - 6)$ **85.** $(x + 5)(x + 1)(x - 1)$
87. ☐   **89.** About 69.2%   **90.** 5.75 billionaires per
month   **91.** Mother's Day: \$16.3 billion; Father's Day:
\$11.1 billion   **92.** 5 or fewer roses   **93.** ☐
95. $(6 - x + a)(6 - x - a)$ **97.** $-x(x^2 + 9)(x^2 - 2)$
99. $-1(x^2 + 2)(x + 3)(x - 3)$, or $-(x^2 + 2)(x + 3)(x - 3)$
101. $(y + 1)(y - 7)(y + 3)$ **103.** $(y + 4 + x)^2$
105. $(a + 3)^2(2a + b + 4)(a - b + 5)$
107. $(7x^2 + 1 + 5x^3)(7x^2 + 1 - 5x^3)$

Quick Quiz: Sections 5.1–5.6, p. 345

1. $10(m + 3)(m - 3)$ **2.** $(a + 3)(a - 2)$
3. $(2x - 1)(6x^2 - 5)$ **4.** $8(mn - 1)^2$
5. $c(3c + 2)(2c - 3)$

Prepare to Move On, p. 345

1. $\frac{9}{8}$ **2.** $-\frac{7}{2}$ **3.** 3   **4.** $-\frac{5}{3}$ **5.** $\frac{1}{4}$ **6.** 11

Connecting the Concepts, p. 350

1. Expression   **2.** Equation   **3.** Expression
4. Equation   **5.** $2x^3 + x^2 - 8x$ **6.** $-2x^2 - 11$
7. $-10, 10$ **8.** $6a^2 - 19a + 10$ **9.** $(n - 1)(n - 9)$
10. 2, 8

Technology Connection, p. 351

1. $-4.65, 0.65$ **2.** $-0.37, 5.37$ **3.** $-8.98, -4.56$
4. No solution   **5.** 0, 2.76

Exercise Set 5.7, pp. 351–353

1. (c)   **2.** (a)   **3.** (d)   **4.** (b)   **5.** $-9, -2$
7. $-1, 8$ **9.** $-6, \frac{3}{2}$ **11.** $\frac{1}{7}, \frac{3}{10}$ **13.** 0, 7   **15.** $\frac{1}{21}, \frac{18}{11}$
17. $-\frac{8}{3}, 0$ **19.** 50, 70   **21.** 1, 6   **23.** $-7, 3$
25. $-9, -2$ **27.** 0, 10   **29.** $-6, 0$ **31.** $-6, 6$
33. $-\frac{7}{2}, \frac{7}{2}$ **35.** -5 **37.** 8   **39.** 0, 2   **41.** $-\frac{5}{4}, 3$
43. 3   **45.** 0, $\frac{4}{3}$ **47.** $-\frac{7}{6}, \frac{7}{6}$ **49.** $-4, -\frac{2}{3}$ **51.** $-3, 1$
53. $-\frac{5}{2}, \frac{4}{3}$ **55.** $-1, 4$ **57.** $-3, 2$ **59.** $(-2, 0), (3, 0)$
61. $(-4, 0), (2, 0)$ **63.** $(-3, 0), \left(\frac{3}{2}, 0\right)$ **65.** ☐   **67.** 65
68. $\frac{4}{3}$ **69.** 1.65   **70.** 6.8×10^{-4} **71.** $-0.\overline{6}$
72. 125%   **73.** ☐   **75.** $-7, -\frac{8}{3}, \frac{11}{2}$
77. (a) $x^2 - x - 20 = 0$; (b) $x^2 - 6x - 7 = 0$;
(c) $4x^2 - 13x + 3 = 0$; (d) $6x^2 - 5x + 1 = 0$;
(e) $12x^2 - 17x + 6 = 0$; (f) $x^3 - 4x^2 + x + 6 = 0$
79. $-5, 4$ **81.** $-\frac{3}{5}, \frac{3}{5}$ **83.** $-4, 2$ **85.** $-1, 1, 2$
87. (a) $2x^2 + 20x - 4 = 0$; (b) $x^2 - 3x - 18 = 0$;
(c) $(x + 1)(5x - 5) = 0$; (d) $(2x + 8)(2x - 5) = 0$;
(e) $4x^2 + 8x + 36 = 0$; (f) $9x^2 - 12x + 24 = 0$
89. ☐   **91.** 2.33, 6.77   **93.** $-9.15, -4.59$
95. $-3.76, 0$ **97.** -8 and -7, or 7 and 8

Quick Quiz: Sections 5.1–5.7, p. 353

1. $(x - 4)(x + 2)$ **2.** $-2, 4$ **3.** $-10, 10$
4. $(a + 10)(a - 10)$ **5.** $2(a + 10)^2$

Prepare to Move On, p. 353

1. Let n represent the first integer; $[n + (n + 1)]^2$
2. Let n represent the first integer; $n(n + 1)$
3. $140°, 35°, 5°$ **4.** Length: 64 in.; width: 32 in.

Exercise Set 5.8, pp. 359–363

1. $x + 1$ **2.** $2w$ **3.** $90°$ **4.** $c^2 = a^2 + b^2$
5. $-2, 3$ **7.** 11, 12   **9.** -14 and -12; 12 and 14
11. Length: 40 ft; width: 8 ft   **13.** Length: 12 cm; width:
7 cm   **15.** Foot: 7 ft; height: 12 ft   **17.** Base: 8 ft;
height: 16 ft   **19.** Base: 8 ft; height: 15 ft   **21.** 8 teams
23. 66 handshakes   **25.** 12 players   **27.** 1 min, 3 min
29. 10 knots   **31.** 9 ft   **33.** 842 ft   **35.** 300 ft by
400 ft by 500 ft   **37.** 24 m, 25 m   **39.** 12 ft, 35 ft, 37 ft
41. Dining room: 12 ft by 12 ft; kitchen: 12 ft by 10 ft
43. 20 ft   **45.** 1 sec, 2 sec   **47.** ☐
49. $\varnothing$; contradiction   **50.** 0   **51.** $\mathbb{R}$; identity
52. $\{y \,|\, y \le -4\}$, or $(-\infty, -4]$
53. $\{x \,|\, x < -1\}$, or $(-\infty, -1)$ **54.** $y = -\frac{1}{2}x + \frac{7}{2}$
55. ☐   **57.** \$180   **59.** 39 cm   **61.** 4 in., 6 in.
63. 35 ft   **65.** Length: 6 in.; width: $4\frac{1}{4}$ in.
67. 0.8 hr, 6.4 hr   **69.** ☐

Quick Quiz: Sections 5.1–5.8, p. 363

1. $(x - 5)(3x^2 - 7)$ **2.** $-\frac{1}{5}, \frac{3}{4}$ **3.** $(2x - 3)(5x - 1)$
4. $6(x^4 + 1)(x^2 + 1)(x + 1)(x - 1)$ **5.** Longer leg: 40 ft;
hypotenuse: 41 ft

Prepare to Move On, p. 363

1. $\frac{6}{7}$ **2.** $\frac{45}{44}$ **3.** $\frac{4}{5}$ **4.** 0   **5.** Undefined

Translating for Success, p. 364

1. O   **2.** M   **3.** K   **4.** I   **5.** G   **6.** E   **7.** C
8. A   **9.** H   **10.** B

Decision Making: Connection, p. 366

1. 105 games   **2.** 210 games   **3.** Even number of
teams: $n - 1$ rounds; odd number of teams: n rounds
4. ☐   **5.** ☐   **6.** ☐

Study Summary: Chapter 5, pp. 367–369

1. $6x(2x^3 - 3x^2 + 5)$ **2.** $(x - 3)(2x^2 - 1)$
3. $(x - 9)(x + 2)$ **4.** $(3x + 2)(2x - 1)$
5. $(2x - 3)(4x - 5)$ **6.** $(10n + 9)^2$
7. $(12t + 5)(12t - 5)$ **8.** $(a - 1)(a^2 + a + 1)$
9. $3x(x - 6)^2$ **10.** $-10, 3$ **11.** 12, 13

Review Exercises: Chapter 5, pp. 369–370

1. False   **2.** True   **3.** True   **4.** False   **5.** False
6. True   **7.** True   **8.** False   **9.** Answers may vary.

$(4x)(5x^2), (-2x^2)(-10x), (x^3)(20)$ **10.** Answers may vary. $(-3x^2)(6x^3), (2x^4)(-9x), (-18x)(x^4)$
11. $6x^3(2x - 3)$ **12.** $(10t + 1)(10t - 1)$
13. $(x + 4)(x - 3)$ **14.** $(x + 7)^2$ **15.** $3x(2x + 1)^2$
16. $(2x + 3)(3x^2 + 1)$ **17.** $(6a - 5)(a + 1)$
18. $(5t - 3)^2$ **19.** $(9a^2 + 1)(3a + 1)(3a - 1)$
20. $3x(3x - 5)(x + 3)$ **21.** $2(x - 5)(x^2 + 5x + 25)$
22. $(x + 4)(x^3 - 2)$ **23.** $(ab^2 + 8)(ab^2 - 8)$
24. $-4x^4(2x^2 - 8x + 1)$ **25.** $3(2x - 5)^2$ **26.** Prime
27. $-t(t + 6)(t - 7)$ **28.** $(2x + 5)(2x - 5)$
29. $(n + 6)(n - 10)$ **30.** $5(z^2 - 6z + 2)$
31. $(2y + 3x^2)(4y^2 - 6x^2y + 9x^4)$ **32.** $(2t + 1)(t - 4)$
33. $7x(x + 1)(x + 4)$ **34.** $-6x(x + 5)(x - 5)$
35. $(5 - x)(3 - x)$ **36.** Prime   **37.** $(xy + 8)(xy - 2)$
38. $3(2a + 7b)^2$ **39.** $(m + 5)(m + t)$
40. $(3r + 5s)(2r - 3s)$ **41.** $-11, 9$ **42.** $-7, 5$
43. $-\frac{3}{4}, \frac{3}{4}$ **44.** $\frac{2}{3}, 1$ **45.** $-2, 3$ **46.** $0, \frac{3}{5}$
47. 1 **48.** $-3, 4$ **49.** 5 sec   **50.** $(-1, 0), \left(\frac{5}{2}, 0\right)$
51. Height: 14 ft; base: 14 ft   **52.** 10 holes
53. Answers may vary. Because Celia did not first factor out the largest common factor, 4, her factorization will not be "complete" until she removes a common factor of 2 from each binomial. The answer should be $4(x - 5)(x + 5)$. Awarding 3 to 7 points would seem reasonable.   **54.** The principle of zero products is used to solve quadratic equations and is not used to solve linear equations.
55. 2.5 cm   **56.** $0, 2$ **57.** Length: 12 cm; width: 6 cm   **58.** $-3, 2, \frac{5}{2}$ **59.** No real solution

Test: Chapter 5, p. 371

1. [5.2] $(x - 4)(x - 9)$ **2.** [5.4] $(x - 5)^2$
3. [5.1] $2y^2(2y^2 - 4y + 3)$ **4.** [5.1] $(x + 1)(x^2 + 2)$
5. [5.1] $t^5(t^2 - 3)$ **6.** [5.2] $a(a + 4)(a - 1)$
7. [5.3] $2(5x - 6)(x + 4)$ **8.** [5.4] $(2t + 5)(2t - 5)$
9. [5.3] $-3m(2m + 1)(m + 1)$
10. [5.5] $3(r - 1)(r^2 + r + 1)$ **11.** [5.4] $5(3r + 2)^2$
12. [5.4] $3(x^2 + 4)(x + 2)(x - 2)$ **13.** [5.4] $(7t + 6)^2$
14. [5.1] $(x + 2)(x^3 - 3)$ **15.** [5.2] Prime
16. [5.3] $3t(2t + 5)(t - 1)$
17. [5.2] $3(m - 5n)(m + 2n)$ **18.** [5.7] $1, 5$
19. [5.7] $-\frac{3}{2}, 5$ **20.** [5.7] $0, \frac{2}{5}$ **21.** [5.7] $-\frac{1}{5}, \frac{1}{5}$
22. [5.7] $-4, 5$ **23.** [5.7] $(-1, 0), \left(\frac{8}{3}, 0\right)$
24. [5.8] Length: 10 m; width: 4 m   **25.** [5.8] 10 people
26. [5.8] 5 ft   **27.** [5.8] 15 cm by 30 cm
28. [5.2] $(a - 4)(a + 8)$ **29.** [5.7] $-\frac{8}{3}, 0, \frac{2}{5}$

Cumulative Review: Chapters 1–5, p. 372

1. $\frac{1}{2}$ **2.** $\frac{9}{8}$ **3.** 29   **4.** $\frac{1}{9x^4y^6}$ **5.** t^{10}
6. $3x^4 + 5x^3 + x - 10$ **7.** $\frac{t^8}{4s^2}$ **8.** $-\frac{8x^6y^3}{27z^{12}}$
9. 8   **10.** $-x^4$ **11.** $2x^3 - 5x^2 + \frac{1}{2}x - 1$
12. $-4t^{11} + 8t^9 + 20t^8$ **13.** $9x^2 - 30x + 25$
14. $100x^{10} - y^2$ **15.** $(c + 1)(c - 1)$
16. $5(x + y)(1 + 2x)$ **17.** $(2r - t)^2$ **18.** $10(y^2 + 4)$
19. $y(x - 1)(x - 2)$ **20.** $(3x - 2y)(4x + y)$
21. $\frac{1}{12}$ **22.** $-\frac{9}{4}$ **23.** $\{x | x \geq 1\}$, or $[1, \infty)$ **24.** $-4, 3$
25. $-2, 2$ **26.** $0, 4$ **27.** $c = \frac{a}{b + d}$ **28.** 0
29. $y = 5x + \frac{5}{3}$

30.

31.

32.

33.

34. 372 min   **35.** Bottom of ladder to building: 5 ft; top of ladder to ground: 12 ft   **36.** Scores that are 9 and higher
37. **(a)**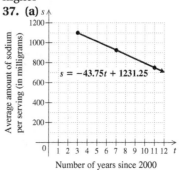

(b) 925 mg per serving   **38.** $b = \dfrac{2}{a + 1}$ **39.** $-1, 0, \frac{1}{3}$

CHAPTER 6

Technology Connection, p. 377

1. Correct   **2.** Not correct

Exercise Set 6.1, pp. 379–380

1. Quotient   **2.** Denominator   **3.** Factors
4. A factor equal to 1   **5.** (a)   **6.** (c)   **7.** (d)
8. (b)   **9.** 0   **11.** -5 **13.** 5   **15.** $-4, 7$
17. $-6, \frac{1}{2}$ **19.** $\dfrac{5a}{4b^2}$ **21.** $\dfrac{t + 2}{t - 3}$ **23.** $\frac{7}{8}$
25. $\dfrac{a - 3}{a + 1}$ **27.** $-\dfrac{2x^3}{3}$ **29.** $\dfrac{y - 3}{4y}$ **31.** $\dfrac{3(2a + 1)}{7(a + 1)}$
33. $\dfrac{t - 4}{t - 5}$ **35.** $\dfrac{a + 4}{2(a - 4)}$ **37.** $\dfrac{x - 4}{x + 4}$
39. $\dfrac{1}{n^2 + 2n + 4}$ **41.** $t - 1$ **43.** $\dfrac{y^2 + 4}{y + 2}$ **45.** $\frac{1}{2}$
47. $\dfrac{y}{2y + 1}$ **49.** $\dfrac{2x - 3}{5x + 2}$ **51.** -1 **53.** -7
55. $-\frac{1}{4}$ **57.** $-\frac{3}{2}$ **59.** -1 **61.**
63. $(x + 5)(3x^2 + 1)$ **64.** $(3x + 1)(x + 5)$
65. $3y^2(6y^2 - 9y + 1)$ **66.** $(5a + 4b)(5a - 4b)$
67. $m(m - 4)^2$ **68.** $5(x - 4)(x - 3)$ **69.**

71. $-(2y + x)$　**73.** $\dfrac{x^3 + 4}{(x^3 + 2)(x^2 + 2)}$

75. $\dfrac{(t - 1)(t - 9)^2}{(t + 1)(t^2 + 9)}$　**77.** $x + 2$　**79.** $\dfrac{(x - y)^3}{(x + y)^2(x - 5y)}$

81.

Prepare to Move On, p. 380

1. $\frac{4}{21}$　**2.** $-\frac{5}{3}$　**3.** $\frac{15}{4}$　**4.** $-\frac{21}{16}$

Technology Connection, p. 383

1. Let $y_1 = ((x^2 + 3x + 2)/(x^2 + 4))/(5x^2 + 10x)$ and $y_2 = (x + 1)/((x^2 + 4)(5x))$. With the table set in AUTO mode, note that the values in the Y1- and Y2-columns match except for $x = -2$.　**2.** ERROR messages occur when division by 0 is attempted. Since the simplified expression has no factor of $x + 5$ or $x + 1$ in a denominator, no ERROR message occurs in Y2 for $x = -5$ or -1.

Exercise Set 6.2, pp. 384–386

1. (d)　**2.** (c)　**3.** (a)　**4.** (b)　**5.** (d)　**6.** (c)
7. (a)　**8.** (e)　**9.** (b)　**10.** (f)　**11.** $\dfrac{3x(x + 2)}{8(5x - 1)}$

13. $\dfrac{(a - 4)(a + 2)}{(a + 6)^2}$　**15.** $\dfrac{(n - 4)(n + 4)}{(n^2 + 4)(n^2 - 4)}$　**17.** $\dfrac{6t}{5}$

19. $\dfrac{4}{c^2d}$　**21.** $\dfrac{y + 4}{4}$　**23.** $\dfrac{x + 2}{x - 2}$

25. $\dfrac{(n - 5)(n - 1)(n - 6)}{(n + 6)(n^2 + 36)}$　**27.** $\dfrac{7(a + 3)}{a(a + 4)}$　**29.** $\dfrac{y(y - 1)}{y + 1}$

31. $\dfrac{3v}{v - 2}$　**33.** $\dfrac{t - 5}{t + 5}$　**35.** $\dfrac{9(y - 5)}{10(y - 1)}$　**37.** 1

39. $\dfrac{(t - 2)(t + 5)}{(t - 5)(t - 5)}$　**41.** $(2x - 1)^2$　**43.** $\dfrac{(7x + 5)(3x + 4)}{8}$

45. $\dfrac{2x + 5y}{x^2y}$　**47.** $c(c - 2)$　**49.** $\dfrac{9}{2x}$　**51.** $\dfrac{1}{a^4 + 3a}$

53. $\dfrac{x^2}{20}$　**55.** $\dfrac{a^3}{b^3}$　**57.** $\dfrac{4(t - 3)}{3(t + 1)}$　**59.** $4(y - 2)$

61. $-\dfrac{a}{b}$　**63.** $\dfrac{(n + 3)(n + 3)}{n - 2}$　**65.** $\dfrac{a - 5}{3(a - 1)}$

67. $\dfrac{(2x - 1)(2x + 1)}{x - 5}$　**69.** $\dfrac{(w - 7)(w - 8)}{(2w - 7)(3w + 1)}$

71. $\dfrac{1}{(c - 5)(5c - 3)}$　**73.** $\frac{15}{16}$　**75.** $\dfrac{-x^2 - 4}{x + 2}$

77. $\dfrac{(x - 4y)(x - y)}{(x + y)^3}$　**79.** $\dfrac{x^2 + 4x + 16}{(x + 4)^2}$

81. $\dfrac{(2a + b)^2}{2(a + b)}$　**83.**

85.

86.

87.

88.

89.

90.

91. 　**93.** $\dfrac{3}{7x}$　**95.** 1　**97.** $\dfrac{1}{b^3(a - 3b)}$

99. $\dfrac{(z + 4)^3}{3(z - 4)^2}$　**101.** $\dfrac{a - 3b}{c}$　**103.** $\dfrac{(x + 1)^2}{(x - 1)^2}$

105. 1　**107.** $\dfrac{(2n - 1)(3n + 2)}{(2n + 1)(3n - 2)}$　**109.** ▨

Quick Quiz: Sections 6.1–6.2, p. 386

1. $\dfrac{6(x + 3)}{x - 4}$　**2.** $\dfrac{y - 3}{2y + 1}$　**3.** $\dfrac{(x - 1)^2}{4x}$

4. $\dfrac{m + 3}{6(m + 2)}$　**5.** $\dfrac{(x + 4)^2}{(x + 5)(x - 4)}$

Prepare to Move On, p. 386

1. $\frac{41}{24}$　**2.** $\frac{1}{6}$　**3.** $x^2 + 3$　**4.** $-2x^2 - 4x + 1$

Exercise Set 6.3, pp. 393–395

1. Numerators; denominator　**2.** Term　**3.** Least common denominator; LCD　**4.** Factor　**5.** $\dfrac{8}{t}$

7. $\dfrac{3x + 5}{12}$　**9.** $\dfrac{9}{a + 3}$　**11.** $\dfrac{8}{4x - 7}$　**13.** $\dfrac{2y + 7}{2y}$

15. 6　**17.** $\dfrac{4(x - 1)}{x + 3}$　**19.** $a + 5$　**21.** $y - 7$

23. 0　**25.** $\dfrac{1}{x + 2}$　**27.** $\dfrac{(3a - 7)(a - 2)}{(a + 6)(a - 1)}$

29. $\dfrac{t - 4}{t + 3}$　**31.** $\dfrac{y + 2}{y - 4}$　**33.** $-\dfrac{5}{x - 4}$, or $\dfrac{5}{4 - x}$

35. $-\dfrac{1}{x - 1}$, or $\dfrac{1}{1 - x}$　**37.** 180　**39.** 72　**41.** 60

43. $18t^5$　**45.** $30a^4b^8$　**47.** $6(y - 3)$

49. $(x - 5)(x + 3)(x - 3)$　**51.** $t(t - 4)(t + 2)^2$

53. $120x^2y^3z^2$　**55.** $(a + 1)(a - 1)^2$

57. $(2n - 1)(n + 1)(n + 2)$　**59.** $(t + 3)(t - 3)$

61. $12x^3(x - 5)(x - 3)(x - 1)$

63. $2(x + 1)(x - 1)(x^2 + x + 1)$

65. $\dfrac{15}{18t^4}, \dfrac{st^2}{18t^4}$　**67.** $\dfrac{21y}{9x^4y^3}, \dfrac{4x^3}{9x^4y^3}$

69. $\dfrac{2x(x+3)}{(x-2)(x+2)(x+3)}$, $\dfrac{4x(x-2)}{(x-2)(x+2)(x+3)}$

71. 📋   **73.** $-\dfrac{10}{3}$ **74.** $\{x \mid x > 15\}$, or $(15, \infty)$

75. $-2, 10$ **76.** $\{x \mid x \le -8\}$, or $(-\infty, -8]$ **77.** -1

78. $\frac{8}{3}$ **79.** 📋   **81.** $\dfrac{18x+5}{x-1}$ **83.** $\dfrac{x}{3x+1}$

85. 30 strands   **87.** 60 strands

89. $(2x+5)(2x-5)(3x+4)^4$ **91.** 12 sec

93. 6:15 A.M.   **95.** 📋   **97.** 🖥

Quick Quiz: Sections 6.1–6.3, p. 395

1. $\dfrac{1}{x+7}$ **2.** $x(x-6)(x-1)$ **3.** $\dfrac{1}{(x+3)(x-1)}$

4. $\dfrac{4}{3t^2(t-2)}$ **5.** $\dfrac{8}{x-2}$

Prepare to Move On, p. 395

1. $\dfrac{-5}{8}, \dfrac{5}{-8}$ **2.** $\dfrac{-4}{11}, -\dfrac{4}{11}$ **3.** $-x+y$, or $y-x$

4. $-3+a$, or $a-3$ **5.** $-2x+7$, or $7-2x$

6. $-a+b$, or $b-a$

Exercise Set 6.4, pp. 400–402

1. LCD   **2.** Missing; denominator   **3.** Numerators;

LCD   **4.** Simplify   **5.** $\dfrac{3+5x}{x^2}$ **7.** $-\dfrac{5}{24r}$

9. $\dfrac{3u^2+4v}{u^3v^2}$ **11.** $\dfrac{-2(xy+9)}{3x^2y^3}$ **13.** $\dfrac{7x+1}{24}$

15. $\dfrac{-x-4}{6}$ **17.** $\dfrac{a^2+13a-5}{15a^2}$ **19.** $\dfrac{7z-12}{12z}$

21. $\dfrac{(3c-d)(c+d)}{c^2d^2}$ **23.** $\dfrac{4x^2-13xt+9t^2}{3x^2t^2}$

25. $\dfrac{6x}{(x+2)(x-2)}$ **27.** $\dfrac{(t-3)(t+1)}{(t-1)(t+3)}$ **29.** $\dfrac{11x+2}{3x(x+1)}$

31. $\dfrac{-5t+3}{2t(t-1)}$ **33.** $\dfrac{a^2}{(a-3)(a+3)}$ **35.** $\dfrac{16}{3(z+4)}$

37. $\dfrac{5q-3}{(q-1)^2}$ **39.** $\dfrac{9a}{4(a-5)}$ **41.** $\dfrac{2y-1}{y(y-1)}$

43. $\dfrac{10}{(a-3)(a+2)}$ **45.** $\dfrac{x-5}{(x+5)(x+3)}$

47. $\dfrac{3z^2+19z-20}{(z-2)^2(z+3)}$ **49.** $\dfrac{-7}{x^2+25x+24}$ **51.** $\dfrac{6x+7}{2x+1}$

53. $\dfrac{10-3x}{4-x}$ **55.** $\dfrac{3x-1}{2}$ **57.** 0   **59.** $y+3$

61. 0   **63.** $\dfrac{1}{t^2+t+1}$ **65.** $\dfrac{p^2+7p+1}{(p-5)(p+5)}$

67. $\dfrac{(x+1)(x+3)}{(x-4)(x+4)}$ **69.** $\dfrac{-a-2}{(a+1)(a-1)}$, or

$\dfrac{a+2}{(1+a)(1-a)}$ **71.** $\dfrac{2(5x+3y)}{(x-y)(x+y)}$ **73.** $\dfrac{2x-3}{2-x}$

75. 3   **77.** 0   **79.** $\dfrac{2}{(x+3)(x+4)}$ **81.** 📋

83. 6   **84.** 7   **85.** 3×10^{14} **86.** $\dfrac{-6a^4}{b}$ **87.** $\dfrac{a^2}{9b^2}$

88. 12   **89.** 📋   **91.** Perimeter: $\dfrac{2(5x-7)}{(x-5)(x+4)}$; area:

93. $\dfrac{6}{(x-5)(x+4)}$ **93.** $\dfrac{x}{3x+1}$ **95.** $\dfrac{-29}{(x-3)(x+1)}$

97. $\dfrac{x^4+4x^3-5x^2-126x-441}{(x+2)^2(x+7)^2}$

99. $\dfrac{5(a^2+2ab-b^2)}{(a-b)(3a+b)(3a-b)}$ **101.** $\dfrac{a}{a-b} + \dfrac{3b}{b-a}$;

answers may vary.   **103.** 📋, 📈

Quick Quiz: Sections 6.1–6.4, p. 402

1. $\dfrac{x-8}{4x}$ **2.** $\dfrac{(x-1)(x+6)}{(x-4)(x+2)}$ **3.** $x+2$

4. $\dfrac{t(4t-1)}{(2t+1)(t-1)}$ **5.** $\dfrac{(x-1)^2(2x+1)}{(x-2)^3}$

Prepare to Move On, p. 402

1. $\frac{9}{10}$ **2.** $\frac{16}{27}$ **3.** $\frac{2}{3}$ **4.** $\dfrac{(x-3)(x+2)}{(x-2)(x+3)}$

Mid-Chapter Review: Chapter 6, pp. 403–404

1. $\dfrac{a^2}{a-10} \div \dfrac{a^2+5a}{a^2-100} = \dfrac{a^2}{a-10} \cdot \dfrac{a^2-100}{a^2+5a}$

$= \dfrac{a \cdot a \cdot (a+10) \cdot (a-10)}{(a-10) \cdot a \cdot (a+5)}$

$= \dfrac{a(a-10)}{a(a-10)} \cdot \dfrac{a(a+10)}{a+5}$

$= \dfrac{a(a+10)}{a+5}$

2. $\dfrac{2}{x} + \dfrac{1}{x^2+x} = \dfrac{2}{x} + \dfrac{1}{x(x+1)}$

$= \dfrac{2}{x} \cdot \dfrac{x+1}{x+1} + \dfrac{1}{x(x+1)}$

$= \dfrac{2x+2}{x(x+1)} + \dfrac{1}{x(x+1)}$

$= \dfrac{2x+3}{x(x+1)}$

3. $\dfrac{3x+10}{5x^2}$ **4.** $\dfrac{6}{5x^3}$ **5.** $\dfrac{3x}{10}$ **6.** $\dfrac{3x-10}{5x^2}$

7. $\dfrac{x-3}{15(x-2)}$ **8.** $\frac{1}{3}$ **9.** $\dfrac{x^2-2x-2}{(x-1)(x+2)}$

10. $\dfrac{5x+17}{(x+3)(x+4)}$ **11.** -5 **12.** $\dfrac{5}{x-4}$

13. $\dfrac{(2x+3)(x+3)}{(x+1)^2}$ **14.** $\frac{1}{6}$ **15.** $\dfrac{x(x+4)}{(x-1)^2}$

16. $\dfrac{x+7}{(x-5)(x+1)}$ **17.** $\dfrac{9(u-1)}{16}$ **18.** $(t+5)^2$

19. $\dfrac{a-1}{(a+2)(a-2)^2}$ **20.** $\dfrac{-3x^2+9x-14}{2x}$

Exercise Set 6.5, pp. 408–410

1. Complex   **2.** Denominator   **3.** Least common

denominator   **4.** Reciprocal   **5.** (b)   **6.** (a)

7. (a)   **8.** (b)   **9.** 10   **11.** $\frac{5}{11}$ **13.** $\dfrac{5x^2}{4(x^2+4)}$

15. $\dfrac{(x+2)(x-3)}{(x-1)(x+4)}$ **17.** $\dfrac{-10t}{5t-2}$ **19.** $\dfrac{2(2a-5)}{a-7}$

21. $\dfrac{x^2 - 18}{2(x + 3)}$ **23.** $-\frac{1}{5}$ **25.** $\dfrac{1 + t^2}{t(1 - t)}$ **27.** $\dfrac{x}{x - y}$

29. $\dfrac{c(4c + 7)}{3(2c^2 - 1)}$ **31.** $\dfrac{15(4 - a^3)}{14a^2(9 + 2a)}$ **33.** 1

35. $\dfrac{3a^2 + 4b^3}{b^3(5 - 3a^2)}$ **37.** $\dfrac{(t - 3)(t + 3)}{t^2 + 4}$ **39.** $\dfrac{y^2 + 1}{(y + 1)(y - 1)}$

41. $\dfrac{1}{a(a - h)}$ **43.** $\dfrac{1}{x - y}$ **45.** $\dfrac{a^2 b^2}{b^2 - ab + a^2}$

47. $\dfrac{t^2 + 5t + 3}{(t + 1)^2}$ **49.** $\dfrac{x^2 - 2x - 1}{x^2 - 5x - 4}$ **51.** $\dfrac{(a - 2)(a - 7)}{(a + 1)(a - 6)}$

53. $\dfrac{x + 2}{x + 3}$ **55.** 📝   **57.** $(2x - 3)(3x^2 - 2)$
58. $4ab(3a + b - 2)$ **59.** $3n(2n + 1)(5n - 3)$
60. $(5a - 4b)^2$ **61.** $(n^2 + 1)(n + 1)(n - 1)$
62. $(pw + 10)(pw - 12)$ **63.** 📝   **65.** 6, 7, 8
67. $-3, -\frac{4}{5}, 3$

69. $\dfrac{A}{B} \div \dfrac{C}{D} = \dfrac{\frac{A}{B}}{\frac{C}{D}} = \dfrac{\frac{A}{B}}{\frac{C}{D}} \cdot \dfrac{BD}{BD} = \dfrac{AD}{BC} = \dfrac{A}{B} \cdot \dfrac{D}{C}$

71. $\dfrac{x^2 + 5x + 15}{-x^2 + 10}$ **73.** 0   **75.** $\dfrac{x - 5}{x - 3}$

77. $\dfrac{(x - 1)(3x - 2)}{5x - 3}$

Quick Quiz: Sections 6.1–6.5, p. 410

1. $\dfrac{2(2x + 1)}{2x - 1}$ **2.** $\dfrac{2x(x + 3)}{3}$ **3.** $\dfrac{a + 3}{a + 1}$

4. $\dfrac{-5x^2 + 21x - 2}{(x - 3)(x + 1)}$ **5.** $\dfrac{5x + 8}{6x}$

Prepare to Move On, p. 410

1. -4 **2.** $-\frac{14}{27}$ **3.** 3, 4   **4.** $-15, 2$

Connecting the Concepts, pp. 415–416

1. Expression; $\dfrac{19n - 2}{5n(2n - 1)}$ **2.** Equation; 8

3. Equation; $-\frac{1}{2}$ **4.** Expression; $\dfrac{8(t + 1)}{(t - 1)(2t - 1)}$

5. Expression; $\dfrac{2a}{a - 1}$ **6.** Equation; $-10, 10$

Exercise Set 6.6, pp. 416–417

1. False   **2.** True   **3.** True   **4.** True   **5.** $-\frac{2}{5}$
7. $\frac{24}{5}$ **9.** $-6, 6$ **11.** 12   **13.** $\frac{14}{3}$ **15.** $-6, 6$
17. $-4, -1$ **19.** -10 **21.** $-4, -3$ **23.** $\frac{23}{2}$
25. $\frac{5}{2}$ **27.** -1 **29.** No solution   **31.** -10
33. $-\frac{7}{3}$ **35.** $-2, \frac{7}{3}$ **37.** $-3, 13$ **39.** No solution
41. 2   **43.** -8 **45.** No solution   **47.** No solution
49. 📝   **51.** x-intercept: $(3, 0)$; y-intercept: $(0, -18)$
52. $\frac{1}{9}$ **53.** Slope: -2; y-intercept: $(0, 5)$ **54.** Yes
55. $y = \frac{1}{3}x - 2$ **56.** $y - (-5) = -4(x - 1)$
57. 📝   **59.** -2 **61.** 3   **63.** 4   **65.** 4
67. -2 **69.** ⚿

Quick Quiz: Sections 6.1–6.6, p. 417

1. $\dfrac{7(x - 11)}{x + 7}$ **2.** $x(x + 2)(x - 2)(x + 1)$

3. $\dfrac{-2n^2 + 5n + 6}{2n(n + 2)}$ **4.** $\dfrac{x - 2}{x + 2}$ **5.** -7

Prepare to Move On, p. 417

1. 137, 139   **2.** $-8, -6; 6, 8$ **3.** Base: 9 cm;
height: 12 cm   **4.** 0.06 cm per day

Exercise Set 6.7, pp. 426–431

1. False   **2.** True   **3.** True   **4.** True   **5.** True
6. False   **7.** $\frac{1}{2}$ cake per hour   **8.** $\frac{1}{3}$ cake per hour
9. $\frac{5}{6}$ cake per hour   **10.** 1 lawn per hour   **11.** $\frac{1}{3}$ lawn
per hour   **12.** $\frac{2}{3}$ lawn per hour   **13.** 6 hr
15. $3\frac{3}{7}$ hr   **17.** $8\frac{4}{7}$ hr   **19.** GT-S50: $7\frac{1}{2}$ min; GT-1500:
15 min   **21.** Anita: 3 days; Tori: 6 days   **23.** Tristan:
$\frac{4}{3}$ months; Sara: 4 months   **25.** 300 min, or 5 hr
27. AMTRAK: 80 km/h; CSX: 66 km/h

	Distance (in km)	Speed (in km/h)	Time (in hours)
CSX	330	$r - 14$	$\dfrac{330}{r - 14}$
AMTRAK	400	r	$\dfrac{400}{r}$

29. Rita: 50 mph; Sean: 65 mph   **31.** 7 mph
33. 5.2 ft/sec   **35.** 3 hr   **37.** 40 mph   **39.** 20 mph
41. 10.5   **43.** $\frac{8}{3}$ **45.** 12.6   **47.** $3\frac{3}{4}$ in.
49. 20 ft   **51.** 15 ft   **53.** About 26.7 cm   **55.** $65.25
57. 702 photos   **59.** 52 bulbs   **61.** $7\frac{1}{2}$ oz
63. 90 whales   **65.** 📝   **67.** $x^3 - x^2 + x - 15$
68. $2x^4 + 6x^3 - 7x - 21$ **69.** $3y^2z + 2yz^2 + 6y^2 - 6yz$
70. $2ab^2 + 4b - a$ **71.** $64n^6 - 9$ **72.** $x^2 + x + \dfrac{7}{x - 1}$
73. 📝   **75.** $49\frac{1}{2}$ hr   **77.** Michelle: 6 hr; Sal: 3 hr;
Kristen: 4 hr   **79.** 30 min   **81.** 2250 people per hour
83. $14\frac{7}{8}$ mi   **85.** About 13 sec   **87.** $21\frac{9}{11}$ min after 4:00
89. 48 km/h   **91.** 45 mph

93. Equation 1: $\dfrac{1}{a} \cdot t + \dfrac{1}{b} \cdot t = 1$;

Equation 2: $\left(\dfrac{1}{a} + \dfrac{1}{b}\right) t = 1$;

Equation 3: $\dfrac{t}{a} + \dfrac{t}{b} = 1$;

Equation 4: $\dfrac{1}{a} + \dfrac{1}{b} = \dfrac{1}{t}$

$\dfrac{1}{a} \cdot t + \dfrac{1}{b} \cdot t = 1$ Equation 1

$$t\left(\frac{1}{a} + \frac{1}{b}\right) = 1 \qquad \text{Factoring out } t; \text{ equation 1} = \text{equation 2}$$

$$t \cdot \frac{1}{a} + t \cdot \frac{1}{b} = 1 \qquad \text{Using the distributive law}$$

$$\frac{t}{a} + \frac{t}{b} = 1 \qquad \text{Multiplying; equation 2} = \text{equation 3}$$

$$\frac{1}{t} \cdot \left(\frac{t}{a} + \frac{t}{b}\right) = \frac{1}{t} \cdot 1 \qquad \text{Multiplying both sides by } \frac{1}{t}$$

$$\frac{1}{t} \cdot \frac{t}{a} + \frac{1}{t} \cdot \frac{t}{b} = \frac{1}{t} \cdot 1 \qquad \text{Using the distributive law}$$

$$\frac{1}{a} + \frac{1}{b} = \frac{1}{t} \qquad \text{Multiplying; equation 3} = \text{equation 4}$$

95. 📝

Quick Quiz: Sections 6.1–6.7, p. 431

1. $\dfrac{(y - 3)(y - 2)}{7x(y - 1)}$ **2.** 35   **3.** $\dfrac{2x}{(x - 2)(x + 1)(x + 2)}$

4. -7 **5.** $\frac{100}{3}$ min, or $33\frac{1}{3}$ min

Prepare to Move On, p. 431

1.
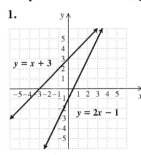
$y = x + 3$
$y = 2x - 1$

2.
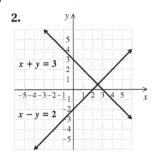
$x + y = 3$
$x - y = 2$

3.
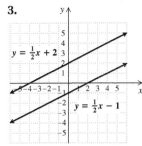
$y = \frac{1}{2}x + 2$
$y = \frac{1}{2}x - 1$

4.

$x + y = 2$ $2x + 2y = 4$

Translating for Success, p. 432

1. K   **2.** C   **3.** N   **4.** D   **5.** E   **6.** O   **7.** F
8. H   **9.** B   **10.** A

Decision Making: Connection, p. 433

1. Yes   **2.** No   **3.** $84.99   **4.** Yes

Study Summary: Chapter 6, pp. 434–437

1. $\dfrac{3(x - 1)}{(x - 3)}$ **2.** $\dfrac{5(a + 1)}{2a}$ **3.** $\dfrac{t^2(t - 10)}{(t - 2)^2}$
4. $\dfrac{3x - 1}{x + 5}$ **5.** 1   **6.** $(a + 5)(a - 5)(a - 1)$

7. $\dfrac{(x - 3)(2x - 1)}{(x - 1)(x - 2)}$ **8.** $\dfrac{3}{3x + 2}$ **9.** 2   **10.** $\frac{6}{5}$ hr, or $1\frac{1}{5}$ hr   **11.** Jogging: 9 mph; walking: 4 mph   **12.** $\frac{15}{2}$

Review Exercises: Chapter 6, pp. 437–438

1. False   **2.** True   **3.** False   **4.** True   **5.** True
6. False   **7.** False   **8.** False   **9.** 0   **10.** $-6, 6$
11. $-6, 5$ **12.** -2 **13.** $\dfrac{x - 3}{x + 5}$ **14.** $\dfrac{7x + 3}{x - 3}$
15. $\dfrac{3(y - 3)}{2(y + 3)}$ **16.** $-5(x + 2y)$ **17.** $\dfrac{a - 6}{5}$
18. $\dfrac{3(y - 2)^2}{4(2y - 1)(y - 1)}$ **19.** $-32t$ **20.** $\dfrac{2x(x - 1)}{x + 1}$
21. $\dfrac{(x^2 + 1)(2x + 1)}{(x - 2)(x + 1)}$ **22.** $\dfrac{(t + 4)^2}{t + 1}$ **23.** $60a^5b^8$
24. $x^4(x - 1)(x + 1)$ **25.** $(y - 2)(y + 2)(y + 1)$
26. $\dfrac{15 - 3x}{x + 3}$ **27.** $\dfrac{4}{x - 4}$ **28.** $\dfrac{x + 5}{2x}$
29. $\dfrac{2a^2 - 21ab + 15b^2}{5a^2b^2}$ **30.** $y - 4$ **31.** $\dfrac{t(t - 2)}{(t - 1)(t + 1)}$
32. $d + 2$ **33.** $\dfrac{-x^2 + x + 26}{(x + 1)(x - 5)(x + 5)}$ **34.** $\dfrac{2(x - 2)}{x + 2}$
35. $\dfrac{3(7t + 2)}{4t(3t + 2)}$ **36.** $\dfrac{z}{1 - z}$ **37.** $\dfrac{10x}{3x^2 + 16}$
38. $c - d$ **39.** 4   **40.** $\frac{7}{2}$ **41.** $-6, -1$
42. $-1, 4$ **43.** $5\frac{1}{7}$ hr   **44.** Ben: 30 hr; Jon: 45 hr
45. 24 mph   **46.** Jennifer: 70 mph; Elizabeth: 62 mph
47. 55 seals   **48.** 6   **49.** 72 radios
50. 📝 The LCM of denominators is used to clear fractions when simplifying a complex rational expression using the method of multiplying by the LCD, and when solving rational equations.   **51.** 📝 Although multiplying the denominators of the expressions being added results in a common denominator, it is often not the *least* common denominator. Using a common denominator other than the LCD makes the expressions more complicated, requires additional simplifying after the addition has been performed, and leaves more room for error.
52. $\dfrac{5(a + 3)^2}{a}$ **53.** $\dfrac{10a}{(a - b)(b - c)}$ **54.** 0   **55.** 44%

Test: Chapter 6, p. 439

1. [6.1] 0   **2.** [6.1] 1, 2   **3.** [6.1] $\dfrac{3x + 7}{x + 3}$
4. [6.2] $\dfrac{2t(t + 3)}{3(t - 1)}$ **5.** [6.2] $\dfrac{(5y + 1)(y + 1)}{3y(y + 2)}$
6. [6.2] $\dfrac{(2a + 1)(4a^2 + 1)}{4a^2(2a - 1)}$ **7.** [6.2] $(x + 3)(x - 3)$
8. [6.3] $(y - 3)(y + 3)(y + 7)$ **9.** [6.3] $\dfrac{-3x + 9}{x^3}$
10. [6.3] $\dfrac{-2t + 8}{t^2 + 1}$ **11.** [6.4] 1   **12.** [6.4] $\dfrac{3x - 5}{x - 3}$
13. [6.4] $\dfrac{11t - 8}{t(t - 2)}$ **14.** [6.4] $\dfrac{y^2 + 3}{(y - 1)(y + 3)^2}$
15. [6.4] $\dfrac{x^2 + 2x - 7}{(x + 1)(x - 1)^2}$ **16.** [6.5] $\dfrac{3y + 1}{y}$
17. [6.5] $x - 8$ **18.** [6.6] $\frac{8}{3}$ **19.** [6.6] $-3, 5$

20. [6.7] 12 min   **21.** [6.5] Tyler: 4 hr; Katie: 10 hr
22. [6.7] $1\frac{1}{4}$ mi   **23.** [6.7] Ryan: 65 km/h; Alicia: 45 km/h
24. [6.5] a **25.** [6.7] -1

Cumulative Review: Chapters 1–6, p. 440

1. $a + cb$ **2.** -25 **3.** 25   **4.** $-3x + 33$ **5.** 4
6. $-10, -1$ **7.** $-7, 7$ **8.** -8 **9.** 1, 4   **10.** -17
11. $-4, \frac{1}{2}$ **12.** $\{x \mid x > 43\}$, or $(43, \infty)$ **13.** -13
14. $b = 3a - c + 9$
15.

16.

17.

18.

19. -2 **20.** Slope: $\frac{1}{2}$; y-intercept: $\left(0, -\frac{1}{4}\right)$

21. $y = -\frac{5}{8}x - 4$ **22.** $\dfrac{1}{x^2}$ **23.** $-4a^4b^{14}$

24. $-y^3 - 2y^2 - 2y + 7$ **25.** $2x^5 + x^3 - 6x^2 - x + 3$
26. $36x^2 - 60xy + 25y^2$ **27.** $3n^2 - 13n - 10$
28. $4x^6 - 1$ **29.** $2x(3 - x - 12x^3)$ **30.** $(4x + 9)(4x - 9)$
31. $(t - 4)(t - 6)$ **32.** $10(t + 1)(t^2 - t + 1)$
33. $2(3x - 2)(x - 4)$ **34.** $(5t + 4)^2$ **35.** $(xy - 5)(xy + 4)$

36. $(x + 2)(x^3 - 3)$ **37.** $\dfrac{4}{t + 4}$ **38.** 1

39. $\dfrac{a^2 + 7ab + b^2}{(a + b)(a - b)}$ **40.** $\dfrac{2x + 5}{4 - x}$ **41.** $\dfrac{x}{x - 2}$

42. $15x^3 - 57x^2 + 177x - 529 + \dfrac{1605}{x + 3}$ **43.** 15 books

44. 12 ft   **45.** $\frac{75}{4}$ min, or $18\frac{3}{4}$ min   **46.** 150 calories
47. $-144, 144$ **48.** $-7, 4, 12$ **49.** 18

CHAPTER 7

Exercise Set 7.1, pp. 448–452

1. Correspondence   **2.** Exactly   **3.** Domain
4. Range   **5.** Horizontal   **6.** Vertical   **7.** "f of 3"
8. Vertical   **9.** Yes   **11.** Yes   **13.** No   **15.** Yes
17. Function   **19.** Function   **21.** (a) $\{-3, -2, 0, 4\}$;
(b) $\{-10, 3, 5, 9\}$; **(c)** yes   **23.** (a) $\{1, 2, 3, 4, 5\}$; **(b)** $\{1\}$;
(c) yes   **25.** (a) $\{-2, 3, 4\}$; **(b)** $\{-8, -2, 4, 5\}$; **(c)** no
27. (a) -2; **(b)** 4   **29.** (a) -2; **(b)** -2 **31.** (a) 3;
(b) -3 **33.** (a) 3; **(b)** $-2, 0$ **35.** (a) 4; **(b)** $-1, 3$

37. Yes   **39.** Yes   **41.** No   **43.** (a) 5; **(b)** -3;
(c) -9; **(d)** 21; **(e)** $2a + 9$; **(f)** $2a + 7$ **45.** (a) 0;
(b) 1; **(c)** 57; **(d)** $5t^2 + 4t$; **(e)** $20a^2 + 8a$; **(f)** 48

47. (a) $\frac{3}{5}$; **(b)** $\frac{1}{3}$; **(c)** $\frac{4}{7}$; **(d)** 0; **(e)** $\dfrac{x - 1}{2x - 1}$; **(f)** $\dfrac{a + h - 3}{2a + 2h - 5}$

49. 11   **51.** 0   **53.** $-\frac{21}{2}$ **55.** $\frac{25}{6}$ **57.** -3
59. -25 **61.** $4\sqrt{3}$ cm$^2 \approx 6.93$ cm^2
63. 36π in$^2 \approx 113.10$ in^2 **65.** 75 heart attacks per
10,000 men   **67.** 250 mg/dl   **69.** 🖉   **71.** 6
72. $-4, 8$ **73.** $-6, 6$ **74.** $-\frac{1}{2}$ **75.** $-1, 1$
76. $-4, 3$ **77.** $\frac{9}{32}$ **78.** $\frac{1}{7}$ **79.** 🖉   **81.** 26; 99
83. Worm   **85.** (a) 2; **(b)** 2; **(c)** $\{x \mid 0 < x \leq 2\}$, or $(0, 2]$
87. About 22 mm   **89.** 1 every 3 min
91.

Prepare to Move On, p. 452

1. 0   **2.** $\frac{1}{3}$ **3.** $-3, 4$ **4.** $-6, 6$

Exercise Set 7.2, pp. 457–460

1. Domain   **2.** Range   **3.** Domain   **4.** Range
5. Domain   **6.** Domain   **7.** (c)   **8.** (d)   **9.** (d)
10. (b)   **11.** (c)   **12.** (b)   **13.** Domain:
$\{-4, -2, 0, 2, 4\}$; range, $\{-2, -1, 0, 1, 2\}$ **15.** Domain:
$\{-5, -3, -1, 0, 2, 4\}$; range: $\{-1, 1\}$ **17.** Domain:
$\{x \mid -4 \leq x \leq 3\}$, or $[-4, 3]$; range: $\{y \mid -3 \leq y \leq 4\}$, or
$[-3, 4]$ **19.** Domain: $\{x \mid -4 \leq x \leq 5\}$, or $[-4, 5]$;
range: $\{y \mid -2 \leq y \leq 4\}$, or $[-2, 4]$ **21.** Domain:
$\{x \mid -4 \leq x \leq 4\}$, or $[-4, 4]$; range: $\{-3, -1, 1\}$
23. Domain: $\mathbb{R}$; range: $\mathbb{R}$ **25.** Domain: $\mathbb{R}$; range: $\{4\}$
27. Domain: $\mathbb{R}$; range: $\{y \mid y \geq 1\}$, or $[1, \infty)$
29. Domain: $\{x \mid x$ is a real number $and\ x \neq -2\}$; range:
$\{y \mid y$ is a real number $and\ y \neq -4\}$ **31.** Domain:
$\{x \mid x \geq 0\}$, or $[0, \infty)$; range: $\{y \mid y \geq 0\}$, or $[0, \infty)$
33. $\{x \mid x$ is a real number $and\ x \neq 3\}$
35. $\{x \mid x$ is a real number $and\ x \neq \frac{1}{2}\}$ **37.** $\mathbb{R}$ **39.** $\mathbb{R}$
41. $\{x \mid x$ is a real number $and\ x \neq 3\ and\ x \neq -3\}$ **43.** $\mathbb{R}$
45. $\{x \mid x$ is a real number $and\ x \neq -1\ and\ x \neq -7\}$
47. $\{t \mid 0 \leq t \leq 5\}$, or $[0, 5]$
49. $\{p \mid \$0 \leq p \leq \$10.60\}$, or $[0, 10.60]$
51. $\{d \mid d \geq 0\}$, or $[0, \infty)$ **53.** $\{t \mid 0 \leq t \leq 5\}$, or $[0, 5]$
55. (a) -5; **(b)** 1; **(c)** 21   **57.** (a) -15; **(b)** 0; **(c)** -6
59. (a) 100; **(b)** 100; **(c)** 131   **61.** 🖉   **63.** -3

64. $15x - 29$ **65.** $4x^{12}y^2$ **66.** $-\dfrac{12b^{26}}{7a^{12}}$ **67.** 🖉

69.   **71.**

73. Domain: $\{x \mid x$ is a real number $and\ x \neq 0\}$; range: $\{y \mid y$ is a real number $and\ y \neq 0\}$ **75.** Domain: $\{x \mid x < -2\ or\ x > 0\}$; range: $\{y \mid y < -2\ or\ y > 3\}$
77. Domain: $\mathbb{R}$; range: $\{y \mid y \geq 0\}$, or $[0, \infty)$
79. Domain: $\{x \mid x$ is a real number $and\ x \neq 2\}$; range: $\{y \mid y$ is a real number $and\ y \neq 0\}$
81. $\{h \mid 0 \leq h \leq 144\}$, or $[0, 144]$
83.   **85.**

87.

Quick Quiz: Sections 7.1–7.2, p. 460

1. 0   **2.** 200   **3.** $\{x \mid x$ is a real number $and\ x \neq 0\}$
4. $\mathbb{R}$ **5.** -3

Prepare to Move On, p. 460

1.   **2.**

3. Slope: $\frac{2}{3}$; y-intercept: $(0, -4)$
4. Slope: $-\frac{1}{4}$; y-intercept: $(0, 6)$
5. Slope: $\frac{4}{3}$; y-intercept: $(0, 0)$
6. Slope: -5; y-intercept: $(0, 0)$

Connecting the Concepts, p. 461

1. $\{-2, 1, 3\}$ **2.** $\{-6, 5\}$ **3.** -6 **4.** 1
5. $\{x \mid x$ is a real number $and\ x \neq 0\}$ **6.** 0
7. $\frac{3}{8}$ **8.** 2

Exercise Set 7.3, pp. 466–469

1. False   **2.** True   **3.** False   **4.** True
5. True   **6.** True
7.   **9.**

11.   **13.**

15.   **17.**

19.   **21.**

23.   **25.** $C(d) = 0.75d + 30$;
60 miles
27. $L(t) = \frac{1}{2}t + 5$;
20 months after the haircut
29. $S(t) = 2.2t + 4.5$; 2005

31. (a) $N(t) = 1.02t + 74.8$; **(b)** 91.12 million tons
33. (a) $E(t) = 0.14t + 79.7$; **(b)** 82.5 years
35. (a) $S(t) = \frac{466}{25}t + \frac{2423}{5}$; **(b)** 857.4 tons
37. (a) $P(d) = 0.03d + 1$; **(b)** 21.7 atm   **39.** Linear function; $\mathbb{R}$ **41.** Quadratic function; $\mathbb{R}$ **43.** Rational function; $\left\{ t \mid t \text{ is a real number } and\ t \neq -\frac{4}{3} \right\}$

45. Polynomial function; $\mathbb{R}$ **47.** Rational function; $\{x \mid x \text{ is a real number } and\, x \neq \frac{5}{2}\}$
49. Rational function; $\{n \mid n \text{ is a real number } and\, n \neq -1 \, and\, n \neq -2\}$ **51.** Linear function; $\mathbb{R}$
53. $\{y \mid y \geq 0\}$, or $[0, \infty)$ **55.** $\mathbb{R}$ **57.** $\{y \mid y \leq 0\}$, or $(-\infty, 0]$

59.

61.

Domain: $\mathbb{R}$; range: $\mathbb{R}$ Domain: $\mathbb{R}$; range: $\{-1\}$

63.

65.

Domain: $\mathbb{R}$; range: $\{y \mid y \geq 1\}$, or $[1, \infty)$ Domain: $\mathbb{R}$; range: $\{y \mid y \geq 0\}$, or $[0, \infty)$

67. ☑   **69.** $(2n - 7)^2$ **70.** $(4x + 3)(x - 5)$
71. $2x(x - 1)(x - 6)$ **72.** $(c - 10)(c^2 + 10c + 100)$
73. $d(d + 8)(d - 8)$ **74.** $(a + 4)(a^2 + 2)$
75. ☑   **77.** False   **79.** False   **81.** $21.1°C$
83. $60   **85.** **(a)** $g(x) = x - 8$; **(b)** -10; **(c)** 83

Quick Quiz: Sections 7.1–7.3, p. 469

1. $\frac{5}{4}$ **2.** $\frac{a}{a - 1}$ **3.** $\{x \mid x \text{ is a real number } and\, x \neq 2\}$
4. Quadratic   **5.** $\mathbb{R}$

Prepare to Move On, p. 469

1. $4x^2 + 2x - 1$ **2.** $2x^3 - x^2 - x + 7$
3. $2x^2 - 13x - 7$ **4.** $x^2 + x - 12$

Mid-Chapter Review: Chapter 7, p. 470

1. $f(-5) = 2(-5)^2 - 3(-5) = 2(25) - (-15) = 50 + 15 = 65$ **2.** $x - 7 = 0$
$x = 7$
Domain $= \{x \mid x \text{ is a real number } and\, x \neq 7\}$
3. $\{-1, 0, 3, 4\}$ **4.** $\{-2, 0, 6, 8\}$ **5.** -2
6. $\mathbb{R}$ **7.** $\{x \mid x \text{ is a real number } and\, x \neq 0\}$
8. $\frac{1}{5}$ **9.** Linear function   **10.** Rational function
11. $\mathbb{R}$ **12.** $\{x \mid x \text{ is a real number } and\, x \neq -10 \, and\, x \neq 4\}$ **13.** Yes   **14.** -4 **15.** $-1, 4\frac{1}{2}$
16. $\{x \mid x \geq -3\}$, or $[-3, \infty)$
17. $\{y \mid y \geq -4\}$, or $[-4, \infty)$ **18.** 4   **19.** 10
20. 13

Exercise Set 7.4, pp. 476–479

1. Sum   **2.** Subtract   **3.** Evaluate   **4.** Domains
5. Excluding   **6.** Sum   **7.** 1   **9.** 5   **11.** -7
13. 1   **15.** -5 **17.** $x^2 - 2x - 2$ **19.** $x^2 + 2x - 8$
21. $x^2 - x + 3$ **23.** 5   **25.** $-a^3 + 5a^2 + 2a - 10$
27. $\frac{x^2 - 2}{5 - x}, x \neq 5$ **29.** $\frac{7}{2}$ **31.** -2
33. $\frac{15}{2x^3}$ **35.** $\frac{10 - 3x}{2x^2}$ **37.** $\frac{3x}{10}$
39. $\frac{2x + 7}{(x + 2)(x - 3)(x + 3)}$ **41.** $\frac{2x^2 + 6x + 1}{(x + 2)(x - 3)(x + 3)}$
43. $\frac{(x - 1)(x + 3)}{(x + 2)^2}$ **45.** $1.2 + 2.9 = 4.1$ million
47. $45 - 28 = 17$ **49.** About 85 million; the number of tons of municipal solid waste that was composted or recycled in 2009   **51.** About 240 million; the number of tons of municipal solid waste in 2000   **53.** About 220 million; the number of tons of municipal solid waste that was not composted in 2008   **55.** $\mathbb{R}$ **57.** $\{x \mid x \text{ is a real number } and\, x \neq -5\}$
59. $\{x \mid x \text{ is a real number } and\, x \neq 0\}$
61. $\{x \mid x \text{ is a real number } and\, x \neq 1\}$
63. $\{x \mid x \text{ is a real number } and\, x \neq -\frac{9}{2} \, and\, x \neq 1\}$
65. $\{x \mid x \text{ is a real number } and\, x \neq 3\}$
67. $\{x \mid x \text{ is a real number } and\, x \neq -4\}$
69. $\{x \mid x \text{ is a real number } and\, x \neq 4 \, and\, x \neq 5\}$
71. $\{x \mid x \text{ is a real number } and\, x \neq -1 \, and\, x \neq -\frac{5}{2}\}$
73. 4; 3   **75.** 5; -1 **77.** $\{x \mid 0 \leq x \leq 9\}$; $\{x \mid 3 \leq x \leq 10\}$; $\{x \mid 3 \leq x \leq 9\}$; $\{x \mid 3 \leq x \leq 9\}$
79.

81. ☑
83. $60°, 30°, 90°$
84. 11 points

85. 2.992×10^{-23} g   **86.** 36 ft   **87.** ☑
89. $\{x \mid x \text{ is a real number } and\, x \neq 4 \, and\, x \neq 3 \, and\, x \neq 2 \, and\, x \neq -2\}$
91. Answers may vary.

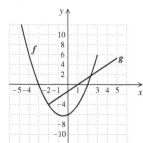

93. $\{x \mid x \text{ is a real number } and\, -1 < x < 5 \, and\, x \neq \frac{3}{2}\}$
95. Answers may vary. $f(x) = \frac{1}{x + 2}, g(x) = \frac{1}{x - 5}$
97. 〰

Quick Quiz: Sections 7.1–7.4, p. 479

1. 8   **2.** −1
3.   **4.** 3

$g(x) = 3x - 2$

5. $-x^2 - x + 3$

Prepare to Move On, p. 479

1. $c = \dfrac{b}{a}$ **2.** $w = \dfrac{x - y}{z}$ **3.** $q = \dfrac{st}{p - r}$

4. $b = \dfrac{d}{a + c}$ **5.** $b = \dfrac{cd + d}{a - 3}$

Exercise Set 7.5, pp. 485–490

1. (d)   **2.** (f)   **3.** (e)   **4.** (b)   **5.** (a)   **6.** (c)
7. Inverse   **8.** Direct   **9.** Direct   **10.** Inverse

11. Inverse   **12.** Direct   **13.** $d = \dfrac{L}{f}$

15. $v_1 = \dfrac{2s}{t} - v_2$, or $\dfrac{2s - tv_2}{t}$ **17.** $b = \dfrac{at}{a - t}$

19. $g = \dfrac{Rs}{s - R}$ **21.** $n = \dfrac{IR}{E - Ir}$ **23.** $q = \dfrac{pf}{p - f}$

25. $t_1 = \dfrac{H}{Sm} + t_2$, or $\dfrac{H + Smt_2}{Sm}$ **27.** $r = \dfrac{Re}{E - e}$

29. $r = 1 - \dfrac{a}{S}$, or $\dfrac{S - a}{S}$ **31.** $a + b = \dfrac{f}{c^2}$

33. $r = \dfrac{A}{P} - 1$, or $\dfrac{A - P}{P}$ **35.** $t_1 = t_2 - \dfrac{d_2 - d_1}{v}$, or

$\dfrac{vt_2 - d_2 + d_1}{v}$ **37.** $t = \dfrac{ab}{b + a}$ **39.** $Q = \dfrac{2Tt - 2AT}{A - q}$

41. $w = \dfrac{4.15c - 98.42}{p + 0.082}$ **43.** $k = 6; y = 6x$

45. $k = 1.7; y = 1.7x$ **47.** $k = 10; y = 10x$

49. $k = 100; y = \dfrac{100}{x}$ **51.** $k = 44; y = \dfrac{44}{x}$

53. $k = 9; y = \dfrac{9}{x}$ **55.** $33\frac{1}{3}$ cm   **57.** 3.5 hr

59. 12 people   **61.** 600 tons   **63.** 286 Hz
65. About 21 min   **67.** About 33.06   **69.** $y = \frac{1}{2}x^2$

71. $y = \dfrac{5000}{x^2}$ **73.** $y = 1.5xz$ **75.** $y = \dfrac{4wx^2}{z}$

77. 61.3 ft   **79.** 64 foot-candles   **81.** About 57 mph
83. 📝   **85.** $9x^2$ **86.** $9 + 6x + x^2$ **87.** $\frac{8}{35}$

88. $\dfrac{5x}{9y^5}$ **89.** −6   **90.** $3x - 10$ **91.** 📝

93. 567 mi   **95.** Ratio is $\dfrac{a + 12}{a + 6}$; percent increase is

$\dfrac{6}{a + 6} \cdot 100\%$, or $\dfrac{600}{a + 6}\%$

97. $t_1 = t_2 + \dfrac{(d_2 - d_1)(t_4 - t_3)}{a(t_4 - t_2)(t_4 - t_3) + d_3 - d_4}$
99. The intensity is halved.   **101.** About 1.7 m
103. $d(s) = \dfrac{28}{s}$; 70 yd

Quick Quiz: Sections 7.1–7.5, p. 490

1. Yes   **2.** Domain: $\{x \mid -4 \le x \le 3\}$, or $[-4, 3]$;
range: $\{y \mid -3 \le y \le 1\}$, or $[-3, 1]$ **3.** Domain:
$\{-2, -1, 0, 1, 2\}$; range: $\{-1, 0, 1, 2, 3\}$
4.   **5.** 40 kg

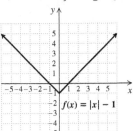

$f(x) = |x| - 1$

Prepare to Move On, p. 490

1. $y = \frac{1}{6}x - \frac{1}{2}$ **2.** $y = \frac{3}{8}x - \frac{5}{8}$ **3.** $y = -\frac{5}{2}x - \frac{3}{2}$
4. Let x represent the number; $\frac{1}{2}x - 3 = 57$
5. Let x represent the first integer; $x + (x + 1) = 145$
6. Let n represent the number; $n - (-n) = 20$

Visualizing for Success, p. 491

1. D   **2.** J   **3.** A   **4.** E   **5.** B   **6.** C   **7.** I
8. F   **9.** G   **10.** H

Decision Making: Connection, p. 492

1. 51.2 gal   **2.** $2250   **3.** $320; $720; $960   **4.** 🖥

Study Summary: Chapter 7, pp. 493–495

1. 5   **2.** Yes   **3.** Domain: $\mathbb{R}$; range: $\{y \mid y \ge -2\}$
4. $\mathbb{R}$
5.   **6.**

$f(x) = -2x + 1$

$f(x) = x^2 - 2$

Domain: $\mathbb{R}$; range: $\{y \mid y \ge -2\}$,
or $[-2, \infty)$

7. $2x - 9$ **8.** 5   **9.** −6   **10.** $\dfrac{x - 2}{x - 7}, x \ne 7$

11. $y = 50x$ **12.** $y = \dfrac{40}{x}$ **13.** $y = \frac{1}{10}xz$

Review Exercises: Chapter 7, pp. 495–497

1. True **2.** True **3.** False **4.** True **5.** False
6. True **7.** True **8.** True **9.** True **10.** False
11. (a) 3; **(b)** $\{x \mid -2 \leq x \leq 4\}$, or $[-2, 4]$; **(c)** -1;
(d) $\{y \mid 1 \leq y \leq 5\}$, or $[1, 5]$ **12.** $\frac{3}{2}$
13. $4a^2 + 4a - 3$ **14.** 19.5% **15. (a)** Yes;
(b) domain: $\mathbb{R}$; range: $\{y \mid y \geq 0\}$, or $[0, \infty)$
16. (a) No **17. (a)** No **18. (a)** Yes; **(b)** domain: $\mathbb{R}$;
range: $\{-2\}$ **19.** $\mathbb{R}$ **20.** $\{x \mid x$ is a real number
$and \ x \neq 1\}$ **21.** $\{t \mid t$ is a real number $and \ t \neq -1$
$and \ t \neq -4\}$ **22.** $\{t \mid 0 \leq t \leq 60\}$, or $[0, 60]$
23. (a) 5; **(b)** 4; **(c)** 16; **(d)** 35 **24.** $C(t) = 30t + 90$;
7 months **25. (a)** $R(t) = -0.02t + 19.81$; **(b)** about
19.11 sec; about 19.01 sec **26.** Absolute-value function
27. Polynomial function **28.** Quadratic function
29. Linear function **30.** Rational function
31.

32.

Domain: $\mathbb{R}$; range: $\{3\}$
33.

Domain: $\mathbb{R}$; range: $\mathbb{R}$
34. 102
35. -17 **36.** $-\frac{9}{2}$
37. $\mathbb{R}$

Domain: $\mathbb{R}$; range: $\{y \mid y \geq 0\}$,
or $[0, \infty)$

38. $\{x \mid x$ is a real number and $x \neq 2\}$ **39.** $r = \dfrac{2V - IR}{2I}$,
or $\dfrac{V}{I} - \dfrac{R}{2}$ **40.** $m = \dfrac{H}{S(t_1 - t_2)}$ **41.** $c = \dfrac{b + 3a}{2}$
42. $t_1 = \dfrac{-A}{vT} + t_2$, or $t_1 = \dfrac{-A + vTt_2}{vT}$ **43.** $y = \frac{15}{2}x$

44. $y = \dfrac{\frac{3}{4}}{x}$ **45.** $y = \dfrac{1}{2} \dfrac{xw^2}{z}$ **46.** 20 cm

47. About 2.9 sec **48.** 56 in. **49.** ⬓ Two functions
that have the same domain and range are not necessarily
identical. For example, the functions f: $\{(-2, 1), (-3, 2)\}$
and g: $\{(-2, 2), (-3, 1)\}$ have the same domain and range
but are different functions. **50.** ⬓ Jenna is not correct.
Any value of the variable that makes a denominator 0 is
not in the domain; 0 itself may or may not make a denominator 0. **51.** $f(x) = 10.94x + 20$ **52.** Domain:
$\{x \mid x \geq -4 \ and \ x \neq 2\}$; range: $\{y \mid y \geq 0 \ and \ y \neq 3\}$

Test: Chapter 7, pp. 498–499

1. [7.1], [7.2] **(a)** 1; **(b)** $\{x \mid -3 \leq x \leq 4\}$, or $[-3, 4]$; **(c)** 3;
(d) $\{y \mid -1 \leq y \leq 2\}$, or $[-1, 2]$ **2. (a)** [7.1] Yes; **(b)** [7.2]
domain: $\mathbb{R}$; range: $\mathbb{R}$ **3. (a)** [7.1] Yes; **(b)** [7.2] domain: $\mathbb{R}$;
range: $\{y \mid y \geq 1\}$, or $[1, \infty)$ **4. (a)** [7.1] No
5. [7.2] $\{t \mid 0 \leq t \leq 4\}$, or $[0, 4]$ **6.** [7.2] **(a)** -5; **(b)** 10
7. [7.3] $C(t) = 55t + 180$; 12 months
8. [7.3] **(a)** $C(m) = 0.3m + 25$; **(b)** $175
9. [7.3] Linear function; $\mathbb{R}$ **10.** [7.3] Rational function;
$\{x \mid x$ is a real number $and \ x \neq -4 \ and \ x \neq 4\}$
11. [7.3] Quadratic function; $\mathbb{R}$
12. [7.3]   **13.** [7.3]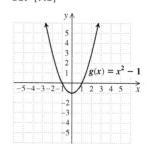

Domain: $\mathbb{R}$; range: $\mathbb{R}$

Domain: $\mathbb{R}$; range:
$\{y \mid y \geq -1\}$, or $[-1, \infty)$
15. [7.1] -1
16. [7.1] $10a + 1$
17. [7.4] $\dfrac{1}{x} + 2x + 1$

14. [7.3]

Domain: $\mathbb{R}$; range: $\left\{-\frac{1}{2}\right\}$
18. [7.1] $\{x \mid x$ is a real number $and \ x \neq 0\}$
19. [7.4] $\{x \mid x$ is a real number $and \ x \neq 0\}$
20. [7.4] $\left\{x \mid x$ is a real number $and \ x \neq 0 \ and \ x \neq -\frac{1}{2}\right\}$
21. [7.5] $s = \dfrac{Rg}{g - R}$ **22.** [7.5] $y = \frac{1}{2}x$
23. [7.5] 30 workers **24.** [7.5] 637 in² **25.** [7.3]
(a) 30 mi; **(b)** 15 mph **26.** [7.4] $h(x) = 7x - 2$

Cumulative Review: Chapters 1–7, p. 500

1. 3.91×10^8 **2.** Slope: $\frac{7}{4}$; y-intercept: $(0, -3)$
3. $y = -2x + 5$ **4. (a)** 0; **(b)** $\{x \mid x$ is a real number and
$x \neq 5 \ and \ x \neq 6\}$
5.   **6.**

7.

$f(x) = -4$

8.

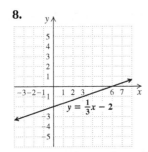

$y = \frac{1}{3}x - 2$

9. $15x^4 - x^3 - 9x^2 + 5x - 2$ **10.** $9x^4 + 6x^2y + y^2$
11. $4x^4 - 81$ **12.** $-m^3n^2 - m^2n^2 - 5mn^3$
13. $x - 1$ **14.** $\dfrac{a^2 + 7ab + b^2}{(a - b)(a + b)}$ **15.** $4x(x^2 + 100)$
16. $(x - 6)(x + 14)$ **17.** $(4y - 5)(4y + 5)$
18. $8(2x + 1)(4x^2 - 2x + 1)$ **19.** $(t - 8)^2$
20. $(3t - 4)(t + 7)$ **21.** $\frac{1}{4}$ **22.** $-12, 12$
23. $\{x \,|\, x \geq -1\}$, or $[-1, \infty)$ **24.** $\frac{3}{5}$ **25.** -1
26. $a = \dfrac{Pb}{4 - P}$ **27.** -5 **28.** $y = -x + 3$
29. 99 **30.** $\dfrac{x^2 - 1}{x + 5}$ **31.** 72 in.   **32.** IQAir
HealthPro: 10 min; Austin Healthmate: 15 min
33. $22\frac{1}{2}$ min   **34.** $x^3 - 12x^2 + 48x - 64$
35. $-3, 3, -5, 5$
36. $C(x) = \begin{cases} 12, & \text{if } x \leq 20, \\ 12 + 0.75(x - 20), & \text{if } x > 20 \end{cases}$

CHAPTER 8

Technology Connection, p. 505

1. $(1.53, 2.58)$ **2.** $(0.87, -0.32)$

Exercise Set 8.1, pp. 507–510

1. False   **2.** True   **3.** True   **4.** True   **5.** True
6. False   **7.** False   **8.** True   **9.** Yes   **11.** No
13. Yes   **15.** Yes   **17.** $(3, 2)$ **19.** $(2, -1)$
21. $(1, 4)$ **23.** $(-3, -2)$ **25.** $(3, -1)$ **27.** $(3, -7)$
29. $(7, 2)$ **31.** $(4, 0)$ **33.** No solution
35. $\{(x, y) \,|\, y = 3 - x\}$ **37.** All except Exercise 33
39. Exercise 35   **41.** Let x represent the first number
and y the second number; $x + y = 10$, $x = \frac{2}{3}y$ **43.** Let s
represent the number of e-mails sent and r the number of
e-mails received; $s + r = 115$, $r = 2s + 1$ **45.** Let x and
y represent the angles; $x + y = 180$, $x = 2y - 3$ **47.** Let
x represent the number of two-point shots and y the number of foul shots; $x + y = 64$, $2x + y = 100$ **49.** Let x
represent the number of hats sold and y the number of tee
shirts sold; $x + y = 45$, $14.50x + 19.50y = 697.50$
51. Let c represent the number of Classic Heart Rate
watches purchased and d the number of Drive Plus Heart
Rate watches; $c + d = 35$, $39.99c + 59.99d = 1639.65$
53. Let l represent the length, in yards, and w the width, in
yards; $2l + 2w = 340$; $l = w + 50$ **55.** 📋   **57.** $-\frac{4}{5}$
58. -0.06 **59.** -29 **60.** $\dfrac{6y^8}{x^5}$ **61.** $-\frac{1}{100}$ **62.** 1

63. 📋   **65.** Answers may vary. **(a)** $x + y = 6$, $x - y = 4$;
(b) $x + y = 1$, $2x + 2y = 3$; **(c)** $x + y = 1$, $2x + 2y = 2$
67. $A = -\frac{17}{4}$, $B = -\frac{12}{5}$ **69.** Let x and y represent the
number of years that Dell and Juanita have taught at the
university, respectively; $x + y = 46$, $x - 2 = 2.5(y - 2)$
71. Let s and v represent the number of ounces of baking
soda and vinegar needed, respectively; $s = 4v$, $s + v = 16$
73. Mineral oil: 12 oz; vinegar: 4 oz   **75.** $(0, 0)$, $(1, 1)$
77. $(0.07, -7.95)$ **79.** $(0.00, 1.25)$ **81.** 🖥

Prepare to Move On, p. 510

1. $\frac{8}{13}$ **2.** -1 **3.** 11 **4.** $y = 3x - 4$
5. $x = \frac{5}{2}y - \frac{7}{2}$

Connecting the Concepts, pp. 515–516

1. $(1, 1)$ **2.** $(9, 1)$ **3.** $(4, 3)$ **4.** $(5, 7)$
5. $\left(1, -\frac{1}{19}\right)$ **6.** $(3, 1)$ **7.** No solution
8. $\{(x, y) \,|\, x = 2 - y\}$

Exercise Set 8.2, pp. 516–518

1. Substitution   **2.** Elimination   **3.** Opposites
4. Inconsistent   **5.** (d)   **6.** (e)   **7.** (a)   **8.** (f)
9. (c)   **10.** (b)   **11.** $(2, -1)$ **13.** $(-4, 3)$
15. $(2, -2)$ **17.** $\{(x, y) \,|\, 2x - 3 = y\}$ **19.** $(-2, 1)$
21. $\left(\frac{1}{2}, \frac{1}{2}\right)$ **23.** $(2, 0)$ **25.** No solution   **27.** $(1, 2)$
29. $(7, -2)$ **31.** $(-1, 2)$ **33.** $\left(\frac{49}{11}, -\frac{12}{11}\right)$ **35.** $(6, 2)$
37. No solution   **39.** $(20, 0)$ **41.** $(3, -1)$
43. $\{(x, y) \,|\, -4x + 2y = 5\}$ **45.** $\left(2, -\frac{3}{2}\right)$ **47.** $(-2, -9)$
49. $(30, 6)$ **51.** $\{(x, y) \,|\, 4x - 2y = 2\}$ **53.** No
solution   **55.** $(140, 60)$ **57.** $\left(\frac{1}{3}, -\frac{2}{3}\right)$ **59.** 📋
61. $4 + (m + n)$ **62.** $-2a^2 + 7$ **63.** $47x - 36$
64. -1 **65.** 3.005×10^7 **66.** 0.00061 **67.** 📋
69. $m = -\frac{1}{2}$, $b = \frac{5}{2}$ **71.** $a = 5$, $b = 2$ **73.** $\left(-\frac{32}{17}, \frac{38}{17}\right)$
75. $\left(-\frac{1}{5}, \frac{1}{10}\right)$ **77.** Toaster oven: 3 kWh; convection
oven: 12 kWh   **79.** 📋

Quick Quiz: Sections 8.1–8.2, p. 518

1. Yes   **2.** $(3, 1)$ **3.** $(-3, -10)$ **4.** $\left(\frac{7}{5}, -\frac{3}{5}\right)$
5. $\left(\frac{1}{11}, \frac{3}{11}\right)$

Prepare to Move On, p. 518

1. $105,000   **2.** 90 **3.** 290 mi

Exercise Set 8.3, pp. 527–531

1. Total value   **2.** Principal   **3.** Distance   **4.** Sum
5. $4, 6$ **7.** e-mails sent: 38; e-mails received: 77
9. $119°, 61°$ **11.** Two-point shots: 36; foul shots: 28
13. Hats: 36; tee shirts: 9   **15.** Classic Heart Rate
watches: 23; Drive Plus Heart Rate watches: 12
17. Length: 110 yd; width: 60 yd   **19.** Wind: 924 trillion Btu's; solar: 109 trillion Btu's   **21.** 3-credit courses:
37; 4-credit courses: 11   **23.** Regular paper: 16 cases;
recycled paper: 11 cases   **25.** 23-watt bulbs: 60; 42-watt
bulbs: 140   **27.** Youths: 78; adults: 32   **29.** Mexican:

14 lb; Peruvian: 14 lb   **31.** Custom-printed M&Ms: 64 oz; bulk M&Ms: 256 oz   **33.** 50%-chocolate: 7.5 lb;10%-chocolate: 12.5 lb   **35.** Deep Thought: 12 lb; Oat Dream: 8 lb   **37.** $7500 at 6.5%; $4500 at 7.2%
39. Steady State: 12.5 L; Even Flow: 7.5 L   **41.** 87-octane: 2.5 gal; 95-octane: 7.5 gal   **43.** Whole milk: $169\frac{3}{13}$ lb; cream: $30\frac{10}{13}$ lb   **45.** 375 km   **47.** 14 km/h
49. About 1489 mi   **51.** Length: 265 ft; width: 165 ft
53. Wii game machines: 92.4 million; PlayStation 3 consoles: 61.6 million   **55.** $7.99 plans: 190; $15.98 plans: 90
57. Quarters: 17; fifty-cent pieces: 13   **59.** 📝   **61.** -7
62. 102   **63.** 0   **64.** $x^2 + x - 5$ **65.** $\mathbb{R}$
66. $\{x \mid x \text{ is a real number } and\, x \neq 7\}$ **67.** 📝
69. 0%: 20 reams; 30%: 40 reams   **71.** $10\frac{2}{3}$ oz
73. 33 boxes   **75.** Brown: 0.8 gal; neutral: 0.2 gal

77. City: 261 mi; highway: 204 mi   **79.** $P(x) = \dfrac{0.1 + x}{1.5}$

(This expresses the percent as a decimal quantity.)

Quick Quiz: Sections 8.1–8.3, p. 531

1. No solution   **2.** $\left(\frac{23}{4}, \frac{25}{16}\right)$ **3.** $(4, 4)$
4. $(3, 0)$ **5.** Large trash bags: 21 rolls; small trash bags: 7 rolls

Prepare to Move On, p. 531

1. 1   **2.** $\frac{1}{2}$ **3.** 17   **4.** 7

Exercise Set 8.4, pp. 537–539

1. True   **2.** False   **3.** False   **4.** True   **5.** True
6. False   **7.** Yes   **9.** $(3, 1, 2)$ **11.** $(1, -2, 2)$
13. $(2, -5, -6)$ **15.** No solution   **17.** $(-2, 0, 5)$
19. $(21, -14, -2)$ **21.** The equations are dependent.
23. $\left(3, \frac{1}{2}, -4\right)$ **25.** $\left(\frac{1}{2}, \frac{1}{3}, \frac{1}{6}\right)$ **27.** $\left(\frac{1}{2}, \frac{2}{3}, -\frac{5}{6}\right)$
29. $(15, 33, 9)$ **31.** $(3, 4, -1)$ **33.** $(10, 23, 50)$
35. No solution   **37.** The equations are dependent.
39. 📝   **41.** Slope: $\frac{1}{3}$; y-intercept: $\left(0, -\frac{7}{3}\right)$ **42.** 0
43. x-intercept: $(10, 0)$; y-intercept: $(0, -4)$ **44.** $\frac{5}{8}$
45. Parallel   **46.** Neither   **47.** 📝   **49.** $(1, -1, 2)$
51. $(1, -2, 4, -1)$ **53.** $\left(-1, \frac{1}{5}, -\frac{1}{2}\right)$ **55.** 14
57. $z = 8 - 2x - 4y$

Quick Quiz: Sections 8.1–8.4, p. 539

1. $\left(\frac{14}{5}, \frac{3}{10}\right)$ **2.** $\{(x, y) \mid 2x - y = 4\}$ **3.** $(5, -6, 9)$
4. 20 mph   **5.** 15% pigment: $1\frac{1}{5}$ gal; 10% pigment: $1\frac{4}{5}$ gal

Prepare to Move On, p. 539

1. Let x represent the first number; $x + (x + 1) + (x + 2) = 100$ **2.** Let $x, y,$ and z represent the numbers; $x + y + z = 100$ **3.** Let $x, y,$ and z represent the numbers; $xy = 5z$ **4.** Let x and y represent the numbers; $xy = 2(x + y)$

Mid-Chapter Review: Chapter 8, p. 540

1.
$$2x - 3(x - 1) = 5$$
$$2x - 3x + 3 = 5$$
$$-x + 3 = 5$$
$$-x = 2$$
$$x = -2$$

$$y = x - 1$$
$$y = -2 - 1$$
$$y = -3$$

The solution is $(-2, -3)$.

2.
$$2x - 5y = 1$$
$$\underline{x + 5y = 8}$$
$$3x = 9$$
$$x = 3$$

$$x + 5y = 8$$
$$3 + 5y = 8$$
$$5y = 5$$
$$y = 1$$

The solution is $(3, 1)$.

3. $(1, 1)$ **4.** $(9, 1)$ **5.** $(4, 3)$ **6.** $(5, 7)$ **7.** $(5, 10)$
8. $\left(2, \frac{2}{5}\right)$ **9.** No solution   **10.** $\{(x, y) \mid x = 2 - y\}$
11. $(1, 1)$ **12.** $\left(\frac{40}{9}, \frac{10}{3}\right)$ **13.** $(2, -10, -3)$
14. $\left(\frac{1}{2}, -4, \frac{1}{3}\right)$ **15.** No solution   **16.** The equations are dependent.   **17.** Microsoft: 4%; Yahoo!: 8.3%
18. 5-cent bottles or cans: 336; 10-cent bottles or cans: 94
19. Pecan Morning: 12 lb; Oat Dream: 8 lb   **20.** 18 mph

Exercise Set 8.5, pp. 544–547

1. (a)   **2.** (c)   **3.** (d)   **4.** (b)   **5.** 8, 15, 62
7. 8, 21, -3 **9.** $32°, 96°, 52°$ **11.** Reading: 497; mathematics: 514; writing: 489   **13.** Bran muffin: 1.5 g; banana: 3 g; 1 cup of Wheaties: 3 g   **15.** Base price: $28,920; tow package: $595; sunroof: $850
17. 12-oz cups: 17; 16-oz cups: 25; 20-oz cups: 13
19. Business-equipment loan: $15,000; small-business loan: $35,000; home-equity loan: $70,000   **21.** Gold: $55.62/g; silver: $1.09/g; copper: $0.01/g   **23.** Roast beef: 2 servings; baked potato: 1 serving; broccoli: 2 servings
25. First mezzanine: 8 tickets; main floor: 12 tickets; second mezzanine: 20 tickets   **27.** Asia: 5.2 billion; Africa: 2.3 billion; rest of the world: 1.9 billion   **29.** 📝

31.

32.

33.

34.

35.

36.

37. 📝   **39.** Applicant: $150; spouse: $154; first child: $116; second child: $117   **41.** 20 years   **43.** 35 tickets

Quick Quiz: Sections 8.1–8.5, p. 547

1. $(4, 3)$ **2.** $(1, 1)$ **3.** $(6, -1)$ **4.** $(0, 0)$
5. $(0, 5, -2)$

Prepare to Move On, p. 547

1. $-4x + 6y$ **2.** $7y$ **3.** $-2a + b + 6c$
4. $-12x + 5y - 8z$ **5.** $23x - 13z$

Exercise Set 8.6, pp. 551–552

1. Matrix   **2.** Rows; vertical   **3.** Entry   **4.** Matrices
5. Rows   **6.** First   **7.** $(3, 4)$ **9.** $(-2, 5)$
11. $\left(\frac{3}{2}, \frac{5}{2}\right)$ **13.** $\left(2, \frac{1}{2}, -2\right)$ **15.** $(2, -2, 1)$
17. $\left(4, \frac{1}{2}, -\frac{1}{2}\right)$ **19.** $(1, -3, -2, -1)$ **21.** Dimes: 18; nickels: 24   **23.** Dried fruit: 9 lb; macadamia nuts: 6 lb
25. $400 at 3%; $500 at 4%; $1600 at 5%   **27.** 📝
29. $x(x + 1)^2$ **30.** $\dfrac{18xy^6}{25z^2}$ **31.** $\dfrac{4}{(3a - 1)(a + 1)^2}$
32. $\dfrac{5t + 10}{3t}$ **33.** 📝   **35.** 1324

Quick Quiz: Sections 8.1–8.6, p. 552

1. $(-1, 5)$ **2.** No solution   **3.** $\left(\frac{1}{2}, \frac{11}{10}, \frac{5}{4}\right)$
4. 4-marker packages: 26; 6-marker packages: 16
5. Drink Fresh: $1\frac{1}{5}$ L; Summer Light: $4\frac{4}{5}$ L

Prepare to Move On, p. 552

1. 17   **2.** -19 **3.** 37   **4.** 422

Exercise Set 8.7, pp. 557–558

1. True   **2.** True   **3.** True   **4.** False   **5.** False
6. False   **7.** 4   **9.** -50 **11.** 27   **13.** -3
15. -5 **17.** $(-3, 2)$ **19.** $\left(\frac{9}{19}, \frac{51}{38}\right)$ **21.** $\left(-1, -\frac{6}{7}, \frac{11}{7}\right)$
23. $(2, -1, 4)$ **25.** $(1, 2, 3)$ **27.** 📝
29. $(6x - 1)(x + 4)$ **30.** $5(a - 1)(a^2 + 3)$
31. $(5y^4 + 7z)(5y^4 - 7z)$ **32.** $8(n + 1)(n^2 - n + 1)$
33. 📝   **35.** 12   **37.** 10

Quick Quiz: Sections 8.1–8.7, p. 558

1. $(3, 5)$ **2.** $(-8, -23)$ **3.** $(-2, 3)$ **4.** $(1, 0)$
5. $\left(\frac{29}{93}, \frac{28}{93}\right)$

Prepare to Move On, p. 558

1. $70x - 2500$ **2.** 4500   **3.** $\frac{250}{7}$ **4.** $\frac{250}{7}$

Exercise Set 8.8, pp. 562–564

1. (b)   **2.** (f)   **3.** (h)   **4.** (a)   **5.** (e)   **6.** (d)
7. (c)   **8.** (g)   **9.** (a) $P(x) = 20x - 200,000$;
(b) (10,000 units, $550,000)   **11. (a)** $P(x) = 25x - 3100$;
(b) (124 units, $4960)   **13. (a)** $P(x) = 45x - 22,500$;
(b) (500 units, $42,500)   **15. (a)** $P(x) = 16x - 50,000$;
(b) (3125 units, $125,000)   **17. (a)** $P(x) = 50x - 100,000$;
(b) (2000 units, $250,000)   **19.** ($60, 1100)
21. ($22, 474)   **23.** ($50, 6250)   **25.** ($10, 1070)
27. (a) $C(x) = 45,000 + 40x$; **(b)** $R(x) = 130x$;
(c) $P(x) = 90x - 45,000$; **(d)** $225,000 profit, $9000 loss
(e) (500 phones, $65,000)   **29. (a)** $C(x) = 10,000 + 30x$;
(b) $R(x) = 80x$; **(c)** $P(x) = 50x - 10,000$; **(d)** $90,000
profit, $7500 loss; **(e)** (200 seats, $16,000)   **31.** 📝
33. $-\frac{1}{5}, \frac{1}{5}$ **34.** 1   **35.** $\frac{5}{2}$ **36.** $-3, 6$
37. 📝   **39.** ($5, 300 yo-yo's)
41. (a) $8.74; **(b)** 24,509 units

Quick Quiz: Sections 8.1–8.8, p. 564

1. Length: 40 ft; width: 30 ft   **2.** Low-fat milk: $9\frac{3}{5}$ oz; whole milk: $6\frac{2}{5}$ oz   **3.** $90°, 67.5°, 22.5°$ **4.** 26
5. -25

Prepare to Move On, p. 564

1. 6   **2.** -2 **3.** $\frac{3}{4}$ **4.** -6 **5.** -5

Visualizing for Success, p. 565

1. C   **2.** H   **3.** J   **4.** G   **5.** D   **6.** I   **7.** A
8. F   **9.** E   **10.** B

Decision Making: Connection, p. 566

1. $28\frac{1}{8}$ years   **2.** $18,750   **3.** $26,250; about 16.4 years
4. $5750   **5.** 🖥

Study Summary: Chapter 8, pp. 567–570

1. $(2, -1)$ **2.** $\left(-\frac{1}{2}, \frac{1}{2}\right)$ **3.** $\left(\frac{16}{7}, -\frac{3}{7}\right)$ **4.** Pens:
32 boxes; pencils: 88 boxes   **5.** 40%-acid: 0.8 L;
15%-acid: 1.2 L   **6.** 8 mph   **7.** $\left(2, -\frac{1}{2}, -5\right)$
8. $(2.5, 3.5, 3)$ **9.** $(4, 1)$ **10.** 28   **11.** -25
12. $\left(\frac{11}{4}, -\frac{3}{4}\right)$ **13. (a)** $P(x) = 75x - 9000$;
(b) (120, $10,800)   **14.** ($9, 141)

Review Exercises: Chapter 8, pp. 570–572

1. Substitution   **2.** Elimination   **3.** Graphical
4. Dependent   **5.** Inconsistent   **6.** Contradiction
7. Parallel   **8.** Square   **9.** Determinant   **10.** Zero
11. $(4, 1)$ **12.** $(3, -2)$ **13.** $\left(\frac{8}{3}, \frac{14}{3}\right)$
14. No solution   **15.** $\left(\frac{9}{4}, \frac{7}{10}\right)$ **16.** $(-2, -3)$
17. $\left(-\frac{4}{5}, \frac{2}{5}\right)$ **18.** $\left(\frac{76}{17}, -\frac{2}{119}\right)$ **19.** $\{(x, y) \mid 3x + 4y = 6\}$
20. $(4, 3)$ **21.** Private lessons: 7 students; group lessons:
5 students   **22.** 4 hr   **23.** 8% juice: 10 L; 15% juice: 4 L

24. $(4, -8, 10)$ **25.** The equations are dependent.
26. $(2, 0, 4)$ **27.** $\left(\frac{8}{9}, -\frac{2}{3}, \frac{10}{9}\right)$ **28.** No solution
29. A: 90°; B: 67.5°; C: 22.5°   **30.** Man: 1.4;
woman: 5.3; one-year-old child: 50   **31.** $\left(55, -\frac{89}{2}\right)$
32. $(-1, 1, 3)$ **33.** -5 **34.** 9   **35.** $(6, -2)$
36. $(-3, 0, 4)$ **37.** (a) $P(x) = 20x - 15,800$;
(b) (790 units, $39,500)   **38.** ($3, 81)
39. (a) $C(x) = 4.75x + 54,000$; (b) $R(x) = 9.25x$;
(c) $P(x) = 4.5x - 54,000$; (d) $31,500 loss, $13,500
profit; (e) (12,000 pints of honey, $111,000)   **40.** To
solve a problem involving four variables, go through the
Familiarize and *Translate* steps as usual. The resulting
system of equations can be solved using the elimination
method just as for three variables but likely with more
steps.   **41.** A system of equations can be both
dependent and inconsistent if it is equivalent to a system
with fewer equations that has no solution. An example is a
system of three equations in three unknowns in which two
of the equations represent the same plane, and the third
represents a parallel plane.   **42.** 20,000 pints
43. $(0, 2), (1, 3)$

Test: Chapter 8, pp. 572–573

1. [8.1] $(2, 4)$ **2.** [8.2] $\left(3, -\frac{11}{3}\right)$ **3.** [8.2] $(2, -1)$
4. [8.2] No solution   **5.** [8.2] $\{(x, y) \mid x = 2y - 3\}$
6. [8.2] $\left(-\frac{3}{2}, -\frac{3}{2}\right)$ **7.** [8.3] Length: 94 ft; width: 50 ft
8. [8.3] Pepperidge Farm Goldfish: 120 g; Rold Gold
Pretzels: 500 g   **9.** [8.3] 20 mph   **10.** [8.4] The equations are dependent.   **11.** [8.4] $\left(2, -\frac{1}{2}, -1\right)$
12. [8.4] No solution   **13.** [8.4] $(0, 1, 0)$
14. [8.6] $\left(\frac{22}{5}, -\frac{28}{5}\right)$ **15.** [8.6] $(3, 1, -2)$ **16.** [8.7] -14
17. [8.7] -59 **18.** [8.7] $\left(\frac{7}{13}, -\frac{17}{26}\right)$
19. [8.5] Electrician: 3.5 hr; carpenter: 8 hr; plumber: 10 hr
20. [8.8] ($3, 55)   **21.** [8.8] (a) $C(x) = 25x + 44,000$;
(b) $R(x) = 80x$; (c) $P(x) = 55x - 44,000$; (d) $27,500 loss,
$5500 profit; (e) (800 hammocks, $64,000)
22. [7.3], [8.3] $m = 7, b = 10$ **23.** [8.3] $\frac{120}{7}$ lb

Cumulative Review: Chapters 1–8, p. 574

1. x^{11} **2.** $-\dfrac{2a^{11}}{5b^{33}}$ **3.** $\dfrac{81x^{36}}{256y^8}$ **4.** 4.00×10^6

5. $b = \dfrac{2A}{h} - t$, or $b = \dfrac{2A - ht}{h}$ **6.** $r = \dfrac{s}{B - 1}$

7. -5 **8.** 1   **9.** $-3, -2$ **10.** 2, 3
11. $\left\{y \mid y \geq -\frac{2}{3}\right\}$, or $\left[-\frac{2}{3}, \infty\right)$ **12.** $(1, 1)$
13. $\left(-3, \frac{2}{5}\right)$ **14.** $(-3, 2, -4)$
15.

16.

17.

18.

19. Slope: $\frac{9}{4}$; y-intercept: $(0, -3)$ **20.** $y = -\frac{1}{10}x + \frac{12}{5}$
21. Parallel   **22.** $y = -2x + 5$
23. $\{x \mid x$ is a real number *and* $x \neq -10\}$ **24.** -31
25. $2a^2 + 4a - 4$ **26.** $5(x + 2y)(x - 2y)$
27. $(3x + 2)(2x + 3)$ **28.** $25a^2 + 70a + 49$

29. $2x + 1$ **30.** $\dfrac{2(x + 2)}{x - 2}$ **31.** $\dfrac{x}{2(x + 1)(x + 2)}$

32. Dog sled: 12 mph; snowmobile: 52 mph
33. 68 professionals; 82 students   **34.** Sea Spray: 90 oz;
Ocean Mist: 30 oz   **35.** 86   **36.** $-12x^{2a}y^{b+y+3}$
37. $m = -\frac{5}{9}, b = -\frac{2}{9}$

CHAPTER 9

Exercise Set 9.1, pp. 580–583

1. Inequality   **2.** Solution   **3.** Negative
4. Above   **5.** Equivalent equations   **6.** Equivalent
expressions   **7.** Equivalent inequalities
8. Not equivalent   **9.** Equivalent equations
10. Equivalent inequalities   **11.** $\{x \mid x < 2\}$, or $(-\infty, 2)$
13. $\{x \mid x \leq -9\}$, or $(-\infty, -9]$ **15.** $\{x \mid x < -26\}$, or
$(-\infty, -26)$ **17.** $\left\{t \mid t \geq -\frac{13}{3}\right\}$, or $\left[-\frac{13}{3}, \infty\right)$
19. $\left\{y \mid y \leq -\frac{3}{2}\right\}$, or $\left(-\infty, -\frac{3}{2}\right]$ **21.** $\left\{t \mid t < \frac{29}{5}\right\}$, or
$\left(-\infty, \frac{29}{5}\right)$ **23.** $\left\{m \mid m > \frac{7}{3}\right\}$, or $\left(\frac{7}{3}, \infty\right)$
25. $\{x \mid x \geq 2\}$, or $[2, \infty)$ **27.** $\{x \mid x > 0\}$, or $(0, \infty)$
29. $\{x \mid x < 7\}$, or $(-\infty, 7)$ **31.** $\{x \mid x \geq 2\}$, or $[2, \infty)$
33. $\{x \mid x < 8\}$, or $(-\infty, 8)$ **35.** $\{x \mid x \leq 2\}$, or $(-\infty, 2]$
37. $\{x \mid x \geq 2\}$, or $[2, \infty)$
39. Lengths of time less than $7\frac{1}{2}$ hr   **41.** At least 56 questions correct   **43.** Gross sales greater than $7000
45. For more than 17 transactions   **47.** Years after 2015
49. (a) Body densities less than $\frac{99}{95}$ kg/L, or about 1.04 kg/L;
(b) body densities less than $\frac{495}{482}$ kg/L, or about 1.03 kg/L
51. Years after 2032   **53.** (a) $\left\{x \mid x < 3913\frac{1}{23}\right\}$, or
$\{x \mid x \leq 3913\}$; (b) $\left\{x \mid x > 3913\frac{1}{23}\right\}$, or $\{x \mid x \geq 3914\}$
55.   **57.** $-\frac{6}{5}$ **58.** $-5, 3$ **59.** $\left(\frac{4}{3}, -\frac{7}{9}\right)$
60. $\left(\frac{8}{5}, \frac{27}{5}\right)$ **61.** $r = \dfrac{b}{a + c}$ **62.** $n = \dfrac{a}{y - b}$

63.   **65.** $\left\{x \mid x \leq \dfrac{2}{a - 1}\right\}$ **67.** $\left\{y \mid y \geq \dfrac{2a + 5b}{b(a - 2)}\right\}$

69. False; $2 < 3$ and $4 < 5$, but $2 - 4 = 3 - 5$.
71. About 7.8 gal or less   **73.** (a) More than $40;
(b) costs greater than $30   **75.**

Prepare to Move On, p. 583

1. $\{x \mid x \text{ is a real number } and \, x \neq 0\}$
2. $\{x \mid x \text{ is a real number } and \, x \neq \frac{7}{5}\}$ **3.** $\mathbb{R}$
4. $\{x \mid x \text{ is a real number } and \, x \neq 0\}$

Exercise Set 9.2, pp. 589–593

1. Intersection   2. Union   3. Intersection
4. Intersection   5. Union   6. Union   7. (h)
8. (j)   9. (f)   10. (a)   11. (e)   12. (d)   13. (b)
14. (g)   15. (c)   16. (i)   17. $\{4, 16\}$
19. $\{0, 5, 10, 15, 20\}$ 21. $\{b, d, f\}$ 23. $\{u, v, x, y, z\}$
25. $\varnothing$ 27. $\{1, 3, 5\}$
29. $(1, 3)$
31. $[-6, 0]$
33. $(-\infty, -1) \cup (4, \infty)$
35. $(-\infty, -2] \cup (1, \infty)$
37. $(-2, 4]$
39. $(-2, 4)$
41. $(-\infty, 5) \cup (7, \infty)$
43. $(-\infty, -4] \cup [5, \infty)$
45. $[-3, 7)$
47. $(-7, 0]$
49. $(-\infty, 5)$
51. $\{x \mid -5 \le x < 7\}$, or $[-5, 7)$
53. $\{t \mid 4 < t \le 8\}$, or $(4, 8]$
55. $\{a \mid -2 \le a < 2\}$, or $[-2, 2)$
57. $\mathbb{R}$, or $(-\infty, \infty)$
59. $\{x \mid -3 \le x \le 2\}$, or $[-3, 2]$
61. $\{x \mid 7 < x < 23\}$, or $(7, 23)$
63. $\{x \mid -32 \le x \le 8\}$, or $[-32, 8]$
65. $\{x \mid 1 \le x \le 3\}$, or $[1, 3]$
67. $\{x \mid -\frac{7}{2} < x \le 7\}$, or $(-\frac{7}{2}, 7]$
69. $\{t \mid t < 0 \text{ or } t > 1\}$, or $(-\infty, 0) \cup (1, \infty)$
71. $\{a \mid a < \frac{7}{2}\}$, or $(-\infty, \frac{7}{2})$
73. $\{a \mid a < -5\}$, or $(-\infty, -5)$
75. $\varnothing$
77. $\{t \mid t \le 6\}$, or $(-\infty, 6]$
79. $(-\infty, -6) \cup (-6, \infty)$ 81. $(-\infty, 0) \cup (0, \infty)$
83. $(-\infty, 4) \cup (4, \infty)$ 85. $\{x \mid x \ge 10\}$, or $[10, \infty)$
87. $\{x \mid x \le 3\}$, or $(-\infty, 3]$ 89. $\{x \mid x \ge -\frac{7}{2}\}$, or
$[-\frac{7}{2}, \infty)$ 91. $\{x \mid x \le 4\}$, or $(-\infty, 4]$ 93. 🖻
95. $(x - 2)(x - 10)$ 96. $2(5c^3 + 3d)(5c^3 - 3d)$
97. $10(c + 1)(c^2 - c + 1)(c - 1)(c^2 + c + 1)$
98. $16x^2z^5(3xz^3 - 5x^2 + 1)$ 99. 🖻

101. $(-1, 6)$ 103. $0 \text{ ft} \le d \le 198 \text{ ft}$ 105. Densities
between 1.03 kg/L and 1.04 kg/L   107. More than
12 trips and fewer than 125 trips
109. $\{m \mid m < \frac{6}{5}\}$, or $(-\infty, \frac{6}{5})$
111. $\{x \mid -\frac{1}{8} < x < \frac{1}{2}\}$, or $(-\frac{1}{8}, \frac{1}{2})$
113. False   115. True   117. $(-\infty, -7) \cup (-7, \frac{3}{4}]$
119. 🖾   121. Between 5.24 words and 15.09 words per
sentence   123. Let w represent the number of ounces in
a bottle; $15.9 \le w \le 16.1$; $[15.9, 16.1]$ 125. 🖾
127. 🖾   129. 🖳

Quick Quiz: Sections 9.1–9.2, p. 593

1. $\{x \mid x > \frac{2}{7}\}$, or $(\frac{2}{7}, \infty)$ 2. $\{x \mid x \ge 6\}$, or $[6, \infty)$
3. $\{m \mid m < -18\}$, or $(-\infty, -18)$
4. $\{y \mid y < 0 \text{ or } y > 2\}$, or $(-\infty, 0) \cup (2, \infty)$
5. $\{x \mid 3 < x < 8\}$, or $(3, 8)$

Prepare to Move On, p. 593

1. $\frac{2}{3}$ 2. 16   3. 0   4. 7   5. 6

Technology Connection, p. 598

1. The x-values on the graph of $y_1 = |4x + 2|$ that are
below the line $y = 6$ solve the inequality $|4x + 2| < 6$.
2. The x-values on the graph of $y_1 = |3x - 2|$ that are
below the line $y = 4$ are in the interval $(-\frac{2}{3}, 2)$.
3. The graphs of $y_1 = |4x + 2|$ and $y_2 = -6$ do not
intersect.

Exercise Set 9.3, pp. 599–601

1. True   2. False   3. True   4. True   5. True
6. True   7. False   8. False   9. (g)   10. (h)
11. (d)   12. (a)   13. (a)   14. (b)   15. $\{-10, 10\}$
17. $\varnothing$ 19. $\{0\}$ 21. $\{-\frac{1}{2}, \frac{7}{2}\}$ 23. $\varnothing$ 25. $\{-4, 8\}$
27. $\{6, 8\}$ 29. $\{-5.5, 5.5\}$ 31. $\{-8, 8\}$ 33. $\{-1, 1\}$
35. $\{-\frac{11}{2}, \frac{13}{2}\}$ 37. $\{-2, 12\}$ 39. $\{-\frac{1}{3}, 3\}$ 41. $\{-7, 1\}$
43. $\{-8.7, 8.7\}$ 45. $\{-\frac{9}{2}, \frac{11}{2}\}$ 47. $\{-8, 2\}$ 49. $\{-\frac{1}{2}\}$
51. $\{-\frac{3}{5}, 5\}$ 53. $\mathbb{R}$ 55. $\{\frac{1}{4}\}$
57. $\{a \mid -3 \le a \le 3\}$, or $[-3, 3]$
59. $\{t \mid t < 0 \text{ or } t > 0\}$, or $(-\infty, 0) \cup (0, \infty)$
61. $\{x \mid -3 < x < 5\}$, or $(-3, 5)$
63. $\{n \mid -8 \le n \le 4\}$, or $[-8, 4]$
65. $\{x \mid x < -2 \text{ or } x > 8\}$, or $(-\infty, -2) \cup (8, \infty)$
67. $\mathbb{R}$, or $(-\infty, \infty)$
69. $\{a \mid a \le -\frac{10}{3} \text{ or } a \ge \frac{2}{3}\}$, or $(-\infty, -\frac{10}{3}] \cup [\frac{2}{3}, \infty)$
71. $\{y \mid -9 < y < 15\}$, or $(-9, 15)$

73. $\{x \mid x \le -8 \ or \ x \ge 0\}$, or $(-\infty, -8] \cup [0, \infty)$

75. $\{x \mid x < -\frac{1}{2} \ or \ x > \frac{7}{2}\}$, or $(-\infty, -\frac{1}{2}) \cup (\frac{7}{2}, \infty)$

77. $\varnothing$

79. $\{x \mid x < -\frac{43}{24} \ or \ x > \frac{9}{8}\}$, or $(-\infty, -\frac{43}{24}) \cup (\frac{9}{8}, \infty)$

81. $\{m \mid -9 \le m \le 3\}$, or $[-9, 3]$

83. $\{a \mid -6 < a < 0\}$, or $(-6, 0)$

85. $\{x \mid -\frac{1}{2} \le x \le \frac{7}{2}\}$, or $[-\frac{1}{2}, \frac{7}{2}]$

87. $\{x \mid x \le -\frac{7}{3} \ or \ x \ge 5\}$, or $(-\infty, -\frac{7}{3}] \cup [5, \infty)$

89. $\{x \mid -4 < x < 5\}$, or $(-4, 5)$

91.   **93.** $y = \frac{1}{3}x - 2$ **94.** $y - 7 = -8(x - 3)$
95. $y = 2x + 5$ **96.** $y = -x - 1$ **97.**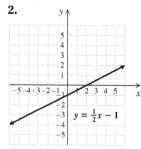
99. $\{\frac{5}{4}, \frac{5}{2}\}$ **101.** $\{x \mid -4 \le x \le -1 \ or \ 3 \le x \le 6\}$,
or $[-4, -1] \cup [3, 6]$ **103.** $\{t \mid t \le \frac{5}{2}\}$, or $(-\infty, \frac{5}{2}]$
105. $|x| < 3$ **107.** $|x| \ge 6$ **109.** $|x + 3| > 5$
111. $|x - 7| < 2$, or $|7 - x| < 2$ **113.** $|x - 3| \le 4$
115. $|x + 4| < 3$ **117.** Between 80 ft and 100 ft
119.

Quick Quiz: Sections 9.1–9.3, p. 601

1. $\{x \mid x \ge -\frac{13}{2}\}$, or $[-\frac{13}{2}, \infty)$ **2.** $\{2, 3, 5, 7\}$
3. $\{1, 2, 3, 4, 6, 8\}$ **4.** $\{-3, 11\}$ **5.** $\{x \mid -5 < x < 5\}$,
or $(-5, 5)$

Prepare to Move On, p. 601

1.

(graph with $3x - y = 6$)

2.

(graph with $y = \frac{1}{2}x - 1$)

3.

(graph with $x = -2$)

4.

(graph with $y = 4$)

5. $\left(4, -\frac{4}{3}\right)$ **6.** $(5, 1)$

Mid-Chapter Review: Chapter 9, p. 602

1. $2 \le x \le 11$
The solution is $[2, 11]$.
2. $x - 1 < -9$ or $9 < x - 1$
     $x < -8$ or $10 < x$
The solution is $(-\infty, -8) \cup (10, \infty)$.
3. $\{-15, 15\}$ **4.** $\{t \mid -10 < t < 10\}$, or $(-10, 10)$
5. $\{p \mid p < -15 \ or \ p > 15\}$, or $(-\infty, -15) \cup (15, \infty)$
6. $\{-4, 3\}$ **7.** $\{x \mid 2 < x < 11\}$, or $(2, 11)$
8. $\{t \mid -4 < t < 4\}$, or $(-4, 4)$
9. $\{x \mid x < -6 \ or \ x > 13\}$, or $(-\infty, -6) \cup (13, \infty)$
10. $\{x \mid -7 \le x \le 3\}$, or $[-7, 3]$ **11.** $\{-\frac{8}{3}, \frac{8}{3}\}$
12. $\{x \mid x < -\frac{13}{2}\}$, or $(-\infty, -\frac{13}{2})$
13. $\{n \mid -9 < n \le \frac{8}{3}\}$, or $(-9, \frac{8}{3}]$
14. $\{x \mid x \le -\frac{17}{2} \ or \ x \ge \frac{7}{2}\}$, or $(-\infty, -\frac{17}{2}] \cup [\frac{7}{2}, \infty)$
15. $\{x \mid x \ge -2\}$, or $[-2, \infty)$ **16.** $\{-42, 38\}$ **17.** $\varnothing$
18. $\{a \mid -7 < a < -5\}$, or $(-7, -5)$ **19.** $\mathbb{R}$, or $(-\infty, \infty)$
20. $\mathbb{R}$, or $(-\infty, \infty)$

Technology Connection, p. 606

1. $y > x + 3.5$

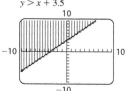

2. $7y \le 2x + 5$

3. $8x - 2y < 11$

4. $11x + 13y + 4 \ge 0$

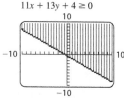

Technology Connection, p. 608

1. $y_1 \le 4 - x, \ y_2 > x - 4$

Connecting the Concepts, pp. 609–610

1.

2.

3.

4.

$x + y = 2$

5.

$x + y < 2$

19.

$2x + 3y < 6$

21.
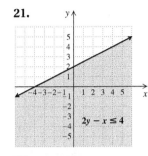
$2y - x \leq 4$

6.
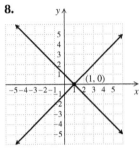
$x + y \geq 2$

7.
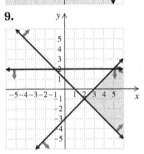
$x + 2 \leq 7$

23.

$2x - 2y \geq 8 + 2y$

25.

$x > -2$

8.

$(1, 0)$

9.

27.

$y \leq 6$

29.

$-2 < y < 7$

31.

$-5 \leq x < 4$

33.

$0 \leq y \leq 3$

Exercise Set 9.4, pp. 610–612

1. (e)   **2.** (c)   **3.** (d)   **4.** (a)   **5.** (b)   **6.** (f)
7. No   **9.** Yes

11.

$y \geq \frac{1}{2}x$

13.

$y > x - 3$

35.

37.

15.

$y \leq x + 2$

17.

$x - y \leq 4$

39.

41.

43.

45.

47.

49.

51.

53.

55.

57.

59. $4p^6 - 12p^3w^4 + 9w^8$

60. $25x^4 - 49$

61. $-3t^4 + 3t^2 - 1$

62. $x - 2 + \dfrac{-8}{x + 1}$

63. $\dfrac{(3x + 2)(x + 1)}{2(2x - 3)(x + 5)}$

64. $\dfrac{x^2 - 13x + 6}{(x - 4)(x + 3)^2}$

65.

67.

69.

71.
$$w > 0,$$
$$h > 0,$$
$$w + h + 30 \le 62, \text{ or}$$
$$w + h \le 32,$$
$$2w + 2h + 30 \le 130, \text{ or}$$
$$w + h \le 50$$

73. $q + v \ge 287,$
$$v \ge 145,$$
$$q \le 170,$$
$$v \le 170$$

75. $35c + 75a > 1000,$
$$c \ge 0,$$
$$a \ge 0$$

77. $h < 2w,$
$$w \le 1.5h,$$
$$h \le 3200,$$
$$h \ge 0,$$
$$w \ge 0$$

79. (a) $3x + 6y > 2$

(b) $x - 5y \le 10$

(c) $13x - 25y + 10 \le 0$

(d) $2x + 5y > 0$

Quick Quiz: Sections 9.1–9.4, p. 612

1. $\{a \,|\, a \ge -3.6\}$, or $[-3.6, \infty)$

2. $\mathbb{R}$, or $(-\infty, \infty)$

3. $\left\{x \mid x < -\frac{11}{2} \, or \, x > 3\right\}$, or $\left(-\infty, -\frac{11}{2}\right) \cup (3, \infty)$

4. $\varnothing$ **5.**

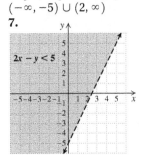

Prepare to Move On, p. 612

1. 3%: $3600; 5%: $6400   **2.** Student tickets: 62; adult tickets: 108   **3.** Corn: 240 acres; soybeans: 160 acres

Exercise Set 9.5, pp. 616–618

1. Objective   **2.** Constraints   **3.** Corner
4. Feasible   **5.** Vertices   **6.** Vertex
7. Maximum 84 when $x = 0$, $y = 6$; minimum 0 when $x = 0$, $y = 0$ **9.** Maximum 76 when $x = 7$, $y = 0$; minimum 16 when $x = 0$, $y = 4$ **11.** Maximum 5 when $x = 3$, $y = 7$; minimum -15 when $x = 3$, $y = -3$
13. Bus: 2 trips; train: 3 trips   **15.** 4-photo pages: 5; 6-photo pages: 15; 110 photos   **17.** Corporate bonds: $22,000; municipal bonds: $18,000; maximum: $1510
19. Short-answer questions: 12; essay questions: 4
21. Merlot: 80 acres; Cabernet: 160 acres   **23.** 2.5 servings of each   **25.** 📋   **27.** $\frac{1}{100}$ **28.** y^{16} **29.** $-2x^{12}$
30. $-\dfrac{8}{a^9 b^{12}}$ **31.** $\dfrac{3d^3}{2c}$ **32.** 1   **33.** 📋
35. T3's: 30; S5's: 10

Quick Quiz: Sections 9.1–9.5, p. 618

1. $\left\{x \mid -\frac{4}{5} < x \leq -\frac{1}{5}\right\}$, or $\left(-\frac{4}{5}, -\frac{1}{5}\right]$ **2.** $\left\{-\frac{2}{3}, \frac{10}{3}\right\}$
3. $\{x \mid -1 < x < 0\}$, or $(-1, 0)$
4.

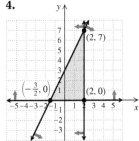

5. Maximum 8 when $x = 2$, $y = 0$; minimum -6 when $x = -\frac{3}{2}$, $y = 0$

Prepare to Move On, p. 618

1. a^{12} **2.** $9t^{10}$ **3.** $x^2 + 4x + 4$ **4.** $9a^2 - 6a + 1$

Visualizing for Success, p. 619

1. B   **2.** F   **3.** J   **4.** A   **5.** E   **6.** G   **7.** C
8. D   **9.** I   **10.** H

Decision Making: Connection, p. 620

1. Bills greater than $9500   **2.** United Health One: $1175.76; SmartSense Plus: $2366.04   **3.** The United Health One plan will save Elisabeth money no matter how great her bills are.

Study Summary: Chapter 9, pp. 621–622

1. $\{x \mid x \geq -4\}$, or $[-4, \infty)$ **2.** $\left\{x \mid -2 < x \leq -\frac{3}{4}\right\}$, or $\left(-2, -\frac{3}{4}\right]$ **3.** $\{x \mid x \leq 13 \, or \, x > 22\}$, or $(-\infty, 13] \cup (22, \infty)$ **4.** $\left\{-1, \frac{9}{2}\right\}$ **5.** $\{x \mid 11 \leq x \leq 13\}$, or $[11, 13]$ **6.** $\{x \mid x < -5 \, or \, x > 2\}$, or $(-\infty, -5) \cup (2, \infty)$
7.

8. Maximum 8 when $x = 4$ and $y = 0$

Review Exercises: Chapter 9, pp. 622–623

1. True   **2.** True   **3.** True   **4.** True   **5.** False
6. False   **7.** $\left\{x \mid x > -\frac{3}{2}\right\}$, or $\left(-\frac{3}{2}, \infty\right)$
8. $\{x \mid x < -3\}$, or $(-\infty, -3)$ **9.** $\left\{x \mid x \leq -\frac{5}{2}\right\}$, or $\left(-\infty, -\frac{5}{2}\right]$ **10.** $\{x \mid x < 5\}$, or $(-\infty, 5)$
11. $\{x \mid x < 1\}$, or $(-\infty, 1)$ **12.** $\{x \mid x \geq -4\}$, or $[-4, \infty)$
13. $\{x \mid x \geq 6\}$, or $[6, \infty)$ **14.** $\{x \mid x \leq 2\}$, or $(-\infty, 2]$
15. More than 125 hr   **16.** $3000   **17.** $\{a, c\}$
18. $\{a, b, c, d, e, f, g\}$
19. ⟵——|———|——|—→ $(-3, 2]$
         -3 0   2
20. ⟵————|————→ $(-\infty, \infty)$
              0
21. $\{x \mid -8 < x \leq 0\}$, or $(-8, 0]$
22. $\left\{x \mid -\frac{5}{4} < x < \frac{5}{2}\right\}$, or $\left(-\frac{5}{4}, \frac{5}{2}\right)$
23. $\{x \mid x < -3 \, or \, x > 1\}$, or $(-\infty, -3) \cup (1, \infty)$
24. $\{x \mid x < -11 \, or \, x \geq -6\}$, or $(-\infty, -11) \cup [-6, \infty)$
25. $\{x \mid x \leq -6 \, or \, x \geq 8\}$, or $(-\infty, -6] \cup [8, \infty)$

26. $\left\{x \mid x < -\frac{2}{5} \text{ or } x > \frac{8}{5}\right\}$, or $\left(-\infty, -\frac{2}{5}\right) \cup \left(\frac{8}{5}, \infty\right)$

27. $(-\infty, -3) \cup (-3, \infty)$ **28.** $[2, \infty)$ **29.** $\left(-\infty, \frac{1}{4}\right]$

30. $\{-11, 11\}$ **31.** $\{t \mid t \leq -21 \text{ or } t \geq 21\}$, or $(-\infty, -21] \cup [21, \infty)$ **32.** $\{5, 11\}$

33. $\left\{a \mid -\frac{7}{2} < a < 2\right\}$, or $\left(-\frac{7}{2}, 2\right)$

34. $\left\{x \mid x \leq -\frac{11}{3} \text{ or } x \geq \frac{19}{3}\right\}$, or $\left(-\infty, -\frac{11}{3}\right] \cup \left[\frac{19}{3}, \infty\right)$

35. $\left\{-14, \frac{4}{3}\right\}$ **36.** $\varnothing$ **37.** $\{x \mid -16 \leq x \leq 8\}$, or $[-16, 8]$ **38.** $\{x \mid x < 0 \text{ or } x > 10\}$, or $(-\infty, 0) \cup (10, \infty)$

39. $\{x \mid -6 \leq x \geq 4\}$, or $[-6, 4]$ **40.** $\varnothing$

41.

$x - 2y \geq 6$

42.

43.

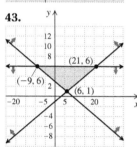

(21, 6)

(-9, 6)

(6, 1)

44. Maximum 40 when $x = 7$, $y = 15$; minimum 10 when $x = 1$, $y = 3$ **45.** East coast: 40 books; West coast: 60 books

46. 📝 The equation $|X| = p$ has two solutions when p is positive because X can be either p or $-p$. The same equation has no solution when p is negative because no number has a negative absolute value.   **47.** 📝 The solution set of a system of inequalities is all ordered pairs that make *all* the individual inequalities true. This consists of ordered pairs that are common to all the individual solution sets, or the intersection of the graphs.   **48.** $\left\{x \mid -\frac{8}{3} \leq x \leq -2\right\}$, or $\left[-\frac{8}{3}, -2\right]$

Test: Chapter 9, p. 624

1. [9.1] $\{y \mid y \leq -2\}$, or $(-\infty, -2]$ **2.** [9.1] $\left\{x \mid x > \frac{16}{5}\right\}$, or $\left(\frac{16}{5}, \infty\right)$ **3.** [9.1] $\left\{x \mid x \leq \frac{9}{16}\right\}$, or $\left(-\infty, \frac{9}{16}\right]$

4. [9.1] $\{x \mid x > 1\}$, or $(1, \infty)$ **5.** [9.1] $\{x \mid x \geq 4\}$, or $[4, \infty)$ **6.** [9.1] $\{x \mid x > 1\}$, or $(1, \infty)$ **7.** [9.1] More than $187\frac{1}{2}$ mi   **8.** [9.1] Less than or equal to 2.5 hr

9. [9.2] $\{a, e\}$ **10.** [9.2] $\{a, b, c, d, e, i, o, u\}$

11. [9.1] $(-\infty, 2]$ **12.** [9.2] $(-\infty, 7) \cup (7, \infty)$

13. [9.2] $\left\{x \mid -\frac{3}{2} < x \leq \frac{1}{2}\right\}$, or $\left(-\frac{3}{2}, \frac{1}{2}\right]$

14. [9.2] $\{x \mid x < 3 \text{ or } x > 6\}$, or $(-\infty, 3) \cup (6, \infty)$

15. [9.2] $\left\{x \mid x < -4 \text{ or } x \geq -\frac{5}{2}\right\}$, or $(-\infty, -4) \cup \left[-\frac{5}{2}, \infty\right)$

16. [9.2] $\{x \mid -3 \leq x \leq 1\}$, or $[-3, 1]$

17. [9.3] $\{-15, 15\}$

18. [9.3] $\{a \mid a < -5 \text{ or } a > 5\}$, or $(-\infty, -5) \cup (5, \infty)$

19. [9.3] $\left\{x \mid -2 < x < \frac{8}{3}\right\}$, or $\left(-2, \frac{8}{3}\right)$

20. [9.3] $\left\{t \mid t \leq -\frac{13}{5} \text{ or } t \geq \frac{7}{5}\right\}$, or $\left(-\infty, -\frac{13}{5}\right] \cup \left[\frac{7}{5}, \infty\right)$

21. [9.3] $\varnothing$ **22.** [9.2] $\left\{x \mid x < \frac{1}{2} \text{ or } x > \frac{7}{2}\right\}$, or $\left(-\infty, \frac{1}{2}\right) \cup \left(\frac{7}{2}, \infty\right)$

23. [9.3] $\left\{-\frac{3}{2}\right\}$

24. [9.4]

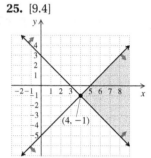

$y \leq 2x + 1$

25. [9.4]

(4, −1)

26. [9.4]

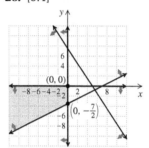

(0, 0)

$\left(0, -\frac{7}{2}\right)$

27. [9.5] Maximum 57 when $x = 6$, $y = 9$; minimum 5 when $x = 1$, $y = 0$

28. [9.5] Manicures: 35; haircuts: 15; maximum: $690

29. [9.3] $[-1, 0] \cup [4, 6]$

30. [9.2] $\left(\frac{1}{5}, \frac{4}{5}\right)$

31. [9.3] $|x + 3| \leq 5$

Cumulative Review: Chapters 1–9, p. 625

1. 22   **2.** $c - 6$ **3.** $-\dfrac{6x^4}{y^3}$ **4.** $\dfrac{9a^6}{4b^4}$

5. $\dfrac{2}{x^2 + 5x + 25}$ **6.** 5   **7.** $\left\{-\frac{7}{2}, \frac{9}{2}\right\}$

8. $\{t \mid t < -3 \text{ or } t > 3\}$, or $(-\infty, -3) \cup (3, \infty)$

9. $\left\{x \mid -2 \leq x \leq \frac{10}{3}\right\}$, or $\left[-2, \frac{10}{3}\right]$ **10.** $\left(\frac{22}{17}, -\frac{2}{17}\right)$

11. No solution   **12.** $\left\{x \mid x < \frac{13}{2}\right\}$, or $\left(-\infty, \frac{13}{2}\right)$

13. $-2, 4$ **14.** $-4, 3$

15.

$y = \frac{2}{3}x - 4$

16.

$x = -3$

17.
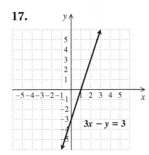
$3x - y = 3$

18.

$x + y \geq -2$

19.

$f(x) = -x + 1$

20.

21. Slope: $\frac{4}{9}$; y-intercept: $(0, -2)$ **22.** $y = \frac{2}{3}x + 4$
23. Domain: $\mathbb{R}$; range: $\{y | y \geq -2\}$, or $[-2, \infty)$
24. 22 **25.** $x^2 + 6x - 9$ **26.** $t = \dfrac{c}{a - d}$
27. Beef: 9300 gal; wheat: 2300 gal
28. (a) $f(t) = 0.7t + 0.56$; (b) \$4.76 billion; (c) approximately 2018 **29.** \$50 billion **30.** 183 cannons
31. $m = \frac{1}{3}, b = \frac{16}{3}$ **32.** $[-4, 0) \cup (0, \infty)$

CHAPTER 10

Technology Connection, p. 630

1. False **2.** True **3.** False

Exercise Set 10.1, pp. 633–636

1. Two **2.** Negative **3.** Positive **4.** Negative
5. Irrational **6.** Real **7.** Nonnegative **8.** Negative
9. $8, -8$ **11.** $10, -10$ **13.** $20, -20$ **15.** $25, -25$
17. 7 **19.** -4 **21.** $\frac{6}{7}$ **23.** $-\frac{4}{9}$ **25.** 0.2
27. 0.09 **29.** $\sqrt{5}$; 0; does not exist; does not exist
31. -7; does not exist; -1; does not exist
33. 1; $\sqrt{2}$; $\sqrt{101}$ **35.** $10|x|$ **37.** $|-4b|$, or $4|b|$
39. $|8 - t|$ **41.** $|y + 8|$ **43.** $|2x + 7|$ **45.** $|a^{11}|$
47. Cannot be simplified **49.** -1 **51.** -4 **53.** $5y$
55. $p^2 + 4$; 2 **57.** $\dfrac{x}{y + 4}$; 5 **59.** -4 **61.** $\frac{2}{3}$
63. $|x|$ **65.** t **67.** $6|a|$ **69.** 6 **71.** $|a + b|$
73. $4x$ **75.** $-3t$ **77.** $5b$ **79.** $a + 1$ **81.** $2x$
83. $x - 1$ **85.** t^9 **87.** $(x - 2)^4$ **89.** 2; 3; -2; -4
91. 2; does not exist; does not exist; 3 **93.** $\{x | x \geq 6\}$, or $[6, \infty)$ **95.** $\{t | t \geq -8\}$, or $[-8, \infty)$ **97.** $\{x | x \leq 5\}$, or $(-\infty, 5]$ **99.** $\mathbb{R}$ **101.** $\{z | z \geq -\frac{2}{5}\}$, or $[-\frac{2}{5}, \infty)$ **103.** $\mathbb{R}$ **105.** 📝 **107.** 0 **108.** $\mathbb{R}$

109. $\{x | x \neq 0\}$, or $(-\infty, 0) \cup (0, \infty)$
110. $(f + g)(x) = 3x - 1 + \dfrac{1}{x}$ **111.** $(fg)(x) = 3 - \dfrac{1}{x}$
112. f **113.** 📝 **115.** About 840 GPM
117. About 1404 species
119. $\{x | x \geq -5\}$, or $[-5, \infty)$ **121.** $\{x | x \geq 0\}$, or $[0, \infty)$

$f(x) = \sqrt{x + 5}$

$g(x) = \sqrt{x} - 2$

123. $\{x | -3 \leq x < 2\}$, or $[-3, 2)$
125. $\{x | x < -1 \text{ or } x > 6\}$, or $(-\infty, -1) \cup (6, \infty)$ **127.** 89%

Prepare to Move On, p. 636

1. $15x^3y^9$ **2.** $\dfrac{a^3}{8b^6c^3}$ **3.** $\dfrac{x^3}{2y^6}$ **4.** $\dfrac{y^4z^8}{16x^4}$

Technology Connection, p. 638

1. Without parentheses, the expression entered would be $\dfrac{7^2}{3}$.

2. For $x = 0$ or $x = 1$, $y_1 = y_2 = y_3$; on $(0, 1)$, $y_1 > y_2 > y_3$; on $(1, \infty)$, $y_1 < y_2 < y_3$.

Technology Connection, p. 640

1. Many graphing calculators do not have keys for radicals of index 3 or higher. On those graphing calculators that offer $\sqrt[x]{\ }$ in a MATH menu, rational exponents still require fewer keystrokes.

Exercise Set 10.2, pp. 640–643

1. Radical **2.** Subtract **3.** Equivalent
4. Rational **5.** (g) **6.** (c) **7.** (e) **8.** (h)
9. (a) **10.** (d) **11.** (b) **12.** (f) **13.** $\sqrt[3]{y}$
15. 6 **17.** 2 **19.** 8 **21.** $\sqrt{xyz}$ **23.** $\sqrt[5]{a^2b^2}$
25. $\sqrt[6]{t^5}$ **27.** 8 **29.** 625 **31.** $27\sqrt[4]{x^3}$
33. $125x^6$ **35.** $18^{1/3}$ **37.** $30^{1/2}$ **39.** $x^{7/2}$
41. $m^{2/5}$ **43.** $(xy)^{1/4}$ **45.** $(xy^2z)^{1/5}$ **47.** $(3mn)^{3/2}$
49. $(8x^2y)^{5/7}$ **51.** $\dfrac{2x}{z^{2/3}}$ **53.** $\frac{1}{2}$ **55.** $\dfrac{1}{(2rs)^{3/4}}$
57. 8 **59.** $8a^{3/5}c$ **61.** $\dfrac{2a^{3/4}c^{2/3}}{b^{1/2}}$ **63.** $\dfrac{a^3}{3^{5/2}b^{7/3}}$
65. $\left(\dfrac{3c}{2ab}\right)^{5/6}$ **67.** $\dfrac{x}{y^{1/4}}$ **69.** $11^{5/6}$ **71.** $3^{3/4}$
73. $4.3^{1/2}$ **75.** $10^{6/25}$ **77.** $a^{23/12}$ **79.** 64 **81.** $\dfrac{m^{1/3}}{n^{1/8}}$
83. $\sqrt[3]{x}$ **85.** y^5 **87.** $\sqrt{a}$ **89.** x^2y^2 **91.** $\sqrt{7a}$

93. $\sqrt[4]{8x^3}$ **95.** $\sqrt[10]{m}$ **97.** x^3y^3 **99.** a^6b^{12}
101. $\sqrt[12]{xy}$ **103.** 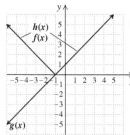   **105.** -6 **106.** $\{y|y < \frac{6}{5}\}$, or $(-\infty, \frac{6}{5})$ **107.** $\{x|-2 \le x \le \frac{3}{5}\}$, or $[-2, \frac{3}{5}]$
108. $-2, 3$ **109.** $-5, 3$ **110.** $(\frac{4}{3}, -\frac{1}{3})$ **111.**
113. $\sqrt[6]{x^5}$ **115.** $\sqrt[7]{c-d}, c \ge d$
117. $2^{7/12} \approx 1.498 \approx 1.5$ **119. (a)** 1.8 m; **(b)** 3.1 m;
(c) 1.5 m; **(d)** 5.3 m   **121.** 338 cubic feet
123. Approximately 0.99 m² **125.**

Quick Quiz: Sections 10.1–10.2, p. 643
1. -9 **2.** $|x|$ **3.** 2   **4.** 4   **5.** 5

Prepare to Move On, p. 643
1. $x^2 - 25$ **2.** $x^3 - 8$ **3.** $(3a - 4)^2$ **4.** $3(n + 2)^2$

Technology Connection, p. 644
1. The graphs differ in appearance because the domain of y_1 is the intersection of $[-3, \infty)$ and $[3, \infty)$, or $[3, \infty)$. The domain of y_2 is $(-\infty, -3] \cup [3, \infty)$.

Exercise Set 10.3, pp. 647–649
1. True   **2.** False   **3.** False   **4.** True   **5.** True
6. True   **7.** $\sqrt{30}$ **9.** $\sqrt[3]{35}$ **11.** $\sqrt[4]{54}$
13. $\sqrt{26xy}$ **15.** $\sqrt[5]{80y^4}$ **17.** $\sqrt{y^2 - b^2}$
19. $\sqrt[3]{0.21y^2}$ **21.** $\sqrt[5]{(x-2)^3}$ **23.** $\sqrt{\dfrac{6s}{11t}}$
25. $\sqrt[7]{\dfrac{5x - 15}{4x + 8}}$ **27.** $2\sqrt{3}$ **29.** $3\sqrt{5}$ **31.** $2x^4\sqrt{2x}$
33. $2\sqrt{30}$ **35.** $6a^2\sqrt{b}$ **37.** $2x\sqrt[3]{y^2}$ **39.** $-2x^2\sqrt[3]{2}$
41. $f(x) = 2x^2\sqrt[3]{5}$ **43.** $f(x) = |7(x - 3)|$, or $7|x - 3|$
45. $f(x) = |x - 1|\sqrt{5}$ **47.** $a^5b^5\sqrt{b}$ **49.** $xy^2z^3\sqrt[3]{x^2z}$
51. $2xy^2\sqrt[4]{xy^3}$ **53.** $x^2yz^3\sqrt[5]{x^3y^3z^2}$ **55.** $-2a^4\sqrt[3]{10a^2}$
57. $5\sqrt{2}$ **59.** $3\sqrt{22}$ **61.** 3   **63.** $24y^5$ **65.** $a\sqrt[3]{10}$
67. $24x^3\sqrt{5x}$ **69.** $s^2t^3\sqrt[3]{t}$ **71.** $(x - y)^4$
73. $2ab^3\sqrt[4]{5a}$ **75.** $x(y + z)^2\sqrt[5]{x}$ **77.**
79. $9abx^2$ **80.** $\dfrac{(x - 1)^2}{(x - 2)^2}$ **81.** $\dfrac{x + 1}{2(x + 5)}$
82. $\dfrac{3(4x^2 + 5y^3)}{50xy^2}$ **83.** $\dfrac{b + a}{a^2b^2}$ **84.** $\dfrac{-x - 2}{4x + 3}$ **85.**
87. 175.6 mi   **89. (a)** $-3.3°$C; **(b)** $-16.6°$C; **(c)** $-25.5°$C;
(d) $-54.0°$C   **91.** $25x^5\sqrt[3]{25x}$ **93.** $a^{10}b^{17}\sqrt{ab}$
95. $f(x) = h(x); f(x) \ne g(x)$

(graph: h(x), f(x), g(x))

97. $\{x|x \le 2 \text{ or } x \ge 4\}$, or $(-\infty, 2] \cup [4, \infty)$ **99.** 6
101.

Quick Quiz: Sections 10.1–10.3, p. 649
1. $(5 - y)^5$ **2.** $2xy^2\sqrt[3]{5x^2}$ **3.** $\sqrt[5]{c}$ **4.** $3^{9/10}$
5. $2xy$

Prepare to Move On, p. 649
1. $41ab$ **2.** $\dfrac{15m^2}{8n^3}$ **3.** $17xy^4$ **4.** $15x^4$

Exercise Set 10.4, pp. 653–655
1. Quotient rule for radicals   **2.** Multiplying by 1
3. Multiplying by 1   **4.** Quotient rule for radicals
5. (f)   **6.** (a)   **7.** (e)   **8.** (b)   **9.** (c)   **10.** (d)
11. $\frac{7}{10}$ **13.** $\frac{5}{2}$ **15.** $\dfrac{11}{t}$ **17.** $\dfrac{6y\sqrt{y}}{x^2}$ **19.** $\dfrac{3a\sqrt[3]{a}}{2b}$
21. $\dfrac{2a}{bc^2}$ **23.** $\dfrac{ab^2}{c^2}\sqrt[4]{\dfrac{a}{c^2}}$ **25.** $\dfrac{2x}{y^2}\sqrt[5]{\dfrac{x}{y}}$ **27.** $\dfrac{xy}{z^2}\sqrt[6]{\dfrac{y^2}{z^3}}$
29. 3   **31.** $\sqrt[3]{2}$ **33.** $y\sqrt{5y}$ **35.** $2\sqrt[3]{a^2b}$
37. $\sqrt{2ab}$ **39.** $2x^2y^3\sqrt[4]{y^3}$ **41.** $\sqrt[3]{x^2 + xy + y^2}$
43. $\dfrac{\sqrt{10}}{5}$ **45.** $\dfrac{2\sqrt{15}}{21}$ **47.** $\dfrac{\sqrt[3]{10}}{2}$ **49.** $\dfrac{\sqrt[3]{75ac^2}}{5c}$
51. $\dfrac{y\sqrt[4]{45y^2x^3}}{3x}$ **53.** $\dfrac{\sqrt[3]{2xy^2}}{xy}$ **55.** $\dfrac{\sqrt{14a}}{6}$
57. $\dfrac{\sqrt[5]{9y^4}}{2xy}$ **59.** $\dfrac{\sqrt{5b}}{6a}$ **61.** $\dfrac{5}{\sqrt{55}}$ **63.** $\dfrac{12}{5\sqrt{42}}$
65. $\dfrac{2}{\sqrt{6x}}$ **67.** $\dfrac{7}{\sqrt[3]{98}}$ **69.** $\dfrac{7x}{\sqrt{21xy}}$ **71.** $\dfrac{2a^2}{\sqrt[3]{20ab}}$
73. $\dfrac{x^2y}{\sqrt{2xy}}$ **75.**   **77.** $-\frac{1}{3}$ **78.** $\frac{4}{27}$ **79.** -65
80. $9x^3 - x^2 + 9x$ **81.** $12x^2 - 12x + 6 + \dfrac{-14}{x + 1}$
82. $49m^2 - 28mn + 4n^2$ **83.**   **85. (a)** 1.62 sec;
(b) 1.99 sec; **(c)** 2.20 sec   **87.** $9\sqrt[3]{9n^2}$
89. $\dfrac{-3\sqrt{a^2 - 3}}{a^2 - 3}$, or $\dfrac{-3}{\sqrt{a^2 - 3}}$ **91.** Step 1: $\sqrt[n]{a} = a^{1/n}$,
by definition; Step 2: $\left(\dfrac{a}{b}\right)^n = \dfrac{a^n}{b^n}$, raising a quotient to a
power; Step 3: $a^{1/n} = \sqrt[n]{a}$, by definition
93. $(f/g)(x) = 3x$, where x is a real number and
$x > 0$ **95.** $(f/g)(x) = \sqrt{x + 3}$, where x is a real
number and $x > 3$

Quick Quiz: Sections 10.1–10.4, p. 655
1. $\frac{3}{10}$ **2.** $x^{1/3}$ **3.** $6mn^2\sqrt{10mp}$ **4.** $4x\sqrt{x}$
5. $\{x|x \ge -8\}$, or $[-8, \infty)$

Prepare to Move On, p. 655
1. $-\frac{1}{4}$ **2.** $\frac{11}{18}$ **3.** $a^2 - b^2$ **4.** $a^4 - 4y^2$
5. $15 + 4x - 4x^2$ **6.** $6x^6 + 6x^5$

Connecting the Concepts, p. 658

1. $\dfrac{6\sqrt{7}}{7}$ **2.** $\dfrac{3+\sqrt{2}}{7}$ **3.** $\dfrac{2\sqrt{xy}}{xy}$ **4.** $\dfrac{5\sqrt{2}}{4}$

5. $\dfrac{\sqrt{10}-\sqrt{6}}{2}$ **6.** $\dfrac{-1-\sqrt{5}}{2}$ **7.** $\dfrac{\sqrt[3]{xy^2}}{xy}$

8. $\dfrac{\sqrt[4]{ab^2}}{b}$

Exercise Set 10.5, pp. 660–662

1. Radicands; indices   **2.** Indices   **3.** Bases
4. Denominators   **5.** Numerator; conjugate
6. Bases   **7.** $11\sqrt{3}$ **9.** $2\sqrt[3]{4}$ **11.** $10\sqrt[3]{y}$
13. $12\sqrt{2}$ **15.** $13\sqrt[3]{7}+\sqrt{3}$ **17.** $9\sqrt{3}$
19. $-7\sqrt{5}$ **21.** $9\sqrt[3]{2}$ **23.** $(1+12a)\sqrt{a}$
25. $(x-2)\sqrt[3]{6x}$ **27.** $3\sqrt{a-1}$ **29.** $(x+3)\sqrt{x-1}$
31. $5\sqrt{2}+2$ **33.** $3\sqrt{30}-3\sqrt{35}$ **35.** $6\sqrt{5}-4$
37. $3-4\sqrt[3]{63}$ **39.** $a+2a\sqrt[3]{3}$ **41.** $4+3\sqrt{6}$
43. $\sqrt{6}-\sqrt{14}+\sqrt{21}-7$ **45.** 1 **47.** -5
49. $2-8\sqrt{35}$ **51.** $23+8\sqrt{7}$ **53.** $5-2\sqrt{6}$
55. $2t+5+2\sqrt{10t}$ **57.** $14+x-6\sqrt{x+5}$
59. $6\sqrt[4]{63}+4\sqrt[4]{35}-3\sqrt[4]{54}-2\sqrt[4]{30}$
61. $\dfrac{18+6\sqrt{2}}{7}$ **63.** $\dfrac{12-2\sqrt{3}+6\sqrt{5}-\sqrt{15}}{33}$
65. $\dfrac{a-\sqrt{ab}}{a-b}$ **67.** -1 **69.** $\dfrac{12-3\sqrt{10}-2\sqrt{14}+\sqrt{35}}{6}$
71. $\dfrac{1}{\sqrt{5}-1}$ **73.** $\dfrac{2}{14+2\sqrt{3}+3\sqrt{2}+7\sqrt{6}}$
75. $\dfrac{x-y}{x+2\sqrt{xy}+y}$ **77.** $\dfrac{1}{\sqrt{a+h}+\sqrt{a}}$ **79.** $\sqrt{a}$
81. $b^2\sqrt[10]{b^3}$ **83.** $xy\sqrt[6]{xy^5}$ **85.** $3a^2b\sqrt[4]{ab}$
87. $a^2b^2c^2\sqrt[6]{a^2bc^2}$ **89.** $\sqrt[12]{a^5}$ **91.** $\sqrt[12]{x^2y^5}$ **93.** $\sqrt[10]{ab^9}$
95. $\sqrt[6]{(7-y)^5}$ **97.** $\sqrt[12]{5+3x}$ **99.** $x\sqrt[6]{xy^5}-\sqrt[15]{x^{13}y^{14}}$
101. $2m^2+m\sqrt[4]{n}+2m\sqrt[3]{n^2}+\sqrt[12]{n^{11}}$
103. $2\sqrt[4]{x^3}-\sqrt[12]{x^{11}}$ **105.** x^2-7 **107.** $11-6\sqrt{2}$
109. $27+6\sqrt{14}$ **111.** 🖊   **113.** IV   **114.** 1
115. x-intercept: $(10,0)$; y-intercept: $(0,-10)$
116. Slope: $-\frac{5}{3}$; y-intercept: $(0,\frac{1}{3})$ **117.** $y=-2x+12$
118. $y=-2x-8$ **119.** 🖊   **121.** $f(x)=2x\sqrt{x-1}$
123. $f(x)=(x+3x^2)\sqrt[4]{x-1}$ **125.** $(7x^2-2y^2)\sqrt{x+y}$
127. $4x(y+z)^3\sqrt[6]{2x(y+z)}$ **129.** $1-\sqrt{w}$
131. $(\sqrt{x}+\sqrt{5})(\sqrt{x}-\sqrt{5})$
133. $(\sqrt{x}+\sqrt{a})(\sqrt{x}-\sqrt{a})$ **135.** $2x-2\sqrt{x^2-4}$
137. (a) $(A+B+\sqrt{2AB})(A+B-\sqrt{2AB})=$
$(A+B)^2-(\sqrt{2AB})^2=A^2+2AB+B^2-2AB=A^2+B^2$;
(b) $2AB$ must be a perfect square.

Quick Quiz: Sections 10.1–10.5, p. 662

1. $|10t+1|$ **2.** $\sqrt[8]{(3xy)^7}$, or $(\sqrt[8]{3xy})^7$ **3.** $(17ab)^{1/2}$

4. $\dfrac{\sqrt[3]{10xy^2}}{2x^2y}$ **5.** $\dfrac{1}{2\sqrt{10}-\sqrt{30}}$

Prepare to Move On, p. 662

1. 42   **2.** $-7,3$ **3.** 11   **4.** 3, 11

Mid-Chapter Review: Chapter 10, p. 663

1. $\sqrt{6x^9}\cdot\sqrt{2xy}=\sqrt{6x^9\cdot 2xy}$
$\quad\quad\quad\quad\quad = \sqrt{12x^{10}y}$
$\quad\quad\quad\quad\quad = \sqrt{4x^{10}\cdot 3y}$
$\quad\quad\quad\quad\quad = \sqrt{4x^{10}}\cdot\sqrt{3y}$
$\quad\quad\quad\quad\quad = 2x^5\sqrt{3y}$
2. $\sqrt{12}-3\sqrt{75}+\sqrt{8}=2\sqrt{3}-3\cdot 5\sqrt{3}+2\sqrt{2}$
$\quad\quad\quad\quad\quad\quad\quad = 2\sqrt{3}-15\sqrt{3}+2\sqrt{2}$
$\quad\quad\quad\quad\quad\quad\quad = -13\sqrt{3}+2\sqrt{2}$
3. 9   **4.** $-\frac{3}{10}$ **5.** $|8t|$, or $8|t|$ **6.** x **7.** -4
8. $\{x\,|\,x\le 10\}$, or $(-\infty,10]$ **9.** 4   **10.** $\sqrt[12]{a}$ **11.** y^8
12. $t+5$ **13.** $-3a^4$ **14.** $3x\sqrt{10}$ **15.** $\frac{2}{3}$
16. $2\sqrt{15}-3\sqrt{22}$ **17.** $\sqrt[8]{t}$ **18.** $\dfrac{a^2}{2}$ **19.** $-8\sqrt{3}$
20. -4 **21.** $25+10\sqrt{6}$ **22.** $2\sqrt{x-1}$
23. $xy\sqrt[10]{x^7y^3}$ **24.** $15\sqrt[3]{5}$ **25.** $6x^3y^2$

Technology Connection, p. 666

1. The x-coordinates of the points of intersection should approximate the solutions of the examples.

Exercise Set 10.6, pp. 668–670

1. Powers   **2.** Radical   **3.** Isolate   **4.** Even
5. True   **6.** True   **7.** False   **8.** True   **9.** 3
11. $\frac{16}{3}$ **13.** 20   **15.** -1 **17.** 5   **19.** 91
21. 0, 36   **23.** 100   **25.** -125 **27.** 16
29. No solution   **31.** $\frac{80}{3}$ **33.** 45   **35.** $-\frac{5}{3}$ **37.** 4
39. 1   **41.** $\frac{106}{27}$ **43.** 3, 7   **45.** $\frac{80}{9}$ **47.** -1
49. No solution   **51.** 2, 6   **53.** 2   **55.** 4
57. 🖊   **59.** At least 84%   **60.** $-191{,}800$ permits per year   **61.** 4 mph   **62.** Swiss chocolate: 45 oz; whipping cream: 20 oz   **63.** 🖊   **65.** About 68 psi   **67.** About 278 Hz   **69.** 524.8°C   **71.** $t=\dfrac{1}{9}\left(\dfrac{S^2\cdot 2457}{1087.7^2}-2617\right)$

73. $r=\dfrac{v^2h}{2gh-v^2}$ **75.** $-\frac{8}{9}$ **77.** $-8,8$ **79.** 1, 8
81. $\left(\frac{1}{36},0\right),(36,0)$ **83.** 📊

Quick Quiz: Sections 10.1–10.6, p. 670

1. $11n$ **2.** $\sqrt[6]{a}$ **3.** $-\sqrt{3}$ **4.** $x\sqrt[10]{x}$ **5.** 1

Prepare to Move On, p. 670

1. Length: 200 ft; width: 15 ft   **2.** Base: 34 in.; height: 15 in.   **3.** Length: 30 yd; width: 16 yd   **4.** 13 cm

Exercise Set 10.7, pp. 676–680

1. (d)   **2.** (c)   **3.** (e)   **4.** (b)   **5.** (f)   **6.** (a)
7. $\sqrt{34}$; 5.831   **9.** $9\sqrt{2}$; 12.728   **11.** 8   **13.** 4 m
15. $\sqrt{19}$ in.; 4.359 in.   **17.** 1 m   **19.** 250 ft
21. $\sqrt{643{,}600}$ ft = $20\sqrt{1609}$ ft; 802.247 ft   **23.** 24 in.
25. $(\sqrt{340} + 8)$ ft = $(2\sqrt{85} + 8)$ ft; 26.439 ft
27. $(110 - \sqrt{6500})$ paces = $(110 - 10\sqrt{65})$ paces;
29.377 paces   **29.** Leg = 5; hypotenuse = $5\sqrt{2} \approx 7.071$
31. Shorter leg = 7; longer leg = $7\sqrt{3} \approx 12.124$
33. Leg = $5\sqrt{3} \approx 8.660$; hypotenuse = $10\sqrt{3} \approx 17.321$
35. Both legs = $\dfrac{13\sqrt{2}}{2} \approx 9.192$ **37.** Leg = $14\sqrt{3} \approx$
24.249; hypotenuse = 28   **39.** $5\sqrt{3} \approx 8.660$
41. $7\sqrt{2} \approx 9.899$ **43.** $\dfrac{15\sqrt{2}}{2} \approx 10.607$
45. $\sqrt{10{,}561}$ ft ≈ 102.767 ft   **47.** $\dfrac{1089}{4}\sqrt{3}$ ft$^2 \approx$
471.551 ft^2 **49.** $(0, -4), (0, 4)$ **51.** 5
53. $\sqrt{10} \approx 3.162$ **55.** $\sqrt{200} = 10\sqrt{2} \approx 14.142$
57. 17.8   **59.** $\dfrac{\sqrt{13}}{6} \approx 0.601$ **61.** $\sqrt{12} \approx 3.464$
63. $\sqrt{101} \approx 10.050$ **65.** $(3, 4)$ **67.** $\left(\frac{7}{2}, \frac{7}{2}\right)$
69. $(-1, -3)$ **71.** $(0.7, 0)$ **73.** $\left(-\frac{1}{12}, \frac{1}{24}\right)$
75. $\left(\dfrac{\sqrt{2} + \sqrt{3}}{2}, \dfrac{3}{2}\right)$ **77.**

79.

80.

81.

82.

83.

84.

85. 🖊   **87.** $36\sqrt{3}$ cm^2; 62.354 cm^2
89. (a) $d = s + s\sqrt{2}$, or $d = s(1 + \sqrt{2})$;
(b) $A = 2s^2 + 2\sqrt{2}s^2$, or $A = 2s^2(1 + \sqrt{2})$
91. 60.28 ft by 60.28 ft   **93.** $\sqrt{75}$ cm

Quick Quiz: Sections 10.1–10.7, p. 680

1. $\dfrac{3x\sqrt[3]{2x}}{5t^2}$ **2.** $x\sqrt[4]{2x}(2 - x^2)$ **3.** $30x^2\sqrt{2}$
4. $\frac{144}{25}$ **5.** $\sqrt{85} \approx 9.220$

Prepare to Move On, p. 680

1. $2 + \sqrt{3}$ **2.** $\sqrt{7} - 6$ **3.** $9x^2 - 4y^2$
4. $25w^2 - 20wx + 4x^2$ **5.** $-8ac + 28c^2$
6. $24a^2 - 14ap - 5p^2$

Exercise Set 10.8, pp. 686–687

1. False   **2.** False   **3.** True   **4.** True   **5.** True
6. True   **7.** False   **8.** True   **9.** $10i$ **11.** $i\sqrt{5}$, or
$\sqrt{5}i$ **13.** $2i\sqrt{2}$, or $2\sqrt{2}i$ **15.** $-i\sqrt{11}$, or $-\sqrt{11}i$
17. $-7i$ **19.** $-10i\sqrt{3}$, or $-10\sqrt{3}i$ **21.** $6 - 2i\sqrt{21}$, or
$6 - 2\sqrt{21}i$ **23.** $(-2\sqrt{19} + 5\sqrt{5})i$ **25.** $(3\sqrt{2} - 8)i$
27. $5 - 3i$ **29.** $7 + 2i$ **31.** $2 - i$ **33.** $-12 - 5i$
35. -40 **37.** -24 **39.** -18 **41.** $-\sqrt{30}$
43. $-3\sqrt{14}$ **45.** $-30 + 10i$ **47.** $28 - 21i$
49. $1 + 5i$ **51.** $38 + 9i$ **53.** $2 - 46i$ **55.** 73
57. 50   **59.** $12 - 16i$ **61.** $-5 + 12i$ **63.** $-5 - 12i$
65. $3 - i$ **67.** $\frac{6}{13} + \frac{4}{13}i$ **69.** $\frac{3}{17} + \frac{5}{17}i$ **71.** $-\frac{5}{6}i$
73. $-\frac{3}{4} - \frac{5}{4}i$ **75.** $1 - 2i$ **77.** $-\frac{23}{58} + \frac{43}{58}i$
79. $\frac{19}{29} - \frac{4}{29}i$ **81.** $\frac{6}{25} - \frac{17}{25}i$ **83.** 1   **85.** $-i$
87. -1 **89.** i **91.** -1 **93.** $-125i$ **95.** 0
97. 🖊   **99.** $(x + 10)(x - 10)$
100. $(t + 10)(t^2 - 10t + 100)$ **101.** $(x + 9)(x - 7)$
102. $a(4a - 3)(3a + 1)$ **103.** $(w + 2)(w - 2)(w + 3)$
104. $12x^2y^2(2x - 5y^2 - 1)$ **105.** 🖊
107.

Imaginary axis / Real axis plot: $-1 + 4i$, $3 + 2i$, $3 - i$, $-5i$

109. 5   **111.** $\sqrt{2}$
113. $-9 - 27i$
115. $50 - 120i$
117. $\frac{250}{41} + \frac{200}{41}i$ **119.** 8
121. $\frac{3}{5} + \frac{9}{5}i$ **123.** 1

Quick Quiz: Sections 10.1–10.8, p. 687

1. 3   **2.** $\left\{x \mid x \geq \frac{1}{2}\right\}$, or $\left[\frac{1}{2}, \infty\right)$ **3.** 25
4. $5 - 15\sqrt{6} - \sqrt{2} + 6\sqrt{3}$ **5.** $17 + i$

Prepare to Move On, p. 687

1. $-2, 3$ **2.** 5   **3.** $-5, 5$ **4.** $-\frac{2}{5}, \frac{4}{3}$

Visualizing for Success, p. 688

1. B   **2.** H   **3.** C   **4.** I   **5.** D   **6.** A
7. F   **8.** J   **9.** G   **10.** E

Decision Making: Connection, p. 689

1. Approximately 47.4 mi   **2.** 600 ft
3. (a) Approximately 12.2 mi;   **(b)** approximately 24.4 mi;
(c) approximately 32.5 mi

Study Summary: Chapter 10, pp. 690–692

1. -9 **2.** -1 **3.** $|6x|$, or $6|x|$ **4.** x **5.** $\frac{1}{10}$
6. $\sqrt{21xy}$ **7.** $10x^2y^9\sqrt{2x}$ **8.** $\frac{2x\sqrt{3x}}{5}$ **9.** $\frac{\sqrt{6xy}}{3y}$
10. $-5\sqrt{2}$ **11.** $31 - 19\sqrt{3}$ **12.** $\frac{3\sqrt{15} - 5\sqrt{3}}{4}$
13. $x^2\sqrt[6]{x}$ **14.** 3 **15.** $\sqrt{51}$ m ≈ 7.141 m
16. $a = 6$ **17.** $b = 5\sqrt{3} \approx 8.660; c = 10$
18. $\sqrt{185} \approx 13.601$ **19.** $\left(2, -\frac{9}{2}\right)$ **20.** $-3 - 12i$
21. $3 - 2i$ **22.** $-32 - 26i$ **23.** i **24.** $-i$

Review Exercises: Chapter 10, pp. 693–694

1. True   **2.** False   **3.** False   **4.** True   **5.** True
6. True   **7.** True   **8.** False   **9.** $\frac{10}{11}$ **10.** -0.6
11. 5 **12.** $\{x | x \geq -10\}$, or $[-10, \infty)$ **13.** $8|t|$
14. $|c + 7|$ **15.** $|2x + 1|$ **16.** -2 **17.** $(5ab)^{4/3}$
18. $\sqrt[5]{3a^4}$ **19.** x^3y^5 **20.** $\sqrt[3]{x^2y}$ **21.** $\frac{1}{x^{2/5}}$
22. $7^{1/6}$ **23.** $f(x) = 5|x - 6|$ **24.** $2x^5y^2$
25. $5xy\sqrt{10x}$ **26.** $\sqrt{35ab}$ **27.** $3xb\sqrt[3]{x^2}$
28. $-6x^5y^4\sqrt[3]{2x^2}$ **29.** $y\sqrt[3]{6}$ **30.** $\frac{5\sqrt{x}}{2}$ **31.** $\frac{2a^2\sqrt[4]{3a^3}}{c^2}$
32. $7\sqrt[3]{4y}$ **33.** $\sqrt{3}$ **34.** $15\sqrt{2}$ **35.** -1
36. $\sqrt{15} + 4\sqrt{6} - 6\sqrt{10} - 48$ **37.** $\sqrt[4]{x^3}$ **38.** $\sqrt[12]{x^5}$
39. $4 - 4\sqrt{a} + a$ **40.** $\frac{\sqrt{2xy}}{4y}$ **41.** $-4\sqrt{10} + 4\sqrt{15}$
42. $\frac{20}{\sqrt{10} + \sqrt{15}}$ **43.** 19 **44.** -126 **45.** 4
46. 2 **47.** $5\sqrt{2}$ cm; 7.071 cm   **48.** $\sqrt{32}$ ft; 5.657 ft
49. Short leg $= 10$; long leg $= 10\sqrt{3} \approx 17.321$
50. $\sqrt{26} \approx 5.099$ **51.** $\left(-2, -\frac{3}{2}\right)$ **52.** $3i\sqrt{5}$, or $3\sqrt{5}i$
53. $-2 - 9i$ **54.** $6 + i$ **55.** 29 **56.** -1
57. $9 - 12i$ **58.** $\frac{13}{25} - \frac{34}{25}i$ **59.** ✒ A complex number
$a + bi$ is real when $b = 0$. It is imaginary when $b \neq 0$.
60. ✒ An absolute-value sign must be used to simplify
$\sqrt[n]{x^n}$ when n is even, since x may be negative. If x is negative while n is even, the radical expression cannot be
simplified to x, since $\sqrt[n]{x^n}$ represents the principal, or nonnegative, root. When n is odd, there is only one root, and
it will be positive or negative depending on the sign of x.
Thus there is no absolute-value sign when n is odd.
61. $\frac{2i}{3i}$; answers may vary   **62.** 3 **63.** $-\frac{2}{5} + \frac{9}{10}i$
64. The isosceles right triangle is larger by about 1.206 ft².

Test: Chapter 10, p. 695

1. [10.3] $5\sqrt{2}$ **2.** [10.4] $-\frac{2}{x^2}$ **3.** [10.1] $9|a|$
4. [10.1] $|x - 4|$ **5.** [10.2] $(7xy)^{1/2}$ **6.** [10.2] $\sqrt[6]{(4a^3b)^5}$
7. [10.1] $\{x | x \geq 5\}$, or $[5, \infty)$ **8.** [10.5] $27 + 10\sqrt{2}$
9. [10.3] $2x^3y^2\sqrt[5]{x}$ **10.** [10.3] $2\sqrt[3]{2wv^2}$ **11.** [10.4] $\frac{10a^2}{3b^3}$
12. [10.4] $\sqrt[5]{3x^4y}$ **13.** [10.5] $x\sqrt[4]{x}$ **14.** [10.5] $\sqrt[5]{y^2}$
15. [10.5] $6\sqrt{2}$ **16.** [10.5] $9\sqrt{2xy}$
17. [10.5] $14 - 19\sqrt{x} - 3x$ **18.** [10.4] $\frac{\sqrt[3]{2xy^2}}{2y}$
19. [10.6] 4 **20.** [10.6] $-1, 2$ **21.** [10.6] 8
22. [10.7] $\sqrt{10{,}600}$ ft ≈ 102.956 ft   **23.** [10.7] 5 cm;
$5\sqrt{3}$ cm ≈ 8.660 cm   **24.** [10.7] $\sqrt{17} \approx 4.123$
25. [10.7] $\left(\frac{3}{2}, -6\right)$ **26.** [10.8] $5i\sqrt{2}$, or $5\sqrt{2}i$
27. [10.8] $12 + 2i$ **28.** [10.8] $15 - 8i$
29. [10.8] $-\frac{11}{34} - \frac{7}{34}i$ **30.** [10.8] i **31.** [10.6] 3
32. [10.8] $-\frac{17}{4}i$ **33.** [10.6] $22{,}500$ ft

Cumulative Review: Chapters 1–10, p. 696

1. $-7, 5$ **2.** $\frac{5}{2}$ **3.** -1 **4.** $\frac{1}{5}$
5. $\{x | -3 \leq x \leq 7\}$, or $[-3, 7]$ **6.** $\mathbb{R}$, or $(-\infty, \infty)$
7. $-3, 2$ **8.** 7 **9.** $(1, -1, -2)$
10.   **11.**

12.   **13.**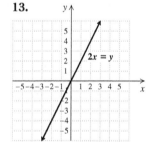

14. $y = 7x - 11$ **15.** 6 **16.** $4a^2 - 20ab + 25b^2$
17. $c^4 - 9d^2$ **18.** $\frac{x + 13}{(x - 2)(x + 1)}$ **19.** $\frac{(a + 2)(2a + 1)}{(a - 3)(a - 1)}$
20. $\frac{2x + 1}{x^2}$ **21.** 0 **22.** $-1 + 3\sqrt{5}$ **23.** $\sqrt[15]{y^8}$
24. $(x - 7)(x + 2)$ **25.** $4y^5(y - 1)(y^2 + y + 1)$
26. $(3t - 8)(t + 1)$ **27.** $(y - x)(t - z^2)$
28. $\{x | x$ is a real number $and \ x \neq 3\}$, or $(-\infty, 3) \cup (3, \infty)$
29. $\{x | x \geq \frac{11}{2}\}$, or $\left[\frac{11}{2}, \infty\right)$ **30.** $6 - 2\sqrt{5}$
31. $(f + g)(x) = x^2 + \sqrt{2x - 3}$
32. $2\sqrt{3}$ ft ≈ 3.464 ft   **33. (a)** $m(t) = 0.08t + 25.02$;
(b) 26.62; **(c)** 2037 **34.** $\$36{,}650$ **35.** 5 ft
36. $5x - 3y = -15$ **37.** -2 **38.** 9

CHAPTER 11

Technology Connection, p. 705

1. x-intercepts should be approximations of $-5/2 + \sqrt{37}/2$ and $-5/2 - \sqrt{37}/2$.
2. The graph of $y = x^2 - 6x + 11$ has no x-intercepts.

Exercise Set 11.1, pp. 706–708

1. Quadratic function   **2.** Parabola   **3.** Standard form
4. Zero products   **5.** Square roots   **6.** Complete the
square   **7.** ± 10 **9.** $\pm 5\sqrt{2}$ **11.** $\pm\sqrt{6}$
13. $\pm\frac{7}{3}$ **15.** $\pm\sqrt{\frac{5}{6}}$, or $\pm\frac{\sqrt{30}}{6}$ **17.** $\pm i$ **19.** $\pm\frac{9}{2}i$
21. $-1, 7$ **23.** $-5 \pm 2\sqrt{3}$ **25.** $-1 \pm 3i$
27. $-\frac{3}{4} \pm \frac{\sqrt{17}}{4}$, or $\frac{-3 \pm \sqrt{17}}{4}$ **29.** $-3, 13$ **31.** $\pm\sqrt{19}$
33. $1, 9$ **35.** $-4 \pm \sqrt{13}$ **37.** $-14, 0$
39. $x^2 + 16x + 64 = (x + 8)^2$
41. $t^2 - 10t + 25 = (t - 5)^2$
43. $t^2 - 2t + 1 = (t - 1)^2$ **45.** $x^2 + 3x + \frac{9}{4} = (x + \frac{3}{2})^2$
47. $x^2 + \frac{2}{5}x + \frac{1}{25} = (x + \frac{1}{5})^2$
49. $t^2 - \frac{5}{6}t + \frac{25}{144} = (t - \frac{5}{12})^2$ **51.** $-7, 1$ **53.** $5 \pm \sqrt{2}$
55. $-8, -4$ **57.** $-4 \pm \sqrt{19}$
59. $(-3 - \sqrt{2}, 0), (-3 + \sqrt{2}, 0)$
61. $\left(-\frac{9}{2} - \frac{\sqrt{181}}{2}, 0\right), \left(-\frac{9}{2} + \frac{\sqrt{181}}{2}, 0\right)$, or
$\left(\frac{-9 - \sqrt{181}}{2}, 0\right), \left(\frac{-9 + \sqrt{181}}{2}, 0\right)$
63. $(5 - \sqrt{47}, 0), (5 + \sqrt{47}, 0)$ **65.** $-\frac{4}{3}, -\frac{2}{3}$
67. $-\frac{1}{3}, 2$ **69.** $-\frac{2}{5} \pm \frac{\sqrt{19}}{5}$, or $\frac{-2 \pm \sqrt{19}}{5}$
71. $\left(-\frac{1}{4} - \frac{\sqrt{13}}{4}, 0\right), \left(-\frac{1}{4} + \frac{\sqrt{13}}{4}, 0\right)$, or $\left(\frac{-1 - \sqrt{13}}{4}, 0\right)$,
$\left(\frac{-1 + \sqrt{13}}{4}, 0\right)$ **73.** $\left(\frac{3}{4} - \frac{\sqrt{17}}{4}, 0\right), \left(\frac{3}{4} + \frac{\sqrt{17}}{4}, 0\right)$,
or $\left(\frac{3 - \sqrt{17}}{4}, 0\right), \left(\frac{3 + \sqrt{17}}{4}, 0\right)$ **75.** 5%   **77.** 4%
79. About 2.8 sec   **81.** About 15.0 sec   **83.** 🖊
85. $3y(y + 10)(y - 10)$ **86.** $(t + 6)^2$
87. $6(x^2 + x + 1)$ **88.** $10a^3(a + 2)(a - 3)$
89. $(4x + 3)(5x - 2)$
90. $(n + 1)(n^2 - n + 1)(n - 1)(n^2 + n + 1)$
91. 🖊   **93.** ± 18 **95.** $-\frac{7}{2}, -\sqrt{5}, 0, \sqrt{5}, 8$
97. Barge: 8 km/h; fishing boat: 15 km/h   **99.** 📈
101. 🖊, 📈

Prepare to Move On, p. 708

1. 64   **2.** -15 **3.** $10\sqrt{2}$ **4.** $2i$
5. $2i\sqrt{2}$, or $2\sqrt{2}i$

Connecting the Concepts, p. 712

1. $-2, 5$ **2.** ± 11 **3.** $-3 \pm \sqrt{19}$ **4.** $-\frac{1}{2} \pm \frac{\sqrt{13}}{2}$
5. $-1 \pm \sqrt{2}$ **6.** 5   **7.** $1 \pm \sqrt{7}$ **8.** $\pm\frac{\sqrt{11}}{2}$

Exercise Set 11.2, pp. 713–714

1. True   **2.** True   **3.** False   **4.** False   **5.** False
6. True   **7.** $-\frac{5}{2}, 1$ **9.** $-1 \pm \sqrt{5}$ **11.** $3 \pm \sqrt{6}$
13. $\frac{3}{2} \pm \frac{\sqrt{29}}{2}$ **15.** $-1 \pm \frac{2\sqrt{3}}{3}$ **17.** $-\frac{4}{3} \pm \frac{\sqrt{19}}{3}$
19. $3 \pm i$ **21.** $\frac{1}{2} \pm \frac{\sqrt{3}}{2}i$ **23.** $-2 \pm \sqrt{2}i$ **25.** $-\frac{8}{3}, \frac{5}{4}$
27. $\frac{2}{5}$ **29.** $-\frac{11}{8} \pm \frac{\sqrt{41}}{8}$ **31.** $5, 10$ **33.** $\frac{3}{2}, 24$
35. $2 \pm \sqrt{5}i$ **37.** $2, -1 \pm \sqrt{3}i$ **39.** $-\frac{4}{3}, \frac{5}{2}$
41. $5 \pm \sqrt{53}$ **43.** $\frac{3}{2} \pm \frac{\sqrt{5}}{2}$ **45.** $-5.236, -0.764$
47. $0.764, 5.236$ **49.** $-1.266, 2.766$ **51.** 🖊
53. 1   **54.** 1000   **55.** $x^{11/12}$ **56.** $\frac{1}{9}$ **57.** $\frac{3a^{10}c^7}{4}$
58. $\frac{9w^8}{4x^{10}}$ **59.** 🖊   **61.** $(-2, 0), (1, 0)$
63. $4 - 2\sqrt{2}, 4 + 2\sqrt{2}$ **65.** $-1.179, 0.339$
67. $\frac{-5\sqrt{2} \pm \sqrt{34}}{4}$ **69.** $\frac{1}{2}$ **71.** 📈

Quick Quiz: Sections 11.1–11.2, p. 714

1. $-3, \frac{5}{2}$ **2.** $2 \pm \sqrt{3}$ **3.** $3 \pm \sqrt{5}$ **4.** $\frac{3}{2} \pm \frac{\sqrt{13}}{2}$
5. $-\frac{1}{4} \pm \frac{\sqrt{39}}{4}i$

Prepare to Move On, p. 714

1. $x^2 + 4$ **2.** $x^2 - 180$ **3.** $x^2 - 4x - 3$
4. $x^2 + 6x + 34$

Exercise Set 11.3, pp. 718–719

1. (b)   **2.** (a)   **3.** (d)   **4.** (b)   **5.** (c)   **6.** (c)
7. Two irrational   **9.** Two imaginary   **11.** Two irrational
13. Two rational   **15.** Two imaginary   **17.** One rational
19. Two rational   **21.** Two irrational
23. Two imaginary   **25.** Two rational
27. Two irrational   **29.** $x^2 + x - 20 = 0$
31. $x^2 - 6x + 9 = 0$ **33.** $x^2 + 4x + 3 = 0$
35. $4x^2 - 23x + 15 = 0$ **37.** $8x^2 + 6x + 1 = 0$
39. $x^2 - 2x - 0.96 = 0$ **41.** $x^2 - 3 = 0$
43. $x^2 - 20 = 0$ **45.** $x^2 + 16 = 0$
47. $x^2 - 4x + 53 = 0$ **49.** $x^2 - 6x - 5 = 0$
51. $3x^2 - 6x - 4 = 0$ **53.** $x^3 - 4x^2 - 7x + 10 = 0$

55. $x^3 - 2x^2 - 3x = 0$ **57.**   **59.** $3a^3b^6\sqrt{30a}$
60. $2w^2\sqrt[4]{2w^2}$ **61.** $\sqrt[6]{x^5}$ **62.** $-\sqrt{6}$ **63.** $7 - i$
64. -1 **65.**   **67.** $a = 1, b = 2, c = -3$
69. (a) $-\frac{3}{5}$; (b) $-\frac{1}{3}$ **71.** (a) $9 + 9i$; (b) $3 + 3i$
73. The solutions of $ax^2 + bx + c = 0$ are
$x = \dfrac{-b \pm \sqrt{b^2 - 4ac}}{2a}$. When there is just one solution,
$b^2 - 4ac$ must be 0, so $x = \dfrac{-b \pm 0}{2a} = \dfrac{-b}{2a}$.
75. $a = 8, b = 20, c = -12$ **77.** $x^2 - 2 = 0$
79. $x^4 - 8x^3 + 21x^2 - 2x - 52 = 0$ **81.**

Quick Quiz: Sections 11.1–11.3, p. 719

1. $-8 \pm \sqrt{3}$ **2.** $\dfrac{1}{6} \pm \dfrac{\sqrt{13}}{6}$ **3.** $(-2\sqrt{2}, 0), (2\sqrt{2}, 0)$
4. $-2.414, 0.414$ **5.** Two irrational solutions

Prepare to Move On, p. 719

1. $c = \dfrac{d^2}{1 - d}$ **2.** $y = \dfrac{x - 3}{x}$, or $1 - \dfrac{3}{x}$
3. 10 mph   **4.** Homer: 3.5 mph; Gladys: 2 mph

Exercise Set 11.4, pp. 723–726

1. (c)   **2.** (d)   **3.** (a)   **4.** (b)
5. $r = \dfrac{1}{2}\sqrt{\dfrac{A}{\pi}}$ **7.** $r = \dfrac{-\pi h + \sqrt{\pi^2 h^2 + 2\pi A}}{2\pi}$
9. $r = \dfrac{\sqrt{Gm_1 m_2}}{F}$ **11.** $H = \dfrac{c^2}{g}$
13. $b = \sqrt{c^2 - a^2}$ **15.** $t = \dfrac{-v_0 + \sqrt{(v_0)^2 + 2gs}}{g}$
17. $n = \dfrac{1 + \sqrt{1 + 8N}}{2}$ **19.** $d = \dfrac{I^2 s}{T^2}$
21. $t = \dfrac{-b \pm \sqrt{b^2 - 4ac}}{2a}$ **23.** (a) 10.1 sec; (b) 7.49 sec;
(c) 272.5 m   **25.** 2.9 sec   **27.** 0.872 sec   **29.** 2.5 m/sec
31. 4.5%   **33.** First part: 60 mph; second part: 50 mph
35. 40 mph   **37.** Cessna: 150 mph, Beechcraft: 200 mph;
or Cessna: 200 mph, Beechcraft: 250 mph
39. To Hillsboro: 12 mph; return trip: 9 mph
41. About 14 mph   **43.** 12 hr   **45.** About 3.24 mph
47. About 11 days   **49.**   **51.** 45   **52.** $-\frac{1}{8}$
53. $-\frac{4}{3}, 0$ **54.** $\left(\frac{11}{5}, \frac{2}{5}\right)$ **55.** $\frac{233}{2}$ **56.** $\frac{1}{16}$ **57.**
59. $t = \dfrac{-10.2 + 6\sqrt{-A^2 + 13A - 39.36}}{A - 6.5}$ **61.** $\pm\sqrt{2}$
63. $l = \dfrac{w + w\sqrt{5}}{2}$
65. $n = \pm\sqrt{\dfrac{r^2 \pm \sqrt{r^4 + 4m^4 r^2 p - 4mp}}{2m}}$
67. $A(S) = \dfrac{\pi S}{6}$

Quick Quiz: Sections 11.1–11.4, p. 726

1. $10 \pm \sqrt{115}$ **2.** $1 \pm \sqrt{26}$ **3.** 2%
4. $x^2 - 12 = 0$ **5.** $d = -1 \pm \sqrt{1 + n}$

Prepare to Move On, p. 726

1. m^{-2}, or $\dfrac{1}{m^2}$ **2.** $y^{1/3}$ **3.** 2   **4.** 81

Exercise Set 11.5, pp. 731–732

1. True   **2.** True   **3.** True   **4.** True   **5.** $\sqrt{p}$
6. $x^{1/4}$ **7.** $x^2 + 3$ **8.** t^{-3} **9.** $(1 + t)^2$ **10.** $w^{1/6}$
11. $\pm 2, \pm 3$ **13.** $\pm\sqrt{3}, \pm 2$ **15.** $\pm\dfrac{\sqrt{5}}{2}, \pm 1$
17. 4   **19.** $\pm 2\sqrt{2}, \pm 3$ **21.** $\pm 2, \pm 3i$ **23.** $\pm i, \pm 2i$
25. $8 + 2\sqrt{7}$ **27.** No solution   **29.** $-\frac{1}{2}, \frac{1}{3}$
31. $-4, 1$ **33.** $-27, 8$ **35.** 729   **37.** 1
39. No solution   **41.** $\frac{12}{5}$ **43.** $\left(\frac{4}{25}, 0\right)$
45. $\left(\dfrac{3}{2} + \dfrac{\sqrt{33}}{2}, 0\right), \left(\dfrac{3}{2} - \dfrac{\sqrt{33}}{2}, 0\right), (4, 0), (-1, 0)$
47. $(-243, 0), (32, 0)$ **49.** No x-intercepts   **51.**
53.

$2x = -5y$

54.

$y = \frac{1}{3}x - 2$

55.

$2x - 5y = 10$

56.

$3x = -9$

57.

58.

$2(y - 7) = y - 10$

59.   **61.** $\pm\sqrt{\dfrac{-5 \pm \sqrt{37}}{6}}$ **63.** $\frac{100}{99}$
65. 9   **67.** $-2, 1, 1 + \sqrt{3}i, 1 - \sqrt{3}i, -\dfrac{1}{2} + \dfrac{\sqrt{3}}{2}i,$
$-\dfrac{1}{2} - \dfrac{\sqrt{3}}{2}i$ **69.** $-3, -1, 1, 4$

Quick Quiz: Sections 11.1–11.5, p. 732

1. $\frac{1}{2}, 1$ **2.** $-\frac{1}{2} \pm \frac{\sqrt{3}}{2}i$ **3.** $-3, -1, 1, 3$

4. $\frac{7}{4} \pm \frac{\sqrt{33}}{4}$ **5.** $x = \frac{9c^2}{80y}$

Prepare to Move On, p. 732

1.

2.

3.

4.

5.

6.

Mid-Chapter Review: Chapter 11, p. 733

1. $x - 7 = \pm\sqrt{5}$
$\quad x = 7 \pm \sqrt{5}$
The solutions are $7 + \sqrt{5}$ and $7 - \sqrt{5}$.

2. $a = 1, b = -2, c = -1$
$$x = \frac{-(-2) \pm \sqrt{(-2)^2 - 4 \cdot 1 \cdot (-1)}}{2 \cdot 1}$$
$$x = \frac{2 \pm \sqrt{8}}{2}$$
$$x = \frac{2}{2} \pm \frac{2\sqrt{2}}{2}$$
The solutions are $1 + \sqrt{2}$ and $1 - \sqrt{2}$.

3. $-7, 3$ **4.** ± 14 **5.** $1 \pm \sqrt{6}$ **6.** $1 \pm 2i$
7. $\pm 2, \pm 2i$ **8.** $-3 \pm \sqrt{7}$ **9.** $-5, 0$ **10.** $-\frac{5}{6}, 2$
11. $0, \frac{7}{16}$ **12.** $-\frac{5}{6} \pm \frac{\sqrt{37}}{6}$ **13.** $-6, 5$ **14.** $\pm\sqrt{2}, \pm 2i$
15. Two irrational   **16.** Two rational   **17.** Two imaginary
18. $v = 20\sqrt{\frac{F}{A}}$, or $\frac{20\sqrt{FA}}{A}$ **19.** $D = d + \sqrt{d^2 + 2hd}$
20. South: 75 mph; north: 45 mph

Technology Connection, p. 735

1. The graphs of y_1, y_2, and y_3 open upward. The graphs of y_4, y_5, and y_6 open downward. The graph of y_1 is wider than the graph of y_2. The graph of y_3 is narrower than the graph of y_2. Similarly, the graph of y_4 is wider than the graph of y_5, and the graph of y_6 is narrower than the graph of y_5.
2. If A is positive, the graph opens upward. If A is negative, the graph opens downward. Compared with the graph of $y = x^2$, the graph of $y = Ax^2$ is wider if $|A| < 1$ and narrower if $|A| > 1$.

Technology Connection, p. 737

1. Compared with the graph of $y = ax^2$, the graph of $y = a(x - h)^2$ is shifted left or right. It is shifted left if h is negative and right if h is positive.   **2.** The value of A makes the graph wider or narrower, and makes the graph open downward if A is negative. The value of B shifts the graph left or right.

Technology Connection, p. 738

1. The graph of y_2 looks like the graph of y_1 shifted up 2 units, and the graph of y_3 looks like the graph of y_1 shifted down 4 units.   **2.** Compared with the graph of $y = a(x - h)^2$, the graph of $y = a(x - h)^2 + k$ is shifted up or down $|k|$ units. It is shifted down if k is negative and up if k is positive.   **3.** The value of A makes the graph wider or narrower, and makes the graph open downward if A is negative. The value of B shifts the graph left or right. The value of C shifts the graph up or down.

Exercise Set 11.6, pp. 740–742

1. False   **2.** True   **3.** True   **4.** False

5.

7.

9.

11.

13.

$f(x) = \frac{5}{2}x^2$

15. Vertex: $(-1, 0)$; axis of symmetry: $x = -1$

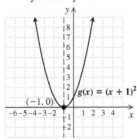

$(-1, 0)$ $g(x) = (x + 1)^2$

17. Vertex $(2, 0)$; axis of symmetry: $x = 2$

$f(x) = (x - 2)^2$

$(2, 0)$

19. Vertex: $(-1, 0)$; axis of symmetry: $x = -1$

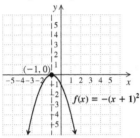

$(-1, 0)$ $f(x) = -(x + 1)^2$

21. Vertex: $(2, 0)$; axis of symmetry: $x = 2$

$(2, 0)$ $g(x) = -(x - 2)^2$

23. Vertex: $(-1, 0)$; axis of symmetry: $x = -1$

$f(x) = 2(x + 1)^2$

25. Vertex: $(4, 0)$; axis of symmetry: $x = 4$

$g(x) = 3(x - 4)^2$

27. Vertex: $(4, 0)$; axis of symmetry: $x = 4$

$(4, 0)$

$h(x) = -\frac{1}{2}(x - 4)^2$

29. Vertex: $(1, 0)$; axis of symmetry: $x = 1$

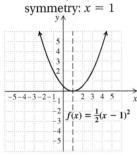

$f(x) = \frac{1}{2}(x - 1)^2$

31. Vertex: $(-5, 0)$; axis of symmetry: $x = -5$

$f(x) = -2(x + 5)^2$

33. Vertex: $\left(\frac{1}{2}, 0\right)$; axis of symmetry: $x = \frac{1}{2}$

$h(x) = -3\left(x - \frac{1}{2}\right)^2$

35. Vertex: $(5, 2)$; axis of symmetry: $x = 5$; minimum: 2

$f(x) = (x - 5)^2 + 2$

37. Vertex: $(-1, -3)$; axis of symmetry: $x = -1$; minimum: -3

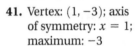

$f(x) = (x + 1)^2 - 3$

39. Vertex: $(-4, 1)$; axis of symmetry: $x = -4$; minimum: 1

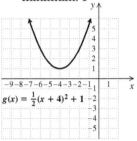

$g(x) = \frac{1}{2}(x + 4)^2 + 1$

41. Vertex: $(1, -3)$; axis of symmetry: $x = 1$; maximum: -3

$h(x) = -2(x - 1)^2 - 3$

43. Vertex: $(-3, 1)$; axis of symmetry: $x = -3$; minimum: 1

$f(x) = 2(x + 3)^2 + 1$

45. Vertex: $(2, 4)$; axis of symmetry: $x = 2$; maximum: 4

$g(x) = -\frac{3}{2}(x - 2)^2 + 4$

47. Vertex: $(3, 9)$; axis of symmetry: $x = 3$; minimum: 9
49. Vertex: $(-8, 2)$; axis of symmetry: $x = -8$; maximum: 2
51. Vertex: $\left(\frac{7}{2}, -\frac{29}{4}\right)$; axis of symmetry: $x = \frac{7}{2}$; minimum: $-\frac{29}{4}$
53. Vertex: $(-2.25, -\pi)$; axis of symmetry: $x = -2.25$;

maximum: $-\pi$ **55.** ☐   **57.** $\dfrac{x^2 + 3x + 6}{x(x + 2)}$

58. $8\sqrt{2x}$ **59.** $-\sqrt[3]{t} + 5\sqrt{t}$ **60.** $-7a^2 + 3a - 8$

61. $\dfrac{-x^2 + 4x + 1}{(x - 1)(x + 3)}$ **62.** $\dfrac{-3}{x + 4}$ **63.** ☐

65. $f(x) = \frac{3}{5}(x-1)^2 + 3$ **67.** $f(x) = \frac{3}{5}(x-4)^2 - 7$
69. $f(x) = \frac{3}{5}(x+2)^2 - 5$ **71.** $f(x) = 2(x-2)^2$
73. $g(x) = -2x^2 - 5$ **75.** The graph will move to the
right. **77.** The graph will be reflected across the x-axis.
79. $F(x) = 3(x-5)^2 + 1$

81.

83.

85.

87.   **89.**

Quick Quiz: Sections 11.1–11.6, p. 742

1. $-7 \pm \sqrt{13}$ **2.** $\frac{3}{2} \pm \frac{\sqrt{3}}{2}i$ **3.** $-\frac{2}{5}, \frac{1}{3}$

4. $z = \pm \sqrt{\frac{xy}{3t}}$, or $z = \pm \frac{\sqrt{3txy}}{3t}$

5. Vertex: $(3, -2)$; axis of symmetry: $x = 3$; minimum: -2

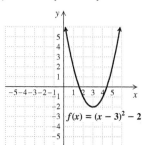

Prepare to Move On, p. 742

1. x-intercept: $(3, 0)$; y-intercept: $(0, -4)$
2. x-intercept: $\left(\frac{8}{3}, 0\right)$; y-intercept: $(0, 2)$
3. $(-5, 0), (-3, 0)$ **4.** $(-1, 0), \left(\frac{3}{2}, 0\right)$
5. $x^2 - 14x + 49 = (x-7)^2$
6. $x^2 + 7x + \frac{49}{4} = \left(x + \frac{7}{2}\right)^2$

Exercise Set 11.7, pp. 747–749

1. True **2.** False **3.** True **4.** True **5.** False
6. True **7.** False **8.** True
9. $f(x) = (x-4)^2 + (-14)$

11. $f(x) = \left(x - \left(-\frac{3}{2}\right)\right)^2 + \left(-\frac{29}{4}\right)$
13. $f(x) = 3(x - (-1))^2 + (-5)$
15. $f(x) = -(x - (-2))^2 + (-3)$
17. $f(x) = 2\left(x - \frac{5}{4}\right)^2 + \frac{55}{8}$

19. (a) Vertex: $(-2, 1)$; axis of symmetry: $x = -2$;
(b)

21. (a) Vertex: $(-4, 4)$; axis of symmetry: $x = -4$;
(b)

$f(x) = x^2 + 8x + 20$

23. (a) Vertex: $(4, -7)$; axis of symmetry: $x = 4$;
(b)

25. (a) Vertex: $(1, 6)$; axis of symmetry: $x = 1$;
(b)

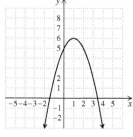

$f(x) = -x^2 + 2x + 5$

27. (a) Vertex: $\left(-\frac{3}{2}, -\frac{49}{4}\right)$; axis of symmetry: $x = -\frac{3}{2}$;
(b)

$g(x) = x^2 + 3x - 10$

29. (a) Vertex: $\left(-\frac{7}{2}, -\frac{49}{4}\right)$; axis of symmetry: $x = -\frac{7}{2}$;
(b)

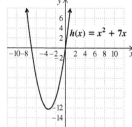

31. (a) Vertex: $(-1, -4)$; axis of symmetry: $x = -1$;
(b)

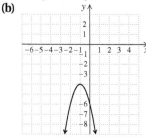

$f(x) = -2x^2 - 4x - 6$

33. (a) Vertex: $(3, 4)$; axis of symmetry: $x = 3$; minimum: 4;
(b)

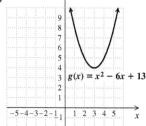

35. (a) Vertex: $(2, -5)$;
axis of symmetry: $x = 2$;
minimum: -5;
(b)

$g(x) = 2x^2 - 8x + 3$

37. (a) Vertex: $(4, 2)$;
axis of symmetry: $x = 4$;
minimum: 2;
(b)

$f(x) = 3x^2 - 24x + 50$

39. (a) Vertex: $\left(\frac{5}{6}, \frac{1}{12}\right)$;
axis of symmetry: $x = \frac{5}{6}$;
maximum: $\frac{1}{12}$;
(b)

$f(x) = -3x^2 + 5x - 2$

41. (a) Vertex: $\left(-4, -\frac{5}{3}\right)$;
axis of symmetry: $x = -4$;
minimum: $-\frac{5}{3}$;
(b)

$h(x) = \frac{1}{2}x^2 + 4x + \frac{19}{3}$

43. $(3 - \sqrt{6}, 0), (3 + \sqrt{6}, 0)$; $(0, 3)$ **45.** $(-1, 0), (3, 0)$;
$(0, 3)$ **47.** $(0, 0); (9, 0); (0, 0)$ **49.** $(2, 0); (0, -4)$

51. $\left(-\frac{1}{2} - \frac{\sqrt{21}}{2}, 0\right), \left(-\frac{1}{2} + \frac{\sqrt{21}}{2}, 0\right)$; $(0, -5)$

53. No x-intercept; $(0, 6)$ **55.** 📝   **57.** $x^4 - 4x^2 - 21$

58. $\dfrac{(x - 2)(x + 4)}{x(x - 3)}$ **59.** $3x^2\sqrt[3]{4y^2}$

60. $2x^2 + 2x + 1 + \dfrac{-2}{x - 1}$ **61.** $\dfrac{3a(2a - b)}{b(a - b)}$ **62.** $\dfrac{1}{\sqrt[12]{x^7}}$

63. 📝   **65. (a)** Minimum: -6.953660714;
(b) $(-1.056433682, 0), (2.413576539, 0); (0, -5.89)$
67. (a) $-2.4, 3.4$; **(b)** $-1.3, 2.3$

69. $f(x) = m\left(x - \dfrac{n}{2m}\right)^2 + \dfrac{4mp - n^2}{4m}$

71. $f(x) = \frac{5}{16}x^2 - \frac{15}{8}x - \frac{35}{16}$, or $f(x) = \frac{5}{16}(x - 3)^2 - 5$

73.

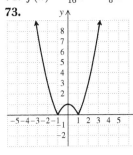

$f(x) = |x^2 - 1|$

75.

$f(x) = |2(x - 3)^2 - 5|$

Quick Quiz: Sections 11.1–11.7, p. 749

1. $\pm\dfrac{\sqrt{15}}{3}$ **2.** $-\dfrac{3}{4} \pm \dfrac{\sqrt{57}}{4}$ **3.** $5x^2 + 3x - 2 = 0$

4.

$f(x) = -3(x + 1)^2$

5.

$f(x) = x^2 - 2x + 3$

Prepare to Move On, p. 749

1. $(-2, 5, 1)$ **2.** $(-3, 6, -5)$ **3.** $\left(\frac{1}{3}, \frac{1}{6}, \frac{1}{2}\right)$

Exercise Set 11.8, pp. 753–758

1. (e)   **2.** (b)   **3.** (c)   **4.** (a)   **5.** (d)   **6.** (f)
7. $3\frac{1}{4}$ weeks; 8.3 lb of milk per day   **9.** \$120/dulcimer;
350 dulcimers   **11.** 180 ft by 180 ft   **13.** 450 ft²; 15 ft
by 30 ft (The house serves as a 30-ft side.)   **15.** 3.5 in.
17. 81; 9 and 9   **19.** -16; 4 and -4 **21.** 25; -5 and -5
23. $f(x) = ax^2 + bx + c, a < 0$ **25.** $f(x) = mx + b$
27. Neither quadratic nor linear
29. $f(x) = ax^2 + bx + c, a > 0$ **31.** $f(x) = mx + b$
33. $f(x) = mx + b$ **35.** $f(x) = 2x^2 + 3x - 1$
37. $f(x) = -\frac{1}{4}x^2 + 3x - 5$
39. (a) $A(s) = \frac{3}{16}s^2 - \frac{135}{4}s + 1750$; **(b)** about 531
accidents for every 200 million km driven
41. $h(d) = -0.0068d^2 + 0.8571d$ **43.** 📝
45. $y = -\frac{1}{3}x + 16$ **46.** $y = 2x + 13$
47. $y = -\frac{4}{3}x + \frac{40}{3}$ **48.** $y = \frac{2}{3}x - \frac{23}{3}$ **49.** $y = \frac{1}{2}x - 6$
50. $y = -4$ **51.** 📝   **53.** 158 ft   **55.** \$15
57. The radius of the circular portion of the window and the
height of the rectangular portion should each be $\dfrac{24}{\pi + 4}$ ft.

59. (a) $a(x) = 18.78035714x^2 + 35.54107143x + 165.1107143$; **(b)** 1,651,382 subscriptions   **61.** 🖥

Quick Quiz: Sections 11.1–11.8, p. 758

1. $-\frac{5}{4}, \frac{2}{3}$ **2.** 2, 7   **3.** $x^2 + 25 = 0$

4. $h = \dfrac{V^2}{12.25}$ **5.**

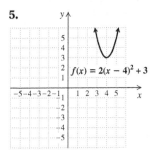

$f(x) = 2(x - 4)^2 + 3$

Prepare to Move On, p. 758

1. $\{x \mid x \geq -3\}$, or $[-3, \infty)$ **2.** $\{x \mid -3 < x < \frac{5}{2}\}$, or
$(-3, \frac{5}{2})$ **3.** $f(x) = \dfrac{-4x - 23}{x + 4}, x \neq -4$

4. $f(x) = \dfrac{1}{x - 1}, x \neq 1$ **5.** No solution   **6.** $-6, 9$

Technology Connection, p. 762

1. $\{x \mid -0.78 \leq x \leq 1.59\}$, or $[-0.78, 1.59]$
2. $\{x \mid x \leq -0.21 \, or \, x \geq 2.47\}$, or $(-\infty, -0.21] \cup [2.47, \infty)$
3. $\{x \mid x > -1.37\}$, or $(-1.37, \infty)$

Exercise Set 11.9, pp. 765–767

1. True   **2.** False   **3.** True   **4.** True   **5.** False
6. True   **7.** $\left[-4, \frac{3}{2}\right]$, or $\{x \mid -4 \leq x \leq \frac{3}{2}\}$
9. $(-\infty, -2) \cup (0, 2) \cup (3, \infty)$, or
$\{x \mid x < -2 \, or \, 0 < x < 2 \, or \, x > 3\}$
11. $\left(-\infty, -\frac{7}{2}\right) \cup (-2, \infty)$, or $\{x \mid x < -\frac{7}{2} \, or \, x > -2\}$
13. $(5, 6)$, or $\{x \mid 5 < x < 6\}$
15. $(-\infty, -7] \cup [2, \infty)$, or $\{x \mid x \leq -7 \, or \, x \geq 2\}$
17. $(-\infty, -1) \cup (2, \infty)$, or $\{x \mid x < -1 \, or \, x > 2\}$
19. $\varnothing$ **21.** $[2 - \sqrt{7}, 2 + \sqrt{7}]$, or
$\{x \mid 2 - \sqrt{7} \leq x \leq 2 + \sqrt{7}\}$ **23.** $(-\infty, -2) \cup (0, 2)$,
or $\{x \mid x < -2 \, or \, 0 < x < 2\}$ **25.** $[-2, 1] \cup [4, \infty)$,
or $\{x \mid -2 \leq x \leq 1 \, or \, x \geq 4\}$ **27.** $[-2, 2]$, or
$\{x \mid -2 \leq x \leq 2\}$ **29.** $(-1, 2) \cup (3, \infty)$, or
$\{x \mid -1 < x < 2 \, or \, x > 3\}$ **31.** $(-\infty, 0] \cup [2, 5]$, or
$\{x \mid x \leq 0 \, or \, 2 \leq x \leq 5\}$ **33.** $(-\infty, 5)$, or $\{x \mid x < 5\}$
35. $(-\infty, -1] \cup (3, \infty)$, or $\{x \mid x \leq -1 \, or \, x > 3\}$
37. $(-\infty, -6)$, or $\{x \mid x < -6\}$ **39.** $(-\infty, -1] \cup [2, 5)$,
or $\{x \mid x \leq -1 \, or \, 2 \leq x < 5\}$ **41.** $(-\infty, -3) \cup [0, \infty)$, or
$\{x \mid x < -3 \, or \, x \geq 0\}$ **43.** $(0, \infty)$, or $\{x \mid x > 0\}$
45. $(-\infty, -4) \cup [1, 3)$, or $\{x \mid x < -4 \, or \, 1 \leq x < 3\}$
47. $\left(-\frac{3}{4}, \frac{5}{2}\right]$, or $\{x \mid -\frac{3}{4} < x \leq \frac{5}{2}\}$ **49.** $(-\infty, 2) \cup [3, \infty)$, or
$\{x \mid x < 2 \, or \, x \geq 3\}$ **51.** 📝   **53.** 3.2 hr   **54.** 9 km/h
55. Mileages no greater than 50 mi   **56.** Deanna: 12 hr;
Donna: 6 hr   **57.** 📝   **59.** $(-1 - \sqrt{6}, -1 + \sqrt{6})$, or
$\{x \mid -1 - \sqrt{6} < x < -1 + \sqrt{6}\}$ **61.** $\{0\}$
63. (a) $(10, 200)$, or $\{x \mid 10 < x < 200\}$;
(b) $[0, 10) \cup (200, \infty)$, or $\{x \mid 0 \leq x < 10 \, or \, x > 200\}$
65. $\{n \mid n \text{ is an integer } and \, 12 \leq n \leq 25\}$
67. $f(x) = 0$ for $x = -2, 1, 3$; $f(x) < 0$ for
$(-\infty, -2) \cup (1, 3)$, or $\{x \mid x < -2 \, or \, 1 < x < 3\}$; $f(x) > 0$
for $(-2, 1) \cup (3, \infty)$, or $\{x \mid -2 < x < 1 \, or \, x > 3\}$
69. $f(x)$ has no zeros; $f(x) < 0$ for $(-\infty, 0)$,
or $\{x \mid x < 0\}$; $f(x) > 0$ for $(0, \infty)$, or $\{x \mid x > 0\}$
71. $f(x) = 0$ for $x = -1, 0$; $f(x) < 0$ for
$(-\infty, -3) \cup (-1, 0)$, or $\{x \mid x < -3 \, or \, -1 < x < 0\}$;
$f(x) > 0$ for $(-3, -1) \cup (0, 2) \cup (2, \infty)$, or
$\{x \mid -3 < x < -1 \, or \, 0 < x < 2 \, or \, x > 2\}$
73. $(-\infty, -5] \cup [9, \infty)$, or $\{x \mid x \leq -5 \, or \, x \geq 9\}$
75. $(-\infty, -8] \cup [0, \infty)$, or $\{x \mid x \leq -8 \, or \, x \geq 0\}$ **77.** 📝

Quick Quiz: Sections 11.1–11.9, p. 767

1. $\pm \dfrac{\sqrt{3}}{3} i$ **2.** 16   **3.** $\dfrac{1}{10} \pm \dfrac{\sqrt{21}}{10}$
4. $(-\infty, -1] \cup [\frac{3}{2}, \infty)$, or $\{x \mid x \leq -1 \, or \, x \geq \frac{3}{2}\}$
5. x-intercepts: $(0, 0)$, $(\frac{3}{4}, 0)$; y-intercept: $(0, 0)$

Prepare to Move On, p. 767

1. [graph of $f(x) = x^3 - 2$]   **2.** [graph of $g(x) = \dfrac{2}{x}$]

3. $a - 8$ **4.** $4a^2 + 20a + 27$

Visualizing for Success, p. 768

1. B   **2.** E   **3.** A   **4.** H   **5.** C   **6.** J
7. F   **8.** G   **9.** I   **10.** D

Decision Making: Connection, p. 769

1. Quadratic   **2. (a)** $p(x) = x - 1$; **(b)** $p(x) = \frac{3}{2}x - 6$;
(c) $p(x) = \frac{1}{8}x^2 - 2x + 16.5$; The quadratic function is
the best fit.   **3.** (b)   **4.** Quadratic   **5.** 🖥

Study Summary: Chapter 11, pp. 770–772

1. 1, 11   **2.** $9 \pm \sqrt{5}$ **3.** $-21, 1$ **4.** $-\frac{3}{2}, 3$ **5.** Two
imaginary-number solutions   **6.** $n = \pm \sqrt{a - 1}$ **7.** 36
8.

9. 30 ft by 30 ft   **10.** $\{x \mid -1 < x < 12\}$, or $(-1, 12)$

Review Exercises: Chapter 11, pp. 772–774

1. False   **2.** True   **3.** True   **4.** True   **5.** False
6. True   **7.** True   **8.** True   **9.** False   **10.** True
11. $\pm \dfrac{\sqrt{2}}{3}$ **12.** $0, -\frac{3}{4}$ **13.** 3, 9   **14.** $2 \pm 2i$

15. 3, 5   **16.** $-\dfrac{9}{2} \pm \dfrac{\sqrt{85}}{2}$ **17.** $-0.372, 5.372$

18. $-\frac{1}{4}, 1$ **19.** $x^2 - 18x + 81 = (x - 9)^2$
20. $x^2 + \frac{3}{5}x + \frac{9}{100} = \left(x + \frac{3}{10}\right)^2$ **21.** $3 \pm 2\sqrt{2}$ **22.** 4%
23. 5.3 sec   **24.** Two irrational real numbers
25. Two imaginary numbers   **26.** $x^2 + 9 = 0$
27. $x^2 + 10x + 25 = 0$ **28.** About 153 mph   **29.** 6 hr
30. $(-3, 0), (-2, 0), (2, 0), (3, 0)$ **31.** $-5, 3$
32. $\pm\sqrt{2}, \pm\sqrt{7}$
33.

$f(x) = -3(x + 2)^2 + 4$
Maximum: 4

34. **(a)** Vertex: $(3, 5)$; axis of symmetry: $x = 3$;
(b)

35. $(2, 0), (7, 0); (0, 14)$ **36.** $p = \dfrac{9\pi^2}{N^2}$

37. $T = \dfrac{1 \pm \sqrt{1 + 24A}}{6}$ **38.** Linear   **39.** Quadratic

40. 225 ft²; 15 ft by 15 ft   **41.** **(a)** $f(x) = \frac{17}{12}x^2 - \frac{1}{12}x + 7$;
(b) approximately \$109,000   **42.** $(-1, 0) \cup (3, \infty)$,
or $\{x | -1 < x < 0\ or\ x > 3\}$ **43.** $(-3, 5]$, or
$\{x | -3 < x \le 5\}$ **44.** ⬜ The x-coordinate of the
maximum or minimum point lies halfway between the
x-coordinates of the x-intercepts.   **45.** ⬜ The first
coordinate of each x-intercept of the graph of f is a solution of $f(x) = 0$. Suppose the first coordinates of the
x-intercepts are a and b. Then $(x - a)$ and $(x - b)$ are
factors of $f(x)$. If the graph of a quadratic function has
one x-intercept $(a, 0)$, then $(x - a)$ is a repeated factor of
$f(x)$.   **46.** ⬜ Completing the square was used to solve
quadratic equations and to graph quadratic functions by
rewriting the function in the form $f(x) = a(x - h)^2 + k$.
47. $f(x) = \frac{7}{15}x^2 - \frac{14}{15}x - 7$ **48.** $h = 60, k = 60$
49. 18, 324

Test: Chapter 11, p. 775

1. [11.1] $\pm\dfrac{\sqrt{7}}{5}$ **2.** [11.1] 2, 9   **3.** [11.2] $-1 \pm \sqrt{2}i$
4. [11.2] $1 \pm \sqrt{6}$ **5.** [11.5] $-2, \frac{2}{3}$
6. [11.2] $-4.193, 1.193$ **7.** [11.2] $-\frac{3}{4}, \frac{7}{3}$
8. [11.1] $x^2 - 20x + 100 = (x - 10)^2$
9. [11.1] $x^2 + \frac{2}{7}x + \frac{1}{49} = \left(x + \frac{1}{7}\right)^2$ **10.** [11.1] $-5 \pm \sqrt{10}$

11. [11.3] Two imaginary numbers   **12.** [113] $x^2 - 11 = 0$
13. [11.4] 16 km/h   **14.** [11.4] 2 hr   **15.** [11.5] $(-4, 0), (4, 0)$
16. [11.6]   **17.** [11.7] **(a)** $(-1, -8), x = -1$;
(b)

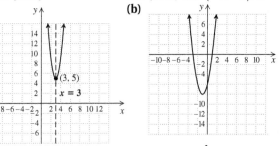

$f(x) = 4(x - 3)^2 + 5$
Minimum: 5

$f(x) = 2x^2 + 4x - 6$

18. [11.7] $(-2, 0), (3, 0); (0, -6)$ **19.** [11.4] $r = \sqrt{\dfrac{3V}{\pi} - R^2}$

20. [11.8] Quadratic   **21.** [11.8] Minimum: \$129/cabinet
when 325 cabinets are built   **22.** [11.8] $f(x) = \frac{1}{5}x^2 - \frac{3}{5}x$
23. [11.9] $(-6, 1)$, or $\{x | -6 < x < 1\}$
24. [11.9] $[-1, 0) \cup [1, \infty)$, or $\{x | -1 \le x < 0\ or\ x \ge 1\}$
25. [11.3] $\frac{1}{2}$ **26.** [11.3] $x^4 + x^2 - 12 = 0$; answers may vary
27. [11.5] $\pm\sqrt{\sqrt{5} + 2}, \pm\sqrt{\sqrt{5} - 2}i$

Cumulative Review: Chapters 1–11, p. 776

1. 24   **2.** $14x^2y - 10xy - 9xy^2$ **3.** $81p^4q^2 - 64t^2$
4. $\dfrac{t(t + 1)(t + 5)}{(3t + 4)^3}$ **5.** $13 - \sqrt{2}i$
6. $3(2x^2 + 5y^2)(2x^2 - 5y^2)$ **7.** $x(x - 20)(x - 4)$
8. $100(m + 1)(m^2 - m + 1)(m - 1)(m^2 + m + 1)$
9. $(2t + 9)(3t + 4)$ **10.** 7   **11.** $\{x | x < 7\}$, or
$(-\infty, 7)$ **12.** $\left(3, \frac{1}{2}\right)$ **13.** $-6, 11$ **14.** $\frac{1}{2}, 2$ **15.** 4
16. $-5 \pm \sqrt{2}$ **17.** $\dfrac{1}{6} \pm \dfrac{\sqrt{11}}{6}i$

18.   **19.**

20.   **21.**

22. $y = -5x + \frac{1}{2}$ **23.** $-\frac{7}{10}$
24. $(-\infty, 10]$, or $\{x | x \le 10\}$
25. $\{x | x$ is a real number $and\ x \ne 4\}$, or $(-\infty, 4) \cup (4, \infty)$

26. $a = \dfrac{c}{2b - 1}$ **27.** $t = \dfrac{4r}{3p^2}$

28. (a) 1.74 oz; **(b)** \$1200 per ounce; **(c)** 75%

29. (a) $f(t) = -t + 52$; **(b)** 18 million Americans; **(c)** 2032

30. Number tiles: 26 sets; alphabet tiles: 10 sets

31. \$125/bunk bed; 400 bunk beds

32. $\dfrac{1}{3} \pm \dfrac{\sqrt{2}}{6}i$ **33.** $\{0\}$

34. $(1 - \sqrt{6}, 16 - 10\sqrt{6}), (1 + \sqrt{6}, 16 + 10\sqrt{6})$

CHAPTER 12

Technology Connection, p. 780

1. To check $(f \circ g)(x)$, we let $y_1 = \sqrt{x}$, $y_2 = x - 1$, $y_3 = \sqrt{x - 1}$, and $y_4 = y_1(y_2)$. A table shows that we have $y_3 = y_4$. The check for $(g \circ f)(x)$ is similar. Graphs can also be used.

Technology Connection, p. 786

1. Graph each pair of functions in a square window along with the line $y = x$ and determine whether the first two functions are reflections of each other across $y = x$. For further verification, examine a table of values for each pair of functions.   **2.** Yes; most graphing calculators do not require that the inverse relation be a function.

Exercise Set 12.1, pp. 787–789

1. True   **2.** True   **3.** False   **4.** False   **5.** False
6. False   **7.** True   **8.** True   **9. (a)** $(f \circ g)(1) = 5$;
(b) $(g \circ f)(1) = -1$; **(c)** $(f \circ g)(x) = x^2 - 6x + 10$;
(d) $(g \circ f)(x) = x^2 - 2$ **11. (a)** $(f \circ g)(1) = -24$;
(b) $(g \circ f)(1) = 65$; **(c)** $(f \circ g)(x) = 10x^2 - 34$;
(d) $(g \circ f)(x) = 50x^2 + 20x - 5$
13. (a) $(f \circ g)(1) = 8$; **(b)** $(g \circ f)(1) = \frac{1}{64}$;
(c) $(f \circ g)(x) = \dfrac{1}{x^2} + 7$; **(d)** $(g \circ f)(x) = \dfrac{1}{(x + 7)^2}$
15. (a) $(f \circ g)(1) = 2$; **(b)** $(g \circ f)(1) = 4$;
(c) $(f \circ g)(x) = \sqrt{x + 3}$; **(d)** $(g \circ f)(x) = \sqrt{x} + 3$
17. (a) $(f \circ g)(1) = 2$; **(b)** $(g \circ f)(1) = \frac{1}{2}$;
(c) $(f \circ g)(x) = \sqrt{\dfrac{4}{x}}$; **(d)** $(g \circ f)(x) = \dfrac{1}{\sqrt{4x}}$
19. (a) $(f \circ g)(1) = 4$; **(b)** $(g \circ f)(1) = 2$;
(c) $(f \circ g)(x) = x + 3$; **(d)** $(g \circ f)(x) = \sqrt{x^2 + 3}$
21. $f(x) = x^4$; $g(x) = 3x - 5$ **23.** $f(x) = \sqrt{x}$;
$g(x) = 9x + 1$ **25.** $f(x) = \dfrac{6}{x}$; $g(x) = 5x - 2$ **27.** Yes
29. No   **31.** Yes   **33.** No   **35. (a)** Yes;
(b) $f^{-1}(x) = x - 3$ **37. (a)** Yes; **(b)** $f^{-1}(x) = \dfrac{x}{2}$
39. (a) Yes; **(b)** $g^{-1}(x) = \dfrac{x + 1}{3}$ **41. (a)** Yes;
(b) $f^{-1}(x) = 2x - 2$ **43. (a)** No   **45. (a)** Yes;

(b) $h^{-1}(x) = -10 - x$ **47. (a)** Yes; **(b)** $f^{-1}(x) = \dfrac{1}{x}$

49. (a) No   **51. (a)** Yes; **(b)** $f^{-1}(x) = \dfrac{3x - 1}{2}$

53. (a) Yes; **(b)** $f^{-1}(x) = \sqrt[3]{x} - 5$ **55. (a)** Yes;
(b) $g^{-1}(x) = \sqrt[3]{x} + 2$ **57. (a)** Yes;
(b) $f^{-1}(x) = x^2, x \geq 0$

59. (a) 40, 44, 52, 60; **(b)** Yes; $f^{-1}(x) = (x - 24)/2$, or $\dfrac{x}{2} - 12$

(c) 8, 10, 14, 18

61.

63.

65.

67.

69.

71. (1) $(f^{-1} \circ f)(x) = f^{-1}(f(x))$
$= f^{-1}(\sqrt[3]{x - 4}) = (\sqrt[3]{x - 4})^3 + 4$
$= x - 4 + 4 = x$;
(2) $(f \circ f^{-1})(x) = f(f^{-1}(x))$
$= f(x^3 + 4) = \sqrt[3]{x^3 + 4 - 4}$
$= \sqrt[3]{x^3} = x$

73. (1) $(f^{-1} \circ f)(x) = f^{-1}(f(x)) = f^{-1}\!\left(\dfrac{1 - x}{x}\right)$

$= \dfrac{1}{\left(\dfrac{1 - x}{x}\right) + 1}$

$= \dfrac{1}{\dfrac{1 - x + x}{x}}$

$= x$;

(2) $(f \circ f^{-1})(x) = f(f^{-1}(x)) = f\left(\dfrac{1}{x+1}\right)$

$= \dfrac{1 - \left(\dfrac{1}{x+1}\right)}{\left(\dfrac{1}{x+1}\right)}$

$= \dfrac{\dfrac{x+1-1}{x+1}}{\dfrac{1}{x+1}} = x$

75.   **77.** $t^{13/15}$ **78.** $2ab^4 \sqrt[3]{5a^2}$ **79.** $\dfrac{x^{12}}{9y^8}$

80. $-i$ **81.** 25 **82.** 6.3×10^{-15} **83.**

85.

87. $g(x) = \dfrac{x}{2} + 20$ **89.**

91. Suppose that $h(x) = (f \circ g)(x)$. First, note that for $I(x) = x$, $(f \circ I)(x) = f(I(x)) = f(x)$ for any function f.
(i) $((g^{-1} \circ f^{-1}) \circ h)(x) = ((g^{-1} \circ f^{-1}) \circ (f \circ g))(x)$
$= ((g^{-1} \circ (f^{-1} \circ f)) \circ g)(x)$
$= ((g^{-1} \circ I) \circ g)(x)$
$= (g^{-1} \circ g)(x) = x$
(ii) $(h \circ (g^{-1} \circ f^{-1}))(x) = ((f \circ g) \circ (g^{-1} \circ f^{-1}))(x)$
$= ((f \circ (g \circ g^{-1})) \circ f^{-1})(x)$
$= ((f \circ I) \circ f^{-1})(x)$
$= (f \circ f^{-1})(x) = x.$
Therefore, $(g^{-1} \circ f^{-1})(x) = h^{-1}(x).$
93. Yes **95.** No **97. (1)** C; **(2)** A; **(3)** B; **(4)** D
99.

Prepare to Move On, p. 789

1. $\frac{1}{8}$ **2.** $\frac{1}{25}$ **3.** 32 **4.** Approximately 2.1577
5.

6.

Technology Connection, p. 792

1.

2.

3.

$y_1 = \left(\frac{3}{7}\right)^x;\ y_2 = \left(\frac{7}{3}\right)^x$

4. $y_1 = 5000(1.08)^x;\ y_2 = 5000(1.08)^{x-3}$

Xscl = 5, Yscl = 1000

Exercise Set 12.2, pp. 794–797

1. True **2.** True **3.** True **4.** False **5.** False
6. True

7.

9.

11.

13.

15.

17.

19.

21.

23.

25.

27.

29.

31.

33.

35.

37.

39. (a) $3.2 billion; $4.8 billion; $7.3 billion;
(b)

41. (a) 19.6%; 16.3%; 7.3%;
(b)

43. (a) About 44,079 whales; about 12,953 whales;
(b)
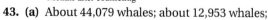

45. (a) About 8706 whales; about 15,107 whales;
(b)

47. (a) About 50 moose; about 1421 moose; about 8470
moose; **(b)**

49. 🖉   **51.** $3(x + 4)(x - 4)$ **52.** $(x - 10)^2$
53. $(2x + 3)(3x - 4)$
54. $8(x^2 - 2y^2)(x^4 + 2x^2y^2 + 4y^4)$
55. $(t - y + 1)(t + y - 1)$ **56.** $x(x - 2)(5x^2 - 3)$
57. 🖉   **59.** $\pi^{2.4}$

61.

63.

65.

67.

69.

71. $N(t) = 136(1.85)^t$;
about 5550 ruffe
73. 🖉   **75.** 〰

Quick Quiz: Sections 12.1–12.2, p. 797

1. $(f \circ g)(x) = -3x^2 + x + 9$

2. $f(x) = x^4;\ g(x) = x - 6$ **3.** $g^{-1}(x) = \dfrac{x - 5}{2}$

4.

5.

Prepare to Move On, p. 797

1.

2.

3.

4.

Exercise Set 12.3, pp. 802–804

1. Logarithmic   **2.** Exponent   **3.** Positive   **4.** 1
5. (g)   **6.** (d)   **7.** (a)   **8.** (h)   **9.** (b)   **10.** (c)
11. (e)   **12.** (f)   **13.** 3   **15.** 2   **17.** −2   **19.** −1
21. 4   **23.** 1   **25.** 0   **27.** 5   **29.** −2   **31.** $\frac{1}{2}$
33. $\frac{3}{2}$ **35.** $\frac{2}{3}$ **37.** 29

39.

41.

43.

45.

47.

49. $10^x = 8$ **51.** $9^1 = 9$
53. $10^{-1} = 0.1$
55. $10^{0.845} = 7$
57. $c^8 = m$ **59.** $r^t = C$
61. $e^{-1.3863} = 0.25$
63. $r^{-x} = T$
65. $2 = \log_{10} 100$
67. $-3 = \log_5 \frac{1}{125}$
69. $\frac{1}{4} = \log_{16} 2$
71. $0.4771 = \log_{10} 3$
73. $m = \log_z 6$

75. $t = \log_p q$ **77.** $3 = \log_e 20.0855$ **79.** 36
81. 5   **83.** 9   **85.** 49   **87.** $\frac{1}{9}$ **89.** 4   **91.** 📝
93. $30a^2b^4$ **94.** $12 - 2\sqrt{30} + 2\sqrt{15} - 5\sqrt{2}$
95. $3\sqrt{3x}$ **96.** $\sqrt[12]{x}$ **97.** $2y^2\sqrt[3]{y}$ **98.** $\sqrt[10]{a^3y^7}$
99. 📝
101.

103.

105. 6   **107.** $-25, 4$ **109.** -2 **111.** 0
113. Let $b = 0$, and suppose that $x_1 = 1$ and $x_2 = 2$. Then
$0^1 = 0^2$, but $1 \neq 2$. Then let $b = 1$, and suppose that
$x_1 = 1$ and $x_2 = 2$. Then $1^1 = 1^2$, but $1 \neq 2$.

Quick Quiz: Sections 12.1–12.3, p. 804

1. No   **2.**

3. 4   **4.** $3^x = t$
5. $\frac{1}{16}$

Prepare to Move On, p. 804

1. c^{16} **2.** x^{30} **3.** a^{12} **4.** $3^{1/2}$ **5.** $t^{2/3}$

Exercise Set 12.4, pp. 809–811

1. (e)   **2.** (f)   **3.** (a)   **4.** (b)   **5.** (c)   **6.** (d)
7. $\log_3 81 + \log_3 27$ **9.** $\log_4 64 + \log_4 16$
11. $\log_c r + \log_c s + \log_c t$ **13.** $\log_a (2 \cdot 10)$, or $\log_a 20$
15. $\log_c (t \cdot y)$ **17.** $8 \log_a r$ **19.** $\frac{1}{3} \log_2 y$
21. $-3 \log_b C$ **23.** $\log_2 5 - \log_2 11$
25. $\log_b m - \log_b n$ **27.** $\log_a \frac{19}{2}$ **29.** $\log_b \frac{36}{4}$, or $\log_b 9$
31. $\log_a \dfrac{x}{y}$ **33.** $\log_a x + \log_a y + \log_a z$
35. $3 \log_a x + 4 \log_a z$ **37.** $2 \log_a w - 2 \log_a x + \log_a y$
39. $5 \log_a x - 3 \log_a y - \log_a z$
41. $\log_b x + 2 \log_b y - \log_b w - 3 \log_b z$
43. $\frac{1}{2}(7 \log_a x - 5 \log_a y - 8 \log_a z)$
45. $\frac{1}{3}(6 \log_a x + 3 \log_a y - 2 - 7 \log_a z)$ **47.** $\log_a 3x$
49. $\log_a (x^8 z^3)$ **51.** $\log_b \dfrac{w^2}{zy^4}$ **53.** $\log_a x$
55. $\log_a \dfrac{y^5}{x^{3/2}}$ **57.** $\log_a (x - 3)$ **59.** 1.953
61. -0.369 **63.** -1.161 **65.** $\frac{3}{2}$ **67.** Cannot be
found   **69.** 10   **71.** m **73.**
75. $\{x \mid -\frac{11}{3} \le x \le -1\}$, or $[-\frac{11}{3}, -1]$ **76.** $-\frac{3}{4}, \frac{5}{6}$
77. $-2 \pm i$ **78.** $\frac{1}{2}$ **79.** 16, 256   **80.** $\frac{1}{4}, 9$
81.   **83.** $\log_a (x^6 - x^4 y^2 + x^2 y^4 - y^6)$
85. $\frac{1}{2} \log_a (1 - s) + \frac{1}{2} \log_a (1 + s)$ **87.** $\frac{10}{3}$
89. -2 **91.** $\frac{2}{5}$ **93.** True

Quick Quiz: Sections 12.1–12.4, p. 811

1. $(g \circ f)(x) = 2x^2 - 20x + 50$ **2.** $\log_m 5 = 10$
3. 5   **4.** $2 \log_a x + 3 \log_a y - \log_a z$
5. $\frac{1}{2} \log_a x + \frac{1}{2} \log_a y + \log_a z$

Prepare to Move On, p. 811

1. $(-\infty, -7) \cup (-7, \infty)$, or
$\{x \mid x \text{ is a real number } and \, x \neq -7\}$
2. $(-\infty, -3) \cup (-3, 2) \cup (2, \infty)$, or
$\{x \mid x \text{ is a real number } and \, x \neq -3 \, and \, x \neq 2\}$
3. $(-\infty, 10]$, or $\{x \mid x \le 10\}$ **4.** $(-\infty, \infty)$, or $\mathbb{R}$

Mid-Chapter Review: Chapter 12, p. 812

1.
$$y = 2x - 5$$
$$x = 2y - 5$$
$$x + 5 = 2y$$
$$\frac{x + 5}{2} = y$$
$$f^{-1}(x) = \frac{x + 5}{2}$$
2. $\log_4 x = 1$
$$4^1 = x$$
$$4 = x$$
3. $x^2 - 10x + 26$ **4.** $f(x) = \sqrt{x}; g(x) = 5x - 3$

5. $g^{-1}(x) = 6 - x$ **6.**

7. 2   **8.** -1 **9.** $\frac{1}{2}$ **10.** 1   **11.** 19   **12.** 0
13. $x^m = 3$ **14.** $2^{10} = 1024$ **15.** $t = \log_e x$
16. $\frac{2}{3} = \log_{64} 16$ **17.** $\log x - \frac{1}{2} \log y - \frac{3}{2} \log z$
18. $\log \dfrac{a}{b^2 c}$ **19.** 4   **20.** $\frac{1}{3}$

Technology Connection, p. 813

1.

Technology Connection, p. 814

1. As x gets larger, the value of y_1 approaches
2.7182818284. . . .   **2.** For large values of x, the graphs of
y_1 and y_2 will be very close or appear to be the same curve,
depending on the window chosen.   **3.** Using (TRACE),
no y-value is given for $x = 0$. Using a table, an error message appears for y_1 when $x = 0$. The domain does not
include 0 because division by 0 is undefined.

Technology Connection, p. 817

1. $y = \log x / \log 7$ **2.** $y = \log (x+2)/\log 5$

3. $y = \log x / \log 7 + 2$

Exercise Set 12.5, pp. 818–819

1. True   **2.** True   **3.** True   **4.** False   **5.** True
6. True   **7.** True   **8.** True   **9.** True   **10.** True
11. 0.8451   **13.** 1.1367   **15.** 3   **17.** -0.1249
19. 13.0014   **21.** 50.1187   **23.** 0.0011   **25.** 2.1972
27. -5.0832 **29.** 96.7583   **31.** 15.0293   **33.** 0.0305
35. 3.0331   **37.** 6.6439   **39.** 1.1610   **41.** -0.3010
43. -3.3219 **45.** 2.0115

47. Domain: $\mathbb{R}$;
range: $(0, \infty)$

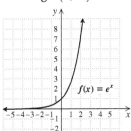

49. Domain: $\mathbb{R}$;
range: $(3, \infty)$

67. Domain: $(0, \infty)$;
range: $\mathbb{R}$

69. Domain: $(0, \infty)$;
range: $\mathbb{R}$

51. Domain: $\mathbb{R}$;
range: $(-2, \infty)$

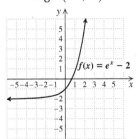

53. Domain: $\mathbb{R}$;
range: $(0, \infty)$

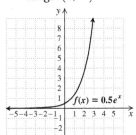

71. Domain: $(-2, \infty)$;
range: $\mathbb{R}$

73. Domain: $(1, \infty)$;
range: $\mathbb{R}$

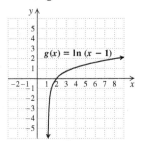

55. Domain: $\mathbb{R}$;
range: $(0, \infty)$

57. Domain: $\mathbb{R}$;
range: $(0, \infty)$

75.   **77.** 1   **78.** $-7\frac{1}{2}$

79. $(g - f)(x) = 5x - 8 - \dfrac{1}{x + 2}$

80. $\{x \mid x \text{ is a real number } and \, x \neq -2\}$, or
$(-\infty, -2) \cup (-2, \infty)$

81. $\{x \mid x \text{ is a real number } and \, x \neq -2 \, and \, x \neq \frac{8}{5}\}$, or
$(-\infty, -2) \cup (-2, \frac{8}{5}) \cup (\frac{8}{5}, \infty)$

82. $gg(x) = 25x^2 - 80x + 64$ **83.**   **85.** 2.452

87. 1.442   **89.** $\log M = \dfrac{\ln M}{\ln 10}$ **91.** 1086.5129

93. 4.9855   **95. (a)** Domain: $\{x \mid x > 0\}$, or $(0, \infty)$;
range: $\{y \mid y < 0.5135\}$, or $(-\infty, 0.5135)$;
(b) $[-1, 5, -10, 5]$; **(c)** $y = 3.4 \ln x - 0.25e^x$

59. Domain: $\mathbb{R}$;
range: $(0, \infty)$

61. Domain: $\mathbb{R}$;
range: $(-\infty, 0)$

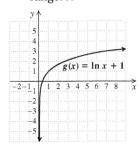

97. (a) Domain: $\{x \mid x > 0\}$, or $(0, \infty)$; range:
$\{y \mid y > -0.2453\}$, or $(-0.2453, \infty)$;
(b) $[-1, 5, -1, 10]$; **(c)** $y = 2x^3 \ln x$

63. Domain: $(0, \infty)$;
range: $\mathbb{R}$

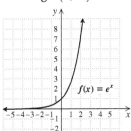

65. Domain: $(0, \infty)$;
range: $\mathbb{R}$

99.

Quick Quiz: Sections 12.1–12.5, p. 819

1. $f(x) = \sqrt{x}$; $g(x) = 3x - 7$ **2.** $\log_a \dfrac{x^2}{y^3}$

3. $\log_a (x^2 - 1)$

4.

$y = 2^{x-5}$

5.

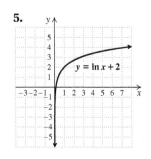

$y = \ln x + 2$

Prepare to Move On, p. 819

1. $-4, 7$ **2.** $0, \frac{7}{5}$ **3.** $\frac{15}{17}$ **4.** $\frac{5}{6}$ **5.** $\frac{56}{9}$ **6.** 4

Technology Connection, p. 823

1. 0.38 **2.** -1.96 **3.** 0.90 **4.** -1.53
5. 0.13, 8.47 **6.** $-0.75, 0.75$

Connecting the Concepts, p. 824

1. 500 **2.** 8 **3.** $\ln 5 \approx 1.6094$ **4.** $-5, 5$ **5.** 4

6. $\dfrac{\ln 4}{5 \ln 3} \approx 0.2524$ **7.** $-\frac{1}{2}$ **8.** $-\frac{2}{5}$

Exercise Set 12.6, pp. 825–826

1. False **2.** True **3.** True **4.** True **5.** (d)
6. (a) **7.** (b) **8.** (c) **9.** 2 **11.** $\frac{5}{2}$

13. $\dfrac{\log 10}{\log 2} \approx 3.322$ **15.** -1 **17.** $\dfrac{\log 19}{\log 8} + 3 \approx 4.416$

19. $\ln 50 \approx 3.912$ **21.** $\dfrac{\ln 8}{-0.02} \approx -103.972$

23. $\dfrac{\log 87}{\log 4.9} \approx 2.810$ **25.** $\dfrac{\ln\left(\frac{19}{2}\right)}{4} \approx 0.563$

27. $\dfrac{\ln 2}{-1} \approx -0.693$ **29.** 81 **31.** $\frac{1}{16}$

33. $e^5 \approx 148.413$ **35.** $\dfrac{e^3}{4} \approx 5.021$

37. $10^{1.2} \approx 15.849$ **39.** $\dfrac{e^4 - 1}{2} \approx 26.799$

41. $e \approx 2.718$ **43.** $e^{-3} \approx 0.050$ **45.** -4
47. 10 **49.** No solution **51.** 2 **53.** $\frac{83}{15}$ **55.** 1
57. 6 **59.** 1 **61.** 5 **63.** $\frac{17}{2}$ **65.** 4 **67.** ☑
69. $\dfrac{(a+2)(a-2)^2}{a^4}$ **70.** $\dfrac{t(2t-3)(t-1)}{2t+3}$

71. $\dfrac{5m-7}{(m+1)(m-5)}$ **72.** $\dfrac{-x^2 + 4x + 2}{x(x-2)}$

73. $\dfrac{x(3y-2)}{2y+x}$ **74.** $\dfrac{x+2}{x+1}$ **75.** ☑ **77.** -4
79. 2 **81.** $\pm\sqrt{34}$ **83.** $-3, -1$ **85.** $-625, 625$
87. $\frac{1}{2}, 5000$ **89.** $-3, -1$ **91.** $\frac{1}{100,000}, 100,000$
93. $-\frac{1}{3}$ **95.** 38 **97.** 1

Quick Quiz: Sections 12.1–12.6, p. 826

1. $g^{-1}(x) = x + 6$ **2.** -1 **3.** 11 **4.** 8
5. $10^{2.7} \approx 501.187$

Prepare to Move On, p. 826

1. Length: 9.5 ft; width: 3.5 ft
2. (a) $w(t) = \frac{5900}{11}t + 15{,}200$, where $w(t)$ is the average
cost of a wedding t years after 1990; (b) about \$28,609
3. $1\frac{1}{5}$ hr

Exercise Set 12.7, pp. 833–838

1. (b) **2.** (d) **3.** (c) **4.** (a) **5.** (a) 2010;
(b) approximately 1.5 years **7.** (a) 6.4 years;
(b) 23.4 years **9.** (a) The 49th key; (b) 12 keys
11. (a) 33 months after March 2011, or in December 2013;
(b) approximately 16 months **13.** 4.9 **15.** 10^{-7}
moles per liter **17.** 130 dB **19.** 7.6 W/m^2
21. Approximately 42.4 million messages per day
23. (a) $P(t) = P_0 e^{0.025t}$; (b) \$5126.58; \$5256.36;
(c) 27.7 years **25.** (a) $P(t) = 314e^{0.00963t}$, where $P(t)$ is
the population, in millions, t years after 2012;
(b) 339 million; (c) about 2037 **27.** 21 years
29. (a) About 2044; (b) about 2060;
(c)

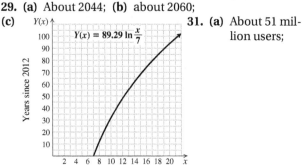

$Y(x) = 89.29 \ln \frac{x}{7}$

World population (in billions)

31. (a) About 51 million users;

(b)

$c(t) = 26 + 36 \ln(t), t \geq 1$

Years since 2010

(c) about 2018

33. (a) $k \approx 0.241$; $P(t) = 4232e^{0.241t}$;
(b) about 2014 **35.** (a) $k \approx 0.341$; $P(t) = 15.5e^{-0.341t}$;
(b) about 5.6 mcg/mL; (c) after about 4 hr; (d) 2 hr
37. About 1964 years **39.** 7.2 days
41. (a) 13.9% per hour; (b) 21.6 hr **43.** (a) $k \approx 0.123$;
$V(t) = 9e^{0.123t}$; (b) about \$360 million; (c) 5.6 years;
(d) 38.3 years **45.** ☑ **47.** $f(x) = 18x + \frac{1}{2}$
48. $f(x) = \frac{11}{6}x$ **49.** $f(x) = \frac{2}{3}x + 9$
50. $f(x) = -2x + 8$ **51.** ☑ **53.** \$14.0 million
55. (a) -26.9; (b) 1.58×10^{-17} W/m^2
57. Consider an exponential growth function $P(t) = P_0 e^{kt}$.
At time T, $P(T) = 2P_0$.
Solve for T:

$$2P_0 = P_0 e^{kT}$$
$$2 = e^{kT}$$
$$\ln 2 = kT$$
$$\frac{\ln 2}{k} = T.$$

Quick Quiz: Sections 12.1–12.7, p. 838

1. Yes   **2.** $\frac{3}{4}$ **3.** 3.9069   **4.** 5
5. Approximately 23.4 years

Prepare to Move On, p. 838

1. $\sqrt{2}$ **2.** $(4, -7)$ **3.** $-4 \pm \sqrt{17}$
4.

Visualizing for Success, p. 839

1. J   **2.** D   **3.** B   **4.** G   **5.** H   **6.** C   **7.** F
8. I   **9.** E   **10.** A

Decision Making: Connection, p. 840

1. $F(t) = 4430e^{0.062t}$, where t is the number of school years since 2000–2001   **2.** $G(t) = 2050e^{0.103t}$, where t is the number of school years since 2000–2001
3. Answers will vary.   **4.** Answers will vary.   **5.** 🖥

Study Summary: Chapter 12, pp. 841–842

1. $(f \circ g)(x) = 19 - 6x^2$ **2.** Yes   **3.** $f^{-1}(x) = \dfrac{x - 1}{5}$
4.

5.

6. $\log_5 625 = 4$ **7.** $\log_9 x + \log_9 y$ **8.** $\log_6 7 - \log_6 10$
9. 0   **10.** 19   **11.** 2.3219   **12.** $\frac{4}{3}$
13. $\dfrac{\ln 10}{0.1} \approx 23.0259$ **14.** (a) $P(t) = 15{,}000e^{0.023t}$;
(b) 30.1 years   **15.** 35 days

Review Exercises: Chapter 12, pp. 843–844

1. True   **2.** True   **3.** True   **4.** False   **5.** False
6. True   **7.** False   **8.** False   **9.** True   **10.** False
11. $(f \circ g)(x) = 4x^2 - 12x + 10$; $(g \circ f)(x) = 2x^2 - 1$
12. $f(x) = \sqrt{x}$; $g(x) = 3 - x$ **13.** No
14. $f^{-1}(x) = x + 10$ **15.** $g^{-1}(x) = \dfrac{2x - 1}{3}$
16. $f^{-1}(x) = \dfrac{\sqrt[3]{x}}{3}$

17.

18.

19.

20. 2   **21.** -2 **22.** 11
23. $\frac{1}{2}$ **24.** $\log_2 \frac{1}{8} = -3$
25. $\log_{25} 5 = \frac{1}{2}$
26. $16 = 4^x$ **27.** $1 = 8^0$

28. $4 \log_a x + 2 \log_a y + 3 \log_a z$
29. $5 \log_a x - (\log_a y + 2 \log_a z)$, or
$5 \log_a x - \log_a y - 2 \log_a z$
30. $\frac{1}{4}(2 \log z - 3 \log x - \log y)$ **31.** $\log_a (5 \cdot 8)$, or $\log_a 40$
32. $\log_a \frac{48}{12}$, or $\log_a 4$ **33.** $\log \dfrac{a^{1/2}}{bc^2}$ **34.** $\log_a \sqrt[3]{\dfrac{x}{y^2}}$
35. 1   **36.** 0   **37.** 17   **38.** 6.93   **39.** -3.2698
40. 8.7601   **41.** 3.2698   **42.** 2.54995   **43.** -3.6602
44. 1.8751   **45.** 61.5177   **46.** -1.2040 **47.** 0.3753
48. 2.4307   **49.** 0.8982
50. Domain: $\mathbb{R}$;   **51.** Domain: $(0, \infty)$;
range: $(-1, \infty)$ range: $\mathbb{R}$

52. 3   **53.** -1 **54.** $\frac{1}{81}$ **55.** 2   **56.** $\frac{1}{1000}$
57. $e^3 \approx 20.0855$ **58.** $\dfrac{1}{2}\left(\dfrac{\log 19}{\log 4} + 5\right) \approx 3.5620$
59. $\dfrac{\log 12}{\log 2} \approx 3.5850$ **60.** $\dfrac{\ln 0.03}{-0.1} \approx 35.0656$
61. $e^{-3} \approx 0.0498$ **62.** $\frac{15}{2}$ **63.** 16   **64.** 5
65. (a) 82; (b) 66.8; (c) 35 months
66. (a) 2.3 years; (b) 3.1 years
67. (a) $k \approx 1.565$; $A(t) = 175e^{1.565t}$;
(b) \$91.6 billion; (c) about 2014; (d) 0.44 year
68. (a) $k \approx 0.060$; $F(t) = 2500e^{-0.060t}$;
(b) approximately 3 fatalities; (c) about 2014
69. 11.553% per year   **70.** 16.5 years   **71.** 3463 years
72. 5.1   **73.** About 114 dB   **74.** 📋 Negative numbers do not have logarithms because logarithm bases are positive, and there is no exponent to which a positive number

can be raised to yield a negative number. **75.** 📋 If $f(x) = e^x$, then to find the inverse function, we let $y = e^x$ and interchange x and y: $x = e^y$. If $x = e^y$, then $\log_e x = y$ by the definition of logarithms. Since $\log_e x = \ln x$, we have $y = \ln x$ or $f^{-1}(x) = \ln x$. Thus, $g(x) = \ln x$ is the inverse of $f(x) = e^x$. Another approach is to find $(f \circ g)(x)$ and $(g \circ f)(x)$:

$$(f \circ g)(x) = e^{\ln x} = x, \text{ and}$$
$$(g \circ f)(x) = \ln e^x = x.$$

Thus, g and f are inverse functions. **76.** e^{e^3}
77. $-3, -1$ **78.** $\left(\frac{8}{3}, -\frac{2}{3}\right)$

Test: Chapter 12, p. 845

1. [12.1] $(f \circ g)(x) = 2 + 6x + 4x^2$; $(g \circ f)(x) = 2x^2 + 2x + 1$

2. [12.1] $f(x) = \frac{1}{x}$; $g(x) = 2x^2 + 1$ **3.** [12.1] No

4. [12.1] $f^{-1}(x) = \frac{x - 4}{3}$ **5.** [12.1] $g^{-1}(x) = \sqrt[3]{x} - 1$

6. [12.2] **7.** [12.3]

8. [12.3] 3 **9.** [12.3] $\frac{1}{2}$ **10.** [12.4] 1 **11.** [12.4] 0
12. [12.3] $\log_5 \frac{1}{625} = -4$ **13.** [12.3] $2^m = \frac{1}{2}$
14. [12.4] $3 \log a + \frac{1}{2} \log b - 2 \log c$
15. [12.4] $\log_a \left(z^2 \sqrt[3]{x}\right)$
16. [12.4] 1.146 **17.** [12.4] 0.477 **18.** [12.4] 1.204
19. [12.5] 1.3979 **20.** [12.5] 0.1585 **21.** [12.5] -0.9163
22. [12.5] 121.5104 **23.** [12.5] 2.4022
24. [12.5]

Domain: $\mathbb{R}$;
range: $(3, \infty)$

25. [12.5]

Domain: $(4, \infty)$;
range: $\mathbb{R}$

26. [12.6] -5 **27.** [12.6] 2 **28.** [12.6] $\frac{1}{100}$
29. [12.6] $\dfrac{\log 1.2}{\log 7} \approx 0.0937$ **30.** [12.6] 4

31. [12.7] **(a)** 2.26 ft/sec; **(b)** 1,290,000
32. [12.7] **(a)** $P(t) = 155e^{0.019t}$, where t is the number of years after 2012 and $P(t)$ is in millions; **(b)** 167 million; 319 million; **(c)** about 2025; **(d)** 36.5 years
33. [12.7] **(a)** $k \approx 0.024$; $C(t) = 30{,}360e^{0.024t}$; **(b)** \$43,516;
(c) about 2022 **34.** [12.7] 4.3% **35.** [12.7] 7.0
36. [12.6] $-309, 316$ **37.** [12.4] 2

Cumulative Review: Chapters 1–12, p. 846

1. $\dfrac{y^{12}}{16x^8}$ **2.** $-\dfrac{y^4}{3z^5}$ **3.** $\dfrac{20x^6z^2}{y}$ **4.** 8 **5.** $(3, -1)$

6. $(1, -2, 0)$ **7.** $-7, 10$ **8.** $\frac{9}{2}$ **9.** $\frac{3}{4}$ **10.** $\pm 4i$

11. $\pm 2, \pm 3$ **12.** 9 **13.** $\dfrac{\log 7}{5 \log 3} \approx 0.3542$

14. $\dfrac{8e}{e - 1} \approx 12.6558$ **15.** $(-\infty, -5) \cup (1, \infty)$, or $\{x \mid x < -5 \text{ or } x > 1\}$ **16.** $-3 \pm 2\sqrt{5}$
17. $\{x \mid x \le -2 \text{ or } x \ge 5\}$, or $(-\infty, -2] \cup [5, \infty)$
18. $\dfrac{a + 2}{6}$ **19.** $\dfrac{7x + 4}{(x + 6)(x - 6)}$ **20.** $\sqrt[10]{(x + 5)^7}$
21. $15 - 4\sqrt{3}i$ **22.** $(3 + 4n)(9 - 12n + 16n^2)$
23. $2(3x - 2y)(x + 2y)$ **24.** $2(m + 3n)^2$
25. $(x - 2y)(x + 2y)(x^2 + 4y^2)$ **26.** $\dfrac{6 + \sqrt{y} - y}{4 - y}$

27. $f^{-1}(x) = \dfrac{x - 9}{-2}$, or $f^{-1}(x) = \dfrac{9 - x}{2}$
28. $f(x) = -10x - 8$
29.

30.

31.

32.

$f(x) = 2x^2 + 12x + 19$
Minimum: 1

33.

Domain: $\mathbb{R}$;
range: $(0, \infty)$

34. 13.5 million acre-feet   **35.** **(a)** $k \approx 0.076$; $D(t) = 15e^{0.076t}$; **(b)** 108 million m³ per day; **(c)** 2020
36. $5\frac{5}{11}$ min   **37.** Thick and Tasty: 6 oz; Light and Lean: 9 oz
38. $\frac{1}{3}, \frac{10,000}{3}$ **39.** 35 mph

CHAPTER 13

Technology Connection, p. 853

1. $x^2 + y^2 - 16 = 0$

2. $(x-1)^2 + (y-2)^2 = 25$

3. $(x+3)^2 + (y-5)^2 = 16$

Exercise Set 13.1, pp. 853–857

1. Conic sections   **2.** Circle   **3.** Horizontal
4. Vertex   **5.** Center   **6.** Center   **7.** (f)   **8.** (e)
9. (c)   **10.** (b)   **11.** (d)   **12.** (a)

13.

15.

17.

19.

21.

23.

25.

27.

29.

31.

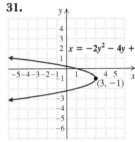

33. $x^2 + y^2 = 64$ **35.** $(x-7)^2 + (y-3)^2 = 6$
37. $(x+4)^2 + (y-3)^2 = 18$
39. $(x+5)^2 + (y+8)^2 = 300$ **41.** $x^2 + y^2 = 25$
43. $(x+4)^2 + (y-1)^2 = 20$
45. $(0,0)$; 1   **47.** $(-1,-3)$; 7

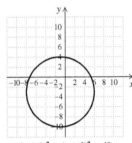

$(x+1)^2 + (y+3)^2 = 49$

49. $(4,-3)$; $\sqrt{10}$ **51.** $(0,0)$; $2\sqrt{2}$

$(x-4)^2 + (y+3)^2 = 10$

53. $(5,0)$; $\frac{1}{2}$ **55.** $(-4,3)$; $\sqrt{40}$, or $2\sqrt{10}$

$(x-5)^2 + y^2 = \frac{1}{4}$

$x^2 + y^2 + 8x - 6y - 15 = 0$

57. $(4, -1); 2$ **59.** $(0, -5); 10$

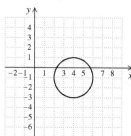

$x^2 + y^2 - 8x + 2y + 13 = 0$

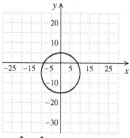

$x^2 + y^2 + 10y - 75 = 0$

61. $\left(-\dfrac{7}{2}, \dfrac{3}{2}\right); \sqrt{\dfrac{98}{4}}, \text{ or } \dfrac{7\sqrt{2}}{2}$ **63.** $(0,0); \dfrac{1}{6}$

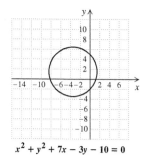

$x^2 + y^2 + 7x - 3y - 10 = 0$

$36x^2 + 36y^2 = 1$

65.   **67.** $2xy^3\sqrt[4]{3x^3}$ **68.** $y\sqrt[6]{y}$ **69.** $10x^2\sqrt{w}$
70. $\sqrt[30]{t^7}$ **71.** $2\sqrt{3}$ **72.** $12\sqrt{3} - 3\sqrt{2} + 4\sqrt{6} - 2$
73. 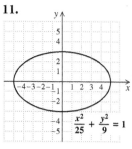   **75.** $(x - 3)^2 + (y + 5)^2 = 9$
77. $(x - 3)^2 + y^2 = 25$ **79.** $\dfrac{17}{4}\pi \text{ m}^2$, or
approximately 13.4 m²   **81.** 7169 mm
83. (a) $(0, -3)$; **(b)** 5 ft   **85.** $x^2 + (y - 30.6)^2 = 590.49$
87. 7 in.   **89.**

Prepare to Move On, p. 857

1. ± 4 **2.** $\pm a$ **3.** $-4, 6$ **4.** $-3 \pm 3\sqrt{3}$

Exercise Set 13.2, pp. 861–863

1. A   **2.** C   **3.** B   **4.** D   **5.** True   **6.** False
7. True   **8.** True
9.   **11.**

13.

$4x^2 + 9y^2 = 36$

15.

$16x^2 + 9y^2 = 144$

17.

$2x^2 + 3y^2 = 6$

19.

$5x^2 + 5y^2 = 125$

21.

$3x^2 + 7y^2 - 63 = 0$

23.

$16x^2 = 16 - y^2$

25.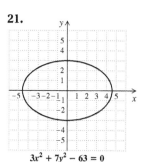

$16x^2 + 25y^2 = 1$

27.

$\dfrac{(x - 3)^2}{9} + \dfrac{(y - 2)^2}{25} = 1$

29.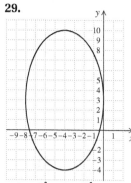

$\dfrac{(x + 4)^2}{16} + \dfrac{(y - 3)^2}{49} = 1$

31.

$12(x - 1)^2 + 3(y + 4)^2 = 48$

33.

$4(x + 3)^2 + 4(y + 1)^2 - 10 = 90$

35.   **37.** $\dfrac{5}{2} \pm \dfrac{\sqrt{13}}{2}$

38. 3   **39.** $-\dfrac{3}{4}, 2$

40. $\dfrac{5}{2}$ **41.** $-\sqrt{11}, \sqrt{11}$

42. $-10, 6$ **43.**

45. $\dfrac{x^2}{81} + \dfrac{y^2}{121} = 1$

47. $\dfrac{(x - 2)^2}{16} + \dfrac{(y + 1)^2}{9} = 1$

49. $\dfrac{x^2}{9} + \dfrac{y^2}{25} = 1$

51. (a) Let $F_1 = (-c, 0)$ and $F_2 = (c, 0)$. Then the sum of the distances from the foci to P is $2a$. By the distance formula,
$$\sqrt{(x + c)^2 + y^2} + \sqrt{(x - c)^2 + y^2} = 2a, \text{ or}$$
$$\sqrt{(x + c)^2 + y^2} = 2a - \sqrt{(x - c)^2 + y^2}.$$
Squaring, we get
$$(x + c)^2 + y^2 = 4a^2 - 4a\sqrt{(x - c)^2 + y^2} + (x - c)^2 + y^2,$$
or
$$x^2 + 2cx + c^2 + y^2 = 4a^2 - 4a\sqrt{(x - c)^2 + y^2} + x^2 - 2cx + c^2 + y^2.$$
Thus,
$$-4a^2 + 4cx = -4a\sqrt{(x - c)^2 + y^2}$$
$$a^2 - cx = a\sqrt{(x - c)^2 + y^2}.$$
Squaring again, we get
$$a^4 - 2a^2cx + c^2x^2 = a^2(x^2 - 2cx + c^2 + y^2)$$
$$a^4 - 2a^2cx + c^2x^2 = a^2x^2 - 2a^2cx + a^2c^2 + a^2y^2,$$
or
$$x^2(a^2 - c^2) + a^2y^2 = a^2(a^2 - c^2)$$
$$\dfrac{x^2}{a^2} + \dfrac{y^2}{a^2 - c^2} = 1.$$

(b) When P is at $(0, b)$, it follows that $b^2 = a^2 - c^2$. Substituting, we have
$$\dfrac{x^2}{a^2} + \dfrac{y^2}{b^2} = 1.$$

53. 5.66 ft   **55.**

$\dfrac{(x - 2)^2}{16} + \dfrac{(y + 1)^2}{4} = 1$

57.

Quick Quiz: Sections 13.1–13.2, p. 863

1. $(-5, -1); 2$ **2.** $(x - 9)^2 + (y - (-23))^2 = 200$, or $(x - 9)^2 + (y + 23)^2 = 200$

3.

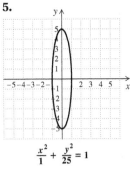

$(x + 3)^2 + (y + 1)^2 = 4$

4.

$y = x^2 - 2x - 2$

5.

$\dfrac{x^2}{1} + \dfrac{y^2}{25} = 1$

Prepare to Move On, p. 863

1. $y = \dfrac{4}{x}$ **2.** $y = 2x - 4$ **3.** $x^2 - 5x - 7 = 0$

Technology Connection, p. 868

1. $y_1 = \dfrac{\sqrt{15x^2 - 240}}{2}$; $y_2 = -\dfrac{\sqrt{15x^2 - 240}}{2}$

2. $y_1 = \sqrt{\dfrac{16x^2 - 64}{3}}$; $y_2 = -\sqrt{\dfrac{16x^2 - 64}{3}}$

3. $y_1 = \dfrac{\sqrt{5x^2 + 320}}{4}$; $y_2 = -\dfrac{\sqrt{5x^2 + 320}}{4}$

4. $y_1 = \sqrt{\dfrac{9x^2 + 441}{45}}$; $y_2 = -\sqrt{\dfrac{9x^2 + 441}{45}}$

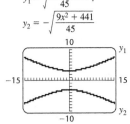

Connecting the Concepts, p. 870

1. $(4, 1); x = 4$ **2.** $(2, -1); y = -1$ **3.** $(3, 2)$
4. $(-3, -5)$ **5.** $(-12, 0), (12, 0), (0, -9), (0, 9)$
6. $(-3, 0), (3, 0)$ **7.** $(0, -1), (0, 1)$ **8.** $y = \frac{3}{2}x, y = -\frac{3}{2}x$

Exercise Set 13.3, pp. 871–872

1. B   **2.** E   **3.** A   **4.** D   **5.** F   **6.** C

7.

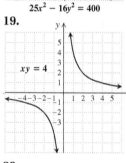

$$\frac{y^2}{16} - \frac{x^2}{16} = 1$$

9.

$$\frac{x^2}{4} - \frac{y^2}{25} = 1$$

11.

$$\frac{y^2}{36} - \frac{x^2}{9} = 1$$

13.

$$y^2 - x^2 = 25$$

15.

$$25x^2 - 16y^2 = 400$$

17.

$xy = -6$

19.

$xy = 4$

21.

$xy = -2$

23.

$xy = 1$

25. Circle   **27.** Ellipse
29. Hyperbola   **31.** Circle
33. Parabola
35. Hyperbola   **37.** Parabola
39. Hyperbola   **41.** Circle
43. Ellipse   **45.**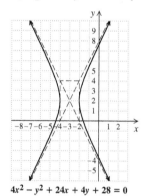
47. $(4 + y^2)(2 + y)(2 - y)$
48. $(3xy - 5)^2$

49. $10c(c - 3)(c - 5)$ **50.** $(x + 1)(x^2 + 3)$
51. $8t(t - 1)(t^2 + t + 1)$ **52.** $(3a - 2b)(2a + 5b)$
53. 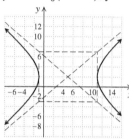   **55.** $\dfrac{y^2}{36} - \dfrac{x^2}{4} = 1$

57. $C: (5, 2); V: (-1, 2), (11, 2);$ asymptotes:
$y - 2 = \frac{5}{6}(x - 5), y - 2 = -\frac{5}{6}(x - 5)$

$$\frac{(x - 5)^2}{36} - \frac{(y - 2)^2}{25} = 1$$

59. $\dfrac{(y + 3)^2}{4} - \dfrac{(x - 4)^2}{16} = 1; C: (4, -3); V: (4, -5), (4, -1);$
asymptotes: $y + 3 = \frac{1}{2}(x - 4), y + 3 = -\frac{1}{2}(x - 4)$

$$8(y + 3)^2 - 2(x - 4)^2 = 32$$

61. $\dfrac{(x + 3)^2}{1} - \dfrac{(y - 2)^2}{4} = 1; C: (-3, 2); V: (-4, 2), (-2, 2);$
asymptotes: $y - 2 = 2(x + 3), y - 2 = -2(x + 3)$

63.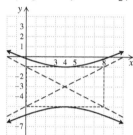

$4x^2 - y^2 + 24x + 4y + 28 = 0$

Quick Quiz: Sections 13.1–13.3, p. 872

1.

$(x - 2)^2 + y^2 = 16$

2.

$xy = 6$

3.

$$\frac{x^2}{36} + \frac{y^2}{4} = 1$$

4.

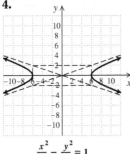

$$\frac{x^2}{36} - \frac{y^2}{4} = 1$$

5.

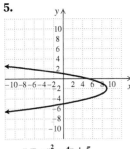

$$x = -y^2 - 4y + 5$$

Prepare to Move On, p. 872

1. $(-3, 6)$ **2.** $(3, 7)$ **3.** $-2, 2$ **4.** $-4, \frac{2}{3}$

5. $\frac{3}{2} \pm \frac{\sqrt{13}}{2}$ **6.** $\pm 1, \pm 5$

Mid-Chapter Review: Chapter 13, p. 873

1.
$$(x^2 - 4x) + (y^2 + 2y) = 6$$
$$(x^2 - 4x + 4) + (y^2 + 2y + 1) = 6 + 4 + 1$$
$$(x - 2)^2 + (y + 1)^2 = 11$$

The center of the circle is $(2, -1)$. The radius is $\sqrt{11}$.

2. (a) Is there both an x^2-term and a y^2-term? Yes;
(b) Do both the x^2-term and the y^2-term have the same sign? No; **(c)** The graph of the equation is a hyperbola.

3. $(x + 4)^2 + (y - 9)^2 = 20$ **4.** Center: $(5, -1)$; radius: 6

5. Circle   **6.** Parabola

$$x^2 + y^2 = 36$$

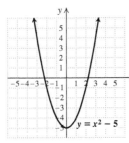

$$y = x^2 - 5$$

7. Ellipse   **8.** Hyperbola

$$\frac{x^2}{25} + \frac{y^2}{49} = 1$$

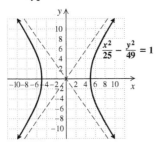

$$\frac{x^2}{25} - \frac{y^2}{49} = 1$$

9. Parabola   **10.** Ellipse

$$x = (y + 3)^2 + 2$$

$$4x^2 + 9y^2 = 36$$

11. Hyperbola   **12.** Circle

$$xy = -4$$

$$(x + 2)^2 + (y - 3)^2 = 1$$

13. Circle   **14.** Parabola

$$x^2 + y^2 - 8y - 20 = 0$$

$$x = y^2 + 2y$$

15. Hyperbola   **16.** Hyperbola

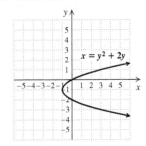

$$16y^2 - x^2 = 16$$

$$x = \frac{9}{y}$$

Technology Connection, p. 876

1. $(-1.50, -1.17); (3.50, 0.50)$
2. $(-2.77, 2.52); (-2.77, -2.52)$

Technology Connection, p. 878

1. $y_1 = \sqrt{(20 - x^2)/4}; \; y_2 = -\sqrt{(20 - x^2)/4}; \; y_3 = 4/x$

Exercise Set 13.4, pp. 879–881

1. True　**2.** True　**3.** False　**4.** False　**5.** True
6. True　**7.** $(-5, -4), (4, 5)$　**9.** $(0, 2), (3, 0)$
11. $(-2, 1)$

13. $\left(\dfrac{5 + \sqrt{70}}{3}, \dfrac{-1 + \sqrt{70}}{3}\right), \left(\dfrac{5 - \sqrt{70}}{3}, \dfrac{-1 - \sqrt{70}}{30}\right)$

15. $\left(4, \frac{3}{2}\right), (3, 2)$　**17.** $\left(\frac{7}{3}, \frac{1}{3}\right), (1, -1)$　**19.** $\left(\frac{11}{4}, -\frac{5}{4}\right), (1, 4)$
21. $(2, 4), (4, 2)$　**23.** $(3, -5), (-1, 3)$
25. $(-5, -8), (8, 5)$　**27.** $(0, 0), (1, 1),$

$\left(-\dfrac{1}{2} + \dfrac{\sqrt{3}}{2}i, -\dfrac{1}{2} - \dfrac{\sqrt{3}}{2}i\right), \left(-\dfrac{1}{2} - \dfrac{\sqrt{3}}{2}i, -\dfrac{1}{2} + \dfrac{\sqrt{3}}{2}i\right)$

29. $(-4, 0), (4, 0)$　**31.** $(-4, -3), (-3, -4), (3, 4), (4, 3)$

33. $\left(\dfrac{16}{3}, \dfrac{5\sqrt{7}}{3}i\right), \left(\dfrac{16}{3}, -\dfrac{5\sqrt{7}}{3}i\right), \left(-\dfrac{16}{3}, \dfrac{5\sqrt{7}}{3}i\right),$

$\left(-\dfrac{16}{3}, -\dfrac{5\sqrt{7}}{3}i\right)$　**35.** $(-3, -\sqrt{5}), (-3, \sqrt{5}), (3, -\sqrt{5}),$

$(3, \sqrt{5})$　**37.** $(-3, -1), (-1, -3), (1, 3), (3, 1)$
39. $(4, 1), (-4, -1), (2, 2), (-2, -2)$　**41.** $(2, 1), (-2, -1)$
43. $\left(2, -\frac{4}{5}\right), \left(-2, -\frac{4}{5}\right), (5, 2), (-5, 2)$　**45.** $(-\sqrt{2}, \sqrt{2}),$
$(\sqrt{2}, -\sqrt{2})$　**47.** Length: 8 cm; width: 6 cm
49. Length: 2 in.; width: 1 in.　**51.** Length: 12 ft; width: 5 ft
53. 6 and 15; −6 and −15　**55.** Length: 12 in.; width: 7.5 in.

57. Length: $\sqrt{3}$ m; width: 1 m　**59.** 🖉　**61.** $\dfrac{9}{2a^3}$
62. $\frac{1}{4}$　**63.** 4　**64.** $-i$　**65.** -253
66. $10\sqrt{5}$　**67.** 🖉　**69.** $(-2, 3), (2, -3), (-3, 2),$
$(3, -2)$　**71.** Length: 55 ft; width: 45 ft　**73.** 10 in.
by 7 in. by 5 in.

Quick Quiz: Sections 13.1–13.4, p. 881

1. Circle　**2.** Hyperbola　**3.** Ellipse　**4.** Parabola
5. $(2, -1), (1, -2)$

Prepare to Move On, p. 881

1. -9　**2.** -27　**3.** $\frac{1}{5}$　**4.** 77　**5.** $\frac{21}{2}$

Visualizing for Success, p. 882

1. C　**2.** A　**3.** F　**4.** B　**5.** J　**6.** D　**7.** H
8. I　**9.** G　**10.** E

Decision Making: Connection, p. 883

1. $b \approx 34.9$ in.; $h \approx 19.6$ in.　**2.** $b = 32$ in.; $h = 24$ in.

3. An older TV　**4.** $h = \dfrac{d}{\sqrt{1 + r^2}}$　**5.** 🖥

Study Summary: Chapter 13, pp. 884–885

1.

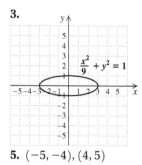

2. Center: $(3, 0)$; radius: 2

3.

4.

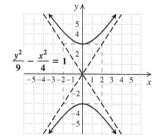

5. $(-5, -4), (4, 5)$

Review Exercises: Chapter 13, pp. 886–887

1. True　**2.** False　**3.** False　**4.** True　**5.** True
6. True　**7.** False　**8.** True　**9.** $(-3, 2), 4$
10. $(5, 0), \sqrt{11}$　**11.** $(3, 1), 3$　**12.** $(-4, 3), 3\sqrt{5}$
13. $(x + 4)^2 + (y - 3)^2 = 16$
14. $(x - 7)^2 + (y + 2)^2 = 20$
15. Circle　**16.** Ellipse

17. Parabola　**18.** Hyperbola

19. Hyperbola

20. Parabola

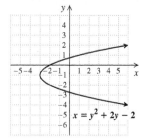
$x = y^2 + 2y - 2$

21. Ellipse

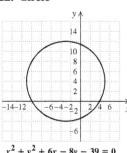
$\dfrac{(x + 1)^2}{3} + (y - 3)^2 = 1$

22. Circle

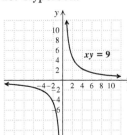
$x^2 + y^2 + 6x - 8y - 39 = 0$

23. $(5, -2)$ **24.** $(2, 2), \left(\frac{32}{9}, -\frac{10}{9}\right)$ **25.** $(0, -5), (2, -1)$
26. $(4, 3), (4, -3), (-4, 3), (-4, -3)$ **27.** $(2, 1), (\sqrt{3}, 0),$
$(-2, 1), (-\sqrt{3}, 0)$ **28.** $(3, -3), \left(-\frac{3}{5}, \frac{21}{5}\right)$ **29.** $(6, 8),$
$(6, -8), (-6, 8), (-6, -8)$ **30.** $(2, 2), (-2, -2),$
$(2\sqrt{2}, \sqrt{2}), (-2\sqrt{2}, -\sqrt{2})$ **31.** Length: 12 m; width: 7 m
32. Length: 12 in.; width: 9 in.   **33.** Board: 32 cm; mirror:
20 cm   **34.** 3 ft, 11 ft   **35.** ☑ The graph of a parabola
has one branch whereas the graph of a hyperbola has two
branches. A hyperbola has asymptotes, but a parabola does
not.   **36.** ☑ Function notation rarely appears in this
chapter because many of the relations are not functions.
Function notation could be used for vertical parabolas and
for hyperbolas that have the axes as asymptotes.
37. $(-5, -4\sqrt{2}), (-5, 4\sqrt{2}), (3, -2\sqrt{2}), (3, 2\sqrt{2})$
38. $(x - 2)^2 + (y + 1)^2 = 25$ **39.** $\dfrac{x^2}{100} + \dfrac{y^2}{1} = 1$

Test: Chapter 13, p. 887

1. [13.1] $(x - 3)^2 + (y + 4)^2 = 12$ **2.** [13.1] $(4, -1), \sqrt{5}$
3. [13.1] $(-2, 3), 3$
4. [13.1], [13.3] Parabola   **5.** [13.1], [13.3] Circle

$y = x^2 - 4x - 1$

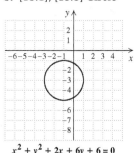
$x^2 + y^2 + 2x + 6y + 6 = 0$

6. [13.3] Hyperbola

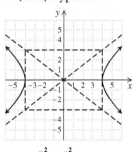
$\dfrac{x^2}{16} - \dfrac{y^2}{9} = 1$

7. [13.2], [13.3] Ellipse

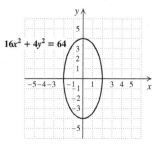
$16x^2 + 4y^2 = 64$

8. [13.3] Hyperbola

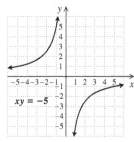
$xy = -5$

9. [13.1], [13.3] Parabola

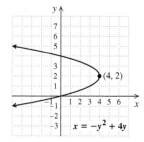
$x = -y^2 + 4y$

10. [13.4] $(0, 6), \left(\frac{144}{25}, \frac{42}{25}\right)$ **11.** [13.4] $(-4, 13), (2, 1)$
12. [13.4] $(3, 2), (-3, -2), \left(-2\sqrt{2}\,i, \dfrac{3\sqrt{2}}{2}\,i\right),$
$\left(2\sqrt{2}\,i, -\dfrac{3\sqrt{2}}{2}\,i\right)$ **13.** [13.4] $(\sqrt{6}, 2), (\sqrt{6}, -2),$
$(-\sqrt{6}, 2), (-\sqrt{6}, -2)$ **14.** [13.4] 2 by 11
15. [13.4] $\sqrt{5}$ m, $\sqrt{3}$ m
16. [13.4] Length: 32 ft; width: 24 ft
17. [13.4] \$1200, 6%   **18.** [13.2] $\dfrac{(x - 6)^2}{25} + \dfrac{(y - 3)^2}{9} = 1$
19. [13.4] 9   **20.** [13.2] $\dfrac{x^2}{16} + \dfrac{y^2}{49} = 1$

Cumulative Review: Chapters 1–13, p. 888

1. $16t^4 - 40t^2s + 25s^2$ **2.** $\dfrac{4t - 3}{3t(t - 3)}$ **3.** $3t^2\sqrt{10w}$
4. $27a^{1/2}b^{3/16}$ **5.** -4 **6.** 25   **7.** $-\frac{1}{64}$
8. $(10x - 3y)^2$ **9.** $3(m^2 - 2)(m^4 + 2m^2 + 4)$
10. $(x - y)(a - b)$ **11.** $(4x - 3)(8x + 1)$
12. $\left(-\infty, -\frac{25}{3}\right]$, or $\left\{x \mid x \le -\frac{25}{3}\right\}$ **13.** $0, \frac{9}{8}$ **14.** 1, 4
15. $\pm i$ **16.** 4   **17.** $\dfrac{\log 1.5}{\log 3} \approx 0.3691$ **18.** 7
19. $(-\sqrt{3}, -1), (-\sqrt{3}, 1), (\sqrt{3}, -1), (\sqrt{3}, 1)$
20.

$3x - y = 9$

21.

$y = \log_5 x$

22.

$$\frac{x^2}{25} + \frac{y^2}{1} = 1$$

23.

$f(x) = 2^{x-1}$

24.

$x^2 + (y - 3)^2 = 4$

25.

$x < 2y + 1$

26.

Maximum: 3
$(-2, 3)$
$x = -2$
$f(x) = -(x + 2)^2 + 3$

27. $y = -x + 3$
28. $x^2 - 3 = 0$
29. 2640 mi

30. **(a)** $g(t) = -687.5t + 48{,}750$; **(b)** 43,250 ft²;
(c) about 2019   **31. (a)** $P(t) = 2.19e^{-0.0084t}$;
(b) 1.96 million; **(c)** 83 years   **32.** 8 in. by 8 in.
33. y is divided by 10.   **34.** $(-\infty, 0) \cup (0, 1]$, or
$\{x \mid x < 0 \ or \ 0 < x \le 1\}$

CHAPTER 14

Exercise Set 14.1, pp. 894–896

1. B   **2.** A   **3.** B   **4.** A   **5.** A   **6.** B   **7.** (f)
8. (a)   **9.** (d)   **10.** (b)   **11.** (c)   **12.** (e)
13. 43   **15.** 364   **17.** -23.5 **19.** -363 **21.** $\frac{441}{400}$
23. 2, 5, 8, 11; 29; 44   **25.** 3, 6, 11, 18; 102; 227
27. $\frac{1}{2}, \frac{2}{3}, \frac{3}{4}, \frac{4}{5}, \frac{10}{11}, \frac{15}{16}$ **29.** $1, -\frac{1}{2}, \frac{1}{4}, -\frac{1}{8}, -\frac{1}{512}, \frac{1}{16{,}384}$
31. $-1, \frac{1}{2}, -\frac{1}{3}, \frac{1}{4}, \frac{1}{10}, -\frac{1}{15}$ **33.** $0, 7, -26, 63; 999; -3374$
35. $2n$ **37.** $(-1)^n$ **39.** $(-1)^{n+1} \cdot n$ **41.** $2n + 1$
43. $n^2 - 1$, or $(n + 1)(n - 1)$ **45.** $\dfrac{n}{n + 1}$
47. $(0.1)^n$, or 10^{-n} **49.** $(-1)^n \cdot n^2$ **51.** 5
53. 1.11111, or $1\frac{11{,}111}{100{,}000}$ **55.** $\frac{1}{2} + \frac{1}{4} + \frac{1}{6} + \frac{1}{8} + \frac{1}{10} = \frac{137}{120}$
57. $10^0 + 10^1 + 10^2 + 10^3 + 10^4 = 11{,}111$
59. $2 + \frac{3}{2} + \frac{4}{3} + \frac{5}{4} + \frac{6}{5} + \frac{7}{6} + \frac{8}{7} = \frac{1343}{140}$
61. $(-1)^2 2^1 + (-1)^3 2^2 + (-1)^4 2^3 + (-1)^5 2^4 +$
$(-1)^6 2^5 + (-1)^7 2^6 + (-1)^8 2^7 + (-1)^9 2^8 = -170$
63. $(0^2 - 2 \cdot 0 + 3) + (1^2 - 2 \cdot 1 + 3) +$
$(2^2 - 2 \cdot 2 + 3) + (3^2 - 2 \cdot 3 + 3) +$
$(4^2 - 2 \cdot 4 + 3) + (5^2 - 2 \cdot 5 + 3) = 43$
65. $\dfrac{(-1)^3}{3 \cdot 4} + \dfrac{(-1)^4}{4 \cdot 5} + \dfrac{(-1)^5}{5 \cdot 6} = -\dfrac{1}{15}$ **67.** $\displaystyle\sum_{k=1}^{5} \dfrac{k+1}{k+2}$

69. $\displaystyle\sum_{k=1}^{6} k^2$ **71.** $\displaystyle\sum_{k=2}^{n} (-1)^k k^2$ **73.** $\displaystyle\sum_{k=1}^{\infty} 6k$
75. $\displaystyle\sum_{k=1}^{\infty} \dfrac{1}{k(k + 1)}$ **77.** 📋   **79.** $t^2 - t + 1$ **80.** $\dfrac{x}{a}$
81. $\dfrac{5a - 3}{a(a - 1)(a + 1)}$ **82.** $\dfrac{2t}{t - 1}$ **83.** $\dfrac{x - 4}{4(x + 2)}$
84. $\dfrac{3(y + 1)(y - 1)}{y}$ **85.** 📋   **87.** 1, 3, 13, 63, 313, 1563
89. $2500, $2000, $1600, $1280, $1024, $819.20, $655.36,
$524.29, $419.43, $335.54   **91.** $S_{100} = 0; S_{101} = -1$
93. $i, -1, -i, 1, i; i$ **95.** 11th term

Prepare to Move On, p. 896

1. 98   **2.** -15 **3.** $a_1 + a_n$ **4.** d

Exercise Set 14.2, pp. 902–904

1. Arithmetic series   **2.** Common difference
3. First term   **4.** Sum   **5.** $a_1 = 8, d = 5$
7. $a_1 = 7, d = -4$ **9.** $a_1 = \frac{3}{2}, d = \frac{3}{4}$
11. $a_1 = $8.16, d = 0.30 **13.** 154   **15.** -94
17. $-$1628.16$ **19.** 26th   **21.** 57th   **23.** 178
25. 5   **27.** 28   **29.** $a_1 = 8; d = -3; 8, 5, 2, -1, -4$
31. $a_1 = 1; d = 1$ **33.** 780   **35.** 31,375   **37.** 2550
39. 918   **41.** 1030   **43.** 35 musicians; 315 musicians
45. 180 stones   **47.** $49.60   **49.** 📋
51. $y = \frac{1}{3}x + 10$ **52.** $y = -4x + 11$ **53.** $y = -2x + 10$
54. $y = -\frac{4}{3}x - \frac{16}{3}$ **55.** $x^2 + y^2 = 16$
56. $(x + 2)^2 + (y - 1)^2 = 20$ **57.** 📋
59. 33 jumps   **61.** Let $d = $ the common difference.
Since $p, m,$ and q form an arithmetic sequence, $m = p + d$
and
$$q = p + 2d. \text{ Then } \frac{p + q}{2} = \frac{p + (p + 2d)}{2} = p + d = m.$$
63. 156,375

Quick Quiz: Sections 14.1–14.2, p. 904

1. 19   **2.** $a_n = (n - 1)^2$ **3.** $\displaystyle\sum_{k=1}^{\infty} 2k$ **4.** -0.5 **5.** 1

Prepare to Move On, p. 904

1. 315   **2.** 50   **3.** $\frac{2}{3}$

Connecting the Concepts, p. 909

1. -3 **2.** $-\frac{1}{2}$ **3.** 110   **4.** 640   **5.** 4410
6. $1146.39   **7.** 1   **8.** No

Exercise Set 14.3, pp. 911–914

1. Infinite; geometric; sequence   **2.** Finite; geometric;
series   **3.** Ratio; less; does   **4.** $0.22\ldots$; geometric;
series   **5.** Geometric sequence   **6.** Arithmetic sequence
7. Geometric series   **8.** Arithmetic series
9. Geometric series   **10.** None of these   **11.** 2
13. -0.1 **15.** $-\frac{1}{2}$ **17.** $\frac{1}{5}$ **19.** $\dfrac{6}{m}$ **21.** 1458

23. 243 **25.** 52,488 **27.** \$1423.31 **29.** $a_n = 5^{n-1}$
31. $a_n = (-1)^{n-1}$, or $a_n = (-1)^{n+1}$
33. $a_n = \dfrac{1}{x^n}$, or $a_n = x^{-n}$ **35.** 3066 **37.** $\frac{547}{18}$
39. $\dfrac{1 - x^8}{1 - x}$, or $(1 + x)(1 + x^2)(1 + x^4)$ **41.** \$5134.51
43. 27 **45.** $\frac{49}{4}$ **47.** No **49.** No **51.** $\frac{43}{99}$
53. \$25,000 **55.** $\frac{5}{9}$ **57.** $\frac{343}{99}$ **59.** $\frac{5}{33}$ **61.** $\frac{5}{1024}$ ft
63. 155,797 **65.** 2710 flies **67.** About 1456 GW
69. 3100.35 ft **71.** 20.48 in. **73.**
75. $\{-8, 14\}$ **76.** $\left(x \mid -\frac{11}{2} < x < \frac{1}{2}\right)$, or $\left(-\frac{11}{2}, \frac{1}{2}\right)$
77. $\left\{x \mid x \le 2 \, or \, x \ge \frac{8}{3}\right\}$, or $\left(-\infty, 2\right] \cup \left[\frac{8}{3}, \infty\right)$
78. $\left\{x \mid -\frac{1}{3} < x < \frac{11}{3}\right\}$, or $\left(-\frac{1}{3}, \frac{11}{3}\right)$
79. $\{x \mid -2 < x < 7\}$, or $(-2, 7)$
80. $\{x \mid -1 \le x < 0 \, or \, x \ge 1\}$, or $[-1, 0) \cup [1, \infty)$
81.   **83.** 54 **85.** $\dfrac{x^2[1 - (-x)^n]}{1 + x}$ **87.** 512 cm^2
89.   **91.**

Quick Quiz: Sections 14.1–14.3, p. 914

1. $-1, 2, -3, 4; 20$ **2.** 140 **3.** 435 **4.** $511\frac{1}{2}$
5. $\frac{155}{99}$

Prepare to Move On, p. 914

1. $x^2 + 2xy + y^2$ **2.** $x^3 + 3x^2y + 3xy^2 + y^3$
3. $x^3 - 3x^2y + 3xy^2 - y^3$
4. $x^4 - 4x^3y + 6x^2y^2 - 4xy^3 + y^4$
5. $8x^3 + 12x^2y + 6xy^2 + y^3$
6. $8x^3 - 12x^2y + 6xy^2 - y^3$

Mid-Chapter Review: Chapter 14, p. 915

1. $a_n = a_1 + (n - 1)d$ **2.** $a_n = a_1r^{n-1}$
$\quad n = 14, a_1 = -6, d = 5$ $\qquad n = 7, a_1 = \frac{1}{9}, r = -3$
$\quad a_{14} = -6 + (14 - 1)5$ $\qquad a_7 = \frac{1}{9} \cdot (-3)^{7-1}$
$\quad a_{14} = 59$ $\qquad\qquad a_7 = 81$
3. 300 **4.** $\dfrac{1}{n + 1}$ **5.** 78 **6.** $2^2 + 3^2 + 4^2 + 5^2 = 54$
7. $\displaystyle\sum_{k=1}^{6}(-1)^{k+1} \cdot k$ **8.** 61st **9.** -39 **10.** $\dfrac{1}{10^8}$
11. $2(-1)^{n+1}$ **12.** Yes, a limit exists; $\frac{250}{3}$, or $83\frac{1}{3}$
13. \$465 **14.** \$1,073,741,823

Technology Connection, p. 919

1. 479,001,600 **2.** 56; 792

Exercise Set 14.4, pp. 921–923

1. Binomial **2.** Expansion **3.** First **4.** Third
5. Factorial **6.** Binomial **7.** 2^5, or 32 **8.** 8
9. 9 **10.** 1 **11.** 24 **13.** 3,628,800 **15.** 90
17. 126 **19.** 210 **21.** 1 **23.** 435 **25.** 780
27. $a^4 - 4a^3b + 6a^2b^2 - 4ab^3 + b^4$
29. $p^7 + 7p^6q + 21p^5q^2 + 35p^4q^3 + 35p^3q^4 +$
$21p^2q^5 + 7pq^6 + q^7$

31. $2187c^7 - 5103c^6d + 5103c^5d^2 - 2835c^4d^3 +$
$945c^3d^4 - 189c^2d^5 + 21cd^6 - d^7$
33. $t^{-12} + 12t^{-10} + 60t^{-8} + 160t^{-6} + 240t^{-4} + 192t^{-2} + 64$
35. $19,683s^9 + \dfrac{59,049s^8}{t} + \dfrac{78,732s^7}{t^2} + \dfrac{61,236s^6}{t^3} +$
$\dfrac{30,618s^5}{t^4} + \dfrac{10,206s^4}{t^5} + \dfrac{2268s^3}{t^6} + \dfrac{324s^2}{t^7} + \dfrac{27s}{t^8} + \dfrac{1}{t^9}$
37. $x^{15} - 10x^{12}y + 40x^9y^2 - 80x^6y^3 + 80x^3y^4 - 32y^5$
39. $125 + 150\sqrt{5}t + 375t^2 + 100\sqrt{5}t^3 + 75t^4 +$
$6\sqrt{5}t^5 + t^6$
41. $x^{-3} - 6x^{-2} + 15x^{-1} - 20 + 15x - 6x^2 + x^3$
43. $15a^4b^2$ **45.** $-64,481,508a^3$ **47.** $1120x^{12}y^2$
49. $1,959,552u^5v^{10}$ **51.** y^8 **53.**
55.   **56.**

57.   **58.**

59.   **60.**

61.   **63.** List all the subsets of size 3: $\{a, b, c\}$, $\{a, b, d\}$,
$\{a, b, e\}, \{a, c, d\}, \{a, c, e\}, \{a, d, e\}, \{b, c, d\}, \{b, c, e\}$,
$\{b, d, e\}, \{c, d, e\}$. There are exactly 10 subsets of size 3 and
$\dbinom{5}{3} = 10$, so there are exactly $\dbinom{5}{3}$ ways of forming a
subset of size 3 from $\{a, b, c, d, e\}$.
65. $\dbinom{8}{5}(0.15)^3(0.85)^5 \approx 0.084$ **67.** $\dbinom{8}{6}(0.15)^2(0.85)^6 +$
$\dbinom{8}{7}(0.15)(0.85)^7 + \dbinom{8}{8}(0.85)^8 \approx 0.89$
69. $\dbinom{n}{n - r} = \dfrac{n!}{[n - (n - r)]!(n - r)!}$
$\qquad\qquad = \dfrac{n!}{r!(n - r)!} = \dbinom{n}{r}$

71. $-4320x^6y^{9/2}$ **73.** $-\dfrac{35}{x^{1/6}}$ **75.** 12

Quick Quiz: Sections 14.1–14.4, p. 923

1. $\dfrac{1+1}{1} + \dfrac{2+1}{2} + \dfrac{3+1}{3} + \dfrac{4+1}{4} = \dfrac{73}{12}$ **2.** -0.4
3. $-\frac{1}{2}$ **4.** 220   **5.** $x^4 + 4x^3w + 6x^2w^2 + 4xw^3 + w^5$

Visualizing for Success, p. 924

1. J   **2.** G   **3.** A   **4.** H   **5.** I   **6.** B   **7.** E
8. D   **9.** F   **10.** C

Decision Making: Connection, p. 925

1. (a) $1000, 1040, 1080, 1120, \ldots$;
(b) $a_n = 1000 + 40(n-1)$;   **(c)** \$1800
2. (a) $1000, 1040, 1081.60, 1124.87, \ldots$;
(b) $a_n = 1000\,(1.04)^{n-1}$;   **(c)** \$2191.12
3. (a) $1000, 1010, 1020, 1030, \ldots$; or
$a_n = 1000 + 10(n-1)$; \$1800
(b) $1000, 1010, 1020.10, 1030.30, \ldots$; or $a_n = 1000(1.01)^{n-1}$;
\$2216.72   **4.** 🖥

Study Summary: Chapter 14, pp. 926–927

1. 143   **2.** -25 **3.** $5 \cdot 0 + 5 \cdot 1 + 5 \cdot 2 + 5 \cdot 3 = 30$
4. 15.5   **5.** 215   **6.** -640 **7.** $-20{,}475$
8. 16   **9.** 39,916,800   **10.** 84
11. $x^{10} - 10x^8 + 40x^6 - 80x^4 + 80x^2 - 32$ **12.** $3240t^7$

Review Exercises: Chapter 14, pp. 927–928

1. False   **2.** True   **3.** True   **4.** False   **5.** False
6. True   **7.** False   **8.** False   **9.** 1, 11, 21, 31; 71; 111
10. $0, \frac{1}{5}, \frac{1}{5}, \frac{3}{17}, \frac{7}{65}, \frac{11}{145}$ **11.** $a_n = -5n$
12. $a_n = (-1)^n(2n-1)$
13. $-2 + 4 + (-8) + 16 + (-32) = -22$
14. $-3 + (-5) + (-7) + (-9) + (-11) + (-13) = -48$
15. $\displaystyle\sum_{k=1}^{6} 7k$ **16.** $\displaystyle\sum_{k=1}^{5}\dfrac{1}{(-2)^k}$ **17.** -55 **18.** $\frac{1}{5}$
19. $a_1 = -15$, $d = 5$ **20.** -544 **21.** $25{,}250$
22. $1024\sqrt{2}$ **23.** $\frac{3}{4}$ **24.** $a_n = 2(-1)^n$
25. $a_n = 3\left(\dfrac{x}{4}\right)^{n-1}$ **26.** 11,718   **27.** $-4095x$ **28.** 12
29. $\frac{49}{11}$ **30.** No   **31.** No   **32.** \$40,000   **33.** $\frac{5}{9}$
34. $\frac{16}{11}$ **35.** \$24.30   **36.** 903 poles   **37.** \$15,791.18
38. 6 m   **39.** 5040   **40.** 120   **41.** $190a^{18}b^2$
42. $x^4 - 8x^3y + 24x^2y^2 - 32xy^3 + 16y^4$

43. ✏ For a geometric sequence with $|r| < 1$, as n gets larger, the absolute value of the terms gets smaller, since $|r^n|$ gets smaller.   **44.** ✏ The first form of the binomial theorem draws the coefficients from Pascal's triangle; the second form uses factorial notation. The second form avoids the need to compute all preceding rows of Pascal's triangle, and is generally easier to use when only one term of an expansion is needed. When several terms of an expansion are needed and n is not large (say, $n \le 8$), it is often easier to use Pascal's triangle.   **45.** $\dfrac{1-(-x)^n}{x+1}$
46. $x^{-15} + 5x^{-9} + 10x^{-3} + 10x^3 + 5x^9 + x^{15}$

Test: Chapter 14, p. 929

1. [14.1] $\frac{1}{2}, \frac{1}{5}, \frac{1}{10}, \frac{1}{17}, \frac{1}{26}; \frac{1}{145}$ **2.** [14.1] $a_n = 4\left(\frac{1}{3}\right)^n$
3. [14.1] $-3 + (-7) + (-15) + (-31) = -56$
4. [14.1] $\displaystyle\sum_{k=1}^{5}(-1)^{k+1}k^3$ **5.** [14.2] $\frac{13}{2}$
6. [14.2] $a_1 = 31.2$; $d = -3.8$ **7.** [14.2] 2508
8. [14.3] 1536   **9.** [14.3] $\frac{2}{3}$ **10.** [14.3] 3^n
11. [14.3] 5621   **12.** [14.3] 1   **13.** [14.3] No
14. [14.3] $\frac{\$25{,}000}{23} \approx \$1086.96$ **15.** [14.3] $\frac{85}{99}$
16. [14.2] 63 seats   **17.** [14.2] \$17,100
18. [14.3] \$5987.37   **19.** [14.3] 36 m   **20.** [14.4] 220
21. [14.4] $x^5 - 15x^4y + 90x^3y^2 - 270x^2y^3 +$
$405xy^4 - 243y^5$ **22.** [14.4] $220a^9x^3$

23. [14.2] $n(n+1)$ **24.** [14.3] $\dfrac{1 - \left(\dfrac{1}{x}\right)^n}{1 - \dfrac{1}{x}}$, or $\dfrac{x^n - 1}{x^{n-1}(x-1)}$

Cumulative Review/Final Exam: Chapters 1–14, pp. 930–931

1. $\frac{7}{15}$ **2.** $-4y + 17$ **3.** 280   **4.** 8.4×10^{-15}
5. $3a^2 - 8ab - 15b^2$ **6.** $4a^2 - 1$
7. $9a^4 - 30a^2y + 25y^2$ **8.** $\dfrac{4}{x+2}$
9. $\dfrac{(x+y)(x^2 + xy + y^2)}{x^2 + y^2}$ **10.** $x - a$ **11.** $12a^2\sqrt{b}$
12. $-27x^{10}y^{-2}$, or $-\dfrac{27x^{10}}{y^2}$ **13.** $25x^4y^{1/3}$
14. $y\sqrt[12]{x^5y^2}$, $y \ge 0$ **15.** $14 + 8i$
16. $(2x - 3)^2$ **17.** $(3a - 2)(9a^2 + 6a + 4)$
18. $12(s^2 + 2t)(s^2 - 2t)$ **19.** $3(y^2 + 3)(5y^2 - 4)$
20. $7x^3 + 9x^2 + 19x + 38 + \dfrac{72}{x - 2}$
21. $[4, \infty)$, or $\{x \mid x \ge 4\}$ **22.** $(-\infty, 5) \cup (5, \infty)$,
or $\{x \mid x < 5 \text{ or } x > 5\}$ **23.** $y = 3x - 8$
24. $x^2 - 50 = 0$ **25.** $(2, -3)$; 6
26. $\log_a \dfrac{\sqrt[3]{x^2} \cdot z^5}{\sqrt{y}}$ **27.** $a^5 = c$ **28.** 2.0792
29. 0.6826   **30.** 5   **31.** -121 **32.** 875
33. $16\left(\frac{1}{4}\right)^{n-1}$ **34.** $13{,}440a^4b^6$ **35.** $\frac{3}{5}$ **36.** $-\frac{6}{5}, 4$
37. $\mathbb{R}$, or $(-\infty, \infty)$ **38.** $\left(-1, \frac{1}{2}\right)$ **39.** $(2, -1, 1)$
40. 2   **41.** $\pm 2, \pm 5$ **42.** $(\sqrt{5}, \sqrt{3})$, $(\sqrt{5}, -\sqrt{3})$,
$(-\sqrt{5}, \sqrt{3})$, $(-\sqrt{5}, -\sqrt{3})$ **43.** 1.7925   **44.** 1005
45. $-\frac{1}{2}$ **46.** $\{x \mid -2 \le x \le 3\}$, or $[-2, 3]$
47. $\pm i\sqrt{3}$ **48.** $-2 \pm \sqrt{7}$ **49.** $\{y \mid y < -5 \text{ or } y > 2\}$,
or $(-\infty, -5) \cup (2, \infty)$ **50.** $-8, 10$ **51.** $R = \dfrac{Ir}{1 - I}$

52.

53.

54.

55.

56.

57.

58.

59. 5000 ft²   **60.** 5 ft by 12 ft
61. More than 25 downloads
62. $2.68 herb: 10 oz; $4.60
herb: 14 oz   **63.** 350 mph
64. $8\frac{2}{5}$ hr, or 8 hr 24 min
65. **(a)** $1.5 trillion per year;
(b) $f(t) = 1.5t + 9$;
(c) $P(t) = 9e^{0.128t}$;
(d) $27 trillion;
(e) 41.8 trillion;
(f) about 5.4 years
66. All real numbers except 0 and −12   **67.** 81
68. y gets divided by 8   **69.** 84 years

CHAPTER R

Exercise Set R.1, pp. 938–939

1. >   **3.** <   **5.** >   **7.** 22   **9.** 1.3
11. −25   **13.** $-\frac{11}{15}$ **15.** −6.5   **17.** −9   **19.** 0
21. $-\frac{1}{2}$ **23.** 5.8   **25.** −3   **27.** 39   **29.** 175
31. −32   **33.** 16   **35.** −6   **37.** 9   **39.** −3
41. −16   **43.** 100   **45.** 2   **47.** −23   **49.** 36
51. 10   **53.** 10   **55.** −7   **57.** 32   **59.** 28 cm²
61. $8x + 28$ **63.** $-30 + 6x$ **65.** $8a + 12b - 6c$
67. $-6x + 3y - 3z$ **69.** $2(4x + 3y)$ **71.** $3(1 + w)$
73. $10(x + 5y + 10)$ **75.** p **77.** $-m + 22$
79. $-5x + 7$ **81.** $6p - 7$ **83.** $-x + 12y$
85. $36a - 48b$ **87.** $-10x + 104y + 9$ **89.** Let n
represent the number; $3n = 348$ **91.** Let c represent
the international per capita consumption of Coca-Cola
beverages; $412 = 5.15c$ **93.** Let h represent the number
of calories in an order of McDonald's hotcakes and sausage;
$1060 = 2h + 20$

Exercise Set R.2, pp. 946–948

1. 16   **3.** $-\frac{1}{12}$ **5.** −0.8   **7.** $-\frac{5}{3}$ **9.** 42   **11.** −5
13. $\frac{5}{3}$ **15.** $-\frac{4}{9}$ **17.** −4   **19.** $\frac{69}{5}$ **21.** $\frac{9}{32}$

23. −2   **25.** −15   **27.** $\frac{43}{2}$ **29.** $-\frac{61}{115}$ **31.** $l = \dfrac{A}{w}$

33. $P = IV$ **35.** $p = 2q - r$ **37.** $\pi = \dfrac{A}{r^2 + r^2 h}$

39. $\{x \,|\, x \le 12\}$, or $(-\infty, 12]$

41. $\{m \,|\, m > 12\}$, or $(12, \infty)$

43. $\{x \,|\, x \ge -\frac{3}{2}\}$, or $[-\frac{3}{2}, \infty)$

45. $\{t \,|\, t < -3\}$, or $(-\infty, -3)$

47. $\{y \,|\, y > 10\}$, or $(10, \infty)$ **49.** $\{a \,|\, a \ge 1\}$, or $[1, \infty)$
51. $\{x \,|\, x \ge \frac{64}{17}\}$, or $[\frac{64}{17}, \infty)$ **53.** $\{x \,|\, x > \frac{39}{11}\}$, or $(\frac{39}{11}, \infty)$
55. $\{x \,|\, x \le -10.875\}$, or $(-\infty, -10.875]$ **57.** 7
59. 16, 18   **61.** $166\frac{2}{3}$ pages   **63.** 4.5 cm, 9.5 cm
65. 900 cubic feet   **67.** 110¢, or $1.10   **69.** 30 min
or more   **71.** For $2\frac{7}{9}$ hr or less

Exercise Set R.3, p. 954

1.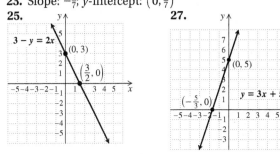

3. II   **5.** x-axis
7. IV   **9.** No
11. Yes

13.   **15.**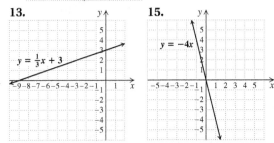

17. −1   **19.** 0   **21.** Slope: 2; y-intercept: $(0, -5)$
23. Slope: $-\frac{2}{7}$; y-intercept: $\left(0, \frac{1}{7}\right)$

29.

31.

33.

35. 0

37. Undefined

39. $y = 5x + 9$

41. $y = -x + 3$

43. Perpendicular

45. Neither

Exercise Set R.4, pp. 961–962

1. 1   **3.** -3 **5.** $\dfrac{1}{8^2} = \dfrac{1}{64}$ **7.** $\dfrac{10}{x^5}$ **9.** $\dfrac{1}{(ab)^2}$

11. y^{10} **13.** x^{15} **15.** a^6 **17.** $(4x)^9$ **19.** 7^{40}

21. $x^8 y^{12}$ **23.** $\dfrac{y^6}{64}$ **25.** $\dfrac{9q^8}{4p^6}$ **27.** $8x^3, -6x^2, x, -7$

29. $18, 36, -7, 3; 3, 9, 1, 0; 9$ **31.** $-1, 4, -2; 3, 3, 2; 3$

33. $8p^4; 8$ **35.** $x^4 + 3x^3$ **37.** $-7t^2 + 5t + 10$

39. 36   **41.** -14 **43.** 9 words

45. $4x^3 - 3x^2 + 8x + 7$ **47.** $-y^2 + 5y - 2$

49. $-3x^2y - y^2 + 8y$ **51.** $12x^5 - 28x^3 + 28x^2$

53. $8a^2 + 2ab + 4ay + by$ **55.** $x^3 + 4x^2 - 20x + 7$

57. $x^2 - 49$ **59.** $x^2 + 2xy + y^2$ **61.** $6x^4 + 17x^2 - 14$

63. $42a^2 - 17ay - 15y^2$ **65.** $-t^4 - 3t^2 + 2t - 5$

67. $5x + 3$ **69.** $2x^2 - 3x + 3 + \dfrac{-2}{x + 1}$

71. $5x + 3 + \dfrac{3}{x^2 - 1}$

Exercise Set R.5, p. 970

1. $6t^3(3t^2 - 2t + 1)$ **3.** $(y - 3)^2$

5. $(p + 2)(2p^3 + 1)$ **7.** Prime

9. $(2t + 3)(4t^2 - 6t + 9)$ **11.** $(m + 6)(m + 7)$

13. $(x^2 + 9)(x + 3)(x - 3)$ **15.** $(2x + 3)(4x + 5)$

17. $(x + 2)(x + 1)(x - 1)$

19. $(0.1t^2 - 0.2)(0.01t^4 + 0.02t^2 + 0.04)$

21. $\left(x^2 + \frac{1}{4}\right)\left(x + \frac{1}{2}\right)\left(x - \frac{1}{2}\right)$ **23.** $(n - 2)(m + 3)$

25. $(m + 15n)(m - 10n)$ **27.** $2y(3x + 1)(4x - 3)$

29. $(y - 11)^2$ **31.** $-3, 1$ **33.** $0, 11$ **35.** $-3, 3$

37. $-\frac{5}{2}, 7$ **39.** $0, 5$ **41.** $-2, 6$ **43.** $-11, 5$

45. -5 **47.** Base: 8 ft; height: 5 ft   **49.** 6 ft

Exercise Set R.6, pp. 980–981

1. $-\frac{1}{3}$ **3.** $-2, 2$ **5.** $\dfrac{8x}{9y}$ **7.** $\dfrac{t + 2}{t + 4}$ **9.** $\dfrac{-1}{x + 2}$

11. $\dfrac{6}{x}$ **13.** $\dfrac{(a + 1)^3(a - 1)}{a^3}$ **15.** 1   **17.** $\dfrac{5x + 4}{x^2}$

19. $\dfrac{6a + 3b - 4}{3a - 3b}$ **21.** $\dfrac{-3}{5x(x + 2)}$ **23.** $\dfrac{(x + 1)^2}{x^2(x + 2)}$

25. $\dfrac{x + 3}{(x + 1)^2}$ **27.** 1   **29.** $\dfrac{2t + 1}{(t + 1)(t - 1)}$

31. $\dfrac{-3x}{2}$ **33.** $\dfrac{-7(2x + 1)}{(x + 5)(x - 4)}$ **35.** $\dfrac{8x - 4}{x^3}$

37. $\dfrac{3(x + 1)}{(x - 7)(4x + 3)}$ **39.** $\dfrac{(x + 1)^2}{(x - 2)(x + 4)}$ **41.** $\dfrac{-1}{x}$

43. $\frac{6}{5}$ **45.** 1   **47.** $\frac{31}{2}$ **49.** $-4, 4$ **51.** $22\frac{2}{9}$ hr

53. Jessica: 45 km/h; Josh: 25 km/h   **55.** 50

APPENDIXES

Exercise Set A, pp. 985–986

1. Mean: 17; median: 18; mode: 13   **3.** Mean: $10.\overline{6}$; median: 9; modes: 3, 20   **5.** Mean: 4.06; median: 4.6; mode: none   **7.** Mean: $239.\overline{3}$; median: 234; mode: 234

9. Average: 34.875; median: 22; mode: 0   **11.** Average: $218.\overline{3}$; median: 222; mode: 202   **13.** 10 home runs

15. $a = 30, b = 58$

Exercise Set B, pp. 987–988

1. $\{8, 9, 10, 11\}$ **3.** $\{41, 43, 45, 47, 49\}$ **5.** $\{-3, 3\}$

7. True   **9.** True   **11.** False   **13.** True   **15.** False

17. True   **19.** $\{c, d, e\}$ **21.** $\{1, 2, 3, 6\}$ **23.** $\varnothing$

25. $\{a, e, i, o, u, q, c, k\}$ **27.** $\{1, 2, 3, 4, 6, 9, 12, 18\}$

29. $\{1, 2, 3, 4, 5, 6, 7, 8\}$ **31.** ◫   **33.** The set of integers   **35.** The set of real numbers   **37.** $\varnothing$

39. (a) A; **(b)** A; **(c)** A; **(d)** $\varnothing$ **41.** True   **43.** True

45. True

Exercise Set C, pp. 992–993

1. True   **2.** True   **3.** False   **4.** False   **5.** True

6. True   **7.** $x^2 - 3x - 5$ **9.** $a + 5 + \dfrac{-4}{a + 3}$

11. $2x^2 - 5x + 3 + \dfrac{8}{x + 2}$ **13.** $a^2 + 2a - 6$

15. $3y^2 + 2y + 6 + \dfrac{-2}{y - 3}$ **17.** $x^4 + 2x^3 + 4x^2 + 8x + 16$

19. $3x^2 + 6x - 3 + \dfrac{2}{x + \frac{1}{3}}$ **21.** 6   **23.** 125   **25.** 0

27. ◫   **29.** ◫   **31. (a)** The degree of R must be less than 1, the degree of $x - r$, **(b)** Let $x = r$. Then $P(r) = (r - r) \cdot Q(r) + R = 0 \cdot Q(r) + R = R$.

33. $0; -3; -\frac{5}{2}, \frac{3}{2}$ **35.** ◫   **37.** 0

GLOSSARY

Absolute value [R.1, 1.4] The distance that a number is from 0 on the number line

Additive identity [1.5] The number 0

Additive inverse [1.6] A number's opposite; two numbers are additive inverses of each other if when added the result is zero

Algebraic expression [R.1, 1.1] An expression consisting of variables and/or numerals, often with operation signs and grouping symbols

Arithmetic sequence (or Progression) [14.2] A sequence in which the difference between any two successive terms is constant

Arithmetic series [14.2] A series for which the associated sequence is arithmetic

Ascending order [4.4] A polynomial in one variable written with the terms arranged according to degree, from least to greatest

Associative law for addition [R.1, 1.2] The statement that when three numbers are added, changing the grouping does not change the result

Associative law for multiplication [R.1, 1.2] The statement that when three numbers are multiplied, changing the grouping does not change the result

Asymptote [13.3] A line that a graph approaches more and more closely as x increases or as x decreases

Average [2.7, App A] Most commonly, the *mean* of a set of numbers, found by adding the numbers and then dividing by the number of addends

Axes (singular, Axis) [R.3, 3.1] Two perpendicular number lines used to identify points in a plane

Axis of symmetry [11.6] A line that can be drawn through a graph such that the part of the graph on one side of the line is an exact reflection of the part on the opposite side

Bar graph [3.1] A graphic display of data using bars proportional in length to the numbers represented

Base [1.8] In exponential notation, the number being raised to a power

Binomial [R.4, 4.3] A polynomial with two terms

Branches [13.3] The two curves that comprise a hyperbola

Break-even point [8.8] In business, the point of intersection of the revenue function and the cost function

Center point [App A] A single representative number used to analyze a set of data; also called *measure of central tendency*

Circle [13.1] A set of points in a plane that are a fixed distance r, called the radius, from a fixed point (h, k), called the center

Circle graph [3.1] A graphic display of data often used to show what percent of the whole each item in a group represents

Circumference [2.3] The distance around a circle

Closed interval [a, b] [R.2, 2.6] The set of all numbers x for which $a \leq x \leq b$; thus, $[a, b] = \{x \mid a \leq x \leq b\}$

Coefficient [R.4, 2.1, 4.3] The numerical multiplier of a variable

Combined variation [7.5] A mathematical relationship in which a variable varies directly and/or inversely, at the same time, with more than one other variable

Common factor [R.5, 1.2] A factor that appears in every term in an expression

Common logarithm [12.5] A logarithm with base 10

Commutative law for addition [R.1, 1.2] The statement that when two numbers are added, changing the order of addition does not affect the answer

Commutative law for multiplication [R.1, 1.2] The statement that when two numbers are multiplied, changing the order of multiplication does not affect the answer

Completing the square [11.1] A method of adding a particular constant to an expression so that the resulting sum is a perfect square

Complex number [10.8] Any number that can be written in the form $a + bi$, where a and b are real numbers and $i = \sqrt{-1}$

Complex rational expression [R.6, 6.5] A rational expression that contains rational expressions within its numerator and/or its denominator

Complex-number system [10.8] A number system that contains the real-number system and is designed so that negative numbers have defined square roots

Composite function [12.1] A function in which some quantity depends on a variable that, in turn, depends on another variable

Composite number [1.3] A natural number other than 1 that is not prime

Compound inequality [9.2] A statement in which two or more inequalities are joined by the word "and" or the word "or"

Compound interest [11.1] Interest earned on both the initial investment and the interest from previous periods

Conditional equation [R.2, 2.2] An equation that is true for some replacements and false for others

Conic section [13.1] A curve formed by the intersection of a plane and a cone

Conjugate of a complex number [10.8] The *conjugate* of a complex number $a + bi$ is $a - bi$, and the *conjugate* of $a - bi$ is $a + bi$.

Conjugates [10.5] Pairs of radical expressions like $\sqrt{a} + \sqrt{b}$ and $\sqrt{a} - \sqrt{b}$

Conjunction [9.2] A sentence in which two or more statements are joined by the word "and"

Consecutive even integers [2.5] Integers that are even and two units apart

Consecutive integers [2.5] Integers that are one unit apart

Consecutive odd integers [2.5] Integers that are odd and two units apart

Consistent system of equations [8.1, 8.4] A system of equations that has at least one solution

Constant [R.1, 1.1]   A particular number that never changes

Constant of proportionality [7.5]   The constant, k, in an equation of variation; also called *variation constant*

Constant function [7.3]   A function given by an equation of the form $f(x) = b$, where b is a real number

Constant polynomial [R.4]   A polynomial of degree 0

Contradiction [R.2, 2.2]   An equation that is never true

Coordinates [R.3, 3.1]   The numbers in an ordered pair

Counting numbers [1.3]   The set of numbers used for counting: $\{1, 2, 3, 4, 5, \ldots\}$; also called *natural numbers*

Cube root [10.1]   The number c is the *cube root* of a if $c^3 = a$.

Cubic polynomial [R.4]   A polynomial in one variable of degree 3

Data [1.1]   A set of numbers used to represent information

Decay rate [12.7]   The rate of decay of a population or other quantity at any instant in time

Degree of a monomial [R.4, 4.3]   The number of variable factors in the monomial

Degree of a polynomial [R.4, 4.3, 4.7]   The degree of the term of highest degree in a polynomial

Demand function [8.8]   A function modeling the relationship between the price of a good and the quantity of that good demanded

Denominator [1.3]   The number below the fraction bar in a fraction

Dependent equations [8.1, 8.4]   Equations in a system from which one equation can be removed without changing the solution set

Descending order [R.4, 4.4]   A polynomial in one variable written with the terms arranged according to degree, from greatest to least

Determinant [8.7]   A descriptor of a square matrix; the determinant of a two-by-two matrix $\begin{bmatrix} a & c \\ b & d \end{bmatrix}$ is denoted by $\begin{vmatrix} a & c \\ b & d \end{vmatrix}$ and is defined as $ad - bc$.

Difference [1.2]   The result when two numbers are subtracted

Difference of cubes [R.5, 5.5]   An expression that can be written in the form $A^3 - B^3$

Difference of squares [R.4, R.5, 4.6, 5.4]   An expression that can be written in the form $A^2 - B^2$

Direct variation [7.5]   A situation that can be modeled by a linear function of the form $f(x) = kx$, or $y = kx$, where k is a nonzero constant

Discriminant [11.3]   The radicand $b^2 - 4ac$ from the quadratic formula

Disjunction [9.2]   A sentence in which two or more statements are joined by the word "or"

Distance formula [10.7]   The formula $d = \sqrt{(x_2 - x_1)^2 + (y_2 - y_1)^2}$, where d is the distance between any two points (x_1, y_1) and (x_2, y_2)

Distributive law [R.1, 1.2]   The statement that multiplying a factor by the sum of two numbers gives the same result as multiplying the factor by each of the two numbers and then adding

Domain [7.1, 7.2]   The set of all first coordinates of the ordered pairs in a function

Doubling time [12.7]   The amount of time necessary for a population to double in size

Elements [App B]   The objects of a set

Elements of a matrix [8.6]   The individual entries in a matrix

Elimination method [8.2]   An algebraic method that uses the addition principle to solve a system of equations

Ellipse [13.2]   The set of all points in a plane for which the sum of the distances from two fixed points F_1 and F_2 is constant

Empty set [2.2, App B]   The set containing no elements, written $\varnothing$ or $\{\ \}$

Equation [1.1]   A number sentence formed by placing an equals sign between two expressions

Equilibrium point [8.8]   The point of intersection between the demand function and the supply function

Equivalent equations [R.2, 2.1]   Equations that have the same solutions

Equivalent expressions [R.1, 1.2]   Expressions that have the same value for all allowable replacements

Equivalent inequalities [R.2, 2.6]   Inequalities that have the same solution set

Evaluate [R.1, 1.1]   To substitute a number for each variable in the expression and calculate the result

Even root [10.1]   A root with an even index

Exponent [1.8]   In an expression of the form b^n, the number n is an exponent.

Exponential decay [12.7]   A decrease in quantity over time that can be modeled by an exponential function of the form $P(t) = P_0 e^{-kt}$, $k > 0$, where P_0 is the quantity present at time 0, $P(t)$ is the amount present at time t, and k is the exponential decay rate

Exponential equation [12.6]   An equation with a variable in an exponent.

Exponential function [12.2]   A function $f(x) = a^x$, where a is a positive constant, $a \neq 1$, and x is any real number

Exponential growth [12.7]   An increase in quantity over time that can be modeled by an exponential function of the form $P(t) = P_0 e^{kt}$, $k > 0$, where P_0 is the quantity present at time 0, $P(t)$ is the amount present at time t, and k is the exponential growth rate

Exponential notation [R.1, 1.8]   A representation of a number using a base raised to an exponent

Extrapolation [3.7]   The process of estimating a value that goes beyond the given data

Factor [R.1, 1.2, 5.1]   *Verb*: To write an equivalent expression that is a product; *noun*: part of a product

Factoring [1.2]   The process of rewriting an expression as a product

Factoring by grouping [R.5, 5.1]   If a polynomial can be split into groups of terms and the groups share a common factor, then the original polynomial can be factored. This method can be tried on any polynomial with four or more terms.

Finite sequence [14.1]   A function having for its domain a set of natural numbers: $\{1, 2, 3, 4, 5, \ldots, n\}$, for some natural number n

Finite series [14.1]   The sum of the first n terms of a sequence: $a_1 + a_2 + a_3 + \cdots + a_n$; also called *partial sum*

Fixed costs [8.8]   In business, costs that must be paid regardless of how many items are produced

Foci (singular, **Focus**) **[13.2]** Two fixed points that determine the points of an ellipse

FOIL method [R.4, 4.6] To multiply two binomials $A + B$ and $C + D$, multiply the First terms AC, the Outside terms AD, the Inner terms BC, and then the Last terms BD. Then add the results.

Formula [R.2, 2.3] An equation using numbers and/or letters to represent a relationship between two or more quantities

Fraction notation [1.3] A number written using a numerator and a denominator

Function [7.1] A correspondence between a first set, called the *domain*, and a second set, called the *range*, such that each member of the domain corresponds to *exactly one* member of the range

General term of a sequence [14.1] The nth term, denoted a_n

Geometric sequence [14.3] A sequence in which the ratio of every pair of successive terms is constant

Geometric series [14.3] A series for which the associated sequence is geometric

Grade [3.5] The ratio of the vertical distance a road rises over the horizontal distance it runs, expressed as a percent

Graph [R.2, 2.6] A picture or a diagram of the data in a table; a line, a curve, a plane, a collection of points, etc., that represents all the solutions of an equation or an inequality

Grouping method [5.3] A method for factoring a trinomial of the type $ax^2 + bx + c$, that uses factoring by grouping

Growth rate [12.7] The rate of growth of a population or other quantity at any instant in time

Half-life [12.7] The amount of time necessary for half of a quantity to decay

Half-open intervals $(a, b]$ and $[a, b)$ [R.2, 2.6] An interval that contains one endpoint and not the other; thus, $(a, b] = \{x \mid a < x \le b\}$ and $[a, b) = \{x \mid a \le x < b\}$

Horizontal line [R.3, 3.3, 3.7] The graph of $y = b$ is a horizontal line, with y-intercept $(0, b)$.

Horizontal-line test [12.1] If it is impossible to draw a horizontal line that intersects a function's graph more than once, then the function is one-to-one.

Hyperbola [13.3] The set of all points P in the plane such that the difference of the distance from P to two fixed points is constant

Hypotenuse [R.5, 5.8, 10.7] In a right triangle, the side opposite the 90° angle

i [10.8] The square root of -1; that is, $i = \sqrt{-1}$ and $i^2 = -1$

Identity [R.2, 2.2] An equation that is true for all replacements

Identity property of 0 [R.1, 1.5] The statement that the sum of 0 and a number is the original number

Identity property of 1 [R.1, 1.3] The statement that the product of 1 and a number is the original number

Imaginary number [10.8] A number that can be written in the form $a + bi$, where a and b are real numbers and $b \ne 0$ and $i = \sqrt{-1}$

Inconsistent system of equations [8.1, 8.4] A system of equations for which there is no solution

Independent equations [8.1, 8.4] Equations that are not dependent

Index (plural, **Indices**) **[10.1]** In the radical, $\sqrt[n]{a}$, the number n is called the index.

Inequality [1.4, 9.1] A mathematical sentence using $<, >, \le, \ge,$ or $\ne$

Infinite geometric series [14.3] The sum of the terms of an infinite geometric sequence

Infinite sequence [14.1] A function having for its domain the set of natural numbers: $\{1, 2, 3, 4, 5, \ldots\}$

Infinite series [14.1] Given the infinite sequence $a_1, a_2, a_3, a_4, \ldots a_n, \ldots$, the sum of the terms $a_1 + a_2 + a_3 + a_4 + \cdots a_n + \cdots$ is called an infinite series.

Input [7.1] An element of the domain of a function

Integers [R.1, 1.4] The set of all whole numbers and their opposites: $\{\ldots, -4, -3, -2, -1, 0, 1, 2, 3, 4, \ldots\}$

Interpolation [3.7] The process of estimating a value between given values

Intersection of sets A and B [9.2, App B] The set of all elements that are common to both A and B; denoted $A \cap B$

Interval notation [R.2, 2.6] The use of a pair of numbers inside parentheses and/or brackets to represent the set of all numbers between and sometimes including those two numbers; see also *open, closed,* and *half-open intervals*

Inverse relation [12.1] The relation formed by interchanging the members of the domain and the range of a relation

Inverse variation [7.5] A situation that can be modeled by a rational function of the form $f(x) = k/x$, or $y = k/x$, where k is a nonzero constant

Irrational number [R.1, 1.4, 10.1] A real number that cannot be written as the ratio of two integers; when written in decimal notation, an irrational number neither terminates nor repeats

Isosceles right triangle [10.7] A right triangle in which both legs have the same length

Joint variation [7.5] A situation that can be modeled by an equation of the form $y = kxz$, where k is a nonzero constant

Largest common factor [R.5, 5.1] The largest common factor of a polynomial is the largest common factor of the coefficients times the largest common factor of the variable(s) in all of the terms.

Leading coefficient [R.4, 4.3] The coefficient of the term of highest degree in a polynomial

Leading term [R.4, 4.3] The term of highest degree in a polynomial

Least common denominator (LCD) [R.6, 6.3] The least common multiple of the denominators of two or more fractions

Least common multiple (LCM) [R.6, 6.3] The smallest number that is a multiple of two or more numbers

Legs [R.5, 5.8, 10.7] In a right triangle, the two sides that form the 90° angle

Like radicals [10.5] Radical expressions that have the same indices and radicands

Like terms [R.1, R.4, 1.5, 1.8, 4.7] Terms containing the same variable(s) raised to the same power(s); also called *similar terms*

Line graph [3.1] A graph in which quantities are represented as points connected by straight-line segments

Linear equation [R.3, 2.2, 3.2] In two variables, any equation whose graph is a straight line and can be written in the form $y = mx + b$ or $Ax + By = C$, where x and y are variables and m, b, A, B, and C are constants

Linear equation in three variables [8.4] An equation equivalent to one of the form $Ax + By + Cz = D$, where A, B, C, and D are constants

Linear function [7.3] A function whose graph is a straight line and can be described by an equation of the form $f(x) = mx + b$, where m and b are constants

Linear inequality [9.4] An inequality whose related equation is a linear equation

Linear polynomial [R.4] A polynomial of degree 1

Linear regression [3.7] A method for finding an equation for a line that best fits a set of data

Logarithmic equation [12.6] An equation containing a logarithmic expression

Logarithmic function, base a [12.3] The inverse of an exponential function $f(x) = a^x$, written $f^{-1}(x) = \log_a x$

Mathematical model [1.1] A mathematical representation of a real-world situation

Matrix (plural, Matrices) [8.6] A rectangular array of numbers

Maximum value [11.6] The greatest function value (output) achieved by a function

Mean [2.7, App A] The sum of a set of numbers, divided by the number of addends

Measure of central tendency [App A] A single representative number used to analyze a set of data; also called *center point*

Median [App A] After arranging a set of data from smallest to largest, the middle number if there is an odd number of data numbers, or the average of the two middle numbers if there is an even number of data numbers

Midpoint formula [10.7] The formula $\left(\dfrac{x_1 + x_2}{2}, \dfrac{y_1 + y_2}{2}\right)$, which represents the midpoint of the line segment with endpoints (x_1, y_1) and (x_2, y_2)

Minimum value [11.6] The least function value (output) achieved by a function

Mode [App A] In a set of data, the number or numbers that occur most often; if each number occurs the same number of times, then there is *no* mode

Monomial [R.4, 4.3] A constant, a variable, or a product of a constant and one or more variables

Motion problem [R.6, 2.5, 6.7, 8.3] A problem dealing with distance, rate (or speed), and time

Multiplicative identity [1.3] The number 1

Multiplicative inverses [1.3] *Reciprocals*; two numbers whose product is 1

Multiplicative property of zero [R.1, 1.7] The statement that the product of 0 and any real number is 0

Natural logarithm [12.5] A logarithm with base e; also called Napierian logarithm

Natural numbers [R.1, 1.3] The numbers used for counting: $\{1, 2, 3, 4, 5, \ldots\}$; also called *counting numbers*

Nonlinear equation [3.2] An equation whose graph is not a straight line

Nonlinear function [7.3] A function for which the graph is not a straight line

nth root [10.1] A number c is called the nth root of a if $c^n = a$.

Numerator [1.3] The number above the fraction bar in a fraction

Odd root [10.1] A root with an odd index

One-to-one function [12.1] A function for which different inputs have different outputs

Open interval (a, b) [R.2, 2.6] The set of all numbers x for which $a < x < b$; thus, $(a, b) = \{x \mid a < x < b\}$

Opposite of a polynomial [R.4, 4.4] To find the *opposite* of a polynomial, change the sign of every term; this is the same as multiplying the polynomial by -1

Opposites [R.1, 1.6] Two expressions whose sum is 0; *additive inverses*

Ordered pair [R.3, 3.1] A pair of numbers of the form (x, y) for which the order in which the numbers are listed is important

Origin [R.3, 3.1] The point on a coordinate plane where the two axes intersect

Output [7.1] An element of the range of a function

Parabola [11.1, 11.6, 13.1] A graph of a quadratic function

Parallel lines [R.3, 3.6] Lines in the same plane that never intersect; two lines are parallel if they have the same slope or if both lines are vertical

Partial sum [14.1] The sum of the first n terms of a sequence: $a_1 + a_2 + a_3 + \cdots + a_n$; also called *finite series*

Pascal's triangle [14.4] A triangular array of coefficients of the expansion $(a + b)^n$ for $n = 0, 1, 2, \ldots$

Percent notation [2.4] The percent symbol % means "per hundred."

Perfect-square trinomial [R.5, 5.4] A trinomial that is the square of a binomial

Perpendicular lines [R.3, 3.6] Two lines that intersect to form a right angle; two lines are perpendicular if the product of their slopes is -1 or if one line is vertical and the other line is horizontal

Piecewise-defined function [7.2] A function defined by different equations for various parts of the domain

Point–slope form [R.3, 3.7, 7.3] Any equation of the form $y - y_1 = m(x - x_1)$, where the slope of the line is m and the line passes through (x_1, y_1)

Polynomial [R.4, 4.3] A monomial or a sum of monomials

Polynomial equation [R.5] An equation in which two polynomials are set equal to each other

Polynomial inequality [11.9] An inequality that is equivalent to an inequality with a polynomial as one side and 0 as the other

Prime factorization [1.3] The factorization of a composite number into a product of prime numbers

Prime number [1.3] A natural number that has exactly two different natural number factors: the number itself and 1

Prime polynomial [R.5, 5.2] A polynomial that cannot be factored using rational numbers

Principal square root [10.1] The nonnegative square root of a number

Product [1.2] The result when two numbers are multiplied

Progression [14.1] A function for which the domain is a set of counting numbers beginning with 1; also called *sequence*

Proportion [R.6, 6.7] An equation stating that two ratios are equal

Pure imaginary number [10.8] A complex number of the form $a + bi$, in which $a = 0$ and $b \neq 0$

Pythagorean theorem [R.5, 5.8, 10.7] In any right triangle, if a and b are the lengths of the legs and c is the length of the hypotenuse, then $a^2 + b^2 = c^2$.

Quadrants [R.3, 3.1] The four regions into which the horizontal axis and the vertical axis divide a plane

Quadratic equation [R.5, 5.7, 11.1] An equation equivalent to one of the form $ax^2 + bx + c = 0$, where a, b, and c are constants, with $a \neq 0$

Quadratic formula [11.2] The formula
$$x = \frac{-b \pm \sqrt{b^2 - 4ac}}{2a},$$
which gives the solutions of $ax^2 + bx + c = 0, a \neq 0$

Quadratic function [11.2] A second-degree polynomial function in one variable

Quadratic inequality [11.9] A second-degree polynomial inequality in one variable

Quadratic polynomial [R.4] A polynomial in one variable of degree 2

Quartic polynomial [R.4] A polynomial in one variable of degree 4

Quotient [1.2] The result when two numbers are divided

Radical equation [10.6] An equation in which a variable appears in a radicand

Radical expression [10.1] Any expression in which a radical sign appears

Radical sign [10.1] The symbol $\sqrt{}$

Radical term [10.5] A term in which a radical sign appears

Radicand [10.1] The expression under a radical sign

Radius (plural, Radii) [13.1] The distance from the center of a circle to a point on the circle; a segment connecting a point on the circle to the center of the circle

Range [7.1, 7.2] The set of all second coordinates of the ordered pairs in a function

Rate [3.4] A ratio that indicates how two quantities change with respect to each other

Ratio [R.6, 6.7] The quotient of two quantities

Rational equation [R.6, 6.6] An equation that contains one or more rational expressions

Rational expression [R.6, 6.1] A quotient of two polynomials

Rational inequality [11.9] An inequality involving a rational expression

Rational numbers [R.1, 1.4] The set of all numbers a/b, such that a and b are integers and $b \neq 0$

Rationalizing the denominator [10.4] A procedure for finding an equivalent expression without a radical expression in the denominator

Rationalizing the numerator [10.4] A procedure for finding an equivalent expression without a radical expression in the numerator

Real numbers [R.1, 1.4] The set of all numbers corresponding to points on the number line

Reciprocals [1.3] Two numbers whose product is 1; *multiplicative inverses*

Reflection [12.2] The mirror image of a graph

Relation [7.1] A correspondence between a first set, called the *domain*, and a second set, called the *range*, such that each member of the domain corresponds to at least one member of the range

Remainder theorem [App C] The remainder obtained by dividing the polynomial $P(x)$ by $x - r$ is $P(r)$.

Repeating decimal [R.1, 1.4] A decimal in which a block of digits repeats indefinitely

Revenue [4.8] The price per item times the quantity of items sold

Right triangle [5.8] A triangle that has a 90° angle

Roster notation [App B] Set notation in which the elements of a set are listed within { }

Row-equivalent operations [8.6] Operations used to produce equivalent systems of equations

Scientific notation [4.2] An expression of the type $N \times 10^m$, where N is at least 1 but less than 10 (that is, $1 \leq N < 10$), N is expressed in decimal notation, and m is an integer

Sequence [14.1] A function for which the domain is a set of consecutive counting numbers beginning with 1; also called *progression*

Series [14.1] The sum of specified terms in a sequence

Set [1.4, App B] A collection of objects

Set-builder notation [R.2, 2.6, App B] The naming of a set by describing basic characteristics of the elements in the set

Sigma notation [14.1] The naming of a sum using the Greek letter Σ (sigma) as part of an abbreviated form; also called *summation notation*

Similar terms [R.1, R.4, 1.5, 1.8, 4.7] Terms containing the same variable(s) raised to the same power(s); also called *like terms*

Similar triangles [6.7] Triangles in which corresponding angles have the same measure and corresponding sides are proportional

Slope [R.3, 3.5] The ratio of vertical change to horizontal change for any two points on a line

Slope–intercept equation [R.3, 3.6, 7.3] An equation of the form $y = mx + b$, with slope m and y-intercept $(0, b)$

Solution [R.2, 2.1, 2.6, 9.1] Any replacement or substitution for a variable that makes an equation or inequality true

Solution of a system [8.1] A solution of a system of two equations makes *both* equations true.

Solution set [2.2, 2.6, 9.1] The set of all solutions of an equation, an inequality, or a system of equations or inequalities

Solve [R.2, 2.1, 2.6, 9.1] To find all solutions of an equation, an inequality, or a system of equations or inequalities

Speed [3.4] The speed of an object is found by dividing the distance traveled by the time required to travel that distance.

Square matrix [8.7] A matrix with the same number of rows and columns

Square root [10.1] The number c is a *square root* of a if $c^2 = a$.

Standard form of a linear equation [R.3, 3.7, 7.3] Any equation of the form $Ax + By = C$, where A, B, and C are real numbers and A and B are not both 0

Subset [App B]   If every element of A is also an element of B, then A is a *subset* of B; denoted $A \subseteq B$

Substitute [R.1, 1.1]   To replace a variable with a number or an expression

Substitution method [8.2]   An algebraic method for solving a system of equations

Sum [1.2]   The result when two numbers are added

Sum of cubes [R.5, 5.5]   An expression that can be written in the form $A^3 + B^3$

Summation notation [14.1]   The naming of a sum using the Greek letter Σ (sigma) as part of an abbreviated form; also called *sigma notation*

Supply function [8.8]   A function modeling the relationship between the price of a good and the quantity of that good supplied

Synthetic division [App C]   A method used to divide a polynomial by a binomial of the type $x - a$

System of equations [8.1]   A set of two or more equations, in two or more variables, for which a common solution is sought

Term [R.1, 1.2, 4.3]   A number, a variable, a product of numbers and/or variables, or a quotient of numbers and/or variables

Terminating decimal [R.1, 1.4]   A decimal that can be written using a finite number of decimal places

Total cost [8.8]   The amount spent to produce a product

Total profit [8.8]   The money taken in less the money spent, or total revenue minus total cost

Total revenue [8.8]   The amount taken in from the sale of a product

Trinomial [R.4, 4.3]   A polynomial with three terms

Undefined [R.1, 1.7]   An expression that has no meaning attached to it

Union of sets A and B [9.2, App B]   The collection of elements belonging to A and/or B; denoted $A \cup B$

Value [1.1]   The numerical result after a number has been substituted for a variable in an expression and calculations have been carried out

Variable [R.1, 1.1]   A letter that represents an unknown number

Variable costs [8.8]   In business, costs that vary according to the quantity being produced

Variable expression [1.1]   An expression containing a variable

Variation constant [7.5]   The constant k in an equation of direct variation or inverse variation; also called *constant of proportionality*

Vertex [11.6]   The "turning point" of the graph of a quadratic equation

Vertical line [R.3, 3.3, 3.7]   The graph of $x = a$ is a vertical line, with x-intercept $(a, 0)$.

Vertical-line test [7.1]   The statement that if it is possible for a vertical line to cross a graph more than once, then the graph is not the graph of a function

Whole numbers [R.1, 1.4]   The set of natural numbers and 0: $\{0, 1, 2, 3, 4, 5, \ldots\}$

x-axis [R.3, 3.1]   The horizontal axis in a coordinate plane

x-intercept [R.3, 3.3]   A point at which a graph crosses the x-axis

y-axis [R.3, 3.1]   The vertical axis in a coordinate plane

y-intercept [R.3, 3.3]   A point at which a graph crosses the y-axis

Zeros [11.9]   The x-values for which $f(x)$ is 0, for any function f

INDEX

INDEX OF APPLICATIONS

Formulas

$$m = \frac{y_2 - y_1}{x_2 - x_1}$$ Slope of a line

$$y = mx + b$$ Slope–intercept form of a linear equation

$$y - y_1 = m(x - x_1)$$ Point–slope form of a linear equation

$$(A + B)(A - B) = A^2 - B^2$$ Product of the sum and difference of the same two terms

$$\left.\begin{array}{l}(A + B)^2 = A^2 + 2AB + B^2, \\ (A - B)^2 = A^2 - 2AB + B^2\end{array}\right\}$$ Square of a binomial

$$d = rt$$ Formula for distance traveled

$$\frac{1}{a} \cdot t + \frac{1}{b} \cdot t = 1$$ Work principle

$$s = 16t^2$$ Free-fall distance

$$y = kx$$ Direct variation

$$y = \frac{k}{x}$$ Inverse variation

$$x = \frac{-b \pm \sqrt{b^2 - 4ac}}{2a}$$ Quadratic formula

Plane Geometry

Rectangle
Area: $A = lw$
Perimeter: $P = 2l + 2w$

Square
Area: $A = s^2$
Perimeter: $P = 4s$

Triangle
Area: $A = \frac{1}{2}bh$

Triangle
Sum of Angle Measures:
$A + B + C = 180°$

Right Triangle
Pythagorean Theorem
(Equation):
$a^2 + b^2 = c^2$

Parallelogram
Area: $A = bh$

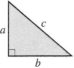

Trapezoid
Area: $A = \frac{1}{2}h(b_1 + b_2)$

Circle
Area: $A = \pi r^2$
Circumference:
$C = \pi d = 2\pi r$
$\left(\frac{22}{7}\text{ and 3.14 are different approximations for }\pi\right)$

Solid Geometry

Rectangular Solid
Volume: $V = lwh$

Cube
Volume: $V = s^3$

Right Circular Cylinder
Volume: $V = \pi r^2 h$
Total Surface Area:
$S = 2\pi rh + 2\pi r^2$

Right Circular Cone
Volume: $V = \frac{1}{3}\pi r^2 h$
Total Surface Area:
$S = \pi r^2 + \pi rs$
Slant Height:
$s = \sqrt{r^2 + h^2}$

Sphere
Volume: $V = \frac{4}{3}\pi r^3$
Surface Area: $S = 4\pi r^2$

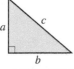

Selected Keys of the Scientific Calculator

This secondary function takes the square root of number displayed.

Squares number displayed.

Activates secondary functions printed above certain keys. Also denoted INV or 2nd.

Used when entering numbers in scientific notation. Also denoted EXP.

Finds reciprocal of number displayed.

Used to raise any base to a power. Also denoted y^x, a^x, or ⌃.

Stores number displayed in memory. Also denoted MIN or M.

Recalls number stored in memory. Also denoted MR.

This secondary function raises 10 to any power entered.

Clears all preceding numbers and operations. Also used to turn calculator on.

Used as an approximation for pi.

Used to perform indicated operation.

Used to control order in which certain operations are performed.

Clears last number displayed but not preceding operations.

Used when entering decimal notation.

Used to change sign of number displayed.

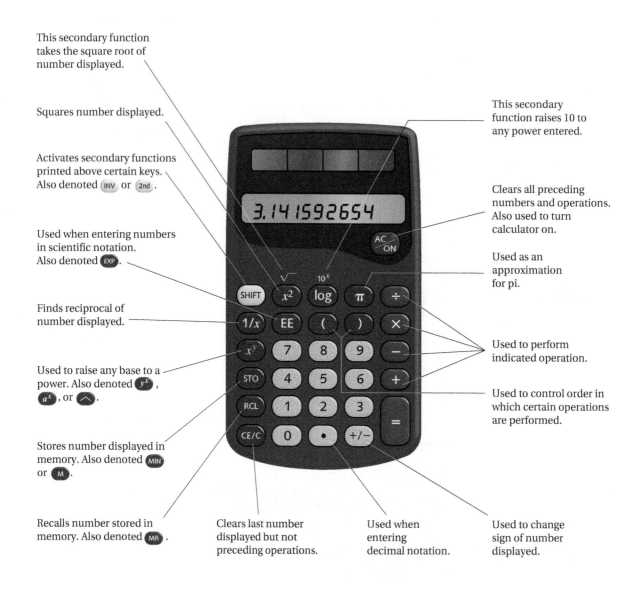

Selected Keys of the Graphing Calculator*

Controls the values that are used when creating a table.

Determines the portion of the curve(s) shown and the scale of the graph.

Used to enter the equation(s) that is to be graphed.

Controls whether graphs are drawn sequentially or simultaneously and if the window is split.

Activates the secondary functions printed above many keys in blue or green.

Used to delete previously entered characters.

Accesses preprogrammed applications and tutorials.

These keys are similar to those found on a scientific calculator.

Magnifies or reduces a portion of the curve being viewed and can "square" the graph to reduce distortion.

Used to determine certain important values associated with a graph.

Used to display the coordinates of points on a curve.

Used to display x- and y-values in a table.

Used to graph equations that were entered using the Y= key.

Used to move the cursor and adjust contrast.

Used to fit curves to data.

Used to access a previously named function or equation.

Used to raise a base to a power.

Used to write the variable, x.

Used as a negative sign.

*Key functions and locations are the same for the TI-83 Plus.